Neural Networks and Learning Machines

Neural Networks and Learning Machines
Third Edition

Simon Haykin
McMaster University
Hamilton, Ontario, Canada

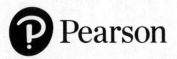

Authorized adaptation from the United States edition, entitled *Neural Networks and Learning Machines,* 3rd edition, ISBN 978-0-13-147139-9, by Haykin, Simon O., published by Pearson Education Inc., Copyright © 2009.

Indian Subcontinent Adaptation
Copyright © 2016 Pearson India Education Services Pvt. Ltd

ISBN 978-93-3257-031-3

First Impression, 2016
Third Impression, 2018
Fourth Impression, 2019

This edition is manufactured in India and is authorized for sale only in India, Bangladesh, Bhutan, Pakistan, Nepal, Sri Lanka and the Maldives. Circulation of this edition outside of these territories is UNAUTHORIZED.

Published by Pearson India Education Services Pvt. Ltd, CIN: U72200TN2005PTC057128.

Head Office: 15th Floor, Tower-B, World Trade Tower, Plot No. 1, Sector 16, Noida 201 301, Uttar Pardesh, India.

Registered Office:4th Floor, Software Block, Elnet Software City, TS -140, Block 2 & 9 Rajiv Gandhi Salai, Taramani, Chennai, Tamil Nadu 600113.Fax: 080-30461003,Phone: 080-30461060, Website: in.pearson.com Email: companysecetary.india@pearson.com

Printed in India by Pushp Print Services.

To my wife, Nancy, for her patience and tolerance,

and

to the countless researchers in neural networks for their original contributions, the many reviewers for their critical inputs, and many of my graduate students for their keen interest.

Contents

Preface

In writing this third edition of a classic book, I have been guided by the same underlying philosophy of the first edition of the book:

> *Write an up-to-date treatment of neural networks in a comprehensive, thorough, and readable manner.*

The new edition has been retitled *Neural Networks and Learning Machines*, in order to reflect two realities:

1. The perceptron, the multilayer perceptron, self-organizing maps, and neurodynamics, to name a few topics, have always been considered integral parts of neural networks, rooted in ideas inspired by the human brain.
2. Kernel methods, exemplified by support-vector machines and kernel principal-components analysis, are rooted in statistical learning theory.

Although, indeed, they share many fundamental concepts and applications, there are some subtle differences between the operations of neural networks and learning machines. The underlying subject matter is therefore much richer when they are studied together, under one umbrella, particularly so when

- ideas drawn from neural networks and machine learning are hybridized to perform improved learning tasks beyond the capability of either one operating on its own, and
- ideas inspired by the human brain lead to new perspectives wherever they are of particular importance.

Moreover, the scope of the book has been broadened to provide detailed treatments of dynamic programming and sequential state estimation, both of which have affected the study of reinforcement learning and supervised learning, respectively, in significant ways.

Organization of the Book

The book begins with an introductory chapter that is motivational, paving the way for the rest of the book which is organized into six parts as follows:

1. Chapters 1 through 4, constituting the first part of the book, follow the classical approach on supervised learning. Specifically,

- Chapter 1 describes Rosenblatt's perceptron, highlighting the perceptron convergence theorem, and the relationship between the perceptron and the Bayesian classifier operating in a Gaussian environment.
- Chapter 2 describes the method of least squares as a basis for model building. The relationship between this method and Bayesian inference for the special case of a Gaussian environment is established. This chapter also includes a discussion of the minimum description length (MDL) principle for model selection.
- Chapter 3 is devoted to the least-mean-square (LMS) algorithm and its convergence analysis. The theoretical framework of the analysis exploits two principles: Kushner's direct method and the Langevin equation (well known in nonequilibrium thermodynamics).

These three chapters, though different in conceptual terms, share a common feature: They are all based on a single computational unit. Most importantly, they provide a great deal of insight into the learning process in their own individual ways—a feature that is exploited in subsequent chapters.

Chapter 4, on the multilayer perceptron, is a generalization of Rosenblatt's perceptron. This rather long chapter covers the following topics:

- the back-propagation algorithm, its virtues and limitations, and its role as an optimum method for computing partial derivations;
- optimal annealing and adaptive control of the learning rate;
- cross-validation;
- convolutional networks, inspired by the pioneering work of Hubel and Wiesel on visual systems;
- supervised learning viewed as an optimization problem, with attention focused on conjugate-gradient methods, quasi-Newton methods, and the Marquardt–Levenberg algorithm;
- nonlinear filtering;
- last, but by no means least, a contrasting discussion of small-scale versus large-scale learning problems.

2. The next part of the book, consisting of Chapters 5 and 6, discusses kernel methods based on radial-basis function (RBF) networks.

In a way, Chapter 5 may be viewed as an insightful introduction to kernel methods. Specifically, it does the following:

- presents Cover's theorem as theoretical justification for the architectural structure of RBF networks;
- describes a relatively simple two-stage hybrid procedure for supervised learning, with stage 1 based on the idea of clustering (namely, the K-means algorithm) for computing the hidden layer, and stage 2 using the LMS or the method of least squares for computing the linear output layer of the network;
- presents kernel regression and examines its relation to RBF networks.

Chapter 6 is devoted to support vector machines (SVMs), which are commonly recognized as a method of choice for supervised learning. Basically, the SVM is a binary classifier, in the context of which the chapter covers the following topics:

- the condition for defining the maximum margin of separation between a pair of linearly separable binary classes;
- quadratic optimization for finding the optimal hyperplane when the two classes are linearly separable and when they are not;
- the SVM viewed as a kernel machine, including discussions of the kernel trick and Mercer's theorem;
- the design philosophy of SVMs;
- the ϵ-insensitive loss function and its role in the optimization of regression problems;
- the Representer Theorem, and the roles of Hilbert space and reproducing kernel Hilbert space (RKHS) in its formulation.

  From this description, it is apparent that the underlying theory of support vector machines is built on a strong mathematical background—hence their computational strength as an elegant and powerful tool for supervised learning.

3. The third part of the book involves a single chapter, Chapter 7. This broadly based chapter is devoted to regularization theory, which is at the core of machine learning. The following topics are studied in detail:

   - Tikhonov's classic regularization theory, which builds on the RKHS discussed in Chapter 6. This theory embodies some profound mathematical concepts: the Fréchet differential of the Tikhonov functional, the Riesz representation theorem, the Euler–Lagrange equation, Green's function, and multivariate Gaussian functions;
   - generalized RBF networks and their modification for computational tractability;
   - the regularized least-squares estimator, revisited in light of the Representer Theorem;
   - estimation of the regularization parameter, using Wahba's concept of generalized cross-validation;
   - semisupervised learning, using labeled as well as unlabeled examples;
   - differentiable manifolds and their role in manifold regularization—a role that is basic to designing semisupervised learning machines;
   - spectral graph theory for finding a Gaussian kernel in an RBF network used for semisupervised learning;
   - a generalized Representer Theorem for dealing with semisupervised kernel machines;
   - the Laplacian regularized least-squares (LapRLS) algorithm for computing the linear output layer of the RBF network; here, it should be noted that when the intrinsic regularization parameter (responsible for the unlabeled data) is reduced to zero, the algorithm is correspondingly reduced to the ordinary least-squares algorithm.

   This highly theoretical chapter is of profound practical importance. First, it provides the basis for the regularization of supervised-learning machines. Second, it lays down the groundwork for designing regularized semisupervised learning machines.

4. Chapters 8 through 11 constitute the fourth part of the book, dealing with unsupervised learning. Beginning with Chapter 8, four principles of self-organization, intuitively motivated by neurobiological considerations, are presented:

(i) Hebb's postulate of learning for self-amplification;

(ii) Competition among the synapses of a single neuron or a group of neurons for limited resources;

(iii) Cooperation among the winning neuron and its neighbors;

(iv) Structural information (e.g., redundancy) contained in the input data.

The main theme of the chapter is threefold:

• Principles (i), (ii), and (iv) are applied to a single neuron, in the course of which Oja's rule for maximum eigenfiltering is derived; this is a remarkable result obtained through self-organization, which involves bottom-up as well as top-down learning. Next, the idea of maximum eigenfiltering is generalized to principal-components analysis (PCA) on the input data for the purpose of dimensionality reduction; the resulting algorithm is called the generalized Hebbian algorithm (GHA).

• Basically, PCA is a linear method, the computing power of which is therefore limited to second-order statistics. In order to deal with higher-order statistics, the kernel method is applied to PCA in a manner similar to that described in Chapter 6 on support vector machines, but with one basic difference: unlike SVM, kernel PCA is performed in an unsupervised manner.

• Unfortunately, in dealing with natural images, kernel PCA can become unmanageable in computational terms. To overcome this computational limitation, GHA and kernel PCA are hybridized into a new on-line unsupervised learning algorithm called the kernel Hebbian algorithm (KHA), which finds applications in image denoising.

The development of KHA is an outstanding example of what can be accomplished when an idea from machine learning is combined with a complementary idea rooted in neural networks, producing a new algorithm that overcomes their respective practical limitations.

Chapter 9 is devoted to self-organizing maps (SOMs), the development of which follows the principles of self-organization described in Chapter 8. The SOM is a simple algorithm in computational terms, yet highly powerful in its built-in ability to construct organized topographic maps with several useful properties:

• spatially discrete approximation of the input space, responsible for data generation;

• topological ordering, in the sense that the spatial location of a neuron in the topographic map corresponds to a particular feature in the input (data) space;

• input–output density matching;

• input-data feature selection.

The SOM has been applied extensively in practice; the construction of contextual maps and hierarchical vector quantization are presented as two illustrative examples of the SOM's computing power. What is truly amazing is that the SOM exhibits several interesting properties and solves difficult computational tasks, yet it lacks an objective function that could be optimized. To fill this gap and thereby provide the possibility of improved topographic mapping, the self-organizing map is kernelized. This is done by introducing an entropic function as the objective function to be maximized. Here again, we see the practical benefit of hybridizing ideas rooted in neural networks with complementary kernel-theoretic ones.

Chapter 10 exploits principles rooted in Shannon's information theory as tools for unsupervised learning. This rather long chapter begins by presenting a review of Shannon's information theory, with particular attention given to the concepts of entropy, mutual information, and the Kullback–Leibler divergence (KLD). The review also includes the concept of copulas, which, unfortunately, has been largely overlooked for several decades. Most importantly, the copula provides a measure of the statistical dependence between a pair of correlated random variables. In any event, focusing on mutual information as the objective function, the chapter establishes the following principles:

- The Infomax principle, which maximizes the mutual information between the input and output data of a neural system; Infomax is closely related to redundancy reduction.
- The Imax principle, which maximizes the mutual information between the single outputs of a pair of neural systems that are driven by correlated inputs.
- The Imin principle operates in a manner similar to the Imax principle, except that the mutual information between the pair of output random variables is minimized.
- The independent-components analysis (ICA) principle, which provides a powerful tool for the blind separation of a hidden set of statistically independent source signals. Provided that certain operating conditions are satisfied, the ICA principle affords the basis for deriving procedures for recovering the original source signals from a corresponding set of observables that are linearly mixed versions of the source signals. Two specific ICA algorithms are described:

   (i) the natural-gradient learning algorithm, which, except for scaling and permutation, solves the ICA problem by minimizing the KLD between a parameterized probability density function and the corresponding factorial distribution;

   (ii) the maximum-entropy learning algorithm, which maximizes the entropy of a nonlinearly transformed version of the demixer output; this algorithm, commonly known as the Infomax algorithm for ICA, also exhibits scaling and permutation properties.

Chapter 10 also describes another important ICA algorithm, known as FastICA, which, as the name implies, is computationally fast. This algorithm maximizes a contrast function based on the concept of negentropy, which provides a measure of the non-Gaussianity of a random variable. Continuing with ICA, the chapter goes on to describe a new algorithm known as coherent ICA, the development of which rests on fusion of the Infomax and Imax principles via the use of the copula; coherent ICA is useful for extracting the envelopes of a mixture of amplitude-modulated signals. Finally, Chapter 10 introduces another concept rooted in Shannon's information theory, namely, rate distortion theory, which is used to develop the last concept in the chapter: information bottleneck. Given the joint distribution of an input vector and a (relevant) output vector, the method is formulated as a constrained optimization problem in such a way that a tradeoff is created between two amounts of information, one pertaining to information contained in the bottleneck vector about the input and the other pertaining to information contained in the bottle-neck vector about the output. The chapter then goes on to find an optimal manifold for data representation, using the information bottleneck method.

The final approach to unsupervised learning is described in Chapter 11, using stochastic methods that are rooted in statistical mechanics; the study of statistical mechanics is closely related to information theory. The chapter begins by review-ing the fundamental concepts of Helmholtz free energy and entropy (in a statisti-cal mechanics sense), followed by the description of Markov chains. The stage is then set for describing the Metropolis algorithm for generating a Markov chain, the transition probabilities of which converge to a unique and stable distribution. The discussion of stochastic methods is completed by describing simulated an-nealing for global optimization, followed by Gibbs sampling, which can be used as a special form of the Metropolis algorithm. With all this background on statistical mechanics at hand, the stage is set for describing the Boltzmann machine, which, in a historical context, was the first multilayer learning machine discussed in the literature. Unfortunately, the learning process in the Boltzmann machine is very slow, particularly when the number of hidden neurons is large—hence the lack of interest in its practical use. Various methods have been proposed in the literature to overcome the limitations of the Boltzmann machine. The most successful inno-vation to date is the deep belief net, which distinguishes itself in the clever way in which the following two functions are combined into a powerful machine:

- generative modeling, resulting from bottom-up learning on a layer-by-layer basis and without supervision;
- inference, resulting from top-down learning.

Finally, Chapter 10 describes deterministic annealing to overcome the excessive computational requirements of simulated annealing; the only problem with deterministic annealing is that it could get trapped in a local minimum.

5. Up to this point, the focus of attention in the book has been the formulation of al-gorithms for supervised learning, semisupervised learning, and unsupervised learn-ing. Chapter 12, constituting the next part of the book all by itself, addresses reinforcement learning, in which learning takes place in an on-line manner as the result of an agent (e.g., robot) interacting with its surrounding environment. In re-ality, however, dynamic programming lies at the core of reinforcement learning. Accordingly, the early part of Chapter 15 is devoted to an introductory treatment of Bellman's dynamic programming, which is then followed by showing that the two widely used methods of reinforcement learning: Temporal difference (TD) learn-ing, and Q-learning can be derived as special cases of dynamic programming. Both TD-learning and Q-learning are relatively simple, on-line reinforcement learning algorithms that do not require knowledge of transition probabilities. However, their practical applications are limited to situations in which the dimensionality of the state space is of moderate size. In large-scale dynamic systems, the curse of dimensionality becomes a serious issue, making not only dynamic programming,

but also its approximate forms, TD-learning and Q-learning, computationally intractable. To overcome this serious limitation, two indirect methods of approximate dynamic programming are described:

- a linear method called the least-squares policy evaluation (LSPV) algorithm, and
- a nonlinear method using a neural network (e.g., multilayer perceptron) as a universal approximator.

6. The last part of the book, consisting of Chapters 13, 14, and 15, is devoted to the study of nonlinear feedback systems, with an emphasis on recurrent neural networks:

   (i) Chapter 13 studies neurodynamics, with particular attention given to the stability problem. In this context, the direct method of Lyapunov is described. This method embodies two theorems, one dealing with stability of the system and the other dealing with asymptotic stability. At the heart of the method is a Lyapunov function, for which an energy function is usually found to be adequate. With this background theory at hand, two kinds of associative memory are described:

   - the Hopfield model, the operation of which demonstrates that a complex system is capable of generating simple emergent behavior;
   - the brain-state-in-a-box model, which provides a basis for clustering.

   The chapter also discusses properties of chaotic processes and a regularized procedure for their dynamic reconstruction.

   (ii) Chapter 14 is devoted to the Bayesian filter, which provides a unifying basis for sequential state estimation algorithms, at least in a conceptual sense. The findings of the chapter are summarized as follows:

   - The classic Kalman filter for a linear Gaussian environment is derived with the use of the minimum mean-square-error criterion; in a problem at the end of the chapter, it is shown that the Kalman filter so derived is a special case of the Bayesian filter;
   - square-root filtering is used to overcome the divergence phenomenon that can arise in practical applications of the Kalman filter;
   - the extended Kalman filter (EKF) is used to deal with dynamic systems whose nonlinearity is of a mild sort; the Gaussian assumption is maintained;
   - the direct approximate form of the Bayesian filter is exemplified by a new filter called the cubature Kalman filter (CKF); here again, the Gaussian assumption is maintained;
   - indirect approximate forms of the Bayesian filter are exemplified by particle filters, the implementation of which can accommodate nonlinearity as well as non-Gaussianity.

   With the essence of Kalman filtering being that of a predictor–corrector, Chapter 14 goes on to describe the possible role of "Kalman-like filtering" in certain parts of the human brain.

The final chapter of the book, Chapter 15, studies dynamically driven recurrent neural networks. The early part of the chapter discusses different structures (models) for recurrent networks and their computing power, followed by two algorithms for the training of recurrent networks:

- back propagation through time, and
- real-time recurrent learning.

Unfortunately both of these procedures, being gradient based, are likely to suffer from the so-called vanishing-gradients problem. To mitigate the problem, the use of nonlinear sequential state estimators is described at some length for the supervised training of recurrent networks in a rather novel manner. In this context, the advantages and disadvantages of the extended Kalman filter (simple, but derivative dependent) and the cubature Kalman filter (derivative free, but more complicated mathematically) as sequential state estimator for supervised learning are discussed. The emergence of adaptive behavior, unique to recurrent networks, and the potential benefit of using an adaptive critic to further enhance the capability of recurrent networks are also discussed in the chapter.

An important topic featuring prominently in different parts of the book is supervised learning and semisupervised learning applied to large-scale problems. The concluding remarks of the book assert that this topic is in its early stages of development; most importantly, a four-stage procedure is described for its future development.

Distinct Features of the Book

Over and above the broad scope and thorough treatment of the topics summarized under the organization of the book, distinctive features of the text include the following:

1. Chapters 1 through 7 and Chapter 10 include computer experiments involving the double-moon configuration for generating data for the purpose of binary classification. The experiments range from the simple case of linearly separable patterns to difficult cases of nonseparable patterns. The double-moon configuration, as a running example, is used all the way from Chapter 1 to Chapter 7, followed by Chapter 10, thereby providing an experimental means for studying and comparing the learning algorithms described in those eight chapters.

2. Computer experiments are also included in Chapter 8 on PCA, Chapter 9 on SOM and kernel SOM, and Chapter 14 on dynamic reconstruction of the Mackay–Glass attractor using the EKF and CKF algorithms.

3. Several case studies, using real-life data, are presented:

   - Chapter 7 discusses the United States Postal Service (USPS) data for semisupervised learning using the Laplacian RLS algorithm;
   - Chapter 8 examines how PCA is applied to handwritten digital data and describes the coding and denoising of images;
   - Chapter 10 treats the analysis of natural images by using sparse-sensory coding and ICA;
   - Chapter 13 presents dynamic reconstruction applied to the Lorenz attractor by using a regularized RBF network.

Chapter 15 also includes a section on the model reference adaptive control system as a case study.

4. Each chapter ends with notes and references for further study, followed by end-of-chapter problems that are designed to challenge, and therefore expand, the reader's expertise.

    The glossary at the front of the book has been expanded to include explanatory notes on the methodology used on matters dealing with matrix analysis and probability theory.

5. PowerPoint files of all the figures and tables in the book will be available to Instructors and can be found at www.pearsoned.co.in/haykin

6. The book is accompanied by a Manual that includes the solutions to all the end-of-chapter problems as well as computer experiments.

    The manual is available at www.pearsoned.co.in/haykin only to instructors who use the book as the recommended volume for a course.

Last, but by no means least, every effort has been expended to make the book error free and, most importantly, readable.

Simon Haykin
Ancaster, Ontario

Acknowledgments

I am deeply indebted to many renowned authorities on neural networks and learning machines around the world, who have provided invaluable comments on selected parts of the book:

Dr. Sun-Ichi Amari, The RIKEN Brain Science Institute, Wako City, Japan

Dr. Susanne Becker, Department of Psychology, Neuroscience & Behaviour, McMaster University, Hamilton, Ontario, Canada

Dr. Dimitri Bertsekas, MIT, Cambridge, Massachusetts

Dr. Leon Bottou, NEC Laboratories America, Princeton, New Jersey

Dr. Simon Godsill, University of Cambridge, Cambridge, England

Dr. Geoffrey Gordon, Carnegie-Mellon University, Pittsburgh, Pennsylvania

Dr. Peter Grünwald, CWI, Amsterdam, the Netherlands

Dr. Geoffrey Hinton, Department of Computer Science, University of Toronto, Toronto, Ontario, Canada

Dr. Timo Honkela, Helsinki University of Technology, Helsinki, Finland

Dr. Tom Hurd, Department of Mathematics and Statistics, McMaster University, Ontario, Canada.

Dr. Eugene Izhikevich, The Neurosciences Institute, San Diego, California

Dr. Juha Karhunen, Helsinki University of Technology, Helsinki, Finland

Dr. Kwang In Kim, Max-Planck-Institut für Biologische Kybernetik, Tübingen, Germany

Dr. James Lo, University of Maryland at Baltimore County, Baltimore, Maryland

Dr. Klaus Müller, University of Potsdam and Fraunhofer Institut FIRST, Berlin, Germany

Dr. Erkki Oja, Helsinki University of Technology, Helsinki, Finland

Dr. Bruno Olshausen, Redwood Center for Theoretical Neuroscience, University of California, Berkeley, California

Dr. Danil Prokhorov, Toyota Technical Center, Ann Arbor, Michigan

Dr. Kenneth Rose, Electrical and Computer Engineering, University of California, Santa Barbara, California

Dr. Bernhard Schölkopf, Max-Planck-Institut für Biologische Kybernetik, Tübingen, Germany

Dr. Vikas Sindhwani, Department of Computer Science, University of Chicago, Chicago, Illinois

Dr. Sergios Theodoridis, Department of Informatics, University of Athens, Athens, Greece

Dr. Naftali Tishby, The Hebrew University, Jerusalem, Israel

Dr. John Tsitsiklis, Massachusetts Institute of Technology, Cambridge, Massachusetts

Dr. Marc Van Hulle, Katholieke Universiteit, Leuven, Belgium

Several photographs and graphs have been reproduced in the book with permissions provided by Oxford University Press and

Dr. Anthony Bell, Redwood Center for Theoretical Neuroscience, University of California, Berkeley, California

Dr. Leon Bottou, NEC Laboratories America, Princeton, New Jersey

Dr. Juha Karhunen, Helsinki University of Technology, Helsinki, Finland

Dr. Bruno Olshausen, Redwood Center for Theoretical Neuroscience, University of California, Berkeley, California

Dr. Vikas Sindhwani, Department of Computer Science, University of Chicago, Chicago, Illinois

Dr. Naftali Tishby, The Hebrew University, Jerusalem, Israel

Dr. Marc Van Hulle, Katholieke Universiteit, Leuven, Belgium

I thank them all most sincerely.

I am grateful to my graduate students:

1. Yanbo Xue, for his tremendous effort devoted to working on nearly all the computer experiments produced in the book, and also for reading the second page proofs of the book.

2. Karl Wiklund, for proofreading the entire book and making valuable comments for improving it.

3. Haran Arasaratnam, for working on the computer experiment dealing with the Mackay–Glass attractor.

4. Andreas Wendel (Graz University of technology, Austria) while he was on leave at McMaster University, 2008.

I am grateful to Scott Disanno and Alice Dworkin of Prentice Hall for their support and hard work in the production of the book. Authorization of the use of color in the book by Marcia Horton is truly appreciated; the use of color has made a tremendous difference to the appearance of the book from cover to cover.

The tremendous effort by my Technical Coordinator, Lola Brooks, in typing several versions of the chapters in the book over the course of 12 months, almost nonstop, is gratefully acknowledged.

Last, but by no means least, I thank my wife, Nancy, for having allowed me the time and space, which I have needed over the last 12 months, almost nonstop, to complete the book in a timely fashion.

Simon Haykin

Introduction

1 WHAT IS A NEURAL NETWORK?

Work on artificial neural networks, commonly referred to as "neural networks," has been motivated right from its inception by the recognition that the human brain computes in an entirely different way from the conventional digital computer. The brain is a highly *complex, nonlinear, and parallel computer* (information-processing system). It has the capability to organize its structural constituents, known as *neurons*, so as to perform certain computations (e.g., pattern recognition, perception, and motor control) many times faster than the fastest digital computer in existence today. Consider, for example, human *vision*, which is an information-processing task. It is the function of the visual system to provide a *representation* of the environment around us and, more important, to supply the information we need to *interact* with the environment. To be specific, the brain routinely accomplishes perceptual recognition tasks (e.g., recognizing a familiar face embedded in an unfamiliar scene) in approximately 100–200 ms, whereas tasks of much lesser complexity take a great deal longer on a powerful computer.

For another example, consider the *sonar* of a bat. Sonar is an active echolocation system. In addition to providing information about how far away a target (e.g., a flying insect) is, bat sonar conveys information about the relative velocity of the target, the size of the target, the size of various features of the target, and the azimuth and elevation of the target. The complex neural computations needed to extract all this information from the target echo occur within a brain the size of a plum. Indeed, an echolocating bat can pursue and capture its target with a facility and success rate that would be the envy of a radar or sonar engineer.

How, then, does a human brain or the brain of a bat do it? At birth, a brain already has considerable structure and the ability to build up its own rules of behavior through what we usually refer to as "experience." Indeed, experience is built up over time, with much of the development (i.e., hardwiring) of the human brain taking place during the first two years from birth, but the development continues well beyond that stage.

A "developing" nervous system is synonymous with a plastic brain: *Plasticity* permits the developing nervous system to *adapt* to its surrounding environment. Just as plasticity appears to be essential to the functioning of neurons as information-processing units in the human brain, so it is with neural networks made up of artificial neurons. In

1

its most general form, a *neural network* is a machine that is designed to *model* the way in which the brain performs a particular task or function of interest; the network is usually implemented by using electronic components or is simulated in software on a digital computer. In this book, we focus on an important class of neural networks that perform useful computations through a process of *learning*. To achieve good performance, neural networks employ a massive interconnection of simple computing cells referred to as "neurons" or "processing units." We may thus offer the following definition of a neural network viewed as an adaptive machine[1]:

> *A neural network is a massively parallel distributed processor made up of simple processing units that has a natural propensity for storing experiential knowledge and making it available for use. It resembles the brain in two respects:*
>
> 1. *Knowledge is acquired by the network from its environment through a learning process.*
> 2. *Interneuron connection strengths, known as synaptic weights, are used to store the acquired knowledge.*

The procedure used to perform the learning process is called a *learning algorithm*, the function of which is to modify the synaptic weights of the network in an orderly fashion to attain a desired design objective.

The modification of synaptic weights provides the traditional method for the design of neural networks. Such an approach is the closest to linear adaptive filter theory, which is already well established and successfully applied in many diverse fields (Widrow and Stearns, 1985; Haykin, 2002). However, it is also possible for a neural network to modify its own topology, which is motivated by the fact that neurons in the human brain can die and new synaptic connections can grow.

Benefits of Neural Networks

It is apparent that a neural network derives its computing power through, first, its massively parallel distributed structure and, second, its ability to learn and therefore generalize. *Generalization* refers to the neural network's production of reasonable outputs for inputs not encountered during training (learning). These two information-processing capabilities make it possible for neural networks to find good approximate solutions to complex (large-scale) problems that are *intractable*. In practice, however, neural networks cannot provide the solution by working individually. Rather, they need to be integrated into a consistent system engineering approach. Specifically, a complex problem of interest is *decomposed* into a number of relatively simple tasks, and neural networks are assigned a subset of the tasks that *match* their inherent capabilities. It is important to recognize, however, that we have a long way to go (if ever) before we can build a computer architecture that mimics the human brain.

Neural networks offer the following useful properties and capabilities:

1. *Nonlinearity.* An artificial neuron can be linear or nonlinear. A neural network, made up of an interconnection of nonlinear neurons, is itself nonlinear. Moreover, the nonlinearity is of a special kind in the sense that it is *distributed* throughout the network. Nonlinearity is a highly important property, particularly if the underlying physical mechanism responsible for generation of the input signal (e.g., speech signal) is inherently nonlinear.

2. *Input–Output Mapping.* A popular paradigm of learning, called *learning with a teacher*, or *supervised learning*, involves modification of the synaptic weights of a neural network by applying a set of labeled *training examples*, or *task examples.* Each example consists of a unique *input signal* and a corresponding *desired (target) response.* The network is presented with an example picked at random from the set, and the synaptic weights (free parameters) of the network are modified to minimize the difference between the desired response and the actual response of the network produced by the input signal in accordance with an appropriate statistical criterion. The training of the network is repeated for many examples in the set, until the network reaches a steady state where there are no further significant changes in the synaptic weights. The previously applied training examples may be reapplied during the training session, but in a different order. Thus the network learns from the examples by constructing an *input–output mapping* for the problem at hand. Such an approach brings to mind the study of *nonparametric statistical inference*, which is a branch of statistics dealing with model-free estimation, or, from a biological viewpoint, *tabula rasa* learning (Geman et al., 1992); the term "nonparametric" is used here to signify the fact that no prior assumptions are made on a statistical model for the input data. Consider, for example, a *pattern classification* task, where the requirement is to assign an input signal representing a physical object or event to one of several prespecified categories (classes). In a nonparametric approach to this problem, the requirement is to "estimate" arbitrary decision boundaries in the input signal space for the pattern-classification task using a set of examples, and to do so *without* invoking a probabilistic distribution model. A similar point of view is implicit in the supervised learning paradigm, which suggests a close analogy between the input–output mapping performed by a neural network and nonparametric statistical inference.

3. *Adaptivity.* Neural networks have a built-in capability to *adapt* their synaptic weights to changes in the surrounding environment. In particular, a neural network trained to operate in a specific environment can be easily *retrained* to deal with minor changes in the operating environmental conditions. Moreover, when it is operating in a *nonstationary* environment (i.e., one where statistics change with time), a neural network may be designed to change its synaptic weights in real time. The natural architecture of a neural network for pattern classification, signal processing, and control applications, coupled with the adaptive capability of the network, makes it a useful tool in adaptive pattern classification, adaptive signal processing, and adaptive control. As a general rule, it may be said that the more adaptive we make a system, all the time ensuring that the system remains stable, the more robust its performance will likely be when the system is required to operate in a nonstationary environment. It should be emphasized, however, that adaptivity does not always lead to robustness; indeed, it may do the very opposite. For example, an adaptive system with short-time constants may change rapidly and therefore tend to respond to spurious disturbances, causing a drastic degradation in system performance. To realize the full benefits of adaptivity, the principal time constants of the system should be long enough for the system to ignore spurious disturbances, and yet short enough to respond to meaningful changes in the environment; the problem described here is referred to as the *stability–plasticity dilemma* (Grossberg, 1988).

4. *Evidential Response.* In the context of pattern classification, a neural network can be designed to provide information not only about which particular pattern to *select*, but also about the *confidence* in the decision made. This latter information may be used to reject ambiguous patterns, should they arise, and thereby improve the classification performance of the network.

5. *Contextual Information.* Knowledge is represented by the very structure and activation state of a neural network. Every neuron in the network is potentially affected by the global activity of all other neurons in the network. Consequently, contextual information is dealt with naturally by a neural network.

6. *Fault Tolerance.* A neural network, implemented in hardware form, has the potential to be inherently *fault tolerant*, or capable of robust computation, in the sense that its performance degrades gracefully under adverse operating conditions. For example, if a neuron or its connecting links are damaged, recall of a stored pattern is impaired in quality. However, due to the distributed nature of information stored in the network, the damage has to be extensive before the overall response of the network is degraded seriously. Thus, in principle, a neural network exhibits a graceful degradation in performance rather than catastrophic failure. There is some empirical evidence for robust computation, but usually it is uncontrolled. In order to be assured that the neural network is, in fact, fault tolerant, it may be necessary to take corrective measures in designing the algorithm used to train the network (Kerlirzin and Vallet, 1993).

7. *VLSI Implementability.* The massively parallel nature of a neural network makes it potentially fast for the computation of certain tasks. This same feature makes a neural network well suited for implementation using *very-large-scale-integrated* (VLSI) technology. One particular beneficial virtue of VLSI is that it provides a means of capturing truly complex behavior in a highly hierarchical fashion (Mead, 1989).

8. *Uniformity of Analysis and Design.* Basically, neural networks enjoy universality as information processors. We say this in the sense that the same notation is used in all domains involving the application of neural networks. This feature manifests itself in different ways:

- Neurons, in one form or another, represent an ingredient *common* to all neural networks.
- This commonality makes it possible to *share* theories and learning algorithms in different applications of neural networks.
- Modular networks can be built through a *seamless integration of modules*.

9. *Neurobiological Analogy.* The design of a neural network is motivated by analogy with the brain, which is living proof that fault-tolerant parallel processing is not only physically possible, but also fast and powerful. Neurobiologists look to (artificial) neural networks as a research tool for the interpretation of neurobiological phenomena. On the other hand, engineers look to neurobiology for new ideas to solve problems more complex than those based on conventional hardwired design techniques. These two viewpoints are illustrated by the following two respective examples:

- In Anastasio (1993), linear system models of the *vestibulo-ocular reflex* (VOR) are compared to neural network models based on *recurrent networks*, which are described in Section 6 and discussed in detail in Chapter 15. The vestibulo-ocular reflex is part of the oculomotor system. The function of VOR is to maintain visual (i.e., retinal) image stability by making eye rotations that are opposite to head rotations. The VOR is mediated by premotor neurons in the vestibular nuclei that receive and process head rotation signals from vestibular sensory neurons and send the results to the eye muscle motor neurons. The VOR is well suited for modeling because its input (head rotation) and its output (eye rotation) can be precisely specified. It is also a relatively simple reflex, and the neurophysiological properties of its constituent neurons have been well described. Among the three neural types, the premotor neurons (reflex interneurons) in the vestibular nuclei are the most complex and therefore most interesting. The VOR has previously been modeled using lumped, linear system descriptors and control theory. These models were useful in explaining some of the overall properties of the VOR, but gave little insight into the properties of its constituent neurons. This situation has been greatly improved through neural network modeling. Recurrent network models of VOR (programmed using an algorithm called real-time recurrent learning, described in Chapter 15) can reproduce and help explain many of the static, dynamic, nonlinear, and distributed aspects of signal processing by the neurons that mediate the VOR, especially the vestibular nuclei neurons.

- The *retina*, more than any other part of the brain, is where we begin to put together the relationships between the outside world represented by a visual sense, its *physical image* projected onto an array of receptors, and the first *neural images*. The retina is a thin sheet of neural tissue that lines the posterior hemisphere of the eyeball. The retina's task is to convert an optical image into a neural image for transmission down the optic nerve to a multitude of centers for further analysis. This is a complex task, as evidenced by the synaptic organization of the retina. In all vertebrate retinas, the transformation from optical to neural image involves three stages (Sterling, 1990):

   (i) photo transduction by a layer of receptor neurons;
   (ii) transmission of the resulting signals (produced in response to light) by chemical synapses to a layer of bipolar cells;
   (iii) transmission of these signals, also by chemical synapses, to output neurons that are called ganglion cells.

At both synaptic stages (i.e., from receptor to bipolar cells, and from bipolar to ganglion cells), there are specialized laterally connected neurons called *horizontal cells* and *amacrine cells*, respectively. The task of these neurons is to modify the transmission across the synaptic layers. There are also centrifugal elements called *inter-plexiform cells*; their task is to convey signals from the inner synaptic layer back to the outer one. Some researchers have built electronic chips that mimic the structure of the retina. These electronic chips are called *neuromorphic* integrated circuits, a term coined by Mead (1989). A neuromorphic imaging sensor consists of an array of photoreceptors combined with analog circuitry at each picture element (pixel). It emulates the retina in that it can adapt locally to changes in brightness, detect edges, and detect motion. The neurobiological analogy, exemplified by neuromorphic integrated circuits, is useful in another important way: It provides a hope and belief, and to a certain extent an existence of proof, that physical understanding of neurobiological structures could have a productive influence on the art of electronics and VLSI technology for the implementation of neural networks.

With inspiration from neurobiology in mind, it seems appropriate that we take a brief look at the human brain and its structural levels of organization.[2]

2 THE HUMAN BRAIN

The human nervous system may be viewed as a three-stage system, as depicted in the block diagram of Fig. 1 (Arbib, 1987). Central to the system is the *brain*, represented by the *neural (nerve) net*, which continually receives information, perceives it, and makes appropriate decisions. Two sets of arrows are shown in the figure. Those pointing from left to right indicate the *forward* transmission of information-bearing signals through the system. The arrows pointing from right to left (shown in red) signify the presence of *feedback* in the system. The *receptors* convert stimuli from the human body or the external environment into electrical impulses that convey information to the neural net (brain). The *effectors* convert electrical impulses generated by the neural net into discernible responses as system outputs.

The struggle to understand the brain has been made easier because of the pioneering work of Ramón y Cajál (1911), who introduced the idea of *neurons* as structural constituents of the brain. Typically, neurons are five to six orders of magnitude slower than silicon logic gates; events in a silicon chip happen in the nanosecond range, whereas neural events happen in the millisecond range. However, the brain makes up for the relatively slow rate of operation of a neuron by having a truly staggering number of neurons (nerve cells) with massive interconnections between them. It is estimated that there are approximately 10 billion neurons in the human cortex, and 60 trillion synapses or connections (Shepherd and Koch, 1990). The net result is that the brain is an enormously efficient structure. Specifically, the *energetic efficiency* of the brain is approximately 10^{-16} joules (J) per operation per second, whereas the corresponding value for the best computers is orders of magnitude larger.

Synapses, or *nerve endings*, are elementary structural and functional units that mediate the interactions between neurons. The most common kind of synapse is a *chemical synapse*, which operates as follows: A presynaptic process liberates a *transmitter* substance that diffuses across the synaptic junction between neurons and then acts on a postsynaptic process. Thus a synapse converts a presynaptic electrical signal into a chemical

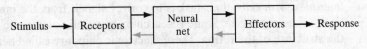

FIGURE 1 Block diagram representation of nervous system.

signal and then back into a postsynaptic electrical signal (Shepherd and Koch, 1990). In electrical terminology, such an element is said to be a *nonreciprocal two-port device*. In traditional descriptions of neural organization, it is assumed that a synapse is a simple connection that can impose *excitation* or *inhibition*, but not both on the receptive neuron.

Earlier we mentioned that plasticity permits the developing nervous system to adapt to its surrounding environment (Eggermont, 1990; Churchland and Sejnowski, 1992). In an adult brain, plasticity may be accounted for by two mechanisms: the creation of new synaptic connections between neurons, and the modification of existing synapses. *Axons*, the transmission lines, and *dendrites*, the receptive zones, constitute two types of cell filaments that are distinguished on morphological grounds; an axon has a smoother surface, fewer branches, and greater length, whereas a dendrite (so called because of its resemblance to a tree) has an irregular surface and more branches (Freeman, 1975). Neurons come in a wide variety of shapes and sizes in different parts of the brain. Figure 2 illustrates the shape of a *pyramidal cell*, which is one of the most common types of cortical neurons. Like many other types of neurons, it receives most of its inputs through dendritic spines; see the segment of dendrite in the insert in Fig. 2 for detail. The pyramidal cell can receive 10,000 or more synaptic contacts, and it can project onto thousands of target cells.

The majority of neurons encode their outputs as a series of brief voltage pulses. These pulses, commonly known as *action potentials*, or *spikes*,[3] originate at or close to the cell body of neurons and then propagate across the individual neurons at constant velocity and amplitude. The reasons for the use of action potentials for communication among neurons are based on the physics of axons. The axon of a neuron is very long and thin and is characterized by high electrical resistance and very large capacitance. Both of these elements are distributed across the axon. The axon may therefore be modeled as resistance-capacitance (RC) transmission line, hence the common use of "cable equation" as the terminology for describing signal propagation along an axon. Analysis of this propagation mechanism reveals that when a voltage is applied at one end of the axon, it decays exponentially with distance, dropping to an insignificant level by the time it reaches the other end. The action potentials provide a way to circumvent this transmission problem (Anderson, 1995).

In the brain, there are both small-scale and large-scale anatomical organizations, and different functions take place at lower and higher levels. Figure 3 shows a hierarchy of interwoven levels of organization that has emerged from the extensive work done on the analysis of local regions in the brain (Shepherd and Koch, 1990; Churchland and Sejnowski, 1992). The *synapses* represent the most fundamental level, depending on molecules and ions for their action. At the next levels, we have neural microcircuits, dendritic trees, and then neurons. A *neural microcircuit* refers to an assembly of synapses organized into patterns of connectivity to produce a functional operation of interest. A neural microcircuit may be likened to a silicon chip made up of an assembly of transistors. The smallest size of microcircuits is measured in micrometers (μm), and their fastest speed of operation is measured in milliseconds. The neural microcircuits are grouped to form *dendritic subunits* within the *dendritic trees* of individual neurons. The whole *neuron*, about 100 μm in size, contains several dendritic subunits. At the next level of complexity, we have *local circuits* (about 1 mm in size) made up of neurons with similar or different properties; these neural

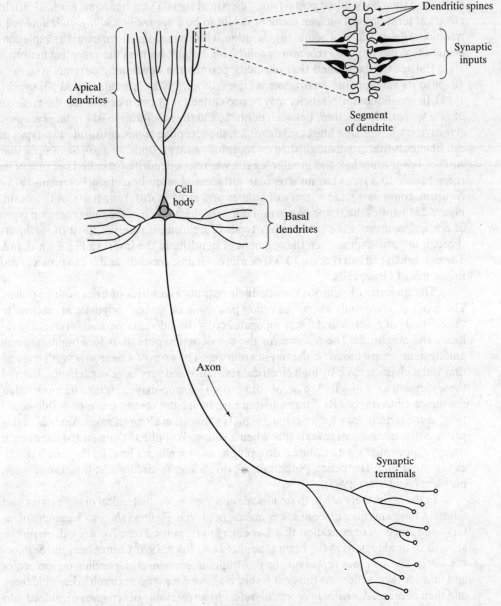

Apical dendrites

Cell body

Basal dendrites

Axon

Dendritic spines

Synaptic inputs

Segment of dendrite

Synaptic terminals

FIGURE 2   The pyramidal cell.

assemblies perform operations characteristic of a localized region in the brain. They are followed by *interregional circuits* made up of pathways, columns, and topographic maps, which involve multiple regions located in different parts of the brain.

Topographic maps are organized to respond to incoming sensory information. These maps are often arranged in sheets, as in the *superior colliculus*, where the visual,

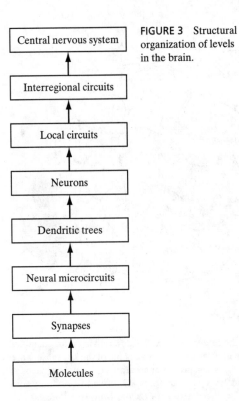

FIGURE 3   Structural organization of levels in the brain.

auditory, and somatosensory maps are stacked in adjacent layers in such a way that stimuli from corresponding points in space lie above or below each other. Figure 4 presents a cytoarchitectural map of the cerebral cortex as worked out by Brodmann (Brodal, 1981). This figure shows clearly that different sensory inputs (motor, somatosensory, visual, auditory, etc.) are mapped onto corresponding areas of the cerebral cortex in an orderly fashion. At the final level of complexity, the topographic maps and other interregional circuits mediate specific types of behavior in the *central nervous system.*

It is important to recognize that the structural levels of organization described herein are a unique characteristic of the brain. They are nowhere to be found in a digital computer, and we are nowhere close to re-creating them with artificial neural networks. Nevertheless, we are inching our way toward a hierarchy of computational levels similar to that described in Fig. 3. The artificial neurons we use to build our neural networks are truly primitive in comparison with those found in the brain. The neural networks we are presently able to design are just as primitive compared with the local circuits and the interregional circuits in the brain. What is really satisfying, however, is the remarkable progress that we have made on so many fronts. With neurobiological analogy as the source of inspiration, and the wealth of theoretical and computational tools that we are bringing together, it is certain that our understanding of artificial neural networks and their applications will continue to grow in depth as well as breadth, year after year.

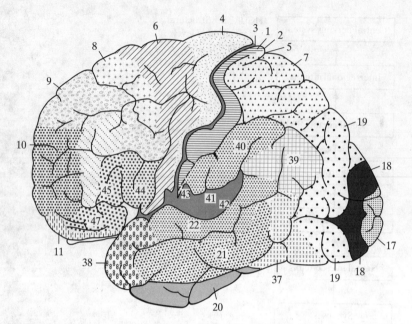

FIGURE 4 Cytoarchitectural map of the cerebral cortex. The different areas are identified by the thickness of their layers and types of cells within them. Some of the key sensory areas are as follows: Motor cortex: motor strip, area 4; premotor area, area 6; frontal eye fields, area 8. Somatosensory cortex: areas 3, 1, and 2. Visual cortex: areas 17, 18, and 19. Auditory cortex: areas 41 and 42. *(From A. Brodal, 1981; with permission of Oxford University Press.)*

3 MODELS OF A NEURON

A *neuron* is an information-processing unit that is fundamental to the operation of a neural network. The block diagram of Fig. 5 shows the *model* of a neuron, which forms the basis for designing a large family of neural networks studied in later chapters. Here, we identify three basic elements of the neural model:

1. A set of *synapses*, or *connecting links*, each of which is characterized by a *weight* or *strength* of its own. Specifically, a signal x_j at the input of synapse j connected to neuron k is multiplied by the synaptic weight w_{kj}. It is important to make a note of the manner in which the subscripts of the synaptic weight w_{kj} are written. The first subscript in w_{kj} refers to the neuron in question, and the second subscript refers to the input end of the synapse to which the weight refers. Unlike the weight of a synapse in the brain, the synaptic weight of an artificial neuron may lie in a range that includes negative as well as positive values.

2. An *adder* for summing the input signals, weighted by the respective synaptic strengths of the neuron; the operations described here constitute a *linear combiner*.

3. An *activation function* for limiting the amplitude of the output of a neuron. The activation function is also referred to as a *squashing function*, in that it squashes (limits) the permissible amplitude range of the output signal to some finite value.

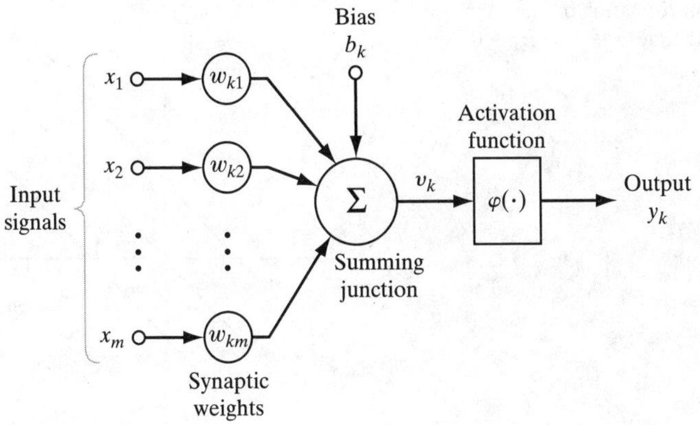

FIGURE 5 Nonlinear model of a neuron, labeled k.

Typically, the normalized amplitude range of the output of a neuron is written as the closed unit interval [0,1], or, alternatively, [−1,1].

The neural model of Fig. 5 also includes an externally applied *bias*, denoted by b_k. The bias b_k has the effect of increasing or lowering the net input of the activation function, depending on whether it is positive or negative, respectively.

In mathematical terms, we may describe the neuron k depicted in Fig. 5 by writing the pair of equations:

$$u_k = \sum_{j=1}^{m} w_{kj} x_j \qquad (1)$$

and

$$y_k = \varphi(u_k + b_k) \qquad (2)$$

where $x_1, x_2, ..., x_m$ are the input signals; $w_{k1}, w_{k2}, ..., w_{km}$ are the respective synaptic weights of neuron k; u_k (not shown in Fig. 5) is the *linear combiner output* due to the input signals; b_k is the bias; $\varphi(\cdot)$ is the *activation function*; and y_k is the output signal of the neuron. The use of bias b_k has the effect of applying an *affine transformation* to the output u_k of the linear combiner in the model of Fig. 5, as shown by

$$v_k = u_k + b_k \qquad (3)$$

In particular, depending on whether the bias b_k is positive or negative, the relationship between the *induced local field*, or *activation potential*, v_k of neuron k and the linear combiner output u_k is modified in the manner illustrated in Fig. 6; hereafter, these two terms are used interchangeably. Note that as a result of this affine transformation, the graph of v_k versus u_k no longer passes through the origin.

The bias b_k is an external parameter of neuron k. We may account for its presence as in Eq. (2). Equivalently, we may formulate the combination of Eqs. (1) to (3) as follows:

$$v_k = \sum_{j=0}^{m} w_{kj} x_j \qquad (4)$$

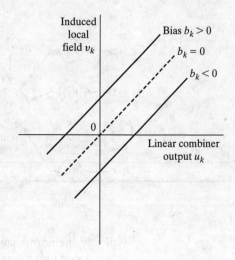

FIGURE 6 Affine transformation produced by the presence of a bias; note that $v_k = b_k$ at $u_k = 0$.

and

$$y_k = \varphi(v_k) \tag{5}$$

In Eq. (4), we have added a new synapse. Its input is

$$x_0 = +1 \tag{6}$$

and its weight is

$$w_{k0} = b_k \tag{7}$$

We may therefore reformulate the model of neuron k as shown in Fig. 7. In this figure, the effect of the bias is accounted for by doing two things: (1) adding a new input signal fixed at $+1$, and (2) adding a new synaptic weight equal to the bias b_k. Although the models of Figs. 5 and 7 are different in appearance, they are mathematically equivalent.

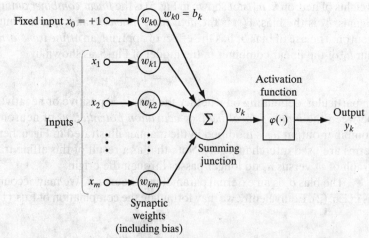

FIGURE 7 Another nonlinear model of a neuron; w_{k0} accounts for the bias b_k.

Types of Activation Function

The activation function, denoted by $\varphi(v)$, defines the output of a neuron in terms of the induced local field v. In what follows, we identify two basic types of activation functions:

1. *Threshold Function.* For this type of activation function, described in Fig. 8a, we have

$$\varphi(v) = \begin{cases} 1 & \text{if } v \geq 0 \\ 0 & \text{if } v < 0 \end{cases} \tag{8}$$

In engineering, this form of a threshold function is commonly referred to as a *Heaviside function.* Correspondingly, the output of neuron k employing such a threshold function is expressed as

$$y_k = \begin{cases} 1 & \text{if } v_k \geq 0 \\ 0 & \text{if } v_k < 0 \end{cases} \tag{9}$$

where v_k is the induced local field of the neuron; that is,

$$v_k = \sum_{j=1}^{m} w_{kj} x_j + b_k \tag{10}$$

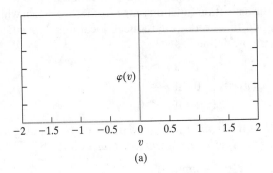

$\varphi(v)$

v

(a)

FIGURE 8   (a) Threshold function. (b) Sigmoid function for varying slope parameter a.

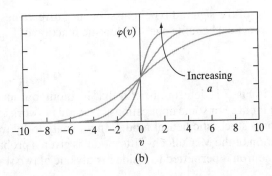

$\varphi(v)$

Increasing
a

v

(b)

In neural computation, such a neuron is referred to as the *McCulloch–Pitts model*, in recognition of the pioneering work done by McCulloch and Pitts (1943). In this model, the output of a neuron takes on the value of 1 if the induced local field of that neuron is nonnegative, and 0 otherwise. This statement describes the *all-or-none property* of the McCulloch–Pitts model.

2. *Sigmoid Function.*[4] The sigmoid function, whose graph is "S"-shaped, is by far the most common form of activation function used in the construction of neural networks. It is defined as a strictly increasing function that exhibits a graceful balance between linear and nonlinear behavior. An example of the sigmoid function is the *logistic function*,[5] defined by

$$\varphi(v) = \frac{1}{1 + \exp(-av)} \tag{11}$$

where a is the *slope parameter* of the sigmoid function. By varying the parameter a, we obtain sigmoid functions of different slopes, as illustrated in Fig. 8b. In fact, the slope at the origin equals $a/4$. In the limit, as the slope parameter approaches infinity, the sigmoid function becomes simply a threshold function. Whereas a threshold function assumes the value of 0 or 1, a sigmoid function assumes a continuous range of values from 0 to 1. Note also that the sigmoid function is differentiable, whereas the threshold function is not. (Differentiability is an important feature of neural network theory, as described in Chapter 4).

The activation functions defined in Eqs. (8) and (11) range from 0 to +1. It is sometimes desirable to have the activation function range from −1 to +1, in which case, the activation function is an odd function of the induced local field. Specifically, the threshold function of Eq. (8) is now defined as

$$\varphi(v) = \begin{cases} 1 & \text{if } v > 0 \\ 0 & \text{if } v = 0 \\ -1 & \text{if } v < 0 \end{cases} \tag{12}$$

which is commonly referred to as the *signum function*. For the corresponding form of a sigmoid function, we may use the *hyperbolic tangent function*, defined by

$$\varphi(v) = \tanh(v) \tag{13}$$

Allowing an activation function of the sigmoid type to assume negative values as prescribed by Eq. (13) may yield practical benefits over the logistic function of Eq. (11).

Stochastic Model of a Neuron

The neural model described in Fig. 7 is deterministic in that its input–output behavior is precisely defined for all inputs. For some applications of neural networks, it is desirable to base the analysis on a stochastic neural model. In an analytically tractable approach, the activation function of the McCulloch–Pitts model is given a probabilistic interpretation. Specifically, a neuron is permitted to reside in only one of two states: +1 or −1, say. The decision for a neuron to *fire* (i.e., switch its state from "off" to "on") is probabilistic. Let x denote the state of the neuron and $P(v)$ denote the *probability* of firing, where v is the induced local field of the neuron. We may then write

$$x = \begin{cases} +1 & \text{with probability } P(v) \\ -1 & \text{with probability } 1 - P(v) \end{cases} \tag{14}$$

A standard choice for $P(v)$ is the sigmoid-shaped function

$$P(v) = \frac{1}{1 + \exp(-v/T)} \tag{15}$$

where T is a *pseudotemperature* used to control the noise level and therefore the uncertainty in firing (Little, 1974). It is important to realize, however, that T is *not* the physical temperature of a neural network, be it a biological or an artificial neural network. Rather, as already stated, we should think of T merely as a parameter that controls the thermal fluctuations representing the effects of synaptic noise. Note that when $T \to 0$, the stochastic neuron described by Eqs. (14) and (15) reduces to a noiseless (i.e., deterministic) form, namely, the McCulloch–Pitts model.

4   NEURAL NETWORKS VIEWED AS DIRECTED GRAPHS

The *block diagram* of Fig. 5 or that of Fig. 7 provides a functional description of the various elements that constitute the model of an artificial neuron. We may simplify the appearance of the model by using the idea of signal-flow graphs without sacrificing any of the functional details of the model. Signal-flow graphs, with a well-defined set of rules, were originally developed by Mason (1953, 1956) for linear networks. The presence of nonlinearity in the model of a neuron limits the scope of their application to neural networks. Nevertheless, signal-flow graphs do provide a neat method for the portrayal of the flow of signals in a neural network, which we pursue in this section.

A *signal-flow graph* is a network of directed *links* (*branches*) that are interconnected at certain points called *nodes*. A typical node j has an associated *node signal* x_j. A typical directed link originates at node j and terminates on node k; it has an associated *transfer function*, or *transmittance*, that specifies the manner in which the signal y_k at node k depends on the signal x_j at node j. The flow of signals in the various parts of the graph is dictated by three basic rules:

Rule 1. A signal flows along a link only in the direction defined by the arrow on the link.

Two different types of links may be distinguished:

- *Synaptic links*, whose behavior is governed by a *linear* input–output relation. Specifically, the node signal x_j is multiplied by the synaptic weight w_{kj} to produce the node signal y_k, as illustrated in Fig. 9a.
- *Activation links*, whose behavior is governed in general by a *nonlinear* input–output relation. This form of relationship is illustrated in Fig. 9b, where $\varphi(\cdot)$ is the nonlinear activation function.

FIGURE 9   Illustrating basic rules for
the construction of signal-flow graphs.

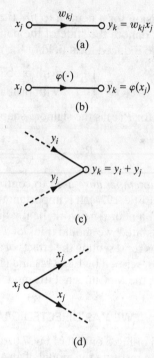

$$x_j \circ \xrightarrow{w_{kj}} \circ\, y_k = w_{kj}x_j$$

(a)

$$x_j \circ \xrightarrow{\varphi(\cdot)} \circ\, y_k = \varphi(x_j)$$

(b)

$$y_k = y_i + y_j$$

(c)

(d)

Rule 2.   A node signal equals the algebraic sum of all signals entering the pertinent
node via the incoming links.

This second rule is illustrated in Fig. 9c for the case of *synaptic convergence*, or *fan-in*.

Rule 3.   The signal at a node is transmitted to each outgoing link originating from
that node, with the transmission being entirely independent of the transfer
functions of the outgoing links.

This third rule is illustrated in Fig. 9d for the case of *synaptic divergence*, or *fan-out*.
For example, using these rules, we may construct the signal-flow graph of Fig. 10 as
the model of a neuron, corresponding to the block diagram of Fig. 7. The representation
shown in Fig. 10 is clearly simpler in appearance than that of Fig. 7, yet it contains all the
functional details depicted in the latter diagram. Note that in both figures, the input $x_0 = +1$
and the associated synaptic weight $w_{k0} = b_k$, where b_k is the bias applied to neuron k.
Indeed, based on the signal-flow graph of Fig. 10 as the model of a neuron, we may
now offer the following mathematical definition of a neural network:

*A neural network is a directed graph consisting of nodes with interconnecting synaptic and
activation links and is characterized by four properties:*

1.   *Each neuron is represented by a set of linear synaptic links, an externally applied bias,
     and a possibly nonlinear activation link. The bias is represented by a synaptic link con-
     nected to an input fixed at +1.*
2.   *The synaptic links of a neuron weight their respective input signals.*

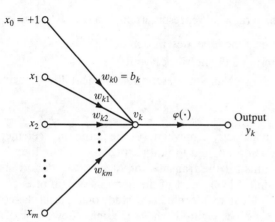

FIGURE 10   Signal-flow graph of a neuron.

3. *The weighted sum of the input signals defines the induced local field of the neuron in question.*
4. *The activation link squashes the induced local field of the neuron to produce an output.*

A directed graph, defined in this manner is *complete* in the sense that it describes not only the signal flow from neuron to neuron, but also the signal flow inside each neuron. When, however, the focus of attention is restricted to signal flow from neuron to neuron, we may use a reduced form of this graph by omitting the details of signal flow inside the individual neurons. Such a directed graph is said to be *partially complete*. It is characterized as follows:

1. *Source nodes* supply input signals to the graph.
2. Each neuron is represented by a single node called a *computation node*.
3. The *communication links* interconnecting the source and computation nodes of the graph carry no weight; they merely provide directions of signal flow in the graph.

A partially complete directed graph defined in this way is referred to as an *architectural graph*, describing the layout of the neural network. It is illustrated in Fig. 11 for the simple case of a single neuron with m source nodes and a single node fixed at $+1$ for the bias. Note that the computation node representing the neuron is shown shaded, and the source node is shown as a small square. This convention is followed throughout the book. More elaborate examples of architectural layouts are presented later in Section 6.

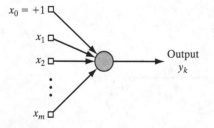

FIGURE 11   Architectural graph of a neuron.

To sum up, we have three graphical representations of a neural network:

- block diagram, providing a functional description of the network;
- architectural graph, describing the network layout;
- signal-flow graph, providing a complete description of signal flow in the network.

5 FEEDBACK

Feedback is said to exist in a dynamic system whenever the output of an element in the system influences in part the input applied to that particular element, thereby giving rise to one or more closed paths for the transmission of signals around the system. Indeed, feedback occurs in almost every part of the nervous system of every animal (Freeman, 1975). Moreover, it plays a major role in the study of a special class of neural networks known as *recurrent networks.* Figure 12 shows the signal-flow graph of a *single-loop feedback system,* where the input signal $x_j(n)$, internal signal $x_j'(n)$, and output signal $y_k(n)$ are functions of the discrete-time variable n. The system is assumed to be *linear,* consisting of a forward path and a feedback path that are characterized by the "operators" $\mathbf{A}$ and $\mathbf{B}$, respectively. In particular, the output of the forward channel determines in part its own output through the feedback channel. From Fig. 12, we readily note the input–output relationships

$$y_k(n) = \mathbf{A}[x_j'(n)] \tag{16}$$

and

$$x_j'(n) = x_j(n) + \mathbf{B}[y_k(n)] \tag{17}$$

where the square brackets are included to emphasize that $\mathbf{A}$ and $\mathbf{B}$ act as *operators.* Eliminating $x_j'(n)$ between Eqs. (16) and (17), we get

$$y_k(n) = \frac{\mathbf{A}}{1 - \mathbf{AB}}[x_j(n)] \tag{18}$$

We refer to $\mathbf{A}/(1 - \mathbf{AB})$ as the *closed-loop operator* of the system, and to $\mathbf{AB}$ as the *open-loop operator.* In general, the open-loop operator is noncommutative in that $\mathbf{BA} \neq \mathbf{AB}$.

Consider, for example, the single-loop feedback system shown in Fig. 13a, for which $\mathbf{A}$ is a fixed weight w and $\mathbf{B}$ is a *unit-delay operator* z^{-1}, whose output is delayed with respect to the input by one time unit. We may then express the closed-loop operator of the system as

$$\frac{\mathbf{A}}{1 - \mathbf{AB}} = \frac{w}{1 - wz^{-1}}$$

$$= w(1 - wz^{-1})^{-1}$$

FIGURE 12 Signal-flow graph of a single-loop feedback system.

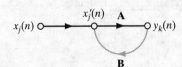

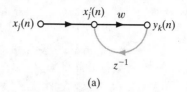

(a)

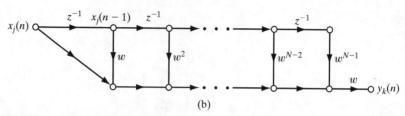

(b)

FIGURE 13   (a) Signal-flow graph of a first-order, infinite-duration impulse response (IIR) filter. (b) Feedforward approximation of part (a) of the figure, obtained by truncating Eq. (20).

Using the binomial expansion for $(1 - wz^{-1})^{-1}$, we may rewrite the closed-loop operator of the system as

$$\frac{A}{1 - AB} = w \sum_{l=0}^{\infty} w^l z^{-l} \tag{19}$$

Hence, substituting Eq. (19) into (18), we get

$$y_k(n) = w \sum_{l=0}^{\infty} w^l z^{-l} [x_j(n)] \tag{20}$$

where again we have included square brackets to emphasize the fact that z^{-1} is an operator. In particular, from the definition of z^{-1}, we have

$$z^{-l}[x_j(n)] = x_j(n - l) \tag{21}$$

where $x_j(n - l)$ is a sample of the input signal delayed by l time units. Accordingly, we may express the output signal $y_k(n)$ as an infinite weighted summation of present and past samples of the input signal $x_j(n)$, as shown by

$$y_k(n) = \sum_{l=0}^{\infty} w^{l+1} x_j(n - l) \tag{22}$$

We now see clearly that the dynamic behavior of a feedback system represented by the signal-flow graph of Fig. 13 is controlled by the weight w. In particular, we may distinguish two specific cases:

1. $|w| < 1$, for which the output signal $y_k(n)$ is exponentially *convergent*; that is, the system is *stable*. This case is illustrated in Fig. 14a for a positive w.
2. $|w| \geq 1$, for which the output signal $y_k(n)$ is *divergent*; that is, the system is *unstable*. If $|w| = 1$ the divergence is linear, as in Fig. 14b, and if $|w| > 1$ the divergence is exponential, as in Fig. 14c.

FIGURE 14   Time response of
Fig. 13 for three different values
of feedforward weight w.
(a) Stable.
(b) Linear divergence.
(c) Exponential divergence.

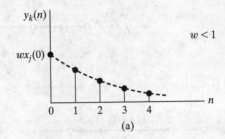

(a)

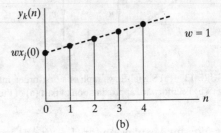

(b)

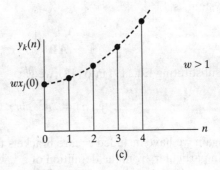

(c)

The issue of stability features prominently in the study of closed-loop feedback systems.
      The case of $|w| < 1$ corresponds to a system with *infinite memory* in the sense that
the output of the system depends on samples of the input extending into the infinite
past. Moreover, the memory is *fading* in that the influence of a past sample is reduced
exponentially with time n. Suppose that, for some power N, $|w|$ is small enough relative
to unity such that w^N is negligible for all practical purposes. In such a situation, we may
approximate the output y_k by the finite sum

$$y_k(n) \approx \sum_{l=0}^{N-1} w^{l+1} x_j(n-l)$$

$$= w x_j(n) + w^2 x_j(n-1) + w^3 x_j(n-2) + \cdots + w^N x_j(n-N+1)$$

In a corresponding way, we may use the feedforward signal-flow graph of Fig. 13b as
the approximation for the feedback signal-flow graph of Fig. 13a. In making this approximation, we speak of the "unfolding" of a feedback system. Note, however, that
the unfolding operation is of practical value only when the feedback system is stable.

The analysis of the dynamic behavior of neural networks involving the application of feedback is unfortunately complicated by the fact that the processing units used for the construction of the network are usually *nonlinear.* Further consideration of this important issue is deferred to the latter part of the book.

6   NETWORK ARCHITECTURES

The manner in which the neurons of a neural network are structured is intimately linked with the learning algorithm used to train the network. We may therefore speak of learning algorithms (rules) used in the design of neural networks as being *structured.* The classification of learning algorithms is considered in Section 8. In this section, we focus attention on network architectures (structures).

In general, we may identify three fundamentally different classes of network architectures:

(i)   Single-Layer Feedforward Networks

In a *layered* neural network, the neurons are organized in the form of layers. In the simplest form of a layered network, we have an *input layer* of source nodes that projects directly onto an *output layer* of neurons (computation nodes), but not vice versa. In other words, this network is strictly of a *feedforward* type. It is illustrated in Fig. 15 for the case of four nodes in both the input and output layers. Such a network is called a *single-layer network,* with the designation "single-layer" referring to the output layer of computation nodes (neurons). We do not count the input layer of source nodes because no computation is performed there.

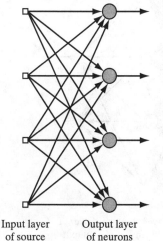

FIGURE 15   Feedforward network
with a single layer of neurons.

Input layer   Output layer
of source   of neurons
nodes

(ii) Multilayer Feedforward Networks

The second class of a feedforward neural network distinguishes itself by the presence of one or more *hidden layers*, whose computation nodes are correspondingly called *hidden neurons* or *hidden units*; the term "hidden" refers to the fact that this part of the neural network is not seen directly from either the input or output of the network. The function of hidden neurons is to intervene between the external input and the network output in some useful manner. By adding one or more hidden layers, the network is enabled to extract higher-order statistics from its input. In a rather loose sense, the network acquires a *global* perspective despite its local connectivity, due to the extra set of synaptic connections and the extra dimension of neural interactions (Churchland and Sejnowski, 1992).

The source nodes in the input layer of the network supply respective elements of the activation pattern (input vector), which constitute the input signals applied to the neurons (computation nodes) in the second layer (i.e., the first hidden layer). The output signals of the second layer are used as inputs to the third layer, and so on for the rest of the network. Typically, the neurons in each layer of the network have as their inputs the output signals of the preceding layer only. The set of output signals of the neurons in the output (final) layer of the network constitutes the overall response of the network to the activation pattern supplied by the source nodes in the input (first) layer. The architectural graph in Fig. 16 illustrates the layout of a multilayer feedforward neural network for the case of a single hidden layer. For the sake of brevity, the network in Fig. 16 is referred to as a 10–4–2 network because it has 10 source nodes, 4 hidden neurons, and 2 output neurons. As another example, a feedforward network with m source nodes, h_1 neurons in the first hidden layer, h_2 neurons in the second hidden layer, and q neurons in the output layer is referred to as an m–h_1–h_2–q network.

FIGURE 16   Fully connected feedforward network with one hidden layer and one output layer.

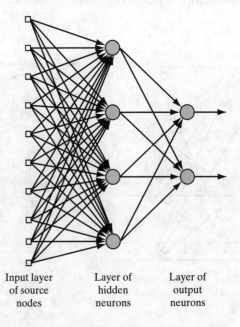

Input layer   Layer of   Layer of
of source   hidden   output
nodes   neurons   neurons

The neural network in Fig. 16 is said to be *fully connected* in the sense that every node in each layer of the network is connected to every other node in the adjacent forward layer. If, however, some of the communication links (synaptic connections) are missing from the network, we say that the network is *partially connected*.

(iii)   Recurrent Networks

A *recurrent neural network* distinguishes itself from a feedforward neural network in that it has at least one *feedback* loop. For example, a recurrent network may consist of a single layer of neurons with each neuron feeding its output signal back to the inputs of all the other neurons, as illustrated in the architectural graph in Fig. 17. In the structure depicted in this figure, there are *no* self-feedback loops in the network; self-feedback refers to a situation where the output of a neuron is fed back into its own input. The recurrent network illustrated in Fig. 17 also has *no* hidden neurons.

In Fig. 18 we illustrate another class of recurrent networks with hidden neurons. The feedback connections shown in Fig. 18 originate from the hidden neurons as well as from the output neurons.

The presence of feedback loops, be it in the recurrent structure of Fig. 17 or in that of Fig. 18, has a profound impact on the learning capability of the network and on its performance. Moreover, the feedback loops involve the use of particular branches composed of unit-time delay elements (denoted by z^{-1}), which result in a nonlinear dynamic behavior, assuming that the neural network contains nonlinear units.

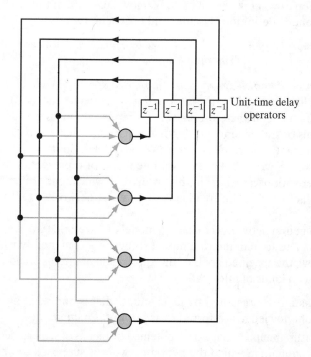

Unit-time delay operators

FIGURE 17   Recurrent network with no self-feedback loops and no hidden neurons.

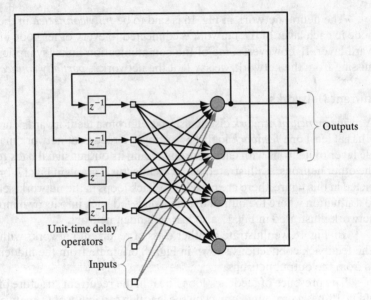

FIGURE 18 Recurrent network with hidden neurons.

7 KNOWLEDGE REPRESENTATION

In Section 1, we used the term "knowledge" in the definition of a neural network without an explicit description of what we mean by it. We now take care of this matter by offering the following generic definition (Fischler and Firschein, 1987):

Knowledge refers to stored information or models used by a person or machine to interpret, predict, and appropriately respond to the outside world.

The primary characteristics of *knowledge representation* are twofold: (1) what information is actually made explicit; and (2) how the information is physically encoded for subsequent use. By the very nature of it, therefore, knowledge representation is goal directed. In real-world applications of "intelligent" machines, it can be said that a good solution depends on a good representation of knowledge (Woods, 1986). So it is with neural networks. Typically, however, we find that the possible forms of representation from the inputs to internal network parameters are highly diverse, which tends to make the development of a satisfactory solution by means of a neural network a real design challenge.

A major task for a neural network is to learn a model of the world (environment) in which it is embedded, and to maintain the model sufficiently consistently with the real world so as to achieve the specified goals of the application of interest. Knowledge of the world consists of two kinds of information:

1. The known world state, represented by facts about what is and what has been known; this form of knowledge is referred to as *prior information*.
2. Observations (measurements) of the world, obtained by means of sensors designed to probe the environment, in which the neural network is supposed to operate.

Ordinarily, these observations are inherently noisy, being subject to errors due to sensor noise and system imperfections. In any event, the observations so obtained provide the pool of information, from which the *examples* used to train the neural network are drawn.

The examples can be *labeled* or *unlabeled*. In labeled examples, each example representing an *input signal* is paired with a corresponding *desired response* (i.e., target output). On the other hand, unlabeled examples consist of different realizations of the input signal all by itself. In any event, a set of examples, labeled or otherwise, represents knowledge about the environment of interest that a neural network can learn through training. Note, however, that labeled examples may be expensive to collect, as they require the availability of a "teacher" to provide a desired response for each labeled example. In contrast, unlabeled examples are usually abundant as there is no need for supervision.

A set of input–output pairs, with each pair consisting of an input signal and the corresponding desired response, is referred to as a *set of training data*, or simply *training sample*. To illustrate how such a data set can be used, consider, for example, the *handwritten-digit recognition problem*. In this problem, the input signal consists of an image with black or white pixels, with each image representing one of 10 digits that are well separated from the background. The desired response is defined by the "identity" of the particular digit whose image is presented to the network as the input signal. Typically, the training sample consists of a large variety of handwritten digits that are representative of a real-world situation. Given such a set of examples, the design of a neural network may proceed as follows:

- An appropriate architecture is selected for the neural network, with an input layer consisting of source nodes equal in number to the pixels of an input image, and an output layer consisting of 10 neurons (one for each digit). A subset of examples is then used to train the network by means of a suitable algorithm. This phase of the network design is called *learning*.

- The recognition performance of the trained network is *tested* with data not seen before. Specifically, an input image is presented to the network, but this time the network is not told the identity of the digit which that particular image represents. The performance of the network is then assessed by comparing the digit recognition reported by the network with the actual identity of the digit in question. This second phase of the network operation is called *testing*, and successful performance on the test patterns is called *generalization*, a term borrowed from psychology.

Herein lies a fundamental difference between the design of a neural network and that of its classical information-processing counterpart: the pattern classifier. In the latter case, we usually proceed by first formulating a mathematical model of environmental observations, validating the model with real data, and then building the design on the basis of the model. In contrast, the design of a neural network is based directly on real-life data, with the *data set being permitted to speak for itself*. Thus, the neural network not only provides the implicit model of the environment in which it is embedded, but also performs the information-processing function of interest.

The examples used to train a neural network may consist of both *positive* and *negative* examples. For instance, in a passive sonar detection problem, positive examples pertain to input training data that contain the target of interest (e.g., a submarine). Now, in a passive sonar environment, the possible presence of marine life in the test data is known to cause occasional false alarms. To alleviate this problem, negative examples (e.g., echos from marine life) are included purposely in the training data to teach the network not to confuse marine life with the target.

In a neural network of specified architecture, knowledge representation of the surrounding environment is defined by the values taken on by the free parameters (i.e., synaptic weights and biases) of the network. The form of this knowledge representation constitutes the very design of the neural network, and therefore holds the key to its performance.

Roles of Knowledge Representation

The subject of how knowledge is actually represented inside an artificial network is, however, very complicated. Nevertheless, there are four rules for knowledge representation that are of a general commonsense nature, as described next.

> **Rule 1.** Similar inputs (i.e., patterns drawn) from similar classes should usually produce similar representations inside the network, and should therefore be classified as belonging to the same class.

There is a plethora of measures for determining the similarity between inputs. A commonly used *measure of similarity* is based on the concept of Euclidian distance. To be specific, let $\mathbf{x}_i$ denote an m-by-1 vector

$$\mathbf{x}_i = [x_{i1}, x_{i2}, ..., x_{im}]^T$$

all of whose elements are real; the superscript T denotes matrix *transposition*. The vector $\mathbf{x}_i$ defines a point in an m-dimensional space called *Euclidean space* and denoted by $\mathbb{R}^m$. As illustrated in Fig. 19, the *Euclidean distance* between a pair of m-by-1 vectors $\mathbf{x}_i$ and $\mathbf{x}_j$ is defined by

$$
\begin{aligned}
d(\mathbf{x}_i, \mathbf{x}_j) &= \|\mathbf{x}_i - \mathbf{x}_j\| \\
&= \left[\sum_{k=1}^{m} (x_{ik} - x_{jk})^2 \right]^{1/2}
\end{aligned}
\tag{23}
$$

where x_{ik} and x_{jk} are the kth elements of the input vectors $\mathbf{x}_i$ and $\mathbf{x}_j$, respectively. Correspondingly, the similarity between the inputs represented by the vectors $\mathbf{x}_i$ and $\mathbf{x}_j$ is defined as the Euclidean distance $d(\mathbf{x}_i, \mathbf{x}_j)$. The closer the individual elements of the input vectors $\mathbf{x}_i$ and $\mathbf{x}_j$ are to each other, the smaller the Euclidean distance $d(\mathbf{x}_i, \mathbf{x}_j)$ is and therefore the greater the similarity between the vectors $\mathbf{x}_i$ and $\mathbf{x}_j$ will be. Rule 1 states that if the vectors $\mathbf{x}_i$ and $\mathbf{x}_j$ are similar, they should be assigned to the same class.

Another measure of similarity is based on the idea of a *dot product*, or *inner product*, which is also borrowed from matrix algebra. Given a pair of vectors $\mathbf{x}_i$ and $\mathbf{x}_j$ of the same dimension, their inner product is $\mathbf{x}_i^T\mathbf{x}_j$, defined as the *projection* of the vector $\mathbf{x}_i$ onto the vector $\mathbf{x}_j$, as illustrated in Fig. 19. We thus write

$$
\begin{aligned}
(\mathbf{x}_i, \mathbf{x}_j) &= \mathbf{x}_i^T \mathbf{x}_j \\
&= \sum_{k=1}^{m} x_{ik} x_{jk}
\end{aligned}
\tag{24}
$$

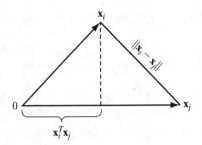

The inner product $(\mathbf{x}_i, \mathbf{x}_j)$ divided by the product $\|\mathbf{x}_i\| \|\mathbf{x}_j\|$ is the *cosine of the angle* subtended between the vectors $\mathbf{x}_i$ and $\mathbf{x}_j$.

The two measures of similarity defined here are indeed intimately related to each other, as illustrated in Fig. 19. This figure shows clearly that the smaller the Euclidean distance $\|\mathbf{x}_i - \mathbf{x}_j\|$, and therefore the more similar the vectors $\mathbf{x}_i$ and $\mathbf{x}_j$ are, the larger the inner product $\mathbf{x}_i^T \mathbf{x}_j$ will be.

To put this relationship on a formal basis, we first normalize the vectors $\mathbf{x}_i$ and $\mathbf{x}_j$ to have unit length, that is,

$$\|\mathbf{x}_i\| = \|\mathbf{x}_j\| = 1$$

We may then use Eq. (23) to write

$$\begin{aligned} d^2(\mathbf{x}_i, \mathbf{x}_j) &= (\mathbf{x}_i - \mathbf{x}_j)^T(\mathbf{x}_i - \mathbf{x}_j) \\ &= 2 - 2\mathbf{x}_i^T \mathbf{x}_j \end{aligned} \tag{25}$$

Equation (25) shows that minimization of the Euclidean distance $d(\mathbf{x}_i, \mathbf{x}_i)$ corresponds to maximization of the inner product $(\mathbf{x}_i, \mathbf{x}_j)$ and, therefore, the similarity between the vectors $\mathbf{x}_i$, and $\mathbf{x}_j$.

The Euclidean distance and inner product described here are defined in deterministic terms. What if the vectors $\mathbf{x}_i$ and $\mathbf{x}_j$ are *stochastic*, drawn from two different populations, or ensembles, of data? To be specific, suppose that the difference between these two populations lies solely in their mean vectors. Let $\boldsymbol{\mu}_i$ and $\boldsymbol{\mu}_j$ denote the mean values of the vectors $\mathbf{x}_i$ and $\mathbf{x}_j$, respectively. That is,

$$\boldsymbol{\mu}_i = \mathbb{E}[\mathbf{x}_i] \tag{26}$$

where $\mathbb{E}$ is the *statistical expectation operator* over the *ensemble* of data vectors $\mathbf{x}_i$. The mean vector $\boldsymbol{\mu}_j$ is similarly defined. For a measure of the distance between these two populations, we may use the *Mahalanobis distance*, denoted by d_{ij}. The squared value of this distance from $\mathbf{x}_i$ to $\mathbf{x}_j$ is defined by

$$d_{ij}^2 = (\mathbf{x}_i - \boldsymbol{\mu}_i)^T \mathbf{C}^{-1}(\mathbf{x}_j - \boldsymbol{\mu}_j) \tag{27}$$

where $\mathbf{C}^{-1}$ is the *inverse* of the covariance matrix $\mathbf{C}$. It is assumed that the *covariance matrix* is the same for both populations, as shown by

$$\begin{aligned} \mathbf{C} &= \mathbb{E}[(\mathbf{x}_i - \boldsymbol{\mu}_i)(\mathbf{x}_i - \boldsymbol{\mu}_i)^T] \\ &= \mathbb{E}[(\mathbf{x}_j - \boldsymbol{\mu}_j)(\mathbf{x}_j - \boldsymbol{\mu}_j)^T] \end{aligned} \tag{28}$$

Then, for a prescribed $\mathbf{C}$, the smaller the distance d_{ij} is, the more similar the vectors $\mathbf{x}_i$ and $\mathbf{x}_j$ will be.

For the special case when $\mathbf{x}_j = \mathbf{x}_i$, $\boldsymbol{\mu}_i = \boldsymbol{\mu}_j = \boldsymbol{\mu}$, and $\mathbf{C} = \mathbf{I}$, where $\mathbf{I}$ is the identity matrix, the Mahalanobis distance reduces to the Euclidean distance between the sample vector $\mathbf{x}_i$ and the mean vector $\boldsymbol{\mu}$.

Regardless of whether the data vectors $\mathbf{x}_i$ and $\mathbf{x}_j$ are deterministic or stochastic, Rule 1 addresses the issue of how these two vectors are *correlated* to each other. *Correlation* plays a key role not only in the human brain, but also in signal processing of various kinds (Chen et al., 2007).

Rule 2. Items to be categorized as separate classes should be given widely different representations in the network.

According to Rule 1, patterns drawn from a particular class have an algebraic measure (e.g., Euclidean distance) that is small. On the other hand, patterns drawn from different classes have a large algebraic measure. We may therefore say that Rule 2 is the dual of Rule 1.

Rule 3. If a particular feature is important, then there should be a large number of neurons involved in the representation of that item in the network.

Consider, for example, a radar application involving the detection of a target (e.g., aircraft) in the presence of clutter (i.e., radar reflections from undesirable targets such as buildings, trees, and weather formations). The detection performance of such a radar system is measured in terms of two probabilities:

- *probability of detection*, defined as the probability that the system decides that a target is present when it is;
- *probability of false alarm*, defined as the probability that the system decides that a target is present when it is not.

According to the *Neyman–Pearson criterion*, the probability of detection is maximized, subject to the constraint that the probability of false alarm does not exceed a prescribed value (Van Trees, 1968). In such an application, the actual presence of a target in the received signal represents an important feature of the input. Rule 3, in effect, states that there should be a large number of neurons involved in making the decision that a target is present when it actually is. By the same token, there should be a very large number of neurons involved in making the decision that the input consists of clutter only when it actually does. In both situations, the large number of neurons assures a high degree of accuracy in decision making and tolerance with respect to faulty neurons.

Rule 4. Prior information and invariances should be built into the design of a neural network whenever they are available, so as to simplify the network design by its not having to learn them.

Rule 4 is particularly important because proper adherence to it results in a neural network with a *specialized structure*. This is highly desirable for several reasons:

1. Biological visual and auditory networks are known to be very specialized.

2. A neural network with specialized structure usually has a smaller number of free parameters available for adjustment than a fully connected network. Consequently, the specialized network requires a smaller data set for training, learns faster, and often generalizes better.

3. The rate of information transmission through a specialized network (i.e., the network throughput) is accelerated.

4. The cost of building a specialized network is reduced because of its smaller size, relative to that of its fully connected counterpart.

Note, however, that the incorporation of prior knowledge into the design of a neural network *restricts* application of the network to the particular problem being addressed by the knowledge of interest.

How to Build Prior Information into Neural Network Design

An important issue that has to be addressed, of course, is how to develop a specialized structure by building prior information into its design. Unfortunately, there are currently no well-defined rules for doing this; rather, we have some *ad hoc* procedures that are known to yield useful results. In particular, we may use a combination of two techniques:

1. *restricting the network architecture*, which is achieved through the use of local connections known as *receptive fields*[6];
2. *constraining the choice of synaptic weights*, which is implemented through the use of *weight-sharing.*[7]

These two techniques, particularly the latter one, have a profitable side benefit: The number of free parameters in the network could be reduced significantly.

To be specific, consider the partially connected feedforward network of Fig. 20. This network has a restricted architecture by construction. The top six source nodes constitute

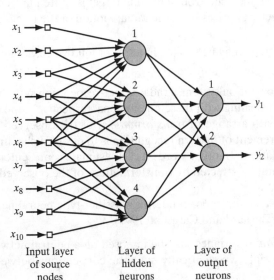

FIGURE 20   Illustrating the combined use of a receptive field and weight sharing. All four hidden neurons share the same set of weights exactly for their six synaptic connections.

Input layer of source nodes

Layer of hidden neurons

Layer of output neurons

the receptive field for hidden neuron 1, and so on for the other hidden neurons in the network. The *receptive* field of a neuron is defined as that region of the input field over which the incoming stimuli can influence the output signal produced by the neuron. The mapping of the receptive field is a powerful and shorthand description of the neuron's behavior, and therefore its output.

To satisfy the weight-sharing constraint, we merely have to use the same set of synaptic weights for each one of the neurons in the hidden layer of the network. Then, for the example shown in Fig. 20 with six local connections per hidden neuron and a total of four hidden neurons, we may express the induced local field of hidden neuron j as

$$v_j = \sum_{i=1}^{6} w_i x_{i+j-1}, \qquad j = 1, 2, 3, 4 \tag{29}$$

where $\{w_i\}_{i=1}^{6}$ constitutes the same set of weights shared by all four hidden neurons, and x_k is the signal picked up from source node $k = i + j - 1$. Equation (29) is in the form of a *convolution sum*. It is for this reason that a feedforward network using local connections and weight sharing in the manner described herein is referred to as a *convolutional network* (LeCun and Bengio, 2003).

The issue of building prior information into the design of a neural network pertains to one part of Rule 4; the remaining part of the rule involves the issue of invariances, which is discussed next.

How to Build Invariances into Neural Network Design

Consider the following physical phenomena:

- When an object of interest rotates, the image of the object as perceived by an observer usually changes in a corresponding way.
- In a coherent radar that provides amplitude as well as phase information about its surrounding environment, the echo from a moving target is shifted in frequency, due to the Doppler effect that arises from the radial motion of the target in relation to the radar.
- The utterance from a person may be spoken in a soft or loud voice, and in a slow or quick manner.

In order to build an object-recognition system, a radar target-recognition system, and a speech-recognition system for dealing with these phenomena, respectively, the system must be capable of coping with a range of *transformations* of the observed signal. Accordingly, a primary requirement of pattern recognition is to design a classifier that is *invariant* to such transformations. In other words, a class estimate represented by an output of the classifier must not be affected by transformations of the observed signal applied to the classifier input.

There are at least three techniques for rendering classifier-type neural networks invariant to transformations (Barnard and Casasent, 1991):

1. *Invariance by Structure.* Invariance may be imposed on a neutral network by structuring its design appropriately. Specifically, synaptic connections between the neurons of the network are created so that transformed versions of the same input are forced to produce the same output. Consider, for example, the classification of an input image by a neural network that is required to be independent of in-plane rotations of the image about its center. We may impose rotational invariance on the network structure as follows: Let w_{ji} be the synaptic weight of neuron j connected to pixel i in the input image. If the condition $w_{ji} = w_{jk}$ is enforced for all pixels i and k that lie at equal distances from the center of the image, then the neural network is invariant to in-plane rotations. However, in order to maintain rotational invariance, the synaptic weight w_{ji} has to be duplicated for every pixel of the input image at the same radial distance from the origin. This points to a shortcoming of invariance by structure: The number of synaptic connections in the neural network becomes prohibitively large even for images of moderate size.

2. *Invariance by Training.* A neural network has a natural ability for pattern classification. This ability may be exploited directly to obtain transformation invariance as follows: The network is trained by presenting it with a number of different examples of the same object, with the examples being chosen to correspond to different transformations (i.e., different aspect views) of the object. Provided that the number of examples is sufficiently large, and if the the network is trained to learn to discriminate between the different aspect views of the object, we may then expect the network to generalize correctly to transformations other than those shown to it. However, from an engineering perspective, invariance by training has two disadvantages. First, when a neural network has been trained to recognize an object in an invariant fashion with respect to known transformations, it is not obvious that this training will also enable the network to recognize other objects of different classes invariantly. Second, the computational demand imposed on the network may be too severe to cope with, especially if the dimensionality of the feature space is high.

3. *Invariant Feature Space.* The third technique of creating an invariant classifier-type neural network is illustrated in Fig. 21. It rests on the premise that it may be possible to extract *features* that characterize the essential information content of an input data set and that are invariant to transformations of the input. If such features are used, then the network as a classifier is relieved of the burden of having to delineate the range of transformations of an object with complicated decision boundaries. Indeed, the only differences that may arise between different instances of the same object are due to unavoidable factors such as noise and occlusion. The use of an invariant-feature space offers three distinct advantages. First, the number of features applied to the network may be reduced to realistic levels. Second, the requirements imposed on network design are relaxed. Third, invariance for all objects with respect to known transformations is assured.

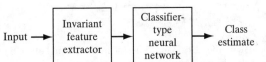

FIGURE 21   Block diagram of an invariant-feature-space type of system.

EXAMPLE 1:   Autoregressive Models

To illustrate the idea of invariant-feature space, consider the example of a coherent radar system used for air surveillance, where the targets of interest include aircraft, weather systems, flocks of migrating birds, and ground objects. The radar echoes from these targets possess different spectral characteristics. Moreover, experimental studies have shown that such radar signals can be modeled fairly closely as an *autoregressive* (AR) *process* of moderate order (Haykin and Deng, 1991). An AR model is a special form of regressive model defined for complex-valued data by

$$x(n) = \sum_{i=1}^{M} a_i^* x(n - i) + e(n) \tag{30}$$

where $\{a_i\}_{i=1}^{M}$ are the *AR coefficients*, M is the *model order*, $x(n)$ is the *input*, and $e(n)$ is the *error* described as white noise. Basically, the AR model of Eq. (30) is represented by a *tapped-delay-line filter* as illustrated in Fig. 22a for $M = 2$. Equivalently, it may be represented by a *lattice filter* as shown in Fig. 22b, the coefficients of which are called *reflection coefficients*. There is a one-to-one correspondence between the AR coefficients of the model in Fig. 22a and the reflection coefficients of the model in Fig. 22b. The two models depicted here assume that the input $x(n)$ is complex valued, as in the case of a coherent radar, in which case the AR coefficients and the reflection coefficients are all complex valued. The asterisk in Eq. (30) and Fig. 22 signifies *complex conjugation*. For now, it suffices to say that the coherent radar data may be described by a set of *autoregressive coefficients*, or by a corresponding set of *reflection coefficients*. The latter set of coefficients has

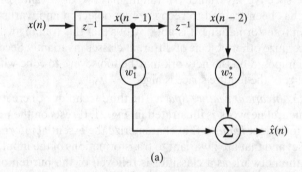

(a)

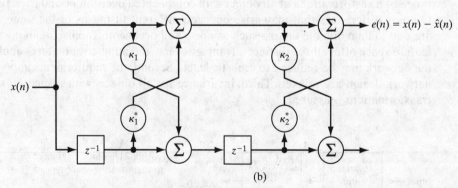

(b)

FIGURE 22   Autoregressive model of order 2: (a) tapped-delay-line model; (b) lattice-filter model. (The asterisk denotes complex conjugation.)

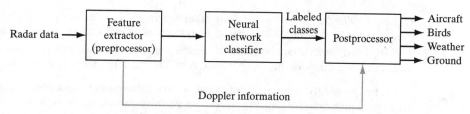

FIGURE 23   Doppler-shift-invariant classifier of radar signals.

a computational advantage in that efficient algorithms exist for their computation directly from the input data. The feature extraction problem, however, is complicated by the fact that moving objects produce varying Doppler frequencies that depend on their radial velocities measured with respect to the radar, and that tend to obscure the spectral content of the reflection coefficients as feature discriminants. To overcome this difficulty, we must build *Doppler invariance* into the computation of the reflection coefficients. The phase angle of the first reflection coefficient turns out to be equal to the Doppler frequency of the radar signal. Accordingly, Doppler frequency *normalization* is applied to all coefficients so as to remove the mean Doppler shift. This is done by defining a new set of reflection coefficients $\{\kappa'_m\}$ related to the set of ordinary reflection coefficients $\{\kappa_m\}$ computed from the input data as:

$$\kappa'_m = \kappa_m e^{-jm\theta} \qquad \text{for } m = 1, 2, ..., M \tag{31}$$

where θ is the phase angle of the first reflection coefficient. The operation described in Eq. (31) is referred to as *heterodyning*. A set of *Doppler-invariant radar features* is thus represented by the normalized reflection coefficients $\kappa'_1, \kappa'_2, ..., \kappa'_M$, with κ'_1 being the only real-valued coefficient in the set. As mentioned previously, the major categories of radar targets of interest in air surveillance are weather, birds, aircraft, and ground. The first three targets are moving, whereas the last one is not. The *heterodyned* spectral parameters of radar echoes from ground have echoes similar in characteristic to those from aircraft. A ground echo can be discriminated from an aircraft echo because of its small Doppler shift. Accordingly, the radar classifier includes a postprocessor as shown in Fig. 23, which operates on the classified results (encoded labels) for the purpose of identifying the ground class (Haykin and Deng, 1991). Thus, the *preprocessor* in Fig. 23 takes care of Doppler-shift-invariant feature extraction at the classifier input, whereas the *postprocessor* uses the stored Doppler signature to distinguish between aircraft and ground returns. ∎

EXAMPLE 2:   Echolocating Bat

A much more fascinating example of knowledge representation in a neural network is found in the biological sonar system of echolocating bats. Most bats use *frequency-modulated* (FM, or "chirp") signals for the purpose of acoustic imaging; in an FM signal, the instantaneous frequency of the signal varies with time. Specifically, the bat uses its mouth to broadcast short-duration FM sonar signals and uses its auditory system as the sonar receiver. Echoes from targets of interest are represented in the auditory system by the activity of neurons that are selective to different combinations of acoustic parameters. There are three principal neural dimensions of the bat's auditory representation (Simmons et al., 1992):

- *Echo frequency*, which is encoded by "place" originating in the frequency map of the cochlea; it is preserved throughout the entire auditory pathway as an orderly arrangement across certain neurons tuned to different frequencies.

- *Echo amplitude*, which is encoded by other neurons with different dynamic ranges; it is manifested both as amplitude tuning and as the number of discharges per stimulus.
- *Echo delay*, which is encoded through neural computations (based on cross-correlation) that produce delay-selective responses; it is manifested as target-range tuning.

The two principal characteristics of a target echo for image-forming purposes are *spectrum* for target shape and *delay* for target range. The bat perceives "shape" in terms of the arrival time of echoes from different reflecting surfaces (glints) within the target. For this to occur, *frequency* information in the echo spectrum is converted into estimates of the *time* structure of the target. Experiments conducted by Simmons and coworkers on the big brown bat, *Eptesicus fuscus,* critically identify this conversion process as consisting of parallel time-domain and frequency-to-time-domain transforms whose converging outputs create the common delay of range axis of a perceived image of the target. It appears that the unity of the bat's perception is due to certain properties of the transforms themselves, despite the separate ways in which the auditory time representation of the echo delay and frequency representation of the echo spectrum are initially performed. Moreover, feature invariances are built into the sonar image-forming process so as to make it essentially independent of the target's motion and the bat's own motion. ∎

Some Final Remarks

The issue of knowledge representation in a neural network is directly related to that of network architecture. Unfortunately, there is no well-developed theory for optimizing the architecture of a neural network required to interact with an environment of interest, or for evaluating the way in which changes in the network architecture affect the representation of knowledge inside the network. Indeed, satisfactory answers to these issues are usually found through an exhaustive experimental study for a specific application of interest, with the designer of the neural network becoming an essential part of the structural learning loop.

8 LEARNING PROCESSES

Just as there are different ways in which we ourselves learn from our own surrounding environments, so it is with neural networks. In a broad sense, we may categorize the learning processes through which neural networks function as follows: learning with a teacher and learning without a teacher. By the same token, the latter form of learning may be subcategorized into unsupervised learning and reinforcement learning. These different forms of learning as performed on neural networks parallel those of human learning.

Learning with a Teacher

Learning with a teacher is also referred to as *supervised learning.* Figure 24 shows a block diagram that illustrates this form of learning. In conceptual terms, we may think of the teacher as having knowledge of the environment, with that knowledge being represented by a set of *input–output examples.* The environment is, however, *unknown* to the neural network. Suppose now that the teacher and the neural network are both exposed to a training vector (i.e., example) drawn from the same environment. By virtue of built-in

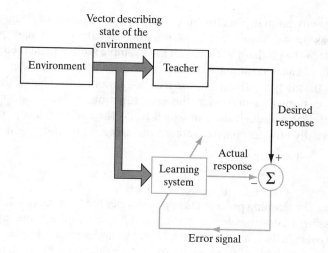

FIGURE 24   Block diagram of learning with a teacher; the part of the figure printed in red constitutes a feedback loop.

knowledge, the teacher is able to provide the neural network with a desired response for that training vector. Indeed, the desired response represents the "optimum" action to be performed by the neural network. The network parameters are adjusted under the combined influence of the training vector and the error signal. The *error signal* is defined as the difference between the desired response and the actual response of the network. This adjustment is carried out iteratively in a step-by-step fashion with the aim of eventually making the neural network *emulate* the teacher; the emulation is presumed to be optimum in some statistical sense. In this way, knowledge of the environment available to the teacher is transferred to the neural network through training and stored in the form of "fixed" synaptic weights, representing *long-term memory*. When this condition is reached, we may then dispense with the teacher and let the neural network deal with the environment completely by itself.

The form of supervised learning we have just described is the basis of *error-correction learning*. From Fig. 24, we see that the supervised-learning process constitutes a closed-loop feedback system, but the unknown environment is outside the loop. As a performance measure for the system, we may think in terms of the *mean-square error*, or the *sum of squared errors* over the training sample, defined as a function of the free parameters (i.e., synaptic weights) of the system. This function may be visualized as a multidimensional *error-performance surface*, or simply *error surface*, with the free parameters as coordinates. The true error surface is *averaged* over all possible input–output examples. Any given operation of the system under the teacher's supervision is represented as a point on the error surface. For the system to improve performance over time and therefore learn from the teacher, the operating point has to move down successively toward a minimum point of the error surface; the minimum point may be a local minimum or a global minimum. A supervised learning system is able to do this with the useful information it has about the *gradient* of the error surface corresponding to the current behavior of the system. The gradient of the error surface at any point is a vector that points in the direction of *steepest descent*. In fact, in the case of supervised learning from examples, the system may use an *instantaneous estimate* of the gradient vector, with the example indices presumed to be those of time. The use of such an estimate results in a motion of the operating point on the error surface that is typically in the form of a "random walk." Nevertheless, given an algorithm designed to minimize the cost function, an adequate set of input–output examples, and enough time in which to do the training, a supervised learning system is usually able to approximate an unknown input–output mapping reasonably well.

Learning without a Teacher

In supervised learning, the learning process takes place under the tutelage of a teacher. However, in the paradigm known as *learning without a teacher*, as the name implies, there is *no teacher* to oversee the learning process. That is to say, there are no labeled examples of the function to be learned by the network. Under this second paradigm, two subcategories are identified:

1. Reinforcement Learning

In *reinforcement learning*, the learning of an input–output mapping is performed through continued interaction with the environment in order to minimize a scalar index of performance. Figure 25 shows the block diagram of one form of a reinforcement-learning system built around a *critic* that converts a *primary reinforcement signal* received from the environment into a higher quality reinforcement signal called the *heuristic reinforcement signal*, both of which are scalar inputs (Barto et al., 1983). The system is designed to learn under *delayed reinforcement*, which means that the system observes a temporal sequence of stimuli also received from the environment, which eventually result in the generation of the heuristic reinforcement signal.

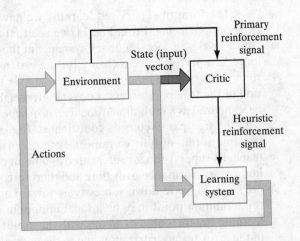

FIGURE 25 Block diagram of reinforcement learning; the learning system and the environment are both inside the feedback loop.

The goal of reinforcement learning is to minimize a *cost-to-go function*, defined as the expectation of the cumulative cost of *actions* taken over a sequence of steps instead of simply the immediate cost. It may turn out that certain actions taken earlier in that sequence of time steps are in fact the best determinants of overall system behavior. The function of the *learning system* is to *discover* these actions and feed them back to the environment.

Delayed-reinforcement learning is difficult to perform for two basic reasons:

- There is no teacher to provide a desired response at each step of the learning process.
- The delay incurred in the generation of the primary reinforcement signal implies that the learning machine must solve a *temporal credit assignment problem*. By this we mean that the learning machine must be able to assign credit and blame individually to each action in the sequence of time steps that led to the final outcome, while the primary reinforcement may only evaluate the outcome.

Notwithstanding these difficulties, delayed-reinforcement learning is appealing. It provides the basis for the learning system to interact with its environment, thereby developing the ability to learn to perform a prescribed task solely on the basis of the outcomes of its experience that result from the interaction.

2. Unsupervised Learning

In *unsupervised*, or *self-organized*, *learning*, there is no external teacher or critic to oversee the learning process, as indicated in Fig. 26. Rather, provision is made for a *task-independent measure* of the quality of representation that the network is required to learn, and the free parameters of the network are optimized with respect to that measure. For a specific task-independent measure, once the network has become tuned to the statistical regularities of the input data, the network develops the ability to form internal representations for encoding features of the input and thereby to create new classes automatically (Becker, 1991).

To perform unsupervised learning, we may use a competitive-learning rule. For example, we may use a neural network that consists of two layers—an input layer and a competitive layer. The input layer receives the available data. The competitive layer consists of neurons that compete with each other (in accordance with a learning rule) for the "opportunity" to respond to features contained in the input data. In its simplest form, the network operates in accordance with a "winner-takes-all" strategy. In such a strategy, the neuron with the greatest total input "wins" the competition and turns on; all the other neurons in the network then switch off.

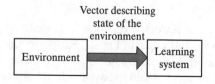

Vector describing
state of the
environment

FIGURE 26 Block diagram
of unsupervised learning.

9 LEARNING TASKS

In the previous section, we discussed different learning paradigms. In this section, we describe some basic learning tasks. The choice of a particular learning rule, is of course, influenced by the learning task, the diverse nature of which is testimony to the universality of neural networks.

Pattern Association

An *associative memory* is a brainlike distributed memory that learns by *association*. Association has been known to be a prominent feature of human memory since the time of Aristotle, and all models of cognition use association in one form or another as the basic operation (Anderson, 1995).

Association takes one of two forms: *autoassociation* and *heteroassociation*. In autoassociation, a neural network is required to *store* a set of patterns (vectors) by repeatedly presenting them to the network. The network is subsequently presented with a partial description or distorted (noisy) version of an original pattern stored in it, and the task is to *retrieve* (*recall*) that particular pattern. Heteroassociation differs from autoassociation in that an arbitrary set of input patterns is *paired* with another arbitrary set of output patterns. Autoassociation involves the use of unsupervised learning, whereas the type of learning involved in heteroassociation is supervised.

Let $\mathbf{x}_k$ denote a *key pattern* (vector) applied to an associative memory and $\mathbf{y}_k$ denote a *memorized pattern* (vector). The pattern association performed by the network is described by

$$\mathbf{x}_k \rightarrow \mathbf{y}_k, \qquad k = 1, 2, ..., q \tag{32}$$

where q is the number of patterns stored in the network. The key pattern $\mathbf{x}_k$ acts as a stimulus that not only determines the storage location of memorized pattern $\mathbf{y}_k$, but also holds the key for its retrieval.

In an autoassociative memory, $\mathbf{y}_k = \mathbf{x}_k$, so the input and output (data) spaces of the network have the same dimensionality. In a heteroassociative memory, $\mathbf{y}_k \neq \mathbf{x}_k$; hence, the dimensionality of the output space in this second case may or may not equal the dimensionality of the input space.

There are two phases involved in the operation of an associative memory:

- *storage phase*, which refers to the training of the network in accordance with Eq. (32);
- *recall phase*, which involves the retrieval of a memorized pattern in response to the presentation of a noisy or distorted version of a key pattern to the network.

Let the stimulus (input) $\mathbf{x}$ represent a noisy or distorted version of a key pattern $\mathbf{x}_j$. This stimulus produces a response (output) $\mathbf{y}$, as indicated in Fig. 27. For perfect recall, we should find that $\mathbf{y} = \mathbf{y}_j$, where $\mathbf{y}_j$ is the memorized pattern associated with the key pattern $\mathbf{x}_j$. When $\mathbf{y} \neq \mathbf{y}_j$ for $\mathbf{x} = \mathbf{x}_j$, the associative memory is said to have made an *error in recall*.

FIGURE 27 Input–output relation of pattern associator.

The number of patterns q stored in an associative memory provides a direct measure of the *storage capacity* of the network. In designing an associative memory, the challenge is to make the storage capacity q (expressed as a percentage of the total number N of neurons used to construct the network) as large as possible, yet insist that a large fraction of the memorized patterns is recalled correctly.

Pattern Recognition

Humans are good at pattern recognition. We receive data from the world around us via our senses and are able to recognize the source of the data. We are often able to do so almost immediately and with practically no effort. For example, we can recognize the familiar face of a person even though that person has aged since our last encounter, identify a familiar person by his or her voice on the telephone despite a bad connection, and distinguish a boiled egg that is good from a bad one by smelling it. Humans perform pattern recognition through a learning process; so it is with neural networks.

Pattern recognition is formally defined as *the process whereby a received pattern/signal is assigned to one of a prescribed number of classes*. A neural network performs pattern recognition by first undergoing a training session during which the network is repeatedly presented with a set of input patterns along with the category to which each particular pattern belongs. Later, the network is presented with a new pattern that has not been seen before, but which belongs to the same population of patterns used to train the network. The network is able to identify the class of that particular pattern because of the information it has extracted from the training data. Pattern recognition performed by a neural network is statistical in nature, with the patterns being represented by points in a multidimensional *decision space*. The decision space is divided into regions, each one of which is associated with a class. The decision boundaries are determined by the training process. The construction of these boundaries is made statistical by the inherent variability that exists within and between classes.

In generic terms, pattern-recognition machines using neural networks may take one of two forms:

- The machine is split into two parts, an unsupervised network for *feature extraction* and a supervised network for *classification*, as shown in the hybridized system of Fig. 28a. Such a method follows the traditional approach to statistical pattern recognition (Fukunaga, 1990; Duda et al., 2001; Theodoridis and Koutroumbas, 2003). In conceptual terms, a pattern is represented by a set of m observables, which may be viewed as a point $\mathbf{x}$ in an m-dimensional *observation (data) space*.

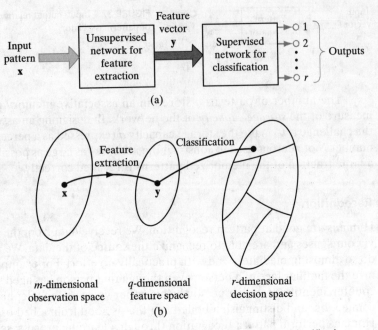

(a)

(b)

m-dimensional   *q*-dimensional   *r*-dimensional
observation space   feature space   decision space

FIGURE 28   Illustration of the classical approach to pattern classification.

Feature extraction is described by a transformation that maps the point $\mathbf{x}$ into an intermediate point $\mathbf{y}$ in a q-dimensional *feature space* with $q < m$, as indicated in Fig. 28b. This transformation may be viewed as one of dimensionality reduction (i.e., data compression), the use of which is justified on the grounds that it simplifies the task of classification. The classification is itself described as a transformation that maps the intermediate point $\mathbf{y}$ into one of the classes in an r-dimensional decision space, where r is the number of classes to be distinguished.

- The machine is designed as a feedforward network using a supervised learning algorithm. In this second approach, the task of feature extraction is performed by the computational units in the hidden layer(s) of the network.

Function Approximation

The third learning task of interest is that of function approximation. Consider a nonlinear input–output mapping described by the functional relationship

$$\mathbf{d} = \mathbf{f}(\mathbf{x}) \tag{33}$$

where the vector $\mathbf{x}$ is the input and the vector $\mathbf{d}$ is the output. The vector-valued function $\mathbf{f}(\cdot)$ is assumed to be unknown. To make up for the lack of knowledge about the function $\mathbf{f}(\cdot)$, we are given the set of labeled examples:

$$\mathcal{T} = \{(\mathbf{x}_i, \mathbf{d}_i)\}_{i=1}^{N} \tag{34}$$

The requirement is to design a neural network that approximates the unknown function $\mathbf{f}(\cdot)$ such that the function $\mathbf{F}(\cdot)$ describing the input–output mapping actually realized by the network, is close enough to $\mathbf{f}(\cdot)$ in a Euclidean sense over all inputs, as shown by

$$\|\mathbf{F}(\mathbf{x}) - \mathbf{f}(\mathbf{x})\| < \varepsilon \quad \text{for all } \mathbf{x} \tag{35}$$

where ε is a small positive number. Provided that the size N of the training sample $\mathcal{T}$ is large enough and the network is equipped with an adequate number of free parameters, then the approximation error ε can be made small enough for the task.

The approximation problem described here is a perfect candidate for supervised learning, with $\mathbf{x}_i$ playing the role of input vector and $\mathbf{d}_i$ serving the role of desired response. We may turn this issue around and view supervised learning as an approximation problem.

The ability of a neural network to approximate an unknown input–output mapping may be exploited in two important ways:

(i) *System identification.* Let Eq. (33) describe the input–output relation of an unknown memoryless *multiple input–multiple output (MIMO) system*; by a "memoryless" system, we mean a system that is time invariant. We may then use the set of labeled examples in Eq. (34) to train a neural network as a model of the system. Let the vector $\mathbf{y}_i$ denote the actual output of the neural network produced in response to an input vector $\mathbf{x}_i$. The difference between $\mathbf{d}_i$ (associated with $\mathbf{x}_i$) and the network output $\mathbf{y}_i$ provides the error signal vector $\mathbf{e}_i$, as depicted in Fig. 29. This error signal is, in turn, used to adjust the free parameters of the network to minimize the squared difference between the outputs of the unknown system and the neural network in a statistical sense, and is computed over the entire training sample $\mathcal{T}$.

(ii) *Inverse modeling.* Suppose next we are given a known memoryless MIMO system whose input–output relation is described by Eq. (33). The requirement in this case is to construct an *inverse model* that produces the vector $\mathbf{x}$ in response to the vector $\mathbf{d}$. The inverse system may thus be described by

$$\mathbf{x} = \mathbf{f}^{-1}(\mathbf{d}) \tag{36}$$

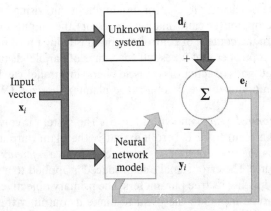

FIGURE 29 Block diagram of system identification: The neural network, doing the identification, is part of the feedback loop.

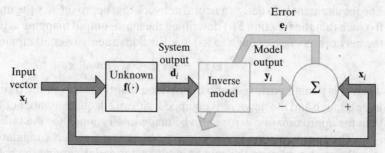

FIGURE 30   Block diagram of inverse system modeling. The neural network, acting as the inverse model, is part of the feedback loop.

where the vector-valued function $\mathbf{f}^{-1}(\cdot)$ denotes the inverse of $\mathbf{f}(\cdot)$. Note, however, that $\mathbf{f}^{-1}(\cdot)$ is not the reciprocal of $\mathbf{f}(\cdot)$; rather, the use of superscript -1 is merely a flag to indicate an inverse. In many situations encountered in practice, the vector-valued function $\mathbf{f}(\cdot)$ is much too complex and inhibits a straightforward formulation of the inverse function $\mathbf{f}^{-1}(\cdot)$. Given the set of labeled examples in Eq. (34), we may construct a neural network approximation of $\mathbf{f}^{-1}(\cdot)$ by using the scheme shown in Fig. 30. In the situation described here, the roles of $\mathbf{x}_i$ and $\mathbf{d}_i$ are interchanged: The vector $\mathbf{d}_i$ is used as the input, and $\mathbf{x}_i$ is treated as the desired response. Let the error signal vector $\mathbf{e}_i$ denote the difference between $\mathbf{x}_i$ and the actual output $\mathbf{y}_i$ of the neural network produced in response to $\mathbf{d}_i$. As with the system identification problem, this error signal vector is used to adjust the free parameters of the neural network to minimize the squared difference between the outputs of the unknown inverse system and the neural network in a statistical sense, and is computed over the complete training set $\mathcal{T}$. Typically, inverse modeling is a more difficult learning task than system identification, as there may not be a unique solution for it.

Control

The control of a *plant* is another learning task that is well suited for neural networks; by a "plant" we mean a process or critical part of a system that is to be maintained in a controlled condition. The relevance of learning to control should not be surprising because, after all, the human brain is a computer (i.e., information processor), the outputs of which as a whole system are *actions*. In the context of control, the brain is living proof that it is possible to build a generalized controller that takes full advantage of parallel distributed hardware, can control many thousands of actuators (muscle fibers) in parallel, can handle nonlinearity and noise, and can optimize over a long-range planning horizon (Werbos, 1992).

Consider the *feedback control system* shown in Fig. 31. The system involves the use of unity feedback around a plant to be controlled; that is, the plant output is fed back directly to the input. Thus, the plant output $\mathbf{y}$ is subtracted from a *reference signal* $\mathbf{d}$ supplied from an external source. The error signal $\mathbf{e}$ so produced is applied to a neural *controller* for the purpose of adjusting its free parameters. The primary objective of the controller is to supply appropriate inputs to the plant to make its output $\mathbf{y}$ track the

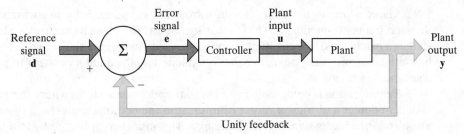

FIGURE 31   Block diagram of feedback control system.

reference signal **d**. In other words, the controller has to invert the plant's input–output behavior.

We note that in Fig. 31, the error signal **e** has to propagate through the neural controller before reaching the plant. Consequently, to perform adjustments on the free parameters of the plant in accordance with an error-correction learning algorithm, we need to know the *Jacobian,* made up of a matrix of partial derivatives as shown by

$$\mathbf{J} = \left\{ \frac{\partial y_k}{\partial u_j} \right\}_{j,\,k} \tag{37}$$

where y_k is an element of the plant output **y** and u_j is an element of the plant input **u**. Unfortunately, the partial derivatives $\partial y_k / \partial u_j$ for the various k and j depend on the operating point of the plant and are therefore not known. We may use one of two approaches to account for them:

(i) *Indirect learning.* Using actual input–output measurements on the plant, we first construct a neural model to produce a copy of it. This model is, in turn, used to provide an estimate of the Jacobian **J**. The partial derivatives constituting this Jacobian are subsequently used in the error-correction learning algorithm for computing the adjustments to the free parameters of the neural controller (Nguyen and Widrow, 1989; Suykens et al., 1996; Widrow and Walach, 1996).

(ii) *Direct learning.* The signs of the partial derivatives $\partial y_k / \partial u_j$ are generally known and usually remain constant over the dynamic range of the plant. This suggests that we may approximate these partial derivatives by their individual signs. Their absolute values are given a distributed representation in the free parameters of the neural controller (Saerens and Soquet, 1991; Schiffman and Geffers, 1993). The neural controller is thereby enabled to learn the adjustments to its free parameters directly from the plant.

Beamforming

Beamforming is used to distinguish between the spatial properties of a target signal and background noise. The device used to do the beamforming is called a *beamformer.*

The task of beamforming is compatible, for example, with feature mapping in the cortical layers of auditory systems of echolocating bats (Suga, 1990a; Simmons et al.,

1992). The echolocating bat illuminates the surrounding environment by broadcasting short-duration frequency-modulated (FM) sonar signals and then uses its auditory system (including a pair of ears) to focus attention on its prey (e.g., flying insect). The ears provide the bat with a beamforming capability that is exploited by the auditory system to produce *attentional selectivity*.

Beamforming is commonly used in radar and sonar systems where the primary task is to detect and track a target of interest in the combined presence of receiver noise and interfering signals (e.g., jammers). This task is complicated by two factors:

- the target signal originates from an unknown direction, and
- there is no *prior* information available on the interfering signals.

One way of coping with situations of this kind is to use a *generalized sidelobe canceller* (GSLC), the block diagram of which is shown in Fig. 32. The system consists of the following components (Griffiths and Jim, 1982; Haykin, 2002):

- An *array of antenna elements*, which provides a means of sampling the observation-space signal at discrete points in space.
- A *linear combiner* defined by a set of fixed weights $\{w_i\}_{i=1}^m$, the output of which performs the role of a desired response. This linear combiner acts like a "spatial filter," characterized by a radiation pattern (i.e., a polar plot of the amplitude of the antenna output versus the incidence angle of an incoming signal). The mainlobe of this radiation pattern is pointed along a prescribed direction, for which the GSLC is *constrained* to produce a distortionless response. The output of the linear combiner, denoted by $d(n)$, provides a desired response for the beamformer.
- A *signal-blocking matrix* $\mathbf{C}_a$, the function of which is to cancel interference that leaks through the sidelobes of the radiation pattern of the spatial filter representing the linear combiner.

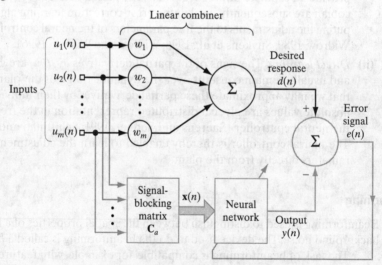

FIGURE 32 Block diagram of generalized sidelobe canceller.

- A *neural network* with adjustable parameters, which is designed to accommodate statistical variations in the interfering signals.

The adjustments to the free parameters of the neural network are performed by an error-correcting learning algorithm that operates on the error signal $e(n)$, defined as the difference between the linear combiner output $d(n)$ and the actual output $y(n)$ of the neural network. Thus the GSLC operates under the supervision of the linear combiner that assumes the role of a "teacher." As with ordinary supervised learning, notice that the linear combiner is outside the feedback loop acting on the neural network. A beamformer that uses a neural network for learning is called a *neuro-beamformer*. This class of learning machines comes under the general heading of *attentional neurocomputers* (Hecht-Nielsen, 1990).

10   CONCLUDING REMARKS

In the material covered in this introductory chapter, we have focused attention on neural networks, the study of which is motivated by the human brain. The one important property of neural networks that stands out is that of *learning*, which is categorized as follows:

(i) *supervised learning*, which requires the availability of a target or desired response for the realization of a specific input–output mapping by minimizing a cost function of interest;

(ii) *unsupervised learning*, the implementation of which relies on the provision of a task-independent measure of the quality of representation that the network is required to learn in a self-organized manner;

(iii) *reinforcement learning*, in which input–output mapping is performed through the continued interaction of a learning system with its environment so as to minimize a scalar index of performance.

Supervised learning relies on the availability of a training sample of *labeled examples*, with each example consisting of an input signal (stimulus) and the corresponding desired (target) response. In practice, we find that the collection of labeled examples is a time-consuming and expensive task, especially when we are dealing with large-scale learning problems; typically, we therefore find that labeled examples are in short supply. On the other hand, unsupervised learning relies solely on unlabeled examples, consisting simply of a set of input signals or stimuli, for which there is usually a plentiful supply. In light of these realities, there is a great deal of interest in another category of learning: *semisupervised learning*, which employs a training sample that consists of labeled as well as unlabeled examples. The challenge in semisupervised learning, discussed in a subsequent chapter, is to design a learning system that scales reasonably well for its implementation to be practically feasible when dealing with large-scale pattern-classification problems.

Reinforcement learning lies between supervised learning and unsupervised learning. It operates through continuing interactions between a learning system (agent) and the environment. The learning system performs an action and learns from the response of the environment to that action. In effect, the role of the teacher in supervised learning is replaced by a critic, for example, that is integrated into the learning machinery.

NOTES AND REFERENCES

1. This definition of a neural network is adapted from Aleksander and Morton (1990).
2. For a readable account of computational aspects of the brain, see Churchland and Sejnowski (1992). For more detailed descriptions, see Kandel et al. (1991), Shepherd (1990), Kuffler et al. (1984), and Freeman (1975).
3. For detailed treatment of spikes and spiking neurons, see Rieke et al. (1997). For a biophysical perspective of computation and information-processing capability of single neurons, see Koch (1999).
4. For a thorough account of sigmoid functions and related issues, see Mennon et al. (1996).
5. The logistic function, or more precisely, the *logistic distribution function*, derives its name from a transcendental "law of logistic growth" that has a huge literature. Measured in appropriate units, all growth processes are supposed to be represented by the logistic distribution function

$$F(t) = \frac{1}{1 + e^{\alpha t - \beta}}$$

where t represents time, and α and β are constants.
6. According to Kuffler et al. (1984), the term "receptive field" was coined originally by Sherrington (1906) and reintroduced by Hartline (1940). In the context of a visual system, the receptive field of a neuron refers to the restricted area on the retinal surface, which influences the discharges of that neuron due to light.
7. The weight-sharing technique was originally described in Rumelhart et al. (1986b).

C H A P T E R   1

Rosenblatt's Perceptron

ORGANIZATION OF THE CHAPTER

The perceptron occupies a special place in the historical development of neural networks: It was the first algorithmically described neural network. Its invention by Rosenblatt, a psychologist, inspired engineers, physicists, and mathematicians alike to devote their research effort to different aspects of neural networks in the 1960s and the 1970s. Moreover, it is truly remarkable to find that the perceptron (in its basic form as described in this chapter) is as valid today as it was in 1958 when Rosenblatt's paper on the perceptron was first published.

The chapter is organized as follows:

1. Section 1.1 expands on the formative years of neural networks, going back to the pioneering work of McCulloch and Pitts in 1943.
2. Section 1.2 describes Rosenblatt's perceptron in its most basic form. It is followed by Section 1.3 on the perceptron convergence theorem. This theorem proves convergence of the perceptron as a linearly separable pattern classifier in a finite number time-steps.
3. Section 1.4 establishes the relationship between the perceptron and the Bayes classifier for a Gaussian environment.
4. The experiment presented in Section 1.5 demonstrates the pattern-classification capability of the perceptron.
5. Section 1.6 generalizes the discussion by introducing the perceptron cost function, paving the way for deriving the batch version of the perceptron convergence algorithm.

Section 1.7 provides a summary and discussion that conclude the chapter.

1.1   INTRODUCTION

In the formative years of neural networks (1943–1958), several researchers stand out for their pioneering contributions:

- McCulloch and Pitts (1943) for introducing the idea of neural networks as computing machines.

- Hebb (1949) for postulating the first rule for self-organized learning.
- Rosenblatt (1958) for proposing the perceptron as the first model for learning with a teacher (i.e., supervised learning).

The idea of Hebbian learning will be discussed at some length in Chapter 8. In this chapter, we discuss Rosenblatt's *perceptron*.

The perceptron is the simplest form of a neural network used for the classification of patterns said to be *linearly separable* (i.e., patterns that lie on opposite sides of a hyperplane). Basically, it consists of a single neuron with adjustable synaptic weights and bias. The algorithm used to adjust the free parameters of this neural network first appeared in a learning procedure developed by Rosenblatt (1958, 1962) for his perceptron brain model.[1] Indeed, Rosenblatt proved that if the patterns (vectors) used to train the perceptron are drawn from two linearly separable classes, then the perceptron algorithm converges and positions the decision surface in the form of a hyperplane between the two classes. The proof of convergence of the algorithm is known as the *perceptron convergence theorem*.

The perceptron built around a *single neuron* is limited to performing pattern classification with only two classes (hypotheses). By expanding the output (computation) layer of the perceptron to include more than one neuron, we may correspondingly perform classification with more than two classes. However, the classes have to be linearly separable for the perceptron to work properly. The important point is that insofar as the basic theory of the perceptron as a pattern classifier is concerned, we need consider only the case of a single neuron. The extension of the theory to the case of more than one neuron is trivial.

1.2   PERCEPTRON

Rosenblatt's perceptron is built around a nonlinear neuron, namely, the *McCulloch–Pitts model* of a neuron. From the introductory chapter we recall that such a neural modeling consists of a linear combiner followed by a hard limiter (performing the signum function), as depicted in Fig. 1.1. The summing node of the neural model computes a linear combination of the inputs applied to its synapses, as well as incorporates an externally applied bias. The resulting sum, that is, the induced local field, is applied to a hard

FIGURE 1.1   Signal-flow graph of the perceptron.

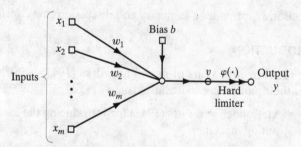

limiter. Accordingly, the neuron produces an output equal to +1 if the hard limiter input is positive, and −1 if it is negative.

In the signal-flow graph model of Fig. 1.1, the synaptic weights of the perceptron are denoted by $w_1, w_2, ..., w_m$. Correspondingly, the inputs applied to the perceptron are denoted by $x_1, x_2, ..., x_m$. The externally applied bias is denoted by b. From the model, we find that the hard limiter input, or induced local field, of the neuron is

$$v = \sum_{i=1}^{m} w_i x_i + b \qquad (1.1)$$

The goal of the perceptron is to correctly classify the set of externally applied stimuli x_1, $x_2, ..., x_m$ into one of two classes, $\mathscr{C}_1$ or $\mathscr{C}_2$. The decision rule for the classification is to assign the point represented by the inputs $x_1, x_2, ..., x_m$ to class $\mathscr{C}_1$ if the perceptron output y is +1 and to class $\mathscr{C}_2$ if it is −1.

To develop insight into the behavior of a pattern classifier, it is customary to plot a map of the decision regions in the m-dimensional signal space spanned by the m input variables $x_1, x_2, ..., x_m$. In the simplest form of the perceptron, there are two decision regions separated by a *hyperplane*, which is defined by

$$\sum_{i=1}^{m} w_i x_i + b = 0 \qquad (1.2)$$

This is illustrated in Fig. 1.2 for the case of two input variables x_1 and x_2, for which the decision boundary takes the form of a straight line. A point (x_1, x_2) that lies above the boundary line is assigned to class $\mathscr{C}_1$, and a point (x_1, x_2) that lies below the boundary line is assigned to class $\mathscr{C}_2$. Note also that the effect of the bias b is merely to shift the decision boundary away from the origin.

The synaptic weights $w_1, w_2, ..., w_m$ of the perceptron can be adapted on an iteration-by-iteration basis. For the adaptation, we may use an error-correction rule known as the perceptron convergence algorithm, discussed next.

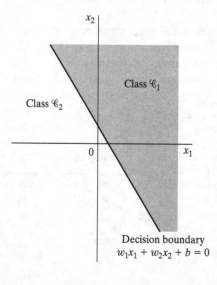

FIGURE 1.2   Illustration of the hyperplane (in this example, a straight line) as decision boundary for a two-dimensional, two-class pattern-classification problem.

Decision boundary
$w_1 x_1 + w_2 x_2 + b = 0$

1.3   THE PERCEPTRON CONVERGENCE THEOREM

To derive the error-correction learning algorithm for the perceptron, we find it more convenient to work with the modified signal-flow graph model in Fig. 1.3. In this second model, which is equivalent to that of Fig. 1.1, the bias $b(n)$ is treated as a synaptic weight driven by a fixed input equal to $+1$. We may thus define the $(m + 1)$-by-1 input vector

$$\mathbf{x}(n) = [+1, x_1(n), x_2(n), ..., x_m(n)]^T$$

where n denotes the time-step in applying the algorithm. Correspondingly, we define the $(m + 1)$-by-1 weight vector as

$$\mathbf{w}(n) = [b, w_1(n), w_2(n), ..., w_m(n)]^T$$

Accordingly, the linear combiner output is written in the compact form

$$
\begin{aligned}
v(n) &= \sum_{i=0}^{m} w_i(n)x_i(n) \\
&= \mathbf{w}^T(n)\mathbf{x}(n)
\end{aligned}
\tag{1.3}
$$

where, in the first line, $w_0(n)$, corresponding to $i = 0$, represents the bias b. For fixed n, the equation $\mathbf{w}^T\mathbf{x} = 0$, plotted in an m-dimensional space (and for some prescribed bias) with coordinates $x_1, x_2, ..., x_m$, defines a hyperplane as the decision surface between two different classes of inputs.

For the perceptron to function properly, the two classes $\mathcal{C}_1$ and $\mathcal{C}_2$ must be *linearly separable*. This, in turn, means that the patterns to be classified must be sufficiently separated from each other to ensure that the decision surface consists of a hyperplane. This requirement is illustrated in Fig. 1.4 for the case of a two-dimensional perceptron. In Fig. 1.4a, the two classes $\mathcal{C}_1$ and $\mathcal{C}_2$ are sufficiently separated from each other for us to draw a hyperplane (in this case, a striaght line) as the decision boundary. If, however, the two classes $\mathcal{C}_1$ and $\mathcal{C}_2$ are allowed to move too close to each other, as in Fig. 1.4b, they become nonlinearly separable, a situation that is beyond the computing capability of the perceptron.

Suppose then that the input variables of the perceptron originate from two linearly separable classes. Let $\mathcal{H}_1$ be the subspace of training vectors $\mathbf{x}_1(1), \mathbf{x}_1(2), ...$ that belong to class $\mathcal{C}_1$, and let $\mathcal{H}_2$ be the subspace of training vectors $\mathbf{x}_2(1), \mathbf{x}_2(2), ...$ that belong to class $\mathcal{C}_2$. The union of $\mathcal{H}_1$ and $\mathcal{H}_2$ is the complete space denoted by $\mathcal{H}$. Given the sets

FIGURE 1.3   Equivalent signal-flow graph of the perceptron; dependence on time has been omitted for clarity.

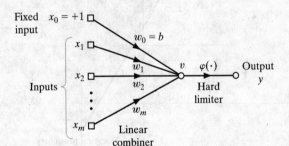

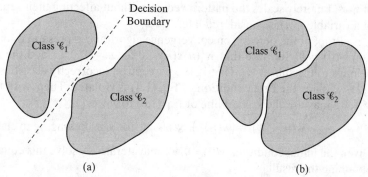

FIGURE 1.4   (a) A pair of linearly separable patterns. (b) A pair of non-linearly separable patterns.

of vectors $\mathcal{H}_1$ and $\mathcal{H}_2$ to train the classifier, the training process involves the adjustment of the weight vector $\mathbf{w}$ in such a way that the two classes $\mathcal{C}_1$ and $\mathcal{C}_2$ are linearly separable. That is, there exists a weight vector $\mathbf{w}$ such that we may state

$$\mathbf{w}^T\mathbf{x} > 0 \text{ for every input vector } \mathbf{x} \text{ belonging to class } \mathcal{C}_1$$
$$\mathbf{w}^T\mathbf{x} \leq 0 \text{ for every input vector } \mathbf{x} \text{ belonging to class } \mathcal{C}_2 \tag{1.4}$$

In the second line of Eq. (1.4), we have arbitrarily chosen to say that the input vector $\mathbf{x}$ belongs to class $\mathcal{C}_2$ if $\mathbf{w}^T\mathbf{x} = 0$. Given the subsets of training vectors $\mathcal{H}_1$ and $\mathcal{H}_2$, the training problem for the perceptron is then to find a weight vector $\mathbf{w}$ such that the two inequalities of Eq. (1.4) are satisfied.

The algorithm for adapting the weight vector of the elementary perceptron may now be formulated as follows:

1. If the nth member of the training set, $\mathbf{x}(n)$, is correctly classified by the weight vector $\mathbf{w}(n)$ computed at the nth iteration of the algorithm, no correction is made to the weight vector of the perceptron in accordance with the rule:

$$\mathbf{w}(n + 1) = \mathbf{w}(n) \quad \text{if } \mathbf{w}^T(n)\mathbf{x}(n) > 0 \text{ and } \mathbf{x}(n) \text{ belongs to class } \mathcal{C}_1$$
$$\mathbf{w}(n + 1) = \mathbf{w}(n) \quad \text{if } \mathbf{w}^T(n)\mathbf{x}(n) \leq 0 \text{ and } \mathbf{x}(n) \text{ belongs to class } \mathcal{C}_2 \tag{1.5}$$

2. Otherwise, the weight vector of the perceptron is updated in accordance with the rule

$$\mathbf{w}(n + 1) = \mathbf{w}(n) - \eta(n)\mathbf{x}(n) \quad \text{if } \mathbf{w}^T(n)\mathbf{x}(n) > 0 \text{ and } \mathbf{x}(n) \text{ belongs to class } \mathcal{C}_2$$
$$\mathbf{w}(n + 1) = \mathbf{w}(n) + \eta(n)\mathbf{x}(n) \quad \text{if } \mathbf{w}^T(n)\mathbf{x}(n) \leq 0 \text{ and } \mathbf{x}(n) \text{ belongs to class } \mathcal{C}_1 \tag{1.6}$$

where the *learning-rate parameter* $\eta(n)$ controls the adjustment applied to the weight vector at iteration n.

If $\eta(n) = \eta > 0$, where η is a constant independent of the iteration number n, then we have a *fixed-increment adaptation rule* for the perceptron.

In the sequel, we first prove the convergence of a fixed-increment adaptation rule for which $\eta = 1$. Clearly, the value of η is unimportant, so long as it is positive. A value of $\eta \neq 1$ merely scales the pattern vectors without affecting their separability. The case of a variable $\eta(n)$ is considered later.

Proof of the perceptron convergence algorithm[2] is presented for the initial condition $\mathbf{w}(0) = \mathbf{0}$. Suppose that $\mathbf{w}^T(n)\mathbf{x}(n) < 0$ for $n = 1, 2, ...,$ and the input vector $\mathbf{x}(n)$ belongs to the subset $\mathcal{H}_1$. That is, the perceptron incorrectly classifies the vectors $\mathbf{x}(1)$, $\mathbf{x}(2), ...,$ since the first condition of Eq. (1.4) is violated. Then, with the constant $\eta(n) = 1$, we may use the second line of Eq. (1.6) to write

$$\mathbf{w}(n + 1) = \mathbf{w}(n) + \mathbf{x}(n) \qquad \text{for } \mathbf{x}(n) \text{ belonging to class } \mathcal{C}_1 \qquad (1.7)$$

Given the initial condition $\mathbf{w}(0) = \mathbf{0}$, we may iteratively solve this equation for $\mathbf{w}(n+1)$, obtaining the result

$$\mathbf{w}(n + 1) = \mathbf{x}(1) + \mathbf{x}(2) + \cdots + \mathbf{x}(n) \qquad (1.8)$$

Since the classes $\mathcal{C}_1$ and $\mathcal{C}_2$ are assumed to be linearly separable, there exists a solution $\mathbf{w}_o$ for which $\mathbf{w}^T\mathbf{x}(n) > 0$ for the vectors $\mathbf{x}(1), ..., \mathbf{x}(n)$ belonging to the subset $\mathcal{H}_1$. For a fixed solution $\mathbf{w}_o$, we may then define a positive number α as

$$\alpha = \min_{\mathbf{x}(n) \in \mathcal{H}_1} \mathbf{w}_o^T \mathbf{x}(n) \qquad (1.9)$$

Hence, multiplying both sides of Eq. (1.8) by the row vector $\mathbf{w}_o^T$, we get

$$\mathbf{w}_o^T\mathbf{w}(n + 1) = \mathbf{w}_o^T\mathbf{x}(1) + \mathbf{w}_o^T\mathbf{x}(2) + \cdots + \mathbf{w}_o^T\mathbf{x}(n)$$

Accordingly, in light of the definition given in Eq. (1.9), we have

$$\mathbf{w}_o^T\mathbf{w}(n + 1) \geq n\alpha \qquad (1.10)$$

Next we make use of an inequality known as the Cauchy–Schwarz inequality. Given two vectors $\mathbf{w}_0$ and $\mathbf{w}(n + 1)$, the *Cauchy–Schwarz inequality* states that

$$\|\mathbf{w}_o\|^2 \|\mathbf{w}(n + 1)\|^2 \geq [\mathbf{w}_o^T\mathbf{w}(n + 1)]^2 \qquad (1.11)$$

where $\|\cdot\|$ denotes the Euclidean norm of the enclosed argument vector, and the inner product $\mathbf{w}_o^T\mathbf{w}(n + 1)$ is a scalar quantity. We now note from Eq. (1.10) that $[\mathbf{w}_o^T\mathbf{w}(n + 1)]^2$ is equal to or greater than $n^2\alpha^2$. From Eq. (1.11) we note that $\|\mathbf{w}_o\|^2 \|\mathbf{w}(n + 1)\|^2$ is equal to or greater than $[\mathbf{w}_o^T\mathbf{w}(n + 1)]^2$. It follows therefore that

$$\|\mathbf{w}_o\|^2 \|\mathbf{w}(n + 1)\|^2 \geq n^2\alpha^2$$

or, equivalently,

$$\|\mathbf{w}(n + 1)\|^2 \geq \frac{n^2\alpha^2}{\|\mathbf{w}_o\|^2} \qquad (1.12)$$

We next follow another development route. In particular, we rewrite Eq. (1.7) in the form

$$\mathbf{w}(k + 1) = \mathbf{w}(k) + \mathbf{x}(k) \qquad \text{for } k = 1, ..., n \text{ and } \mathbf{x}(k) \in \mathcal{H}_1 \qquad (1.13)$$

By taking the squared Euclidean norm of both sides of Eq. (1.13), we obtain

$$\|\mathbf{w}(k + 1)\|^2 = \|\mathbf{w}(k)\|^2 + \|\mathbf{x}(k)\|^2 + 2\mathbf{w}^T(k)\mathbf{x}(k) \qquad (1.14)$$

But, $\mathbf{w}^T(k)\mathbf{x}(k) \leq 0$. We therefore deduce from Eq. (1.14) that

$$\|\mathbf{w}(k + 1)\|^2 \leq \|\mathbf{w}(k)\|^2 + \|\mathbf{x}(k)\|^2$$

or, equivalently,

$$\|\mathbf{w}(k + 1)\|^2 - \|\mathbf{w}(k)\|^2 \leq \|\mathbf{x}(k)\|^2, \qquad k = 1, ..., n \qquad (1.15)$$

Adding these inequalities for $k = 1, ..., n$, and invoking the assumed initial condition $\mathbf{w}(0) = \mathbf{0}$, we get the inequality

$$\|\mathbf{w}(n + 1)\|^2 \leq \sum_{k=1}^{n} \|\mathbf{x}(k)\|^2 \qquad (1.16)$$

$$\leq n\beta$$

where β is a positive number defined by

$$\beta = \max_{\mathbf{x}(k) \in \mathcal{H}_1} \|\mathbf{x}(k)\|^2 \qquad (1.17)$$

Equation (1.16) states that the squared Euclidean norm of the weight vector $\mathbf{w}(n + 1)$ grows at most linearly with the number of iterations n.

The second result of Eq. (1.16) is clearly in conflict with the earlier result of Eq. (1.12) for sufficiently large values of n. Indeed, we can state that n cannot be larger than some value n_{max} for which Eqs. (1.12) and (1.16) are both satisfied with the equality sign. That is, n_{max} is the solution of the equation

$$\frac{n_{max}^2 \alpha^2}{\|\mathbf{w}_o\|^2} = n_{max}\beta$$

Solving for n_{max}, given a solution vector $\mathbf{w}_o$, we find that

$$n_{max} = \frac{\beta\|\mathbf{w}_o\|^2}{\alpha^2} \qquad (1.18)$$

We have thus proved that for $\eta(n) = 1$ for all n and $\mathbf{w}(0) = \mathbf{0}$, and given that a solution vector $\mathbf{w}_o$ exists, the rule for adapting the synaptic weights of the perceptron must terminate after at most n_{max} interations. Surprisingly, this statement, proved for hypothesis $\mathcal{H}_1$, also holds for huypothesis $\mathcal{H}_2$. Note however,

We may now state the *fixed-increment covergence theorem* for the perceptron as follows (Rosenblatt, 1962):

> Let the subsets of training vectors $\mathcal{H}_1$ and $\mathcal{H}_2$ be linearly separable. Let the inputs presented to the perceptron originate from these two subsets. The perceptron converges after some n_o iterations, in the sense that
>
> $$\mathbf{w}(n_o) = \mathbf{w}(n_o + 1) = \mathbf{w}(n_o + 2) = \cdots$$
>
> is a solution vector for $n_0 \leq n_{max}$.

Consider next the *absolute error-correction procedure* for the adaptation of a single-layer perceptron, for which $\eta(n)$ is variable. In particular, let $\eta(n)$ be the smallest integer for which the condition

$$\eta(n)\mathbf{x}^T(n)\mathbf{x}(n) > |\mathbf{w}^T(n)\mathbf{x}(n)|$$

holds. With this procedure we find that if the inner product $\mathbf{w}^T(n)\mathbf{x}(n)$ at iteration n has an incorrect sign, then $\mathbf{w}^T(n+1)\mathbf{x}(n)$ at iteration $n + 1$ would have the correct sign. This suggests that if $\mathbf{w}^T(n)\mathbf{x}(n)$ has an incorrect sign, at iteration n, we may modify the training sequence at iteration $n + 1$ by setting $\mathbf{x}(n + 1) = \mathbf{x}(n)$. In other words, each pattern is presented repeatedly to the perceptron until that pattern is classified correctly.

Note also that the use of an initial value $\mathbf{w}(0)$ different from the null condition merely results in a decrease or increase in the number of iterations required to converge, depending on how $\mathbf{w}(0)$ relates to the solution $\mathbf{w}_o$. Regardless of the value assigned to $\mathbf{w}(0)$, the perceptron is assured of convergence.

In Table 1.1, we present a summary of the *perceptron convergence algorithm* (Lippmann, 1987). The symbol $\mathrm{sgn}(\cdot)$, used in step 3 of the table for computing the actual response of the perceptron, stands for the *signum function*:

$$\mathrm{sgn}(v) = \begin{cases} +1 & \text{if } v > 0 \\ -1 & \text{if } v < 0 \end{cases} \tag{1.19}$$

We may thus express the *quantized response* $y(n)$ of the perceptron in the compact form

$$y(n) = \mathrm{sgn}[\mathbf{w}^T(n)\mathbf{x}(n)] \tag{1.20}$$

Notice that the input vector $\mathbf{x}(n)$ is an $(m + 1)$-by-1 vector whose first element is fixed at $+1$ throughout the computation. Correspondingly, the weight vector $\mathbf{w}(n)$ is an

---

TABLE 1.1   Summary of the Perceptron Convergence Algorithm

Variables and Parameters:

$\mathbf{x}(n) = (m + 1)$-by-1 input vector
$\quad\quad = [+1, x_1(n), x_2(n), ..., x_m(n)]^T$
$\mathbf{w}(n) = (m + 1)$-by-1 weight vector
$\quad\quad = [b, w_1(n), w_2(n), ..., w_m(n)]^T$
$\quad b$ = bias
$\quad y(n)$ = actual response (quantized)
$\quad d(n)$ = desired response
$\quad \eta$ = learning-rate parameter, a positive constant less than unity

1. *Initialization.* Set $\mathbf{w}(0) = \mathbf{0}$. Then perform the following computations for time-step $n = 1, 2, ...$
2. *Activation.* At time-step n, activate the perceptron by applying continuous-valued input vector $\mathbf{x}(n)$ and desired response $d(n)$.
3. *Computation of Actual Response.* Compute the actual response of the perceptron as
$$y(n) = \mathrm{sgn}[\mathbf{w}^T(n)\mathbf{x}(n)]$$
   where $\mathrm{sgn}(\cdot)$ is the signum function.
4. *Adaptation of Weight Vector.* Update the weight vector of the perceptron to obtain
$$\mathbf{w}(n + 1) = \mathbf{w}(n) + \eta[d(n) - y(n)]\mathbf{x}(n)$$

   where

$$d(n) = \begin{cases} +1 & \text{if } \mathbf{x}(n) \text{ belongs to class } \mathscr{C}_1 \\ -1 & \text{if } \mathbf{x}(n) \text{ belongs to class } \mathscr{C}_2 \end{cases}$$

5. *Continuation.* Increment time step n by one and go back to step 2.

$(m + 1)$-by-1 vector whose first element equals the bias b. One other important point to note in Table 1.1 is that we have introduced a *quantized desired response* $d(n)$, defined by

$$d(n) = \begin{cases} +1 & \text{if } \mathbf{x}(n) \text{ belongs to class } \mathscr{C}_1 \\ -1 & \text{if } \mathbf{x}(n) \text{ belongs to class } \mathscr{C}_2 \end{cases} \tag{1.21}$$

Thus, the adaptation of the weight vector $\mathbf{w}(n)$ is summed up nicely in the form of the *error-correction learning rule*

$$\mathbf{w}(n + 1) = \mathbf{w}(n) + \eta[d(n) - y(n)]\mathbf{x}(n) \tag{1.22}$$

where η is the *learning-rate parameter* and the difference $d(n) - y(n)$ plays the role of an *error signal*. The learning-rate parameter is a positive constant limited to the range $0 < \eta \leq 1$. When assigning a value to it inside this range, we must keep in mind two conflicting requirements (Lippmann, 1987):

- *averaging* of past inputs to provide stable weight estimates, which requires a small η;
- *fast adaptation* with respect to real changes in the underlying distributions of the process responsible for the generation of the input vector $\mathbf{x}$, which requires a large η.

1.4   RELATION BETWEEN THE PERCEPTRON AND BAYES CLASSIFIER FOR A GAUSSIAN ENVIRONMENT

The perceptron bears a certain relationship to a classical pattern classifier known as the Bayes classifier. When the environment is Gaussian, the Bayes classifier reduces to a linear classifier. This is the same form taken by the perceptron. However, the linear nature of the perceptron is *not* contingent on the assumption of Gaussianity. In this section, we study this relationship and thereby develop further insight into the operation of the perceptron. We begin the discussion with a brief review of the Bayes classifier.

Bayes Classifier

In the *Bayes classifier*, or *Bayes hypothesis testing procedure*, we minimize the *average risk*, denoted by $\mathscr{R}$. For a two-class problem, represented by classes $\mathscr{C}_1$ and $\mathscr{C}_2$, the average risk is defined by Van Trees (1968) as

$$\begin{aligned}
\mathscr{R} = {}& c_{11}p_1 \int_{\mathscr{H}_1} p_{\mathbf{X}}(\mathbf{x}|\mathscr{C}_1)d\mathbf{x} + c_{22}p_2 \int_{\mathscr{H}_2} p_{\mathbf{X}}(\mathbf{x}|\mathscr{C}_2)d\mathbf{x} \\
& + c_{21}p_1 \int_{\mathscr{H}_2} p_{\mathbf{X}}(\mathbf{x}|\mathscr{C}_1)d\mathbf{x} + c_{12}p_2 \int_{\mathscr{H}_1} p_{\mathbf{X}}(\mathbf{x}|\mathscr{C}_2)d\mathbf{x}
\end{aligned} \tag{1.23}$$

where the various terms are defined as follows:

p_i = *prior probability* that the observation vector $\mathbf{x}$ (representing a realization of the random vector $\mathbf{X}$) corresponds to an object in class C_1, with $i = 1, 2$, and $p_1 + p_2 = 1$

c_{ij} = cost of deciding in favor of class $\mathscr{C}_i$ represented by subspace $\mathscr{H}_i$ when class $\mathscr{C}_j$ is true (i.e., observation vector $\mathbf{x}$ corresponds to an object in class C_1), with $i, j = 1, 2$

$p_{\mathbf{X}}(\mathbf{x}|\mathscr{C}_i)$ = conditional probability density function of the random vector $\mathbf{X}$, given that the observation vector $\mathbf{x}$ corresponds to an object in class C_1, with $i = 1, 2$.

The first two terms on the right-hand side of Eq. (1.23) represent *correct* decisions (i.e., correct classifications), whereas the last two terms represent *incorrect* decisions (i.e., misclassifications). Each decision is weighted by the product of two factors: the cost involved in making the decision and the relative frequency (i.e., *prior* probability) with which it occurs.

The intention is to determine a strategy for the *minimum average risk*. Because we require that a decision be made, each observation vector $\mathbf{x}$ must be assigned in the overall observation space $\mathscr{X}$ to either $\mathscr{X}_1$ or $\mathscr{X}_2$. Thus,

$$\mathscr{X} = \mathscr{X}_1 + \mathscr{X}_2 \tag{1.24}$$

Accordingly, we may rewrite Eq. (1.23) in the equivalent form

$$\mathscr{R} = c_{11}p_1 \int_{\mathscr{X}_1} p_{\mathbf{X}}(\mathbf{x}|\mathscr{C}_1)d\mathbf{x} + c_{22}p_2 \int_{\mathscr{X}-\mathscr{X}_1} p_{\mathbf{X}}(\mathbf{x}|\mathscr{C}_2)d\mathbf{x}$$
$$+ c_{21}p_1 \int_{\mathscr{X}-\mathscr{X}_1} p_{\mathbf{X}}(\mathbf{x}|\mathscr{C}_1)\mathbf{x} + c_{12}p_2 \int_{\mathscr{X}_1} p_{\mathbf{X}}(\mathbf{x}|\mathscr{C}_2)d\mathbf{x} \tag{1.25}$$

where $c_{11} < c_{21}$ and $c_{22} < c_{12}$. We now observe the fact that

$$\int_{\mathscr{X}} p_{\mathbf{X}}(\mathbf{x}|\mathscr{C}_1)d\mathbf{x} = \int_{\mathscr{X}} p_{\mathbf{X}}(\mathbf{x}|\mathscr{C}_2)d\mathbf{x} = 1 \tag{1.26}$$

Hence, Eq. (1.25) reduces to

$$\mathscr{R} = c_{21}p_1 + c_{22}p_2$$
$$+ \int_{\mathscr{X}_1} [p_2(c_{12} - c_{22})\, p_{\mathbf{X}}(\mathbf{x}|\mathscr{C}_2) - p_1(c_{21} - c_{11})\, p_{\mathbf{X}}(\mathbf{x}|\mathscr{C}_1)]d\mathbf{x} \tag{1.27}$$

The first two terms on the right-hand side of Eq. (1.27) represent a fixed cost. Since the requirement is to minimize the average risk $\mathscr{R}$, we may therefore deduce the following strategy from Eq.(1.27) for optimum classification:

1. All values of the observation vector $\mathbf{x}$ for which the integrand (i.e., the expression inside the square brackets) is negative should be assigned to subset $\mathscr{X}_1$ (i.e., class $\mathscr{C}_1$), for the integral would then make a negative contribution to the risk $\mathscr{R}$.

2. All values of the observation vector $\mathbf{x}$ for which the integrand is positive should be excluded from subset $\mathscr{X}_1$ (i.e., assigned to class $\mathscr{C}_2$), for the integral would then make a positive contribution to the risk $\mathscr{R}$.

3. Values of $\mathbf{x}$ for which the integrand is zero have no effect on the average risk $\mathscr{R}$ and may be assingned arbitrarily. We shall assume that these points are assigned to subset $\mathscr{X}_2$ (i.e., class $\mathscr{C}_2$).

On this basis, we may now formulate the Bayes classifier as follows:

If the condition

$$p_1(c_{21} - c_{11})\, p_\mathbf{x}(\mathbf{x}|\mathscr{C}_1) > p_2(c_{12} - c_{22})\, p_\mathbf{x}(\mathbf{x}|\mathscr{C}_2)$$

holds, assign the observation vector $\mathbf{x}$ *to subspace* $\mathscr{X}_1$ *(i.e., class* $\mathscr{C}_1$*). Otherwise assign* $\mathbf{x}$ *to* $\mathscr{X}_2$ *(i.e., class* $\mathscr{C}_2$*).*

To simplify matters, define

$$\Lambda(\mathbf{x}) = \frac{p_\mathbf{x}(\mathbf{x}|\mathscr{C}_1)}{p_\mathbf{x}(\mathbf{x}|\mathscr{C}_2)} \tag{1.28}$$

and

$$\xi = \frac{p_2(c_{12} - c_{22})}{p_1(c_{21} - c_{11})} \tag{1.29}$$

The quantity $\Lambda(\mathbf{x})$, the ratio of two conditional probability density functions, is called the *likelihood ratio*. The quantity ξ is called the *threshold* of the test. Note that both $\Lambda(\mathbf{x})$ and ξ are always positive. In terms of these two quantities, we may now reformulate the Bayes classifier by stating the following

If, for an observation vector $\mathbf{x}$*, the likelihood ratio* $\Lambda(\mathbf{x})$ *is greater than the threshold* ξ*, assign* $\mathbf{x}$ *to class* $\mathscr{C}_1$*. Otherwise, assign it to class* $\mathscr{C}_2$*.*

Figure 1.5a depicts a block-diagram representation of the Bayes classifier. The important points in this block diagram are twofold:

1. The data processing involved in designing the Bayes classifier is confined entirely to the computation of the likelihood ratio $\Lambda(\mathbf{x})$.

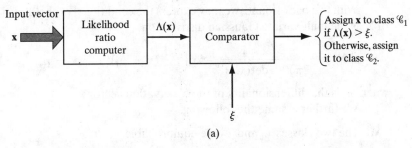

(a)

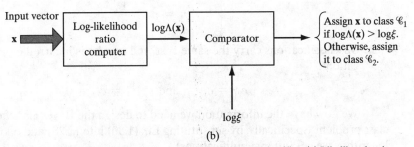

(b)

FIGURE 1.5   Two equivalent implementations of the Bayes classifier: (a) Likelihood ratio test, (b) Log-likelihood ratio test.

2. This computation is completely invariant to the values assigned to the prior probabilities and costs involved in the decision-making process. These quantities merely affect the value of the threshold ξ.

From a computational point of view, we find it more convenient to work with the logarithm of the likelihood ratio rather than the likelihood ratio itself. We are permitted to do this for two reasons. First, the logarithm is a monotonic function. Second, the likelihood ratio $\Lambda(\mathbf{x})$ and threshold ξ are both positive. Therefore, the Bayes classifier may be implemented in the equivalent form shown in Fig. 1.5b. For obvious reasons, the test embodied in this latter figure is called the *log-likelihood ratio test.*

Bayes Classifier for a Gaussian Distribution

Consider now the special case of a two-class problem, for which the underlying distribution is Gaussian. The random vector $\mathbf{X}$ has a mean value that depends on whether it belongs to class $\mathscr{C}_1$ or class $\mathscr{C}_2$, but the covariance matrix of $\mathbf{X}$ is the same for both classes. That is to say,

$$\text{Class } \mathscr{C}_1: \quad \mathbb{E}[\mathbf{X}] = \boldsymbol{\mu}_1$$
$$\mathbb{E}[(\mathbf{X} - \boldsymbol{\mu}_1)(\mathbf{X} - \boldsymbol{\mu}_1)^T] = \mathbf{C}$$
$$\text{Class } \mathscr{C}_2: \quad \mathbb{E}[\mathbf{X}] = \boldsymbol{\mu}_2$$
$$\mathbb{E}[(\mathbf{X} - \boldsymbol{\mu}_2)(\mathbf{X} - \boldsymbol{\mu}_2)^T] = \mathbf{C}$$

The covariance matrix $\mathbf{C}$ is nondiagonal, which means that the samples drawn from classes $\mathscr{C}_1$ and $\mathscr{C}_2$ are *correlated*. It is assumed that $\mathbf{C}$ is nonsingular, so that its inverse matrix $\mathbf{C}^{-1}$ exists.

With this background, we may express the conditional probability density function of $\mathbf{X}$ as the multivariate Gaussian distribution

$$p_{\mathbf{X}}(\mathbf{x}|\mathscr{C}_i) = \frac{1}{(2\pi)^{m/2}(\det(\mathbf{C}))^{1/2}} \exp\left(-\frac{1}{2}(\mathbf{x} - \boldsymbol{\mu}_i)^T \mathbf{C}^{-1}(\mathbf{x} - \boldsymbol{\mu}_i)\right), \quad i = 1, 2 \quad (1.30)$$

where m is the dimensionality of the observation vector $\mathbf{x}$.

We further assume the following:

1. The two classes $\mathscr{C}_1$ and $\mathscr{C}_2$ are equiprobable:

$$p_1 = p_2 = \frac{1}{2} \tag{1.31}$$

2. Misclassifications carry the same cost, and no cost is incurred on correct classifications:

$$c_{21} = c_{12} \quad \text{and} \quad c_{11} = c_{22} = 0 \tag{1.32}$$

We now have the information we need to design the Bayes classifier for the two-class problem. Specifically, by substituting Eq. (1.30) into (1.28) and taking the natural logarithm, we get (after simplifications)

$$\log \Lambda(\mathbf{x}) = -\frac{1}{2}(\mathbf{x} - \boldsymbol{\mu}_1)^T \mathbf{C}^{-1}(\mathbf{x} - \boldsymbol{\mu}_1) + \frac{1}{2}(\mathbf{x} - \boldsymbol{\mu}_2)^T \mathbf{C}^{-1}(\mathbf{x} - \boldsymbol{\mu}_2)$$

$$= (\boldsymbol{\mu}_1 - \boldsymbol{\mu}_2)^T \mathbf{C}^{-1}\mathbf{x} + \frac{1}{2}(\boldsymbol{\mu}_2^T \mathbf{C}^{-1}\boldsymbol{\mu}_2 - \boldsymbol{\mu}_1^T \mathbf{C}^{-1}\boldsymbol{\mu}_1)$$

(1.33)

By substituting Eqs. (1.31) and (1.32) into Eq. (1.29) and taking the natural logarithm, we get

$$\log \xi = 0 \qquad (1.34)$$

Equations (1.33) and (1.34) state that the Bayes classifier for the problem at hand is a *linear classifier*, as described by the relation

$$y = \mathbf{w}^T \mathbf{x} + b \qquad (1.35)$$

where

$$\mathbf{y} = \log \Lambda(\mathbf{x}) \qquad (1.36)$$

$$\mathbf{w} = \mathbf{C}^{-1}(\boldsymbol{\mu}_1 - \boldsymbol{\mu}_2) \qquad (1.37)$$

$$b = \frac{1}{2}(\boldsymbol{\mu}_2^T \mathbf{C}^{-1}\boldsymbol{\mu}_2 - \boldsymbol{\mu}_1^T \mathbf{C}^{-1}\boldsymbol{\mu}_1) \qquad (1.38)$$

More specifically, the classifier consists of a linear combiner with weight vector $\mathbf{w}$ and bias b, as shown in Fig. 1.6.

On the basis of Eq. (1.35), we may now describe the log-likelihood ratio test for our two-class problem as follows:

> *If the output y of the linear combiner (including the bias b) is positive, assign the observation vector* $\mathbf{x}$ *to class* $\mathscr{C}_1$. *Otherwise, assign it to class* $\mathscr{C}_2$.

The operation of the Bayes classifier for the Gaussian environment described herein is analogous to that of the perceptron in that they are both linear classifiers; see Eqs. (1.1) and (1.35). There are, however, some subtle and important differences between them, which should be carefully examined (Lippmann, 1987):

- The perceptron operates on the premise that the patterns to be classified are *linearly separable*. The Gaussian distributions of the two patterns assumed in the derivation of the Bayes classifier certainly do *overlap* each other and are therefore *not* separable. The extent of the overlap is determined by the mean vectors

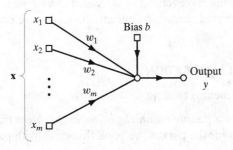

FIGURE 1.6   Signal-flow graph of Gaussian classifier.

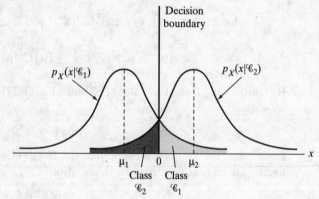

FIGURE 1.7 Two overlapping, one-dimensional Gaussian distributions.

μ_1 and μ_2 and the covariance matrix $\mathbf{C}$. The nature of this overlap is illustrated in Fig. 1.7 for the special case of a scalar random variable (i.e., dimensionality $m = 1$). When the inputs are nonseparable and their distributions overlap as illustrated, the perceptron convergence algorithm develops a problem because decision boundaries between the different classes may oscillate continuously.

- The Bayes classifier minimizes the probability of classification error. This minimization is independent of the overlap between the underlying Gaussian distributions of the two classes. For example, in the special case illustrated in Fig. 1.7, the Bayes classifier always positions the decision boundary at the point where the Gaussian distributions for the two classes $\mathscr{C}_1$ and $\mathscr{C}_2$ cross each other.

- The perceptron convergence algorithm is *nonparametric* in the sense that it makes no assumptions concerning the form of the underlying distributions. It operates by concentrating on errors that occur where the distributions overlap. It may therefore work well when the inputs are generated by nonlinear physical mechanisms and when their distributions are heavily skewed and non-Gaussian. In contrast, the Bayes classifier is *parametric*; its derivation is contingent on the assumption that the underlying distributions be Gaussian, which may limit its area of application.

- The perceptron convergence algorithm is both adaptive and simple to implement; its storage requirement is confined to the set of synaptic weights and bias. On the other hand, the design of the Bayes classifier is fixed; it can be made adaptive, but at the expense of increased storage requirements and more complex computations.

1.5   COMPUTER EXPERIMENT: PATTERN CLASSIFICATION

The objective of this computer experiment is twofold:

(i) to lay down the specifications of a *double-moon classification problem* that will serve as the basis of a prototype for the part of the book that deals with pattern-classification experiments;

(ii) to demonstrate the capability of Rosenblatt's perceptron algorithm to correctly classify linearly separable patterns and to show its breakdown when the condition of linear separability is violated.

Specifications of the Classification Problem

Figure 1.8 shows a pair of "moons" facing each other in an *asymmetrically* arranged manner. The moon labeled "Region A" is positioned symmetrically with respect to the y-axis, whereas the moon labeled "Region B" is displaced to the right of the y-axis by an amount equal to the radius r and below the x-axis by the distance d. The two moons have identical parameters:

$$\text{radius of each moon, } r = 10$$
$$\text{width of each moon, } w = 6$$

The vertical distance d separating the two moons is adjustable; it is measured with respect to the x-axis, as indicated in Fig. 1.8:

- Increasingly positive values of d signify increased separation between the two moons;
- increasingly negative values of d signify the two moons' coming closer to each other.

The training sample $\mathcal{T}$ consists of 1,000 pairs of data points, with each pair consisting of one point picked from region A and another point picked from region B, both randomly. The test sample consists of 2,000 pairs of data points, again picked in a random manner.

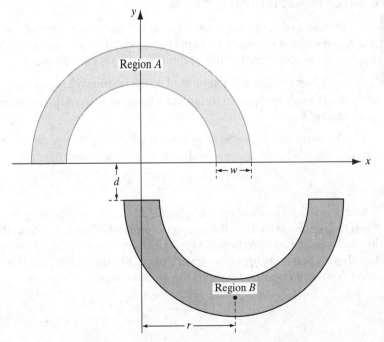

FIGURE 1.8   The double-moon classification problem.

The Experiment

The perceptron parameters picked for the experiment were as follows:

$$\text{size of the input layer} = 2$$
$$\beta = 50; \text{ see Eq. (1.17)}$$

The learning-rate parameter η was varied linearly from 10^{-1} down to 10^{-5}.

The weights were initially all set at zero.

Figure 1.9 presents the results of the experiment for $d = 1$, which corresponds to perfect linear separability. Part (a) of the figure presents the *learning curve*, where the mean-square error (MSE) is plotted versus the number of epochs; the figure shows convergence of the algorithm in three iterations. Part (b) of the figure shows the decision boundary computed through training of the perceptron algorithm, demonstrating perfect separability of all 2,000 test points.

In Fig. 1.10, the separation between the two moons was set at $d = -4$, a condition that violates linear separability. Part (a) of the figure displays the learning curve where the perceptron algorithm is now found to fluctuate continuously, indicating breakdown of the algorithm. This result is confirmed in part (b) of the figure, where the decision boundary (computed through training) intersects both moons, with a classification error rate of $(186/2000) \times 100\% = 9.3\%$.

1.6 THE BATCH PERCEPTRON ALGORITHM

The derivation of the perceptron convergence algorithm summarized in Table 1.1 was presented without reference to a cost function. Moreover, the derivation focused on a single-sample correction. In this section, we will do two things:

1. introduce the generalized form of a perceptron cost function;
2. use the cost function to formulate a batch version of the perceptron convergence algorithm.

The cost function we have in mind is a function that permits the application of a gradient search. Specifically, we define the *perceptron cost function* as

$$J(\mathbf{w}) = \sum_{\mathbf{x}(n)\in\mathcal{X}} (-\mathbf{w}^T\mathbf{x}(n)d(n)) \tag{1.39}$$

where $\mathcal{X}$ is the set of samples $\mathbf{x}$ *misclassified* by a perceptron using $\mathbf{w}$ as its weight vector (Duda et al., 2001). If all the samples are classified correctly, then the set $\mathcal{X}$ is empty, in which case the cost function $J(\mathbf{w})$ is zero. In any event, the nice feature of the cost function $J(\mathbf{w})$ is that it is *differentiable* with respect to the weight vector $\mathbf{w}$. Thus, differentiating $J(\mathbf{w})$ with respect to $\mathbf{w}$ yields the *gradient vector*

$$\nabla J(\mathbf{w}) = \sum_{\mathbf{x}(n)\in\mathcal{X}} (-\mathbf{x}(n)d(n)) \tag{1.40}$$

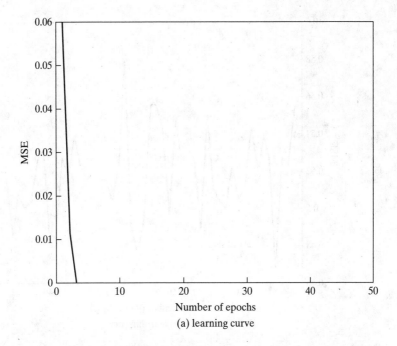

(a) learning curve

Classification using perceptron with distance = 1, radius = 10, and width = 6

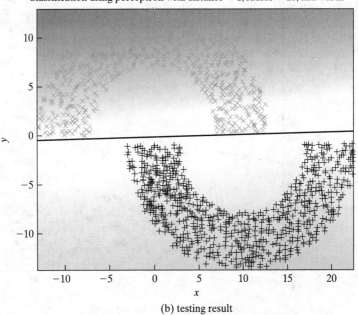

(b) testing result

FIGURE 1.9   Perceptron with the double-moon set at distance $d = 1$.

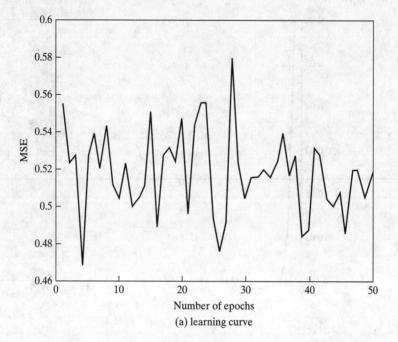

(a) learning curve

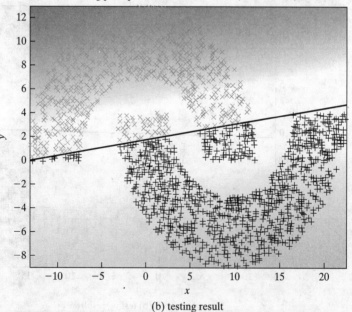

Classification using perceptron with distance = −4, radius = 10, and width = 6

(b) testing result

FIGURE 1.10   Perceptron with the double-moon set at distance $d = -4$.

where the *gradient operator*

$$\nabla = \left[\frac{\partial}{\partial w_1}, \frac{\partial}{\partial w_2}, ..., \frac{\partial}{\partial w_m} \right]^T \tag{1.41}$$

In the *method of steepest descent,* the adjustment to the weight vector **w** at each time-step of the algorithm is applied in a direction *opposite* to the gradient vector $\nabla J(\mathbf{w})$. Accordingly, the algorithm takes the form

$$\mathbf{w}(n + 1) = \mathbf{w}(n) - \eta(n) \nabla J(\mathbf{w})$$
$$= \mathbf{w}(n) + \eta(n) \sum_{\mathbf{x}(n) \in \mathscr{X}} \mathbf{x}(n)d(n) \tag{1.42}$$

which includes the single-sample correction version of the perceptron convergence algorithm as a special case. Moreover, Eq. (1.42) embodies the *batch perceptron algorithm* for computing the weight vector, given the sample set $\mathbf{x}(1), \mathbf{x}(2), ...$ In particular, the adjustment applied to the weight vector at time-step $n + 1$ is defined by the sum of all the samples misclassified by the weight vector $\mathbf{w}(n)$, with the sum being scaled by the learning-rate parameter $\eta(n)$. The algorithm is said to be of the "batch" kind because at each time-step of the algorithm, a batch of misclassified samples is used to compute the adjustment.

1.7 SUMMARY AND DISCUSSION

The perceptron is a single-layer neural network, the operation of which is based on error-correlation learning. The term "single layer" is used here to signify the fact that the computation layer of the network consists of a single neuron for the case of binary classification. The learning process for pattern classification occupies a finite number of iterations and then stops. For the classification to be successful, however, the patterns would have to be linearly separable.

The perceptron uses the McCulloch–Pitts model of a neuron. In this context, it is tempting to raise the question, would the perceptron perform better if it used a sigmoidal nonlinearity in place of the hard limiter? It turns out that the steady-state, decision-making characteristics of the perceptron are basically the same, regardless of whether we use hard limiting or soft limiting as the source of nonlinearity in the neural model (Shynk, 1990; Shynk and Bershad, 1991). We may therefore state formally that so long as we limit ourselves to the model of a neuron that consists of a linear combiner followed by a nonlinear element, then regardless of the form of nonlinearity used, a single-layer perceptron can perform pattern classification only on linearly separable patterns.

The first real critique of Rosenblatt's perceptron was presented by Minsky and Selfridge (1961). Minsky and Selfridge pointed out that the perceptron as defined by Rosenblatt could not even generalize toward the notion of binary parity, let alone make general abstractions. The computational limitations of Rosenblatt's perceptron were subsequently put on a solid mathematical foundation in the famous book *Perceptrons,* by Minsky and Papert (1969, 1988). After the presentation of some brilliant and highly detailed mathematical analyses of the perceptron, Minsky and Papert proved that the perceptron as defined by Rosenblatt is inherently incapable of making some global generalizations on the basis of locally learned examples. In the last chapter of their book, Minsky and Papert make the conjecture that the limitations they had discovered for Rosenblatt's perceptron would also hold true for its variants—more specifically, multilayer neural networks. Section 13.2 of their book (1969) says the following:

> The perceptron has shown itself worthy of study despite (and even because of!) its severe limitations. It has many features to attract attention: its linearity; its intriguing learning theorem; its clear paradigmatic simplicity as a kind of parallel computation. There is no reason to suppose that any of these virtues carry over to the many-layered version. Nevertheless, we consider it to be an important research problem to elucidate (or reject) our intuitive judgement that the extension to multilayer systems is sterile.

This conclusion was largely responsible for casting serious doubt on the computational capabilities of not only the perceptron, but also neural networks in general up to the mid-1980s.

History has shown, however, that the conjecture made by Minsky and Papert seems to be unjustified in that we now have several advanced forms of neural networks and learning machines that are computationally more powerful than Rosenblatt's perceptron. For example, multilayer perceptrons trained with the back-propagation algorithm discussed in Chapter 4, the radial basis-function networks discussed in Chapter 5, and the support vector machines discussed in Chapter 6 overcome the computational limitations of the single-layer perceptron in their own individual ways.

In closing the discussion, we may say that the perceptron is an elegant neural network designed for the classification of linearly separable patterns. Its importance is not only historical but also of practical value in the classification of linearly separable patters.

NOTES AND REFERENCES

1. The network organization of the original version of the perceptron as envisioned by Rosenblatt (1962) has three types of units: sensory units, association units, and response units. The connections from the sensory units to the association units have fixed weights, and the connections from the association units to the response units have variable weights. The association units act as preprocessors designed to extract a pattern from the environmental input. Insofar as the variable weights are concerned, the operation of Rosenblatt's original perceptron is essentially the same as that for the case of a single response unit (i.e., single neuron).

2. Proof of the perceptron convergence algorithm presented in Section 1.3 follows the classic book of Nilsson (1965).

PROBLEMS

1.1 Verify that Eqs. (1.19)–(1.22), summarizing the perceptron convergence algorithm, are consistent with Eqs. (1.5) and (1.6).

1.2 Suppose that in the signal-flow graph of the perceptron shown in Fig. 1.1, the hard limiter is replaced by the sigmoidal nonlinearity

$$\varphi(v) = \tanh\left(\frac{v}{2}\right)$$

where v is the induced local field. The classification decisions made by the perceptron are defined as follows:

> *Observation vector* **x** *belongs to class* $\mathscr{C}_1$ *if the output* $y > \xi$, *where* ξ *is a threshold; otherwise,* **x** *belongs to class* $\mathscr{C}_2$.

Show that the decision boundary so constructed is a hyperplane.

1.3 **(a)** The perceptron may be used to perform numerous logic functions. Demonstrate the implementation of the binary logic functions AND, OR, and COMPLEMENT.

(b) Compare the operation of the Bayes classifier for the Gaussian environment with that of perceptron.

1.4 Consider two one-dimensional, Gaussian-distributed classes $\mathscr{C}_1$ and $\mathscr{C}_2$ that have a common variance equal to 1. Their mean values are

$$\mu_1 = -10$$
$$\mu_2 = +10$$

These two classes are essentially linearly separable. Design a classifier that separates these two classes.

1.5 Equations (1.37) and (1.38) define the weight vector and bias of the Bayes classifier for a Gaussian environment. Determine the composition of this classifier for the case when the covariance matrix **C** is defined by

$$\mathbf{C} = \sigma^2 \mathbf{I}$$

where σ^2 is a constant and **I** is the identity matrix.

Computer Experiment

1.6 Repeat the computer experiment of Section 1.5, this time, however, positioning the two moons of Figure 1.8 to be on the edge of separability, that is, $d = 0$. Determine the classification error rate produced by the algorithm over 2,000 test data points.

CHAPTER 2

Model Building through Regression

ORGANIZATION OF THE CHAPTER

The theme of this chapter is how to use *linear regression*, a special form of function approximation, to model a given set of random variables.

The chapter is organized as follows:

1. Section 2.1 is introductory, followed by Section 2.2 that sets the stage for the rest of the chapter by describing the mathematical framework of linear regression models.

2. Section 2.3 derives the *maximum a posteriori (MAP) estimate* of the parameter vector of a linear regression model.

3. Section 2.4 tackles the parameter estimation problem using the method of least squares and discusses this method's relationship to the Bayesian approach.

4. In Section 2.5, we revisit the pattern-classification experiment considered in Chapter 1, this time using the method of least squares.

5. Section 2.6 addresses the problem of model-order selection.

6. Section 2.7 discusses consequences of finite sample size in parameter estimation, including the bias–variance dilemma.

7. Section 2.8 introduces the notion of instrumental variables to deal with the "errors-in-variables" problem.

Section 2.9 provides a summary and discussion that conclude the chapter.

2.1 INTRODUCTION

The idea of model building shows up practically in every discipline that deals with *statistical data* analysis. Suppose, for example, we are given a set of random variables and the assigned task is to find the relationships that may exist between them, if any. In *regression*, which is a special form of function approximation, we typically find the following scenario:

- One of the random variables is considered to be of particular interest; that random variable is referred to as a dependent variable, or *response*.

- The remaining random variables are called independent variables, or *regressors*; their role is to explain or predict the statistical behavior of the response.

- The dependence of the response on the regressors includes an additive *error* term, to account for uncertainties in the manner in which this dependence is formulated;

the error term is called the *expectational error*, or *explanational error*, both of which are used interchangeably.

Such a model is called the *regression model*.[1]

There are two classes of regression models: linear and nonlinear. In *linear regression models*, the dependence of the response on the regressors is defined by a linear function, which makes their statistical analysis mathematically tractable. On the other hand, in *nonlinear regression models*, this dependence is defined by a nonlinear function, hence the mathematical difficulty in their analysis. In this chapter, we focus attention on linear regression models. Nonlinear regression models are studied in subsequent chapters.

The mathematical tractability of linear regression models shows up in this chapter in two ways. First, we use *Bayesian theory*[2] to derive the *maximum a posteriori estimate* of the vector that parameterizes a linear regression model. Next, we view the parameter estimation problem using another approach, namely, the *method of least squares*, which is perhaps the oldest parameter-estimation procedure; it was first derived by Gauss in the early part of the 19th century. We then demonstrate the equivalence between these two approaches for the special case of a Gaussian environment.

2.2 LINEAR REGRESSION MODEL: PRELIMINARY CONSIDERATIONS

Consider the situation depicted in Fig. 2.1a, where an *unknown stochastic environment* is the focus of attention. The environment is *probed* by applying a set of inputs, constituting the regressor

$$\mathbf{x} = [x_1, x_2, ..., x_M]^T \tag{2.1}$$

where the superscript T denotes matrix *transposition*. The resulting output of the environment, denoted by d, constitutes the corresponding *response*, which is assumed to be scalar merely for the convenience of presentation. Ordinarily, we do not know the functional dependence of the response d on the regressor $\mathbf{x}$, so we propose a linear regression model, parameterized as:

$$d = \sum_{j=1}^{M} w_j x_j + \varepsilon \tag{2.2}$$

where $w_1, w_2, ..., w_M$ denote a set of *fixed*, but *unknown, parameters*, meaning that the environment is *stationary*. The additive term ε, representing the expectational error of the model, accounts for our ignorance about the environment. A signal-flow graph depiction of the input–output behavior of the model described in Eq. (2.2) is presented in Fig. 2.1b.

Using matrix notation, we may rewrite Eq. (2.2) in the compact form

$$d = \mathbf{w}^T \mathbf{x} + \varepsilon \tag{2.3}$$

where the regressor $\mathbf{x}$ is defined in terms of its elements in Eq. (2.1). Correspondingly, the *parameter vector* $\mathbf{w}$ is defined by

$$\mathbf{w} = [w_1, w_2, ..., w_M]^T \tag{2.4}$$

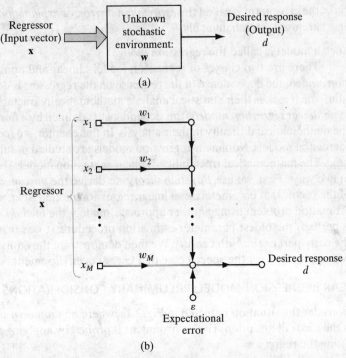

FIGURE 2.1 (a) Unknown stationary stochastic environment. (b) Linear regression model of the environment.

whose dimensionality is the same as that of the regressor $\mathbf{x}$; the common dimension M is called the *model order*. The matrix term $\mathbf{w}^T\mathbf{x}$ is the *inner product* of the vectors $\mathbf{w}$ and $\mathbf{x}$.

With the environment being stochastic, it follows that the regressor $\mathbf{x}$, the response d, and the expectational error ε are *sample* values (i.e., single-shot realizations) of the random vector $\mathbf{X}$, the random variable D, and the random variable E, respectively. With such a stochastic setting as the background, the problem of interest may now be stated as follows:

> *Given the joint statistics of the regressor X and the corresponding response D, estimate the unknown parameter vector* $\mathbf{w}$.

When we speak of the joint statistics, we mean the following set of statistical parameters:

- the correlation matrix of the regressor $\mathbf{X}$;
- the variance of the desired response D;
- the cross-correlation vector of the regressor $\mathbf{X}$ and the desired response D.

It is assumed that the means of both $\mathbf{X}$ and D are zero.

In Chapter 1, we discussed one important facet of Bayesian inference in the context of pattern classification. In this chapter, we study another facet of Bayesian inference that addresses the *parameter estimation* problem just stated.

2.3 MAXIMUM *A POSTERIORI* ESTIMATION OF THE PARAMETER VECTOR

The Bayesian paradigm provides a powerful approach for addressing and quantifying the *uncertainty* that surrounds the choice of the parameter vector $\mathbf{w}$ in the linear regression model of Eq. (2.3). Insofar as this model is concerned, the following two remarks are noteworthy:

1. The regressor $\mathbf{X}$ acts as the "excitation," bearing no relation whatsoever to the parameter vector $\mathbf{w}$.
2. Information about the unknown parameter vector $\mathbf{W}$ is contained solely in the desired response D that acts as the "observable" of the environment.

Accordingly, we focus attention on the joint probablity density function of $\mathbf{W}$ and D, conditional on $\mathbf{X}$.

Let this density function be denoted by $p_{\mathbf{W},\,D|\mathbf{X}}(\mathbf{w},\,d|\mathbf{x})$. From probability theory, we know that this density function may be expressed as

$$p_{\mathbf{W},\,D|\mathbf{X}}(\mathbf{w},\,d\,|\mathbf{x}) = p_{\mathbf{W}|D,\,\mathbf{X}}(\mathbf{w}|d,\,\mathbf{x})p_D(d) \tag{2.5}$$

Moreover, we may also express it in the equivalent form

$$p_{\mathbf{W},\,D|\mathbf{X}}(\mathbf{w},\,d|\mathbf{x}) = p_{D|\mathbf{W},\,\mathbf{X}}(d|\mathbf{w},\,\mathbf{x})p_{\mathbf{W}}(\mathbf{w}) \tag{2.6}$$

In light of this pair of equations, we may go on to write

$$p_{\mathbf{W}|D,\,\mathbf{X}}(\mathbf{w}|d,\,\mathbf{x}) = \frac{p_{D|\,\mathbf{W},\,\mathbf{X}}(d|\mathbf{w},\,\mathbf{x})p_{\mathbf{W}}(\mathbf{w})}{p_D(d)} \tag{2.7}$$

provided that $p_D(d) \neq 0$. Equation (2.7) is a special form of *Bayes's theorem*; it embodies four density functions, characterized as follows:

1. *Observation density*: This stands for the conditional probability density function $p_{D|\mathbf{W},\,\mathbf{X}}(d\,|\,\mathbf{w},\,\mathbf{x})$, referring to the "observation" of the environmental response d due to the regressor $\mathbf{x}$, given the parameter vector $\mathbf{w}$.
2. *Prior*: This stands for the probability density function $p_{\mathbf{W}}(\mathbf{w})$, referring to information about the parameter vector $\mathbf{w}$, prior to any observations made on the environment. Hereafter, the prior is simply denoted by $\pi(\mathbf{w})$.
3. *Posterior density*: This stands for the conditional probability density function $p_{\mathbf{W}|D,\,\mathbf{X}}(\mathbf{w}|d,\,\mathbf{x})$, referring to the parameter vector $\mathbf{w}$ "after" observation of the environment has been completed. Hereafter, the posterior density is denoted by $\pi(\mathbf{w}|d,\,\mathbf{x})$. The conditioning response–regressor pair $(\mathbf{x},\,d)$ is the "observation model," embodying the response d of the environment due to the regressor $\mathbf{x}$.
4. *Evidence*: This stands for the probability density function $p_D(d)$, referring to the "information" contained in the response d for statistical analysis.

The observation density $p_{D|\mathbf{W},\,\mathbf{X}}(d\,|\,\mathbf{w},\,\mathbf{x})$ is commonly reformulated mathematically as the *likelihood function*, defined by

$$l(\mathbf{w}|d,\,\mathbf{x}) = p_{D|\mathbf{W},\,\mathbf{X}}(d|\mathbf{w},\,\mathbf{x}) \tag{2.8}$$

Moreover, insofar as the estimation of the parameter vector $\mathbf{w}$ is concerned, the evidence $p_D(d)$ in the denominator of the right-hand side of Eq. (2.7) plays merely the role of a *normalizing constant*. Accordingly, we may express Eq. (2.7) in words by stating the following:

> *The posterior density of the vector $\mathbf{w}$ parameterizing the regression model is proportional to the product of the likelihood function and the prior.*

That is,

$$\pi(\mathbf{w}|d, \mathbf{x}) \propto l(\mathbf{w}|d, \mathbf{x})\pi(\mathbf{w}) \tag{2.9}$$

where the symbol $\propto$ signifies proportionality.

The likelihood function $l(\mathbf{w}|d, \mathbf{x})$, considered on its own, provides the basis for the *maximum-likelihood (ML) estimate* of the parameter vector $\mathbf{w}$, as shown by

$$\mathbf{w}_{ML} = \arg\max_{\mathbf{w}} l(\mathbf{w}|d, \mathbf{x}) \tag{2.10}$$

For a more profound estimate of the parameter vector $\mathbf{w}$, however, we look to the posterior density $\pi(\mathbf{w}|d, \mathbf{x})$. Specifically, we define the *maximum a posteriori (MAP) estimate* of the parameter vector $\mathbf{w}$ by the formula

$$\mathbf{w}_{MAP} = \arg\max_{\mathbf{w}} \pi(\mathbf{w}|d, \mathbf{x}) \tag{2.11}$$

We say that the MAP estimator is more profound than the ML estimator for two important reasons:

1. The Bayesian paradigm for parameter estimation, rooted in the Bayes' theorem as shown in Eq. (2.7) and exemplified by the MAP estimator of Eq. (2.11), *exploits all the conceivable information about the parameter vector $\mathbf{w}$*. In contrast, the ML estimator of Eq. (2.10) lies on the *fringe* of the Bayesian paradigm, ignoring the prior.

2. The ML estimator relies solely on the observation model $(d, \mathbf{x})$ and may therefore lead to a nonunique solution. To enforce uniqueness and stability on the solution, *the prior $\pi(\mathbf{w})$ has to be incorporated into the formulation of the estimator*; this is precisely what is done in the MAP estimator.

Of course, the challenge in applying the MAP estimation procedure is how to come up with an appropriate prior, which makes MAP more computationally demanding than ML.

One last comment is in order. From a computational perspective, we usually find it more convenient to work with the logarithm of the posterior density rather than the posterior density itself. We are permitted to do this, since the logarithm is a monotonically increasing function of its argument. Accordingly, we may express the MAP estimator in the desired form by writing

$$\mathbf{w}_{MAP} = \arg\max_{\mathbf{w}} \log(\pi(\mathbf{w}|d, \mathbf{x})) \tag{2.12}$$

where "log" denotes the natural logarithm. A similar statement applies to the ML estimator.

Parameter Estimation in a Gaussian Environment

Let $\mathbf{x}_i$ and d_i denote the regressor applied to the environment and the resulting response, respectively, on the ith trial of an experiment performed on the environment. Let the experiment be repeated a total of N times. We thus express the training sample, available for parameter estimation, as

$$\mathcal{T} = \{\mathbf{x}_i, d_i\}_{i=1}^{N} \qquad (2.13)$$

To proceed with the task of parameter estimation, we make the following assumptions:

Assumption 1: Statistical Independence and Identical Distribution

The N examples, constituting the training sample, are statistically *independent and identically distributed* (iid).

Assumption 2: Gaussianity

The environment, responsible for generation of the training sample $\mathcal{T}$, is *Gaussian distributed.*

More specifically, the expectational error in the linear regression model of Eq. (2.3) is described by a Gaussian density function of zero mean and common variance σ^2, as shown by

$$p_E(\varepsilon_i) = \frac{1}{\sqrt{2\pi}\,\sigma} \exp\left(-\frac{\varepsilon_i^2}{2\sigma^2}\right), \qquad i = 1, 2, ..., N \qquad (2.14)$$

Assumption 3: Stationarity

The environment is stationary, which means that the parameter vector $\mathbf{w}$ is *fixed*, but unknown, throughout the N trials of the experiment.

More specifically, the M elements of the weight vector $\mathbf{w}$ are themselves assumed to be iid, with each element being governed by a Gaussian density function of zero mean and common variance σ_w^2. We may therefore express the prior for the kth element of the parameter vector $\mathbf{w}$ as

$$\pi(w_k) = \frac{1}{\sqrt{2\pi}\,\sigma_w} \exp\left(-\frac{w_k^2}{2\sigma_w^2}\right), \qquad k = 1, 2, ..., M \qquad (2.15)$$

Rewriting Eq. (2.3) for the ith trial of the experiment performed on the environment, we have

$$d_i = \mathbf{w}^T \mathbf{x}_i + \varepsilon_i, \qquad i = 1, 2, ..., N \qquad (2.16)$$

where d_i, $\mathbf{x}_i$, and ε_i are sample values (i.e., single-shot realizations) of the random variable D, the random vector $\mathbf{X}$, and the random variable E, respectively.

Let $\mathbb{E}$ denote the statistical expectation operator. Since, under Assumption 2, we have

$$\mathbb{E}[E_i] = 0, \qquad \text{for all } i \qquad (2.17)$$

and

$$\text{var}[E_i] = \mathbb{E}[E_i^2] = \sigma^2, \qquad \text{for all } i \tag{2.18}$$

it follows from Eq. (2.16) that, for a given regressor $\mathbf{x}_i$,

$$\mathbb{E}[D_i] = \mathbf{w}^T\mathbf{x}_i, \qquad i = 1, 2, ..., N \tag{2.19}$$

$$\begin{aligned}\text{var}[D_i] &= \mathbb{E}[(D_i - \mathbb{E}[D_i])^2]\\ &= \mathbb{E}[E_i^2]\\ &= \sigma^2 \end{aligned} \tag{2.20}$$

We thus complete the Gaussian implication of Assumption 2 by expressing the likelihood function for the ith trial, in light of Eq. (2.14), as

$$l(\mathbf{w}|d_i, x_i) = \frac{1}{\sqrt{2\pi}\,\sigma} \exp\left(-\frac{1}{2\sigma^2}(d_i - \mathbf{w}^T\mathbf{x}_i)^2\right), \qquad i = 1, 2, ..., N \tag{2.21}$$

Next, invoking the iid characterization of the N trials of the experiment on the environment under Assumption 1, we express the overall likelihood function for the experiment as

$$\begin{aligned} l(\mathbf{w}|d, \mathbf{x}) &= \prod_{i=1}^{N} l(\mathbf{w}|d_i, \mathbf{x}_i)\\ &= \frac{1}{(\sqrt{2\pi}\sigma)^N} \prod_{i=1}^{N}\exp\left(-\frac{1}{2\sigma^2}(d_i - \mathbf{w}^T\mathbf{x}_i)^2\right)\\ &= \frac{1}{(\sqrt{2\pi}\sigma)^N} \exp\left(-\frac{1}{2\sigma^2}\sum_{i=1}^{N}(d_i - \mathbf{w}^T\mathbf{x}_i)^2\right) \end{aligned} \tag{2.22}$$

which accounts for the total empirical knowledge about the weight vector $\mathbf{w}$ contained in the training sample $\mathcal{T}$ of Eq. (2.13).

The only other source of information that remains to be accounted for is that contained in the prior $\pi(\mathbf{w})$. Invoking the zero-mean Gaussian characterization of the kth element of $\mathbf{w}$ described in Eq. (2.15), followed by the iid characterization of the M elements of $\mathbf{w}$ under Assumption 3, we write

$$\begin{aligned} \pi(\mathbf{w}) &= \prod_{k=1}^{M}\pi(w_k)\\ &= \frac{1}{(\sqrt{2\pi}\sigma_w)^M}\prod_{k=1}^{M}\exp\left(-\frac{w_k^2}{2\sigma_w^2}\right)\\ &= \frac{1}{(\sqrt{2\pi}\sigma_w)^M}\exp\left(-\frac{1}{2\sigma_w^2}\sum_{i=1}^{M}w_k^2\right)\\ &= \frac{1}{(\sqrt{2\pi}\sigma_w)^M}\exp\left(-\frac{1}{2\sigma_w^2}\|\mathbf{w}\|^2\right) \end{aligned} \tag{2.23}$$

where $\|\mathbf{w}\|$ is the *Euclidean norm* of the unknown parameter vector $\mathbf{w}$, defined by

$$\|\mathbf{w}\| = \left(\sum_{k=1}^{M} w_k^2 \right)^{1/2} \tag{2.24}$$

Hence, substituting Eqs. (2.22) and (2.23) into Eq. (2.9), and then simplifying the result, we get the posterior density

$$\pi(\mathbf{w}|d, \mathbf{x}) \propto \exp\left[-\frac{1}{2\sigma^2} \sum_{i=1}^{N} (d_i - \mathbf{w}^T \mathbf{x}_i)^2 - \frac{1}{2\sigma_w^2} \|\mathbf{w}\|^2 \right] \tag{2.25}$$

We are now fully equipped to apply the MAP formula of Eq. (2.12) to the estimation problem at hand. Specifically, substituting Eq. (2.25) into this formula, we get

$$\hat{\mathbf{w}}_{\text{MAP}}(N) = \max_{\mathbf{w}} \left[-\frac{1}{2} \sum_{i=1}^{N} (d_i - \mathbf{w}^T \mathbf{x}_i)^2 - \frac{\lambda}{2} \|\mathbf{w}\|^2 \right] \tag{2.26}$$

where we have introduced the new parameter

$$\lambda = \frac{\sigma^2}{\sigma_w^2} \tag{2.27}$$

Now we define the *quadratic function*

$$\mathscr{E}(\mathbf{w}) = \frac{1}{2} \sum_{i=1}^{N} (d_i - \mathbf{w}^T \mathbf{x}_i)^2 + \frac{\lambda}{2} \|\mathbf{w}\|^2 \tag{2.28}$$

Clearly, maximization of the argument in Eq. (2.26) with respect to $\mathbf{w}$ is equivalent to minimization of the quadratic function $\mathscr{E}(\mathbf{w})$. Accordingly, the optimum estimate $\hat{\mathbf{w}}_{\text{MAP}}$ is obtained by differentiating the function $\mathscr{E}(\mathbf{w})$ with respect to $\mathbf{w}$ and setting the result equal to zero. In so doing, we obtain the desired MAP estimate of the M-by-1 parameter vector as

$$\hat{\mathbf{w}}_{\text{MAP}}(N) = [\mathbf{R}_{xx}(N) + \lambda\mathbf{I}]^{-1}\mathbf{r}_{dx}(N) \tag{2.29}$$

where we have introduced two matrices and a vector:

1. the *time-averaged M-by-M correlation matrix* of the regressor $\mathbf{x}$, which is defined by

$$\hat{\mathbf{R}}_{xx}(N) = -\sum_{i=1}^{N} \sum_{j=1}^{N} \mathbf{x}_i \mathbf{x}_j^T \tag{2.30}$$

where $\mathbf{x}_i \mathbf{x}_j^T$ is the outer product of the regressors $\mathbf{x}_i$ and $\mathbf{x}_j$, applied to the environment on the ith and jth experimental trials;

2. the *M-by-M identity matrix* $\mathbf{I}$ whose M diagonal elements are unity and the remaining elements are all zero;

3. the *time-averaged M-by-1 cross-correlation vector* of the regressor $\mathbf{x}$ and the desired response d, which is defined by

$$\hat{\mathbf{r}}_{dx}(N) = -\sum_{j=1}^{N} \mathbf{x}_i d_i \tag{2.31}$$

The correlations $\hat{\mathbf{R}}_{xx}(N)$ and $\hat{\mathbf{r}}_{dx}(N)$ are both averaged over all the N examples of the training sample $\mathcal{T}$—hence the use of the term "time averaged."

Suppose we assign a large value to the variance σ_w^2, which has the implicit effect of saying that the prior distribution of each element of the parameter vector $\mathbf{w}$ is essentially *uniform* over a wide range of possible values. Under this condition, the parameter λ is essentially zero and the formula of Eq. (2.29) reduces to the ML estimate

$$\hat{\mathbf{w}}_{\mathrm{ML}}(N) = \hat{\mathbf{R}}_{xx}^{-1}(N)\,\hat{\mathbf{r}}_{dx}(N) \tag{2.32}$$

which supports the point we made previously: The ML estimator relies solely on the observation model exemplified by the training sample $\mathcal{T}$. In the statistics literature on linear regression, the equation

$$\hat{\mathbf{R}}_{xx}(N)\,\hat{\mathbf{w}}_{\mathrm{ML}}(N) = \hat{\mathbf{r}}_{dx}(N) \tag{2.33}$$

is commonly referred to as the *normal equation*; the ML estimator $\hat{\mathbf{w}}_{\mathrm{ML}}$ is, of course, the solution of this equation. It is also of interest that the ML estimator is an *unbiased* estimator, in the sense that for an infinitely large training sample $\mathcal{T}$, we find that, in the limit, $\hat{\mathbf{w}}_{\mathrm{ML}}$ converges to the parameter vector $\mathbf{w}$ of the unknown stochastic environment, provided that the regressor $\mathbf{x}(n)$ and the response $d(n)$ are drawn from *jointly ergodic processes*, in which case time averages may be substituted for ensemble averages. Under this condition, in Problem 2.4, it is shown that

$$\lim_{N \to \infty} \hat{\mathbf{w}}_{\mathrm{ML}}(N) = \mathbf{w}$$

In contrast, the MAP estimator of Eq. (2.29) is a *biased* estimator, which therefore prompts us to make the following statement:

> *In improving the stability of the maximum likelihood estimator through the use of regularization (i.e., the incorporation of prior knowledge), the resulting maximum a posteriori estimator becomes biased.*

In short, we have a tradeoff between stability and bias.

2.4   RELATIONSHIP BETWEEN REGULARIZED LEAST-SQUARES ESTIMATION AND MAP ESTIMATION

We may approach the estimation of the parameter vector $\mathbf{w}$ in another way by focusing on a *cost* function $\mathcal{E}_0(\mathbf{w})$ defined as the *squared expectational errors summed over the N experimental trials on the environment*. Specifically, we write

$$\mathcal{E}_0(\mathbf{w}) = \sum_{i=1}^{N} \varepsilon_i^2(\mathbf{w})$$

where we have included $\mathbf{w}$ in the argument of ε_i to stress the fact that the uncertainty in the regression model is due to the vector $\mathbf{w}$. Rearranging terms in Eq. (2.16), we obtain

$$\varepsilon_i(\mathbf{w}) = d_i - \mathbf{w}^T \mathbf{x}_i, \qquad i = 1, 2, ..., N \tag{2.34}$$

Substituting this equation into the expression for $\mathscr{E}_0(\mathbf{w})$ yields

$$\mathscr{E}_0(\mathbf{w}) = \frac{1}{2} \sum_{i=1}^{N} (d_i - \mathbf{w}^T \mathbf{x}_i)^2 \tag{2.35}$$

which relies solely on the training sample $\mathscr{T}$. Minimizing this cost function with respect to $\mathbf{w}$ yields a formula for the *ordinary least-squares estimator* that is identical to the maximum-likelihood estimator of Eq. (2.32), and hence there is a distinct possibility of obtaining a solution that lacks uniqueness and stability.

To overcome this serious problem, the customary practice is to expand the cost function of Eq. (2.35) by adding a new term as follows:

$$\mathscr{E}(\mathbf{w}) = \mathscr{E}_0(\mathbf{w}) + \frac{\lambda}{2} \|\mathbf{w}\|^2$$

$$= \frac{1}{2} \sum_{i=1}^{N} (d_i - \mathbf{w}^T \mathbf{x}_i)^2 + \frac{\lambda}{2} \|\mathbf{w}\|^2 \tag{2.36}$$

This expression is identical to the function defined in Eq. (2.28). The inclusion of the squared Euclidean norm $\|\mathbf{w}\|^2$ is referred to as *structural regularization*. Correspondingly, the scalar λ is referred to as the *regularization parameter*.

When $\lambda = 0$, the implication is that we have complete confidence in the observation model exemplified by the training sample $\mathscr{T}$. At the other extreme, when $\lambda = \infty$, the implication is that we have no confidence in the observation model. In practice, the regularization parameter λ is chosen somewhere between these two limiting cases.

In any event, for a prescribed value of the regularization parameter λ, the solution of the *regularized method of least squares*, obtained by minimizing the regularized cost function of Eq. (2.36) with respect to the parameter vector $\mathbf{w}$, is identical to the MAP estimate of Eq. (2.29). This particular solution is referred to as the *regularized least-squares* (RLS) *solution*.

2.5   COMPUTER EXPERIMENT: PATTERN CLASSIFICATION

In this section, we repeat the computer experiment performed on the pattern-classification problem studied in Chapter 1, where we used the perceptron algorithm. As before, the double-moon structure, providing the training as well as the test data, is that shown in Fig. 1.8. This time, however, we use the method of least squares to perform the classification.

Figure 2.2 presents the results of training the least squares algorithm for the separation distance between the two moons set at $d = 1$. The figure shows the decision boundary constructed between the two moons. The corresponding results obtained using the perceptron algorithm for the same setting $d = 1$ were presented in Fig. 1.9. Comparing these two figures, we make the following interesting observations:

1. The decision boundaries constructed by the two algorithms are both linear, which is intuitively satisfying. The least-squares algorithm discovers the asymmetric

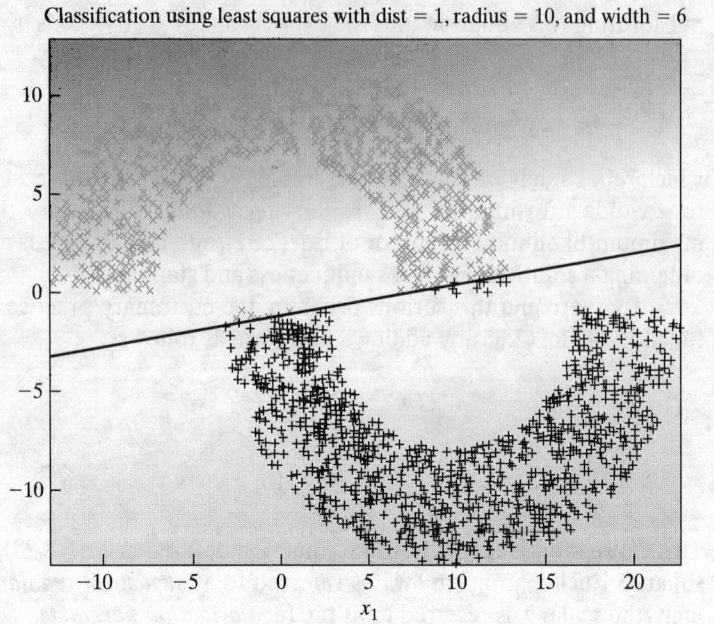

FIGURE 2.2 Least Squares classification of the double-moon of Fig. 1.8 with distance $d = 1$.

manner in which the two moons are positioned relative to each other, as seen by the positive slope of the decision boundary in Fig. 2.2. Interestingly enough, the perceptron algorithm completely ignores this asymmetry by constructing a decision boundary that is parallel to the x-axis.

2. For the separation distance $d = 1$, the two moons are linearly separable. The perceptron algorithm responds perfectly to this setting; on the other hand, in discovering the asymmetric feature of the double-moon figure, the method of least squares ends up misclassifying the test data, incurring a classification error of 0.8%.

3. Unlike the perceptron algorithm, the method of least squares computes the decision boundary in one shot.

Figure 2.3 presents the results of the experiment performed on the double-moon patterns for the separation distance $d = -4$, using the method of least squares. As expected, there is now a noticeable increase in the classification error, namely, 9.5%. Comparing this performance with the 9.3% classification error of the perceptron algorithm for the same setting, which was reported in Fig. 1.10, we see that the classification performance of the method of least squares has degraded slightly.

The important conclusion to be drawn from the pattern-classification computer experiments of Sections 1.5 and 2.5 is as follows:

Although the perceptron and the least-squares algorithms are both linear, they operate differently in performing the task of pattern classification.

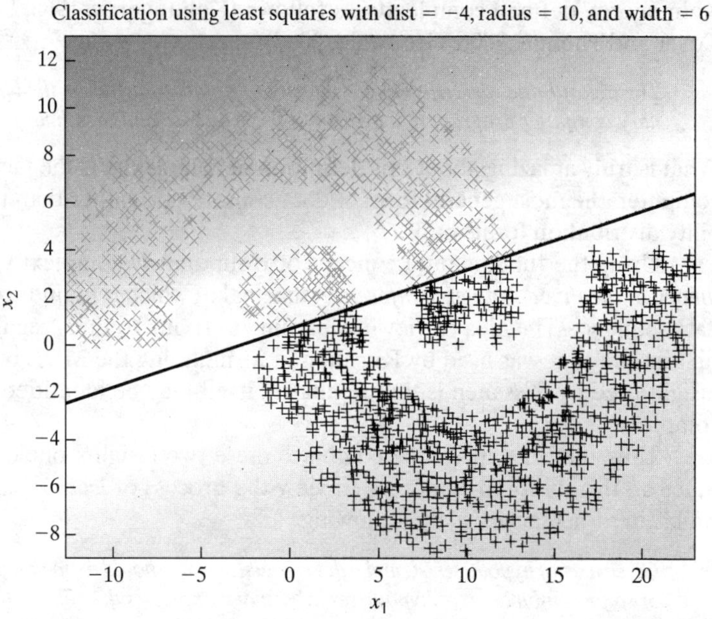

Classification using least squares with dist = −4, radius = 10, and width = 6

FIGURE 2.3   Least-squares classification of the double-moon of Fig. 1.8 with distance $d = -4$.

2.6   THE MINIMUM-DESCRIPTION-LENGTH PRINCIPLE

The representation of a stochastic process by a linear model may be used for synthesis or analysis. In *synthesis*, we generate a desired time series by assigning a formulated set of values to the parameters of the model and feeding it with *white noise* of zero mean and prescribed variance; the model so obtained is referred to as a *generative model*. In *analysis*, on the other hand, we *estimate* the parameters of the model by processing a given time series of finite length, using the Bayesian approach or the regularized method of least squares. Insofar as the estimation is statistical, we need an appropriate measure of the fit between the model and the observed data. We refer to this second problem as that of *model selection*. For example, we may want to estimate the number of degrees of freedom (i.e., adjustable parameters) of the model, or even the general structure of the model.

A plethora of methods for model selection has been proposed in the statistics literature, with each one of them having a goal of its own. With the goals being different, it is not surprising to find that the different methods yield wildly different results when they are applied to the same data set (Grünwald, 2007).

In this section, we describe a well-proven method, called the *minimum-description-length (MDL) principle* for model selection, which was pioneered by Rissanen (1978).

Inspiration for the development of the MDL principle is traced back to *Kolmogorov complexity theory*. In this remarkable theory, the great mathematician

Kolmogorov defined complexity as follows (Kolmogorov, 1965; Li and Vitányi, 1993; Cover and Thomas, 2006; Grünwald, 2007):

> *The algorithmic (descriptive) complexity of a data sequence is the length of the shortest binary computer program that prints out the sequence and then halts.*

What is truly amazing about this definition of complexity is the fact that it looks to the computer, the most general form of data compressor, rather than the notion of probability distribution for its basis.

Using the fundamental concept of Kolmogorov complexity, we may develop a *theory of idealized inductive inference*, the goal of which is to find "regularity" in a given data sequence. The idea of viewing learning as trying to find "regularity" provided the first insight that was used by Rissanen in formulating the MDL principle. The second insight used by Rissanen is that regularity itself may be identified with the "ability to compress."

Thus, the MDL principle combines these two insights, one on regularity and the other on the ability to compress, to view the process of *learning as data compression*, which, in turn, teaches us the following:

> *Given a set of hypotheses, $\mathcal{H}$, and a data sequence d, we should try to find the particular hypothesis or some combination of hypotheses in $\mathcal{H}$, that compresses the data sequence d the most.*

This statement sums up what the MDL principle is all about very succinctly. The symbol d for a sequence should not be confused with the symbol d used previously for desired response.

There are several versions of the MDL principle that have been described in the literature. We will focus on the oldest, but simplest and most well-known version, known as the *simplistic two-part code MDL principle* for probabilistic modeling. By the term "simplistic," we mean that the codelengths under consideration are not determined in an optimal fashion. The terms "code" and "codelengths" used herein pertain to the process of encoding the data sequence in the shortest or *least redundant* manner.

Suppose that we are given a candidate model or model class $\mathcal{M}$. With all the elements of $\mathcal{M}$ being probabilistic sources, we henceforth refer to a point hypothesis as p rather than $\mathcal{H}$. In particular, we look for the probability density function $p \in \mathcal{M}$ that best explains a given data sequence d. The two-part code MDL principle then tells us to look for the (point) hypothesis $p \in \mathcal{M}$ that minimizes the description length of p, which we denote by $L_1(p)$, and the description length of the data sequence d when it is encoded with the help of p, which we denote as $L_2(d \mid p)$. We thus form the sum

$$L_{12}(p, d) = L_1(p) + L_2(d|p)$$

and pick the particular point hypothesis $p \in \mathcal{M}$ that minimizes $L_{12}(p, d)$.

It is crucial that p itself be encoded as well here. Thus, in finding the hypothesis that compresses the data sequence d the most, we must encode (describe or compress) the data in such a way that a decoder can retrieve the data even without knowing the hypothesis in advance. This can be done by explicitly encoding a hypothesis, as in the foregoing two-part code principle; it can also be done in quite different ways—for example, by averaging over hypotheses (Grünwald, 2007).

Model-Order Selection

Let $\mathcal{M}^{(1)}, \mathcal{M}^{(2)}, ..., \mathcal{M}^{(k)}, ...,$ denote a family of linear regression models that are associated with the parameter vector $\mathbf{w}^k \in \mathcal{W}^k$, where the model order $k = 1, 2, ...$; that is, the weight spaces $\mathcal{W}^{(1)}, \mathcal{W}^{(2)}, ..., \mathcal{W}^{(k)}, ...,$ are of increasing dimensionality. The issue of interest is to identify the model that best explains an unknown environment that is responsible for generating the training sample $\{\mathbf{x}_i, d_i\}_{i=1}^{N}$, where $\mathbf{x}_i$ is the stimulus and d_i is the corresponding response. What we have just described is the *model-order selection problem*.

In working through the statistical characterization of the composite length $L_{12}(p, d)$, the two-part code MDL principle tells us to pick the kth model that is the mimimizer

$$\min_k \left\{ \overbrace{- \log p(d_i|\mathbf{w}^{(k)})\pi(\mathbf{w}^{(k)})}^{\text{Error term}} + \overbrace{\frac{k}{2}\log(N) + O(k)}^{\text{Complexity term}} \right\}, \quad \begin{array}{l} k = 1, 2, ... \\ i = 1, 2, ..., N \end{array} \quad (2.37)$$

where $\pi(\mathbf{w}^{(k)})$ is the prior distribution of the parameter vector $\mathbf{w}^{(k)}$, and the last term of the expression is of the order of model order k (Rissanen, 1989; Grünwald, 2007). For a large sample size N, this last term gets overwhelmed by the second term of the expression $\frac{k}{2}\log(N)$. The expression in Eq. (2.37) is usually partitioned into two terms:

- the *error term*, denoted by $-\log(p(d_i|\mathbf{w}^{(k)})\,\pi(\mathbf{w}^{(k)}))$, which relates to the model and the data;
- the *hypothesis complexity term*, denoted by $\frac{k}{2}\log(N) + O(k)$, which relates to the model alone.

In practice, the $O(k)$ term is often ignored to simplify matters when applying Eq. (2.37), with mixed results. The reason for mixed results is that the $O(k)$ term can be rather large. For linear regression models, however, it can be explicitly and efficiently computed, and the resulting procedures tend to work quite well in practice.

Note also that the expression of Eq. (2.37) without the prior distribution $\pi(\mathbf{w}^{(k)})$ was first formulated in Rissanen (1978).

If it turns out that we have more than one minimizer of the expression in Eq. (2.37), then we pick the model with the smallest hypothesis complexity term. And if this move still leaves us with several candidate models, then we do not have any further choice but to work with one of them (Grünwald, 2007).

Attributes of the MDL Principle

The MDL principle for model selection offers two important attributes (Grünwald, 2007):

1. When we have two models that fit a given data sequence equally well, the MDL principle will pick the one that is the "simplest" in the sense that it allows the use of a shorter description of the data. In other words, the MDL principle implements a precise form of *Occam's razor*, which states a preference for simple theories:

   Accept the simplest explanation that fits the data.

2. The MDL principle is a *consistent* model selection estimator in the sense that it converges to the true model order as the sample size increases.

Perhaps the most significant point to note is that, in nearly all of the applications involving the MDL principle, few, if any, anomalous results or models with undesirable properties have been reported in the literature.

2.7 FINITE SAMPLE-SIZE CONSIDERATIONS

A serious limitation of the maximum-likelihood or ordinary least-squares approach to parameter estimation is the nonuniqueness and instability of the solution, which is attributed to complete reliance on the observation model (i.e., the training sample $\mathcal{T}$); the traits of nonuniqueness and instability in characterizing a solution are also referred to as an *overfitting* problem in the literature. To probe more deeply into this practical issue, consider the generic regressive model

$$d = f(\mathbf{x}, \mathbf{w}) + \varepsilon \tag{2.38}$$

where $f(\mathbf{x}, \mathbf{w})$ is a deterministic function of the regressor $\mathbf{x}$ for some $\mathbf{w}$ parameterizing the model and ε is the expectational error. This model, depicted in Fig. 2.4a, is a *mathematical* description of a stochastic environment; its purpose is to *explain* or *predict* the response d produced by the regressor $\mathbf{x}$.

Figure 2.4b is the corresponding *physical* model of the environment, where $\hat{\mathbf{w}}$ denotes an *estimate* of the unknown parameter vector $\mathbf{w}$. The purpose of this second model is to *encode the empirical knowledge represented by the training sample $\mathcal{T}$*, as shown by

$$\mathcal{T} \to \hat{\mathbf{w}} \tag{2.39}$$

In effect, the physical model provides an *approximation* to the regression model of Fig. 2.4a. Let the actual response of the physical model, produced in response to the input vector $\mathbf{x}$, be denoted by

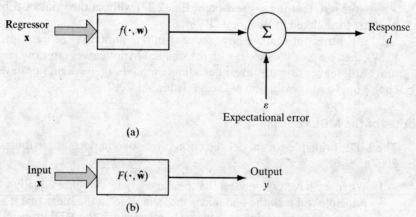

(a)

(b)

FIGURE 2.4   (a) Mathematical model of a stochastic environment, parameterized by the vector $\mathbf{w}$. (b) Physical model of the environment, where $\hat{\mathbf{w}}$ is an estimate of the unknown parameter vector $\mathbf{w}$.

$$y = F(\mathbf{x}, \hat{\mathbf{w}}) \tag{2.40}$$

where $F(\cdot, \hat{\mathbf{w}})$ is the input–output function realized by the physical model; the y in Eq. (2.40) is a sample value of random variable Y. Given the training sample $\mathcal{T}$ of Eq. (2.39), the estimator $\hat{\mathbf{w}}$ is the minimizer of the cost function

$$\mathcal{E}(\hat{\mathbf{w}}) = \frac{1}{2} \sum_{i=1}^{N} (d_i - F(\mathbf{x}_i, \hat{\mathbf{w}}))^2 \tag{2.41}$$

where the factor $\frac{1}{2}$ has been used to be consistent with earlier notations. Except for the scaling factor $\frac{1}{2}$, the cost function $\mathcal{E}(\hat{\mathbf{w}})$ is the squared difference between the environmental (desired) response d and the actual response y of the physical model, computed over the entire training sample $\mathcal{T}$.

Let the symbol $\mathbb{E}_{\mathcal{T}}$ denote the *average operator* taken over the entire training sample $\mathcal{T}$. The variables or their functions that come under the average operator $\mathbb{E}_{\mathcal{T}}$ are denoted by $\mathbf{x}$ and d; the pair $(\mathbf{x}, d)$ represents an example in the training sample $\mathcal{T}$. In contrast, the statistical expectation operator $\mathbb{E}$ acts on the whole ensemble of $\mathbf{x}$ and d, which includes $\mathcal{T}$ as a subset. The difference between the operators $\mathbb{E}$ and $\mathbb{E}_{\mathcal{T}}$ should be very carefully noted in what follows.

In light of the transformation described in Eq. (2.39), we may interchangeably use $F(\mathbf{x}, \hat{\mathbf{w}})$ and $F(\mathbf{x}, \mathcal{T})$ and therefore rewrite Eq. (2.41) in the equivalent form

$$\mathcal{E}(\hat{\mathbf{w}}) = \frac{1}{2} \mathbb{E}_{\mathcal{T}}[(d - F(\mathbf{x}, \mathcal{T}))^2] \tag{2.42}$$

By adding and then subtracting $f(\mathbf{x}, \mathbf{w})$ to the argument $(d - F(\mathbf{x}, \mathcal{T}))$ and next using Eq. (2.38), we may write

$$\begin{aligned} d - f(\mathbf{x}, \mathcal{T}) &= [d - f(\mathbf{x}, \mathbf{w})] + [f(\mathbf{x}, \mathbf{w}) - F(\mathbf{x}, \mathcal{T})] \\ &= \varepsilon + [f(\mathbf{x}, \mathbf{w}) - F(\mathbf{x}, \mathcal{T})] \end{aligned}$$

By substituting this expression into Eq. (2.42) and then expanding terms, we may recast the cost function $\mathcal{E}(\hat{\mathbf{w}})$ in the equivalent form

$$\mathcal{E}(\hat{\mathbf{w}}) = \frac{1}{2} \mathbb{E}_{\mathcal{T}}[\varepsilon^2] + \frac{1}{2} \mathbb{E}_{\mathcal{T}}[(f(\mathbf{x}, \mathbf{w}) - F(\mathbf{x}, \mathcal{T}))^2] + \mathbb{E}_{\mathcal{T}}[\varepsilon f(\mathbf{x}, \mathbf{w}) - \varepsilon F(\mathbf{x}, \mathcal{T})] \tag{2.43}$$

However, the last expectation term on the right-hand side of Eq. (2.43) is zero, for two reasons:

- The expectational error ε is uncorrelated with the regression function $f(\mathbf{x}, \mathbf{w})$.
- The expectational error ε pertains to the regression model of Fig. 2.4a, whereas the approximating function $F(\mathbf{x}, \hat{\mathbf{w}})$ pertains to the physical model of Fig. 2.4b.

Accordingly, Eq. (2.43) reduces to

$$\mathcal{E}(\hat{\mathbf{w}}) = \frac{1}{2} \mathbb{E}_{\mathcal{T}}[\varepsilon^2] + \frac{1}{2} \mathbb{E}_{\mathcal{T}}[(f(\mathbf{x}, \mathbf{w}) - F(\mathbf{x}, \mathcal{T}))^2] \tag{2.44}$$

The term $\mathbb{E}_{\mathcal{T}}[\varepsilon^2]$ on the right-hand side of Eq. (2.44) is the *variance* of the expectational (regressive modeling) error ε, evaluated over the training sample $\mathcal{T}$; here it is assumed that ε has zero mean. This variance represents the *intrinsic error* because it is independent of the estimate $\hat{\mathbf{w}}$. Hence, the estimator $\hat{\mathbf{w}}$ that is the minimizer of the cost function $\mathcal{E}(\hat{\mathbf{w}})$ will also minimize the ensemble average of the squared distance between the regression function $f(\mathbf{x}, \mathbf{w})$ and the approximating function $F(\mathbf{x}, \hat{\mathbf{w}})$. In other words, the *natural measure* of the effectiveness of $F(\mathbf{x}, \hat{\mathbf{w}})$ as a predictor of the desired response d is defined as follows (ignoring the scaling factor ½):

$$L_{av}(f(\mathbf{x}, \mathbf{w}), F(\mathbf{x}, \hat{\mathbf{w}})) = \mathbb{E}_{\mathcal{T}}[(f(\mathbf{x}, \mathbf{w}) - F(\mathbf{x}, \mathcal{T}))^2] \qquad (2.45)$$

This natural measure is fundamentally important because it provides the mathematical basis for the tradeoff between the bias and variance that results from the use of $F(\mathbf{x}, \hat{\mathbf{w}})$ as the approximation to $f(\mathbf{x}, \mathbf{w})$.

Bias–Variance Dilemma

From Eq. (2.38), we find that the function $f(\mathbf{x}, \mathbf{w})$ is equal to the conditional expectation $\mathbb{E}(d|\mathbf{x})$. We may therefore redefine the squared distance between $f(\mathbf{x})$ and $F(\mathbf{x}, \hat{\mathbf{w}})$ as

$$L_{av}(f(\mathbf{x}, \mathbf{w}), F(\mathbf{x}, \hat{\mathbf{w}})) = \mathbb{E}_{\mathcal{T}}[(\mathbb{E}[d|\mathbf{x}] - F(\mathbf{x}, \mathcal{T}))^2] \qquad (2.46)$$

This expression may therefore be viewed as the average value of the estimation error between the regression function $f(\mathbf{x}, \mathbf{w}) = \mathbb{E}[d|\mathbf{x}]$ and the approximating function $F(\mathbf{x}, \hat{\mathbf{w}})$, evaluated over the entire training sample $\mathcal{T}$. Notice that the conditional mean $\mathbb{E}[d|\mathbf{x}]$ has a constant expectation with respect to the training sample $\mathcal{T}$. Next we write

$$\mathbb{E}[d|\mathbf{x}] - F(\mathbf{x}, \mathcal{T}) = (\mathbb{E}[d|\mathbf{x}] - \mathbb{E}_{\mathcal{T}}[F(\mathbf{x}, \mathcal{T})]) + (\mathbb{E}_{\mathcal{T}}[F(\mathbf{x}, \mathcal{T})] - F(\mathbf{x}, \mathcal{T}))$$

where we have simply added and then subtracted the average $\mathbb{E}_{\mathcal{T}}[F(\mathbf{x}, \mathcal{T})]$. By proceeding in a manner similar to that described for deriving Eq. (2.43) from Eq. (2.42), we may reformulate Eq. (2.46) as the sum of two terms (see Problem 2.5):

$$L_{av}(f(\mathbf{x}), F(\mathbf{x}, \mathcal{T})) = B^2(\hat{\mathbf{w}}) + V(\hat{\mathbf{w}}) \qquad (2.47)$$

where $B(\hat{\mathbf{w}})$ and $V(\hat{\mathbf{w}})$ are themselves respectively defined by

$$B(\hat{\mathbf{w}}) = \mathbb{E}_{\mathcal{T}}[F(\mathbf{x}, \mathcal{T})] - \mathbb{E}[d|\mathbf{x}] \qquad (2.49)$$

and

$$V(\hat{\mathbf{w}}) = \mathbb{E}_{\mathcal{T}}[(F(\mathbf{x}, \mathcal{T}) - \mathbb{E}_{\mathcal{T}}[F(\mathbf{x}, \mathcal{T})])^2] \qquad (2.49)$$

We now make two important observations:

1. The first term, $B(\hat{\mathbf{w}})$, is the *bias* of the average value of the approximating function $F(\mathbf{x}, \mathcal{T})$, measured with respect to the regression function $f(\mathbf{x}, \mathbf{w}) = \mathbb{E}[d|\mathbf{x}]$. Thus, $B(\hat{\mathbf{w}})$ represents the inability of the physical model defined by the function $F(\mathbf{x}, \hat{\mathbf{w}})$ to accurately approximate the regression function $f(\mathbf{x}, \mathbf{w}) = \mathbb{E}[d|\mathbf{x}]$. We may therefore view the bias $B(\hat{\mathbf{w}})$ as an *approximation error*.

2. The second term, $V(\hat{\mathbf{w}})$, is the *variance* of the approximating function $F(\mathbf{x}, \mathcal{T})$, measured over the entire training sample $\mathcal{T}$. Thus, $V(\hat{\mathbf{w}})$ represents the inadequacy

of the empirical knowledge contained in the training sample $\mathcal{T}$ about the regression function $f(\mathbf{x}, \mathbf{w})$. We may therefore view the variance $V(\hat{\mathbf{w}})$ as the manifestation of an *estimation error*.

Figure 2.5 illustrates the relations between the target (desired) and approximating functions; it shows how the estimation errors, namely, the bias and variance, accumulate. To achieve good overall performance, the bias $B(\hat{\mathbf{w}})$ and the variance $V(\hat{\mathbf{w}})$ of the approximating function $F(\mathbf{x}, \hat{\mathbf{w}}) = F(\mathbf{x}, \mathcal{T})$ would both have to be small.

Unfortunately, we find that in a complex physical model that learns by example and does so with a training sample of limited size, the price for achieving a small bias is a large variance. For any physical model, it is only when the size of the training sample becomes infinitely large that we can hope to eliminate both bias and variance at the same time. Accordingly, we have a *bias–variance dilemma*, the consequence of which is prohibitively slow convergence (Geman et al., 1992). The bias–variance dilemma may be circumvented if we are willing to *purposely* introduce bias, which then makes it possible to eliminate the variance or to reduce it significantly. Needless to say, we must be sure that the bias built into the design of the physical model is harmless. In the context of pattern classification, for example, the bias is said to be harmless in the sense that it will contribute significantly to the mean-square error only if we try to infer regressions that are not in the anticipated class.

Explanatory notes on what Fig. 2.5 is depicting:

1. The shaded inner space of the figure is a subset of the outer space:

   The outer space represents the ensemble of regression functions $f(\cdot, \mathbf{w})$.
   The inner space represents the ensemble of approximating functions $F(\cdot, \hat{\mathbf{w}})$.

2. The figure shows three points, two fixed and one random:

   $\mathbb{E}[d|\mathbf{x}]$, fixed-point, is averaged over the outer space
   $\mathbb{E}_{\mathcal{T}}[F(\mathbf{x}, \mathcal{T})]$, second fixed-point, is averaged over the inner space
   $F(\mathbf{x}, \mathcal{T})$ is randomly distributed inside the inner space

3. Statistical parameters, embodied in the figure:

   $B(\mathbf{w})$ = bias, denoting the distance between $\mathbb{E}[d|\mathbf{x}]$ and $\mathbb{E}_{\mathcal{T}}[F(\mathbf{x}, \mathcal{T})]$.
   $V(\mathbf{w})$ = variance, denoting the squared distance between $F(\mathbf{x}, \mathcal{T})$ and $\mathbb{E}_{\mathcal{T}}[F(\mathbf{x}, \mathcal{T})]$, averaged over the training sample $\mathcal{T}$.
   $B^2(\mathbf{w}) + V(\mathbf{w})$ = squared distance between $F(\mathbf{x}, \mathcal{T})$ and $\mathbb{E}[d|\mathbf{x}]$ averaged over the training sample $\mathcal{T}$.

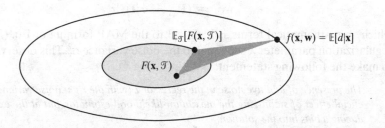

FIGURE 2.5   Decomposition of the natural measure $L_{\mathrm{av}}(f(\mathbf{x}, \mathbf{w}), F(\mathbf{x}, \hat{\mathbf{w}}))$, defined in Eq. (2.46), into bias and variance terms for linear regression models.

In general, the bias must be *designed* for each specific application of interest. A practical way of achieving such an objective is to use a *constrained* network architecture, which usually performs better than a general-purpose architecture.

2.8 THE INSTRUMENTAL-VARIABLES METHOD

In studying the linear regression model, first from the perspective of Bayesian theory in Section 2.3 and then from the perspective of the method of least squares in Section 2.4, we pointed out that both approaches yield the same solution for the parameter vector **w** of the unknown stochastic environment depicted in Fig. 2.1, namely, Eq. (2.29) for the regularized linear regression model and Eq. (2.32) for the unregularized version. Both of these formulas were derived for a Gaussian environment, on the premise that the regressor (i.e., the input signal) **x** and the desired response d are both noiseless. What if, however, we find that the regressor **x** can be observed only in the presence of additive noise, as could happen in practice? That is, the noisy regressor is now defined by

$$\mathbf{z}_i = \mathbf{x}_i + \mathbf{v}_i \tag{2.50}$$

where $\mathbf{v}_i$ is the measurement noise associated with the observation of $\mathbf{x}_i$ in the ith realization of the training sample $\mathcal{T}$. If we were to apply the unregularized formula of Eq. (2.32), we would obtain a modified solution for the parameter vector **w** of the unknown stochastic environment:

$$\hat{\mathbf{w}}_{ML} = \hat{\mathbf{R}}_{zz}^{-1}\hat{\mathbf{r}}_{dz} \tag{2.51}$$

where $\hat{\mathbf{R}}_{zz}$ is the time-averaged correlation function of the noisy regressor **z** and $\hat{\mathbf{r}}_{dz}$ is the corresponding time-averaged cross-correlation function between the desired response d and **z**. To simplify matters, we have ignored the dependence of these two correlation functions on the size of the training sample. Assuming that the measurement noise vector **v** is white noise with zero mean and correlation matrix $\sigma_v^2\mathbf{I}$, where **I** is the identity matrix, we obtain the following correlation functions:

$$\hat{\mathbf{R}}_{zz} = \hat{\mathbf{R}}_{xx} + \sigma_v^2\mathbf{I}$$

and

$$\hat{\mathbf{r}}_{dz} = \hat{\mathbf{r}}_{dx}$$

Correspondingly, the maximum-likelihood estimator assumes the new form

$$\hat{\mathbf{w}}_{ML} = (\hat{\mathbf{R}}_{xx} + \sigma_v^2\mathbf{I})^{-1}\hat{\mathbf{r}}_{dx} \tag{2.52}$$

which, in mathematical terms, is identical to the MAP formula of Eq. (2.29) with the regularization parameter λ set equal to the noise variance σ_v^2. This observation leads us to make the following statement:

> *The presence of additive noise in the regressor* **z** *(with the right noise variance) has the beneficial effect of stabilizing the maximum-likelihood estimator, but at the expense of introducing a bias into the solution.*

This is quite an ironic statement: The addition of noise acts as a regularizer (stabilizer)!

Suppose, however, the requirement is to produce a solution for the unknown parameter vector **w** that is desirably *asymptotically unbiased*. In such a situation, we may resort to the *method of instrumental variables* (Young, 1984). This method relies on the introduction of a set of instrumental variables, denoted by the vector $\hat{\mathbf{x}}$ that has the same dimensionality as the noisy regressor **z** and satisfies the following two properties:

Property 1.   The instrumental vector $\hat{\mathbf{x}}$ is highly correlated with the noiseless regressor **x**, as shown by

$$\mathbb{E}[x_j \hat{x}_k] \neq 0 \qquad \text{for all } j \text{ and } k \tag{2.53}$$

where x_j is the *j*th element of the noiseless regressor **x** and $\hat{x}_k$ is the *k*th element of the instrumental vector $\hat{\mathbf{x}}$.

Property 2.   The instrumental vector $\hat{\mathbf{x}}$ and the measurement noise vector **v** are statistically independent, as shown by

$$\mathbb{E}[v_j \hat{x}_k] = 0 \qquad \text{for all } j \text{ and } k \tag{2.54}$$

Equipped with the instrumental vector $\hat{\mathbf{x}}$ that satisfies these two properties, we compute the following correlation functions:

1. The noisy regressor **z** is correlated with the instrumental vector $\hat{\mathbf{x}}$, obtaining the cross-correlation matrix

$$\hat{\mathbf{R}}_{z\hat{x}} = \sum_{i=1}^{N} \hat{\mathbf{x}}_i \mathbf{z}_i^T \tag{2.55}$$

where $\mathbf{z}_i$ is the *i*th regressor of the noisy training sample $\{\mathbf{z}_i, d_i\}_{i=1}^N$, and $\hat{\mathbf{x}}_i$ is the corresponding instrumental vector.

2. The desired response *d* is correlated with the instrumental vector $\hat{\mathbf{x}}$, obtaining the cross-correlation vector

$$\hat{\mathbf{r}}_{d\hat{x}} = \sum_{i=1}^{N} \hat{\mathbf{x}}_i d_i \tag{2.56}$$

Given these two correlation measurements, we then use the modified formula

$$\hat{\mathbf{w}}(N) = \mathbf{R}_{z\hat{x}}^{-1} \mathbf{r}_{d\hat{x}}$$

$$= \left(\sum_{i=1}^{N} \hat{\mathbf{x}}_i \mathbf{z}_i^T \right)^{-1} \left(\sum_{i=1}^{N} \hat{\mathbf{x}}_i d_i \right) \tag{2.57}$$

for computing an estimate of the unknown parameter vector **w** (Young, 1984). Unlike the ML solution of Eq. (2.51), the modified formula of Eq. (2.57), based on the method of instrumental variables, provides an asymptotically unbiased estimate of the unknown parameter vector **w**; see Problem 2.7.

In applying the method of instrumental variables, however, the key issue is how to obtain or generate variables that satisfy Properties 1 and 2. It turns out that in time-series analysis, the resolution of this issue is surprisingly straightforward (Young, 1984).

2.9   SUMMARY AND DISCUSSION

In this chapter, we studied the method of least squares for linear regression, which is well established in the statistics literature. The study was presented from two different, yet complementary, viewpoints:

- *Bayesian theory*, where the *maximum a posteriori estimate* of a set of unknown parameters is the objective of interest. This approach to parameter estimation requires knowledge of the prior distribution of the unknown parameters. The presentation was demonstrated for a Gaussian environment.
- *Regularization theory*, where the cost function to be minimized with respect to the unknown parameters consists of two components: the squared explanational errors summed over the training data, and a regularizing term defined in terms of the squared Euclidean norm of the parameter vector.

For the special case of an environment in which the prior distribution of the unknown parameters is Gaussian with zero mean and variance σ_w^2, it turns out that the regularization parameter λ is inversely proportional to σ_w^2. The implication of this statement is that when σ_w^2 is very large (i.e., the unknown parameters are uniformly distributed over a wide range), the formula for finding the estimate of the parameter vector $\mathbf{w}$ is defined by the *normal equation*

$$\hat{\mathbf{w}} = \hat{\mathbf{R}}_{xx}^{-1}\hat{\mathbf{r}}_{dx}$$

where $\hat{\mathbf{R}}_{xx}$ is the time-averaged correlation matrix of the input vector $\mathbf{x}$ and $\hat{\mathbf{r}}_{dx}$ is the corresponding time-averaged cross-correlation vector between the input vector $\mathbf{x}$ and the desired response d. Both correlation parameters are computed using the training sample $\{\mathbf{x}_i, d_i\}_{i=1}^N$ and are therefore dependent on its sample size N. Furthermore, this formula is identical to the solution obtained using the maximum-likelihood method that assumes a uniform distribution for the prior.

We also discussed three other important issues:

- The minimum-description-length (MDL) criterion for model-order selection (i.e., the size of the unknown parameter vector in a linear regression model).
- The bias–variance dilemma, which means that in parameter estimation (involving the use of a finite sample size) we have the inevitable task of trading off the variance of the estimate with the bias; the bias is defined as the difference between the expected value of the parameter estimate and the true value, and the variance is a measure of the "volatility" of the estimate around the expected value.
- The method of instrumental variables, the need for which arises when the observables in the training sample are noisy; such a situation is known to arise in practice.

NOTES AND REFERENCES

1. Regression models can be linear or nonlinear. *Linear regression models* are discussed in depth in the classic book by Rao (1973). *Nonlinear regression models* are discussed in Seber and Wild (1989).
2. For a highly readable account of Bayesian theory, see Robert (2001).
3. For a detailed discussion of the method of least squares, see Chapter 8 of Haykin (2002).

PROBLEMS

2.1. Give the basic difference between the classes of regression models.

2.2. Starting with the cost function of Eq. (2.36), $\mathscr{E}(\mathbf{w})$, derive the formula of Eq. (2.29) by minimizing the cost function with respect to the unknown parameter vector $\mathbf{w}$.

2.3. In this problem, we address properties of the least-squares estimator based on the linear regression model of Fig. 2.1:

Property 1. The least-squares estimate

$$\hat{\mathbf{w}} = \mathbf{R}_{xx}^{-1}\mathbf{r}_{dx}$$

is unbiased, provided that the expectational error ε in the linear regression model of Fig. 2.1 has zero mean.

Property 2. When the expectational error ε is drawn from a zero-mean white-noise process with variance σ^2, the covariance matrix of the least-squares estimate $\hat{\mathbf{w}}$ equals

$$\sigma^2\hat{\mathbf{R}}_{xx}^{-1}.$$

Property 3. The estimation error

$$e_o = d - \hat{\mathbf{w}}^T\mathbf{x}$$

produced by the optimized method of least squares is orthogonal to the estimate of the desired response, denoted by $\hat{d}$; this property is a corollary to the *principle of orthogonality*. If we were to use geometric representations of d, $\hat{d}$, and e_o, then we would find that the "vector" representing e_o, is perpendicular (i.e., normal) to that representing $\hat{d}$; indeed it is in light of this geometric representation that the formula

$$\hat{\mathbf{R}}_{xx}\hat{\mathbf{w}} = \hat{\mathbf{r}}_{dx}$$

is called the normal equation.

Starting with the normal equation, prove each of these three properties under the premise that $\hat{\mathbf{R}}_{xx}$ and $\hat{\mathbf{r}}_{dx}$ are time-averaged correlation functions.

2.4. Let $\mathbf{R}_{xx}$ denote the ensemble-averaged correlation function of the regressor $\mathbf{x}$, and let $\mathbf{r}_{dx}$ denote the corresponding ensemble-averaged cross-correlation vector between the regressor $\mathbf{x}$ and response d; that is,

$$\mathbf{R}_{xx} = \mathbb{E}[\mathbf{xx}^T]$$
$$\mathbf{r}_{dx} = \mathbb{E}[d\mathbf{x}]$$

Referring to the linear regression model of Eq. (2.3), show that minimization of the mean-square error

$$J(\mathbf{w}) = \mathbb{E}[\varepsilon^2]$$

leads to the *Wiener–Hopf equation*

$$\mathbf{R}_{xx}\mathbf{w} = \mathbf{r}_{dx}$$

where $\mathbf{w}$ is the parameter vector of the regression model. Compare this equation with the normal equation of Eq. (2.33).

2.5. Equation (2.47) expresses the natural measure of the effectiveness of the approximating function $F(\mathbf{x}, \hat{\mathbf{w}})$ as a predictor of the desired response d. This expression is made up of two components, one defining the squared bias and the other defining the variance. Derive this expression, starting from Eq. (2.46)

2.6. What are the two attributes of the MDL principle?

2.7. The method of instrumental variables described in Eq. (2.57) provides an asymptotically unbiased estimate of the unknown parameter vector $\hat{\mathbf{w}}(N)$; that is,

$$\lim_{N \to \infty} \hat{\mathbf{w}}(N) = \mathbf{w}$$

Prove the validity of this statement, assuming joint ergodicity of the regressor $\mathbf{x}$ and response d.

COMPUTER EXPERIMENT

2.8. Repeat the pattern-classification experiment described in Section 2.5, this time setting the two moons at the very edge of linear separability, that is, $d = 0$. Comment on your results, and compare them with those obtained in Problem 1.6, involving the perceptron.

2.9. In performing the experiments in Section 2.5 and Problem 2.8, there was no regularization included in the method of least squares. Would the use of regularization have made a difference in the performance of the method of least squares?

To substantiate your response to this question, repeat the experiment of Problem 2.7, this time using the regularized least-squares algorithm.

CHAPTER 3

The Least-Mean-Square Algorithm

ORGANIZATION OF THE CHAPTER

In this chapter, we describe a highly popular on-line learning algorithm known as the least-mean-square (LMS) algorithm, which was developed by Widrow and Hoff in 1960.

The chapter is organized as follows:

1. Section 3.1 is introductory, followed by Section 3.2 that sets the stage for the rest of the chapter by describing a linear discrete-time filter of finite-duration impulse response.

2. Section 3.3 reviews two unconstrained optimization techniques: the method of steepest descent and Newton's method.

3. Section 3.4 formulates the Wiener filter, which is optimum in the mean-square-error sense. Traditionally, the average performance of the LMS algorithm is judged against the Wiener filter.

4. Section 3.5 presents the derivation of the LMS algorithm. Section 3.6 portrays a modified form of the LMS algorithm as a Markov model. Then, to prepare the way for studying the convergence behavior of the LMS algorithm, Section 3.7 introduces the Langevin equation, rooted in unstable thermodynamics. The other tool needed for convergence analysis of the algorithm is Kushner's method of direct averaging; this method is discussed in Section 3.8. Section 3.9 presents a detailed statistical analysis of the algorithm; most importantly, it shows that the statistical behavior of the algorithm (using a small learning-rate parameter) is, in fact, the discrete-time version of the Langevin equation.

5. Section 3.10 presents a computer experiment validating the small learning-rate theory of the LMS algorithm. Section 3.11 repeats the pattern-classification experiment of Section 1.5 on the perceptron, this time using the LMS algorithm.

6. Section 3.12 discusses the virtues and limitations of the LMS algorithm. Section 3.13 discusses the related issue of learning-rate annealing schedules.

Section 3.14 provides a summary and discussion that conclude the chapter.

3.1 INTRODUCTION

Rosenblatt's perceptron, discussed in Chapter 1, was the first learning algorithm for solving a linearly separable pattern-classification problem. The *least-mean-square (LMS) algorithm*, developed by Widrow and Hoff (1960), was the first linear adaptive-filtering algorithm for solving problems such as prediction and communication-channel equal-ization. Development of the LMS algorithm was indeed inspired by the perceptron. Though different in applications, these two algorithms share a common feature: They both involve the use of a *linear combiner*, hence the designation "linear."

The amazing thing about the LMS algorithm is that it has established itself not only as the workhorse for adaptive-filtering applications, but also as the benchmark against which other adaptive-filtering algorithms are evaluated. The reasons behind this amazing track record are multifold:

- In terms of computational complexity, the LMS algorithm's complexity is *linear* with respect to adjustable parameters, which makes the algorithm *computationally efficient*, yet the algorithm is effective in performance.
- The algorithm is *simple* to code and therefore easy to build.
- Above all, the algorithm is *robust* with respect to external disturbances.

From an engineering perspective, these qualities are all highly desirable. It is therefore not surprising to see that the LMS algorithm has withstood the test of time.

In this chapter, we derive the LMS algorithm in its most basic form and discuss its virtues and limitations. Most importantly, the material presented herein sets the stage for the back-propagation algorithm to be discussed in the next chapter.

3.2   FILTERING STRUCTURE OF THE LMS ALGORITHM

Figure 3.1 shows the block diagram of an unknown dynamic system that is stimulated by an input vector consisting of the elements $x_1(i), x_2(i), ..., x_M(i)$, where i denotes the instant of time at which the stimulus (excitation) is applied to the system. The time index

FIGURE 3.1 (a) Unknown dynamic system. (b) Signal-flow graph of adaptive model for the system; the graph embodies a feedback loop set in color.

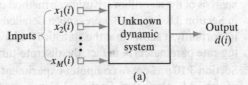

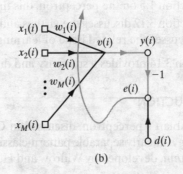

$i = 1, 2, ..., n$. In response to this stimulus, the system produces an output denoted by $y(i)$. Thus, the external behavior of the system is described by the data set

$$\mathcal{T}: \{\mathbf{x}(i), d(i); i = 1, 2, ..., n, ...\} \tag{3.1}$$

where

$$\mathbf{x}(i) = [x_1(i), x_2(i), ..., x_M(i)]^T \tag{3.2}$$

The sample pairs composing $\mathcal{T}$ are identically distributed according to an unknown probability law. The dimension M pertaining to the input vector $\mathbf{x}(i)$ is referred to as the *dimensionality of the input space*, or simply as the *input dimensionality*.

The stimulus vector $\mathbf{x}(i)$ can arise in one of two fundamentally different ways, one spatial and the other temporal:

- The M elements of $\mathbf{x}(i)$ originate at different points in space; in this case, we speak of $\mathbf{x}(i)$ as a *snapshot* of data.
- The M elements of $\mathbf{x}(i)$ represent the set of present and $(M - 1)$ past values of some excitation that are *uniformly spaced in time.*

The problem we address is how to design a multiple-input–single-output *model* of the unknown dynamic system by building it around a *single linear neuron*. The neural model operates under the influence of an algorithm that *controls* necessary adjustments to the synaptic weights of the neuron, with the following points in mind:

- The algorithm starts from an *arbitrary setting* of the neuron's synaptic weights.
- Adjustments to the synaptic weights in response to statistical variations in the system's behavior are made on a *continuous* basis (i.e time is incorporated into the constitution of the algorithm).
- Computations of adjustments to the synaptic weights are completed inside an interval that is one sampling period long.

The neural model just described is referred to as an *adaptive filter*. Although the description is presented in the context of a task clearly recognized as one of *system identification*, the characterization of the adaptive filter is general enough to have wide application.

Figure 3.1b shows a signal-flow graph of the adaptive filter. Its operation consists of two continuous processes:

1. *Filtering process*, which involves the computation of two signals:
   - an output, denoted by $y(i)$, that is produced in response to the M elements of the stimulus vector $\mathbf{x}(i)$, namely, $x_1(i), x_2(i), ..., x_M(i)$;
   - an error signal, denoted by $e(i)$, that is obtained by comparing the output $y(i)$ with the corresponding output $d(i)$ produced by the unknown system. In effect, $d(i)$ acts as a *desired response*, or *target*, signal.
2. *Adaptive process*, which involves the automatic adjustment of the synaptic weights of the neuron in accordance with the error signal $e(i)$.

Thus, the combination of these two processes working together constitutes a *feedback loop* acting around the neuron, as shown in Fig. 3.1b.

Since the neuron is linear, the output $y(i)$ is exactly the same as the induced local field $v(i)$; that is,

$$y(i) = v(i) = \sum_{k=1}^{M} w_k(i)x_k(i) \tag{3.3}$$

where $w_1(i), w_2(i), ..., w_M(i)$ are the M synaptic weights of the neuron, measured at time i. In matrix form, we may express $y(i)$ as an inner product of the vectors $\mathbf{x}(i)$ and $\mathbf{w}(i)$ as

$$y(i) = \mathbf{x}^T(i)\mathbf{w}(i) \tag{3.4}$$

where

$$\mathbf{w}(i) = [w_1(i), w_2(i), ..., w_M(i)]^T$$

Note that the notation for a synaptic weight has been simplified here by *not* including an additional subscript to identify the neuron, since we have only a single neuron to deal with. This practice is followed throughout the book, whenever a single neuron is involved. The neuron's output $y(i)$ is compared with the corresponding output $d(i)$ received from the unknown system at time i. Typically, $y(i)$ is different from $d(i)$; hence, their comparison results in the error signal

$$e(i) = d(i) - y(i) \tag{3.5}$$

The manner in which the error signal $e(i)$ is used to control the adjustments to the neuron's synaptic weights is determined by the cost function used to derive the adaptive-filtering algorithm of interest. This issue is closely related to that of optimization. It is therefore appropriate to present a review of unconstrained-optimization methods. The material is applicable not only to linear adaptive filters, but also to neural networks in general.

3.3 UNCONSTRAINED OPTIMIZATION: A REVIEW

Consider a cost function $\mathcal{E}(\mathbf{w})$ that is a *continuously differentiable* function of some unknown weight (parameter) vector $\mathbf{w}$. The function $\mathcal{E}(\mathbf{w})$ maps the elements of $\mathbf{w}$ into real numbers. It is a measure of how to choose the weight (parameter) vector $\mathbf{w}$ of an adaptive-filtering algorithm so that it behaves in an optimum manner. We want to find an optimal solution $\mathbf{w}^*$ that satisfies the condition

$$\mathcal{E}(\mathbf{w}^*) \leq \mathcal{E}(\mathbf{w}) \tag{3.6}$$

That is, we need to solve an *unconstrained-optimization problem*, stated as follows:

Minimize the cost function $\mathcal{E}(\mathbf{w})$ with respect to the weight vector $\mathbf{w}$.

The necessary condition for optimality is

$$\nabla \mathcal{E}(\mathbf{w}^*) = \mathbf{0} \tag{3.7}$$

where ∇ is the *gradient operator*,

$$\nabla = \left[\frac{\partial}{\partial w_1}, \frac{\partial}{\partial w_2}, ..., \frac{\partial}{\partial w_M} \right]^T \qquad (3.8)$$

and $\nabla\mathscr{E}(\mathbf{w})$ is the *gradient vector* of the cost function,

$$\nabla\mathscr{E}(\mathbf{w}) = \left[\frac{\partial\mathscr{E}}{\partial w_1}, \frac{\partial\mathscr{E}}{\partial w_2}, ..., \frac{\partial\mathscr{E}}{\partial w_M} \right]^T \qquad (3.9)$$

(Differentiation with respect to a vector is discussed in Note 1 at the end of this chapter.)

A class of unconstrained-optimization algorithms that is particularly well suited for the design of adaptive filters is based on the idea of local *iterative descent*:

Starting with an initial guess denoted by $\mathbf{w}(0)$, generate a sequence of weight vectors $\mathbf{w}(1)$, $\mathbf{w}(2), ...$, such that the cost function $\mathscr{E}(\mathbf{w})$ is reduced at each iteration of the algorithm, as shown by

$$\mathscr{E}(\mathbf{w}(n+1)) < \mathscr{E}(\mathbf{w}(n)) \qquad (3.10)$$

where $\mathbf{w}(n)$ is the old value of the weight vector and $\mathbf{w}(n+1)$ is its updated value.

We hope that the algorithm will eventually converge onto the optimal solution $\mathbf{w}^*$. We say "hope" because there is a distinct possibility that the algorithm will diverge (i.e., become unstable) unless special precautions are taken.

In this section, we describe three unconstrained-optimization methods that rely on the idea of iterative descent in one form or another (Bertsekas, 1995).

Method of Steepest Descent

In the method of steepest descent, the successive adjustments applied to the weight vector $\mathbf{w}$ are in the direction of steepest descent, that is, in a direction opposite to the gradient vector $\nabla\mathscr{E}(\mathbf{w})$. For convenience of presentation, we write

$$\mathbf{g} = \nabla\mathscr{E}(\mathbf{w}) \qquad (3.11)$$

Accordingly, the steepest-descent algorithm is formally described by

$$\mathbf{w}(n+1) = \mathbf{w}(n) - \eta\mathbf{g}(n) \qquad (3.12)$$

where η is a positive constant called the *stepsize*, or *learning-rate*, *parameter*, and $\mathbf{g}(n)$ is the gradient vector evaluated at the point $\mathbf{w}(n)$. In going from iteration n to $n+1$, the algorithm applies the *correction*

$$\Delta\mathbf{w}(n) = \mathbf{w}(n+1) - \mathbf{w}(n) \qquad (3.13)$$
$$= -\eta\mathbf{g}(n)$$

Equation (3.13) is in fact a formal statement of the error-correction rule described in the introductory chapter.

To show that the formulation of the steepest-descent algorithm satisfies the condition of Eq. (3.10) for iterative descent, we use a first-order Taylor series expansion around $\mathbf{w}(n)$ to approximate $\mathscr{E}(\mathbf{w}(n+1))$ as

$$\mathscr{E}(\mathbf{w}(n+1)) \approx \mathscr{E}(\mathbf{w}(n)) + \mathbf{g}^T(n)\Delta\mathbf{w}(n)$$

the use of which is justified for small η. Substituting Eq. (3.13) into this approximate relation yields

$$\mathscr{E}(\mathbf{w}(n+1)) \approx \mathscr{E}(\mathbf{w}(n)) - \eta\mathbf{g}^T(n)\mathbf{g}(n)$$
$$= \mathscr{E}(\mathbf{w}(n)) - \eta\|\mathbf{g}(n)\|^2$$

which shows that, for a positive learning-rate parameter η, the cost function is decreased as the algorithm progresses from one iteration to the next. The reasoning presented here is approximate in that this end result is true only for small enough learning rates.

The method of steepest descent converges to the optimal solution $\mathbf{w}^*$ slowly. Moreover, the learning-rate parameter η has a profound influence on its convergence behavior:

- When η is small, the transient response of the algorithm is *overdamped*, in that the trajectory traced by $\mathbf{w}(n)$ follows a smooth path in the $\mathscr{W}$-plane, as illustrated in Fig. 3.2a.
- When η is large, the transient response of the algorithm is *underdamped*, in that the trajectory of $\mathbf{w}(n)$ follows a zigzagging (oscillatory) path, as illustrated in Fig. 3.2b.
- When η exceeds a certain critical value, the algorithm becomes unstable (i.e., it diverges).

Newton's Method

For a more elaborate optimization technique, we may look to *Newton's method*, the basic idea of which is to minimize the quadratic approximation of the cost function $\mathscr{E}(\mathbf{w})$ around the current point $\mathbf{w}(n)$; this minimization is performed at each iteration of the algorithm. Specifically, using a *second-order* Taylor series expansion of the cost function around the point $\mathbf{w}(n)$, we may write

$$\Delta\mathscr{E}(\mathbf{w}(n)) = \mathscr{E}(\mathbf{w}(n+1)) - \mathscr{E}(\mathbf{w}(n))$$
$$\approx \mathbf{g}^T(n)\Delta\mathbf{w}(n) + \frac{1}{2}\Delta\mathbf{w}^T(n)\mathbf{H}(n)\Delta\mathbf{w}(n) \tag{3.14}$$

As before, $\mathbf{g}(n)$ is the M-by-1 gradient vector of the cost function $\mathscr{E}(\mathbf{w})$ evaluated at the point $\mathbf{w}(n)$. The matrix $\mathbf{H}(n)$ is the m-by-m *Hessian* of $\mathscr{E}(\mathbf{w})$, also evaluated at $\mathbf{w}(n)$. The Hessian of $\mathscr{E}(\mathbf{w})$ is defined by

$$\mathbf{H} = \nabla^2\mathscr{E}(\mathbf{w})$$

$$= \begin{bmatrix} \dfrac{\partial^2\mathscr{E}}{\partial w_1^2} & \dfrac{\partial^2\mathscr{E}}{\partial w_1\partial w_2} & \cdots & \dfrac{\partial^2\mathscr{E}}{\partial w_1\partial w_M} \\[2ex] \dfrac{\partial^2\mathscr{E}}{\partial w_2\partial w_1} & \dfrac{\partial^2\mathscr{E}}{\partial w_2^2} & \cdots & \dfrac{\partial^2\mathscr{E}}{\partial w_2\partial w_M} \\[2ex] \vdots & \vdots & \vdots & \vdots \\[2ex] \dfrac{\partial^2\mathscr{E}}{\partial w_M\partial w_1} & \dfrac{\partial^2\mathscr{E}}{\partial w_M\partial w_2} & \cdots & \dfrac{\partial^2\mathscr{E}}{\partial w_M^2} \end{bmatrix} \tag{3.15}$$

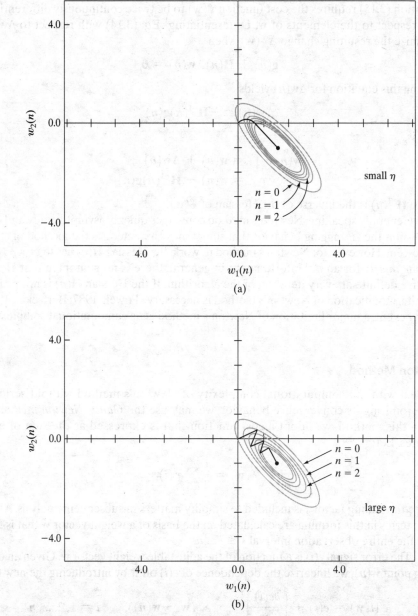

FIGURE 3.2   Trajectory of the method of steepest descent in a two-dimensional space for two different values of learning-rate parameter: (a) small η (b) large η. The coordinates w_1 and w_2 are elements of the weight vector **w**; they both lie in the $\mathcal{W}$-plane.

Equation (3.15) requires the cost function $\mathscr{E}(\mathbf{w})$ to be twice continuously differentiable with respect to the elements of $\mathbf{w}$. Differentiating[1] Eq. (3.14) with respect to $\Delta\mathbf{w}$, we minimize the resulting change $\Delta\mathscr{E}(\mathbf{w})$ when

$$\mathbf{g}(n) + \mathbf{H}(n)\Delta\mathbf{w}(n) = \mathbf{0}$$

Solving this equation for $\Delta\mathbf{w}(n)$ yields

$$\Delta\mathbf{w}(n) = -\mathbf{H}^{-1}(n)\mathbf{g}(n)$$

That is,

$$\begin{aligned}
\mathbf{w}(n+1) &= \mathbf{w}(n) + \Delta\mathbf{w}(n) \\
&= \mathbf{w}(n) - \mathbf{H}^{-1}(n)\mathbf{g}(n)
\end{aligned} \tag{3.16}$$

where $\mathbf{H}^{-1}(n)$ is the inverse of the Hessian of $\mathscr{E}(\mathbf{w})$.

Generally speaking, Newton's method converges quickly asymptotically and does *not* exhibit the zigzagging behavior that sometimes characterizes the method of steepest descent. However, for Newton's method to work, the Hessian $\mathbf{H}(n)$ has to be a *positive definite matrix* for all n. Unfortunately, in general, there is no guarantee that $\mathbf{H}(n)$ is positive definite at every iteration of the algorithm. If the Hessian $\mathbf{H}(n)$ is not positive definite, modification of Newton's method is necessary (Powell, 1987; Bertsekas, 1995). In any event, a major limitation of Newton's method is its computational complexity.

Gauss–Newton Method

To deal with the computational complexity of Newton's method without seriously compromising its convergence behavior, we may use the *Gauss–Newton method*. To apply this method, we adopt a cost function that is expressed as the sum of error squares. Let

$$\mathscr{E}(\mathbf{w}) = \frac{1}{2}\sum_{i=1}^{n} e^2(i) \tag{3.17}$$

where the scaling factor $\frac{1}{2}$ is included to simplify matters in subsequent analysis. All the error terms in this formula are calculated on the basis of a weight vector $\mathbf{w}$ that is fixed over the entire observation interval $1 \le i \le n$.

The error signal $e(i)$ is a function of the adjustable weight vector $\mathbf{w}$. Given an operating point $\mathbf{w}(n)$, we linearize the dependence of $e(i)$ on $\mathbf{w}$ by introducing the new term

$$e'(i, \mathbf{w}) = e(i) + \left[\frac{\partial e(i)}{\partial \mathbf{w}}\right]^T_{\mathbf{w}=\mathbf{w}(n)} \times (\mathbf{w} - \mathbf{w}(n)), \qquad i = 1, 2, ..., n$$

Equivalently, by using matrix notation, we may write

$$e'(n, \mathbf{w}) = e(n) + \mathbf{J}(n)(\mathbf{w} - \mathbf{w}(n)) \tag{3.18}$$

where $\mathbf{e}(n)$ is the error vector

$$\mathbf{e}(n) = [e(1), e(2), ..., e(n)]^T$$

and $\mathbf{J}(n)$ is the n-by-m *Jacobian* of $\mathbf{e}(n)$:

$$\mathbf{J}(n) = \begin{bmatrix} \dfrac{\partial e(1)}{\partial w_1} & \dfrac{\partial e(1)}{\partial w_2} & \cdots & \dfrac{\partial e(1)}{\partial w_M} \\[2mm] \dfrac{\partial e(2)}{\partial w_1} & \dfrac{\partial e(2)}{\partial w_2} & \cdots & \dfrac{\partial e(2)}{\partial w_M} \\[2mm] \vdots & \vdots & & \vdots \\[2mm] \dfrac{\partial e(n)}{\partial w_1} & \dfrac{\partial e(n)}{\partial w_2} & \cdots & \dfrac{\partial e(n)}{\partial w_M} \end{bmatrix}_{\mathbf{w}=\mathbf{w}(n)} \tag{3.19}$$

The Jacobian $\mathbf{J}(n)$ is the transpose of the m-by-n gradient matrix $\nabla \mathbf{e}(n)$, where

$$\nabla \mathbf{e}(n) = [\nabla e(1), \nabla e(2), ..., \nabla e(n)]$$

The updated weight vector $\mathbf{w}(n + 1)$ is now defined by

$$\mathbf{w}(n + 1) = \arg \min_{\mathbf{w}} \left\{ \frac{1}{2} \|\mathbf{e}'(n, \mathbf{w})\|^2 \right\} \tag{3.20}$$

Using Eq. (3.18) to evaluate the squared Euclidean norm of $\mathbf{e}'(n, \mathbf{w})$, we get

$$\frac{1}{2} \|\mathbf{e}'(n, \mathbf{w})\|^2 = \frac{1}{2} \|\mathbf{e}(n)\|^2 + \mathbf{e}^T(n)\mathbf{J}(n)(\mathbf{w} - \mathbf{w}(n))$$

$$+ \frac{1}{2}(\mathbf{w} - \mathbf{w}(n))^T \mathbf{J}^T(n)\mathbf{J}(n)(\mathbf{w} - \mathbf{w}(n))$$

Hence, differentiating this expression with respect to $\mathbf{w}$ and setting the result equal to zero, we obtain

$$\mathbf{J}^T(n)\mathbf{e}(n) + \mathbf{J}^T(n)\mathbf{J}(n)(\mathbf{w} - \mathbf{w}(n)) = \mathbf{0}$$

Solving this equation for $\mathbf{w}$, we may thus write, in light of Eq. 3.20,

$$\mathbf{w}(n + 1) = \mathbf{w}(n) - (\mathbf{J}^T(n)\mathbf{J}(n))^{-1}\mathbf{J}^T(n)\mathbf{e}(n) \tag{3.21}$$

which describes the *pure* form of the Gauss–Newton method.

Unlike Newton's method, which requires knowledge of the Hessian of the cost function $\mathscr{E}(n)$, the Gauss–Newton method requires only the Jacobian of the error vector $\mathbf{e}(n)$. However, for the Gauss–Newton iteration to be computable, the matrix product $\mathbf{J}^T(n)\mathbf{J}(n)$ must be nonsingular.

With regard to the latter point, we recognize that $\mathbf{J}^T(n)\mathbf{J}(n)$ is always nonnegative definite. To ensure that it is nonsingular, the Jacobian $\mathbf{J}(n)$ must have row *rank* n; that is, the n rows of $\mathbf{J}(n)$ in Eq. (3.19) must be linearly independent. Unfortunately, there is no guarantee that this condition will always hold. To guard against the possibility that $\mathbf{J}(n)$ is rank deficient, the customary practice is to add the diagonal matrix $\delta \mathbf{I}$ to the matrix $\mathbf{J}^T(n)\mathbf{J}(n)$, where $\mathbf{I}$ is the identity matrix. The parameter δ is a small positive constant chosen to ensure that

$$\mathbf{J}^T(n)\mathbf{J}(n) + \delta \mathbf{I} \text{ is positive definite for all } n$$

On this basis, the Gauss–Newton method is implemented in the slightly modified form

$$\mathbf{w}(n+1) = \mathbf{w}(n) - (\mathbf{J}^T(n)\mathbf{J}(n) + \delta\mathbf{I})^{-1}\mathbf{J}^T(n)\mathbf{e}(n) \qquad (3.22)$$

The effect of the added term $\delta\mathbf{I}$ is progressively reduced as the number of iterations, n, is increased. Note also that the recursive equation (3.22) is the solution of the *modified cost function*

$$\mathscr{E}(\mathbf{w}) = \frac{1}{2}\left\{ \sum_{i=1}^{n} e^2(i) + \delta\|\mathbf{w} - \mathbf{w}(n)\|^2 \right\} \qquad (3.23)$$

where $\mathbf{w}(n)$ is the *current value* of the weight vector $\mathbf{w}(i)$.

In the literature on signal processing, the addition of the term $\delta\mathbf{I}$ in Eq. (3.22) is referred to as *diagonal loading*. The addition of this term is accounted for by expanding the cost function $\mathscr{E}(\mathbf{w})$ in the manner described in Eq. (3.23), where we now have two terms (ignoring the scaling factor $\frac{1}{2}$):

- The first term, $\sum_{i=1}^{n} e^2(i)$, is the standard sum of squared errors, which depends on the training data.
- The second term contains the squared Euclidean norm, $\|\mathbf{w} - \mathbf{w}(n)\|^2$, which depends on the filter structure. In effect, this term acts as a *stabilizer*.

The scaling factor δ is commonly referred to as a *regularization parameter*, and the resulting modification of the cost function is correspondingly referred to as *structural regularization*. The issue of regularization is discussed in great detail in Chapter 7.

3.4 THE WIENER FILTER

The ordinary least-squares estimator was discussed in Chapter 2, where the traditional approach to minimization was used to find the least-squares solution from an observation model of the environment. To conform to the terminology adopted in this chapter, we will refer to it as the *least-squares filter*. Moreover, we will rederive the formula for this filter by using the Gauss–Newton method.

To proceed then, we use Eqs. (3.3) and (3.4) to define the error vector as

$$\begin{aligned}\mathbf{e}(n) &= \mathbf{d}(n) - [\mathbf{x}(1), \mathbf{x}(2), ..., \mathbf{x}(n)]^T\mathbf{w}(n) \\ &= \mathbf{d}(n) - \mathbf{X}(n)\mathbf{w}(n)\end{aligned} \qquad (3.24)$$

where $\mathbf{d}(n)$ is the n-by-1 *desired response vector*,

$$\mathbf{d}(n) = [d(1), d(2), ..., d(n)]^T$$

and $\mathbf{X}(n)$ is the n-by-M *data matrix*,

$$\mathbf{X}(n) = [\mathbf{x}(n), \mathbf{x}(2), ..., \mathbf{x}(n)]^T$$

Differentiating the error vector $\mathbf{e}(n)$ with respect to $\mathbf{w}(n)$ yields the gradient matrix

$$\nabla\mathbf{e}(n) = -\mathbf{X}^T(n)$$

Correspondingly, the Jacobian of $\mathbf{e}(n)$ is

$$\mathbf{J}(n) = -\mathbf{X}(n) \tag{3.25}$$

Since the error equation (3.18) is already linear in the weight vector $\mathbf{w}(n)$, the Gauss–Newton method converges in a single iteration, as shown here. Substituting Eqs. (3.24) and (3.25) into (3.21) yields

$$\begin{aligned}
\mathbf{w}(n+1) &= \mathbf{w}(n) + (\mathbf{X}^T(n)\mathbf{X}(n))^{-1}\mathbf{X}^T(n)(\mathbf{d}(n) - \mathbf{X}(n)\mathbf{w}(n)) \\
&= (\mathbf{X}^T(n)\mathbf{X}(n))^{-1}\mathbf{X}^T(n)\mathbf{d}(n)
\end{aligned} \tag{3.26}$$

The term $(\mathbf{X}^T(n)\mathbf{X}(n))^{-1}\mathbf{X}^T(n)$ is called the *pseudoinverse* of the data matrix $\mathbf{X}(n)$; that is,[2]

$$\mathbf{X}^+(n) = (\mathbf{X}^T(n)\mathbf{X}(n))^{-1}\mathbf{X}^T(n) \tag{3.27}$$

Hence, we may rewrite Eq. (3.26) in the compact form

$$\mathbf{w}(n+1) = \mathbf{X}^+(n)\mathbf{d}(n) \tag{3.28}$$

This formula represents a convenient way of stating the following:

> The weight vector $\mathbf{w}(n+1)$ solves the linear least-squares problem, defined over an observation interval of duration n, as the product of two terms: the pseudoinverse $\mathbf{X}^+(n)$ and the desired response vector $\mathbf{d}(n)$.

Wiener Filter: Limiting Form of the Least-Squares Filter for an Ergodic Environment

Let $\mathbf{w}_o$ denote the limiting form of the least-squares filter as the number of observations, n, is allowed to approach infinity. We may then use Eq. (3.26) to write

$$\begin{aligned}
\mathbf{w}_o &= \lim_{n\to\infty} \mathbf{w}(n+1) \\
&= \lim_{n\to\infty} (\mathbf{X}^T(n)\mathbf{X}(n))^{-1}\mathbf{X}^T(n)d(n) \\
&= \lim_{n\to\infty} \left(\frac{1}{n}\mathbf{X}^T(n)\mathbf{X}(n) \right)^{-1} \times \lim_{n\to\infty} \frac{1}{n}\mathbf{X}^T(n)\mathbf{d}(n)
\end{aligned} \tag{3.29}$$

Suppose now the input vector $\mathbf{x}(i)$ and the corresponding desired response $d(i)$ are drawn from a jointly *ergodic environment* that is also stationary. We may then substitute time averages for ensemble averages. By definition, the ensemble-averaged form of the correlation matrix of the input vector $\mathbf{x}(i)$ is

$$\mathbf{R}_{xx} = \mathbb{E}[\mathbf{x}(i)\mathbf{x}^T(i)] \tag{3.30}$$

and, correspondingly, the ensemble-averaged form of the *cross-correlation vector* between the input vector $\mathbf{x}(i)$ and the desired response vector $d(i)$ is

$$\mathbf{r}_{dx} = \mathbb{E}[\mathbf{x}(i)d(i)] \tag{3.31}$$

where $\mathbb{E}$ is the expectation operator. Therefore, under the ergodicity assumption, we may now write

$$\mathbf{R}_{xx} = \lim_{n\to\infty} \frac{1}{n}\mathbf{X}(n)\mathbf{X}^T(n)$$

and

$$\mathbf{r}_{dx} = \lim_{n \to \infty} \mathbf{X}^T(n)\mathbf{d}(n)$$

Accordingly, we may recast Eq. (3.29) in terms of ensemble-averaged correlation parameters as

$$\mathbf{w}_o = \mathbf{R}_{xx}^{-1}\mathbf{r}_{dx} \tag{3.32}$$

where $\mathbf{R}_{xx}^{-1}$ is the inverse of the correlation matrix $\mathbf{R}_{xx}$. The formula of Eq. (3.32) is the ensemble-averaged version of the least-squares solution defined in Eq. (2.32).

The weight vector $\mathbf{w}_o$ is called the *Wiener solution* to the optimum linear filtering problem (Widrow and Stearns, 1985; Haykin, 2002). Accordingly, we may make the statement:

> *For an ergodic process, the least-squares filter asymptotically approaches the Wiener filter as the number of observations approaches infinity.*

Designing the Wiener filter requires knowledge of the second-order statistics: the correlation matrix $\mathbf{R}_{xx}$ of the input vector $\mathbf{x}(n)$, and the cross-correlation vector $\mathbf{r}_{xd}$ between $\mathbf{x}(n)$ and the desired response $d(n)$. However, this information is not available when the environment in which the filter operates is unknown. We may deal with such an environment by using a *linear adaptive filter*, adaptive in the sense that the filter is able to adjust its free parameters in response to statistical variations in the environment. A highly popular algorithm for doing this kind of adjustment on a continuing-time basis is the least-mean-square algorithm, discussed next.

3.5   THE LEAST-MEAN-SQUARE ALGORITHM

The *least-mean-square (LMS) algorithm* is configured to minimize the *instantaneous value* of the cost function,

$$\mathcal{E}(\hat{\mathbf{w}}) = \frac{1}{2}e^2(n) \tag{3.33}$$

where $e(n)$ is the error signal measured at time n. Differentiating $\mathcal{E}(\hat{\mathbf{w}})$ with respect to the weight vector $\hat{\mathbf{w}}$ yields

$$\frac{\partial \mathcal{E}(\hat{\mathbf{w}})}{\partial \hat{\mathbf{w}}} = e(n)\frac{\partial e(n)}{\partial \mathbf{w}} \tag{3.34}$$

As with the least-squares filter, the LMS algorithm operates with a linear neuron, so we may express the error signal as

$$e(n) = d(n) - \mathbf{x}^T(n)\hat{\mathbf{w}}(n) \tag{3.35}$$

Hence,

$$\frac{\partial e(n)}{\partial \hat{\mathbf{w}}(n)} = -\mathbf{x}(n)$$

and

$$\frac{\partial \mathcal{E}(\hat{\mathbf{w}})}{\partial \hat{\mathbf{w}}(n)} = -\mathbf{x}(n)e(n)$$

Using this latter result as the *instantaneous estimate* of the gradient vector, we may write

$$\hat{\mathbf{g}}(n) = -\mathbf{x}(n)e(n) \tag{3.36}$$

Finally, using Eq. (3.36) for the gradient vector in Eq. (3.12) for the method of steepest descent, we may formulate the LMS algorithm as follows:

$$\hat{\mathbf{w}}(n + 1) = \hat{\mathbf{w}}(n) + \eta \mathbf{x}(n)e(n) \tag{3.37}$$

It is also noteworthy that the inverse of the learning-rate parameter η acts as a measure of the *memory* of the LMS algorithm: The smaller we make η, the longer the memory span over which the LMS algorithm remembers past data will be. Consequently, when η is small, the LMS algorithm performs accurately, but the convergence rate of the algorithm is slow.

In deriving Eq. (3.37), we have used $\hat{\mathbf{w}}(n)$ in place of $\mathbf{w}(n)$ to emphasize the fact that the LMS algorithm produces an *instantaneous estimate* of the weight vector that would result from the use of the method of steepest-descent. As a consequence, in using the LMS algorithm we sacrifice a distinctive feature of the steepest-descent algorithm. In the steepest-descent algorithm, the weight vector $\mathbf{w}(n)$ follows a well-defined trajectory in the weight space $\mathcal{W}$ for a prescribed η. In contrast, in the LMS algorithm, the weight vector $\hat{\mathbf{w}}(n)$ traces a random trajectory. For this reason, the LMS algorithm is sometimes referred to as a "stochastic gradient algorithm." As the number of iterations in the LMS algorithm approaches infinity, $\hat{\mathbf{w}}(n)$ performs a random walk (Brownian motion) about the Wiener solution $\mathbf{w}_o$. The important point to note, however, is the fact that, unlike the method of steepest descent, the LMS algorithm does *not* require knowledge of the statistics of the environment. This feature of the LMS algorithm is important from a practical perspective.

A summary of the LMS algorithm, based on Eqs. (3.35) and (3.37), is presented in Table 3.1, which clearly illustrates the simplicity of the algorithm. As indicated in this table, *initialization* of the algorithm is done by simply setting the value of the weight vector $\hat{\mathbf{w}}(0) = \mathbf{0}$.

TABLE 3.1   Summary of the LMS Algorithm

Training Sample: Input signal vector = $\mathbf{x}(n)$
Desired response = $d(n)$

User-selected parameter: η
Initialization. Set $\hat{\mathbf{w}}(0) = \mathbf{0}$.
Computation. For $n = 1, 2, ...$, compute

$$e(n) = d(n) - \hat{\mathbf{w}}^T(n)\mathbf{x}(n)$$

$$\hat{\mathbf{w}}(n + 1) = \hat{\mathbf{w}}(n) + \eta \mathbf{x}(n)e(n)$$

FIGURE 3.3   Signal-flow graph
representation of the LMS
algorithm. The graph embodies
feedback depicted in color.

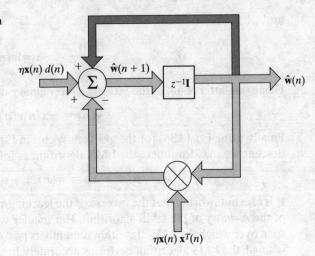

Signal-Flow Graph Representation of the LMS Algorithm

By combining Eqs. (3.35) and (3.37), we may express the evolution of the weight vector in the LMS algorithm as

$$\hat{\mathbf{w}}(n + 1) = \hat{\mathbf{w}}(n) + \eta \mathbf{x}(n)[d(n) - \mathbf{x}^T(n)\hat{\mathbf{w}}(n)]$$
$$= [\mathbf{I} - \eta \mathbf{x}(n)\mathbf{x}^T(n)]\hat{\mathbf{w}}(n) + \eta \mathbf{x}(n)d(n) \tag{3.38}$$

where $\mathbf{I}$ is the identity matrix. In using the LMS algorithm, we recognize that

$$\hat{\mathbf{w}}(n) = z^{-1}[\hat{\mathbf{w}}(n + 1)] \tag{3.39}$$

where z^{-1} is the *unit-time delay operator*, implying storage. Using Eqs. (3.38) and (3.39), we may thus represent the LMS algorithm by the signal-flow graph depicted in Fig. 3.3. This signal-flow graph reveals that the LMS algorithm is an example of a *stochastic feedback system*. The presence of feedback has a profound impact on the convergence behavior of the LMS algorithm.

3.6   MARKOV MODEL PORTRAYING THE DEVIATION OF THE LMS ALGORITHM FROM THE WIENER FILTER

To perform a statistical analysis of the LMS algorithm, we find it more convenient to work with the *weight-error vector*, defined by

$$\boldsymbol{\varepsilon}(n) = \mathbf{w}_o - \hat{\mathbf{w}}(n) \tag{3.40}$$

where $\mathbf{w}_o$ is the optimum Wiener solution defined by Eq. (3.32) and $\hat{\mathbf{w}}(n)$ is the corresponding estimate of the weight vector computed by the LMS algorithm. Thus,

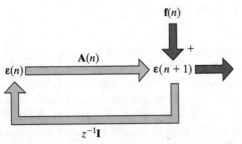

FIGURE 3.4   Signal-flow graph representation of the Markov model described in Eq. (3.41); the graph embodies feedback depicted in color.

in terms of $\varepsilon(n)$, assuming the role of a *state*, we may rewrite Eq. (3.38) in the compact form

$$\varepsilon(n + 1) = \mathbf{A}(n)\varepsilon(n) + \mathbf{f}(n) \tag{3.41}$$

Here, we have

$$\mathbf{A}(n) = \mathbf{I} - \eta\mathbf{x}(n)\mathbf{x}^T(n) \tag{3.42}$$

where $\mathbf{I}$ is the identity matrix. The additive noise term in the right-hand side of Eq. (3.41) is defined by

$$\mathbf{f}(n) = -\eta\mathbf{x}(n)e_o(n) \tag{3.43}$$

where

$$e_o(n) = d(n) - \mathbf{w}_o^T\mathbf{x}(n) \tag{3.44}$$

is the estimation error produced by the Wiener filter.

Equation (3.41) represents a *Markov model* of the LMS algorithm, with the model being characterized as follows:

- The *updated state* of the model, denoted by the vector $\varepsilon(n + 1)$, depends on the old state $\varepsilon(n)$, with the dependence itself being defined by the *transition matrix* $\mathbf{A}(n)$.
- Evolution of the state over time n is perturbed by the intrinsically generated *noise* $\mathbf{f}(n)$, which acts as a "driving force".

Figure 3.4 shows a vector-valued signal-flow graph representation of this model. The branch labeled $z^{-1}\mathbf{I}$ represents the memory of the model, with z^{-1} acting as the *unit-time delay operator*, as shown by

$$z^{-1}[\varepsilon(n + 1)] = \varepsilon(n) \tag{3.45}$$

This figure highlights the presence of feedback in the LMS algorithm in a more compact manner than that in Fig. 3.3.

The signal-flow graph of Fig. 3.4 and the accompanying equations provide the framework for the convergence analysis of the LMS algorithm under the assumption of a small learning-rate parameter η. However, before proceeding with this analysis, we will digress briefly to present two building blocks with that goal in mind: the Langevin equation, presented in Section 3.7, followed by Kushner's direct-averaging method, presented in Section 3.8. With those two building blocks in hand, we will then go on to study convergence analysis of the LMS algorithm in Section 3.9.

3.7   THE LANGEVIN EQUATION: CHARACTERIZATION OF BROWNIAN MOTION

Restating the remarks made towards the end of Section 3.5 in more precise terms insofar as stability or convergence is concerned, we may say that the LMS algorithm (for small enough η) never attains a perfectly stable or convergent condition. Rather, after a large number of iterations, n, the algorithm approaches a "pseudo-equilibrium" condition, which, in qualitative terms, is described by the algorithm executing Brownian motion around the Wiener solution. This kind of stochastic behavior is explained nicely by the Langevin equation of nonequilibrium thermodynamics.[3] So, we will make a brief digression to introduce this important equation.

Let $v(t)$ denote the velocity of a macroscopic particle of mass m immersed in a viscous fluid. It is assumed that the particle is small enough for its velocity due to thermal fluctuations deemed to be significant. Then, from the *equipartition law of thermodynamics*, the mean energy of the particle is given by

$$\frac{1}{2}\mathbb{E}[v^2(t)] = \frac{1}{2}k_{\mathrm{B}}T \qquad \text{for all continuous time } t \tag{3.46}$$

where k_{B} is *Boltzmann's constant* and T is the *absolute temperature*. The total force exerted on the particle by the molecules in the viscous fluid is made up of two components:

(i) a continuous *damping force* equal to $-\alpha v(t)$ in accordance with *Stoke's law*, where α is the coefficient of friction;

(ii) a *fluctuating force* $F_f(t)$, whose properties are specified on the average.

The equation of motion of the particle in the absence of an external force is therefore given by

$$m\frac{dv}{dt} = -\alpha v(t) + F_f(t)$$

Dividing both sides of this equation by m, we get

$$\frac{dv}{dt} = -\gamma v(t) + \Gamma(t) \tag{3.47}$$

where

$$\gamma = \frac{\alpha}{m} \tag{3.48}$$

and

$$\Gamma(t) = \frac{F_f(t)}{m} \tag{3.49}$$

The term $\Gamma(t)$ is the *fluctuating force per unit mass*; it is a stochastic force because it depends on the positions of the incredibly large number of atoms constituting the particle, which are in a state of constant and irregular motion. Equation (3.47) is called the *Langevin equation*, and $\Gamma(t)$ is called the *Langevin force*. The Langevin equation, which describes the motion of the particle in the viscous fluid at all times (if its initial conditions are specified), was the first mathematical equation describing nonequilibrium thermodynamics.

In Section 3.9, we show that a transformed version of the LMS algorithm has the same mathematical form as the discrete-time version of the Langevin equation. But, before doing that, we need to describe our next building block.

3.8   KUSHNER'S DIRECT-AVERAGING METHOD

The Markov model of Eq. (3.41) is a *nonlinear stochastic difference equation*. This equation is nonlinear because the transition matrix $\mathbf{A}(n)$ depends on the outer product $\mathbf{x}(n)\mathbf{x}^T(n)$ of the input vector $\mathbf{x}(n)$. Hence, the dependence of the weight-error vector $\boldsymbol{\varepsilon}(n+1)$ on $\mathbf{x}(n)$ violates the principle of superposition, which is a requirement for linearity. Moreover, the equation is stochastic because the training sample $\{\mathbf{x}(n), d(n)\}$ is drawn from a stochastic environment. Given these two realities, we find that a rigorous statistical analysis of the LMS algorithm is indeed a very difficult task.

However, under certain conditions, the statistical analysis of the LMS algorithm can be simplified significantly by applying *Kushner's direct-averaging method* to the model of Eq. (3.41). For a formal statement of this method, we write the following (Kushner, 1984):

Consider a stochastic learning system described by the Markov model

$$\boldsymbol{\varepsilon}(n+1) = \mathbf{A}(n)\boldsymbol{\varepsilon}(n) + \mathbf{f}(n)$$

where, for some input vector $\mathbf{x}(n)$, *we have*

$$\mathbf{A}(n) = \mathbf{I} - \eta\mathbf{x}(n)\mathbf{x}^T(n)$$

and the additive noise $\mathbf{f}(n)$ *is linearly scaled by the learning-rate parameter* η. *Provided that*

- *the learning-rate parameter* η *is sufficiently small, and*
- *the additive noise* $\mathbf{f}(n)$ *is essentially independent of the state* $\boldsymbol{\varepsilon}(n)$, *the state evolution of a modified Markov model described by the two equations*

$$\boldsymbol{\varepsilon}_0(n+1) = \mathbf{A}(n)\boldsymbol{\varepsilon}_0(n) + \mathbf{f}_0(n) \tag{3.50}$$

$$\overline{\mathbf{A}}(n) = \mathbf{I} - \eta\mathbb{E}[\mathbf{x}(n)\mathbf{x}^T(n)] \tag{3.51}$$

is practically the same as that of the original Markov model for all n.

The deterministic matrix $\overline{\mathbf{A}}(n)$ of Eq. (3.51) is the transition matrix of the modified Markov model. Note also that we have used the symbol $\boldsymbol{\varepsilon}_0(n)$ for the state of the modified Markov model to emphasize the fact that the evolution of this model over time is identically equal to that of the original Markov model *only* for the limiting case of a vanishingly small learning-rate parameter η.

A proof of the statement embodying Eqs. (3.50) and (3.51) is addressed in Problem 3.7, assuming ergodicity (i.e., substituting time averages for ensemble averages). For the discussion presented herein, it suffices to say the following:

1. As mentioned previously, when the learning-rate parameter η is small, the LMS algorithm has a *long memory*. Hence, the evolution of the updated state $\boldsymbol{\varepsilon}_0(n+1)$ can be traced in time, step by step, all the way back to the initial condition $\boldsymbol{\varepsilon}(0)$.
2. When η is small, we are justified in ignoring all second- and higher-order terms in η in the series expansion of $\boldsymbol{\varepsilon}_0(n+1)$.

3. Finally, the statement embodied in Eqs. (3.50) and (3.51) is obtained by invoking ergodicity, whereby ensemble averages are substituted for time agerages.

3.9   STATISTICAL LMS LEARNING THEORY FOR SMALL LEARNING-RATE PARAMETER

Now that we are equipped with Kushner's direct-averaging method, the stage is set for a principled statistical analysis of the LMS algorithm by making three justifiable assumptions:

Assumption I: The learning-rate parameter η is small

By making this assumption, we justify the application of Kushner's direct-averaging method—hence the adoption of the modified Markov model of Eqs. (3.50) and (3.51) as the basis for the statistical analysis of the LMS algorithm.

From a practical perspective, the choice of small η also makes sense. In particular, the LMS algorithm exhibits its most robust behavior with respect to external disturbances when η is small; the issue of robustness is discussed in Section 3.12.

Assumption II: The estimation error $e_o(n)$ produced by the Wiener filter is white.

This assumption is satisfied if the generation of the desired response is described by the *linear regression model*

$$d(n) = \mathbf{w}_o^T\mathbf{x}(n) + e_o(n) \tag{3.52}$$

Equation (3.52) is simply a rewrite of Eq. (3.44), which, in effect, implies that the weight vector of the Wiener filter is matched to the weight vector of the regression model describing the stochastic environment of interest.

Assumption III: The input vector $x(n)$ and the desired response $d(n)$ are jointly Gaussian

Stochastic processes produced by physical phenomena are frequently mechanized such that a Gaussian model is appropriate—hence the justification for the third assumption.

No further assumptions are needed for the statistical analysis of the LMS algorithm (Haykin, 2002, 2006). In what follows, we present a condensed version of that analysis.

Natural Modes of the LMS Algorithm

Let $\mathbf{R}_{xx}$ denote the ensemble-averaged correlation matrix of the input vector $\mathbf{x}(n)$, drawn from a stationary process; that is,

$$\mathbf{R}_{xx} = \mathbb{E}[\mathbf{x}(n)\mathbf{x}^T(n)] \tag{3.53}$$

Correspondingly, we may express the averaged transition matrix in Eq. (3.51) pertaining to the modified Markov model as

$$
\begin{aligned}
\overline{\mathbf{A}} &= \mathbb{E}[\mathbf{I} - \eta \mathbf{x}(n)\mathbf{x}^T(n)] \\
&= [\mathbf{I} - \eta \mathbf{R}_{xx}]
\end{aligned}
\tag{3.54}
$$

We may therefore expand Eq. (3.50) into the form

$$
\boldsymbol{\varepsilon}_0(n + 1) = (\mathbf{I} - \eta \mathbf{R}_{xx})\boldsymbol{\varepsilon}_0(n) + \mathbf{f}_0(n)
\tag{3.55}
$$

where $\mathbf{f}_0(n)$ is the addition noise. Henceforth, Eq. (3.55) is the equation on which the statistical analysis of the LMS algorithm is based.

Natural Modes of the LMS Algorithm

Applying the *orthogonality transformation* of matrix theory[4] to the correlation matrix $\mathbf{R}_{xx}$, we write

$$
\mathbf{Q}^T \mathbf{R}_{xx} \mathbf{Q} = \boldsymbol{\Lambda}
\tag{3.56}
$$

where $\mathbf{Q}$ is an orthogonal matrix whose columns are the eigenvectors of $\mathbf{R}_{xx}$, and $\boldsymbol{\Lambda}$ is a diagonal matrix whose elements are the associated *eigenvalues*. Extending the application of this transformation to the difference equation Eq. (3.55) yields the corresponding *system of decoupled first-order equations* (Haykin, 2002, 2006)

$$
v_k(n + 1) = (1 - \eta \lambda_k)v_k(n) + \phi_k(n), \qquad k = 1, 2, ..., M
\tag{3.57}
$$

where M is the dimensionality of the weight vector $\hat{\mathbf{w}}(n)$. Moreover, $v_k(n)$ is the kth element of the transformed weight-error vector

$$
\mathbf{v}(n) = \mathbf{Q}^T \boldsymbol{\varepsilon}_0(n)
\tag{3.58}
$$

and, correspondingly, $\phi_k(n)$ is the kth element of the transformed noise vector

$$
\boldsymbol{\phi}(n) = \mathbf{Q}^T \mathbf{f}_0(n)
\tag{3.59}
$$

More specifically, $\phi_k(n)$ is the sample function of a white-noise process of zero mean and variance $\mu^2 J_{\min} \lambda_k$, where $J_{\min}$ is the minimum mean-square error produced by the Wiener filter. In effect, the variance of the zero-mean driving force for the kth difference equation Eq. (3.57) is proportional to the kth eigenvalue of the correlation matrix $\mathbf{R}_{xx}$, namely, λ_k.

Define the difference

$$
\Delta v_k(n) = v_k(n + 1) - v_k(n) \qquad \text{for } k = 1, 2, ..., M
\tag{3.60}
$$

We may then recast Eq. (3.57) in the form

$$
\Delta v_k(n) = -\eta \lambda_k v_k(n) + \phi_k(n) \qquad \text{for } k = 1, 2, ..., M
\tag{3.61}
$$

The stochastic equation Eq. (3.61) is now recognized as the discrete-time version of the Langevin equation Eq. (3.47). In particular, as we compare these two equations, term by term, we construct the analogies listed in Table 3.2. In light of this table, we may now make the following important statement:

TABLE 3.2 Analogies between the Langevin equation (in continuous time) and the transformed LMS evolution (in discrete time)

Langevin equation Eq. (3.47)		LMS evolution Eq. (3.61)
$\dfrac{dv(t)}{dt}$	(acceleration)	$\Delta v_k(n)$
$\gamma v(t)$	(damping force)	$\eta \lambda_k v_k(n)$
$\Gamma(t)$	(stochastic driving force)	$\phi_k(n)$

The convergence behavior of the LMS filter resulting from application of the orthogonality transformation to the difference equation Eq. (3.55) is described by a system of M decoupled Langevin equations whose kth component is characterized as follows:

- damping force is defined by $\eta \lambda_k v_k(n)$;
- Langevin force $\phi_k(n)$ is described by a zero-mean white-noise process with the variance $\eta^2 J_{\min} \lambda_k$.

Most important, the Langevin force $\phi_k(n)$ is responsible for the nonequilibrium behavior of the LMS algorithm, which manifests itself in the form of *Brownian motion* performed by the algorithm around the optimum Wiener solution after a large enough number of iterations n. It must, however, be stressed that the findings summarized in Table 3.2 and the foregoing statement rest on the premise that the learning-rate parameter η is small.

Learning Curves of the LMS Algorithm

Following through the solution of the transformed difference equation Eq. (3.57), we arrive at the LMS learning curve described by Haykin, (2002, 2006),

$$J(n) = J_{\min} + \eta J_{\min} \sum_{k=1}^{M} \frac{\lambda_k}{2 - \eta \lambda_k} + \sum_{k=1}^{M} \lambda_k \left(|v_k(0)|^2 - \frac{\eta J_{\min}}{2 - \eta \lambda_k} \right) (1 - \eta \lambda_k)^{2n} \quad (3.62)$$

where

$$J(n) = \mathbb{E}[|e(n)|^2]$$

is the mean-square error and $v_k(0)$ is the initial value of the kth element of the transformed vector $\mathbf{v}(n)$. Under the assumption that the learning-rate parameter η is small, Eq. (3.62) simplifies to

$$J(n) \approx J_{\min} + \frac{\eta J_{\min}}{2} \sum_{k=1}^{M} \lambda_k + \sum_{k=1}^{M} \lambda_k \left(|v_k(0)|^2 - \frac{\eta J_{\min}}{2} \right) (1 - \eta \lambda_k)^{2n} \quad (3.63)$$

The practical validity of the small-learning-rate-parameter theory presented in this section is demonstrated in the computer experiment presented next.

3.10 COMPUTER EXPERIMENT I: LINEAR PREDICTION

The objective of this experiment is to verify the statistical learning theory of the LMS algorithm described in Section 3.9, assuming a small learning-rate parameter η.

For the experiment, we consider a generative model defined by

$$x(n) = ax(n-1) + \varepsilon(n) \tag{3.64}$$

which represents an *autoregressive (AR) process of order one.* The model being of first order, a is the only parameter of the model. The explanational error $\varepsilon(n)$ is drawn from a zero-mean white-noise process of variance σ_ε^2. The generative model is parameterized as follows:

$$a = 0.99$$
$$\sigma_\varepsilon^2 = 0.02$$
$$\sigma_x^2 = 0.995$$

To estimate the model parameter a, we use the LMS algorithm characterized by the learning-rate parameter $\eta = 0.001$. Starting with the initial condition $\hat{w}(0) = 0$, we apply the scalar version of Eq. (3.35), where the estimation error

$$e(n) = x(n) - \hat{a}(n)x(n-1)$$

and where $\hat{a}(n)$ is the estimate of a produced by the LMS algorithm at time n. Then, performing 100 statistically independent application of the LMS algorithm, we plot the *ensemble-averaged learning curve* of the algorithm. The solid (randomly varying) curve plotted in Fig. 3.5 for 5,000 iterations is the result of this ensemble-averaging operation.

In Fig. 3.5, we have also included the result of computing the ensemble-averaged learning curve by using the theoretically derived formula of Eq. (3.63), assuming a small η. It is remarkable to see perfect agreement between theory and practice, as evidenced by

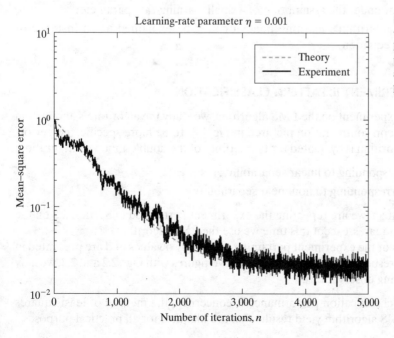

FIGURE 3.5 Experimental verification of the small-learning-rate-parameter theory of the LMS algorithm applied to an autoregressive process of order one.

FIGURE 3.6 LMS classification with distance 1, based on the double-moon configuration of Fig. 1.8.

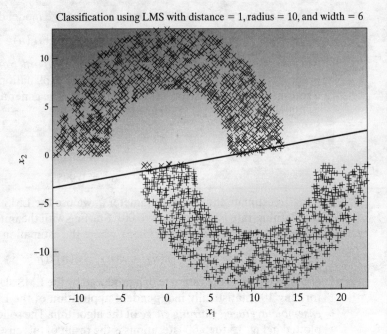

Classification using LMS with distance = 1, radius = 10, and width = 6

the results plotted in Fig. 3.6. Indeed, this remarkable agreement should be viewed as the confirmation of two important theoretical principles:

1. Kushner's method may be used to tackle the theoretical analysis of the LMS learning behavior under the assumption of a small learning-rate parameter.
2. The LMS algorithm's learning behavior may be explained as an instance of Langevin's equation.

3.11 COMPUTER EXPERIMENT II: PATTERN CLASSIFICATION

For the second experiment on the LMS algorithm, we study the algorithm's application to the double-moon configuration pictured in Fig. 1.8. To be more specific, the performance of the algorithm is evaluated for two settings of the double-moon configuration:

(i) $d = 1$, corresponding to linear separability;
(ii) $d = -4$, corresponding to nonlinear separability.

In doing so, in effect, we are repeating the experiment performed in Section 2.5 on the method of least squares, except this time we use the LMS algorithm.

The results of the experiment pertaining to these two values of d are presented in Figs. 3.6 and 3.7, respectively. Comparing these two figures with Figs. 2.2 and 2.3, we may make the following observations:

(a) Insofar as classification performance is concerned, the method of least squares and the LMS algorithm yield results that are identical for all practical purposes.

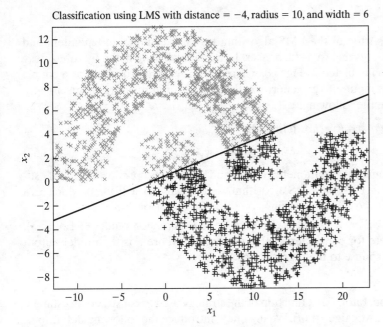

Classification using LMS with distance $= -4$, radius $= 10$, and width $= 6$

FIGURE 3.7   LMS classification with distance -4, based on the double-moon configuration of Fig. 1.8.

(b) In terms of convergence, the LMS algorithm is much slower than the method of least squares. This difference is attributed to the fact that the LMS algorithm is recursive, whereas the method of least squares operates in a batch mode that involves matrix inversion in one time-step.

As a matter of interest, in Chapter 5, we present a recursive implementation of the method of least squares. On account of using second-order information, recursive implementation of the method of least squares remains faster in its convergence behavior than the LMS algorithm.

3.12   VIRTUES AND LIMITATIONS OF THE LMS ALGORITHM

Computational Simplicity and Efficiency

Two virtues of the LMS algorithm are computational simplicity and efficiency, both of which are exemplified by the following summary of the algorithm presented in Table 3.1:

- Coding of the algorithm is composed of two or three lines, which is as simple as anyone could get.
- Computational complexity of the algorithm is linear in the number of adjustable parameters.

From a practical perspective, these are important virtues.

Robustness

Another important virtue of the LMS algorithm is that it is model independent and therefore *robust* with respect to disturbances. To explain what we mean by robustness, consider the situation depicted in Fig. 3.8, where a transfer operator $\mathcal{T}$ maps a couple of disturbances at its input into a "generic" estimation error at the output. Specifically, at the input, we have the following:

- An *initial weight-error vector* defined by

$$\delta \mathbf{w}(0) = \mathbf{w} - \hat{\mathbf{w}}(0) \tag{3.65}$$

where $\mathbf{w}$ is an unknown parameter vector and $\hat{\mathbf{w}}(0)$ is its "proposed" initial estimate at time $n = 0$. In the LMS algorithm, we typically set $\hat{\mathbf{w}}(0) = \mathbf{0}$, which, in a way, is the worst possible initializing condition for the algorithm.

- An *explanational error* ε that traces back to the regression model of Eq. (2.3), reproduced here for convenience of presentation, where d is the model output produced in response to the regressor $\mathbf{x}$:

$$d = \mathbf{w}^T \mathbf{x} + \varepsilon \tag{3.66}$$

Naturally, the operator $\mathcal{T}$ is a function of the strategy used to construct the estimate $\hat{\mathbf{w}}(n)$ (e.g., the LMS algorithm). We may now introduce the following definition:

The energy gain of the estimator is defined as the ratio of the error energy at the output of the operator $\mathcal{T}$ to the total disturbance energy at the input.

To remove this dependence and thereby make the estimator "model independent," we consider the scenario where we have the *largest possible energy gain over all conceivable disturbance sequences* applied to the estimator input. In so doing, we will have defined the H^∞ *norm* of the transfer operator $\mathcal{T}$.

With this brief background, we may now formulate what the H^∞ norm of the transfer operator $\mathcal{T}$ is about:

Find a causal estimator that minimizes the H^∞ norm of $\mathcal{T}$, where $\mathcal{T}$ is a transfer operator that maps the disturbances to the estimation errors.

The optimal estimator designed in accordance with the H^∞ criterion is said to be of a *minimax* kind. More specifically, we may view the H^∞ optimal estimation problem as a "game-theoretic problem" in the following sense: Nature, acting as the "opponent," has access to the unknown disturbances, thereby maximizing the energy gain. On the other hand, the "designer" of the estimation strategy has the task of finding a causal algorithm for which the error energy is minimized. Note that in introducing the idea of the H^∞ criterion, we made no assumptions about the disturbances indicated at the input of Fig. 3.8. We may therefore say that an estimator designed in accordance with the H^∞ criterion is a *worst-case estimator*.

Initial weight-error vector $\delta \mathbf{w}(0)$

Disturbance $\varepsilon(n)$

Transfer operator $\mathcal{T}$

Generic estimation error

FIGURE 3.8 Formulation of the optimal H^∞ estimation problem. The generic estimation error at the transfer operator's output could be the weight-error vector, the explanational error, etc.

In precise mathematical terms, the LMS algorithm is optimal in accordance with the H^∞ (or minimax) criterion.[5] The basic philosophy of optimality in the H^∞ sense is to cater to the worst-case scenario:

If you do not know what you are up against, plan for the worst scenario and optimize.

For a long time, the LMS algorithm was regarded as an instantaneous approximation to the gradient-descent algorithm. However, the H^∞ *optimality of LMS algorithm* provides this widely used algorithm with a rigorous footing. Moreover, the H^∞ theory of the LMS algorithm shows that the most robust performance of the algorithm is attained when the learning-rate parameter η is assigned a small value.

The model-independent behavior of the LMS algorithm also explains the ability of the algorithm to work satisfactorily in both a stationary and a nonstationary environment. By a "nonstationary" environment, we mean an environment in which the statistics vary with time. In such an environment, the optimum Wiener solution takes on a time-varying form, and the LMS algorithm has the additional task of *tracking* variations in the minimum mean-square error of the Wiener filter.

Factors Limiting the LMS Performance

The primary limitations of the LMS algorithm are its slow rate of convergence and its sensitivity to variations in the eigenstructure of the input (Haykin, 2002). The LMS algorithm typically requires a number of iterations equal to about 10 times the dimensionality of the input data space for it to reach a steady-state condition. The slow rate of convergence of the LMS algorithm becomes particularly serious when the dimensionality of the input data space becomes high.

As for sensitivity to changes in environmental conditions, convergence behavior of the LMS algorithm is particularly sensitive to variations in the *condition number*, or *eigenvalue spread*, of the correlation matrix $\mathbf{R}_{xx}$ of the input vector $\mathbf{x}$. The condition number of $\mathbf{R}_{xx}$, denoted by $\chi(\mathbf{R})$, is defined by

$$\chi(\mathbf{R}) = \frac{\lambda_{\max}}{\lambda_{\min}} \tag{3.67}$$

where $\lambda_{\max}$ and $\lambda_{\min}$ are the maximum and minimum eigenvalues of the correlation matrix $\mathbf{R}_{xx}$, respectively. The sensitivity of the LMS algorithm to variations in the condition number $\chi(\mathbf{R})$ becomes particularly acute when the training sample to which the input vector $\mathbf{x}(n)$ belongs is *ill conditioned*—that is, when the condition number of the LMS algorithm is high.[6]

3.13   LEARNING-RATE ANNEALING SCHEDULES

The slow-rate convergence encountered with the LMS algorithm may be attributed to the fact that the learning-rate parameter is maintained constant at some value η_0 throughout the computation, as shown by

$$\eta(n) = \eta_0 \qquad \text{for all } n \tag{3.68}$$

This is the simplest possible form the learning-rate parameter can assume. In contrast, in *stochastic approximation*, which goes back to the classic paper by Robbins and Monro (1951), the learning-rate parameter is time varying. The particular time-varying form most commonly used in the stochastic approximation literature is described by

$$\eta(n) = \frac{c}{n} \tag{3.69}$$

where c is a constant. Such a choice is indeed sufficient to guarantee convergence of the stochastic approximation algorithm (Kushner and Clark, 1978). However, when the constant c is large, there is a danger of parameter blowup for small n.

As an alternative to Eqs. (3.68) and (3.69), we may use the *search-then-converge schedule*, described by Darken and Moody (1992), as

$$\eta(n) = \frac{\eta_0}{1 + (n/\tau)} \tag{3.70}$$

where η_0 and τ are user-selected constants. In the early stages of adaptation involving a number of iterations n that is small compared with the *search-time constant* τ, the learning-rate parameter $\eta(n)$ is approximately equal to η_0, and the algorithm operates essentially as the "conventional" LMS algorithm, as indicated in Fig. 3.9. Hence, by choosing a high value for η_0 within the permissible range, we hope that the adjustable weights of the filter will find and hover about a "good" set of values. Then, for a number n of iterations that is large compared with the search-time constant τ, the learning-rate parameter $\eta(n)$

FIGURE 3.9   Learning-rate annealing schedules: The horizontal axis, printed in color, pertains to the standard LMS algorithm.

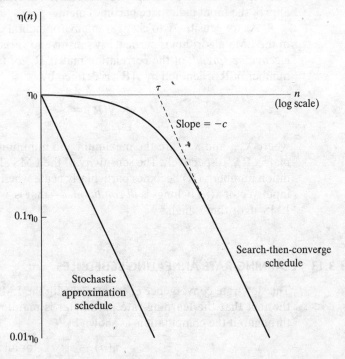

approximates as c/n, where $c = \tau\eta_0$, as illustrated in Fig. 3.9. The algorithm now operates as a traditional stochastic approximation algorithm, and the weights may converge
to their optimum values. Thus, the *search-then-converge schedule* has the potential to
combine the desirable features of the standard LMS algorithm with traditional stochastic approximation theory.

3.14   SUMMARY AND DISCUSSION

In this chapter, we studied the celebrated least-mean-square (LMS) algorithm, developed
by Widrow and Hoff in 1960. Since its inception, this algorithm has withstood the test
of time for a number of important practical reasons:

1. The algorithm is *simple* to formulate and just as simple to implement, be it in hardware or software form.
2. In spite of its simplicity, the algorithm is *effective* in performance.
3. Computationally speaking, the algorithm is *efficient* in that its complexity follows
   a *linear law* with respect to the number of adjustable parameters.
4. Last, but by no means least, the algorithm is model independent and therefore
   robust with respect to disturbances.

Under the assumption that the learning-rate parameter η is a small positive quantity, the convergence behavior of the LMS algorithm—usually difficult to analyze—
becomes mathematically tractable, thanks to Kushner's *direct-averaging method*. The
theoretical virtue of this method is that when η is small, the nonlinear "stochastic"
difference equation, which describes the convergence behavior of the LMS algorithm,
is replaced by a nonlinear "deterministic" version of the original equation. Moreover,
through the clever use of eigendecomposition, the solution of the resulting nonlinear
deterministic equation is replaced by a system of decoupled first-order difference
equations. The important point to note here is that the first-order difference equation
so derived is mathematically identical to the discrete-time version of the *Langevin
equation* of nonequilibrium thermodynamics. This equivalence explains the Brownian motion executed by the LMS algorithm around the optimum Wiener solution after
a large enough number of iterations. The computer experiment presented in Section
3.10 and other computer experiments presented in Haykin (2006) confirm the validity of Eq. (3.63), which describes the ensemble-averaged learning curve of the LMS
algorithm.

It is also noteworthy that the LMS algorithm exhibits its most robust performance
when the learning-rate parameter η is small. However, the price paid for this kind of practically important performance is a relatively slow rate of convergence. To some extent,
this limitation of the LMS algorithm can be alleviated through the use of learning-rate
annealing, as described in Section 3.13.

One last comment is in order. Throughout the chapter, we focused attention on the
ordinary LMS algorithm. Needless to say, the algorithm has several variants, each of
which offers a practical virtue of its own; for details, the interested reader is referred to
(Haykin, 2002).

NOTES AND REFERENCES

1. **Differentiation with respect to a vector**

   Let $f(\mathbf{w})$ denote a real-valued function of parameter vector $\mathbf{w}$. The derivative of $f(\mathbf{w})$ with respect to $\mathbf{w}$ is defined by the vector

   $$\frac{\partial f}{\partial \mathbf{w}} = \left[\frac{\partial f}{\partial w_1}, \frac{\partial f}{\partial w_2}, \ldots, \frac{\partial f}{\partial w_m} \right]^T$$

   where m is the dimension of vector $\mathbf{w}$. The following two cases are of special interest:

   Case 1 The function $f(\mathbf{w})$ is defined by the inner product:

   $$f(\mathbf{w}) = \mathbf{x}^T \mathbf{w}$$
   $$= \sum_{i=1}^{m} x_i w_i$$

   Hence,

   $$\frac{\partial f}{\partial w_i} = x_i, \qquad i = 1, 2, \ldots, m$$

   or, equivalently, in matrix form,

   $$\frac{\partial f}{\partial \mathbf{w}} = \mathbf{x} \tag{3.71}$$

   Case 2 The function $f(\mathbf{w})$ is defined by the quadratic form:

   $$f(\mathbf{w}) = \mathbf{w}^T \mathbf{R} \mathbf{w}$$
   $$= \sum_{i=1}^{m} \sum_{j=1}^{m} w_i r_{ij} w_j$$

   Here, r_{ij} is the ij-th element of the m-by-m matrix $\mathbf{R}$. Hence,

   $$\frac{\partial f}{\partial w_i} = 2 \sum_{j=1}^{m} r_{ij} w_j, \qquad i = 1, 2, \ldots, m$$

   or, equivalently, in matrix form,

   $$\frac{\partial f}{\partial \mathbf{w}} = 2\mathbf{R}\mathbf{w} \tag{3.72}$$

   Equations (3.71) and (3.72) provide two useful rules for the differentiation of a real-valued function with respect to a vector.

2. The pseudoinverse of a rectangular matrix is discussed in Golub and Van Loan (1996); see also Chapter 8 of Haykin (2002).

3. The Langevin equation is discussed in Reif (1965). For a fascinating historical account of the Langevin equation, see the tutorial paper on noise by Cohen (2005).

4. The orthogonality transformation described in Eq. (3.56) follows from the *eigendecomposition* of a square matrix. This topic is described in detail in Chapter 8.

5. For an early (and perhaps the first) motivational treatment of H^∞ control, the reader is referred to Zames (1981).

   The first exposition of optimality of the LMS algorithm in the H^∞ sense was presented in Hassibi et al. (1993). Hassibi et al. (1999) treat the H^∞ theory from an estimation or adaptive-filtering perspective. Hassibi also presents a condensed treatment of robustness of the LMS algorithm in the H^∞ sense in Chapter 5 of Haykin and Widrow (2005).

   For books on H^∞ theory from a control perspective, the reader is referred to Zhou and Doyle (1998) and Green and Limebeer (1995).

6. Sensitivity of convergence behavior of the LMS algorithm to variations in the condition number of the correlation matrix $\mathbf{R}_{xx}$, denoted by $\chi(\mathbf{R})$, is demonstrated experimentally in Section 5.7 of the book by Haykin (2002). In Chapter 9 of Haykin (2002), which deals with recursive implementation of the method of least squares, it is also shown that convergence behavior of the resulting algorithm is essentially independent of the condition number $\chi(\mathbf{R})$.

PROBLEMS

3.1 (a) Let $\mathbf{m}(n)$ denote the mean weight vector of the LMS algorithm at iteration n; that is,

$$\mathbf{m}(n) = \mathbb{E}[\hat{\mathbf{w}}(n)]$$

Using the small-learning-rate parameter theory of Section 3.9, show that

$$\mathbf{m}(n) = (\mathbf{I} - \eta\mathbf{R}_{xx})^n[\mathbf{m}(0) - \mathbf{m}(\infty)] + \mathbf{m}(\infty)$$

where η is the learning-rate parameter, $\mathbf{R}_{xx}$ is the correlation matrix of the input vector $\mathbf{x}(n)$, and $\mathbf{m}(0)$ and $\mathbf{m}(\infty)$ are the initial and final values of $\mathbf{m}(n)$, respectively.

(b) Show that for *convergence of the LMS algorithm in the mean*, the learning-rate parameter η must satisfy the condition

$$0 < \eta < \frac{2}{\lambda_{\max}}$$

where $\lambda_{\max}$ is the largest eigenvalue of the correlation matrix $\mathbf{R}_{xx}$.

3.2 Continuing from Problem 3.1, discuss why convergence of the LMS algorithm in the mean is not an adequate criterion for convergence in practice.

3.3 Discuss the two continuous processes involved in the operation of the adaptive filter. Why is the LMS algorithm considered better as compared to other adaptive-filtering algorithms?

3.4 In a variant of the LMS algorithm called the *leaky LMS algorithm*, the cost function to be minimized is defined by

$$\mathscr{E}(n) = \frac{1}{2}|e(n)|^2 + \frac{1}{2}\lambda\|\mathbf{w}(n)\|^2$$

where $\mathbf{w}(n)$ is the parameter vector, $e(n)$ is the estimation error, and λ is a constant. As in the ordinary LMS algorithm, we have

$$e(n) = d(n) - \mathbf{w}^T(n)\mathbf{x}(n)$$

where $d(n)$ is the desired response corresponding to the input vector $\mathbf{x}(n)$.

(a) Show that the time update for the parameter vector of the leaky LMS algorithm is defined by

$$\hat{\mathbf{w}}(n + 1) = (1 - \eta\lambda)\hat{\mathbf{w}}(n) + \eta\mathbf{x}(n)e(n)$$

which includes the ordinary LMS algorithm as a special case.

(b) Using the small learning-rate parameter theory of Section 3.9, show that

$$\lim_{x \to \infty} \mathbb{E}[\hat{\mathbf{w}}(n)] = (\mathbf{R}_{xx} + \lambda\mathbf{I})^{-1}\mathbf{r}_{dx}$$

where $\mathbf{R}_{xx}$ is the correlation matrix of $\mathbf{x}(n)$, $\mathbf{I}$ is the identity matrix, and $\mathbf{r}_{dx}$ is the cross-correlation vector between $\mathbf{x}(n)$ and $d(n)$.

3.5 Continuing from Problem 3.4, verify that the leaky LMS algorithm can be "simulated" by adding white noise to the input vector $\mathbf{x}(n)$.

(a) What should variance of this noise be for the condition in part (b) of Problem 3.4 to hold?

(b) When will the simulated algorithm take a form that is practically the same as the leaky LMS algorithm? Justify your answer.

3.6 An alternative to the mean-square error (MSE) formulation of the learning curve that we sometimes find in the literature is the *mean-square deviation* (MSD) *learning curve*. Define the weight-error vector

$$\boldsymbol{\varepsilon}(n) = \mathbf{w} - \hat{\mathbf{w}}(n)$$

where $\mathbf{w}$ is the parameter vector of the regression model supplying the desired response. This second learning curve is obtained by computing a plot of the MSD

$$D(n) = \mathbb{E}[\|\boldsymbol{\varepsilon}(n)\|^2]$$

versus the number of iterations n.

Using the small-learning-rate-parameter theory of Section 3.9, show that

$$D(\infty) = \lim_{n \to \infty} D(n)$$
$$= \frac{1}{2}\eta MJ_{\min}$$

where η is the learning-rate parameter, M is the size of the parameter vector $\hat{\mathbf{w}}$, and $J_{\min}$ is the minimum mean-square error of the LMS algorithm.

3.7 In this problem, we address a proof of the direct-averaging method, assuming ergodicity.

Start with Eq. (3.41), which defines the weight-error vector $\boldsymbol{\varepsilon}(n)$ in terms of the transition matrix $\mathbf{A}(n)$ and driving force $\mathbf{f}(n)$, which are themselves defined in terms of the input vector $\mathbf{x}(n)$ in Eqs. (3.42) and (3.43), respectively; then proceed as follows:

- Set $n = 0$, and evaluate $\boldsymbol{\varepsilon}(1)$.
- Set $n = 1$, and evaluate $\boldsymbol{\varepsilon}(2)$.
- Continue in this fashion for a few more iterations.

With these iterated values of $\boldsymbol{\varepsilon}(n)$ at hand, deduce a formula for the transition matrix $\mathbf{A}(n)$.

Next, assume that the learning-rate parameter η is small enough to justify retaining only the terms that are linear in η. Hence, show that

$$\mathbf{A}(n) = \mathbf{I} - \eta \sum_{i=1}^{n} \mathbf{x}(i)\mathbf{x}^T(i)$$

which, assuming ergodicity, takes the form

$$\overline{\mathbf{A}}(n) = \mathbf{I} - \mu \mathbf{R}_{xx}$$

3.8 **(a)** Differentiate between the steepest-descent algorithm and LMS algorithm.

   (b) Discuss the influence of the linear-rate parameter η on the performance and convergence rate of these two algorithms.

3.9 Starting with Eq. (3.55) for a small learning-rate parameter, show that under steady-state conditions, the *Lyapunov equation*

$$\mathbf{R}\mathbf{P}_0(n) + \mathbf{P}_0(n)\mathbf{R} = \eta \sum_{i=0}^{\infty} J_{\min}^{(i)} \mathbf{R}^{(i)}$$

holds, where we have

$$J_{\min}^{(i)} = \mathbb{E}[e_o(n)e_o(n - i)]$$

and

$$\mathbf{R}^{(i)} = \mathbb{E}[\mathbf{x}(n)\mathbf{x}^T(n - i)]$$

for $i = 0, 1, 2, \ldots$. The matrix $\mathbf{P}_0$ is defined by $\mathbb{E}[\boldsymbol{\varepsilon}_o(n)\boldsymbol{\varepsilon}_o^T(n)]$, and $e_o(n)$ is the irreducible estimation error produced by the Wiener filter.

Computer Experiments

3.10 Repeat the computer experiment of Section 3.10 on linear prediction for the following values of the learning-rate parameter:

   (i) $\eta = 0.002$;
   (ii) $\eta = 0.01$;
   (iii) $\eta = 0.02$.

   Comment on your findings in the context of applicability of the small-learning-rate-parameter theory of the LMS algorithm for each value of η.

3.11 Repeat the computer experiment of Section 3.11 on pattern classification for the distance of separation between the two moons of Fig. 1.8 set at $d = 0$. Compare the results of your experiment with those in Problem 1.6 on the perceptron and Problem 2.7 on the method of least squares.

3.12 Plot the pattern-classification learning curves of the LMS algorithm applied to the double-moon configuration of Fig. 1.8 for the following values assigned to the distance of separation:

   $d = 1$
   $d = 0$
   $d = -4$

   Compare the results of the experiment with the corresponding ones obtained using Rosenblatt's perceptron in Chapter 1.

CHAPTER 4

Multilayer Perceptrons

ORGANIZATION OF THE CHAPTER

In this chapter, we study the many facets of the multilayer perceptron, which stands for a neural network with one or more hidden layers. After the introductory material presented in Section 4.1, the study proceeds as follows:

1. Sections 4.2 through 4.7 discuss matters relating to back-propagation learning. We begin with some preliminaries in Section 4.2 to pave the way for the derivation of the back-propagation algorithm. This section also includes a discussion of the credit-assignment problem. In Section 4.3, we describe two methods of learning: batch and on-line. In Section 4.4, we present a detailed derivation of the back-propagation algorithm, using the chain rule of calculus; we take a traditional approach in this derivation. In Section 4.5, we illustrate the use of the back-propagation algorithm by solving the XOR problem, an interesting problem that cannot be solved by Rosenblatt's perceptron. Section 4.6 presents some heuristics and practical guidelines for making the back-propagation algorithm perform better. Section 4.7 presents a pattern-classification experiment on the multilayer perceptron trained with the back-propagation algorithm.

2. Sections 4.8 and 4.9 deal with the error surface. In Section 4.8, we discuss the fundamental role of back-propagation learning in computing partial derivatives of a network-approximating function. We then discuss computational issues relating to the Hessian of the error surface in Section 4.9. In Section 4.10, we discuss two issues: how to fulfill optimal annealing and how to make the learning-rate parameter adaptive.

3. Sections 4.11 through 4.14 focus on various matters relating to the performance of a multilayer perceptron trained with the back-propagation algorithm. In Section 4.11, we discuss the issue of generalization—the very essence of learning. Section 4.12 addresses the approximation of continuous functions by means of multiplayer perceptrons. The use of cross-validation as a statistical design tool is discussed in Section 4.13. In Section 4.14, we discuss the issue of complexity regularization, as well as network-pruning techniques.

4. Section 4.15, summarizes the advantages and limitations of back-propagation learning.

5. Having completed the study of back-propagation learning, we next take a different perspective on learning in Section 4.16 by viewing supervised learning as an optimization problem.

6. Section 4.17 describes an important neural network structure: the *convolutional multilayer perceptron*. This network has been successfully used in the solution of difficult pattern-recognition problems.

7. Section 4.18 deals with nonlinear filtering, where time plays a key role. The discussion begins with short-term memory structures, setting the stage for the universal myopic mapping theorem.

8. Section 4.19 discusses the issue of small-scale versus large-scale learning problems.

The chapter concludes with summary and discussion in Section 4.20.

4.1   INTRODUCTION

In Chapter 1, we studied Rosenblatt's perceptron, which is basically a single-layer neural network. Therein, we showed that this network is limited to the classification of linearly separable patterns. Then we studied adaptive filtering in Chapter 3, using Widrow and Hoff's LMS algorithm. This algorithm is also based on a single linear neuron with adjustable weights, which limits the computing power of the algorithm. To overcome the practical limitations of the perceptron and the LMS algorithm, we look to a neural network structure known as the *multilayer perceptron*.

The following three points highlight the basic features of multilayer perceptrons:

- The model of each neuron in the network includes a nonlinear activation function that is *differentiable*.
- The network contains one or more layers that are *hidden* from both the input and output nodes.
- The network exhibits a high degree of *connectivity*, the extent of which is determined by synaptic weights of the network.

These same characteristics, however, are also responsible for the deficiencies in our knowledge on the behavior of the network. First, the presence of a distributed form of nonlinearity and the high connectivity of the network make the theoretical analysis of a multilayer perceptron difficult to undertake. Second, the use of hidden neurons makes the learning process harder to visualize. In an implicit sense, the learning process must decide which features of the input pattern should be represented by the hidden neurons. The learning process is therefore made more difficult because the search has to be conducted in a much larger space of possible functions, and a choice has to be made between alternative representations of the input pattern.

A popular method for the training of multilayer perceptrons is the back-propagation algorithm, which includes the LMS algorithm as a special case. The training proceeds in two phases:

1. In the *forward phase*, the synaptic weights of the network are fixed and the input signal is propagated through the network, layer by layer, until it reaches the output. Thus, in this phase, changes are confined to the activation potentials and outputs of the neurons in the network.

2. In the *backward phase*, an error signal is produced by comparing the output of the network with a desired response. The resulting error signal is propagated through the network, again layer by layer, but this time the propagation is performed in the backward direction. In this second phase, successive adjustments are made to the synaptic weights of the network. Calculation of the adjustments for the output layer is straightforward, but it is much more challenging for the hidden layers.

Usage of the term "back propagation" appears to have evolved after 1985, when the term was popularized through the publication of the seminal book entitled *Parallel Distributed Processing* (Rumelhart and McClelland, 1986).

The development of the back-propagation algorithm in the mid-1980s represented a landmark in neural networks in that it provided a *computationally efficient* method for the training of multilayer perceptrons, putting to rest the pessimism about learning in multilayer perceptrons that may have been inferred from the book by Minsky and Papert (1969).

4.2 SOME PRELIMINARIES

Figure 4.1 shows the architectural graph of a multiplayer perceptron with two hidden layers and an output layer. To set the stage for a description of the multilayer perceptron in its general form, the network shown here is *fully connected*. This means that a neuron in any layer of the network is connected to all the neurons (nodes) in the previous layer. Signal flow through the network progresses in a forward direction, from left to right and on a layer-by-layer basis.

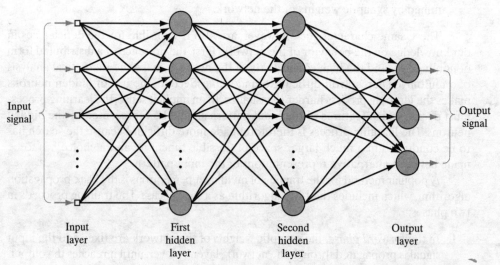

Input
signal

Output
signal

Input
layer

First
hidden
layer

Second
hidden
layer

Output
layer

FIGURE 4.1   Architectural graph of a multilayer perceptron with two hidden layers.

Figure 4.2 depicts a portion of the multilayer perceptron. Two kinds of signals are identified in this network:

1. *Function Signals.* A function signal is an input signal (stimulus) that comes in at the input end of the network, propagates forward (neuron by neuron) through the network, and emerges at the output end of the network as an output signal. We refer to such a signal as a "function signal" for two reasons. First, it is presumed to perform a useful function at the output of the network. Second, at each neuron of the network through which a function signal passes, the signal is calculated as a function of the inputs and associated weights applied to that neuron. The function signal is also referred to as the input signal.

2. *Error Signals.* An error signal originates at an output neuron of the network and propagates backward (layer by layer) through the network. We refer to it as an "error signal" because its computation by every neuron of the network involves an error-dependent function in one form or another.

The output neurons constitute the output layer of the network. The remaining neurons constitute hidden layers of the network. Thus, the hidden units are not part of the output or input of the network—hence their designation as "hidden." The first hidden layer is fed from the input layer made up of sensory units (source nodes); the resulting outputs of the first hidden layer are in turn applied to the next hidden layer; and so on for the rest of the network.

Each hidden or output neuron of a multilayer perceptron is designed to perform two computations:

1. the computation of the function signal appearing at the output of each neuron, which is expressed as a continuous nonlinear function of the input signal and synaptic weights associated with that neuron;

2. the computation of an estimate of the gradient vector (i.e., the gradients of the error surface with respect to the weights connected to the inputs of a neuron), which is needed for the backward pass through the network.

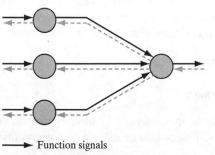

FIGURE 4.2   Illustration of the directions of two basic signal flows in a multilayer perceptron: forward propagation of function signals and back propagation of error signals.

Function signals

Error signals

Function of the Hidden Neurons

The hidden neurons act as *feature detectors*; as such, they play a critical role in the operation of a multilayer perceptron. As the learning process progresses across the multilayer perceptron, the hidden neurons begin to gradually "discover" the salient features that characterize the training data. They do so by performing a nonlinear transformation on the input data into a new space called the *feature space*. In this new space, the classes of interest in a pattern-classification task, for example, may be more easily separated from each other than could be the case in the original input data space. Indeed, it is the formation of this feature space through supervised learning that distinguishes the multilayer perceptron from Rosenblatt's perceptron.

Credit-Assignment Problem

When studying learning algorithms for distributed systems, exemplified by the multilayer perceptron of Figure 4.1, it is instructive to pay attention to the notion of *credit assignment*. Basically, the credit-assignment problem is the problem of assigning *credit* or *blame* for overall outcomes to each of the *internal decisions* made by the hidden computational units of the distributed learning system, recognizing that those decisions are responsible for the overall outcomes in the first place.

In a multilayer perceptron using *error-correlation learning*, the credit-assignment problem arises because the operation of each hidden neuron and of each output neuron in the network is important to the network's correct overall action on a learning task of interest. That is, in order to solve the prescribed task, the network must assign certain forms of behavior to all of its neurons through a specification of the error-correction learning algorithm. With this background, consider the multilayer perceptron depicted in Fig. 4.1. Since each output neuron is visible to the outside world, it is possible to supply a desired response to guide the behavior of such a neuron. Thus, as far as output neurons are concerned, it is a straightforward matter to adjust the synaptic weights of each output neuron in accordance with the error-correction algorithm. But how do we assign credit or blame for the action of the hidden neurons when the error-correction learning algorithm is used to adjust the respective synaptic weights of these neurons? The answer to this fundamental question requires more detailed attention than in the case of output neurons.

In what follows in this chapter, we show that the back-propagation algorithm, basic to the training of a multilayer perceptron, solves the credit-assignment problem in an elegant manner. But before proceeding to do that, we describe two basic methods of supervised learning in the next section.

4.3   BATCH LEARNING AND ON-LINE LEARNING

Consider a multilayer perceptron with an input layer of source nodes, one or more hidden layers, and an output layer consisting of one or more neurons; as illustrated in Fig. 4.1. Let

$$\mathcal{T} = \{\mathbf{x}(n), \mathbf{d}(n)\}_{n=1}^{N} \qquad (4.1)$$

denote the *training sample* used to train the network in a supervised manner. Let $y_j(n)$ denote the function signal produced at the output of neuron j in the output layer by the stimulus $\mathbf{x}(n)$ applied to the input layer. Correspondingly, the *error signal* produced at the output of neuron j is defined by

$$e_j(n) = d_j(n) - y_j(n) \tag{4.2}$$

where $d_j(n)$ is the ith element of the desired-response vector $\mathbf{d}(n)$. Following the terminology of the LMS algorithm studied in Chapter 3, the *instantaneous error energy* of neuron j is defined by

$$\mathscr{E}_j(n) = \frac{1}{2}e_j^2(n) \tag{4.3}$$

Summing the error-energy contributions of all the neurons in the output layer, we express the *total instantaneous error energy* of the whole network as

$$\mathscr{E}(n) = \sum_{j \in C} \mathscr{E}_j(n)$$

$$= \frac{1}{2}\sum_{j \in C} e_j^2(n) \tag{4.4}$$

where the set C includes all the neurons in the output layer. With the training sample consisting of N examples, the *error energy averaged over the training sample*, or the *empirical risk*, is defined by

$$\mathscr{E}_{av}(N) = \frac{1}{N}\sum_{n=1}^{N} \mathscr{E}(n)$$

$$= \frac{1}{2N}\sum_{n=1}^{N}\sum_{j \in C} e_j^2(n) \tag{4.5}$$

Naturally, the instantaneous error energy, and therefore the average error energy, are both functions of all the adjustable synaptic weights (i.e., free parameters) of the multilayer perceptron. This functional dependence has not been included in the formulas for $\mathscr{E}(n)$ and $\mathscr{E}_{av}(N)$, merely to simplify the terminology.

Depending on how the supervised learning of the multilayer perceptron is actually performed, we may identify two different methods—namely, batch learning and on-line learning, as discussed next in the context of gradient descent.

Batch Learning

In the batch method of supervised learning, adjustments to the synaptic weights of the multilayer perceptron are performed *after* the presentation of *all* the N examples in the training sample $\mathscr{T}$ that constitute one *epoch* of training. In other words, the cost function for batch learning is defined by the average error energy $\mathscr{E}_{av}$. Adjustments to the synaptic weights of the multilayer perceptron are made on an *epoch-by-epoch basis*. Correspondingly, one realization of the learning curve is obtained by plotting $\mathscr{E}_{av}$ versus the number of epochs, where, for each epoch of training, the examples in the training sample $\mathcal{T}$ are *randomly shuffled*. The learning curve is then computed by *ensemble averaging* a large enough number of such realizations, where each realization is performed for a *different set of initial conditions* chosen at random.

With the method of gradient descent used to perform the training, the advantages of batch learning include the following:

- *accurate estimation* of the gradient vector (i.e., the derivative of the cost function $\mathcal{E}_{av}$ with respect to the weight vector $\mathbf{w}$), thereby guaranteeing, under simple conditions, convergence of the method of steepest descent to a local minimum;
- *parallelization* of the learning process.

However, from a practical perspective, batch learning is rather demanding in terms of *storage requirements*.

In a statistical context, batch learning may be viewed as a form of *statistical inference*. It is therefore well suited for solving *nonlinear regression problems*.

On-line Learning

In the on-line method of supervised learning, adjustments to the synaptic weights of the multilayer perceptron are performed on an *example-by-example basis*. The cost function to be minimized is therefore the total instantaneous error energy $\mathcal{E}(n)$.

Consider an epoch of N training examples arranged in the order $\{\mathbf{x}(1), \mathbf{d}(1)\}, \{\mathbf{x}(2), \mathbf{d}(2)\}, ..., \{\mathbf{x}(N), \mathbf{d}(N)\}$. The first example pair $\{\mathbf{x}(1), \mathbf{d}(1)\}$ in the epoch is presented to the network, and the weight adjustments are performed using the method of gradient descent. Then the second example $\{\mathbf{x}(2), \mathbf{d}(2)\}$ in the epoch is presented to the network, which leads to further adjustments to weights in the network. This procedure is continued until the last example $\{\mathbf{x}(N), \mathbf{d}(N)\}$ is accounted for. Unfortunately, such a procedure works against the parallalization of on-line learning.

For a given set of initial conditions, a single realization of the learning curve is obtained by plotting the final value $\mathcal{E}(N)$ versus the number of epochs used in the training session, where, as before, the training examples are randomly shuffled after each epoch. As with batch learning, the learning curve for on-line learning is computed by ensemble averaging such realizations over a large enough number of initial conditions chosen at random. Naturally, for a given network structure, the learning curve obtained under on-line learning will be quite different from that under batch learning.

Given that the training examples are presented to the network in a random manner, the use of on-line learning makes the search in the multidimensional weight space *stochastic* in nature; it is for this reason that the method of on-line learning is sometimes referred to as a *stochastic method*. This stochasticity has the desirable effect of making it less likely for the learning process to be trapped in a local minimum, which is a definite advantage of on-line learning over batch learning. Another advantage of on-line learning is the fact that it requires much less storage than batch learning.

Moreover, when the training data are *redundant* (i.e., the training sample $\mathcal{T}$ contains several copies of the same example), we find that, unlike batch learning, on-line learning is able to take advantage of this redundancy because the examples are presented one at a time.

Another useful property of on-line learning is its ability to *track small changes* in the training data, particularly when the environment responsible for generating the data is nonstationary.

To summarize, despite the disadvantages of on-line learning, it is highly popular for solving *pattern-classification problems* for two important practical reasons:

- On-line learning is simple to implement.
- It provides effective solutions to large-scale and difficult pattern-classification problems.

It is for these two reasons that much of the material presented in this chapter is devoted to on-line learning.

4.4   THE BACK-PROPAGATION ALGORITHM

The popularity of on-line learning for the supervised training of multilayer perceptrons has been further enhanced by the development of the back-propagation algorithm. To describe this algorithm, consider Fig. 4.3, which depicts neuron j being fed by a set of

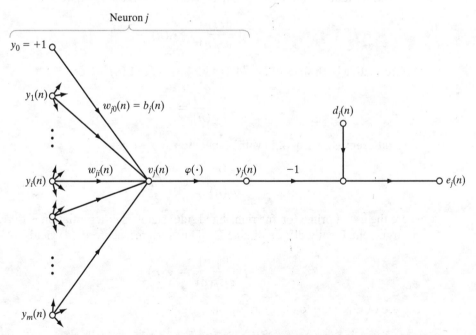

FIGURE 4.3   Signal-flow graph highlighting the details of output neuron j.

function signals produced by a layer of neurons to its left. The induced local field $v_j(n)$ produced at the input of the activation function associated with neuron j is therefore

$$v_j(n) = \sum_{i=0}^{m} w_{ji}(n)y_i(n) \tag{4.6}$$

where m is the total number of inputs (excluding the bias) applied to neuron j. The synaptic weight w_{j0} (corresponding to the fixed input $y_0 = +1$) equals the bias b_j applied to neuron j. Hence, the function signal $y_j(n)$ appearing at the output of neuron j at iteration n is

$$y_j(n) = \varphi_j(v_j(n)) \tag{4.7}$$

In a manner similar to the LMS algorithm studied in Chapter 3, the back-propagation algorithm applies a correction $\Delta w_{ji}(n)$ to the synaptic weight $w_{ji}(n)$, which is proportional to the partial derivative $\partial \mathscr{E}(n)/\partial w_{ji}(n)$. According to the *chain rule* of calculus, we may express this gradient as

$$\frac{\partial \mathscr{E}(n)}{\partial w_{ji}(n)} = \frac{\partial \mathscr{E}(n)}{\partial e_j(n)} \frac{\partial e_j(n)}{\partial y_j(n)} \frac{\partial y_j(n)}{\partial v_j(n)} \frac{\partial v_j(n)}{\partial w_{ji}(n)} \tag{4.8}$$

The partial derivative $\partial \mathscr{E}(n)/\partial w_{ji}(n)$ represents a *sensitivity factor*, determining the direction of search in weight space for the synaptic weight w_{ji}.

Differentiating both sides of Eq. (4.4) with respect to $e_j(n)$, we get

$$\frac{\partial \mathscr{E}(n)}{\partial e_j(n)} = e_j(n) \tag{4.9}$$

Differentiating both sides of Eq. (4.2) with respect to $y_j(n)$, we get

$$\frac{\partial e_j(n)}{\partial y_j(n)} = -1 \tag{4.10}$$

Next, differentiating Eq. (4.7) with respect to $v_j(n)$, we get

$$\frac{\partial y_j(n)}{\partial v_j(n)} = \varphi_j'(v_j(n)) \tag{4.11}$$

where the use of prime (on the right-hand side) signifies differentiation with respect to the argument. Finally, differentiating Eq. (4.6) with respect to $w_{ji}(n)$ yields

$$\frac{\partial v_j(n)}{\partial w_{ji}(n)} = y_i(n) \tag{4.12}$$

The use of Eqs. (4.9) to (4.12) in Eq. (4.8) yields

$$\frac{\partial \mathscr{E}(n)}{\partial w_{ji}(n)} = -e_j(n)\varphi_j'(v_j(n))y_i(n) \tag{4.13}$$

The correction $\Delta w_{ji}(n)$ applied to $w_{ji}(n)$ is defined by the *delta rule*, or

$$\Delta w_{ji}(n) = -\eta \frac{\partial \mathscr{E}(n)}{\partial w_{ji}(n)} \tag{4.14}$$

where η is the *learning-rate parameter* of the back-propagation algorithm. The use of the minus sign in Eq. (4.14) accounts for *gradient descent* in weight space (i.e., seeking a direction for weight change that reduces the value of $\mathscr{E}(n)$). Accordingly, the use of Eq. (4.13) in Eq. (4.14) yields

$$\Delta w_{ji}(n) = \eta \delta_j(n) y_i(n) \tag{4.15}$$

where the *local gradient* $\delta_j(n)$ is defined by

$$\begin{aligned}
\delta_j(n) &= \frac{\partial \mathscr{E}(n)}{\partial v_j(n)} \\
&= \frac{\partial \mathscr{E}(n)}{\partial e_j(n)} \frac{\partial e_j(n)}{\partial y_j(n)} \frac{\partial y_j(n)}{\partial v_j(n)} \\
&= e_j(n) \varphi_j'(v_j(n)) \tag{4.16}
\end{aligned}$$

The local gradient points to required changes in synaptic weights. According to Eq. (4.16), the local gradient $\delta_j(n)$ for output neuron j is equal to the product of the corresponding error signal $e_j(n)$ for that neuron and the derivative $\varphi_j'(v_j(n))$ of the associated activation function.

From Eqs. (4.15) and (4.16), we note that a key factor involved in the calculation of the weight adjustment $\Delta w_{ji}(n)$ is the error signal $e_j(n)$ at the output of neuron j. In this context, we may identify two distinct cases, depending on where in the network neuron j is located. In case 1, neuron j is an output node. This case is simple to handle because each output node of the network is supplied with a desired response of its own, making it a straightforward matter to calculate the associated error signal. In case 2, neuron j is a hidden node. Even though hidden neurons are not directly accessible, they share responsibility for any error made at the output of the network. The question, however, is to know how to penalize or reward hidden neurons for their share of the responsibility. This problem is the *credit-assignment problem* considered in Section 4.2.

Case 1   Neuron j Is an Output Node

When neuron j is located in the output layer of the network, it is supplied with a desired response of its own. We may use Eq. (4.2) to compute the error signal $e_j(n)$ associated with this neuron; see Fig. 4.3. Having determined $e_j(n)$, we find it a straightforward matter to compute the local gradient $\delta_j(n)$ by using Eq. (4.16).

Case 2   Neuron j Is a Hidden Node

When neuron j is located in a hidden layer of the network, there is no specified desired response for that neuron. Accordingly, the error signal for a hidden neuron would have to be determined recursively and working backwards in terms of the error signals of all the neurons to which that hidden neuron is directly connected; this is where the development of the back-propagation algorithm gets complicated. Consider the situation in Fig. 4.4, which depicts neuron j as a hidden node of the network. According to Eq. (4.16), we may redefine the local gradient $\delta_j(n)$ for hidden neuron j as

$$\delta_j(n) = -\frac{\partial \mathcal{E}(n)}{\partial y_j(n)} \frac{\partial y_j(n)}{\partial v_j(n)}$$

$$= -\frac{\partial \mathcal{E}(n)}{\partial y_j(n)} \varphi_j'(v_j(n)), \qquad \text{neuron } j \text{ is hidden} \qquad (4.17)$$

where in the second line we have used Eq. (4.11). To calculate the partial derivative $\partial \mathcal{E}(n)/\partial y_j(n)$, we may proceed as follows: From Fig. 4.4, we see that

$$\mathcal{E}(n) = \frac{1}{2} \sum_{k \in C} e_k^2(n), \qquad \text{neuron } k \text{ is an output node} \qquad (4.18)$$

which is Eq. (4.4) with index k used in place of index j. We have made this substitution in order to avoid confusion with the use of index j that refers to a hidden neuron under case 2. Differentiating Eq. (4.18) with respect to the function signal $y_j(n)$, we get

$$\frac{\partial \mathcal{E}(n)}{\partial y_j(n)} = \sum_k e_k \frac{\partial e_k(n)}{\partial y_j(n)} \qquad (4.19)$$

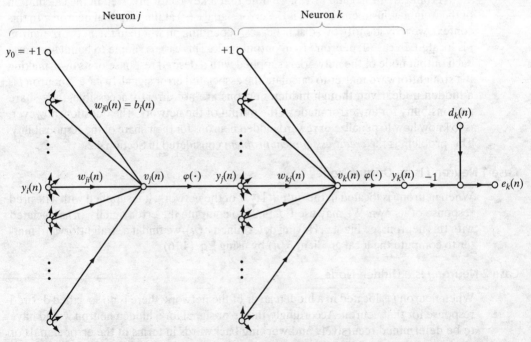

FIGURE 4.4 Signal-flow graph highlighting the details of output neuron k connected to hidden neuron j.

Next we use the chain rule for the partial derivative $\partial e_k(n)/\partial y_j(n)$ and rewrite Eq. (4.19) in the equivalent form

$$\frac{\partial \mathscr{E}(n)}{\partial y_j(n)} = \sum_k e_k(n) \frac{\partial e_k(n)}{\partial v_k(n)} \frac{\partial v_k(n)}{\partial y_j(n)} \tag{4.20}$$

However, from Fig. 4.4, we note that

$$e_k(n) = d_k(n) - y_k(n)$$
$$= d_k(n) - \varphi_k(v_k(n)), \qquad \text{neuron } k \text{ is an output node} \tag{4.21}$$

Hence,

$$\frac{\partial e_k(n)}{\partial v_k(n)} = -\varphi_k'(v_k(n)) \tag{4.22}$$

We also note from Fig. 4.4 that for neuron k, the induced local field is

$$v_k(n) = \sum_{j=0}^{m} w_{kj}(n) y_j(n) \tag{4.23}$$

where m is the total number of inputs (excluding the bias) applied to neuron k. Here again, the synaptic weight $w_{k0}(n)$ is equal to the bias $b_k(n)$ applied to neuron k, and the corresponding input is fixed at the value $+1$. Differentiating Eq. (4.23) with respect to $y_j(n)$ yields

$$\frac{\partial v_k(n)}{\partial y_j(n)} = w_{kj}(n) \tag{4.24}$$

By using Eqs. (4.22) and (4.24) in Eq. (4.20), we get the desired partial derivative

$$\frac{\partial \mathscr{E}(n)}{\partial y_j(n)} = -\sum_k e_k(n) \varphi_k'(v_k(n)) w_{kj}(n) \tag{4.25}$$
$$= -\sum_k \delta_k(n) w_{kj}(n)$$

where, in the second line, we have used the definition of the local gradient $\delta_k(n)$ given in Eq. (4.16), with the index k substituted for j.

Finally, using Eq. (4.25) in Eq. (4.17), we get the *back-propagation formula* for the local gradient $\delta_j(n)$, described by

$$\delta_j(n) = \varphi_j'(v_j(n)) \sum_k \delta_k(n) w_{kj}(n), \qquad \text{neuron } j \text{ is hidden} \tag{4.26}$$

Figure 4.5 shows the signal-flow graph representation of Eq. (4.26), assuming that the output layer consists of m_L neurons.

The outside factor $\varphi_j'(v_j(n))$ involved in the computation of the local gradient $\delta_j(n)$ in Eq. (4.26) depends solely on the activation function associated with hidden neuron j. The remaining factor involved in this computation—namely, the summation over k—depends on two sets of terms. The first set of terms, the $\delta_k(n)$, requires knowledge of the error

FIGURE 4.5   Signal-flow
graph of a part of the adjoint
system pertaining to back-
propagation of error signals.

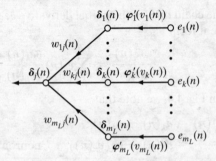

signals $e_k(n)$ for all neurons that lie in the layer to the immediate right of hidden neuron j and that are directly connected to neuron j; see Fig. 4.4. The second set of terms,
the $w_{kj}(n)$, consists of the synaptic weights associated with these connections.

We now summarize the relations that we have derived for the back-propagation
algorithm. First, the correction $\Delta w_{ji}(n)$ applied to the synaptic weight connecting neuron i to neuron j is defined by the delta rule:

$$
\begin{pmatrix} Weight \\ correction \\ \Delta w_{ji}(n) \end{pmatrix} = \begin{pmatrix} learning\text{-} \\ rate\ parameter \\ \eta \end{pmatrix} \times \begin{pmatrix} local \\ gradient \\ \delta_j(n) \end{pmatrix} \times \begin{pmatrix} input\ signal \\ of\ neuron\ j, \\ y_i(n) \end{pmatrix} \quad (4.27)
$$

Second, the local gradient $\delta_j(n)$ depends on whether neuron j is an output node or a
hidden node:

1. If neuron j is an output node, $\delta_j(n)$ equals the product of the derivative $\varphi_j'(v_j(n))$
   and the error signal $e_j(n)$, both of which are associated with neuron j; see Eq. (4.16).
2. If neuron j is a hidden node, $\delta_j(n)$ equals the product of the associated derivative
   $\varphi_j'(v_j(n))$ and the weighted sum of the δs computed for the neurons in the next
   hidden or output layer that are connected to neuron j; see Eq. (4.26).

The Two Passes of Computation

In the application of the back-propagation algorithm, two different passes of computation are distinguished. The first pass is referred to as the forward pass, and the second
is referred to as the backward pass.

In the *forward pass*, the synaptic weights remain unaltered throughout the network, and the function signals of the network are computed on a neuron-by-neuron
basis. The function signal appearing at the output of neuron j is computed as

$$
y_j(n) = \varphi(v_j(n)) \quad (4.28)
$$

where $v_j(n)$ is the induced local field of neuron j, defined by

$$
v_j(n) = \sum_{i=0}^{m} w_{ji}(n)y_i(n) \quad (4.29)
$$

where m is the total number of inputs (excluding the bias) applied to neuron j; $w_{ji}(n)$ is the synaptic weight connecting neuron i to neuron j; and $y_i(n)$ is an input signal of neuron j, or, equivalently, the function signal appearing at the output of neuron i. If neuron j is in the first hidden layer of the network, then $m = m_0$ and the index i refers to the ith input terminal of the network, for which we write

$$y_i(n) = x_i(n) \tag{4.30}$$

where $x_i(n)$ is the ith element of the input vector (pattern). If, on the other hand, neuron j is in the output layer of the network, then $m = m_L$ and the index j refers to the jth output terminal of the network, for which we write

$$y_j(n) = o_j(n) \tag{4.31}$$

where $o_j(n)$ is the jth element of the output vector of the multilayer perceptron. This output is compared with the desired response $d_j(n)$, obtaining the error signal $e_j(n)$ for the jth output neuron. Thus, the forward phase of computation begins at the first hidden layer by presenting it with the input vector and terminates at the output layer by computing the error signal for each neuron of this layer.

The backward pass, on the other hand, starts at the output layer by passing the error signals leftward through the network, layer by layer, and recursively computing the δ (i.e., the local gradient) for each neuron. This recursive process permits the synaptic weights of the network to undergo changes in accordance with the delta rule of Eq. (4.27). For a neuron located in the output layer, the δ is simply equal to the error signal of that neuron multiplied by the first derivative of its nonlinearity. Hence, we use Eq. (4.27) to compute the changes to the weights of all the connections feeding into the output layer. Given the δs for the neurons of the output layer, we next use Eq. (4.26) to compute the δs for all the neurons in the penultimate layer and therefore the changes to the weights of all connections feeding into it. The recursive computation is continued, layer by layer, by propagating the changes to all synaptic weights in the network.

Note that for the presentation of each training example, the input pattern is fixed—that is, "clamped" throughout the round-trip process, which encompasses the forward pass followed by the backward pass.

Activation Function

The computation of the δ for each neuron of the multilayer perceptron requires knowledge of the derivative of the activation function $\varphi(\cdot)$ associated with that neuron. For this derivative to exist, we require the function $\varphi(\cdot)$ to be continuous. In basic terms, *differentiability* is the only requirement that an activation function has to satisfy. An example of a continuously differentiable nonlinear activation function commonly used in multilayer perceptrons is *sigmoidal nonlinearity*,[1] two forms of which are described here:

1. *Logistic Function.* This form of sigmoidal nonlinearity, in its general form, is defined by

$$\varphi_j(v_j(n)) = \frac{1}{1 + \exp(-av_j(n))}, \quad a > 0 \tag{4.32}$$

where $v_j(n)$ is the induced local field of neuron j and a is an adjustable positive parameter. According to this nonlinearity, the amplitude of the output lies inside the range $0 \leq y_j \leq 1$. Differentiating Eq. (4.32) with respect to $v_j(n)$, we get

$$\varphi_j'(v_j(n)) = \frac{a \exp(-av_j(n))}{[1 + \exp(-av_j(n))]^2} \qquad (4.33)$$

With $y_j(n) = \varphi_j(v_j(n))$, we may eliminate the exponential term $\exp(-av_j(n))$ from Eq. (4.33) and consequently express the derivative $\varphi_j'(v_j(n))$ as

$$\varphi_j'(v_j(n)) = ay_j(n)[1 - y_j(n)] \qquad (4.34)$$

For a neuron j located in the output layer, $y_j(n) = o_j(n)$. Hence, we may express the local gradient for neuron j as

$$\begin{aligned} \delta_j(n) &= e_j(n)\varphi_j'(v_j(n)) \\ &= a[d_j(n) - o_j(n)]o_j(n)[1 - o_j(n)], \qquad \text{neuron } j \text{ is an output node} \end{aligned} \qquad (4.35)$$

where $o_j(n)$ is the function signal at the output of neuron j, and $d_j(n)$ is the desired response for it. On the other hand, for an arbitrary hidden neuron j, we may express the local gradient as

$$\begin{aligned} \delta_j(n) &= \varphi_j'(v_j(n)) \sum_k \delta_k(n) w_{kj}(n) \\ &= ay_j(n)[1 - y_j(n)] \sum_k \delta_k(n) w_{kj}(n), \qquad \text{neuron } j \text{ is hidden} \end{aligned} \qquad (4.36)$$

Note from Eq. (4.34) that the derivative $\varphi_j'(v_j(n))$ attains its maximum value at $y_j(n) = 0.5$ and its minimum value (zero) at $y_j(n) = 0$, or $y_j(n) = 1.0$. Since the amount of change in a synaptic weight of the network is proportional to the derivative $\varphi_j'(v_j(n))$, it follows that for a sigmoid activation function, the synaptic weights are changed the most for those neurons in the network where the function signals are in their midrange. According to Rumelhart et al. (1986a), it is this feature of back-propagation learning that contributes to its stability as a learning algorithm.

2. *Hyperbolic tangent function.* Another commonly used form of sigmoidal nonlinearity is the hyperbolic tangent function, which, in its most general form, is defined by

$$\varphi_j(v_j(n)) = a \tanh(bv_j(n)) \qquad (4.37)$$

where a and b are positive constants. In reality, the hyperbolic tangent function is just the logistic function rescaled and biased. Its derivative with respect to $v_j(n)$ is given by

$$\begin{aligned} \varphi_j'(v_j(n)) &= ab \operatorname{sech}^2(bv_j(n)) \\ &= ab(1 - \tanh^2(bv_j(n))) \\ &= \frac{b}{a}[a - y_j(n)][a + y_j(n)] \end{aligned} \qquad (4.38)$$

For a neuron j located in the output layer, the local gradient is

$$\delta_j(n) = e_j(n)\varphi_j'(v_j(n))$$

$$= \frac{b}{a}[d_j(n) - o_j(n)][a - o_j(n)][a + o_j(n)] \qquad (4.39)$$

For a neuron j in a hidden layer, we have

$$\delta_j(n) = \varphi_j'(v_j(n))\sum_k \delta_k(n)w_{kj}(n)$$

$$= \frac{b}{a}[a - y_j(n)][a + y_j(n)]\sum_k \delta_k(n)w_{kj}(n), \qquad \text{neuron } j \text{ is hidden} \qquad (4.40)$$

By using Eqs. (4.35) and (4.36) for the logistic function and Eqs. (4.39) and (4.40) for the hyperbolic tangent function, we may calculate the local gradient δ_j without requiring explicit knowledge of the activation function.

Rate of Learning

The back-propagation algorithm provides an "approximation" to the trajectory in weight space computed by the method of steepest descent. The smaller we make the learning-rate parameter η, the smaller the changes to the synaptic weights in the network will be from one iteration to the next, and the smoother will be the trajectory in weight space. This improvement, however, is attained at the cost of a slower rate of learning. If, on the other hand, we make the learning-rate parameter η too large in order to speed up the rate of learning, the resulting large changes in the synaptic weights assume such a form that the network may become unstable (i.e., oscillatory). A simple method of increasing the rate of learning while avoiding the danger of instability is to modify the delta rule of Eq. (4.15) by including a momentum term, as shown by

$$\Delta w_{ji}(n) = \alpha \Delta w_{ji}(n-1) + \eta \delta_j(n)y_i(n) \qquad (4.41)$$

where α is usually a positive number called the *momentum constant*. It controls the feedback loop acting around $\Delta w_{ji}(n)$, as illustrated in Fig. 4.6, where z^{-1} is the unit-time delay operator. Equation (4.41) is called the *generalized delta rule*[2]; it includes the delta rule of Eq. (4.15) as a special case (i.e., $\alpha = 0$).

In order to see the effect of the sequence of pattern presentations on the synaptic weights due to the momentum constant α, we rewrite Eq. (4.41) as a time series with index t. The index t goes from the initial time 0 to the current time n. Equation (4.41)

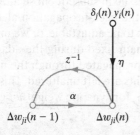

$\delta_j(n)\, y_i(n)$

z^{-1}

η

α

$\Delta w_{ji}(n-1)$

$\Delta w_{ji}(n)$

FIGURE 4.6   Signal-flow graph illustrating the effect of momentum constant α, which lies inside the feedback loop.

may be viewed as a first-order difference equation in the weight correction $\Delta w_{ji}(n)$. Solving this equation for $\Delta w_{ji}(n)$, we have

$$\Delta w_{ji}(n) = \eta \sum_{t=0}^{n} \alpha^{n-t} \delta_j(t) y_i(t) \tag{4.42}$$

which represents a time series of length $n + 1$. From Eqs. (4.13) and (4.16), we note that the product $\delta_j(n)y_i(n)$ is equal to $-\partial \mathscr{E}(n)/\partial w_{ji}(n)$. Accordingly, we may rewrite Eq. (4.42) in the equivalent form

$$\Delta w_{ji}(n) = -\eta \sum_{t=0}^{n} \alpha^{n-t} \frac{\partial \mathscr{E}(t)}{\partial w_{ji}(t)} \tag{4.43}$$

Based on this relation, we may make the following insightful observations:

1. The current adjustment $\Delta w_{ji}(n)$ represents the sum of an exponentially weighted time series. For the time series to be *convergent*, the momentum constant must be restricted to the range $0 \leq |\alpha| < 1$. When α is zero, the back-propagation algorithm operates without momentum. Also, the momentum constant α can be positive or negative, although it is unlikely that a negative α would be used in practice.

2. When the partial derivative $\partial \mathscr{E}(t)/\partial w_{ji}(t)$ has the same algebraic sign on consecutive iterations, the exponentially weighted sum $\Delta w_{ji}(n)$ grows in magnitude, and consequently the weight $w_{ji}(n)$ is adjusted by a large amount. The inclusion of momentum in the back-propagation algorithm tends to *accelerate descent* in steady downhill directions.

3. When the partial derivative $\partial \mathscr{E}(t)/\partial w_{ji}(t)$ has opposite signs on consecutive iterations, the exponentially weighted sum $\Delta w_{ji}(n)$ shrinks in magnitude, and consequently the weight $w_{ji}(n)$ is adjusted by a small amount. The inclusion of momentum in the back-propagation algorithm has a *stabilizing effect* in directions that oscillate in sign.

The incorporation of momentum in the back-propagation algorithm represents a minor modification to the weight update; however, it may have some beneficial effects on the learning behavior of the algorithm. The momentum term may also have the benefit of preventing the learning process from terminating in a shallow local minimum on the error surface.

In deriving the back-propagation algorithm, it was assumed that the learning-rate parameter is a constant denoted by η. In reality, however, it should be defined as η_{ji}; that is, the learning-rate parameter should be *connection dependent*. Indeed, many interesting things can be done by making the learning-rate parameter different for different parts of the network. We provide more detail on this issue in subsequent sections.

It is also noteworthy that in the application of the back-propagation algorithm, we may choose all the synaptic weights in the network to be adjustable, or we may constrain any number of weights in the network to remain fixed during the adaptation process. In the latter case, the error signals are back propagated through the network in the usual manner; however, the fixed synaptic weights are left unaltered. This can be done simply by making the learning-rate parameter η_{ji} for synaptic weight w_{ji} equal to zero.

Stopping Criteria

In general, the back-propagation algorithm cannot be shown to converge, and there are no well-defined criteria for stopping its operation. Rather, there are some reasonable criteria, each with its own practical merit, that may be used to terminate the weight adjustments. To formulate such a criterion, it is logical to think in terms of the unique properties of a *local* or *global minimum* of the error surface.[3] Let the weight vector $\mathbf{w}^*$ denote a minimum, be it local or global. A necessary condition for $\mathbf{w}^*$ to be a minimum is that the gradient vector $\mathbf{g(w)}$ (i.e., first-order partial derivative) of the error surface with respect to the weight vector $\mathbf{w}$ must be zero at $\mathbf{w} = \mathbf{w}^*$. Accordingly, we may formulate a sensible convergence criterion for back-propagation learning as follows (Kramer and Sangiovanni-Vincentelli, 1989):

> The back-propagation algorithm is considered to have converged when the Euclidean norm of the gradient vector reaches a sufficiently small gradient threshold.

The drawback of this convergence criterion is that, for successful trials, learning times may be long. Also, it requires the computation of the gradient vector $\mathbf{g(w)}$.

Another unique property of a minimum that we can use is the fact that the cost function $\mathscr{E}_{av}(\mathbf{w})$ is stationary at the point $\mathbf{w} = \mathbf{w}^*$. We may therefore suggest a different criterion of convergence:

> The back-propagation algorithm is considered to have converged when the absolute rate of change in the average squared error per epoch is sufficiently small.

The rate of change in the average squared error is typically considered to be small enough if it lies in the range of 0.1 to 1 percent per epoch. Sometimes a value as small as 0.01 percent per epoch is used. Unfortunately, this criterion may result in a premature termination of the learning process.

There is another useful, and theoretically supported, criterion for convergence: After each learning iteration, the network is tested for its generalization performance. The learning process is stopped when the generalization performance is adequate or when it is apparent that the generalization performance has peaked; see Section 4.13 for more details.

Summary of the Back-Propagation Algorithm

Figure 4.1 presents the architectural layout of a multilayer perceptron. The corresponding signal-flow graph for back-propagation learning, incorporating both the forward and backward phases of the computations involved in the learning process, is presented in Fig. 4.7 for the case of $L = 2$ and $m_0 = m_1 = m_2 = 3$. The top part of the signal-flow graph accounts for the forward pass. The lower part of the signal-flow graph accounts for the backward pass, which is referred to as a *sensitivity graph* for computing the local gradients in the back-propagation algorithm (Narendra and Parthasarathy, 1990).

Earlier, we mentioned that the sequential updating of weights is the preferred method for on-line implementation of the back-propagation algorithm. For this mode

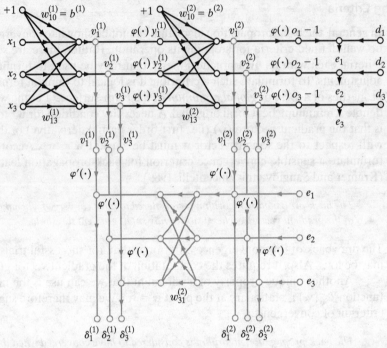

FIGURE 4.7 Signal-flow graphical summary of back-propagation learning. Top part of the graph: forward pass. Bottom part of the graph: backward pass.

of operation, the algorithm cycles through the training sample $\{(\mathbf{x}(n), \mathbf{d}(n))\}_{n=1}^{N}$ as follows:

1. *Initialization.* Assuming that no prior information is available, pick the synaptic weights and thresholds from a uniform distribution whose mean is zero and whose variance is chosen to make the standard deviation of the induced local fields of the neurons lie at the transition between the linear and standards parts of the sigmoid activation function.

2. *Presentations of Training Examples.* Present the network an epoch of training examples. For each example in the sample, ordered in some fashion, perform the sequence of forward and backward computations described under points 3 and 4, respectively.

3. *Forward Computation.* Let a training example in the epoch be denoted by $(\mathbf{x}(n), \mathbf{d}(n))$, with the input vector $\mathbf{x}(n)$ applied to the input layer of sensory nodes and the desired response vector $\mathbf{d}(n)$ presented to the output layer of computation nodes. Compute the induced local fields and function signals of the network by proceeding forward through the network, layer by layer. The induced local field $v_j^{(l)}(n)$ for neuron j in layer l is

$$v_j^{(l)}(n) = \sum_i w_{ji}^{(l)}(n) y_i^{(l-1)}(n) \tag{4.44}$$

where $y_i^{(l-1)}(n)$ is the output (function) signal of neuron i in the previous layer $l-1$ at iteration n, and $w_{ji}^{(l)}(n)$ is the synaptic weight of neuron j in layer l that is fed from neuron i in layer $l-1$. For $i = 0$, we have $y_0^{(l-1)}(n) = +1$, and $w_{j0}^{(l)}(n) = b_j^{(l)}(n)$ is the bias applied to neuron j in layer l. Assuming the use of a sigmoid function, the output signal of neuron j in layer l is

$$y_j^{(l)} = \varphi_j(v_j(n))$$

If neuron j is in the first hidden layer (i.e., $l = 1$), set

$$y_j^{(0)}(n) = x_j(n)$$

where $x_j(n)$ is the jth element of the input vector $\mathbf{x}(n)$. If neuron j is in the output layer (i.e., $l = L$, where L is referred to as the *depth* of the network), set

$$y_j^{(L)} = o_j(n)$$

Compute the error signal

$$e_j(n) = d_j(n) - o_j(n) \tag{4.45}$$

where $d_j(n)$ is the jth element of the desired response vector $\mathbf{d}(n)$.

4. *Backward Computation.* Compute the δs (i.e., local gradients) of the network, defined by

$$\delta_j^{(l)}(n) = \begin{cases} e_j^{(L)}(n)\varphi_j'(v_j^{(L)}(n)) & \text{for neuron } j \text{ in output layer } L \\ \varphi_j'\left(v_j^{(l)}(n)\right) \sum_k \delta_k^{(l+1)}(n)w_{kj}^{(l+1)}(n) & \text{for neuron } j \text{ in hidden layer } l \end{cases} \tag{4.46}$$

where the prime in $\varphi_j'(\cdot)$ denotes differentiation with respect to the argument. Adjust the synaptic weights of the network in layer l according to the generalized delta rule

$$w_{ji}^{(l)}(n+1) = w_{ji}^{(l)}(n) + \alpha[\Delta w_{ji}^{(l)}(n-1)] + \eta\delta_j^{(l)}(n)y_i^{(l-1)}(n) \tag{4.47}$$

where η is the learning-rate parameter and α is the momentum constant.

5. *Iteration.* Iterate the forward and backward computations under points 3 and 4 by presenting new epochs of training examples to the network until the chosen stopping criterion is met.

Notes: The order of presentation of training examples should be randomized from epoch to epoch. The momentum and learning-rate parameter are typically adjusted (and usually decreased) as the number of training iterations increases. Justification for these points will be presented later.

4.5 XOR PROBLEM

In Rosenblatt's single-layer perceptron, there are no hidden neurons. Consequently, it cannot classify input patterns that are not linearly separable. However, nonlinearly separable patterns commonly occur. For example, this situation arises in the *exclusive-OR (XOR) problem*, which may be viewed as a special case of a more general problem, namely, that of classifying points in the *unit hypercube*. Each point in the hypercube is in either class 0 or class 1. However, in the special case of the XOR problem, we need consider only the four corners of a *unit square* that correspond to the input patterns (0,0), (0,1), (1,1), and (1,0), where a single bit (i.e., binary digit) changes as we move from one corner to the next. The first and third input patterns are in class 0, as shown by

$$0 \oplus 0 = 0$$

and

$$1 \oplus 1 = 0$$

where $\oplus$ denotes the exclusive-OR Boolean function operator. The input patterns (0,0) and (1,1) are at opposite corners of the unit square, yet they produce the identical output 0. On the other hand, the input patterns (0,1) and (1,0) are also at opposite corners of the square, but they are in class 1, as shown by

$$0 \oplus 1 = 1$$

and

$$1 \oplus 0 = 1$$

We first recognize that the use of a single neuron with two inputs results in a straight line for a decision boundary in the input space. For all points on one side of this line, the neuron outputs 1; for all points on the other side of the line, it outputs 0. The position and orientation of the line in the input space are determined by the synaptic weights of the neuron connected to the input nodes and the bias applied to the neuron. With the input patterns (0,0) and (1,1) located on opposite corners of the unit square, and likewise for the other two input patterns (0,1) and (1,0), it is clear that we cannot construct a straight line for a decision boundary so that (0,0) and (0,1) lie in one decision region and (0,1) and (1,0) lie in the other decision region. In other words, the single-layer perceptron cannot solve the XOR problem.

However, we may solve the XOR problem by using a single hidden layer with two neurons, as in Fig. 4.8a (Touretzky and Pomerleau, 1989). The signal-flow graph of the network is shown in Fig. 4.8b. The following assumptions are made here:

- Each neuron is represented by a McCulloch–Pitts model, which uses a threshold function for its activation function.
- Bits 0 and 1 are represented by the levels 0 and +1, respectively.

The top neuron, labeled as "Neuron 1" in the hidden layer, is characterized as

$$w_{11} = w_{12} = +1$$

$$b_1 = -\frac{3}{2}$$

The slope of the decision boundary constructed by this hidden neuron is equal to -1 and positioned as in Fig. 4.9a. The bottom neuron, labeled as "Neuron 2" in the hidden layer, is characterized as

$$w_{21} = w_{22} = +1$$

$$b_2 = -\frac{1}{2}$$

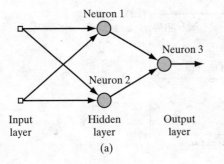

FIGURE 4.8   (a) Architectural graph of network for solving the XOR problem. (b) Signal-flow graph of the network.

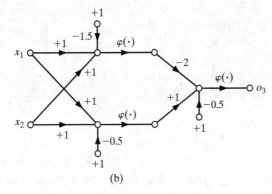

The orientation and position of the decision boundary constructed by this second hidden neuron are as shown in Fig. 4.9b.

The output neuron, labeled as "Neuron 3" in Fig. 4.8a, is characterized as

$$w_{31} = -2$$

$$w_{32} = +1$$

$$b_3 = -\frac{1}{2}$$

The function of the output neuron is to construct a linear combination of the decision boundaries formed by the two hidden neurons. The result of this computation is shown in Fig. 4.9c. The bottom hidden neuron has an excitatory (positive) connection to the output neuron, whereas the top hidden neuron has an inhibitory (negative) connection to the output neuron. When both hidden neurons are off, which occurs when the input pattern is (0,0), the output neuron remains off. When both hidden neurons are on, which occurs when the input pattern is (1,1), the output neuron is switched off again because the inhibitory effect of the larger negative weight connected to the top hidden neuron overpowers the excitatory effect of the positive weight connected to the bottom hidden neuron. When the top hidden neuron is off and the bottom hidden neuron is on, which occurs when the input pattern is (0,1) or (1,0), the output neuron is switched on because of the excitatory effect of the positive weight connected to the bottom hidden neuron. Thus, the network of Fig. 4.8a does indeed solve the XOR problem.

FIGURE 4.9 (a) Decision boundary constructed by hidden neuron 1 of the network in Fig. 4.8. (b) Decision boundary constructed by hidden neuron 2 of the network. (c) Decision boundaries constructed by the complete network.

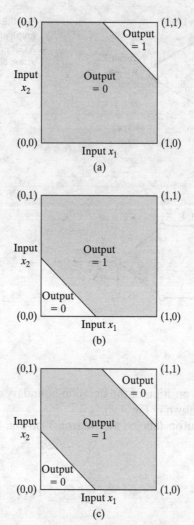

4.6 HEURISTICS FOR MAKING THE BACK-PROPAGATION ALGORITHM PERFORM BETTER

It is often said that the design of a neural network using the back-propagation algorithm is more of an art than a science, in the sense that many of the factors involved in the design are the results of one's own personal experience. There is some truth in this statement. Nevertheless, there are methods that will significantly improve the back-propagation algorithm's performance, as described here:

1. *Stochastic versus batch update.* As mentioned previously, the stochastic (sequential) mode of back-propagation learning (involving pattern-by-pattern updating) is computationally faster than the batch mode. This is especially true when the training data sample is large and highly redundant. (Highly redundant data pose computational problems for the estimation of the Jacobian required for the batch update.)

   2. *Maximizing information content.* As a general rule, every training example presented to the back-propagation algorithm should be chosen on the basis that its information content is the largest possible for the task at hand (LeCun, 1993). Two ways of realizing this choice are as follows:

   • Use an example that results in the largest training error.
   • Use an example that is radically different from all those previously used.

These two heuristics are motivated by a desire to search more of the weight space.

   In pattern-classification tasks using sequential back-propagation learning, a simple and commonly used technique is to randomize (i.e., shuffle) the order in which the examples are presented to the multilayer perceptron from one epoch to the next. Ideally, the randomization ensure that successive examples in an epoch presented to the network rarely belong to the same class.

   3. *Activation function.* Insofar as the speed of learning is concerned, the preferred choice is to use a sigmoid activation function that is an *odd function of its argument*, as shown by

$$\varphi(-v) = -\varphi(v)$$

This condition is satisfied by the hyperbolic function

$$\varphi(v) = a \tanh(bv)$$

as shown in Fig. 4.10, but not the logistic function. Suitable values for the constraints a and b in the formula for $\varphi(v)$ are as follows (LeCun, 1993):

$$a = 1.7159$$

and

$$b = \frac{2}{3}$$

The hyperbolic tangent function $\varphi(v)$ of Fig. 4.10 has the following useful properties:

   • $\varphi(1) = 1$ and $\varphi(-1) = -1$.
   • At the origin, the slope (i.e., effective gain) of the activation function is close to unity, as shown by

$$\varphi(0) = ab$$

$$= 1.7159\left(\frac{2}{3}\right)$$

$$= 1.1424$$

   • The second derivative of $\varphi(v)$ attains its maximum value at $v = 1$.

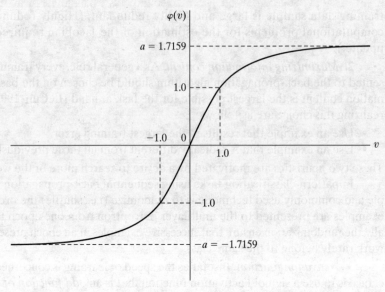

FIGURE 4.10 Graph of the hyperbolic tangent function $\varphi(v) = a\tanh(bv)$ for $a = 1.7159$ and $b = 2/3$. The recommended target values are $+1$ and -1.

4. *Target values.* It is important that the target values (desired response) be chosen within the range of the sigmoid activation function. More specifically, the desired response d_j for neuron j in the output layer of the multilayer perceptron should be *offset* by some amount ε away from the limiting value of the sigmoid activation function, depending on whether the limiting value is positive or negative. Otherwise, the back-propagation algorithm tends to drive the free parameters of the network to infinity and thereby slow down the learning process by driving the hidden neurons into saturation. To be specific, consider the hyperbolic tangent function of Fig. 4.10. For the limiting value $+a$, we set

$$d_j = a - \varepsilon$$

and for the limiting value of $-a$, we set

$$d_j = -a + \varepsilon$$

where ε is an appropriate positive constant. For the choice of $a = 1.7159$ used in Fig. 4.10, we may set $\varepsilon = 0.7159$, in which case the target value (desired response) d_j can be conveniently chosen as ± 1, as indicated in the figure.

5. *Normalizing the inputs.* Each input variable should be *preprocessed* so that its mean value, averaged over the entire training sample, is close to zero, or else it will be small compared to its standard deviation (LeCun, 1993). To appreciate the practical significance of this rule, consider the extreme case where the input variables are consistently positive. In this situation, the synaptic weights of a neuron in the first hidden layer can only increase together or decrease together. Accordingly, if the weight vector of that

neuron is to change direction, it can do so only by zigzagging its way through the error surface, which is typically slow and should therefore be avoided.

In order to accelerate the back-propagation learning process, the normalization of the inputs should also include two other measures (LeCun, 1993):

- The input variables contained in the training set should be *uncorrelated*; this can be done by using principal-components analysis, to be discussed in Chapter 8.
- The decorrelated input variables should be scaled so that their *covariances are approximately equal*, thereby ensuring that the different synaptic weights in the network learn at approximately the same speed.

Figure 4.11 illustrates the results of three normalization steps: mean removal, decorrelation, and covariance equalization, applied in that order.

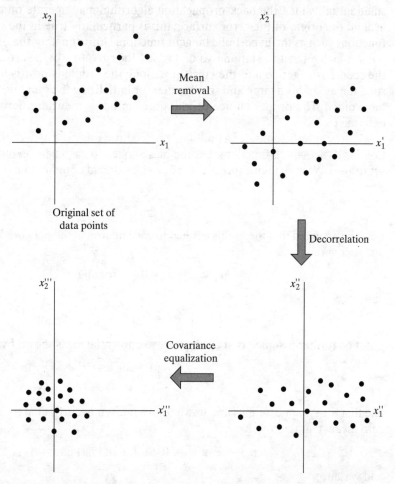

FIGURE 4.11   Illustrating the operation of mean removal, decorrelation, and covariance equalization for a two-dimensional input space.

It is also of interest to note that when the inputs are transformed in the manner illustrated in Fig. 4.11 and used in conjunction with the hyperbolic tangent function specified in Fig. 4.10, the variance of the individual neural outputs in the multilayer perceptron will be close to unity (Orr and Müller, 1998). The rationale for this statement is that the effective gain of the sigmoid function over its useful range is roughly unity.

6. *Initialization.* A good choice for the initial values of the synaptic weights and thresholds of the network can be of tremendous help in a successful network design. The key question is: What is a good choice?

When the synaptic weights are assigned large initial values, it is highly likely that the neurons in the network will be driven into saturation. If this happens, the local gradients in the back-propagation algorithm assume small values, which in turn will cause the learning process to slow down. However, if the synaptic weights are assigned small initial values, the back-propagation algorithm may operate on a very flat area around the origin of the error surface; this is particularly true in the case of sigmoid functions such as the hyperbolic tangent function. Unfortunately, the origin is a *saddle point*, which refers to a stationary point where the curvature of the error surface across the saddle is negative and the curvature along the saddle is positive. For these reasons, the use of both large and small values for initializing the synaptic weights should be avoided. The proper choice of initialization lies somewhere between these two extreme cases.

To be specific, consider a multilayer perceptron using the hyperbolic tangent function for its activation functions. Let the bias applied to each neuron in the network be set to zero. We may then express the induced local field of neuron j as

$$v_j = \sum_{i=1}^{m} w_{ji} y_i$$

Let it be assumed that the inputs applied to each neuron in the network have zero mean and unit variance, as shown by

$$\mu_y = \mathbb{E}[y_i] = 0 \quad \text{for all } i$$

and

$$\sigma_y^2 = \mathbb{E}[(y_i - \mu_i)^2] = \mathbb{E}[y_i^2] = 1 \quad \text{for all } i$$

Let it be further assumed that the inputs are uncorrelated, as shown by

$$\mathbb{E}[y_i y_k] = \begin{cases} 1 & \text{for } k = i \\ 0 & \text{for } k \neq i \end{cases}$$

and that the synaptic weights are drawn from a uniformly distributed set of numbers with zero mean, that is,

$$\mu_w = \mathbb{E}[w_{ji}] = 0 \quad \text{for all } (j, i) \text{ pairs}$$

and variance

$$\sigma_w^2 = \mathbb{E}[(w_{ji} - \mu_w)^2] = \mathbb{E}[w_{ji}^2] \quad \text{for all } (j, i) \text{ pairs}$$

Accordingly, we may express the mean and variance of the induced local field v_j as

$$\mu_v = \mathbb{E}[v_j] = \mathbb{E}\left[\sum_{i=1}^{m} w_{ji} y_i\right] = \sum_{i=1}^{m} \mathbb{E}[w_{ji}]\mathbb{E}[y_i] = 0$$

and

$$\sigma_v^2 = \mathbb{E}[(v_j - \mu_v)^2] = \mathbb{E}[v_j^2]$$

$$= \mathbb{E}\left[\sum_{i=1}^{m}\sum_{k=1}^{m} w_{ji} w_{jk} y_i y_k\right]$$

$$= \sum_{i=1}^{m}\sum_{k=1}^{m} \mathbb{E}[w_{ji} w_{jk}]\mathbb{E}[y_i y_k]$$

$$= \sum_{i=1}^{m} \mathbb{E}[w_{ji}^2]$$

$$= m\sigma_w^2$$

where m is the number of synaptic connections of a neuron.

In light of this result, we may now describe a good strategy for initializing the synaptic weights so that the standard deviation of the induced local field of a neuron lies in the transition area between the linear and saturated parts of its sigmoid activation function. For example, for the case of a hyperbolic tangent function with parameters a and b used in Fig. 4.10, this objective is satisfied by setting $\sigma_v = 1$ in the previous equation, in which case we obtain the following (LeCun, 1993):

$$\sigma_w = m^{-1/2} \tag{4.48}$$

Thus, it is desirable for the uniform distribution, from which the synaptic weights are selected, to have a mean of zero and a variance equal to the reciprocal of the number of synaptic connections of a neuron.

7. *Learning from hints.* Learning from a sample of training examples deals with an unknown input–output mapping function $f(\cdot)$. In effect, the learning process exploits the information contained in the examples about the function $f(\cdot)$ to *infer* an approximate implementation of it. The process of learning from examples may be generalized to *include learning from hints*, which is achieved by allowing prior information that we may have about the function $f(\cdot)$ to be included in the learning process (Abu-Mostafa, 1995). Such information may include invariance properties, symmetries, or any other knowledge about the function $f(\cdot)$ that may be used to accelerate the search for its approximate realization and, more importantly, to improve the quality of the final estimate. The use of Eq. (4.48) is an example of how this is achieved.

8. *Learning rates.* All neurons in the multilayer perceptron should ideally learn at the same rate. The last layers usually have larger local gradients than the layers at the front end of the network. Hence, the learning-rate parameter η should be assigned a smaller value in the last layers than in the front layers of the multilayer perceptron. Neurons with many inputs should have a smaller learning-rate parameter than neurons with few inputs so as to maintain a similar learning time for all neurons in the network. In LeCun (1993), it is suggested that for a given neuron, the learning rate should be inversely proportional to the square root of synaptic connections made to that neuron.

4.7 COMPUTER EXPERIMENT: PATTERN CLASSIFICATION

In this computer experiment, we resume the sequence of pattern-classification experiments performed first in Chapter 1 using Rosenblatt's perceptron and then in Chapter 2 using the method of least squares. For both experiments, we used training and test data generated by randomly sampling the *double-moon* structure pictured in Fig. 1.8. In each of the experiments, we considered two cases, one employing linearly separable patterns and the other employing nonlinearly separable patterns. The perceptron worked perfectly fine for the linearly separable setting of $d = 1$, but the method of least squares required a larger separation between the two moons for perfect classification. In any event, they both failed the nonlinearly separable setting of $d = -4$.

The objective of the computer experiment presented herein is twofold:

1. to demonstrate that the multilayer perceptron, trained with the back-propagation algorithm, is capable of classifying nonlinearly separable test data;
2. to find a more difficult case of nonlinearly separable patterns for which the multilayer perceptron fails the double-moon classification test.

The specifications of the multilayer perceptron used in the experiment are as follows:

Size of the input layer: $m_0 = 2$
Size of the (only) hidden layer: $m_1 = 20$
Size of the output layer: $m_2 = 1$

Activation function: hyperbolic tangent function $\varphi(v) = \dfrac{1 - \exp(-2v)}{1 + \exp(-2v)}$

Threshold setting: zero
Learning-rate parameter η: annealed linearly from 10^{-1} down to 10^{-5}

The experiment is carried out in two parts, one corresponding to the vertical separation $d = -4$, and the other corresponding to $d = -5$:

(a) *Vertical separation d = −4.*
Figure 4.12 presents the results of the MLP experiment for the length of separation between the two moons of $d = -4$. Part (a) of the figure displays the learning curve resulting from the training session. We see that the learning curve reached convergence effectively in about 15 epochs of training. Part (b) of the figure displays the optimal nonlinear decision boundary computed by the MLP. Most important, perfect classification of the two patterns was achieved, with no classification errors. This perfect performance is attributed to the hidden layer of the MLP.

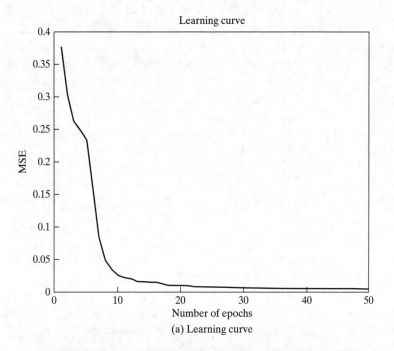

(a) Learning curve

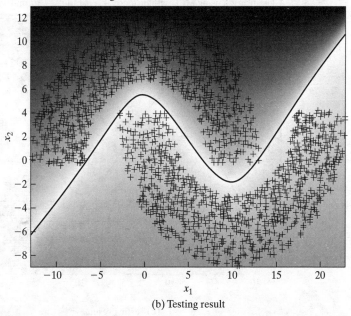

(b) Testing result

FIGURE 4.12   Results of the computer experiment on the back-propagation algorithm applied to the MLP with distance $d = -4$. MSE stands for mean-square error.

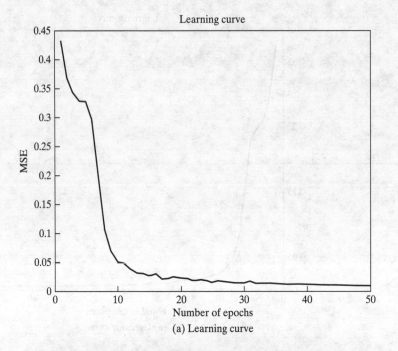

(a) Learning curve

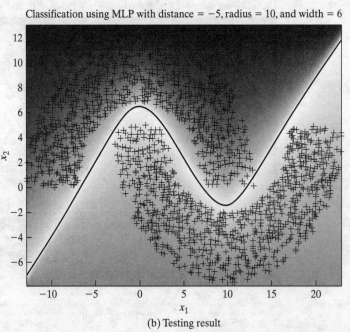

(b) Testing result

FIGURE 4.13 Results of the computer experiment on the back-propagation algorithm applied to the MLP with distance $d = -5$.

(b) *Vertical separation d = −5.*

To challenge the multilayer perceptron with a more difficult pattern-classification task, we reduced the vertical separation between the two moons to $d = -5$. The results of this second part of the experiment are presented in Fig. 4.13. The learning curve of the back-propagation algorithm, plotted in part (a) of the figure, shows a slower rate of convergence, roughly three times that for the easier case of $d = -4$. Moreover, the testing results plotted in part (b) of the figure reveal three classification errors in a testing set of 2,000 data points, representing an error rate of 0.15 percent.

The decision boundary is computed by finding the coordinates x_1 and x_2 pertaining to the input vector **x**, for which the response of the output neuron is zero on the premise that the two classes of the experiment are equally likely. Accordingly, when a threshold of zero is exceeded, a decision is made in favor of one class; otherwise, the decision is made in favor of the other class. This procedure is followed on all the double-moon classification experiments reported in the book.

4.8   BACK PROPAGATION AND DIFFERENTIATION

Back propagation is a specific technique for implementing *gradient descent* in weight space for a multilayer perceptron. The basic idea is to efficiently compute *partial derivatives* of an approximating function $F(\mathbf{w}, \mathbf{x})$ realized by the network with respect to all the elements of the adjustable weight vector **w** for a given value of input vector **x**. Herein lies the computational power of the back-propagation algorithm.[4]

To be specific, consider a multilayer perceptron with an input layer of m_0 nodes, two hidden layers, and a single output neuron, as depicted in Fig. 4.14. The elements of the weight vector **w** are ordered by layer (starting from the first hidden layer), then by neurons in a layer, and then by the number of a synapse within a neuron. Let $w_{ji}^{(l)}$ denote the synaptic weight from neuron i to neuron j in layer $l = 1, 2, \ldots$. For $l = 1$, corresponding to the first hidden layer, the index i refers to a source node rather than to a

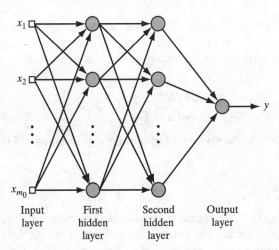

FIGURE 4.14   Multilayer perceptron with two hidden layers and one output neuron.

Input layer   First hidden layer   Second hidden layer   Output layer neuron. For $l = 3$, corresponding to the output layer in Fig. 4.14, we have $j = 1$. We wish to evaluate the derivatives of the function $F(\mathbf{w}, \mathbf{x})$ with respect to all the elements of the weight vector $\mathbf{w}$ for a specified input vector $\mathbf{x} = [x_1, x_2, ..., x_{m_0}]^T$. We have included the weight vector $\mathbf{w}$ as an argument of the function F in order to focus attention on it. For example, for $l = 2$ (i.e., a single hidden layer and a linear output layer), we have

$$F(\mathbf{w}, \mathbf{x}) = \sum_{j=0}^{m_1} w_{oj} \varphi\left(\sum_{i=0}^{m_0} w_{ji} x_i \right) \tag{4.49}$$

where $\mathbf{w}$ is the ordered weight vector and $\mathbf{x}$ is the input vector.

The multilayer perceptron of Fig. 4.14 is parameterized by an *architecture* $\mathcal{A}$ (representing a discrete parameter) and a *weight vector* $\mathbf{w}$ (made up of continuous elements). Let $\mathcal{A}_j^{(l)}$ denote that part of the architecture extending from the input layer ($l = 0$) to node j in layer $l = 1, 2, 3$. Accordingly, we may write

$$F(\mathbf{w}, \mathbf{x}) = \varphi(\mathcal{A}_1^{(3)}) \tag{4.50}$$

where φ is the activation function. However, $\mathcal{A}_1^{(3)}$ is to be interpreted merely as an architectural symbol rather than a variable. Thus, adapting Eqs. (4.2), (4.4), (4.13), and (4.25) for use in this new situation, we obtain the formulas

$$\frac{\partial F(\mathbf{w}, \mathbf{x})}{\partial w_{1k}^{(3)}} = \varphi'(\mathcal{A}_1^{(3)})\varphi(\mathcal{A}_k^{(2)}) \tag{4.51}$$

$$\frac{\partial F(\mathbf{w}, \mathbf{x})}{\partial w_{kj}^{(2)}} = \varphi'(\mathcal{A}_1^{(3)})\varphi'(\mathcal{A}_k^{(2)})\varphi(\mathcal{A}_j^{(1)})w_{1k}^{(3)} \tag{4.52}$$

$$\frac{\partial F(\mathbf{w}, \mathbf{x})}{\partial w_{ji}^{(1)}} = \varphi'(\mathcal{A}_1^{(3)})\varphi'(\mathcal{A}_j^{(1)})x_i\left[\sum_k w_{1k}^{(3)}\varphi'(\mathcal{A}_k^{(2)})w_{kj}^{(2)} \right] \tag{4.53}$$

where φ' is the partial derivative of the nonlinearity φ with respect to its argument and x_i is the ith element of the input vector $\mathbf{x}$. In a similar way, we may derive the equations for the partial derivatives of a general network with more hidden layers and more neurons in the output layer.

Equations (4.51) through (4.53) provide the basis for calculating the sensitivity of the network function $F(\mathbf{w}, \mathbf{x})$ with respect to variations in the elements of the weight vector $\mathbf{w}$. Let ω denote an element of the weight vector $\mathbf{w}$. The *sensitivity* of $F(\mathbf{w}, \mathbf{x})$ with respect to ω, is formally defined by

$$S_\omega^F = \frac{\partial F / F}{\partial \omega / \omega}$$

It is for this reason that we refer to the lower part of the signal-flow graph in Fig. 4.7 as a "sensitivity graph."

The Jacobian

Let W denote the total number of free parameters (i.e., synaptic weights and biases) of a multilayer perceptron, which are ordered in a manner described to form the weight vector $\mathbf{w}$. Let N denote the total number of examples used to train the network. Using back propagation, we may compute a set of W partial derivatives of the approximating function $F[\mathbf{w}, \mathbf{x}(n)]$ with respect to the elements of the weight vector $\mathbf{w}$ for a specific example $\mathbf{x}(n)$ in the training sample. Repeating these computations for $n = 1, 2, ..., N$, we end up with an N-by-W matrix of partial derivatives. This matrix is called the *Jacobian* $\mathbf{J}$ of the multilayer perceptron evaluated at $\mathbf{x}(n)$. Each row of the Jacobian corresponds to a particular example in the training sample.

There is experimental evidence to suggest that many neural network training problems are intrinsically *ill conditioned*, leading to a Jacobian $\mathbf{J}$ that is almost rank deficient (Saarinen et al., 1991). The *rank* of a matrix is equal to the number of linearly independent columns or rows in the matrix, whichever one is smallest. The Jacobian $\mathbf{J}$ is said to be *rank deficient* if its rank is less than min (N, W). Any rank deficiency in the Jacobian causes the back-propagation algorithm to obtain only partial information of the possible search directions. Rank deficiency also causes training times to be long.

4.9 THE HESSIAN AND ITS ROLE IN ON-LINE LEARNING

The *Hessian matrix*, or simply the *Hessian*, of the cost function $\mathscr{E}_{av}(\mathbf{w})$, denoted by $\mathbf{H}$, is defined as the second derivative of $\mathscr{E}_{av}(\mathbf{w})$ with respect to the weight vector $\mathbf{w}$, as shown by

$$\mathbf{H} = \frac{\partial^2 \mathscr{E}_{av}(\mathbf{w})}{\partial \mathbf{w}^2} \tag{4.54}$$

The Hessian plays an important role in the study of neural networks; specifically, we mention the following points[5]:

1. The eigenvalues of the Hessian have a profound influence on the dynamics of back-propagation learning.
2. The inverse of the Hessian provides a basis for pruning (i.e., deleting) insignificant synaptic weights from a multilayer perceptron; this issue will be discussed in Section 4.14.
3. The Hessian is basic to the formulation of second-order optimization methods as an alternative to back-propagation learning, to be discussed in Section 4.16.

In this section, we confine our attention to point 1.

In Chapter 3, we indicated that the eigenstructure of the Hessian has a profound influence on the convergence properties of the LMS algorithm. So it is also with the back-propagation algorithm, but in a much more complicated way. Typically, the Hessian of the error surface pertaining to a multilayer perceptron trained with the back-propagation algorithm has the following composition of eigenvalues (LeCun et al., 1998):

- a small number of small eigenvalues,
- a large number of medium-sized eigenvalues, and
- a small number of large eigenvalues.

There is therefore a wide spread in the eigenvalues of the Hessian.

The factors affecting the composition of the eigenvalues may be grouped as follows:

- nonzero-mean input signals or nonzero-mean induced neural output signals;
- correlations between the elements of the input signal vector and correlations between induced neural output signals;
- wide variations in the second-order derivatives of the cost function with respect to synaptic weights of neurons in the network as we proceed from one layer to the next. These derivatives are often smaller in the lower layers, with the synaptic weights in the first hidden layer learning slowly and those in the last layers learning quickly.

Avoidance of Nonzero-mean Inputs

From Chapter 3, we recall that the *learning time* of the LMS algorithm is sensitive to variations in the condition number $\lambda_{max}/\lambda_{min}$, where λ_{max} is the largest eigenvalue of the Hessian and λ_{min} is its smallest nonzero eigenvalue. Experimental results show that a similar situation holds for the back-propagation algorithm, which is a generalization of the LMS algorithm. For inputs with nonzero mean, the ratio $\lambda_{max}/\lambda_{min}$ is larger than its corresponding value for zero-mean inputs: The larger the mean of the inputs, the larger the ratio $\lambda_{max}/\lambda_{min}$ will be. This observation has a serious implication for the dynamics of back-propagation learning.

For the learning time to be minimized, the use of nonzero-mean inputs should be avoided. Now, insofar as the signal vector **x** applied to a neuron in the first hidden layer of a multilayer perceptron (i.e., the signal vector applied to the input layer) is concerned, it is easy to remove the mean from each element of **x** before its application to the network. But what about the signals applied to the neurons in the remaining hidden and output layers of the network? The answer to this question lies in the type of activation function used in the network. In the case of the logistic function, the output of each neuron is restricted to the interval [0, 1]. Such a choice acts as a source of *systematic bias* for those neurons located beyond the first hidden layer of the network. To overcome this problem, we need to use the hyperbolic tangent function that is odd symmetric. With this latter choice, the output of each neuron is permitted to assume both positive and negative values in the interval [−1, 1], in which case it is likely for its mean to be zero. If the network connectivity is large, back-propagation learning with odd-symmetric activation functions can yield faster convergence than a similar process with nonsymmetric activation functions. This condition provides the justification for heuristic 3 described in Section 4.6.

Asymptotic Behavior of On-line Learning

For a good understanding of on-line learning, we need to know how the ensemble-averaged learning curve evolves across time. Unlike the LMS algorithm, this calculation is unfortunately much too difficult to perform. Generally speaking, the error-performance surface may have exponentially many local minima and multiple global minima because of symmetry properties of the network. Surprisingly, this characteristic of the error-performance surface may turn out to be a useful feature in the following sense: Given that an early-stopping method is used for network training (see Section 4.13) or the network is regularized (see Section 4.14), we may nearly always find ourselves "close" to a local minimum.

In any event, due to the complicated nature of the error-performance surface, we find that in the literature, statistical analysis of the learning curve is confined to its asymptotic behavior in the neighborhood of a local minimum. In this context, we may highlight some important aspects of this asymptotic behavior, assuming a fixed learning-rate parameter, as follows (Murata, 1998):

(i) The learning curve consists of three terms:
   - *minimal loss*, determined by the optimal parameter $\mathbf{w}^*$, which pertains to a local or global minimum;
   - *additional loss*, caused by fluctuations in evolution of the weight-vector estimator $w(n)$ around the mean

$$\lim_{n \to \infty} \mathbb{E}[\hat{\mathbf{w}}(n)] = \mathbf{w}^*$$

   - *a time-dependent term*, describing the effect of decreasing speed of error convergence on algorithmic performance.

(ii) To ensure stability of the on-line learning algorithm, the learning-rate parameter η must be assigned a value smaller than the reciprocal of the largest eigenvalue of the Hessian, $1/\lambda_{\max}$. On the other hand, the speed of convergence of the algorithm is dominated by the smallest eigenvalue of the Hessian, $\lambda_{\min}$.

(iii) Roughly speaking, if the learning-rate parameter η is assigned a large value, then the speed of convergence is fast, but there will be large fluctuations around the local or global minimum, even if the number of iterations, n, approaches infinity. Conversely, if η is small, then the extent of fluctuations is small, but the speed of convergence will be slow.

4.10 OPTIMAL ANNEALING AND ADAPTIVE CONTROL OF THE LEARNING RATE

In Section 4.2, we emphasized the popularity of the on-line learning algorithm for two main reasons:

(i) The algorithm is simple, in that its implementation requires a minimal amount of memory, which is used merely to store the old value of the estimated weight vector from one iteration to the next.

(ii) With each example $\{\mathbf{x}, \mathbf{d}\}$ being used only once at every time-step, the learning rate assumes a more important role in on-line learning than in batch learning, in that the on-line learning algorithm has the built-in ability to *track* statistical variations in the environment responsible for generating the training set of examples.

In Amari (1967) and, more recently, Opper (1996), it is shown that *optimally annealed* on-line learning is enabled to operate as fast as batch learning in an *asymptotic sense*. This issue is explored in what follows.

Optimal Annealing of the Learning Rate

Let **w** denote the vector of synaptic weights in the network, stacked up on top of each other in some orderly fashion. With $\hat{\mathbf{w}}(n)$ denoting the *old estimate* of the weight vector **w** at time-step n, let $\hat{\mathbf{w}}(n+1)$ denote the *updated estimate* of **w** on receipt of the "input-desired response" example $\{\mathbf{x}(n+1), \mathbf{d}(n+1)\}$. Correspondingly, let $\mathbf{F}(\mathbf{x}(n+1); \hat{\mathbf{w}}(n))$ denote the vector-valued output of the network produced in response to the input $\mathbf{x}(n+1)$; naturally the dimension of the function **F** must be the same as that of the desired response vector $\mathbf{d}(n)$. Following the defining equation of Eq. (4.3), we may express the instantaneous energy as the squared Euclidean norm of the estimation error, as shown by

$$\mathscr{E}(\mathbf{x}(n), \mathbf{d}(n); \mathbf{w}) = \frac{1}{2} \|\mathbf{d}(n) - \mathbf{F}(\mathbf{x}(n); \mathbf{w})\|^2 \tag{4.55}$$

The *mean-square error*, or *expected risk*, of the on-line learning problem is defined by

$$J(\mathbf{w}) = \mathbb{E}_{\mathbf{x},\mathbf{d}}[\mathscr{E}(\mathbf{x}, \mathbf{d}; \mathbf{w})] \tag{4.56}$$

where $\mathbb{E}_{\mathbf{x},\mathbf{d}}$ is the expectation operator performed with respect to the example $\{\mathbf{x}, \mathbf{d}\}$. The solution

$$\mathbf{w}^* = \arg \min_{\mathbf{w}}[J(\mathbf{w})] \tag{4.57}$$

defines the *optimal parameter vector*.

The instantaneous *gradient vector* of the learning process is defined by

$$\mathbf{g}(\mathbf{x}(n), \mathbf{d}(n); \mathbf{w}) = \frac{\partial}{\partial \mathbf{w}} \mathscr{E}(\mathbf{x}(n), \mathbf{d}(n); \mathbf{w})$$

$$= -(\mathbf{d}(n) - \mathbf{F}(\mathbf{x}(n); \mathbf{w})\mathbf{F}'(\mathbf{x}(n); \mathbf{w}) \tag{4.58}$$

where

$$\mathbf{F}'(\mathbf{x}; \mathbf{w}) = \frac{\partial}{\partial \mathbf{w}} \mathbf{F}(\mathbf{x}; \mathbf{w}) \tag{4.59}$$

With the definition of the gradient vector just presented, we may now express the on-line learning algorithm as

$$\hat{\mathbf{w}}(n + 1) = \hat{\mathbf{w}}(n) - \eta(n)\mathbf{g}(\mathbf{x}(n + 1), \mathbf{d}(n + 1); \hat{\mathbf{w}}(n)) \tag{4.60}$$

or, equivalently,

$$\underbrace{\hat{\mathbf{w}}(n + 1)}_{\substack{\text{Updated} \\ \text{estimate}}} = \underbrace{\hat{\mathbf{w}}(n)}_{\substack{\text{Old} \\ \text{estimate}}} + \underbrace{\eta(n)}_{\substack{\text{Learning-} \\ \text{rate} \\ \text{parameter}}} \underbrace{[\mathbf{d}(n + 1) - \mathbf{F}(\mathbf{x}(n + 1); \hat{\mathbf{w}}(n))]}_{\text{Error signal}} \underbrace{\mathbf{F}'(\mathbf{x}(n + 1); \hat{\mathbf{w}}(n))}_{\substack{\text{Partial derivative of} \\ \text{the network function } \mathbf{F}}} \tag{4.61}$$

Given this difference equation, we may go on to describe the *ensemble-averaged dynamics* of the weight vector **w** in the neighborhood of the optimal parameter **w*** by the continuous differential equation

$$\frac{d}{dt} \hat{\mathbf{w}}(t) = -\eta(t)\mathbb{E}_{\mathbf{x},\mathbf{d}}[\mathbf{g}(\mathbf{x}(t), \mathbf{d}(t); \hat{\mathbf{w}}(t))] \tag{4.62}$$

where t denotes continuous time. Following Murata (1998), the expected value of the gradient vector is approximated by

$$\mathbb{E}_{x,d}[g(x, d; \hat{w}(t))] \approx -K^*(w^* - \hat{w}(t)) \tag{4.63}$$

where the ensembled-averaged matrix K^* is itself defined by

$$K^* = \mathbb{E}_{x,d}\left[\frac{\partial}{\partial w} g(x, d; w) \right]$$

$$= \mathbb{E}_{x,d}\left[\frac{\partial^2}{\partial w^2} \mathscr{E}(x, d; w) \right] \tag{4.64}$$

The new Hessian K^* is a positive-definite matrix defined differently from the Hessian H of Eq. (4.54). However, if the environment responsible for generating the training examples $\{x, d\}$ is *ergodic*, we may then substitute the Hessian H, based on time averaging, for the Hessian K^*, based on ensemble-averaging. In any event, using Eq. (4.63) in Eq. (4.62), we find that the continuous differential equation describing the evolution of the estimator $\hat{w}(t)$ may be approximated as

$$\frac{d}{dt} \hat{w}(t) \approx -\eta(t)K^*(w^* - \hat{w}(t)) \tag{4.65}$$

Let the vector q denote an eigenvector of the matrix K^*, as shown by the defining equation

$$K^*q = \lambda q \tag{4.66}$$

where λ is the eigenvalue associated with the eigenvector q. We may then introduce the new function

$$\xi(t) = \mathbb{E}_{x,d}[q^T g(x, d; \hat{w}(t))] \tag{4.67}$$

which, in light of Eq. (4.63), may itself be approximated as

$$\xi(t) \approx -q^T K^*(w^* - \hat{w}(t))$$

$$= -\lambda q^T(w^* - \hat{w}(t)) \tag{4.68}$$

At each instant of time t, the function $\xi(t)$ takes on a scalar value, which may be viewed as an approximate measure of the *Euclidean distance* between two projections onto the eigenvector q, one due to the optimal parameter w^* and the other due to the estimator $\hat{w}(t)$. The value of $\xi(t)$ is therefore reduced to zero if, and when, the estimator $\hat{w}(t)$ converges to w^*.

From Eqs. (4.65), (4.66), and (4.68), we find that the function $\xi(t)$ is related to the time-varying learning-rate parameter $\eta(t)$ as follows:

$$\frac{d}{dt} \xi(t) = -\lambda \eta(t)\xi(t) \tag{4.69}$$

This differential equation may be solved to yield

$$\xi(t) = c \exp(-\lambda \int \eta(t)dt) \tag{4.70}$$

where c is a positive integration constant.

Following the annealing schedule due to Darken and Moody (1991) that was discussed in Chapter 3 on the LMS algorithm, let the formula

$$\eta(t) = \frac{\tau}{t + \tau} \eta_0 \tag{4.71}$$

account for dependence of the learning-rate on time t, where τ and η_0 are positive *tuning parameters*. Then, substituting this formula into Eq. (4.70), we find that the corresponding formula tor the function $\xi(t)$ is

$$\xi(t) = c(t + \tau)^{-\lambda\tau\eta_0} \tag{4.72}$$

For $\xi(t)$ to vanish as time t approaches infinity, we require that the product term $\lambda\tau\eta_0$ in the exponent be large compared with unity, which may be satisfied by setting $\eta_0 = \alpha/\lambda$ for positive α.

Now, there remains only the issue of how to choose the eigenvector $\mathbf{q}$. From the previous section, we recall that the convergence speed of the learning curve is dominated by the smallest eigenvalue $\lambda_{\min}$ of the Hessian $\mathbf{H}$. With this Hessian and the new Hessian $\mathbf{K}^*$ tending to behave similarly, a clever choice is to hypothesize that for a sufficiently large number of iterations, the evolution of the estimator $\hat{\mathbf{w}}(t)$ over time t may be considered as a one-dimensional process, running "almost parallel" to the eigenvector of the Hessian $\mathbf{K}^*$ associated with the smallest eigenvalue $\lambda_{\min}$, as illustrated in Fig. 4.15. We may thus set

$$\mathbf{q} = \frac{\mathbb{E}_{\mathbf{x},\mathbf{d}}[\mathbf{g}(\mathbf{x}, \mathbf{d}; \hat{\mathbf{w}})]}{\|\mathbb{E}_{\mathbf{x},\mathbf{d}}[\mathbf{g}(\mathbf{x}, \mathbf{d}; \hat{\mathbf{w}})]\|} \tag{4.73}$$

where the normalization is introduced to make the eigenvector $\mathbf{q}$ assume unit Euclidean length. Correspondingly, the use of this formula in Eq. (4.67) yields

$$\xi(t) = \|\mathbb{E}_{\mathbf{x},\mathbf{d}}[\mathbf{g}(\mathbf{x}, \mathbf{d}; \hat{\mathbf{w}}(t))]\| \tag{4.74}$$

We may now summarize the results of the discussion presented in this section by making the following statements:

1. The choice of the annealing schedule described in Eq. (4.71) satisfies the two conditions

$$\sum_t \eta(t) \to \infty \text{ and } \sum_t \eta^2(t) > \infty, \text{ as } t \to \infty \tag{4.75}$$

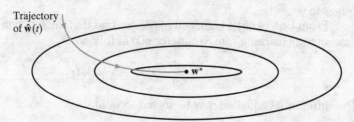

Trajectory of $\hat{\mathbf{w}}(t)$

$\bullet \mathbf{w}^*$

FIGURE 4.15   The evolution of the estimator $\hat{\mathbf{w}}(t)$ over time t. The ellipses represent contours of the expected risk for varying values of $\mathbf{w}$, assumed to be two-dimensional.

In other words, $\eta(t)$ satisfies the requirements of *stochastic approximation theory* (Robbins and Monro, 1951).

2. As time t approaches infinity, the function $\xi(t)$ approaches zero asymptotically. In accordance with Eq. (4.68), it follows that the estimator $\hat{\mathbf{w}}(t)$ approaches the optimal estimator $\mathbf{w}^*$ as t approaches infinity.

3. The ensemble-averaged trajectory of the estimator $\hat{\mathbf{w}}(t)$ is almost parallel to the eigenvector of the Hessian $\mathbf{K}^*$ associated with the smallest eigenvalue $\lambda_{\min}$ after a large enough number of iterations.

4. The optimally annealed on-line learning algorithm for a network characterized by the weight vector $\mathbf{w}$ is collectively described by the following set of three equations:

$$\underbrace{\hat{\mathbf{w}}(n+1)}_{\substack{\text{Updated}\\\text{estimate}}} = \underbrace{\hat{\mathbf{w}}(n)}_{\substack{\text{Old}\\\text{estimate}}} + \underbrace{\eta(n)}_{\substack{\text{Learning-}\\\text{rate}\\\text{parameter}}} (\underbrace{\mathbf{d}(n+1) - \mathbf{F}(\mathbf{x}(n)+1; \hat{\mathbf{w}}(n))}_{\text{Error signal}}) \underbrace{\mathbf{F}'(\mathbf{x}(n+1); \hat{\mathbf{w}}(n))}_{\substack{\text{Partial derivative of}\\\text{the network function } \mathbf{F}}}$$

$$\eta(n) = \frac{n_{\text{switch}}}{n + n_{\text{switch}}} \eta_0 \qquad\qquad (4.76)$$

$$\eta_0 = \frac{\alpha}{\lambda_{\min}}, \qquad \alpha = \text{positive constant}$$

Here, it is assumed that the environment responsible for generating the training examples $\{\mathbf{x}, \mathbf{d}\}$ is ergodic, so that the ensemble-averaged Hessian $\mathbf{K}^*$ assumes the same value as the time-averaged Hessian $\mathbf{H}$.

5. When the learning-rate parameter η_0 is *fixed* in on-line learning based on stochastic gradient descent, stability of the algorithm requires that we choose $\eta_0 < 1/\lambda_{\max}$, where $\lambda_{\max}$ is the largest eigenvalue of the Hessian $\mathbf{H}$. On the other hand, in the case of optimally annealed stochastic gradient descent, according to the third line of Eq. (4.76), the choice is $\eta_0 < 1/\lambda_{\min}$, where $\lambda_{\min}$ is the smallest eigenvalue of $\mathbf{H}$.

6. The *time constant* n_{switch}, a positive integer, defines the *transition* from a regime of fixed η_0 to the annealing regime, where the time-varying learning-rate parameter $\eta(n)$ assumes the desired form c/n, where c is a constant, in accordance with stochastic approximation theory.

Adaptive Control of the Learning Rate

The optimal annealing schedule, described in the second line of Eq. (4.76), provides an important step in improved utilization of on-line learning. However, a practical limitation of this annealing schedule is the requirement that we know the time constant n_{switch} a priori. A practical issue of concern, then, is the fact that when the application of interest builds on the use of on-line learning in a nonstationary environment where the statistics of the training sequence change from one example to the next, the use of a prescribed time constant n_{switch} may no longer be a realistic option. In situations of this kind, which occur frequently in practice, the on-line learning algorithm needs to be equipped with a built-in mechanism for the *adaptive control* of the learning rate. Such a mechanism was first described in the literature by Murata (1998), in which the so-called *learning of the learning algorithm* (Sompolinsky et al., 1995) was appropriately modified.

The adaptive algorithm due to Murata is configured to achieve two objectives:

1. *automatic adjustment* of the learning rate, which accounts for statistical variations in the environment responsible for generation of the training sequence of examples;
2. *generalization* of the on-line learning algorithm so that its applicability is broadened by avoiding the need for a prescribed cost function.

To be specific, the ensemble-averaged dynamics of the weight vector **w**, defined in Eq. (4.62), is now rewritten as[6]

$$\frac{d}{dt}\hat{\mathbf{w}}(t) = -\eta(t)\mathbb{E}_{\mathbf{x},\mathbf{d}}[\mathbf{f}(\mathbf{x}(t), \mathbf{d}(t); \hat{\mathbf{w}}(t))] \tag{4.77}$$

where the vector-valued function $\mathbf{f}(\cdot, \cdot; \cdot)$ denotes *flow* that determines the change applied to the estimator $\hat{\mathbf{w}}(t)$ in response to the incoming example $\{\mathbf{x}(t), \mathbf{d}(t)\}$. The flow **f** is required to satisfy the condition

$$\mathbb{E}_{\mathbf{x},\mathbf{d}}[\mathbf{f}(\mathbf{x}, \mathbf{d}; \mathbf{w}^*)] = \mathbf{0} \tag{4.78}$$

where $\mathbf{w}^*$ is the optimal value of the weight vector **w**, as previously defined in Eq. (4.57). In other words, the flow **f** must asymptotically converge to the optimal parameter $\mathbf{w}^*$ across time t. Moreover, for stability, we also require that the gradient of **f** should be a positive-definite matrix. The flow **f** includes the gradient vector **g** in Eq. (4.62) as a special case.

The previously defined equations of Eqs. (4.63) through (4.69) apply equally well to Murata's algorithm. Thereafter, however, the assumption made is that the evolution of the learning rate $\eta(t)$ across time t is governed by a dynamic system that comprises the pair of differential equations

$$\frac{d}{dt}\xi(t) = -\lambda\eta(t)\xi(t) \tag{4.79}$$

and

$$\frac{d}{dt}\eta(t) = \alpha\eta(t)(\beta\xi(t) - \eta(t)) \tag{4.80}$$

where it should be noted that $\xi(t)$ is always positive and α and β are positive constants. The first equation of this dynamic system is a repeat of Eq. (4.69). The second equation of the system is motivated by the corresponding differential equation in the learning of the learning algorithm described in Sompolinsky et al. (1995).[7]

As before, the λ in Eq. (4.79) is the eigenvalue associated with the eigenvector **q** of the Hessian $\mathbf{K}^*$. Moreover, it is hypothesized that **q** is chosen as the particular eigenvector associated with the smallest eigenvalue λ_{min}. This, in turn, means that the ensemble-averaged flow **f** converges to the optimal parameter $\mathbf{w}^*$ in a manner similar to that previously described, as depicted in Fig. 4.15.

The *asymptotic behavior* of the dynamic system described in Eqs. (4.79) and (4.80) is given by the corresponding pair of equations

$$\xi(t) = \frac{1}{\beta}\left(\frac{1}{\lambda} - \frac{1}{\alpha}\right)\frac{1}{t}, \qquad \alpha > \lambda \tag{4.81}$$

and

$$\eta(t) = \frac{c}{t}, \qquad c = \lambda^{-1} \tag{4.82}$$

The important point to note here is that this new dynamic system exhibits the desired annealing of the learning rate $\eta(t)$—namely, c/t for large t—which is optimal for any estimator $\hat{\mathbf{w}}(t)$ converging to $\mathbf{w}^*$, as previously discussed.

In light of the considerations just presented, we may now formally describe the *Murata adaptive algorithm* for on-line learning in discrete time as follows (Murata, 1998; Müller et al., 1998):

$$\hat{\mathbf{w}}(n + 1) = \hat{\mathbf{w}}(n) - \eta(n)\mathbf{f}(\mathbf{x}(n + 1), \mathbf{d}(n + 1); \hat{\mathbf{w}}(n)) \tag{4.83}$$

$$\mathbf{r}(n + 1) = \mathbf{r}(n) + \delta\mathbf{f}(\mathbf{x}(n + 1), \mathbf{d}(n + 1); \hat{\mathbf{w}}(n)), \qquad 0 < \delta < 1 \tag{4.84}$$

$$\eta(n + 1) = \eta(n) + \alpha\eta(n)(\beta\|\mathbf{r}(n + 1)\| - \eta(n)) \tag{4.85}$$

The following points are noteworthy in the formulation of this discrete-time system of equations:

- Equation (4.83) is simply the instantaneous discrete-time version of the differential equation of Eq. (4.77).
- Equation (4.84) includes an *auxiliary* vector $\mathbf{r}(n)$, which has been introduced to account for the continuous-time function $\xi\chi(t)$. Moreover, this second equation of the Murata adaptive algorithm includes a *leakage factor* whose value δ controls the running average of the flow $\mathbf{f}$.
- Equation (4.85) is a discrete-time version of the differential equation Eq. (4.80). The updated auxiliary vector $\mathbf{r}(n + 1)$ included in Eq. (4.85) links it to Eq. (4.84); in so doing, allowance is made for the linkage between the continuous-time functions $\xi(t)$ and $\eta(t)$ previously defined in Eqs. (4.79) and (4.80).

Unlike the continuous-time dynamic system described in Eqs. (4.79) and (4.80), the asymptotic behavior of the learning-rate parameter $\eta(t)$ in Eq. (4.85), does not converge to zero as the number of iterations, n, approaches infinity, thereby violating the requirement for optimal annealing. Accordingly, in the neighborhood of the optimal parameter $\mathbf{w}^*$, we now find that for the Murata adaptive algorithm:

$$\lim_{n\to\infty} \hat{\mathbf{w}}(n) \neq \mathbf{w}^* \tag{4.86}$$

This asymptotic behavior is different from that of the optimally annealed on-line learning algorithm of Eq. (4.76). Basically, the deviation from optimal annealing is attributed to the use of a running average of the flow in Eq. (4.77), the inclusion of which was motivated by the need to account for the algorithm not having access to a prescribed cost function, as was the case in deriving the optimally annealed on-line learning algorithm of Eq. (4.76).

The learning of the learning rule is useful when the optimal $\hat{\mathbf{w}}^*$ varies with time n slowly (i.e., the environment responsible for generating the examples is nonstationary) or it changes suddenly. On the other hand, the $1/n$ rule is not a good choice in such an environment, because η_n becomes very small for large n, causing the $1/n$ rule to lose its learning capability. Basically, the difference between the optimally annealed on-learning algorithm of Eq. (4.76) and the on-line learning algorithm described in Eqs. (4.83) to (4.85) is that the latter has a built-in mechanism for adaptive control of the learning rate—hence its ability to *track* variations in the optimal $\hat{\mathbf{w}}^*$.

A final comment is in order: Although the Murata adaptive algorithm is indeed *suboptimal* insofar as annealing of the learning-rate parameter is concerned, its important virtue is the broadened applicability of on-line learning in a practically implementable manner.

4.11 GENERALIZATION

In back-propagation learning, we typically start with a training sample and use the back-propagation algorithm to compute the synaptic weights of a multilayer perceptron by loading (encoding) as many of the training examples as possible into the network. The hope is that the neural network so designed will generalize well. A network is said to *generalize* well when the input–output mapping computed by the network is correct (or nearly so) for test data never used in creating or training the network; the term "generalization" is borrowed from psychology. Here, it is assumed that the test data are drawn from the same population used to generate the training data.

The learning process (i.e., training of a neural network) may be viewed as a "curve-fitting" problem. The network itself may be considered simply as a nonlinear input–output mapping. Such a viewpoint then permits us to look at generalization not as a mystical property of neural networks, but rather simply as the effect of a good nonlinear interpolation of the input data. The network performs useful interpolation primarily because multilayer perceptrons with continuous activation functions lead to output functions that are also continuous.

Figure 4.16a illustrates how generalization may occur in a hypothetical network. The nonlinear input–output mapping represented by the curve depicted in this figure is computed by the network as a result of learning the points labeled as "training data." The point marked in red on the curve as "generalization" is thus seen as the result of interpolation performed by the network.

A neural network that is designed to generalize well will produce a correct input–output mapping even when the input is slightly different from the examples used to train the network, as illustrated in the figure. When, however, a neural network learns too many input–output examples, the network may end up memorizing the training data. It may do so by finding a feature (due to noise, for example) that is present in the training data, but not true of the underlying function that is to be modeled. Such a phenomenon is referred to as *overfitting* or *overtraining*. When the network is overtrained, it loses the ability to generalize between similar input–output patterns.

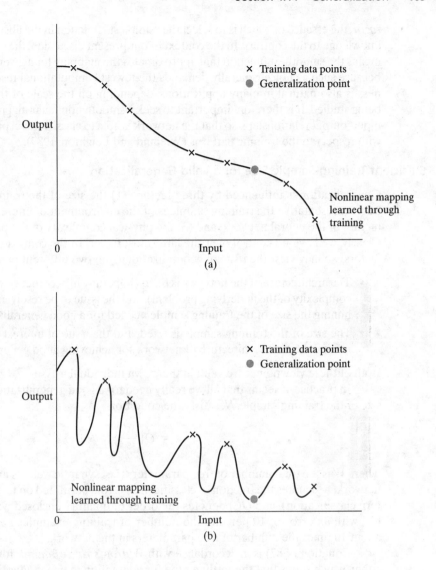

FIGURE 4.16 (a) Properly fitted nonlinear mapping with good generalization. (b) Overfitted nonlinear mapping with poor generalization.

Ordinarily, loading data into a multilayer perceptron in this way requires the use of more hidden neurons than are actually necessary, with the result that undesired contributions in the input space due to noise are stored in synaptic weights of the network. An example of how poor generalization due to memorization in a neural network may occur is illustrated in Fig. 4.16b for the same data as depicted in Fig. 4.16a. "Memorization" is essentially a "look-up table," which implies that the input–output mapping computed by the neural network is not smooth. As pointed out in Poggio and Girosi (1990a), smoothness of input–output mapping is closely related to such model-selection criteria as *Occam's razor*, the essence of which is to select the "simplest" function in the absence of any prior knowledge to the contrary. In the context of our present discussion, the simplest function means the smoothest function that approximates the mapping for a given error criterion, because such a choice generally demands the fewest computational resources. Smoothness is also natural in many applications, depending on the scale of the phenomenon being studied. It is therefore important to seek a smooth nonlinear mapping for ill-posed input–output relationships, so that the network is able to classify novel patterns correctly with respect to the training patterns (Wieland and Leighton, 1987).

Sufficient Training-Sample Size for a Valid Generalization

Generalization is influenced by three factors: (1) the size of the training sample and how representative the training sample is of the environment of interest, (2) the architecture of the neural network, and (3) the physical complexity of the problem at hand. Clearly, we have no control over the lattermost factor. In the context of the other two factors, we may view the issue of generalization from two different perspectives:

- The architecture of the network is fixed (hopefully in accordance with the physical complexity of the underlying problem), and the issue to be resolved is that of determining the size of the training sample needed for a good generalization to occur.
- The size of the training sample is fixed, and the issue of interest is that of determining the best architecture of network for achieving good generalization.

Both of these viewpoints are valid in their own individual ways.

In practice, it seems that all we really need for a good generalization is to have the size of the training sample, N, satisfy the condition

$$N = O\left(\frac{W}{\varepsilon}\right) \tag{4.87}$$

where W is the total number of free parameters (i.e., synaptic weights and biases) in the network, ε denotes the fraction of classification errors permitted on test data (as in pattern classification), and $O(\cdot)$ denotes the order of quantity enclosed within. For example, with an error of 10 percent, the number of training examples needed should be about 10 times the number of free parameters in the network.

Equation (4.87) is in accordance with *Widrow's rule of thumb* for the LMS algorithm, which states that the settling time for adaptation in linear adaptive temporal filtering is approximately equal to the memory span of an adaptive tapped-delay-line filter divided by the misadjustment (Widrow and Stearns, 1985; Haykin, 2002). The misadjustment in the LMS algorithm plays a role somewhat analogous to the error ε in Eq. (4.87). Further justification for this empirical rule is presented in the next section.

4.12   APPROXIMATIONS OF FUNCTIONS

A multilayer perceptron trained with the back-propagation algorithm may be viewed as a practical vehicle for performing a *nonlinear input–output mapping* of a general nature. To be specific, let m_0 denote the number of input (source) nodes of a multilayer perceptron, and let $M = m_L$ denote the number of neurons in the output layer of the network. The input–output relationship of the network defines a mapping from an m_0-dimensional Euclidean input space to an M-dimensional Euclidean output space, which is infinitely continuously differentiable when the activation function is likewise. In assessing the capability of the multilayer perceptron from this viewpoint of input–output mapping, the following fundamental question arises:

> *What is the minimum number of hidden layers in a multilayer perceptron with an input–output mapping that provides an approximate realization of any continuous mapping?*

Universal Approximation Theorem

The answer to this question is embodied in the *universal approximation theorem*[8] for a nonlinear input–output mapping, which may be stated as follows:

> *Let $\varphi(\cdot)$ be a nonconstant, bounded, and monotone-increasing continuous function. Let I_{m_0} denote the m_0-dimensional unit hypercube $[0, 1]^{m_0}$. The space of continuous functions on I_{m_0} is denoted by $C(I_{m_0})$. Then, given any function $f \ni C(I_{m_0})$ and $\varepsilon > 0$, there exist an integer m_1 and sets of real constants $\alpha_i, b_i,$ and w_{ij}, where $i = 1, ..., m_1$ and $j = 1, ..., m_0$ such that we may define*

$$F(x_1, ..., x_{m_0}) = \sum_{i=1}^{m_1} \alpha_i \varphi \left(\sum_{j=1}^{m_0} w_{ij} x_j + b_i \right) \tag{4.88}$$

> *as an approximate realization of the function $f(\cdot)$; that is,*

$$|F(x_1, ..., x_{m_0}) - f(x_1, ..., x_{m_0})| < \varepsilon$$

> *for all $x_1, x_2, ..., x_{m_0}$ that lie in the input space.*

The universal approximation theorem is directly applicable to multilayer perceptrons. We first note, for example, that the hyperbolic tangent function used as the nonlinearity in a neural model for the construction of a multilayer perceptron is indeed a nonconstant, bounded, and monotone-increasing function; it therefore satisfies the conditions imposed on the function $\varphi(\cdot)$ Next, we note that Eq. (4.88) represents the output of a multilayer perceptron described as follows:

1. The network has m_0 input nodes and a single hidden layer consisting of m_1 neurons; the inputs are denoted by $x_1, ..., x_{m_0}$.
2. Hidden neuron i has synaptic weights $w_{i_1}, ..., w_{m_0}$, and bias b_i.
3. The network output is a linear combination of the outputs of the hidden neurons, with $\alpha_1, ..., \alpha_{m_1}$ defining the synaptic weights of the output layer.

The universal approximation theorem is an *existence theorem* in the sense that it provides the mathematical justification for the approximation of an arbitrary continuous function as opposed to exact representation. Equation (4.88), which is the backbone of the theorem, merely generalizes approximations by finite Fourier series. In effect, the theorem states that *a single hidden layer is sufficient for a multilayer perceptron to compute a uniform ε approximation to a given training set represented by the set of inputs $x_1, ..., x_{m_0}$ and a desired (target) output $f(x_1, ..., x_{m_0})$* . However, the theorem does not say that a single hidden layer is optimum in the sense of learning time, ease of implementation, or (more importantly) generalization.

Bounds on Approximation Errors

Barron (1993) has established the approximation properties of a multilayer perceptron, assuming that the network has a single layer of hidden neurons using sigmoid functions and a linear output neuron. The network is trained using the back-propagation algorithm and then tested with new data. During training, the network learns specific points of a target function f in accordance with the training data and thereby produces the approximating function F defined in Eq. (4.88). When the network is exposed to test data that have not been seen before, the network function F acts as an "estimator" of new points of the target function; that is, $F = \hat{f}$.

A smoothness property of the target function f is expressed in terms of its Fourier representation. In particular, the average of the norm of the frequency vector weighted by the Fourier magnitude distribution is used as a measure for the extent to which the function f oscillates. Let $\tilde{f}(\boldsymbol{\omega})$ denote the multidimensional Fourier transform of the function $f(\mathbf{x}), \mathbf{x} \in \mathbb{R}^{m_0}$; the m_0-by-1 vector $\boldsymbol{\omega}$ is the frequency vector. The function $f(x)$ is defined in terms of its Fourier transform $\tilde{f}(\boldsymbol{\omega})$ by the inverse formula

$$f(x) = \int_{\mathbb{R}^{m_0}} \tilde{f}(\boldsymbol{\omega}) \exp(j\boldsymbol{\omega}^T \mathbf{x}) \, d\boldsymbol{\omega} \tag{4.89}$$

where $j = \sqrt{-1}$. For the complex-valued function $\tilde{f}(\boldsymbol{\omega})$ for which $\boldsymbol{\omega}\tilde{f}(\boldsymbol{\omega})$ is integrable, we define the *first absolute moment* of the Fourier magnitude distribution of the function f as

$$C_f = \int_{\mathbb{R}^{m_0}} |\tilde{f}(\boldsymbol{\omega})| \times \|\boldsymbol{\omega}\|^{1/2} \, d\boldsymbol{\omega} \tag{4.90}$$

where $\|\boldsymbol{\omega}\|$ is the Euclidean norm of $\boldsymbol{\omega}$ and $|\tilde{f}(\boldsymbol{\omega})|$ is the absolute value of $\tilde{f}(\boldsymbol{\omega})$. The first absolute moment C_f quantifies the *smoothness* of the function f.

The first absolute moment C_f provides the basis for a *bound* on the error that results from the use of a multilayer perceptron represented by the input–output mapping function $F(\mathbf{x})$ of Eq. (4.88) to approximate $f(\mathbf{x})$. The approximation error is measured by the *integrated squared error* with respect to an arbitrary probability measure μ on the ball $B_r = \{\mathbf{x}: \|\mathbf{x}\| \le r\}$ of radius $r > 0$. On this basis, we may state the following proposition for a bound on the approximation error given by Barron (1993):

For every continuous function $f(\mathbf{x})$ with finite first moment C_f and every $m_1 \ge 1$, there exists a linear combination of sigmoid-based functions $F(\mathbf{x})$ of the form defined in Eq. (4.88) such that when the function $f(\mathbf{x})$ is observed at a set of values of the input vector $\mathbf{x}$ denoted by $\{\mathbf{x}_i\}_{i=1}^N$ that are restricted to lie inside the prescribed ball of radius r, the result provides the following bound on the empirical risk:

$$\mathcal{E}_{av}(N) = \frac{1}{N} \sum_{i=1}^N (f(\mathbf{x}_i) - F(\mathbf{x}_i))^2 \le \frac{C_f'}{m_1} \tag{4.91}$$

where $C_f' = (2rC_f)^2$.

In Barron (1992), the approximation result of Eq. (4.91) is used to express the bound on the risk $\mathscr{E}_{av}(N)$ resulting from the use of a multilayer perceptron with m_0 input nodes and m_1 hidden neurons as follows:

$$\mathscr{E}_{av}(N) \leq O\left(\frac{C_f^2}{m_1}\right) + O\left(\frac{m_0 m_1}{N}\log N\right) \qquad (4.92)$$

The two terms in the bound on the risk $\mathscr{E}_{av}(N)$ express the tradeoff between two conflicting requirements on the size of the hidden layer:

1. *Accuracy of best approximation.* For this requirement to be satisfied, the size of the hidden layer, m_1, must be large in accordance with the universal approximation theorem.

2. *Accuracy of empirical fit to the approximation.* To satisfy this second requirement, we must use a small ratio m_1/N. For a fixed size of training sample, N, the size of the hidden layer, m_1, should be kept small, which is in conflict with the first requirement.

The bound on the risk $\mathscr{E}_{av}(N)$ described in Eq. (4.92) has other interesting implications. Specifically, we see that an exponentially large sample size, large in the dimensionality m_0 of the input space, is *not* required to get an accurate estimate of the target function, provided that the first absolute moment C_f remains finite. This result makes multilayer perceptrons as universal approximators even more important in practical terms.

The error between the empirical fit and the best approximation may be viewed as an *estimation error.* Let ε_0 denote the mean-square value of this estimation error. Then, ignoring the logarithmic factor $\log N$ in the second term of the bound in Eq. (4.92), we may infer that the size N of the training sample needed for a good generalization is about $m_0 m_1/\varepsilon_0$. This result has a mathematical structure similar to the empirical rule of Eq. (4.87), bearing in mind that $m_0 m_1$ is equal to the total number of free parameters W in the network. In other words, we may generally say that for good generalization, the number N of training examples should be larger than the ratio of the total number of free parameters in the network to the mean-square value of the estimation error.

Curse of Dimensionality

Another interesting result that emerges from the bounds described in (4.92) is that when the size of the hidden layer is optimized (i.e., the risk $\mathscr{E}_{av}(N)$ is minimized with respect to N) by setting

$$m_1 \simeq C_f\left(\frac{N}{m_0 \log N}\right)^{1/2}$$

then the risk $\mathscr{E}_{av}(N)$ is bounded by $O(C_f\sqrt{m_0}(\log N/N)$. A surprising aspect of this result is that in terms of the first-order behavior of the risk $\mathscr{E}_{av}(N)$, the rate of convergence expressed as a function of the training-sample size N is·of order $(1/N)^{1/2}$ (times a logarithmic factor). In contrast, for traditional smooth functions (e.g., polynomials and trigonometric functions), we have a different behavior. Let s denote a measure of *smoothness*, defined as the number of continuous derivatives of a function of interest. Then, for traditional smooth functions, we find that the minimax rate of convergence of the total risk $\mathscr{E}_{av}(N)$ is of order $(1/N)^{2s/(2s+mo)}$. The dependence of this rate on the dimensionality of the input space, m_0, is responsible for the *curse of dimensionality*, which severely restricts the practical application of these functions. The use of a multilayer perceptron for function approximation appears to offer an advantage over the use of traditional smooth functions. This advantage is, however, subject to the condition that the first absolute moment C_f remains finite; this is a smoothness constraint.

The curse of dimensionality was introduced by Richard Bellman in his studies of adaptive control processes (Bellman, 1961). For a geometric interpretation of this notion, let $\mathbf{x}$ denote an m_0-dimensional input vector and $\{(\mathbf{x}_i, d_i)\}$, $i = 1, 2, ..., N$, denote the training sample. The *sampling density* is proportional to N^{1/m_0}. Let a function $f(\mathbf{x})$ represent a surface lying in the m_0-dimensional input space that passes near the data points $\{(\mathbf{x}_i, d_i)\}_{i=1}^{N}$. Now, if the function $f(\mathbf{x})$ is arbitrarily complex and (for the most part) completely unknown, we need *dense* sample (data) points to learn it well. Unfortunately, dense samples are hard to find in "high dimensions"—hence the curse of dimensionality. In particular, there is an *exponential* growth in complexity as a result of an increase in dimensionality, which, in turn, leads to the deterioration of the space-filling properties for uniformly randomly distributed points in higher-dimension spaces. The basic reason for the curse of dimensionality is as follows (Friedman, 1995):

> *A function defined in high-dimensional space is likely to be much more complex than a function defined in a lower-dimensional space, and those complications are harder to discern.*

Basically, there are only two ways of mitigating the curse-of-dimensionality problem:

1. Incorporate *prior knowledge* about the unknown function to be approximated. This knowledge is provided over and above the training data. Naturally, the acquisition of knowledge is problem dependent. In pattern classification, for example, knowledge may be acquired from understanding the pertinent classes (categories) of the input data.

2. Design the network so as to provide increasing *smoothness* of the unknown function with increasing input dimensionality.

Practical Considerations

The universal approximation theorem is important from a theoretical viewpoint because it provides the *necessary mathematical tool* for the viability of feedforward networks with a single hidden layer as a class of approximate solutions. Without such a theorem, we could conceivably be searching for a solution that cannot exist. However, the theorem is not constructive; that is, it does not actually specify how to determine a multilayer perceptron with the stated approximation properties.

The universal approximation theorem assumes that the continuous function to be approximated is given and that a hidden layer of unlimited size is available for the approximation. Both of these assumptions are violated in most practical applications of multilayer perceptrons.

The problem with multilayer perceptrons using a single hidden layer is that the neurons therein tend to interact with each other globally. In complex situations, this interaction makes it difficult to improve the approximation at one point without worsening it at some other point. On the other hand, with two hidden layers, the approximation (curve-fitting) process becomes more manageable. In particular, we may proceed as follows (Funahashi, 1989; Chester, 1990):

1. *Local features* are extracted in the first hidden layer. Specifically, some neurons in the first hidden layer are used to partition the input space into regions, and other neurons in that layer learn the local features characterizing those regions.

2. *Global features* are extracted in the second hidden layer. Specifically, a neuron in the second hidden layer combines the outputs of neurons in the first hidden layer operating on a particular region of the input space and thereby learns the global features for that region and outputs zero elsewhere.

Further justification for the use of two hidden layers is presented in Sontag (1992) in the context of *inverse problems*.

4.13 CROSS-VALIDATION

The essence of back-propagation learning is to encode an input–output mapping (represented by a set of labeled examples) into the synaptic weights and thresholds of a multilayer perceptron. The hope is that the network becomes well trained so that it learns enough about the past to generalize to the future. From such a perspective, the learning process amounts to a choice of network parameterization for a given set of data. More specifically, we may view the network selection problem as choosing, within a set of candidate model structures (parameterizations), the "best" one according to a certain criterion.

In this context, a standard tool in statistics, known as *cross-validation*, provides an appealing guiding principle[9] (Stone, 1974, 1978). First the available data set is randomly partitioned into a training sample and a test set. The training sample is further partitioned into two disjoint subsets:

- *an estimation subset*, used to select the model;
- *a validation subset*, used to test or validate the model.

The motivation here is to validate the model on a data set different from the one used for parameter estimation. In this way, we may use the training sample to assess the performance of various candidate models and thereby choose the "best" one. There is, however, a distinct possibility that the model with the best-performing parameter values so selected may end up overfitting the validation subset. To guard against this possibility, the generalization performance of the selected model is measured on the test set, which is different from the validation subset.

The use of cross-validation is appealing particularly when we have to design a large neural network with good generalization as the goal. For example, we may use cross-validation to determine the multilayer perceptron with the best number of hidden neurons and to figure out when it is best to stop training, as described in the next two subsections.

Model Selection

To expand on the idea of selecting a model in accordance with cross-validation, consider a nested *structure* of Boolean function classes denoted by

$$\mathcal{F}_1 \subset \mathcal{F}_2 \subset \cdots \subset \mathcal{F}_n \tag{4.93}$$
$$\mathcal{F}_k = \{F_k\}$$
$$= \{F(\mathbf{x}, \mathbf{w}); \mathbf{w} \in \mathcal{W}_k\}, \quad k = 1, 2, ..., n$$

In words, the kth function class $\mathcal{F}_k$ encompasses a family of multilayer perceptrons with similar architecture and weight vectors $\mathbf{w}$ drawn from a multidimensional weight space $\mathcal{W}_k$. A member of this class, characterized by the function or hypothesis $F_k = F(\mathbf{x}, \mathbf{w})$, $\mathbf{w} \in \mathcal{W}_k$, maps the input vector $\mathbf{x}$ into $\{0, 1\}$, where $\mathbf{x}$ is drawn from an input space $\mathcal{X}$ with some unknown probability P. Each multilayer perceptron in the structure described is trained with the back-propagation algorithm, which takes care of training the parameters of the multilayer perceptron. The model-selection problem is essentially that of choosing the multilayer perceptron with the best value of $\mathbf{w}$, the number of free parameters (i.e., synaptic weights and biases). More precisely, given that the scalar desired response for an input vector $\mathbf{x}$ is $d = \{0, 1\}$, we define the generalization error as the probability

$$\varepsilon_g(F) = P(F(\mathbf{x}) \neq d) \quad \text{for } \mathbf{x} \in \mathcal{X}$$

We are given a training sample of labeled examples

$$\mathcal{T} = \{(\mathbf{x}_i, d_i)\}_{i=1}^N$$

The objective is to select the particular hypothesis $F(\mathbf{x}, \mathbf{w})$ that minimizes the generalization error $\varepsilon_g(F)$, which results when it is given inputs from the test set.

In what follows, we assume that the structure described by Eq. (4.93) has the property that, for any sample size N, we can always find a multilayer perceptron with a large enough number of free parameters $W_{max}(N)$ such that the training sample $\mathcal{T}$ can be fitted adequately. This assumption is merely restating the universal approximation theorem of Section 4.12. We refer to $W_{max}(N)$ as the *fitting number*. The significance of $W_{max}(N)$ is that a reasonable model-selection procedure would choose a hypothesis $F(\mathbf{x}, \mathbf{w})$ that requires $W \leq W_{max}(N)$; otherwise, the network complexity would be increased.

Let a parameter r, lying in the range between 0 and 1, determine the split of the training sample $\mathcal{T}$ between the estimation subset and validation subset. With $\mathcal{T}$ consisting of N examples, $(1 - r)N$ examples are allotted to the estimation subset, and the remaining rN examples are allotted to the validation subset. The estimation subset, denoted by $\mathcal{T}'$, is used to train a nested sequence of multilayer perceptrons, resulting in the hypotheses $\mathcal{F}_1, \mathcal{F}_2, ..., \mathcal{F}_n$ of increasing complexity. With $\mathcal{T}'$ made up of $(1-r)N$ examples, we consider values of W smaller than or equal to the corresponding fitting number $W_{max}((1-r)N)$.

The use of cross-validation results in the choice

$$\mathcal{F}_{cv} = \min_{k=1,2,\ldots,v} \{e_t''(\mathcal{F}_k)\} \tag{4.94}$$

where v corresponds to $W_v \leq W_{\max}((1-r)N)$, and $e_t''(\mathcal{F}_k)$ is the classification error produced by hypothesis $\mathcal{F}_k$ when it is tested on the validation subset $\mathcal{T}''$, consisting of rN examples.

The key issue is how to specify the parameter r that determines the split of the training sample $\mathcal{T}$ between the estimation subset $\mathcal{T}'$ and validation subset $\mathcal{T}''$. In a study described in Kearns (1996) involving an analytic treatment of this issue and supported with detailed computer simulations, several qualitative properties of the optimum r are identified:

- When the complexity of the target function, which defines the desired response d in terms of the input vector $\mathbf{x}$, is small compared with the sample size N, the performance of cross-validation is relatively insensitive to the choice of r.
- As the target function becomes more complex relative to the sample size N, the choice of optimum r has a more pronounced effect on cross-validation performance, and the value of the target function itself decreases.
- A single *fixed* value of r works *nearly* optimally for a wide range of target-function complexity.

On the basis of the results reported in Kearns (1996), a fixed value of r equal to 0.2 appears to be a sensible choice, which means that 80 percent of the training sample $\mathcal{T}$ is assigned to the estimation subset and the remaining 20 percent is assigned to the validation subset.

Early-Stopping Method of Training

Ordinarily, a multilayer perceptron trained with the back-propagation algorithm learns in stages, moving from the realization of fairly simple to more complex mapping functions as the training session progresses. This process is exemplified by the fact that in a typical situation, the mean-square error decreases with an increasing number of epochs used for training: It starts off at a large value, decreases rapidly, and then continues to decrease slowly as the network makes its way to a local minimum on the error surface. With good generalization as the goal, it is very difficult to figure out when it is best to stop training if we were to look at the learning curve for training all by itself. In particular, in light of what was said in Section 4.11 on generalization, it is possible for the network to end up overfitting the training data if the training session is not stopped at the right point.

We may identify the onset of overfitting through the use of cross-validation, for which the training data are split into an estimation subset and a validation subset. The estimation subset of examples is used to train the network in the usual way, except for a minor modification: The training session is stopped periodically (i.e., every so many epochs), and the network is tested on the validation subset after each period of training. More specifically, the periodic "estimation-followed-by-validation process" proceeds as follows:

- After a period of estimation (training)—every five epochs, for example—the synaptic weights and bias levels of the multilayer perceptron are all fixed, and the network is operated in its forward mode. The validation error is thus measured for each example in the validation subset.

- When the validation phase is completed, the estimation (training) is resumed for another period, and the process is repeated.

This procedure is referred to as the *early-stopping method of training*, which is simple to understand and therefore widely used in practice.

Figure 4.17 shows conceptualized forms of two learning curves, one pertaining to measurements on the estimation subset and the other pertaining to the validation subset. Typically, the model does not do as well on the validation subset as it does on the estimation subset, on which its design was based. The *estimation learning curve* decreases monotonically for an increasing number of epochs in the usual manner. In contrast, the *validation learning curve* decreases monotonically to a minimum and then starts to increase as the training continues. When we look at the estimation learning curve, it may appear that we could do better by going beyond the minimum point on the validation learning curve. In reality, however, what the network is learning beyond this point is essentially noise contained in the training data. This heuristic suggests that the minimum point on the validation learning curve be used as a sensible criterion for stopping the training session.

However, a word of caution is in order here. In reality, the validation-sample error does *not* evolve over the number of epochs used for training as smoothly as the idealized curve shown in Fig. 4.17. Rather, the validation-sample error may exhibit few local minima of its own before it starts to increase with an increasing number of epochs. In such situations, a stopping criterion must be selected in some systematic manner. An empirical investigation on multilayer perceptrons carried out by Prechelt (1998) demonstrates experimentally that there is, in fact, a tradeoff between training time and generalization performance. Based on experimental results obtained therein on 1,296 training sessions, 12 different problems, and 24 different network architectures, it is concluded that, in the presence of two or more local minima, the selection of a "slower" stopping criterion (i.e., a criterion that stops later than other criteria) permits the attainment of a small improvement in generalization performance (typically, about 4 percent, on average) at the cost of a much longer training time (about a factor of four, on average).

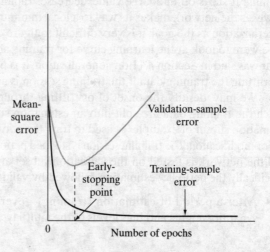

FIGURE 4.17 Illustration of the early-stopping rule based on cross-validation.

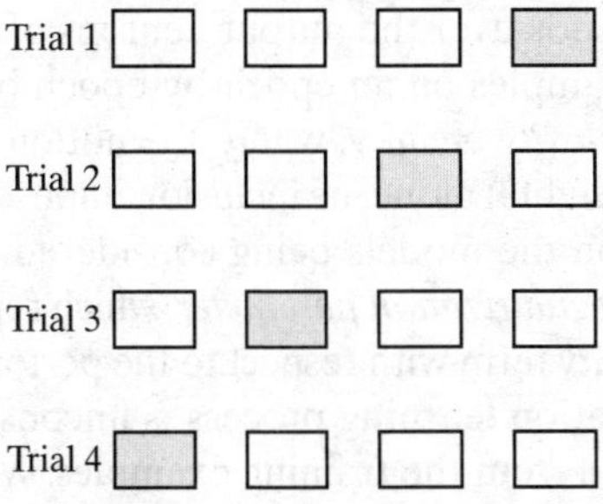

Trial 1 ☐ ☐ ☐ ▨

Trial 2 ☐ ☐ ▨ ☐

Trial 3 ☐ ▨ ☐ ☐

Trial 4 ▨ ☐ ☐ ☐

FIGURE 4.18 Illustration of the multifold method of cross-validation. For a given trial, the subset of data shaded in red is used to validate the model trained on the remaining data.

Variants of Cross-Validation

The approach to cross-validation just described is also referred to as the *holdout method*. There are other variants of cross-validation that find their own uses in practice, particularly when there is a scarcity of labeled examples. In such a situation, we may use *multifold cross-validation* by dividing the available set of N examples into K subsets, where $K > 1$; this procedure assumes that K is divisible into N. The model is trained on all the subsets except for one, and the validation error is measured by testing it on the subset that is left out. This procedure is repeated for a total of K trials, each time using a different subset for validation, as illustrated in Fig. 4.18 for $K = 4$. The performance of the model is assessed by averaging the squared error under validation over all the trials of the experiment. There is a disadvantage to multifold cross-validation: It may require an excessive amount of computation, since the model has to be trained K times, where $1 < K \le N$.

When the available number of labeled examples, N, is severely limited, we may use the extreme form of multifold cross-validation known as the *leave-one-out method*. In this case, $N - 1$ examples are used to train the model, and the model is validated by testing it on the example that is left out. The experiment is repeated for a total of N times, each time leaving out a different example for validation. The squared error under validation is then averaged over the N trials of the experiment.

4.14   COMPLEXITY REGULARIZATION AND NETWORK PRUNING

In designing a multilayer perceptron by whatever method, we are in effect building a non-linear *model* of the physical phenomenon responsible for the generation of the input–output examples used to train the network. Insofar as the network design is statistical in nature, we need an appropriate tradeoff between reliability of the training data and goodness of the model (i.e., a method for solving the bias–variance dilemma discussed in Chapter 2). In the context of back-propagation learning, or any other supervised learning procedure for that matter, we may realize this tradeoff by minimizing the *total risk*, expressed as a function of the parameter vector $\mathbf{w}$, as follows:

$$R(\mathbf{w}) = \mathscr{E}_{av}(\mathbf{w}) + \lambda \mathscr{E}_c(\mathbf{w}) \tag{4.95}$$

The first term, $\mathscr{E}_{av}(\mathbf{w})$, is the standard *performance metric*, which depends on both the network (model) and the input data. In back-propagation learning, it is typically defined as a mean-square error whose evaluation extends over the output neurons of the network and is carried out for all the training examples on an epoch-by-epoch basis, see Eq. (4.5). The second term, $\mathcal{E}_c(\mathbf{w})$, is the *complexity penalty*, where the notion of complexity is measured in terms of the network (weights) alone; its inclusion imposes on the solution prior knowledge that we may have on the models being considered. For the present discussion, it suffices to think of λ as a *regularization parameter*, which represents the relative importance of the complexity-penalty term with respect to the performance-metric term. When λ is zero, the back-propagation learning process is unconstrained, with the network being completely determined from the training examples. When λ is made infinitely large, on the other hand, the implication is that the constraint imposed by the complexity penalty is by itself sufficient to specify the network, which is another way of saying that the training examples are unreliable. In practical applications of complexity regularization, the regularization parameter λ is assigned a value somewhere between these two limiting cases. The subject of regularization theory is discussed in great detail in Chapter 7.

Weight-Decay Procedure

In a simplified, yet effective, form of complex regularization called the *weight-decay procedure* (Hinton, 1989), the complexity penalty term is defined as the squared norm of the weight vector $\mathbf{w}$ (i.e., all the free parameters) in the network, as shown by

$$\begin{aligned}
\mathcal{E}_c(\mathbf{w}) &= \|\mathbf{w}\|^2 \\
&= \sum_{i \in \mathcal{C}_{\text{total}}} w_i^2
\end{aligned} \tag{4.96}$$

where the set $\mathcal{C}_{\text{total}}$ refers to all the synaptic weights in the network. This procedure operates by forcing some of the synaptic weights in the network to take values close to zero, while permitting other weights to retain their relatively large values. Accordingly, the weights of the network are grouped roughly into two categories:

  (i) weights that have a significant influence on the network's performance;

  (ii) weights that have practically little or no influence on the network's performance.

The weights in the latter category are referred to as *excess weights*. In the absence of complexity regularization, these weights result in poor generalization by virtue of their high likelihood of taking on completely arbitrary values or causing the network to overfit the data in order to produce a slight reduction in the training error (Hush and Horne, 1993). The use of complexity regularization encourages the excess weights to assume values close to zero and thereby improve generalization.

Hessian-Based Network Pruning: Optimal Brain Surgeon

The basic idea of an analytic approach to network pruning is to use information on second-order derivatives of the error surface in order to make a trade-off between network complexity and training-error performance. In particular, a local model of the error surface is constructed for analytically predicting the effect of perturbations in synaptic weights. The starting point in the construction of such a model is the local approximation of the cost function $\mathcal{E}_{av}$ by using a *Taylor series* about the operating point, described as

$$\mathcal{E}_{av}(\mathbf{w} + \Delta\mathbf{w}) = \mathcal{E}_{av}(\mathbf{w}) + \mathbf{g}^T(\mathbf{w})\Delta\mathbf{w} + \frac{1}{2}\Delta\mathbf{w}^T\mathbf{H}\Delta\mathbf{w} + O(\|\Delta\mathbf{w}\|^3) \quad (4.97)$$

where $\Delta\mathbf{w}$ is a perturbation applied to the operating point $\mathbf{w}$ and $\mathbf{g}(\mathbf{w})$ is the gradient vector evaluated at $\mathbf{w}$. The Hessian is also evaluated at the point $\mathbf{w}$, and therefore, to be correct, we should denote it by $\mathbf{H}(\mathbf{w})$. We have not done so in Eq. (4.97) merely to simplify the notation.

The requirement is to identify a set of parameters whose deletion from the multilayer perceptron will cause the least increase in the value of the cost function $\mathcal{E}_{av}$. To solve this problem in practical terms, we make the following approximations:

1. *Extremal Approximation.* We assume that parameters are deleted from the network only after the training process has converged (i.e., the network is fully trained). The implication of this assumption is that the parameters have a set of values corresponding to a local minimum or global minimum of the error surface. In such a case, the gradient vector $\mathbf{g}$ may be set equal to zero, and the term $\mathbf{g}^T\Delta\mathbf{w}$ on the right-hand side of Eq. (4.97) may therefore be ignored; otherwise, the saliency measures (defined later) will be invalid for the problem at hand.

2. *Quadratic Approximation.* We assume that the error surface around a local minimum or global minimum is "nearly quadratic." Hence, the higher-order terms in Eq. (4.97) may also be neglected.

Under these two assumptions, Eq. (4.97) is simplified as

$$\begin{aligned} \Delta\mathcal{E}_{av} &= \mathcal{E}(\mathbf{w} + \Delta\mathbf{w}) - \mathcal{E}(\mathbf{w}) \\ &= \frac{1}{2}\Delta\mathbf{w}^T\mathbf{H}\Delta\mathbf{w} \end{aligned} \quad (4.98)$$

Equation (4.98) provides the basis for the pruning procedure called *optimal brain surgeon* (OBS), which is due to Hassibi and Stork (1993).

The goal of OBS is to set one of the synaptic weights to zero in order to minimize the incremental increase in $\mathcal{E}_{av}$ given in Eq. (4.98). Let $w_i(n)$ denote this particular synaptic weight. The elimination of this weight is equivalent to the condition

$$\mathbf{1}_i^T \Delta\mathbf{w} + w_i = 0 \quad (4.99)$$

where $\mathbf{1}_i$ is the *unit vector* whose elements are all zero, except for the ith element, which is equal to unity. We may now restate the goal of OBS as follows:

Minimize the quadratic form $\frac{1}{2}\Delta\mathbf{w}^T\mathbf{H}\Delta\mathbf{w}$ with respect to the incremental change in the weight vector, $\Delta\mathbf{w}$, subject to the constraint that $\mathbf{1}_i^T\Delta\mathbf{w} + w_i$ is zero, and then minimize the result with respect to the index i.

There are two levels of minimization going on here. One minimization is over the synaptic-weight vectors that remain after the ith weight vector is set equal to zero. The second minimization is over which particular vector is pruned.

To solve this constrained-optimization problem, we first construct the *Lagrangian*

$$S = \frac{1}{2}\Delta\mathbf{w}^T\mathbf{H}\Delta\mathbf{w} - \lambda(\mathbf{1}_i^T\Delta\mathbf{w} + w_i) \tag{4.100}$$

where λ is the *Lagrange multiplier*. Then, taking the derivative of the Lagrangian S with respect to $\Delta\mathbf{w}$, applying the constraint of Eq. (4.99), and using matrix inversion, we find that the optimum change in the weight vector $\mathbf{w}$ is given by

$$\Delta\mathbf{w} = -\frac{w_i}{[\mathbf{H}^{-1}]_{i,i}}\mathbf{H}^{-1}\mathbf{1}_i \tag{4.101}$$

and the corresponding optimum value of the Lagrangian S for element w_i is

$$S_i = \frac{w_i^2}{2[\mathbf{H}^{-1}]_{i,i}} \tag{4.102}$$

where $\mathbf{H}^{-1}$ is the inverse of the Hessian $\mathbf{H}$, and $[\mathbf{H}^{-1}]_{i,i}$ is the ii-th element of this inverse matrix. The Lagrangian S_i optimized with respect to $\Delta\mathbf{w}$, subject to the constraint that the ith synaptic weight w_i be eliminated, is called the *saliency* of w_i. In effect, the saliency S_i represents the increase in the mean-square error (performance measure) that results from the deletion of w_i. Note that the saliency S_i, is proportional to w_i^2. Thus, small weights have a small effect on the mean-square error. However, from Eq. (4.102), we see that the saliency S_i, is also inversely proportional to the diagonal elements of the inverse Hessian. Thus, if $[\mathbf{H}^{-1}]_{i,i}$ is small, then even small weights may have a substantial effect on the mean-square error.

In the OBS procedure, the weight corresponding to the smallest saliency is the one selected for deletion. Moreover, the corresponding optimal changes in the remainder of the weights are given in Eq. (4.101), which show that they should be updated along the direction of the i-th column of the inverse of the Hessian.

According to Hassibi and coworkers commenting on some benchmark problems, the OBS procedure resulted in smaller networks than those obtained using the weight-decay procedure. It is also reported that as a result of applying the OBS procedure to the NETtalk multilayer perceptron, involving a single hidden layer and well over 18,000 weights, the network was pruned to a mere 1,560 weights, a dramatic reduction in the size of the network. NETtalk, due to Sejnowski and Rosenberg (1987), is described in Section 4.18.

Computing the inverse Hessian. The inverse Hessian $\mathbf{H}^{-1}$ is fundamental to the formulation of the OBS procedure. When the number of free parameters, W, in the network is large, the problem of computing $\mathbf{H}^{-1}$ may be intractable. In what follows, we describe a manageable procedure for computing $\mathbf{H}^{-1}$, assuming that the multilayer perceptron is fully trained to a local minimum on the error surface (Hassibi and Stork, 1993).

To simplify the presentation, suppose that the multilayer perceptron has a single output neuron. Then, for a given training sample, we may redefine the cost function of Eq. (4.5) as

$$\mathcal{E}_{av}(\mathbf{w}) = \frac{1}{2N}\sum_{n=1}^{N}(d(n) - o(n))^2$$

where $o(n)$ is the actual output of the network on the presentation of the nth example, $d(n)$ is the corresponding desired response, and N is the total number of examples in the training sample. The output $o(n)$ may itself be expressed as

$$o(n) = F(\mathbf{w}, \mathbf{x})$$

where F is the input–output mapping function realized by the multilayer perceptron, $\mathbf{x}$ is the input vector, and $\mathbf{w}$ is the synaptic-weight vector of the network. The first derivative of $\mathscr{E}_{av}$ with respect to $\mathbf{w}$ is therefore

$$\frac{\partial \mathscr{E}_{av}}{\partial \mathbf{w}} = -\frac{1}{N}\sum_{n=1}^{N}\frac{\partial F(\mathbf{w}, \mathbf{x}(n))}{\partial \mathbf{w}}(d(n) - o(n)) \tag{4.103}$$

and the second derivative of $\mathscr{E}_{av}$ with respect to $\mathbf{w}$ or the Hessian is

$$\begin{aligned}
\mathbf{H}(N) &= \frac{\partial^2 \mathscr{E}_{av}}{\partial \mathbf{w}^2} \\
&= \frac{1}{N}\sum_{n=1}^{N}\left\{\left(\frac{\partial F(\mathbf{w}, \mathbf{x}(n))}{\partial \mathbf{w}}\right)\left(\frac{\partial F(\mathbf{w}, \mathbf{x}(n))}{\partial \mathbf{w}}\right)^T\right. \\
&\quad \left. -\frac{\partial^2 F(\mathbf{w}, \mathbf{x}(n))}{\partial \mathbf{w}^2}(d(n) - o(n))\right\}
\end{aligned} \tag{4.104}$$

where we have emphasized the dependence of the Hessian on the size of the training sample, N.

Under the assumption that the network is fully trained—that is, the cost function $\mathscr{E}_{av}$ has been adjusted to a local minimum on the error surface—it is reasonable to say that $o(n)$ is close to $d(n)$. Under this condition, we may ignore the second term and approximate Eq. (4.104) as

$$\mathbf{H}(N) \approx \frac{1}{N}\sum_{n=1}^{N}\left(\frac{\partial F(\mathbf{w}, \mathbf{x}(n))}{\partial \mathbf{w}}\right)\left(\frac{\partial F(\mathbf{w}, \mathbf{x}(n))}{\partial \mathbf{w}}\right)^T \tag{4.105}$$

To simplify the notation, define the W-by-1 vector

$$\boldsymbol{\xi}(n) = \frac{1}{\sqrt{N}}\frac{\partial F(\mathbf{w}, \mathbf{x}(n))}{\partial \mathbf{w}} \tag{4.106}$$

which may be computed using the procedure described in Section 4.8. We may then rewrite Eq. (4.105) in the form of a recursion as follows:

$$\begin{aligned}
\mathbf{H}(n) &= \sum_{k=1}^{n}\boldsymbol{\xi}(k)\boldsymbol{\xi}^T(k) \\
&= \mathbf{H}(n-1) + \boldsymbol{\xi}(n)\boldsymbol{\xi}^T(n), \qquad n = 1, 2, ..., N
\end{aligned} \tag{4.107}$$

This recursion is in the right form for application of the so-called *matrix inversion lemma*, also known as *Woodbury's equality*.

Let $\mathbf{A}$ and $\mathbf{B}$ denote two positive-definite matrices related by

$$\mathbf{A} = \mathbf{B}^{-1} + \mathbf{CDC}^T$$

where $\mathbf{C}$ and $\mathbf{D}$ are two other matrices. According to the matrix inversion lemma, the inverse of matrix $\mathbf{A}$ is defined by

$$\mathbf{A}^{-1} = \mathbf{B} - \mathbf{BC}(\mathbf{D} + \mathbf{C}^T\mathbf{BC})^{-1}\mathbf{C}^T\mathbf{B}$$

For the problem described in Eq. (4.107) we have

$$\mathbf{A} = \mathbf{H}(n)$$
$$\mathbf{B}^{-1} = \mathbf{H}(n-1)$$
$$\mathbf{C} = \boldsymbol{\xi}(n)$$
$$\mathbf{D} = 1$$

Application of the matrix inversion lemma therefore yields the desired formula for recursive computation of the inverse Hessian:

$$\mathbf{H}^{-1}(n) = \mathbf{H}^{-1}(n-1) - \frac{\mathbf{H}^{-1}(n-1)\boldsymbol{\xi}(n)\boldsymbol{\xi}^T(n)\mathbf{H}^{-1}(n-1)}{1 + \boldsymbol{\xi}^T(n)\mathbf{H}^{-1}(n-1)\boldsymbol{\xi}(n)} \qquad (4.108)$$

Note that the denominator in Eq. (4.108) is a scalar; it is therefore straightforward to calculate its reciprocal. Thus, given the past value of the inverse Hessian, $\mathbf{H}^{-1}(n-1)$, we may compute its updated value $\mathbf{H}^{-1}(n)$ on the presentation of the nth example, represented by the vector $\boldsymbol{\xi}(n)$. This recursive computation is continued until the entire set of N examples has been accounted for. To initialize the algorithm, we need to make $\mathbf{H}^{-1}(0)$ large, since it is being constantly reduced according to Eq. (4.108). This requirement is satisfied by setting

$$\mathbf{H}^{-1}(0) = \delta^{-1}\mathbf{I}$$

where δ is a small positive number and $\mathbf{I}$ is the identity matrix. This form of initialization assures that $\mathbf{H}^{-1}(n)$ is always positive definite. The effect of δ becomes progressively smaller as more and more examples are presented to the network.

A summary of the optimal-brain-surgeon algorithm is presented in Table 4.1.

4.15 VIRTUES AND LIMITATIONS OF BACK-PROPAGATION LEARNING

First and foremost, it should be understood that the back-propagation algorithm is *not* an algorithm intended for the optimum design of a multilayer perceptron. Rather, the correct way to describe it is to say:

> *The back-propagation algorithm is a computationally efficient technique for computing the gradients (i.e., first-order derivatives) of the cost function $\mathcal{E}(w)$, expressed as a function of the adjustable parameters (synaptic weights and bias terms) that characterize the multilayer perceptron.*

The computational power of the algorithm is derived from two distinct properties:

1. The back-propagation algorithm is *simple to compute locally.*
2. It performs *stochastic gradient descent* in weight space, when the algorithm is implemented in its on-line (sequential) mode of learning.

TABLE 4.1   Summary of the Optimal-Brain-Surgeon Algorithm

1. Train the given multilayer perceptron to minimum mean-square error.
2. Use the procedure described in Section 4.8 to compute the vector

$$\xi(n) = \frac{1}{\sqrt{N}} \frac{\partial F(\mathbf{w}, \mathbf{x}(n))}{\partial \mathbf{w}}$$

   where $F(\mathbf{w}, \mathbf{x}(n))$ is the input–output mapping realized by the multilayer perceptron with an overall weight vector $\mathbf{w}$, and $\mathbf{x}(n)$ is the input vector.
3. Use the recursion in Eq. (4.108) to compute the inverse Hessian $\mathbf{H}^{-1}$.
4. Find the i that corresponds to the smallest saliency

$$S_i = \frac{w_i^2}{2[\mathbf{H}^{-1}]_{i,i}}$$

   where $[\mathbf{H}^{-1}]_{i,i}$ is the (i, i)th element of $\mathbf{H}^{-1}$. If the saliency S_i is much smaller than the mean-square error $\mathcal{E}_{av}$, then delete the synaptic weight w_i and proceed to step 5. Otherwise, go to step 6.
5. Update all the synaptic weights in the network by applying the adjustment

$$\Delta \mathbf{w} = -\frac{w_i}{[\mathbf{H}^{-1}]_{i,i}} \mathbf{H}^{-1} \mathbf{1}_i$$

   Go to step 2.
6. Stop the computation when no more weights can be deleted from the network without a large increase in the mean-square error. (It may be desirable to retrain the network at this point).

Connectionism

The back-propagation algorithm is an example of a *connectionist paradigm* that relies on local computations to discover the information-processing capabilities of neural networks. This form of computational restriction is referred to as the *locality constraint*, in the sense that the computation performed by each neuron in the network is influenced solely by those other neurons that are in physical contact with it. The use of local computations in the design of (artificial) neural networks is usually advocated for three principal reasons:

1. Neural networks that perform local computations are often held up as *metaphors* for biological neural networks.
2. The use of local computations permits a graceful degradation in performance caused by hardware errors and therefore provides the basis for a *fault-tolerant* network design.
3. Local computations favor the use of *parallel architectures* as an efficient method for the implementation of neural networks.

Replicator (Identity) Mapping

The hidden neurons of a multilayer perceptron trained with the back-propagation algorithm play a critical role as feature detectors. A novel way in which this important property of the multilayer perceptron can be exploited is in its use as a *replicator* or *identity map* (Rumelhart et al., 1986b; Cottrel et al., 1987). Figure 4.19 illustrates

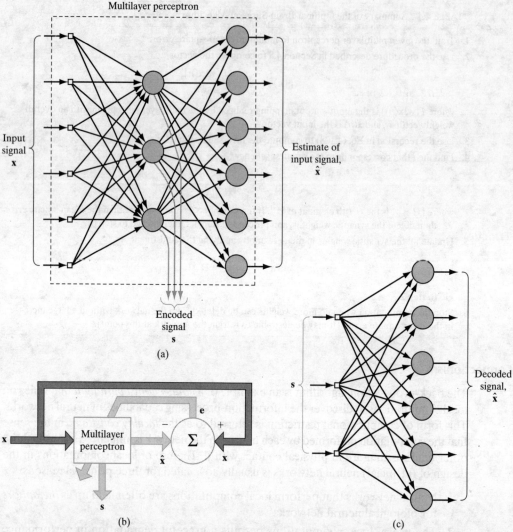

FIGURE 4.19 (a) Replicator network (identity map) with a single hidden layer used as an encoder. (b) Block diagram for the supervised training of the replicator network. (c) Part of the replicator network used as a decoder.

how this can be accomplished for the case of a multilayer perceptron using a single hidden layer. The network layout satisfies the following structural requirements, as illustrated in Fig. 4.19a:

- The input and output layers have the same size, m.
- The size of the hidden layer, M, is smaller than m.
- The network is fully connected.

A given pattern $\mathbf{x}$ is simultaneously applied to the input layer as the stimulus and to the output layer as the desired response. The actual response of the output layer, $\hat{\mathbf{x}}$, is intended to be an "estimate" of **x**. The network is trained using the back-propagation algorithm in the usual way, with the estimation error vector $(\mathbf{x} - \hat{\mathbf{x}})$ treated as the error signal, as illustrated in Fig. 4.19b. The training is performed in an *unsupervised* manner (i.e., without the need for a teacher). By virtue of the special structure built into the design of the multilayer perceptron, the network is *constrained* to perform identity mapping through its hidden layer. An *encoded* version of the input pattern, denoted by **s**, is produced at the output of the hidden layer, as indicated in Fig. 4.19a. In effect, the fully trained multilayer perceptron performs the role of an "encoder." To reconstruct an estimate $\hat{\mathbf{x}}$ of the original input pattern **x** (i.e., to perform *decoding*), we apply the encoded signal to the hidden layer of the replicator network, as illustrated in Fig. 4.19c. In effect, this latter network performs the role of a "decoder." The smaller we make the size M of the hidden layer compared with the size m of the input–output layer, the more effective the configuration of Fig. 4.19a will be as a *data-compression system.*[10]

Function Approximation

A multilayer perceptron trained with the back-propagation algorithm manifests itself as a *nested sigmoidal structure*, written for the case of a single output in the compact form

$$F(\mathbf{x}, \mathbf{w}) = \varphi\left(\sum_k w_{ok}\varphi\left(\sum_j w_{kj}\varphi\left(\cdots\varphi\left(\sum_i w_{li}x_i\right)\right)\right)\right) \tag{4.109}$$

where $\varphi(\cdot)$ is a sigmoid activation function; w_{ok} is the synaptic weight from neuron k in the last hidden layer to the single output neuron o, and so on for the other synaptic weights; and x_i is the ith element of the input vector **x**. The weight vector **w** denotes the entire set of synaptic weights ordered by layer, then neurons in a layer, and then synapses in a neuron. The scheme of nested nonlinear functions described in Eq. (4.109) is unusual in classical approximation theory. It is a *universal approximator*, as discussed in Section 4.12.

Computational Efficiency

The *computational complexity* of an algorithm is usually measured in terms of the number of multiplications, additions, and storage requirement involved in its implementation. A learning algorithm is said to be *computationally efficient* when its computational complexity is *polynomial* in the number of adjustable parameters that are to be updated from one iteration to the next. On this basis, it can be said that the back-propagation algorithm is computationally efficient, as stated in the summarizing description àt the beginning of this section. Specifically, in using the algorithm to train a multilayer perceptron containing a total of W synaptic weights (including biases), its computational complexity is linear in W. This important property of the back-propagation algorithm can be readily verified by examining the computations involved in performing the forward and backward passes summarized in Section 4.4. In the forward pass, the only computations involving the synaptic weights are those that pertain to the induced local fields of the various neurons in the network. Here, we see from Eq. (4.44) that these computations are all linear in the synaptic weights of the network. In the backward pass, the only computations involving the synaptic weights are those that pertain to (1) the local gradients of the hidden neurons, and (2) the updating of the synaptic weights themselves, as shown in Eqs. (4.46) and (4.47), respectively. Here again, we also see that these computations are all linear in the synaptic weights of the network. The conclusion is therefore that the computational complexity of the back-propagation algorithm is *linear* in W; that is, it is $O(W)$.

Sensitivity Analysis

Another computational benefit gained from the use of back-propagation learning is the efficient manner in which we can carry out a sensitivity analysis of the input–output mapping realized by the algorithm. The *sensitivity* of an input–output mapping function F with respect to a parameter of the function, denoted by ω, is defined by

$$S_\omega^F = \frac{\partial F / F}{\partial \omega / \omega} \tag{4.110}$$

Consider then a multilayer perceptron trained with the back-propagation algorithm. Let the function $F(\mathbf{w})$ be the input–output mapping realized by this network; $\mathbf{w}$ denotes the vector of all synaptic weights (including biases) contained in the network. In Section 4.8, we showed that the partial derivatives of the function $F(\mathbf{w})$ with respect to all the elements of the weight vector $\mathbf{w}$ can be computed efficiently. In particular, we see that the complexity involved in computing each of these partial derivatives is linear in W, the total number of weights contained in the network. This linearity holds regardless of where the synaptic weight in question appears in the chain of computations.

Robustness

In Chapter 3, we pointed out that the LMS algorithm is robust in the sense that disturbances with small energy can give rise only to small estimation errors. If the underlying observation model is linear, the LMS algorithm is an H^∞-optimal filter (Hassibi et al., 1993, 1996). What this means is that the LMS algorithm minimizes the *maximum energy gain* from the disturbances to the estimation errors.

If, on the other hand, the underlying observation model is nonlinear, Hassibi and Kailath (1995) have shown that the back-propagation algorithm is a *locally* H^∞-optimal filter. The term "local" means that the initial value of the weight vector used in the back-propagation algorithm is sufficiently close to the optimum value $\mathbf{w}^*$ of the weight vector to ensure that the algorithm does not get trapped in a poor local minimum. In conceptual terms, it is satisfying to see that the LMS and back-propagation algorithms belong to the same class of H^∞-optimal filters.

Convergence

The back-propagation algorithm uses an "instantaneous estimate" for the gradient of the error surface in weight space. The algorithm is therefore *stochastic* in nature; that is, it has a tendency to zigzag its way about the true direction to a minimum on the error surface. Indeed, back-propagation learning is an application of a statistical method known as *stochastic approximation* that was originally proposed by Robbins and Monro (1951). Consequently, it tends to converge slowly. We may identify two fundamental causes for this property (Jacobs, 1988):

1. The error surface is fairly flat along a weight dimension, which means that the derivative of the error surface with respect to that weight is small in magnitude. In such a situation, the adjustment applied to the weight is small, and consequently many itera-tions of the algorithm may be required to produce a significant reduction in the error performance of the network. Alternatively, the error surface is highly curved along a weight dimension, in which case the derivative of the error surface with respect to that weight is large in magnitude. In this second situation, the adjustment applied to the weight is large, which may cause the algorithm to overshoot the minimum of the error surface.

2. The direction of the negative gradient vector (i.e., the negative derivative of the cost function with respect to the vector of weights) may point away from the mini-mum of the error surface: hence, the adjustments applied to the weights may induce the algorithm to move in the wrong direction.

To avoid the slow rate of convergence of the back-propagation algorithm used to train a multilayer perceptron, we may opt for the optimally annealed on-line learning algorithm described in Section 4.10.

Local Minima

Another peculiarity of the error surface that affects the performance of the back-propagation algorithm is the presence of *local minima* (i.e., isolated valleys) in addition to global minima; in general, it is difficult to determine the numbers of local and global minima. Since back-propagation learning is basically a hill-climbing technique, it runs the risk of being trapped in a local minimum where every small change in synaptic weights increases the cost function. But somewhere else in the weight space, there exists another set of synaptic weights for which the cost function is smaller than the local minimum in which the network is stuck. It is clearly undesirable to have the learning process termi-nate at a local minimum, especially if it is located far above a global minimum.

Scaling

In principle, neural networks such as multilayer perceptrons trained with the back-propagation algorithm have the potential to be universal computing machines. However, for that potential to be fully realized, we have to overcome the *scaling problem*, which addresses the issue of how well the network behaves (e.g., as measured by the time required for training or the best generalization performance attainable) as the compu-tational task increases in size and complexity. Among the many possible ways of mea-suring the size or complexity of a computational task, the predicate order defined by Minsky and Papert (1969, 1988) provides the most useful and important measure.

To explain what we mean by a predicate, let $\psi(X)$ denote a function that can have only two values. Ordinarily, we think of the two values of $\psi(X)$ as 0 and 1. But by tak-ing the values to be FALSE or TRUE, we may think of $\psi(X)$ as a *predicate*—that is, a variable statement whose falsity or truth depends on the choice of argument X. For example, we may write

$$\psi_{\text{CIRCLE}}(X) = \begin{cases} 1 & \text{if the figure } X \text{ is a circle} \\ 0 & \text{if the figure } X \text{ is not a circle} \end{cases}$$

Using the idea of a predicate, Tesauro and Janssens (1988) performed an empirical study involving the use of a multilayer perceptron trained with the back-propagation algorithm to learn to compute the parity function. The *parity function* is a Boolean predicate defined by

$$\psi_{\text{PARITY}}(X) = \begin{cases} 1 & \text{if } |X| \text{ is an odd number} \\ 0 & \text{otherwise} \end{cases}$$

and whose order is equal to the number of inputs. The experiments performed by Tesauro and Janssens appear to show that the time required for the network to learn to compute the parity function scales exponentially with the number of inputs (i.e., the predicate order of the computation), and that projections of the use of the back-propagation algorithm to learn arbitrarily complicated functions may be overly optimistic.

It is generally agreed that it is inadvisable for a multilayer perceptron to be fully connected. In this context, we may therefore raise the following question: Given that a multilayer perceptron should not be fully connected, how should the synaptic connections of the network be allocated? This question is of no major concern in the case of small-scale applications, but it is certainly crucial to the successful application of back-propagation learning for solving large-scale, real-world problems.

One effective method of alleviating the scaling problem is to develop insight into the problem at hand (possibly through neurobiological analogy) and use it to put ingenuity into the architectural design of the multilayer perceptron. Specifically, the network architecture and the constraints imposed on synaptic weights of the network should be designed so as to incorporate prior information about the task into the makeup of the network. This design strategy is illustrated in Section 4.17 for the optical character recognition problem.

4.16 SUPERVISED LEARNING VIEWED AS AN OPTIMIZATION PROBLEM

In this section, we take a viewpoint on supervised learning that is quite different from that pursued in previous sections of the chapter. Specifically, we view the supervised training of a multilayer perceptron as a problem in *numerical optimization*. In this context, we first point out that the error surface of a multilayer perceptron with supervised learning is a nonlinear function of a weight vector $\mathbf{w}$; in the case of a multilayer perceptron, $\mathbf{w}$ represents the synaptic weight of the network arranged in some orderly fashion. Let $\mathcal{E}_{\text{av}}(\mathbf{w})$ denote the cost function, averaged over the training sample. Using the Taylor series, we may expand $\mathcal{E}_{\text{av}}(\mathbf{w})$ about the current operating point on the error surface as in Eq. (4.97), reproduced here in the form:

$$\mathcal{E}_{\text{av}}(\mathbf{w}(n) + \Delta\mathbf{w}(n)) = \mathcal{E}_{\text{av}}(\mathbf{w}(n)) + \mathbf{g}^T(n)\Delta\mathbf{w}(n) + \frac{1}{2}\Delta\mathbf{w}^T(n)\mathbf{H}(n)\Delta\mathbf{w}(n)$$
$$+ \text{ (third- and higher-order terms)} \tag{4.111}$$

where $\mathbf{g}(n)$ is the local *gradient vector*, defined by

$$\mathbf{g}(n) = \left. \frac{\partial\mathcal{E}_{\text{av}}(\mathbf{w})}{\partial\mathbf{w}} \right|_{\mathbf{w}=\mathbf{w}(n)} \tag{4.112}$$

The matrix $\mathbf{H}(n)$ is the local *Hessian* representing "curvature" of the error performance surface, defined by

$$\mathbf{H}(n) = \left. \frac{\partial^2 \mathcal{E}_{av}(\mathbf{w})}{\partial \mathbf{w}^2} \right|_{\mathbf{w}=\mathbf{w}(n)} \tag{4.113}$$

The use of an ensemble-averaged cost function $\mathcal{E}_{av}(\mathbf{w})$ presumes a *batch* mode of learning.

In the steepest-descent method, exemplified by the back-propagation algorithm, the adjustment $\Delta\mathbf{w}(n)$ applied to the synaptic weight vector $\mathbf{w}(n)$ is defined by

$$\Delta\mathbf{w}(n) = -\eta\mathbf{g}(n) \tag{4.114}$$

where η is a fixed learning-rate parameter. In effect, the steepest-descent method operates on the basis of a *liner approximation* of the cost function in the local neighborhood of the operating point $\mathbf{w}(n)$. In so doing, it relies on the gradient vector $\mathbf{g}(n)$ as the only source of local *first-order* information about the error surface. This restriction has a beneficial effect: simplicity of implementation. Unfortunately, it also has a detrimental effect: a slow rate of convergence, which can be excruciating, particularly in the case of large-scale problems. The inclusion of the momentum term in the update equation for the synaptic weight vector is a crude attempt at using second-order information about the error surface, which is of some help. However, its use makes the training process more delicate to manage by adding one more item to the list of parameters that have to be "tuned" by the designer.

In order to produce a significant improvement in the convergence performance of a multilayer perceptron (compared with back-propagation learning), we have to use *higher-order information* in the training process. We may do so by invoking a *quadratic approximation* of the error surface around the current point $\mathbf{w}(n)$. We then find from Eq. (4.111) that the optimum value of the adjustment $\Delta\mathbf{w}(n)$ applied to the synaptic weight vector $\mathbf{w}(n)$ is given by

$$\Delta\mathbf{w}^*(n) = \mathbf{H}^{-1}(n)\mathbf{g}(n) \tag{4.115}$$

where $\mathbf{H}^{-1}(n)$ is the inverse of the Hessian $\mathbf{H}(n)$, assuming that it exists. Equation (4.115) is the essence of *Newton's method.* If the cost function $\mathcal{E}_{av}(\mathbf{w})$ is quadratic (i.e., the third- and higher-order terms in Eq. (4.109) are zero), Newton's method converges to the optimum solution in one iteration. However, the practical application of Newton's method to the supervised training of a multilayer perceptron is handicapped by three factors:

(i) Newton's method requires calculation of the inverse Hessian $\mathbf{H}^{-1}(n)$, which can be computationally expensive.

(ii) For $\mathbf{H}^{-1}(n)$ to be computable, $\mathbf{H}(n)$ has to be nonsingular. In the case where $\mathbf{H}(n)$ is positive definite, the error surface around the current point $\mathbf{w}(n)$ is describable by a "convex bowl." Unfortunately, there is no guarantee that the Hessian of the error surface of a multilayer perceptron will always fit this description. Moreover, there is the potential problem of the Hessian being rank deficient (i.e., not all the columns of $\mathbf{H}$ are linearly independent), which results from the intrinsically ill-conditioned nature of supervised-learning problems (Saarinen et al., 1992); this factor only makes the computational task more difficult.

(iii) When the cost function $\mathscr{E}_{av}(\mathbf{w})$ is nonquadratic, there is no guarantee for convergence of Newton's method, which makes it unsuitable for the training of a multilayer perceptron.

To overcome some of these difficulties, we may use a *quasi-Newton method*, which requires only an estimate of the gradient vector $\mathbf{g}$. This modification of Newton's method maintains a positive-definite estimate of the inverse matrix $\mathbf{H}^{-1}$ directly without matrix inversion. By using such an estimate, a quasi-Newton method is assured of going downhill on the error surface. However, we still have a computational complexity that is $O(W^2)$, where W is the size of weight vector $\mathbf{w}$. Quasi-Newton methods are therefore computationally impractical, except for in the training of very small-scale neural networks. A description of quasi-Newton methods is presented later in the section.

Another class of second-order optimization methods includes the conjugate-gradient method, which may be regarded as being somewhat intermediate between the method of steepest descent and Newton's method. Use of the conjugate-gradient method is motivated by the desire to accelerate the typically slow rate of convergence experienced with the method of steepest descent, while avoiding the computational requirements associated with the evaluation, storage, and inversion of the Hessian in Newton's method.

Conjugate-Gradient Method[11]

The conjugate-gradient method belongs to a class of second-order optimization methods known collectively as *conjugate-direction methods*. We begin the discussion of these methods by considering the minimization of the *quadratic function*

$$f(\mathbf{x}) = \frac{1}{2}\mathbf{x}^T\mathbf{A}\mathbf{x} - \mathbf{b}^T\mathbf{x} + c \tag{4.116}$$

where $\mathbf{x}$ is a W-by-1 parameter vector; $\mathbf{A}$ is a W-by-W symmetric, positive-definite matrix; $\mathbf{b}$ is a W-by-1 vector; and c is a scalar. Minimization of the quadratic function $f(\mathbf{x})$ is achieved by assigning to $\mathbf{x}$ the unique value

$$\mathbf{x}^* = \mathbf{A}^{-1}\mathbf{b} \tag{4.117}$$

Thus, minimizing $f(\mathbf{x})$ and solving the linear system of equations $\mathbf{A}\mathbf{x}^* = \mathbf{b}$ are equivalent problems.

Given the matrix $\mathbf{A}$, we say that a set of nonzero vectors $\mathbf{s}(0), \mathbf{s}(1), ..., \mathbf{s}(W-1)$ is $\mathbf{A}$-*conjugate* (i.e., noninterfering with each other in the context of matrix $\mathbf{A}$) if the following condition is satisfied:

$$\mathbf{s}^T(n)\mathbf{A}\mathbf{s}(j) = 0 \qquad \text{for all } n \text{ and } j \text{ such that } n \neq j \tag{4.118}$$

If $\mathbf{A}$ is equal to the identity matrix, conjugacy is equivalent to the usual notion of orthogonality.

EXAMPLE 1   Interpretation of A-conjugate vectors

For an interpretation of **A**-conjugate vectors, consider the situation described in Fig. 4.20a, pertaining to a two-dimensional problem. The elliptic locus shown in this figure corresponds to a plot of Eq. (4.116) for

$$\mathbf{x} = [x_0, x_1]^T$$

at some constant value assigned to the quadratic function $f(\mathbf{x})$. Figure 4.20a also includes a pair of direction vectors that are conjugate with respect to the matrix **A**. Suppose that we define a new parameter vector **v** related to **x** by the transformation

$$\mathbf{v} = \mathbf{A}^{1/2}\mathbf{x}$$

where $\mathbf{A}^{1/2}$ is the square root of **A**. Then the elliptic locus of Fig. 4.20a is transformed into a circular locus, as shown in Fig. 4.20b. Correspondingly, the pair of **A**-conjugate direction vectors in Fig. 4.20a is transformed into a pair of orthogonal direction vectors in Fig. 4.20b.   ∎

An important property of **A**-conjugate vectors is that they are *linearly independent*. We prove this property by contradiction. Let one of these vectors—say, $\mathbf{s}(0)$—be expressed as a linear combination of the remaining $W-1$ vectors as follows:

$$\mathbf{s}(0) = \sum_{j=1}^{W-1} \alpha_j \mathbf{s}(j)$$

Multiplying by **A** and then taking the inner product of $\mathbf{A}\mathbf{s}(0)$ with $\mathbf{s}(0)$ yields

$$\mathbf{s}^T(0)\mathbf{A}\mathbf{s}(0) = \sum_{j=1}^{W-1} \alpha_j \mathbf{s}^T(0)\mathbf{A}\mathbf{s}(j) = 0$$

However, it is impossible for the quadratic form $\mathbf{s}^T(0)\mathbf{A}\mathbf{s}(0)$ to be zero, for two reasons: The matrix **A** is positive definite by assumption, and the vector $\mathbf{s}(0)$ is nonzero by definition. It follows therefore that the **A**-conjugate vectors $\mathbf{s}(0), \mathbf{s}(1), ..., \mathbf{s}(W-1)$ cannot be linearly dependent; that is, they must be linearly independent.

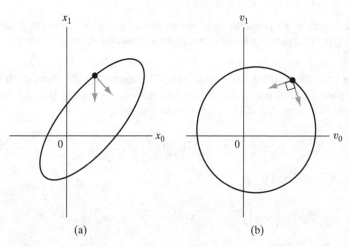

FIGURE 4.20   Interpretation of **A**-conjugate vectors. (a) Elliptic locus in two-dimensional weight space. (b) Transformation of the elliptic locus into a circular locus.

(a)   (b)

For a given set of **A**-conjugate vectors $\mathbf{s}(0), \mathbf{s}(1), ..., \mathbf{s}(W-1)$, the corresponding *conjugate-direction method* for unconstrained minimization of the quadratic error function $f(\mathbf{x})$ is defined by

$$\mathbf{x}(n+1) = \mathbf{x}(n) + \eta(n)\mathbf{s}(n), \qquad n = 0, 1, ..., W - 1 \tag{4.119}$$

where $\mathbf{x}(0)$ is an arbitrary starting vector and $\eta(n)$ is a scalar defined by

$$f(\mathbf{x}(n) + \eta(n)\mathbf{s}(n)) = \min_{\eta} f(\mathbf{x}(n) + \eta\mathbf{s}(n)) \tag{4.120}$$

(Fletcher, 1987; Bertsekas, 1995). The procedure of choosing η so as to minimize the function $f(\mathbf{x}(n) + \eta\mathbf{s}(n))$ for some fixed n is referred to as a *line search*, which represents a one-dimensional minimization problem.

In light of Eqs. (4.118), (4.119) and (4.120), we now offer some observations:

1. Since the **A**-conjugate vectors $\mathbf{s}(0), \mathbf{s}(1), ..., \mathbf{s}(W-1)$ are linearly independent, they form a basis that spans the vector space of **w**.
2. The update equation (4.119) and the line minimization of Eq. (4.120) lead to the same formula for the learning-rate parameter, namely,

$$\eta(n) = -\frac{\mathbf{s}^T(n)\mathbf{A}\mathbf{e}(n)}{\mathbf{s}^T(n)\mathbf{A}\mathbf{s}(n)}, \qquad n = 0, 1, ..., W - 1 \tag{4.121}$$

where $\mathbf{e}(n)$ is the *error vector* defined by

$$\mathbf{e}(n) = \mathbf{x}(n) - \mathbf{x}^* \tag{4.122}$$

3. Starting from an arbitrary point $\mathbf{x}(0)$, the conjugate-direction method is guaranteed to find the optimum solution $\mathbf{x}^*$ of the quadratic equation $f(\mathbf{x}) = 0$ in at most W iterations.

The principal property of the conjugate-direction method is described in the following statement (Fletcher, 1987; Bertsekas, 1995):

At successive iterations, the conjugate-direction method minimizes the quadratic function $f(\mathbf{x})$ over a progressively expanding linear vector space that eventually includes the global minimum of $f(\mathbf{x})$.

In particular, for each iteration n, the iterate $\mathbf{x}(n+1)$ minimizes the function $f(\mathbf{x})$ over a linear vector space $\mathscr{D}_n$ that passes through some arbitrary point $\mathbf{x}(0)$ and is spanned by the **A**-conjugate vectors $\mathbf{s}(0), \mathbf{s}(1), ..., \mathbf{s}(n)$, as shown by

$$\mathbf{x}(n+1) = \arg \min_{\mathbf{x} \in \mathscr{D}_n} f(\mathbf{x}) \tag{4.123}$$

where the space $\mathscr{D}_n$ is defined by

$$\mathscr{D}_n = \left\{ \mathbf{x}(n) \mid \mathbf{x}(n) = \mathbf{x}(0) + \sum_{j=0}^{n} \eta(j)\mathbf{s}(j) \right\} \tag{4.124}$$

For the conjugate-direction method to work, we require the availability of a set of $\mathbf{A}$-conjugate vectors $\mathbf{s}(0), \mathbf{s}(1), ..., \mathbf{s}(W-1)$. In a special form of this method known as the *scaled conjugate-gradient method*,[12] the successive direction vectors are generated as $\mathbf{A}$-conjugate versions of the successive gradient vectors of the quadratic function $f(\mathbf{x})$ as the method progresses—hence the name of the method. Thus, except for $n = 0$, the set of direction vectors $\{\mathbf{s}(n)\}$ is not specified beforehand, but rather it is determined in a sequential manner at successive steps of the method.

First, we define the *residual* as the steepest-descent direction:

$$\mathbf{r}(n) = \mathbf{b} - \mathbf{A}\mathbf{x}(n) \tag{4.125}$$

Then, to proceed, we use a linear combination of $\mathbf{r}(n)$ and $\mathbf{s}(n-1)$, as shown by

$$\mathbf{s}(n) = \mathbf{r}(n) + \beta(n)\mathbf{s}(n-1), \qquad n = 1, 2, ..., W-1 \tag{4.126}$$

where $\beta(n)$ is a scaling factor to be determined. Multiplying this equation by $\mathbf{A}$, taking the inner product of the resulting expression with $\mathbf{s}(n-1)$, invoking the $\mathbf{A}$-conjugate property of the direction vectors, and then solving the resulting expression for $\beta(n)$, we get

$$\beta(n) = -\frac{\mathbf{s}^T(n-1)\mathbf{A}\mathbf{r}(n)}{\mathbf{s}^T(n-1)\mathbf{A}\mathbf{s}(n-1)} \tag{4.127}$$

Using Eqs. (4.126) and (4.127), we find that the vectors $\mathbf{s}(0), \mathbf{s}(1), ..., \mathbf{s}(W-1)$ so generated are indeed $\mathbf{A}$-conjugate.

Generation of the direction vectors in accordance with the recursive equation (4.126) depends on the coefficient $\beta(n)$. The formula of Eq. (4.127) for evaluating $\beta(n)$, as it presently stands, requires knowledge of matrix $\mathbf{A}$. For computational reasons, it would be desirable to evaluate $\beta(n)$ without explicit knowledge of $\mathbf{A}$. This evaluation can be achieved by using one of two formulas (Fletcher, 1987):

1. *the Polak–Ribière formula*, for which $\beta(n)$ is defined by

$$\beta(n) = \frac{\mathbf{r}^T(n)(\mathbf{r}(n) - \mathbf{r}(n-1))}{\mathbf{r}^T(n-1)\mathbf{r}(n-1)} \tag{4.128}$$

2. *the Fletcher–Reeves formula*, for which $\beta(n)$ is defined by

$$\beta(n) = \frac{\mathbf{r}^T(n)\mathbf{r}(n)}{\mathbf{r}^T(n-1)\mathbf{r}(n-1)} \tag{4.129}$$

To use the conjugate-gradient method to attack the unconstrained minimization of the cost function $\mathscr{E}_{\text{av}}(\mathbf{w})$ pertaining to the unsupervised training of multilayer perceptron, we do two things:

- Approximate the cost function $\mathscr{E}_{\text{av}}(\mathbf{w})$ by a quadratic function. That is, the third- and higher-order terms in Eq. (4.111) are ignored, which means that we are operating close to a local minimum on the error surface. On this basis, comparing Eqs. (4.111) and (4.116), we can make the associations indicated in Table 4.2.
- Formulate the computation of coefficients $\beta(n)$ and $\eta(n)$ in the conjugate-gradient algorithm so as to require only gradient information.

TABLE 4.2 Correspondence Between $f(\mathbf{x})$ and $\mathscr{E}_{av}(\mathbf{w})$

Quadratic function $f(\mathbf{x})$	Cost function $\mathscr{E}_{av}(\mathbf{w})$
Parameter vector $\mathbf{x}(n)$	Synaptic weight vector $\mathbf{w}(n)$
Gradient vector $\partial f(\mathbf{x})/\partial \mathbf{x}$	Gradient vector $\mathbf{g} = \partial \mathscr{E}_{av}/\partial \mathbf{w}$
Matrix $\mathbf{A}$	Hessian matrix $\mathbf{H}$

The latter point is particularly important in the context of multilayer perceptrons because it avoids using the Hessian $\mathbf{H}(n)$, the evaluation of which is plagued with computational difficulties.

To compute the coefficient $\beta(n)$ that determines the search direction $\mathbf{s}(n)$ without explicit knowledge of the Hessian $\mathbf{H}(n)$, we can use the Polak–Ribière formula of Eq. (4.128) or the Fletcher–Reeves formula of Eq. (4.129). Both of these formulas involve the use of residuals only. In the linear form of the conjugate-gradient method, assuming a quadratic function, the Polak–Ribière and Fletcher–Reeves formulas are equivalent. On the other hand, in the case of a nonquadratic cost function, they are not.

For nonquadratic optimization problems, the Polak–Ribière form of the conjugate-gradient algorithm is typically superior to the Fletcher–Reeves form of the algorithm, for which we offer the following heuristic explanation (Bertsekas, 1995): Due to the presence of third- and higher-order terms in the cost function $\mathscr{E}_{av}(\mathbf{w})$ and possible inaccuracies in the line search, conjugacy of the generated search directions is progressively lost. This condition may in turn cause the algorithm to "jam" in the sense that the generated direction vector $\mathbf{s}(n)$ is nearly orthogonal to the residual $\mathbf{r}(n)$. When this phenomenon occurs, we have $\mathbf{r}(n) = \mathbf{r}(n-1)$, in which case the scalar $\beta(n)$ will be nearly zero. Correspondingly, the direction vector $\mathbf{s}(n)$ will be close to $\mathbf{r}(n)$, thereby breaking the jam. In contrast, when the Fletcher–Reeves formula is used, the conjugate-gradient algorithm typically continues to jam under similar conditions.

In rare cases, however, the Polak–Ribière method can cycle indefinitely without converging. Fortunately, convergence of the Polak–Ribière method can be guaranteed by choosing

$$\beta = \max\{\beta_{PR}, 0\} \tag{4.130}$$

where β_{PR} is the value defined by the Polak–Ribière formula of Eq. (4.128) (Shewchuk, 1994). Using the value of β defined in Eq. (4.130) is equivalent to restarting the conjugate gradient algorithm if $\beta_{PR} < 0$. To restart the algorithm is equivalent to forgetting the last search direction and starting it anew in the direction of steepest descent.

Consider next the issue of computing the parameter $\eta(n)$, which determines the learning rate of the conjugate-gradient algorithm. As with $\beta(n)$, the preferred method for computing $\eta(n)$ is one that avoids having to use the Hessian $\mathbf{H}(n)$. We recall that the line minimization based on Eq. (4.120) leads to the same formula for $\eta(n)$ as that derived from the update equation Eq. (4.119). We therefore need a *line search*,[12] the purpose of which is to minimize the function $\mathscr{E}_{av}(\mathbf{w} + \eta\mathbf{s})$ with respect to η. That is, given fixed values of the vectors $\mathbf{w}$ and $\mathbf{s}$, the problem is to vary η such that this function is minimized. As η varies, the argument $\mathbf{w} + \eta\mathbf{s}$ traces a line in the W-dimensional vector space of **w**—hence the name "line search." A *line-search algorithm* is an iterative procedure that generates a sequence of estimates $\{\eta(n)\}$ for each iteration of the conjugate-gradient algorithm. The line search is terminated when a satisfactory solution is found. The computation of a line search must be performed along each search direction.

Several line-search algorithms have been proposed in the literature, and a good choice is important because it has a profound impact on the performance of the conjugate-gradient algorithm in which it is embedded. There are two phases to any line-search algorithm (Fletcher, 1987):

- *the bracketing phase*, which searches for a *bracket* (that is, a nontrivial interval that is known to contain a minimum), and
- *the sectioning phase*, in which the bracket is *sectioned* (i.e., divided), thereby generating a sequence of brackets whose length is progressively reduced.

We now describe a *curve-fitting procedure* that takes care of these two phases in a straightforward manner.

Let $\mathscr{E}_{av}(\eta)$ denote the cost function of the multilayer perceptron, expressed as a function of η. It is assumed that $\mathscr{E}_{av}(\eta)$ is strictly *unimodal* (i.e., it has a single minimum in the neighborhood of the current point $\mathbf{w}(n)$) and is twice continuously differentiable. We initiate the search procedure by searching along the line until we find three points η_1, η_2, and η_3 such that the following condition is satisfied, as illustrated in Fig. 4.21:

$$\mathscr{E}_{av}(\eta_1) \geq \mathscr{E}_{av}(\eta_3) \geq \mathscr{E}_{av}(\eta_2) \qquad \text{for } \eta_1 < \eta_2 < \eta_3 \qquad (4.131)$$

Since $\mathscr{E}_{av}(\eta)$ is a continuous function of η, the choice described in Eq. (4.131) ensures that the bracket $[\eta_1, \eta_3]$ contains a minimum of the function $\mathscr{E}_{av}(\eta)$. Provided that the function $\mathscr{E}_{av}(\eta)$ is sufficiently smooth, we may consider this function to be parabolic in the immediate neighborhood of the minimum. Accordingly, we may use *inverse parabolic interpolation* to do the sectioning (Press et al., 1988). Specifically, a parabolic function is fitted through the three original points η_1, η_2, and η_3, as illustrated in Fig. 4.22, where the solid line corresponds to $\mathscr{E}_{av}(\eta)$ and the dashed line corresponds to the first iteration

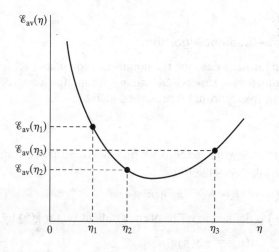

FIGURE 4.21   Illustration of the line search.

FIGURE 4.22 Inverse parabolic interpolation.

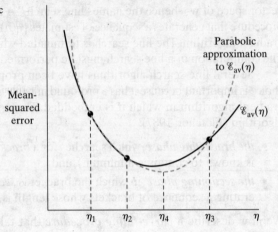

of the sectioning procedure. Let the minimum of the parabola passing through the three points η_1, η_2, and η_3 be denoted by η_4. In the example illustrated in Fig. 4.22, we have $\mathscr{E}_{av}(\eta_4) < \mathscr{E}_{av}(\eta_2)$ and $\mathscr{E}_{av}(\eta_4) < \mathscr{E}_{av}(\eta_1)$. Point η_3 is replaced in favor of η_4, making $[\eta_1, \eta_4]$ the new bracket. The process is repeated by constructing a new parabola through the points η_1, η_2, and η_4. The bracketing-followed-by-sectioning procedure, as illustrated in Fig. 4.22, is repeated several times until a point close enough to the minimum of $\mathscr{E}_{av}(\eta)$ is located, at which time the line search is terminated.

Brent's method constitutes a highly refined version of the three-point curve-fitting procedure just described (Press et al., 1988). At any particular stage of the computation, Brent's method keeps track of six points on the function $\mathscr{E}_{av}(\eta)$, which may not all be necessarily distinct. As before, parabolic interpolation is attempted through three of these points. For the interpolation to be acceptable, certain criteria involving the remaining three points must be satisfied. The net result is a robust line-search algorithm.

Summary of the Nonlinear Conjugate-Gradient Algorithm

All the ingredients we need to formally describe the nonlinear (nonquadratic) form of the conjugate-gradient algorithm for the supervised training of a multilayer perceptron are now in place. A summary of the algorithm is presented in Table 4.3.

Quasi-Newton Methods

Resuming the discussion on quasi-Newton methods, we find that these are basically gradient methods described by the update equation

$$\mathbf{w}(n + 1) = \mathbf{w}(n) + \eta(n)\mathbf{s}(n) \tag{4.132}$$

where the direction vector $\mathbf{s}(n)$ is defined in terms of the gradient vector $\mathbf{g}(n)$ by

$$\mathbf{s}(n) = -\mathbf{S}(n)\mathbf{g}(n) \tag{4.133}$$

TABLE 4.3 Summary of the Nonlinear Conjugate-Gradient Algorithm for the Supervised Training of a Multilayer Perceptron

Initialization

Unless prior knowledge on the weight vector **w** is available, choose the initial value **w**(0) by using a procedure similar to that described for the back-propagation algorithm.

Computation

1. For **w**(0), use back propagation to compute the gradient vector **g**(0).
2. Set **s**(0) = **r**(0) = −**g**(0).
3. At time-step n, use a line search to find $\eta(n)$ that minimizes $\mathscr{E}_{av}(\eta)$ sufficiently, representing the cost function $\mathscr{E}_{av}$ expressed as a function of η for fixed values of **w** and **s**.
4. Test to determine whether the Euclidean norm of the residual **r**(n) has fallen below a specified value, that is, a small fraction of the initial value $\|\mathbf{r}(0)\|$.
5. Update the weight vector:

$$\mathbf{w}(n+1) = \mathbf{w}(n) + \eta(n)\mathbf{s}(n)$$

6. For **w**(n + 1), use back propagation to compute the updated gradient vector **g**(n + 1).
7. Set **r**(n + 1) = −**g**(n + 1).
8. Use the Polak–Ribière method to calculate:

$$\beta(n+1) = \max\left\{\frac{\mathbf{r}^T(n+1)(\mathbf{r}(n+1) - \mathbf{r}(n))}{\mathbf{r}^T(n)\mathbf{r}(n)}, 0\right\}$$

9. Update the direction vector:

$$\mathbf{s}(n+1) = \mathbf{r}(n+1) + \beta(n+1)\mathbf{s}(n)$$

10. Set $n = n + 1$, and go back to step 3.

Stopping criterion. Terminate the algorithm when the condition

$$\|\mathbf{r}(n)\| \leq \varepsilon\|\mathbf{r}(0)\|$$

is satisfied, where ε is a prescribed small number.

The matrix **S**(n) is a positive-definite matrix that is adjusted from one iteration to the next. This is done in order to make the direction vector **s**(n) approximate the *Newton direction*, namely,

$$-(\partial^2\mathscr{E}_{av}/\partial\mathbf{w}^2)^{-1}\,(\partial\mathscr{E}_{av}/\partial\mathbf{w})$$

Quasi-Newton methods use second-order (curvature) information about the error surface without actually requiring knowledge of the Hessian. They do so by using two successive iterates **w**(n) and **w**(n + 1), together with the respective gradient vectors **g**(n) and **g**(n + 1). Let

$$\mathbf{q}(n) = \mathbf{g}(n+1) - \mathbf{g}(n) \tag{4.134}$$

and

$$\Delta\mathbf{w}(n) = \mathbf{w}(n+1) - \mathbf{w}(n) \tag{4.135}$$

We may then derive curvature information by using the approximate formula

$$\mathbf{q}(n) \simeq \left(\frac{\partial}{\partial \mathbf{w}} \mathbf{g}(n) \right) \Delta \mathbf{w}(n) \tag{4.136}$$

In particular, given W linearly independent weight increments $\Delta \mathbf{w}(0), \Delta \mathbf{w}(1), ...,$ $\Delta \mathbf{w}(W-1)$ and the respective gradient increments $\mathbf{q}(0), \mathbf{q}(1), ..., \mathbf{q}(W-1)$, we may approximate the Hessian as

$$\mathbf{H} \simeq [\mathbf{q}(0), \mathbf{q}(1), ..., \mathbf{q}(W-1)] [\Delta \mathbf{w}(0), \Delta \mathbf{w}(1), ..., \Delta \mathbf{w}(W-1)]^{-1} \tag{4.137}$$

We may also approximate the inverse Hessian as follows[13]:

$$\mathbf{H}^{-1} \simeq [\Delta \mathbf{w}(0), \Delta \mathbf{w}(1), ..., \Delta \mathbf{w}(W-1)] [\mathbf{q}(0), \mathbf{q}(1), ..., \mathbf{q}(W-1)]^{-1} \tag{4.138}$$

When the cost function $\mathscr{E}_{av}(\mathbf{w})$ is quadratic, Eqs. (4.137) and (4.138) are exact.

In the most popular class of quasi-Newton methods, the updated matrix $\mathbf{S}(n+1)$ is obtained from its previous value $\mathbf{S}(n)$, the vectors $\Delta \mathbf{w}(n)$ and $\mathbf{q}(n)$, by using the following recursion (Fletcher, 1987; Bertsekas, 1995):

$$\mathbf{S}(n+1) = \mathbf{S}(n) + \frac{\Delta \mathbf{w}(n) \Delta \mathbf{w}^T(n)}{\mathbf{q}^T(n) \mathbf{q}(n)} - \frac{\mathbf{S}(n) \mathbf{q}(n) \mathbf{q}^T(n) \mathbf{S}(n)}{\mathbf{q}^T(n) \mathbf{S}(n) \mathbf{q}(n)} \tag{4.139}$$
$$+ \xi(n) [\mathbf{q}^T(n) \mathbf{S}(n) \mathbf{q}(n)] [\mathbf{v}(n) \mathbf{v}^T(n)]$$

where

$$\mathbf{v}(n) = \frac{\Delta \mathbf{w}(n)}{\Delta \mathbf{w}^T(n) \Delta \mathbf{w}(n)} - \frac{\mathbf{S}(n) \mathbf{q}(n)}{\mathbf{q}^T(n) \mathbf{S}(n) \mathbf{q}(n)} \tag{4.140}$$

and

$$0 \le \xi(n) \le 1 \quad \text{for all } n \tag{4.141}$$

The algorithm is initiated with some arbitrary positive- definite matrix $\mathbf{S}(0)$. The particular form of the quasi-Newton method is parameterized by how the scalar $\xi(n)$ is defined, as indicated by the following two points (Fletcher, 1987):

1. For $\xi(n) = 0$ for all n, we obtain the *Davidon–Fletcher–Powell (DFP) algorithm*, which is historically the first quasi-Newton method.
2. For $\xi(n) = 1$ for all n, we obtain the *Broyden–Fletcher–Goldfarb–Shanno (BFGS) algorithm*, which is considered to be the best form of quasi-Newton methods currently known.

Comparison of Quasi-Newton Methods with Conjugate-Gradient Methods

We conclude this brief discussion of quasi-Newton methods by comparing them with conjugate-gradient methods in the context of nonquadratic optimization problems (Bertsekas, 1995):

- Both quasi-Newton and conjugate-gradient methods avoid the need to use the Hessian. However, quasi-Newton methods go one step further by generating an approximation to the inverse Hessian. Accordingly, when the line search is accurate and we are in close proximity to a local minimum with a positive-definite Hessian, a quasi-Newton method tends to approximate Newton's method, thereby attaining faster convergence than would be possible with the conjugate-gradient method.

- Quasi-Newton methods are not as sensitive to accuracy in the line-search stage of the optimization as the conjugate-gradient method.
- Quasi-Newton methods require storage of the matrix $\mathbf{S}(n)$, in addition to the matrix-vector multiplication overhead associated with the computation of the direction vector $\mathbf{s}(n)$. The net result is that the computational complexity of quasi-Newton methods is $O(W^2)$. In contrast, the computational complexity of the conjugate-gradient method is $O(W)$. Thus, when the dimension W (i.e., size of the weight vector $\mathbf{w}$) is large, conjugate-gradient methods are preferable to quasi-Newton methods in computational terms.

It is because of the lattermost point that the use of quasi-Newton methods is restricted, in practice, to the design of small-scale neural networks.

Levenberg–Marquardt Method

The Levenberg–Marquardt method, due to Levenberg (1994) and Marquardt (1963), is a compromise between the following two methods:

- Newton's method, which converges rapidly near a local or global minimum, but may also diverge;
- Gradient descent, which is assured of convergence through a proper selection of the step-size parameter, but converges slowly.

To be specific, consider the optimization of a second-order function $F(\mathbf{w})$, and let $\mathbf{g}$ be its gradient vector and $\mathbf{H}$ be its Hessian. According to the Levenberg–Marquardt method, the optimum adjustment $\Delta\mathbf{w}$ applied to the parameter vector $\mathbf{w}$ is defined by

$$\Delta\mathbf{w} = [\mathbf{H} + \lambda\mathbf{I}]^{-1}\mathbf{g} \tag{4.142}$$

where $\mathbf{I}$ is the identity matrix of the same dimensions as $\mathbf{H}$ and λ is a *regularizing*, or *loading*, *parameter* that forces the sum matrix $(\mathbf{H} + \lambda\mathbf{I})$ to be positive definite and safely well conditioned throughout the computation. Note also that the adjustment $\Delta\mathbf{w}$ of Eq. (4.142) is a minor modification of the formula defined in Eq. (4.115).

With this background, consider a multilayer perceptron with a single output neuron. The network is trained by minimizing the cost function

$$\mathscr{E}_{\text{av}}(\mathbf{w}) = \frac{1}{2N}\sum_{i=1}^{N}[d(i) - F(\mathbf{x}(i); \mathbf{w})]^2 \tag{4.143}$$

where $\{\mathbf{x}(i), d(i)\}_{i=1}^{N}$ is the training sample and $F(\mathbf{x}(i); \mathbf{w})$ is the approximating function realized by the network; the synaptic weights of the network are arranged in some orderly manner to form the weight vector $\mathbf{w}$. The gradient and the Hessian of the cost function $\mathscr{E}_{\text{av}}(\mathbf{w})$ are respectively defined by

$$g(\mathbf{w}) = \frac{\partial \mathscr{E}_{av}(\mathbf{w})}{\partial \mathbf{w}}$$

$$= -\frac{1}{N} \sum_{i=1}^{N} [d(i) - F(\mathbf{x}(i); \mathbf{w})] \frac{\partial F(\mathbf{x}(i); \mathbf{w})}{\partial \mathbf{w}} \qquad (4.144)$$

and

$$\mathbf{H}(\mathbf{w}) = \frac{\partial^2 \mathscr{E}_{av}(\mathbf{w})}{\partial \mathbf{w}^2} = \frac{1}{N} \sum_{i=1}^{N} \left[\frac{\partial F(\mathbf{x}(i); \mathbf{w})}{\partial \mathbf{w}} \right] \left[\frac{\partial F(\mathbf{x}(i); \mathbf{w})}{\partial \mathbf{w}} \right]^T$$

$$- \frac{1}{N} \sum_{i=1}^{N} [d(i) - F(\mathbf{x}(i); \mathbf{w})] \frac{\partial^2 F(\mathbf{x}(i); \mathbf{w})}{\partial \mathbf{w}^2} \qquad (4.145)$$

Thus, substituting Eqs. (4.144) and (4.145) into Eq. (4.142), the desired adjustment $\Delta \mathbf{w}$ is computed for each iteration of the Levenberg-Marquardt algorithm.

However, from a practical perspective, the computational complexity of Eq. (4.145) can be demanding, particularly when the dimensionality of the weight vector $\mathbf{w}$ is high; the computational difficulty is attributed to the complex nature of the Hessian $\mathbf{H}(\mathbf{w})$. To mitigate this difficulty, the recommended procedure is to ignore the second term on the right-hand side of Eq. (4.145), thereby approximating the Hessian simply as

$$\mathbf{H}(\mathbf{w}) \approx \frac{1}{N} \sum_{i=1}^{N} \left[\frac{\partial F(\mathbf{x}(i); \mathbf{w})}{\partial \mathbf{w}} \right] \left[\frac{\partial F(\mathbf{x}(i); \mathbf{w})}{\partial \mathbf{w}} \right]^T \qquad (4.146)$$

This approximation is recognized as the outer product of the partial derivative $\partial F(\mathbf{w}, \mathbf{x}(i))/\partial \mathbf{w}$ with itself, averaged over the training sample; accordingly, it is referred to as the *outer-product approximation* of the Hessian. The use of this approximation is justified when the Levenberg-Marquardt algorithm is operating in the neighborhood of a local or global minimum.

Clearly, the approximate version of the Levenberg–Marquardt algorithm, based on the gradient vector of Eq. (4.144) and the Hessian of Eq. (4.146), is a first-order method of optimization that is well suited for nonlinear least-squares estimation problems. Moreover, because of the fact that both of these equations involve averaging over the training sample, the algorithm is of a batch form.

The regularizing parameter λ plays a critical role in the way the Levenberg-Marquardt algorithm functions. If we set λ equal to zero, then the formula of Eq. (4.142) reduces to Newton's method. On the other hand, if we assign a large value to λ such that $\lambda \mathbf{I}$ overpowers the Hessian $\mathbf{H}$, the Levenberg-Marquardt algorithm functions effectively as a gradient descent method. From these two observations, it follows that at each iteration of the algorithm, the value assigned to λ should be just large enough to maintain the sum matrix $(\mathbf{H} + \lambda \mathbf{I})$ in its positive-definite form. In specific terms, the recommended *Marquardt recipe* for the selection of λ is as follows (Press et al.,) 1988:

1. Compute $\mathscr{E}_{av}(\mathbf{w})$ at iteration $n - 1$.
2. Choose a modest value for λ, say $\lambda = 10^{-3}$.

3. Solve Eq. (4.142) for the adjustment $\Delta\mathbf{w}$ at iteration n and evaluate $\mathcal{E}_{av}(\mathbf{w} + \Delta\mathbf{w})$.
4. If $\mathcal{E}_{av}(\mathbf{w} + \Delta\mathbf{w}) \geq \mathcal{E}_{av}(\mathbf{w})$, increase λ by a factor of 10 (or any other substantial factor) and go back to step 3.
5. If, on the other hand, $\mathcal{E}_{av}(\mathbf{w} + \Delta\mathbf{w}) < \mathcal{E}_{av}(w)$, decrease λ by a factor of 10, update the trial solution $\mathbf{w} \rightarrow \mathbf{w} + \Delta\mathbf{w}$, and go back to step 3.

For obvious reasons, a rule for stopping the iterative process is necessary. In Press et al. (1998), it is pointed out that an adjustment in the parameter vector $\mathbf{w}$ that changes $\mathcal{E}_{av}(\mathbf{w})$ by an incrementally small amount is *never* statistically meaningful. We may therefore use this insightful comment as a basis for the stopping rule.

One last comment is in order: To evaluate the partial derivative $\partial F(\mathbf{x}; \mathbf{w})/\partial \mathbf{w}$ at each iteration of the algorithm, we may use back-propagation in the manner described in Section 4.8.

Second-Order Stochastic Gradient Descent for On-line Learning

Up to this point, this section has focused on second-order optimization techniques for batch learning. Hereafter, we turn our attention to second-order stochastic gradient-descent methods for on-line learning. Although these two families of techniques are entirely different, they do share a common purpose:

> *The second-order information contained in the Hessian (curvature) of the cost function is used to improve the performance of supervised-learning algorithms.*

A simple way of expanding on the performance of the optimally annealed on-line learning algorithm considered in Section 4.10 is to replace the learning-rate parameter $\eta(n)$ in Eq. (4.60) with the scaled inverse of the Hessian $\mathbf{H}$, as shown by

$$\underbrace{\hat{\mathbf{w}}(n+1)}_{\substack{\text{Updated}\\\text{estimate}}} = \underbrace{\hat{\mathbf{w}}(n)}_{\substack{\text{Old}\\\text{estimate}}} - \underbrace{\frac{1}{n}\mathbf{H}^{-1}}_{\substack{\text{Annealed}\\\text{inverse}\\\text{of the}\\\text{Hessian }\mathbf{H}}} \underbrace{\mathbf{g}(\mathbf{x}(n+1), \mathbf{d}(n+1); \hat{\mathbf{w}}(n))}_{\substack{\text{Gradient vector}\\\mathbf{g}}} \qquad (4.147)$$

The replacement of $\eta(n)$ with the new term $\frac{1}{n}\mathbf{H}^{-1}$ is intended to accelerate the speed of convergence of the on-line algorithm in an optimally annealed fashion. It is assumed that the Hessian $\mathbf{H}$ is known a priori and its inverse $\mathbf{H}^{-1}$ can therefore be precomputed.

Recognizing the fact that "there is no such thing as a free lunch," the price paid for the accelerated convergence is summarized as follows (Bottou, 2007):

(i) Whereas in the stochastic gradient descent of Eq. (4.60), the computation cost per iteration of the algorithm is $O(W)$, where W is the dimension of the weight vector $\mathbf{w}$ being estimated, the corresponding computation cost per iteration of the second-order stochastic gradient-descent algorithm in Eq. (4.147) is $O(W^2)$.

(ii) For each training example $(\mathbf{x}, \mathbf{d})$ processed by the algorithm of Eq. (4.147), the algorithm requires multiplication of the W-by-1 gradient vector $\mathbf{g}$ and the W-by-W inverse matrix $\mathbf{H}^{-1}$ and storage of the product.

(iii) In a general context, whenever some form of *sparsity* exists in the training sample, the natural move is to exploit the sparsity for the purpose of improved algorithmic performance. Unfortunately, the Hessian **H** is typically a full matrix and therefore not sparse, which rules out the possibility of exploiting training-sample sparsity.

To overcome these limitations, we may resort to one of the following *approximation procedures*:

(i) *Diagonal approximation:* (Becker and LeCun, 1989). In this procedure, only the diagonal elements of the Hessian are retained, which means that the inverse matrix $\mathbf{H}^{-1}$ will likewise be a diagonal matrix. Matrix theory teaches us that the matrix product $\mathbf{H}^{-1}\mathbf{g}$ will consist of a sum of terms of the form $h_{ii}^{-1}g_i$, where h_{ii} is the ith diagonal element of the Hessian **H** and g_i is the corresponding element of the gradient **g** for $i = 1, 2, ..., W$. With the gradient vector **g** being linear in the weights, it follows that the computational complexity of the approximated second-order on-line learning algorithm is $O(W)$.

(ii) *Low-rank approximation:* (LeCun et al., 1998). By definition, the rank of a matrix equals the number of algebraically independent columns of the matrix. Given a Hessian **H**, the use of *singular value decomposition* (SVD) provides an important procedure for the low-rank approximation of the Hessian **H**. Let the rank of **H** be denoted by p and a rank r approximation of **H** be denoted by $\mathbf{H}_r$, where $r < p$. The squared error between the Hessian and its approximation is defined by the *Frobenius norm*

$$e^2 = \text{tr}[(\mathbf{H} - \mathbf{H}_r)^T(\mathbf{H} - \mathbf{H}_r)] \qquad (4.148)$$

where tr[·] denotes the *trace* (i.e., sum of the diagonal components) of the square matrix enclosed inside the square brackets. Applying the SVD to the matrices **H** and $\mathbf{H}_r$, we write

$$\mathbf{H} = \mathbf{V}\Sigma\mathbf{U}^T \qquad (4.149)$$

and

$$\mathbf{H}_r = \mathbf{V}\Sigma_r\mathbf{U}^T \qquad (4.150)$$

where the orthogonal matrices **U** and **V** define the common *right* and *left singular vectors*, respectively, and the rectangular matrix

$$\Sigma_r = \text{diag}[\lambda_1, \lambda_2, ..., \lambda_r, 0 ..., 0] \qquad (4.151)$$

defines the *singular values* of the low-rank approximation $\mathbf{H}_r$. The new square matrix

$$\mathbf{H}_r = \mathbf{U}\Sigma_r\mathbf{V}^T \qquad (4.152)$$

provides the *least-squares, rank r approximation* to the Hessian **H** (Scharf, 1991). Correspondingly, the use of the new matrix $\mathbf{H}_r$ in place of the Hessian **H** in the on-line learning algorithm of Eq. (4.147) reduces the computational complexity of the algorithm to somewhere between $O(W)$ and $O(W^2)$.

(iii) *BFGS approximation:* (Schraudolph et al., 2007). As pointed out previously in this section, the BFGS algorithm is considered to be the best form of a quasi-Newton method. In the 2007 paper by Schraudolph et al., the BFGS algorithm is modified in both its full and limited versions of memory such that it becomes usable for the stochastic aproximation of gradients. The modified algorithm appears to provide a fast, scalable, stochastic quasi-Newton procedure for on-line convex optimization. In Yu et al. (2008), the BFGS quasi-Newton method and its limited-memory variant are extended to deal with non-smooth convex objective functions.

4.17   CONVOLUTIONAL NETWORKS

Up to this point, we have been concerned with the algorithmic design of multilayer perceptrons and related issues. In this section, we focus on the structural layout of the multilayer perceptron itself. In particular, we describe a special class of multilayer perceptrons known collectively as *convolutional networks*, which are well suited for pattern classification. The idea behind the development of these networks is neurobiologically motivated, going back to the pioneering work of Hubel and Wiesel (1962, 1977) on locally sensitive and orientation-selective neurons of the visual cortex of a cat.

A *convolutional network* is a multilayer perceptron designed specifically to recognize two-dimensional shapes with a high degree of invariance to translation, scaling, skewing, and other forms of distortion. This difficult task is learned in a supervised manner by means of a network whose structure includes the following forms of *constraints* (LeCun and Bengio, 2003):

1. *Feature extraction.* Each neuron takes its synaptic inputs from a local *receptive field* in the previous layer, thereby forcing it to extract local features. Once a feature has been extracted, its exact location becomes less important, so long as its position relative to other features is approximately preserved.

2. *Feature mapping.* Each computational layer of the network is composed of multiple *feature maps*, with each feature map being in the form of a plane within which the individual neurons are *constrained* to share the same set of synaptic weights. This second form of structural constraint has the following beneficial effects:

- *shift invariance*, forced into the operation of a feature map through the use of *convolution* with a kernel of small size, followed by a sigmoid function;
- *reduction in the number of free parameters*, accomplished through the use of *weight sharing*.

3. *Subsampling.* Each convolutional layer is followed by a computational layer that performs *local averaging* and *subsampling*, whereby the resolution of the feature map is reduced. This operation has the effect of reducing the sensitivity of the feature map's output to shifts and other forms of distortion.

We emphasize that all weights in all layers of a convolutional network are learned through training. Moreover, the network learns to extract its own features automatically.

Figure 4.23 shows the architectural layout of a convolutional network made up of an input layer, four hidden layers, and an output layer. This network is designed to perform *image processing* (e.g., recognition of handwritten characters). The input layer, made up of 28×28 sensory nodes, receives the images of different characters that have

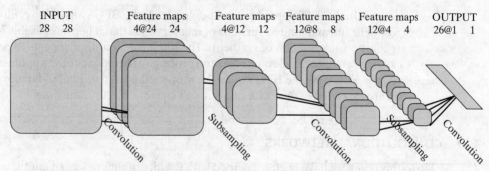

FIGURE 4.23 Convolutional network for image processing such as handwriting recognition. (Reproduced with permission of MIT Press.)

been approximately centered and normalized in size. Thereafter, the computational layouts alternate between convolution and subsampling:

1. The first hidden layer performs convolution. It consists of four feature maps, with each feature map consisting of 24×24 neurons. Each neuron is assigned a receptive field of size 5×5.

2. The second hidden layer performs subsampling and local averaging. It also consists of four feature maps, but each feature map is now made up of 12×12 neurons. Each neuron has a receptive field of size 2×2, a trainable coefficient, a trainable bias, and a sigmoid activation function. The trainable coefficient and bias control the operating point of the neuron; for example, if the coefficient is small, the neuron operates in a quasilinear mode.

3. The third hidden layer performs a second convolution. It consists of 12 feature maps, with each feature map consisting of 8×8 neurons. Each neuron in this hidden layer may have synaptic connections from several feature maps in the previous hidden layer. Otherwise, it operates in a manner similar to the first convolutional layer.

4. The fourth hidden layer performs a second subsampling and local averaging. It consists of 12 feature maps, but with each feature map consisting of 4×4 neurons. Otherwise, it operates in a manner similar to the first subsampling layer.

5. The output layer performs one final stage of convolution. It consists of 26 neurons, with each neuron assigned to one of 26 possible characters. As before, each neuron is assigned a receptive field of size 4×4.

With the successive computational layers alternating between convolution and subsampling, we get a "bipyramidal" effect. That is, at each convolutional or subsampling layer, the number of feature maps is increased while the spatial resolution is reduced, compared with the corresponding previous layer. The idea of convolution followed by subsampling is inspired by the notion of "simple" cells followed by "complex" cells[14] that was first described in Hubel and Wiesel (1962).

The multilayer perceptron described in Fig. 4.23 contains approximately 100,000 synaptic connections, but only about 2,600 free parameters. This dramatic reduction in the number of free parameters is achieved through the use of weight sharing. The capacity of the learning machine is thereby reduced, which in turn improves the machine's generalization ability. What is even more remarkable is the fact that the adjustments to the free parameters of the network are made by using the stochastic mode of back-propagation learning.

Another noteworthy point is that the use of weight sharing makes it possible to implement the convolutional network in parallel form. This is another advantage of the convolutional network over a fully connected multilayer perceptron.

The lesson to be learned from the convolutional network of Fig. 4.23 is twofold. First, a multilayer perceptron of manageable size is able to learn a complex, high-dimensional, nonlinear mapping by *constraining* its design through the incorporation of prior knowledge about the task at hand. Second, the synaptic weights and bias levels can be learned by cycling the simple back-propagation algorithm through the training sample.

4.18   NONLINEAR FILTERING

The prototypical use of a static neural network, exemplified by the multilayer perceptron, is in *structural pattern recognition*; insofar as applications are concerned, much of the material presented in this chapter has focused on structural pattern recognition. In contrast, in *temporal pattern recognition*, or *nonlinear filtering*, the requirement is to process patterns that evolve over time, with the response at a particular instant of time depending not only on the present value of the input signal, but also on past values. Simply put, *time* is an ordered quantity that constitutes an important ingredient of the learning process in temporal-pattern-recognition tasks.

For a neural network to be dynamic, it must be given *short-term memory* in one form or another. A simple way of accomplishing this modification is through the use of *time delays*, which can be implemented at the synaptic level inside the network or externally at the input layer of the network. Indeed, the use of time delays in neural networks is neurobiologically motivated, since it is well known that signal delays are omnipresent in the brain and play an important role in neurobiological information processing (Braitenberg, 1967, 1977, 1986; Miller, 1987). Time may therefore be built into the operation of a neural network in two basic ways:

- *Implicit representation.* Time is represented by the effect it has on signal processing in an implicit manner. For example, in a digital implementation of the neural network, the input signal is *uniformly sampled*, and the sequence of synaptic weights of each neuron connected to the input layer of the network is convolved with a different sequence of input samples. In so doing, the temporal structure of the input signal is embedded in the spatial structure of the network.

- *Explicit representation.* Time is given its own particular representation inside the network structure. For example, the echolocation system of a bat operates by emitting a short frequency-modulated (FM) signal, so that the same intensity level is maintained for each frequency channel restricted to a very short period within the

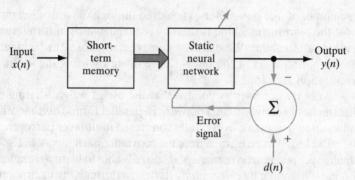

FIGURE 4.24 Nonlinear filter built on a static neural network.

FM sweep. Multiple comparisons between several different frequencies encoded by an array of auditory receptors are made for the purpose of extracting accurate distance (range) information about a target (Suga and Kanwal, 1995). When an echo is received from the target with an unknown delay, a neuron (in the auditory system) with a matching delay line responds, thereby providing an estimate of the range to the target.

In this section, we are concerned with the implicit representation of time, whereby a static neural network (e.g., multilayer perceptron) is provided with *dynamic* properties by external means.

Figure 4.24 shows the block diagram of a *nonlinear filter* consisting of the cascade connection of two subsystems: short-term memory and a static neural network (e.g., multilayer perceptron). This structure provides for a clear-cut separation of processing roles: The static network accounts for nonlinearity, and the memory accounts for time. To be specific, suppose we are given a multilayer perceptron with an input layer of size m. Then, in a corresponding way, the memory is a *single-input, multiple-output* (SIMO) structure providing m differently delayed versions of the input signal for stimulating the neural network.

Short-Term Memory Structures

Figure 4.25 shows the block diagram of a *discrete-time memory structure* consisting of p identical sections connected in cascade. Each section is characterized by an impulse response, denoted by $h(n)$, where n denotes discrete time. The number of sections, p, is

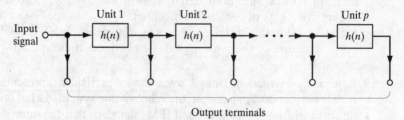

FIGURE 4.25 Generalized tapped-delay-line memory of order p.

called the *order of the memory*. Correspondingly, the number of output terminals (i.e., taps) provided by the memory is $p + 1$, which includes the direct connection from the input to the output. Thus, with m denoting the size of the input layer of the static neural network, we may set

$$m = p + 1$$

The impulse response of each delay section of the memory satisfies two properties:

- *causality*, which means that $h(n)$ is zero for $n < 0$;
- *normalization*, which means that $\sum_{n=0}^{\infty} |h(n)| = 1$.

On this basis, we may refer to $h(n)$ as the *generating kernel* of the discrete-time memory.

The attributes of a memory structure are measured in terms of depth and resolution (deVries and Principe, 1992). Let $h_{\text{overall}}(n)$ denote the overall impulse response of the memory. With p memory sections, it follows that $h_{\text{overall}}(n)$ is defined by p successive convolutions of the impulse response $h(n)$. Accordingly, the *memory depth D* is defined as the *first time moment* of $h_{\text{overall}}(n)$, namely,

$$D = \sum_{n=0}^{\infty} n h_{\text{overall}}(n) \tag{4.153}$$

A memory of low depth D holds information content for a relatively short time interval, whereas a high-depth memory holds it much further into the past. *Memory resolution R* is defined as *the number of taps in the memory structure per unit of time*. A memory of high resolution is therefore able to hold information about the input sequence at a fine level, whereas a low-resolution memory can do so only at a coarser level. For a fixed memory order p, the product of memory depth D and memory resolution R is a constant that turns out to be equal to p.

Naturally, different choices of the generating kernel $h(n)$ result in different values for the depth D and memory resolution R, as illustrated by the following two memory structures:

1. *Tapped-delay-line memory*, for which the generating kernel is simply defined by the unit impulse $\delta(n)$; that is,

$$h(n) = \delta(n) = \begin{cases} 1, & n = 0 \\ 0, & n \neq 0 \end{cases} \tag{4.154}$$

   Correspondingly, the overall impulse response is

$$h_{\text{overall}}(n) = \delta(n - p) = \begin{cases} 1, & n = p \\ 0, & n \neq p \end{cases} \tag{4.155}$$

   Substituting Eq. (4.155) into Eq. (4.153) yields the memory depth $D = p$, which is intuitively satisfying. Moreover, since there is only one tap per time unit, it follows that the resolution $R = 1$, yielding a depth-resolution product equal to p.

2. *Gamma memory*, for which the generating kernel is defined by

$$h(n) = \mu(1 - \mu)^{n-1}, \qquad n \geq 1 \tag{4.156}$$

where μ is an adjustable parameter (deVries and Principe, 1992). For $h(n)$ to be convergent (i.e., for the short-term memory to be stable), we require that

$$0 < \mu < 2$$

Correspondingly, the overall impulse response of the gamma memory is

$$h_{overall}(n) = \binom{n - 1}{p - 1}\mu^{p}(1 - \mu)^{n-p}, \qquad n \geq p \tag{4.157}$$

where $\binom{\cdot}{\cdot}$ is a binomial coefficient. The impulse response $h_{overall}(n)$ for varying p represents a discrete version of the integrand of the gamma function (deVries and Principe, 1992)—hence the name "gamma memory." Figure 4.26 plots the impulse response $h_{overall}(n)$, normalized with respect to μ, for varying memory order $p = 1, 2, 3, 4$ and $\mu = 0.7$. Note also that the time axis has been scaled by the parameter μ, which has the effect of positioning the peak value of $h_{overall}(n)$ at $n = p - 1$.

It turns out that the depth of gamma memory is (p/μ) and the resolution is μ, again producing a depth-resolution product equal to p. Accordingly, by choosing μ to be less than unity, the gamma memory produces improvement in depth at the expense of resolution. For the special case of $\mu = 1$, the gamma memory reduces to an ordinary tapped-delay-line memory where each section consists simply of a unit-time delay operator.

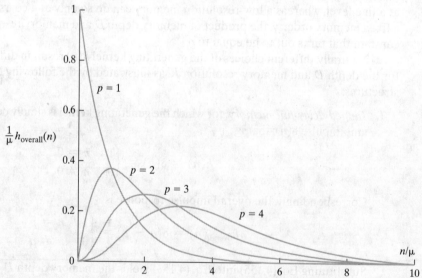

FIGURE 4.26 Family of impulse responses of the gamma memory for order $p = 1, 2, 3, 4$ and $\mu = 0.7$.

Universal Myopic Mapping Theorem

The nonlinear filter of Fig. 4.24 may be generalized to that shown in Fig. 4.27. This generic dynamic structure consists of two functional blocks. The block labeled $\{h_j\}_{j=1}^{L}$ represents *multiple convolutions* in the time domain, that is, a bank of *linear filters* operating in parallel. The h_j are drawn from a large set of real-valued kernels, each one of which represents the impulse response of a linear filter. The block labeled $\mathcal{N}$ represents a static (i.e., memoryless) nonlinear feedforward network such as the multilayer perceptron. The structure of Fig. 4.27 is a *universal dynamic mapper.* In Sandberg and Xu (1997a), it is shown that any shift-invariant *myopic map* can be uniformly approximated arbitrarily well by a structure of the form depicted in Fig. 4.27 under mild conditions. The requirement that a map be myopic is equivalent to "uniformly fading memory"; it is assumed here that the map is *causal*, which means that an output signal is produced by the map at time $n \geq 0$ only when the input signal is applied at time $n = 0$. By "shift invariant," we mean the following: If $y(n)$ is the output of the map generated by an input $x(n)$, then the output of the map generated by the shifted input $x(n - n_0)$ is $y(n - n_0)$, where the time shift n_0 is an integer. In Sandberg and Xu (1997b), it is further shown that for any single-variable, shift-invariant, causal, uniformly fading memory map, there is a gamma memory and static neural network, the combination of which approximates the map uniformly and arbitrarily well.

We may now formally state the *universal myopic mapping theorem*[15] as follows (Sandberg and Xu, 1997a, 1997b):

> Any shift-invariant myopic dynamic map can be uniformly approximated arbitrarily well by a structure consisting of two functional blocks: a bank of linear filters feeding a static neural network.

As already mentioned, a multilayer perceptron may serve the role of the static network. It is also noteworthy that this theorem holds when the input and output signals are functions of a finite number of variables, as in image processing, for example.

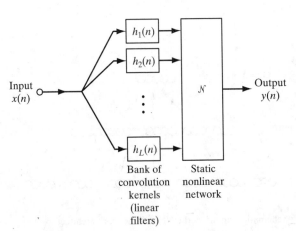

Bank of convolution kernels (linear filters)

Static nonlinear network

FIGURE 4.27 Generic structure for universal myopic mapping theorem.

Practical Implications of the Theorem

The universal myopic mapping theorem has profound practical implications:

1. The theorem provides justification for *NETtalk*, which was the first demonstration of a massively parallel distributed network that converts English speech to phonemes; a *phoneme* is a basic linguistic unit (Sejnowski and Rosenberg, 1987). Figure 4.28 shows a schematic diagram of the NETtalk system, based on a multilayer perceptron with an input layer of 203 sensory (source) nodes, a hidden layer of 80 neurons, and an output layer of 26 neurons. All the neurons used sigmoid (logistic) activation functions. The synaptic connections in the network were specified by a total of 18,629 weights, including a variable threshold for each neuron; threshold is the negative of bias. The standard back-propagation algorithm was used to train the network. The network had seven groups of nodes in the input layer, with each group encoding one letter of the input text. Strings of seven letters were thus presented to the input layer at any one time. The desired response for the training process was specified as the correct phoneme associated with the center (i.e., fourth) letter in the seven-letter window. The other six letters (three on either side of the center letter) provided a partial *context* for each decision made by the network. The text was stepped through the window on a letter-by-letter basis. At each step in the process, the network computed a phoneme, and after each word the synaptic weights of the network were adjusted according to how closely the computed pronunciation matched the correct one.

   The performance of NETtalk exhibited some similarities with observed human performance, as summarized here (Sejnowski and Rosenberg, 1987):

   • The training followed a power law.
   • The more words the network learned, the better it was at generalizing and correctly pronouncing new words.
   • The performance of the network degraded very slowly as synaptic connections in the network were purposely damaged.
   • Relearning after damage to the network was much faster than learning during the original training.

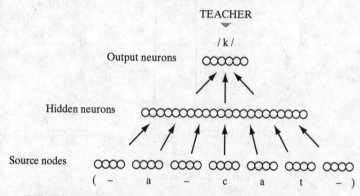

FIGURE 4.28 Schematic diagram of the NETtalk network architecture.

NETtalk was a brilliant illustration in miniature of many aspects of learning, starting out with considerable "innate" knowledge of its input patterns and then gradually acquiring competence at converting English speech to phonemes through practice.

2. The universal myopic theorem lays down the framework for the design of more elaborate models of nonlinear systems. The multiple convolutions at the front end of the structure in Fig. 4.27 may be implemented using linear filters with a finite-duration impulse response (FIR) or infinite-duration impulse response (IIR). Most importantly, the structure of Fig. 4.27 is *inherently stable*, provided that the linear filters are themselves stable. We thus have a clear-cut separation of roles as to how to take care of short-term memory and memoryless nonlinearity in building a stable dynamic system.

3. Given a stationary time series $x(1), x(2), ..., x(n)$, we may use the universal myopic mapping structure of Fig. 4.27 to build a predictive model of the underlying nonlinear physical laws responsible for generating the time series by setting $y(n) = x(n + 1)$, no matter how complex the laws are. In effect, the future sample $x(n + 1)$ plays the role of desired response. When a multilayer perceptron is used as the static network in Fig. 4.27 for such an application, it is advisable to provide a linear neuron for the output unit in the network. This provision will ensure that no amplitude limitation is placed on the dynamic range of the predictive model.

4.19   SMALL-SCALE VERSUS LARGE-SCALE LEARNING PROBLEMS

At various points along the way in this chapter and other parts of the book, we have made references to small-scale and large-scale learning problems. However, we did not elaborate rigorously on the meaning of these two kinds of supervised learning. The purpose of this section is to sharpen the statistical and computational issues that distinguish them from each other.

We begin the discussion with structural risk minimization (SRM), which is entirely statistical in nature; SRM is adequate for dealing with small-scale learning problems. Then we broaden the discussion by considering computational issues that assume a prominent role in dealing with large-scale learning problems.

Structural Risk Minimization

The feasibility of supervised learning depends on the following key question:

Does a training sample consisting of N independent and identically distributed examples

$$(\mathbf{x}_1, d_1), (\mathbf{x}_2, d_2), ..., (\mathbf{x}_N, d_N)$$

contain sufficient information to construct a learning machine capable of good generalization performance?

The answer to this fundamental question lies in the method of *structural risk minimization*, described by Vapnik (1982, 1998).

To describe what we mean by this method, let the natural source or environment responsible for generating the training sample be represented by the *nonlinear* regression model

$$d = f(\mathbf{x}) + \varepsilon \tag{4.158}$$

where, following the terminology introduced in Chapter 2, the vector $\mathbf{x}$ is the regressor, the scalar d is the response, and ε is the explanational (modeling) error. The function f is the unknown, and the objective is to estimate it. To do this estimation, we define the expected risk (i.e., the ensemble-averaged cost function) as

$$J_{\text{actual}}(f) = \mathbb{E}_{\mathbf{x},d}\left[\frac{1}{2}(d - f(\mathbf{x}))^2\right] \tag{4.159}$$

where the expectation is performed jointly with respect to the regressor–response pair $(\mathbf{x}, d)$. In Chapter 5, we will show that the *conditional mean estimator*

$$\hat{f}^* = \mathbb{E}[d|\mathbf{x}] \tag{4.160}$$

is the minimizer of the cost function $J_{\text{actual}}(f)$. Correspondingly, we write $J_{\text{actual}}(\hat{f}^*)$ as the minimum value of the cost function defined in Eq. (4.159); it serves as the *absolute optimum* that is achievable.

Determination of the conditional mean estimator $\hat{f}^*$ requires knowledge of the underlying joint probability distribution of the regressor $\mathbf{x}$ and the response d. Typically, however, we find that this knowledge is not available. To circumvent this difficulty, we look to machine learning for a viable solution. Suppose, for example, we choose a single-layer multilayer perceptron to do the machine learning. Let the function $F(\mathbf{x}; \mathbf{w})$ denote the input–output relationship of the neural network parameterized by the weight vector $\mathbf{w}$. We then make our *first approximation* by setting

$$f(\mathbf{x}) = F(\mathbf{x}; \mathbf{w}) \tag{4.161}$$

Correspondingly, we formulate the model's cost function as

$$J(\mathbf{w}) = \mathbb{E}_{\mathbf{x},d}\left[\frac{1}{2}(d - F(\mathbf{x}; \mathbf{w}))^2\right] \tag{4.162}$$

where, as before, the expectation is performed jointly with respect to the pair $(\mathbf{x}, d)$. This second cost function is naturally formulated differently from the cost function $J_{\text{actual}}(f)$ pertaining to the source—hence the use of different symbols for them. In imposing the equality of Eq. (4.161) on the neural network, we have in effect restricted the choice of the approximating function $F(\mathbf{x}; \mathbf{w})$.

Let

$$\hat{\mathbf{w}}^* = \arg\min_{\mathbf{w}} J(\mathbf{w}) \tag{4.163}$$

be the minimizer of the cost function $J(\mathbf{w})$. The reality, however, is that even if we can find the minimizer $\hat{\mathbf{w}}^*$, it is highly likely that the resulting cost function $J(\hat{\mathbf{w}}^*)$ will be worse than the minimized cost function $J_{\text{actual}}(\hat{f}^*)$. In any event, we cannot do better than $J_{\text{actual}}(\hat{f}^*)$, and thus we write

$$J(\hat{\mathbf{w}}^*) > J_{\text{actual}}(\hat{f}^*) \tag{4.164}$$

Unfortunately, we are still faced with the same practical problem as before in that we may not know the underlying joint probability distribution of the pair $(\mathbf{x}, d)$. To alleviate this difficulty, we make our *second approximation* by using the empirical risk (i.e., the time-averaged energy function)

$$\mathscr{E}_{av}(N; \mathbf{w}) = \frac{1}{2N} \sum_{n=1}^{N} (d(n) - F(\mathbf{x}(n); \mathbf{w}))^2 \qquad (4.165)$$

whose minimizer is defined by

$$\hat{\mathbf{w}}_N = \arg \min_{\mathbf{w}} \mathscr{E}_{av}(N; \mathbf{w}) \qquad (4.166)$$

Clearly, the minimized cost function $J(\hat{\mathbf{w}}_N)$ cannot be smaller than $J(\hat{\mathbf{w}}^*)$. Indeed, it is highly likely to find that

$$J(\hat{\mathbf{w}}_N) > J(\hat{\mathbf{w}}^*) > J_{actual}(\hat{f}^*) \qquad (4.167)$$

With the two approximations that have been made, we may wonder why we should compute the minimum $\hat{\mathbf{w}}_N$ exactly. Before addressing this question, let us examine what happens when the example multilayer perceptron is changed by enlarging the size of the hidden layer.

From Section 4.12, we recall that the multilayer perceptron is a universal approximator of the unknown function $f(\mathbf{x})$. In theory, the parameterized function $F(\mathbf{x}; \mathbf{w})$ approximates the unknown function $f(\mathbf{x})$ with any desired accuracy provided that the size of the hidden layer is large enough. This, in turn, means that $J(\hat{\mathbf{w}}^*)$ becomes closer to the absolute optimum $J_{actual}(\hat{f}^*)$. However, by enlarging the size of the hidden layer, we may compromise the generalization capability of the multilayer perceptron. In particular, it is possible for the error $(J(\hat{\mathbf{w}}^*) - J_{actual}(\hat{f}^*))$ to increase as a result of enlarging the hidden layer, unless the size of the training sample, N, is correspondingly increased. The issue just discussed is the essence of Vapnik's *structural risk minimization*, which manifests itself in the "approximation–estimation trade-off."

To elaborate further on this trade-off, let the *excess error* $(J(\hat{\mathbf{w}}_N) - J_{actual}(\hat{f}^*))$ be decomposed into two terms as follows:

$$\underbrace{J(\hat{\mathbf{w}}_N) - J_{actual}(\hat{f}^*)}_{\text{Excess error}} = \underbrace{J(\hat{\mathbf{w}}_N) - J(\hat{\mathbf{w}}^*)}_{\text{Estimation error}} + \underbrace{J(\hat{\mathbf{w}}^*) - J_{actual}(\hat{f}^*)}_{\text{Approximation error}} \qquad (4.168)$$

In this classical decomposition of errors, the following points are noteworthy:

(i) The *estimation error* provides a measure of how much performance is lost as a result of using a training sample of some prescribed size N. Moreover, with $\hat{\mathbf{w}}_N$ being dependent on the training sample, the approximation error is therefore relevant in the assessment of network training.

(ii) The *approximation error* provides a measure of how much performance is lost by choosing a model characterized by the approximating function $F(\mathbf{x}, \mathbf{w})$. Moreover, with $\hat{f}^*$ being a conditional estimator of the response d given the regressor $\mathbf{x}$, the estimation error is therefore relevant in the assessment of network testing.

In Vapnik's theoretical framework, the approximation and estimation errors are formulated in terms of the *VC dimension,* commonly denoted by h. This new parameter, short for the *Vapnik–Chervonenkis dimension* (Vapnik and Chervonenkis, 1971), is a measure of the *capacity,* or *expressive power,* of a family of binary classification functions realized by the learning machine.[16] For the example of a single-layer multilayer perceptron, the VC dimension is determined by the size of the hidden layer; the larger this size is, the larger the VC dimension h will be.

To put Vapnik's theory in a practical context, consider a family of *nested* approximating network functions denoted by

$$\mathcal{F}_k = \{F(\mathbf{x}; \mathbf{w})(\mathbf{w} \in \mathcal{W}_k)\}, \qquad k = 1, 2, ..., K \tag{4.169}$$

such that we have

$$\mathcal{F}_1 \subset \mathcal{F}_2 \subset \cdots \subset \mathcal{F}_K$$

where the symbol $\subset$ means "is contained in." Correspondingly, the VC dimensions of the individual subsets of $\mathcal{F}_K$ satisfy the condition

$$h_1 < h_2 < \cdots < h_K$$

In effect, the size of $\mathcal{F}_K$ is a measure of the machine capacity. Hereafter, we use the definition of Eq. (4.169) in place of the VC dimension.

Figure 4.29 plots variations of the approximation and estimation errors versus the size K of the family of approximating network functions $\mathcal{F}_K$. For the example of a single-layer multilayer perceptron, the optimum size of the hidden layer is determined by the point at which the approximation error and the estimation error assume a common value. Before the optimum condition is reached, the learning problem is *overdetermined,* which means that the machine capacity is too small for the amount of detail contained in the training sample. Beyond the minimum point, the learning problem is *underdetermined,* which means that the machine capacity is too large for the training sample.

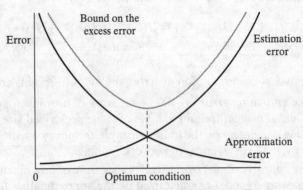

FIGURE 4.29 Variations of the approximation and estimation errors with the size K.

Computational Considerations

The neural network model (e.g., the single-layer multilayer perceptron) must be a *controlled variable*, so that it can be freely adjusted to achieve the best test performance on data not seen before. Another controlled variable is the number of examples to do the training. In order to add practical realism to the supervised-training process, Bottou (2007) has introduced the cost of computation by considering a new controlled variable: *optimization accuracy*.

In practice, it is possible to find that the task of computing the minimizer $\hat{\mathbf{w}}_N$ is rather *costly*. Moreover, in the course of coming up with a satisfactory network design, we usually make many approximations. Suppose, then, we settle on a network model characterized by the weight vector $\tilde{\mathbf{w}}_N$, which is different from $\hat{\mathbf{w}}_N$; in so doing, we will have made our *third, and final, approximation*. For example, the on-line learning algorithm could be stopped long before convergence has been reached, due to limited computing time. In any event, $\tilde{\mathbf{w}}_N$ is a suboptimal solution that satisfies the condition

$$\mathscr{E}_{\text{av}}(N; \tilde{\mathbf{w}}_N) \leq \mathscr{E}_{\text{av}}(N; \hat{\mathbf{w}}_N) + \rho \tag{4.170}$$

where ρ constitutes a new controlled variable; it provides a measure of *computational accuracy*.

In light of this new practicality, we now have a more complicated problem than that encountered in the method of structural risk minimization. Specifically, we must now adjust three variables:

- the network model (for instance, through the number of hidden neurons in a multilayer perceptron),
- the number of training examples, and
- the optimization accuracy (for instance by prematurely terminating computation of the minimizer $\hat{\mathbf{w}}_N$ and settling on the suboptimal solution $\tilde{\mathbf{w}}_N$).

In order to hit the best test performance, we have to satisfy *budget constraints*, which define the maximum number of training examples that we can use and the maximum computing time that we can afford. In a practical context, we are therefore confronted with a trade-off that is rather complicated. In solving this *constrained-optimization problem*, the trade-off will depend on whether we first hit a limit on the number of examples or impose a limit on the computing time. Which of these two limits is the active budget constraint depends on whether the supervised-learning process is of a small-scale or large-scale kind, as discussed next.

Definitions

According to Bottou (2007), small-scale and large-scale learning problems are respectively defined as follows:

Definition I. Small-scale learning

A supervised-learning problem is said to be of a small-scale kind when the *size of the training sample* (i.e., the number of examples) is the active budget constraint imposed on the learning process.

Definition II. Large-scale learning

A supervised-learning problem is said to be of a large-scale kind when the *computing time* is the active budget constraint imposed on the learning process.

In other words, it is the *active budget constraint* that distinguishes one learning problem from the other.

For an illustrative example of a small-scale learning problem, we may mention the design of an *adaptive equalizer*, the purpose of which is to compensate for the inevitable distortion of information-bearing data transmitted over a communication channel. The LMS algorithm, rooted in stochastic gradient descent and discussed in Chapter 3, is widely used for solving this on-line learning problem (Haykin, 2002).

For an illustrative example of a large-scale learning problem, we may mention the design of a check reader where the training examples consist of joint pairs, each of which describes a particular {*image, amount*} pair, where "image" pertains to a check and "amount" pertains to the amount of money inscribed in the check. Such a learning problem has strong structure that is complicated by the following issues (Bottou, 2007):

- field segmentation;
- character segmentation;
- character recognition;
- syntactical interpretation.

The *convolutional network*, embodying differentiable modules as described in Section 4.17 and trained with a stochastic gradient algorithm for a few weeks, is widely used for solving this challenging learning problem (LeCun et al., 1998). Indeed, this novel network has been deployed in industry since 1996, running billions of checks.

Small-Scale Learning Problems

Insofar as small-scale learning problems are concerned, there are three variables available to the designer of a learning machine:

- the number of training examples, N;
- the permissible size K of the family of approximating network functions $\mathcal{F}$;
- the computational error ρ introduced in Eq. (4.170).

With the active budget constraint being the number of examples, the design options in learning problems of the first kind are as follows (Bottou, 2007):

- Reduce the estimation error by making N as large as the budget permits.
- Reduce the optimization error by setting the computational error $\rho = 0$, which means setting $\widetilde{\mathbf{w}}_N = \hat{\mathbf{w}}_N$.
- Adjust the size of $\mathcal{F}$ to the extent deemed to be reasonable.

With $\rho = 0$, the method of structural risk minimization, involving the approximation–estimation tradeoff illustrated in Fig. 4.29, is adequate for dealing with small-scale learning problems.

Large-Scale Learning Problems

As pointed out previously, the active budget constraint in large-scale learning problems is the computing time. In tackling learning problems of this second kind, we face *more complicated trade-offs* because we now have to account for the computing time T.

In large-scale learning problems, the excess error is defined by the difference $(J(\widetilde{\mathbf{w}}_N) - J_{\text{actual}}(\hat{f}^*))$, which is decomposed into three terms, as shown by the following (Bottou, 2007):

$$\underbrace{J(\widetilde{\mathbf{w}}_N) - J_{\text{actual}}(\hat{f}^*)}_{\text{Excess error}} = \underbrace{J(\widetilde{\mathbf{w}}_N) - J(\hat{\mathbf{w}}_N)}_{\text{Optimization error}} + \underbrace{J(\hat{\mathbf{w}}_N) - J(\hat{\mathbf{w}}^*)}_{\text{Estimation error}} + \underbrace{J(\hat{\mathbf{w}}^*) - J_{\text{actual}}(\hat{f}^*)}_{\text{Approximation error}} \qquad (4.171)$$

The last two terms, constituting the approximation and estimation errors, are common to both small-scale and large-scale learning problems. It is the first term in Eq. (4.171) that distinguishes large-scale learning problems from small-scale ones. This new term, called the *optimization error*, is obviously related to the computational error ρ.

Computation of the *bound* on the approximation error, depicted in Fig. 4.29, is reasonably well understood (in terms of the VC theory) for small-scale learning problems. Unfortunately, the constants involved in the formula for this bound are quite bad when the formula is applied to large-scale learning problems. In these more difficult situations, it is therefore more productive to analyze Eq. (4.171) in terms of convergence rates rather than bounds.

The requirement is to minimize the sum of the three terms in Eq. (4.171) by adjusting the available variables:

- the number of examples, N;
- the permissible size K of approximating network functions, $\mathcal{F}_K$;
- the computational error ρ, which is no longer zero.

Doing this minimization analytically is extremely difficult, due to the fact that the computing time T is actually dependent on all three variables N, $\mathcal{F}$, and ρ. To illustrate the consequences of this dependence, suppose we assign a small value to the error ρ so as to reduce the optimization error. To realize this reduction, unfortunately, we must also increase N, $\mathcal{F}$, or both, any of which would have undesirable effects on the approximation and estimation errors.

Nevertheless, in some cases, it is possible to compute the exponents with respect to which the three errors tend to decrease when ρ decreases and both $\mathcal{F}$ and N increase. Similarly, it is possible to identify the exponents with respect to which the computing time T increases when ρ decreases and both $\mathcal{F}$ and N increase. Putting these pieces together, we have the elements for an approximate solution to trade-offs in tackling large-scale

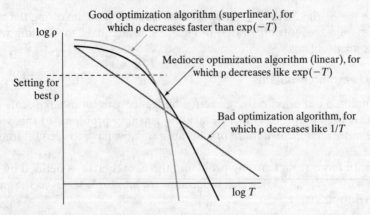

FIGURE 4.30   Variations of the computational error ρ versus the computation time T for three classes of optimization algorithm: bad, mediocre, and good. (This figure is reproduced with the permission of Dr. Leon Bottou.)

learning problems. Most importantly, in the final analysis, the trade-offs depend on the choice of the optimization algorithm.

Figure 4.30 illustrates how a plot of log ρ versus log T is affected by the type of optimization algorithm used to solve a large-scale learning problem. Three categories of optimization algorithms are identified in this figure—namely, *bad*, *mediocre*, and *good*—examples of which respectively include stochastic gradient descent (i.e., on-line learning), gradient descent (i.e., batch learning), and second-order gradient descent (e.g., quasi-Newton optimization algorithm of the BFGS kind or its extension). Table 4.4 summarizes the distinguishing features of these three categories of optimization algorithms.

TABLE 4.4   Summary of Statistical Characteristics of Three Optimization Algorithms*

Algorithm	Cost per iteration	Time to reach ρ
1. Stochastic gradient descent (on-line learning)	$O(m)$	$O\left(\dfrac{1}{\rho}\right)$
2. Gradient descent (batch learning)	$O(Nm)$	$O\left(\log\dfrac{1}{\rho}\right)$
3. Second-order gradient descent (on-line learning)	$O(m(m+N))$	$O\left(\log\left(\log\dfrac{1}{\rho}\right)\right)$

m : dimension of input vector **x**
N : number of examples used in training
ρ : computational error

*This table is compiled from Bottou (2007).

The message to take from the material presented in this section on supervised learning may now be summed up as follows:

> *Whereas the study of small-scale learning problems is well-developed, the study of large-scale learning problems is in its early stages of development.*

4.20 SUMMARY AND DISCUSSION

The back-propagation algorithm has established itself as a computationally efficient and useful algorithm for the training of multilayer perceptrons. The algorithm derives its name from the fact that the partial derivatives of the cost function (performance measure) with respect to the free parameters (synaptic weights and biases) of the network are determined by back-propagating the error signals (computed by the output neurons) through the network, layer by layer. In so doing, the algorithm solves the credit-assignment problem in a most elegant fashion. The computing power of the algorithm lies in its two main attributes:

- the *local* method, for updating the synaptic weights and biases of the multilayer perceptron;
- the *efficient* method, for computing *all* the partial derivatives of the cost function with respect to these free parameters.

Stochastic and Batch Methods of Training

For a given epoch of training data, the back-propagation algorithm operates in one of two modes: stochastic or batch. In the stochastic mode, the synaptic weights of all neurons in the network are adjusted in a sequential manner, pattern by pattern. Consequently, estimation of the gradient vector of the error surface used in the computation is stochastic in nature—hence the name "stochastic back-propagation learning." On the other hand, in the batch mode, the adjustments to all synaptic weights and biases are made on an epoch-by-epoch basis, with the result that a more accurate estimate of the gradient vector is utilized in the computation. Despite its disadvantages, the stochastic form of back-propagation learning is most frequently used for the training of multilayer perceptrons, particularly for large-scale problems. To achieve the best results, however, careful tuning of the algorithm is required.

Pattern Classification and Nonlinear Filtering

The specific details involved in the design of a multilayer perceptron naturally depend on the application of interest. We may, however, make two distinctions:

1. In pattern classification involving nonlinearly separable patterns, all the neurons in the network are *nonlinear*. The nonlinearity is achieved by employing a sigmoid function, two commonly used forms of which are (a) the logistic function, and (b) the hyperbolic tangent function. Each neuron is responsible for producing a hyperplane of its own in decision space. Through a supervised learning process, the combination of hyperplanes formed by all the neurons in the network is iteratively adjusted in order to separate patterns drawn from the different classes and not seen before, with the fewest classification errors on average. For pattern classfication, the stochastic back-propagation algorithm is widely used to perform the training, particularly for large-scale problems (e.g., optical character recognition).

2. In nonlinear filtering, the *dynamic range* at the output of the multilayer perceptron should be sufficiently large to accommodate the process values; in this context, the use of linear output neurons is the most sensible choice. As for learning algorithms, we offer the following observations:

- On-line learning is much slower than batch learning.
- Assuming that batch learning is the desired choice, the standard back-propagation algorithm is slower than the conjugate gradient algorithm.

The method of nonlinear filtering, discussed in this chapter, focused on the use of a static network, exemplified by the multilayer perceptron; the input signal is applied to the multilayer perceptron through a short-term memory structure (e.g., tapped delay line or gamma filter) that provides for time, which is an essential dimension of filtering. In Chapter 15, we revisit the design of nonlinear filters for which feedback is applied to a multilayer perceptron, turning it into a recurrent neural network.

Small-scale versus Large-scale Learning Problems

Generally speaking, there are three kinds of error that can arise in the study of machine-learning problems:

1. *Approximation error*, which refers to the error incurred in the training of a neural network or learning machine, given a training sample of some finite size N.

2. *Estimation error*, which refers to the error incurred when the training of the machine is completed and its performance is tested using data not seen before; in effect, estimation error is another way of referring to generalization error.

3. *Optimization error*, the presence of which is attributed to accuracy of the computation involved in training the machine for some prescribed computing time T.

In small-scale learning problems, we find that the *active budget constraint* is the size of the training sample, which implicitly means that the optimization error is usually zero in practice. Vapnik's theory of structural risk minimization is therefore adequately equipped to handle small-scale learning problems. On the other hand, in large-scale learning problems, the active budget constraint is the available computing time, T, with the result that the optimization error takes on a critical role of its own. In particular, computational accuracy of the learning process and therefore the optimization error are both strongly affected by the type of optimization algorithm employed to solve the learning problem.

NOTES AND REFERENCES

1. Sigmoid functions are "S" shaped graphs; Mennon et al. (1996) present a detailed study of two classes of sigmoids:

   - *simple sigmoids*, defined to be odd, asymptotically bounded, and completely monotone functions of one variable;
   - *hyperbolic sigmoids*, representing a proper subset of simple sigmoids and a natural generalization of the hyperbolic tangent function.

2. For the special case of the LMS algorithm, it has been shown that use of the momentum constant α reduces the stable range of the learning-rate parameter η and could thus lead to instability if η is not adjusted appropriately. Moreover, the misadjustment increases with increasing α; for details, see Roy and Shynk (1990).

3. A vector $\mathbf{w}^*$ is said to be a *local minimum* of an input—output function F if it is no worse than its *neighbors*—that is, if there exists an ε such that

$$F(\mathbf{w}^*) \le F(\mathbf{w}) \qquad \text{for all } \mathbf{w} \text{ with } \|\mathbf{w} - \mathbf{w}^*\| < \varepsilon$$

(Bertsekas, 1995). The vector $\mathbf{w}^*$ is said to be a *global minimum* of the function F if it is no worse than *all* other vectors—that is,

$$F(\mathbf{w}^*) \le F(\mathbf{w}) \qquad \text{for all } \mathbf{w} \in \mathbb{R}^n$$

where n is the dimension of $\mathbf{w}$.

4. The first documented description of the use of back propagation for efficient gradient evaluation is attributed to Werbos (1974). The material presented in Section 4.8 follows the treatment given in Saarinen et al. (1992); a more general discussion of the topic is presented by Werbos (1990).

5. Battiti (1992) presents a review of exact and approximate algorithms for computing the Hessian, with particular reference to neural networks.

6. Müller et al. (1998) have studied the application of the annealed on-line learning algorithm of Eq. (4.77) to a nonstationary blind source separation problem, which illustrates the broad algorithmic applicability of adaptive control of the learning rate due to Murata (1998). The issue of blind source separation is discussed in Chapter 10.

7. The formulation of Eq. (4.80) follows a corresponding part of the optimally annealed on-line learning algorithm due to Sompolinski et al. (1995) that deals with adaptation of the learning-rate parameter. Practical limitations of this algorithm include the need to compute the Hessian at each iteration and the need to know the minimal loss of the learning curve.

8. The universal approximation theorem may be viewed as a natural extension of the *Weierstrass theorem* (Weierstrass, 1885; Kline, 1972). This theorem states

   Any continuous function over a closed interval on the real axis can be expressed in that interval as an absolutely and uniformly convergent series of polynomials.

   Research interest in the virtues of multilayer perceptrons as devices for the representation of arbitrary continuous functions was perhaps first put into focus by Hecht-Nielsen (1987), who invoked an improved version of Kolomogorov's superposition theorem due to Sprecher (1965). Then, Gallant and White (1988) showed that a single-hidden-layer multilayer perceptron with monotone "cosine" squashing at the hidden layer and no squashing at the output behaves like as a special case of a "Fourier network" that yields a Fourier series approximation to a given function as its output. However, in the context of traditional multilayer perceptrons, it was Cybenko who demonstrated rigorously for the first time that a single hidden layer is sufficient to uniformly approximate any continuous function with support in a unit hypercube; this work was published as a University of Illinois Technical Report in 1988 and republished as a paper one year later (Cybenko, 1988, 1989). In 1989, two other papers were published independently on multilayer perceptrons as universal approximators, one by Funahashi (1989) and the other by Hornik et al. (1990). For subsequent contributions to the approximation problem, see Light (1992b).

9. The history of the development of cross-validation is documented in Stone (1974). The idea of cross-validation had been around at least since the 1930s, but refinement of the technique was accomplished in the 1960s and 1970s. Two important papers from that era are by Stone (1974) and Geisser (1975), who independently and almost simultaneously propounded the idea of cross-validation. The technique was termed the "cross-validating method" by Stone and the "predictive sample reuse method" by Geisser.

10. Hecht-Nielsen (1995) describes a replicator neural network in the form of a multilayer perceptron with an input layer of source nodes, three hidden layers and an output layer:

   • The activation functions of neurons in the first and third hidden layers are defined by the hyperbolic tangent function

   $$\varphi^{(1)}(v) = \varphi^{(3)}(v) = \tanh(v)$$

   where v is the induced local field of a neuron in those layers.
   • The activation function for each neuron in the second hidden layer is given by

   $$\varphi^{(2)}(v) = \frac{1}{2} + \frac{2}{2(N-1)} \sum_{j=1}^{N-1} \tanh\left(a\left(v - \frac{j}{N}\right)\right)$$

   where a is a gain parameter and v is the induced local filed of a neuron in that layer. The function $\varphi^{(2)}(v)$ describes a smooth staircase activation function with N treadles, thereby essentially quantizing the vector of the respective neural outputs into $K = N^n$, where n is the number of neurons in the middle hidden layer.
   • The neurons in the output layer are linear, with their activation functions defined by

   $$\varphi^{(4)}(v) = v$$

   • Based on this neural network structure, Hecht-Nielsen describes a theorem showing that optimal data compression for arbitrary input data vector can be carried out.

11. The classic reference for the conjugate-gradient method is Hestenes and Stiefel (1952). For a discussion of the convergence behavior of the conjugate-gradient algorithm, see Luenberger (1984) and Bertsekas (1995). For a tutorial treatment of the many facets of the conjugate-gradient algorithm, see Shewchuk (1994). For a readable account of the algorithm in the context of neural networks, see Johansson et al. (1990).

12. The conventional form of the conjugate-gradient algorithm requires the use of a line search, which can be time consuming because of its trial-and-error nature. Møller (1993) describes a modified version of the conjugate-gradient algorithm called the scaled conjugate-gradient algorithm, which avoids the use of a line search. Essentially, the line search is replaced by a one-dimensional Levenberg–Marquardt form of algorithm. The motivation for using such methods is to circumvent the difficulty caused by nonpositive-definite Hessian matrices (Fletcher, 1987).

13. The so-called $\mathcal{R}$-*technique*, due to Pearlmutter (1994), provides an efficient procedure for computing a matrix-vector product; as such, this technique can be of practical use in computing the inverse Hessian $\mathbf{H}^{-1}$ in Eq. (4.138). The $\mathcal{R}$-technique is addressed in Problem 4.6.

14. Hubel and Wiesel's notion of "simple" and "complex" cells was first exploited in the neural network literature by Fukushima (1980, 1995) in the design of a learning machine called the *neocognitron*. This learning machine, however, operates in a self-organized manner, whereas the convolutional network described in Fig. 4.23 operates in a supervised manner using labeled examples.

15. For the origins of the universal myopic mapping theorem, see Sandberg (1991).

16. For a detailed account of the VC-dimension and the related bound on empirical risk, see the classic book on statistical learning theory by Vapnik (1998). The VC-dimension is also discussed in the books by Schölkopf and Smola (2002) and Herbrich (2002). A noteworthy comment is in order: the VC-dimension is related to Cover's separating capacity, which will be discussed in the next chapter, Chapter 5.

PROBLEMS

Back-Propagation Learning

4.1 Figure P4.1 shows a neural network involving a single hidden neuron for solving the XOR problem; this network may be viewed as an alternative to that considered in Section 4.5. Show that the network of Fig. P4.1 solves the XOR problem by constucting (a) decision regions, and (b) a truth table for the network.

4.2 How does the learning-rate parameter η in back-propagation algorithm affect the trajectory in weight space and the rate of learning? Is there any method to avoid the danger of instability of the algorithm?

4.3 The momentum constant α is normally assigned a positive value in the range $0 < \alpha \leq 1$. Investigate the difference that would be made in the behavior of Eq. (4.43) with respect to time t if α were assigned a negative value in the range $-1 \leq \alpha < 0$.

4.4 Consider the simple example of a network involving a single weight, for which the cost function is

$$\mathcal{E}(w) = k_1(w - w_0)^2 + k_2$$

where w_0, k_1, and k_2 are constants. A back-propagation algorithm with momentum α is used to minimize $\mathcal{E}(w)$.

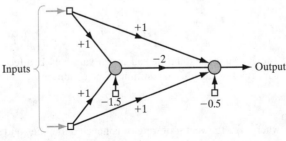

FIGURE P4.1

Explore the way in which the inclusion of the momentum constant α influences the learning process, with particular reference to the number of steps required for convergence versus α.

4.5 Equations (4.51) through (4.53) define the partial derivatives of the approximating function $F(\mathbf{w}, \mathbf{x})$ realized by the multilayer perceptron in Fig. 4.14. Derive these equations from the scenario described by the following conditions:

(a) *Cost function:*

$$\mathcal{E}(n) = \frac{1}{2} [d - F(\mathbf{w}, \mathbf{x})]^2$$

(b) *Output of neuron j:*

$$y_j = \varphi \left(\sum_i w_{ji} \, y_i \right)$$

where w_{ji} is the synaptic weight from neuron i to neuron j, and y_i is the output of neuron i;

(c) *Nonlinearity:*

$$\varphi(v) = \frac{1}{1 + \exp(-v)}$$

4.6 The $\mathcal{R}$ *technique*, developed by Pearlmutter (1994), provides a computationally fast procedure for evaluating a matrix–vector product. To illustrate this procedure, consider a multilayer perceptron with a single hidden layer; the forward-propagation equations of the network are defined by

$$v_j = \sum_i w_{ji} x_i$$

$$z_j = \varphi(v_j)$$

$$y_k = \sum_j w_{kj} z_j$$

$\mathcal{R}[\cdot]$ denotes an *operator* that acts on the quantity enclosed inside the brackets to produce the following results for the example network at hand:

$$\mathcal{R}[v_j] = \sum_i a_{ji} x_i, \qquad \mathcal{R}[w_{ji}] = a_{ji}$$

$$\mathcal{R}[v_j] = \varphi'(v_j) \mathcal{R}[v_j], \qquad \varphi'(v_j) = \frac{\partial}{\partial v_j} \varphi(v_j)$$

$$\mathcal{R}[y_k] = \sum_j w_{kj} \mathcal{R}[z_j] + \sum_i a_{ji} z_j, \qquad \mathcal{R}[w_{kj}] = a_{kj}$$

The $\mathcal{R}$ results are to be viewed as *new* variables. In effect, the operator $\mathcal{R}[\cdot]$ follows the ordinary rules of calculus in addition to the condition

$$\mathcal{R}[\mathbf{w}_j] = \mathbf{a}_j$$

where $\mathbf{w}_j$ is the vector of weights connected to node j and $\mathbf{a}_j$ is the associated vector resulting from application of the $\mathcal{R}$ operator.

(a) Applying the $\mathcal{R}$ technique to the back-propagation algorithm, derive expressions for the elements of the matrix–vector product $\mathbf{Ha}$, identifying the new variables for the hidden and output neurons, the matrix $\mathbf{H}$ is the Hessian. For this application, use the multilayer perceptron described at the beginning of the problem.

(b) Justify the statement that the $\mathcal{R}$ technique is computationally fast.

Supervised Learning Issues

4.7 In this problem, we study the output representation and decision rule performed by a multilayer perceptron. In theory, for an M-class *classification problem* in which the union of the M distinct classes forms the entire input space, we need a total of M outputs to represent all possible classification decisions, as depicted in Fig. P4.7. In this figure, the vector $\mathbf{x}_j$ denotes the jth *prototype* (i.e., unique sample) of an m-dimensional random vector $\mathbf{x}$ to be classified by a multilayer perceptron. The kth of M possible classes to which $\mathbf{x}$ can belong is denoted by $\mathcal{C}_k$. Let y_{kj} be the kth output of the network produced in response to the prototype $\mathbf{x}_j$, as shown by

$$y_{kj} = F_k(\mathbf{x}_j), \quad k = 1, 2, ..., M$$

where the function $F_k(\cdot)$ defines the mapping learned by the network from the input to the k-th output. For convenience of presentation, let

$$\mathbf{y}_j = [y_{1j}, y_{2j}, ..., y_{Mj}]^T$$
$$= [F_1(\mathbf{x}_j), F_2(\mathbf{x}_j), ..., F_M(\mathbf{x}_j)]^T$$
$$= \mathbf{F}(\mathbf{x}_j)$$

where $\mathbf{F}(\cdot)$ is a vector-valued function. The basic question we wish to address in this problem is the following:

> After a multilayer perceptron is trained, what should the optimum decision rule be for classifying the M outputs of the network?

To address this problem, consider the use of a multilayer perceptron embodying a logistic function for its hidden neurons and operating under the following assumptions:

- The size of the training sample is sufficiently large to make a reasonably accurate estimate of the probability of correct classification.
- The back-propagation algorithm used to train the multilayer perceptron does not get stuck in a local minimum.

Specifically, develop mathematical arguments for the property that the M outputs of the multilayer perceptron provide estimates of the a posteriori class probabilities.

4.8 In this problem, we revisit the adaptive control of the learning rate discussed in Section 4.10. The issue of interest is to demonstrate that the asymptotic behavior of the learning-rate parameter $\eta(n)$ in Eq. (4.85) does not converge to zero as the number of iterations increases to infinity.

FIGURE P4.7   Block diagram of a pattern classifier for Problem 4.7.

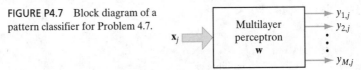

(a) Let $\bar{r}(n)$ denote the expectation of the auxiliary vector $\mathbf{r}(n)$ with respect to the example $\{\mathbf{x}, \mathbf{d}\}$. Show that if the estimator $\hat{\mathbf{w}}(n)$ is in the close vicinity of the optimal estimator $\mathbf{w}^*$, we may then write

$$\bar{\mathbf{r}}(n+1) \approx (1-\delta)\,\bar{\mathbf{r}}(n) + \delta\mathbf{K}^*(\hat{\mathbf{w}}(n) - \bar{\mathbf{w}}(n))$$

where $\bar{\mathbf{w}}(n)$ is the mean value of the estimator $\hat{\mathbf{w}}(n)$ and δ is a small positive parameter.

(b) In Heskas and Kappen (1991), it is shown that the estimator $\hat{\mathbf{w}}(n)$ is closely approximated by a Gaussian-distributed random vector. Hence, justify the following asymptotic behavior:

$$\lim_{n\to\infty} \hat{\mathbf{w}}(n) \neq \tilde{\mathbf{w}}(n)$$

What does this condition teach us about the asymptotic behavior of the learning-rate parameter $\eta(n)$?

4.9 Describe the factors which handicap the practical application of Newton's method to the supervised training of a multilayer perceptron.

4.10 In the *optimal-brain-damage (OBD)* algorithm for network pruning, due to LeCun et al. (1990b), the Hessian $\mathbf{H}$ is approximated by its diagonal version. Using this approximation, derive the OBD procedure as a special case of the optimal-brain-surgeon (OBS) algorithm, studied in Section 4.14.

4.11 In Jacobs (1988), the following heuristics are proposed to accelerate the convergence of on-line back-propagation learning:

(i) Every adjustable network parameter of the cost function should have its own learning-rate parameter.

(ii) Every learning-rate parameter should be allowed to vary from one iteration to the next.

(iii) When the derivative of the cost function with respect to a synaptic weight has the same algebraic sign for several consecutive iterations of the algorithm, the learning-rate parameter for that particular weight should be increased.

(iv) When the algebraic sign of the cost function with respect to a particular synaptic weight alternates for several consecutive iterations of the algorithm, the learning-rate parameter for that weight should be decreased.

These four heuristics satisfy the locality constraint of the back-propagation algorithm.

(a) Use intuitive arguments to justify these four heuristics.

(b) The inclusion of a momentum in the weight update of the back-propagation algorithm may be viewed as a mechanism for satisfying heuristics (iii) and (iv). Demonstrate the validity of this statement.

Second-Order Optimization Methods

4.12 Compare quasi-Newton methods with conjugate-gradient methods.

4.13 Starting with the formula for $\beta(n)$ in Eq. (4.127), derive the *Hesteness-Stiefel formula*,

$$\beta(n) = \frac{\mathbf{r}^T(n)(\mathbf{r}(n) - \mathbf{r}(n-1))}{\mathbf{s}^T(n-1)\mathbf{r}(n-1)}$$

where $\mathbf{s}(n)$ is the direction vector and $\mathbf{r}(n)$ is the residual in the conjugate-gradient method. Use this result to derive the Polak–Ribière formula of Eq. (4.128) and the Fletcher–Reeves formula of Eq. (4.129).

Temporal Processing

4.14 Figure P4.14 illustrates the use of a *Gaussian-shaped time window* as a method for temporal processing, which is motivated by neurobiological considerations (Bodenhausen and Waibel, 1991). The time window associated with synapse i of neuron j is denoted by $\theta(n, \tau_{ji}, \sigma_{ji})$, where τ_{ji} and σ_{ji} are measures of *time delay* and *width* of the windows, respectively, as shown by

$$\theta(n, \tau_{ji}, \sigma_{ji}) = \frac{1}{\sqrt{2\pi}\sigma_{ji}} \exp\left(-\frac{1}{2\sigma_{ji}^2}(n - \tau_{ji})^2\right), \quad i = 1, 2, ..., m_0$$

The output of neuron j is thus defined as

$$y_j(n) = \varphi\left(\sum_{i=1}^{m_0} w_{ji} u_i(n)\right)$$

where $u_i(n)$ is the convolution of the input $x_i(n)$ and the time window $\theta(n, \tau_{ji}, \sigma_{ji})$. The requirement is for the weight w_{ji}, and time delay τ_{ji} of synapse i belonging to neuron j are all to be *learned* in a supervised manner.

This process of learning may be accomplished by using the standard back-propagation algorithm. Demonstrate this learning process by deriving update equations for w_{ji}, τ_{ji}, and σ_{ji}.

Computer Experiments

4.15 Investigate the use of back-propagation learning employing a sigmoidal nonlinearity to achieve one-to-one mappings, as described here:

1. $f(x) = \dfrac{1}{x}$, $\qquad 1 \le x \le 100$

2. $f(x) = \log_{10}x$, $\qquad 1 \le x \le 10$
3. $f(x) = \exp(-x)$, $\qquad 1 \le x \le 10$

4. $f(x) = \sin x$, $\qquad 0 \le x \le \dfrac{\pi}{2}$

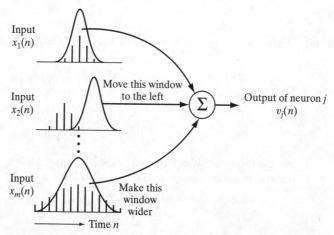

FIGURE P4.14   The figure for Problem 4.14; the instructions appended to the Gaussian windows are aimed at the learning algorithm.

For each mapping, do the following:

(a) Set up two sets of data, one for network training, and the other for testing.

(b) Use the training data set to compute the synaptic weights of the network, assumed to have a single hidden layer.

(c) Evaluate the computation accuracy of the network by using the test data.

Use a single hidden layer, but with a variable number of hidden neurons. Investigate how the network performance is affected by varying the size of the hidden layer.

4.16 Repeat the computer experiment of Section 4.7 for the MLP classifier, where the distance between the two moons is set at $d = 0$. Comment on the findings of your experiment in light of the corresponding experiment performed on the perceptron in Problem 1.6 for the same setting.

4.17 In this computer experiment, we consider a pattern-classification experiment for which the decision boundary is theoretically known. The primary objective of the experiment is to see how the design of the multilayer perceptron could be optimized experimentally in relation to the optimum decision boundary.

Specifically, the requirement is to distinguish between two *equiprobable* classes of "overlapping" two-dimensional Gaussian-distributed patterns, labeled $\mathscr{C}_1$ and $\mathscr{C}_2$. The conditional probability density functions of the two classes are

Class $\mathscr{C}_1$: $p_{\mathbf{X}|\mathscr{C}_1}(\mathbf{x}|\mathscr{C}_1) = \dfrac{1}{2\pi\sigma_1^2} \exp\left(-\dfrac{1}{2\sigma_1^2}\|\mathbf{x} - \boldsymbol{\mu}_1\|^2\right)$

where

$\boldsymbol{\mu}_1$ = mean vector. = $[0, 0]^T$

σ_1^2 = variance = 1

Class $\mathscr{C}_2$: $p_{\mathbf{X}|\mathscr{C}_2}(\mathbf{x}|\mathscr{C}_2) = \dfrac{1}{2\pi\sigma_2^2} \exp\left(-\dfrac{1}{2\sigma_2^2}\|\mathbf{x} - \boldsymbol{\mu}_2\|^2\right)$

where

$\boldsymbol{\mu}_2 = [2, 0]^T$

$\sigma_2^2 = 4$

(a) The optimum Bayesian decision boundary is defined by the likelihood ratio test

$$\Lambda(\mathbf{x}) \underset{\mathscr{C}_2}{\overset{\mathscr{C}_1}{\gtrless}} \lambda$$

where

$$\Lambda(\mathbf{x}) = \frac{p_{\mathbf{X}|\mathscr{C}_1}(\mathbf{x}|\mathscr{C}_1)}{p_{\mathbf{X}|\mathscr{C}_2}(\mathbf{x}|\mathscr{C}_2)}$$

and λ is the *threshold* determined by the prior probabilities of the two classes. Show that the optimum decision boundary is a *circle* whose center is located at

$$\mathbf{x}_\mathscr{C} = \begin{bmatrix} -2/3 \\ 0 \end{bmatrix}$$

and radius $r = 2.34$.

(b) Assume the use of a single hidden layer. The requirement is to experimentally determine the optimal number of hidden neurons.

- Starting with a multilayer perceptron with two hidden neurons, and using the back-propagation algorithm with learning-rate parameter $\eta = 0.1$ and momentum constant $\alpha = 0$ to train the network, calculate the probability of correct classification for the following scenarios:

Training-sample size	Number of epochs
500	320
2,000	80
8,000	20

- Repeat the experiment, this time using four hidden neurons, with everything else remaining the same as before. Compare the results of this second experiment with those of the previous one and thereby select the network configuration, with two *or* four hidden neurons, that you consider to be the optimal choice.

(c) For the "optimal" network selection made in part (b), we now turn to experimentally find the optimal values of the learning-rate parameter η and momentum constant α. To do this, perform experiments using the following combination of parameters:

$$\eta \in [0.01, 0.1, 0.5]$$
$$\alpha \in [0.0, 0.1, 0.5]$$

Hence, determine the values of η and α that yield the best probability of correct classification.

(d) Having identified the optimum size of hidden layer and the optimum set of η and α, perform one last experiment to find the optimum decision boundary and the corresponding probability of correct classification. Compare the optimum performance so obtained experimentally against the theoretical optimum, and comment on your results.

4.18 In this problem, we use the standard back-propagation algorithm to solve a difficult nonlinear prediction problem and compare its performance with that of the LMS algorithm. The time series to be considered is created using a discrete *Volterra model* that has the form

$$x(n) = \sum_i g_i v(n - i) + \sum_i \sum_j g_{ij} v(n - i)v(n - j) + \cdots$$

where $g_i, g_{ij}, \ldots$, are the Volterra coefficients; the $v(n)$ are samples of a white, independently distributed Gaussian noise sequence; and $x(n)$ is the resulting output of the Volterra model. The first summation term is the familiar moving-average (MA) time-series model, and the remaining summation terms are nonlinear components of ever increasing order. In general, the estimation of the Volterra coefficients is considered to be difficult, primarily because of their nonlinear relationship to the data.

We consider the simple example

$$x(n) = v(n) + \beta v(n - 1)v(n - 2)$$

The time series has zero mean, is uncorrelated, and therefore has a white spectrum. However, the time-series samples are not independent of each other, and therefore a higher-order predictor can be constructed. The variance of the model output is given by

$$\sigma_x^2 = \sigma_\nu^2 + \beta^2\sigma_\nu^4$$

where σ_ν^2 is the white-noise variance.

(a) Construct a multilayer perceptron with an input layer of six nodes, a hidden layer of 16 neurons, and a single output neuron. A tapped-delay-line memory is used to feed the input layer of the network. The hidden neurons use sigmoid activation functions limited to the interval [0, 1], whereas the output neuron operates as a linear combiner. The network is trained with the standard back-propagation algorithm having the following description:

Learning-rate parameter	$\eta = 0.001$
Momentum constant	$\alpha = 0.6$
Total number of samples processed	100,000
Number of samples per epoch	1,000
Total number of epochs	2,500

The white-noise variance σ_ν^2 is set equal to unity. Hence, with $\beta = 0.5$, we find that the output variance of the predictor is $\sigma_x^2 = 1.25$.

   Compute the learning curve of the nonlinear predictor, with the variance of the predictor output $x(n)$ plotted as a function of the number of epochs of training samples up to 2,500 epochs. For the preparation of each epoch used to perform the training, explore the following two modes:

   (i) The time ordering of the training sample is maintained from one epoch to the next in exactly the same form as it is generated.

   (ii) The ordering of the training sample is randomized from one pattern (state) to another.

   Also, use cross-validation (described in Section 4.13) with a validation set of 1,000 samples to monitor the learning behavior of the predictor.

(b) Repeat the experiment, using the LMS algorithm designed to perform a linear prediction on an input of six samples. The learning-rate parameter of the algorithm is set equal to $\eta = 10^{-5}$.

(c) Repeat the entire experiment for $\beta = 1, \sigma_\nu^2 = 2$, and then for $\beta = 2, \sigma_\nu^2 = 5$.

The results of each experiment should reveal that initially the back-propagation algorithm and the LMS algorithm follow essentially a similar path, and then the back-propagation algorithm continues to improve, finally producing a prediction variance approaching the prescribed value of σ_x^2.

4.19 In this experiment, we use a multilayer perceptron trained with the back-propagation algorithm to perform one-step prediction on the *Lorenz attractor*. The dynamics of this attractor are defined by three equations:

$$\frac{dx(t)}{dt} = -\sigma x(t) + \sigma y(t)$$

$$\frac{dy(t)}{dt} = -x(t)z(t) + rx(t) - y(t)$$

$$\frac{dz(t)}{dt} = x(t)y(t) - bz(t)$$

where σ, r, and b are dimensionless parameters. Typical values for these parameters are $\sigma = 10, b = \frac{8}{3}$, and $r = 28$.

The specifications of the multilayer perceptron are as follows:

Number of source nodes: 20
Number of hidden neurons: 200
Number of output neurons: 1

The particulars of the data sets are as follows:

Training sample: 700 data points
Testing sample: 800 data points
Number of epochs used for training: 50

The parameters of the back-propagation algorithm are as follows:

The learning-rate parameter η is annealed linearly from 10^{-1} down to 10^{-5}.
Momentum: $\alpha = 0$

(a) Compute the learning curve of the MLP, plotting the mean-square error versus the number of epochs used to do the training.

(b) Compute the one-step prediction to the Lorenz attractor; specifically, plot the results obtained as a function of time, and compare the prediction against the evolution of the Lorenz attractor.

CHAPTER 5

Kernel Methods and Radial-Basis Function Networks

ORGANIZATION OF THE CHAPTER

In this chapter, we study another approach to machine learning : a kernel method based on clustering. After the introductory material presented in Section 5.1, the rest of the chapter is organized as follows:

1. Section 5.2 deals with Cover's theorem on the separability of patterns. This theorem is illustrated by revisiting the XOR problem.
2. Section 5.3 discusses a solution of the interpolation problem that uses radial-basis functions, setting the stage for the construction of radial-basis function (RBF) networks in Section 5.4; this latter section also includes practical considerations pertaining to RBF networks.
3. The *K*-means algorithm, discussed in Section 5.5, provides a simple, yet highly popular, algorithm for clustering, which is well suited for training the hidden layer in an unsupervised manner. Section 5.6 follows up on the *K*-means clustering algorithm to describe a recursive implementation of least-squares estimation (discussed in Chapter 2) for training the output layer of the RBF network in a supervised manner. Section 5.7 addresses practical considerations pertaining to this two-stage procedure for designing RBF networks. This procedure is illustrated in the computer experiment presented in Section 5.8, where comparisons are made with the results of the same computer experiment performed in Chapter 4 using the back-propagation algorithm.
4. Section 5.9 examines interpretations of Gaussian hidden units, followed by Section 5.10 on the relationship between kernel regression in statistics and RBF networks.

The chapter concludes with a summary and discussion in Section 5.11.

5.1 INTRODUCTION

The supervised training of a neural network may be approached in several different ways. The back-propagation learning algorithm for multilayer perceptrons, described in Chapter 4, may be viewed as the application of a recursive technique known in statistics as *stochastic approximation*.

In this chapter, we take a completely different approach. Specifically, we solve the problem of classifying nonlinearly separable patterns by proceeding in a *hybrid* manner, involving two stages:

- The first stage transforms a given set of nonlinearly separable patterns into a new set for which, under certain conditions, the likelihood of the transformed patterns becoming linearly separable is high; the mathematical justification of this transformation is traced to an early paper by Cover (1965).
- The second stage completes the solution to the prescribed classification problem by using least-squares estimation that was discussed in Chapter 2.

Through a discussion of the interpolation problem, we first describe an implementation of this hybrid approach to pattern classification by using a *radial-basis function (RBF) network*,[1] the structure of which consists of only three layers:

- The input layer is made up of source nodes (sensory units) that connect the network to its environment.
- The second layer, consisting of *hidden units*, applies a nonlinear transformation from the input space to the hidden (feature) space. For most applications, the dimensionality of the only hidden layer of the network is high; this layer is trained in an unsupervised manner using stage 1 of the hybrid learning procedure.
- The output layer is *linear*, designed to supply the response of the network to the activation pattern applied to the input layer; this layer is trained in a supervised manner using stage 2 of the hybrid procedure.

The nonlinear transformation from the input space to the hidden space and the high dimensionality of the hidden space satisfy the only two conditions of Cover's theorem.

Much of the theory developed on RBF networks builds on the Gaussian function, an important member of the class of radial-basis functions. The Gaussian function may also be viewed as a *kernel*—hence the designation of the two-stage procedure based on the Gaussian function as a *kernel method*.

Speaking of kernels, in the latter part of the chapter, we also discuss the relationship between kernel regression in statistics and radial-basis function networks.

5.2 COVER'S THEOREM ON THE SEPARABILITY OF PATTERNS

When a radial-basis function (RBF) network is used to perform a *complex* pattern-classification task, the problem is basically solved by first transforming it into a high-dimensional space in a nonlinear manner and then separating the classes in the output layer. The underlying justification is found in *Cover's theorem* on the *separability of patterns*, which, in qualitative terms, may be stated as follows (Cover, 1965):

> *A complex pattern-classification problem, cast in a high-dimensional space nonlinearly, is more likely to be linearly separable than in a low-dimensional space, provided that the space is not densely populated.*

From the work we did on single-layer structures in Chapter 1 through 3, we know that once we have linearly separable patterns, the classification problem is easy to solve. Accordingly, we may develop a great deal of insight into the operation of an RBF network as a pattern classifier by studying the critical issue of separability of patterns.

Consider a family of surfaces where each naturally divides an input space into two regions. Let $\mathcal{X}$ denote a set of N patterns (vectors) $\mathbf{x}_1, \mathbf{x}_2, ..., \mathbf{x}_N$, each of which is assigned to one of two classes $\mathcal{X}_1$ and $\mathcal{X}_2$. This *dichotomy* (binary partition) of the points is said to be separable with respect to the family of surfaces if a surface exists in the family that separates the points in the class $\mathcal{X}_1$ from those in the class $\mathcal{X}_2$. For each pattern $\mathbf{x} \in \mathcal{X}$, define a vector made up of a set of real-valued functions $\{\varphi_i(\mathbf{x}) | i = 1, 2, ..., m_1\}$, as shown by

$$\boldsymbol{\phi}(\mathbf{x}) = [\varphi_1(\mathbf{x}), \varphi_2(\mathbf{x}), ..., \varphi_{m_1}(\mathbf{x})]^T \tag{5.1}$$

Suppose that the pattern $\mathbf{x}$ is a vector in an m_0-dimensional input space. The vector $\boldsymbol{\phi}(\mathbf{x})$ then maps the points in the m_0-dimensional input space into corresponding points in a new space of dimension m_1. We refer to $\varphi_i(\mathbf{x})$ as a *hidden function*, because it plays a role similar to that of a hidden unit in a feedforward neural network. Correspondingly, the space spanned by the set of hidden functions $\{\varphi_i(\mathbf{x})\}_{i=1}^{m_1}$ is referred to as the *feature space*.

A dichotomy $\{\mathcal{X}_1, \mathcal{X}_2\}$ of $\mathcal{X}$ is said to be φ *separable* if there exists an m_1-dimensional vector $\mathbf{w}$ such that we may write the following (Cover, 1965):

$$\begin{aligned} \mathbf{w}^T \boldsymbol{\phi}(\mathbf{x}) > 0, \quad & \mathbf{x} \in \mathcal{X}_1 \\ \mathbf{w}^T \boldsymbol{\phi}(\mathbf{x}) < 0, \quad & \mathbf{x} \in \mathcal{X}_2 \end{aligned} \tag{5.2}$$

The hyperplane defined by the equation

$$\mathbf{w}^T \boldsymbol{\phi}(\mathbf{x}) = 0$$

describes the separating surface in the $\boldsymbol{\phi}$-space (i.e., feature space). The inverse image of this hyperplane, that is,

$$\mathbf{x}: \quad \mathbf{w}^T \boldsymbol{\phi}(\mathbf{x}) = 0 \tag{5.3}$$

defines the *separating surface* (i.e., decision boundary) in the input space.

Consider a natural class of mappings obtained by using a linear combination of r-wise products of the pattern vector coordinates. The separating surfaces corresponding to such mappings are referred to as *rth-order rational varieties*. A rational variety of order r in a space of dimension m_0 is described by an rth-degree homogeneous equation in the coordinates of the input vector $\mathbf{x}$, as shown by

$$\sum_{0 \le i_1 \le i_2 \le \cdots \le i_r \le m_0} a_{i_1 i_2 \ldots i_r} x_{i_1} x_{i_2} \cdots x_{i_r} = 0 \tag{5.4}$$

where x_i is the ith component of input vector $\mathbf{x}$ and x_0 is set equal to unity in order to express the equation in a homogeneous form. An rth-order product of entries x_i of $\mathbf{x}$—that is, $x_{i_1} x_{i_2} \cdots x_{i_r}$—is called a *monomial*. For an input space of dimensionality m_0, there are

$$\frac{m_0!}{(m_0 - r)! \, r!}$$

monomials in Eq. (5.4). Examples of the type of separating surfaces described by Eq. (5.4) are *hyperplanes* (first-order rational varieties), *quadrices* (second-order rational varieties), and *hyperspheres* (quadrics with certain linear constraints on the coefficients).

These examples are illustrated in Fig. 5.1 for a configuration of five points in a two-dimensional input space. In general, linear separability implies spherical separability, which implies quadric separability; however, the converses are not necessarily true.

In a probabilistic experiment, the separability of a set of patterns becomes a random event that depends on the dichotomy chosen and the distribution of the patterns in the input space. Suppose that the activation patterns $\mathbf{x}_1, \mathbf{x}_2, ..., \mathbf{x}_N$ are chosen independently, according to a probability measure imposed on the input space. Suppose also that all the possible dichotomies of $\mathcal{X} = \{\mathbf{x}_i\}_{i=1}^{N}$ are equiprobable. Let $P(N, m_1)$ denote the probability that a particular dichotomy picked at random is φ separable, where the class of separating surfaces chosen has m_1 degrees of freedom. Following Cover (1965), we may then state that

$$P(N, m_1) = \begin{cases} (2^{1-N}) \displaystyle\sum_{m=0}^{m_1-1} \binom{N-1}{m} & \text{for } N > m_1 - 1 \\ 1 & \text{for } N \le m_1 - 1 \end{cases} \tag{5.5}$$

where the binomial coefficients composing $N-1$ and m are themselves defined for all integers l and m by

$$\binom{l}{m} = \frac{l!}{(l-m)!m!}$$

For a graphical interpretation of Eq. (5.5), it is best to normalize the equation by setting $N = \lambda m_1$ and plotting the probability $P(\lambda m_1, m_1)$ versus λ for various values of m_1. This plot reveals two interesting characteristics (Nilsson, 1965):

- a pronounced *threshold effect* around $\lambda = 2$;
- the value $P(2m_1, m_1) = 1/2$ for each value of m_1.

Equation (5.5) embodies the essence of *Cover's separability theorem* for random patterns.[2] It is a statement of the fact that the cumulative binomial distribution corresponding to the probability that $(N-1)$ flips of a fair coin will result in $(m_1 - 1)$ or fewer heads.

FIGURE 5.1   Three examples of φ-separable dichotomies of different sets of five points in two dimensions: (a) linearly separable dichotomy; (b) spherically separable dichotomy; (c) quadrically separable dichotomy.

Although the hidden-unit surfaces envisioned in the derivation of Eq. (5.5) are of a polynomial form and therefore different from those commonly used in radial-basis-function networks, the essential content of the equation has general applicability. Specifically, the higher we make the dimension m_1 of the hidden space, the closer the probability $P(N, m_1)$ will be to unity. To sum up, Cover's theorem on the separability of patterns encompasses two basic ingredients:

1. *nonlinear formulation of the hidden function defined by $\varphi_i(\mathbf{x})$, where $\mathbf{x}$ is the input vector and $i = 1, 2, ..., m_1$;*
2. *high dimensionality of the hidden (feature) space compared with the input space, where the dimensionality of the hidden space is determined by the value assigned to m_1 (i.e., the number of hidden units).*

In general, as stated previously, a complex pattern-classification problem cast in high-dimensional space nonlinearly is more likely to be linearly separable than in a low-dimensional space. We emphasize, however, that in some cases the use of nonlinear mapping (i.e., point 1) may be sufficient to produce linear separability without having to increase the dimensionality of the hidden-unit space, as illustrated in the following example.

EXAMPLE 1   The XOR Problem

To illustrate the significance of the idea of φ separability of patterns, consider the simple, yet important, XOR problem. In the XOR problem, there are four points (patterns)—(1, 1), (0, 1), (0, 0), and (1, 0)—in a two-dimensional input space, as depicted in Fig. 5.2a. The requirement is to construct a pattern classifier that produces the binary output 0 in response to the input pattern (1, 1), or (0, 0), and the binary output 1 in response to the input pattern (0, 1) or (1, 0). Thus, points that are closest in the input space, in terms of the Hamming distance, map to regions that are maximally apart in the output space. The *Hamming distance* of a sequence as defined is the number of changes from symbol 1 to symbol 0, and vice versa, that are found in a binary sequence. Thus, the Hamming distance of both 11 and 00 is zero, whereas the Hamming distance of both 01 and 10 is one.

Define a pair of Gaussian hidden functions as follows:

$$\varphi_1(\mathbf{x}) = \exp(-\|\mathbf{x} - t_1\|^2), \quad \mathbf{t}_1 = [1, 1]^T$$
$$\varphi_2(\mathbf{x}) = \exp(-\|\mathbf{x} - t_2\|^2), \quad \mathbf{t}_2 = [0, 0]^T$$

We may then construct the results summarized in Table 5.1 for the four different input patterns of interest. The input patterns are mapped onto the (φ_1, φ_2) plane as shown in Fig. 5.2b. Here, we now see that the input patterns (0, 1) and (1, 0) are linearly separable from the remaining input patterns (1, 1) and (0, 0). Thereafter, the XOR problem may be readily solved by using the functions $\varphi_1(\mathbf{x})$ and $\varphi_2(\mathbf{x})$ as the inputs to a linear classifier such as the perceptron. ∎

In this example, there is no increase in the dimensionality of the hidden space compared with the input space. In other words, nonlinearity exemplified by the use of Gaussian hidden functions is sufficient to transform the XOR problem into a linearly separable one.

FIGURE 5.2   (a) The four patterns of the XOR problem; (b) decision-making diagram.

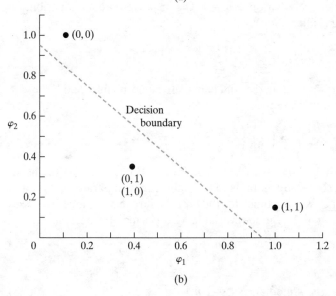

TABLE 5.1   Specification of the Hidden Functions for the XOR Problem of Example 1

Input Pattern $\mathbf{x}$	First Hidden Function $\varphi_1(\mathbf{x})$	Second Hidden Function $\varphi_2(\mathbf{x})$
(1,1)	1	0.1353
(0,1)	0.3678	0.3678
(0,0)	0.1353	1
(1,0)	0.3678	0.3678

Separating Capacity of a Surface

Equation (5.5) has an important bearing on the expected maximum number of randomly assigned patterns that are linearly separable in a multidimensional space. To explore this issue, let $\mathbf{x}_1, \mathbf{x}_2, ..., \mathbf{x}_N$ be a sequence of random patterns (vectors) as previously described. Let N be a random variable defined as the largest integer such that this sequence is φ separable, where φ has m_1 *degrees of freedom*. Then, from Eq. (5.5), we deduce that the probability that $N = n$ is given by

$$\text{Prob}(N = n) = P(n, m_1) - P(n + 1, m_1)$$

$$= \left(\frac{1}{2}\right)^n \binom{n-1}{m_1 - 1}, \quad n = 0, 1, 2, ... \tag{5.6}$$

For an interpretation of this result, recall the definition of a *negative binomial distribution*. This distribution equals the probability that k failures precede the rth success in a long, repeated sequence of *Bernoulli trials*. In such a probabilistic experiment, there are only two possible outcomes for each trial—success or failure—and their probabilities remain the same throughout the experiment. Let p and q denote the probabilities of success and failure, respectively, with $p + q = 1$. The negative binomial distribution is defined by the following (Feller, 1968):

$$f(k; r, p) = p^r q^k \binom{r + k - 1}{k}$$

For the special case of $p = q = \frac{1}{2}$ (i.e., success and failure are equiprobable) and $k + r = n$, the negative binomial distribution reduces to

$$f\left(k; n - k, \frac{1}{2}\right) = \left(\frac{1}{2}\right)^n \binom{n - 1}{k}, \quad n = 0, 1, 2, \ldots$$

With this definition, we now see that the result described in Eq. (5.6) is just the negative binomial distribution, shifted by m_1 units to the right, and with parameters m_1 and $\frac{1}{2}$. Thus, N corresponds to the "waiting time" for the m_1-th failure in a sequence of tosses of a fair coin. The expectation of the random variable N and its median are, respectively,

$$\mathbb{E}[N] = 2m_1 \tag{5.7}$$

and

$$\text{median}[N] = 2m_1 \tag{5.8}$$

We therefore have a corollary to Cover's theorem in the form of a celebrated asymptotic result that may be stated as follows (Cover, 1965):

> *The expected maximum number of randomly assigned patterns (vectors) that are linearly separable in a space of dimensionality m_1 is equal to $2m_1$.*

This result suggests that $2m_1$ is a natural definition of the *separating capacity* of a family of decision surfaces having m_1 degrees of freedom. In a loose-sense, it can be argued that Cover's separating capacity is related to the VC-dimension, discussed previously in Chapter 4.

5.3 THE INTERPOLATION PROBLEM

The important point that emerges from Cover's theorem on the separability of patterns is that in solving a nonlinearly separable pattern-classification problem, there is usually practical benefit to be gained by mapping the input space into a new space of high enough dimension. Basically, a nonlinear mapping is used to transform a nonlinearly separable classification problem into a linearly separable one with high probability. In a similar way, we may use a nonlinear mapping to transform a difficult nonlinear filtering problem into an easier one that involves linear filtering.

Consider then a feedforward network with an input layer, a single hidden layer, and an output layer consisting of a single unit. We have purposely chosen a single output unit to simplify the exposition without loss of generality. The network is designed to perform a *nonlinear mapping* from the input space to the hidden space, followed by a *linear mapping* from the hidden space to the output space. Let m_o denote the dimension of the input space. Then, in an overall fashion, the network represents a map from the m_o-dimensional input space to the single-dimensional output space, written as

$$s: \mathbb{R}^{m_0} \to \mathbb{R}^1 \tag{5.9}$$

We may think of the map s as a *hypersurface* (graph) $\Gamma \subset \mathbb{R}^{m_0+1}$, just as we think of the elementary map $s: \mathbb{R}^1 \to \mathbb{R}^1$, where $s(x) = x^2$, as a parabola drawn in $\mathbb{R}^2$ space. The surface Γ is a multidimensional plot of the output as a function of the input. In a practical situation, the surface Γ is unknown and the training data are usually contaminated with noise. The training phase and generalization phase of the learning process may be respectively viewed as follows (Broomhead and Lowe, 1988):

- The training phase constitutes the optimization of a fitting procedure for the surface Γ, based on known data points presented to the network in the form of input–output examples (patterns).
- The generalization phase is synonymous with interpolation between the data points, with the interpolation being performed along the constrained surface generated by the fitting procedure as the optimum approximation to the true surface Γ.

Thus, we are led to the theory of *multivariable interpolation* in high-dimensional space, which has a long history (Davis, 1963). The interpolation problem, in its *strict* sense, may be stated as follows:

Given a set of N different points $\{\mathbf{x}_i \in \mathbb{R}^{m_0} | i = 1, 2, ..., N\}$ *and a corresponding set of N real numbers* $\{d_i \in \mathbb{R}^1 | i = 1, 2, ..., N\}$, *find a function* $F: \mathbb{R}^N \to \mathbb{R}^1$ *that satisfies the interpolation condition:*

$$F(\mathbf{x}_i) = d_i, \quad i = 1, 2, ..., N \tag{5.10}$$

For strict interpolation as specified here, the interpolating surface (i.e., function F) is constrained to pass through *all* the training data points.

The *radial-basis-functions* (RBF) technique consists of choosing a function F that has the form

$$F(\mathbf{x}) = \sum_{i=1}^{N} w_i \varphi(\|\mathbf{x} - \mathbf{x}_i\|) \tag{5.11}$$

where $\{\varphi(\|\mathbf{x} - \mathbf{x}_i\|) | i = 1, 2, ..., N\}$ is a set of N arbitrary (generally nonlinear) functions, known as *radial-basis functions*, and $\|\cdot\|$ denotes a *norm* that is usually Euclidean (Powell, 1988). The known data points $\mathbf{x}_i \in \mathbb{R}^{m_0}$, $i = 1, 2, ..., N$ are taken to be the *centers* of the radial-basis functions.

Inserting the interpolation conditions of Eq. (5.10) into Eq. (5.11), we obtain a set of simultaneous linear equations for the unknown coefficients (weights) of the expansion $\{w_i\}$ given by

$$
\begin{bmatrix}
\varphi_{11} & \varphi_{12} & \cdots & \varphi_{1N} \\
\varphi_{21} & \varphi_{22} & \cdots & \varphi_{2N} \\
\vdots & \vdots & \vdots & \vdots \\
\varphi_{N1} & \varphi_{N2} & \cdots & \varphi_{NN}
\end{bmatrix}
\begin{bmatrix}
w_1 \\
w_2 \\
\vdots \\
w_N
\end{bmatrix}
=
\begin{bmatrix}
d_1 \\
d_2 \\
\vdots \\
d_N
\end{bmatrix}
\tag{5.12}
$$

where

$$\varphi_{ij} = \varphi(\|\mathbf{x}_j - \mathbf{x}_j\|), \quad i, j = 1, 2, ..., N$$

Let

$$\mathbf{d} = [d_1, d_2, ..., d_N]^T$$
$$\mathbf{w} = [w_1, w_2, ..., w_N]^T$$

The N-by-1 vectors $\mathbf{d}$ and $\mathbf{w}$ represent the *desired response vector* and *linear weight vector*, respectively, where N is the *size of the training sample*. Let $\mathbf{\Phi}$ denote an N-by-N matrix with elements φ_{ij}:

$$\mathbf{\Phi} = \{\varphi_{ij}\}_{i,j=1}^N \tag{5.14}$$

We call this matrix the *interpolation matrix*. We may then rewrite Eq. (5.12) in the compact form

$$\mathbf{\Phi}\mathbf{w} = \mathbf{x} \tag{5.15}$$

Assuming that $\mathbf{\Phi}$ is nonsingular, and therefore that the inverse matrix $\mathbf{\Phi}^{-1}$ exists, we may go on to solve Eq. (5.15) for the weight vector $\mathbf{w}$, obtaining

$$\mathbf{w} = \mathbf{\Phi}^{-1}\mathbf{x} \tag{5.16}$$

The vital question is: How can we be sure that the interpolation matrix $\mathbf{\Phi}$ is nonsingular?

It turns out that for a large class of radial-basis functions and under certain conditions, the answer to this basic question is given in an important theorem discussed next.

Micchelli's Theorem

In Micchelli (1986), the following theorem is proved:

> Let $\{\mathbf{x}_i\}_{i=1}^N$ be a set of distinct points in $\mathbb{R}^{m_0}$. Then the N-by-N interpolation matrix $\mathbf{\Phi}$, whose ij-th element is $\varphi_{ij} = \varphi(\|\mathbf{x}_i - \mathbf{x}_j\|)$, is nonsingular.

There is a large class of radial-basis functions that is covered by Micchelli's theorem; it includes the following functions that are of particular interest in the study of RBF networks:

1. *Multiquadrics:*

$$\varphi(r) = (r^2 + c^2)^{1/2} \quad \text{for some } c > 0 \text{ and } r \in \mathbb{R} \tag{5.17}$$

2. *Inverse multiquadrics:*

$$\varphi(r) = \frac{1}{(r^2 + c^2)^{1/2}} \quad \text{for some } c > 0 \text{ and } r \in \mathbb{R} \tag{5.18}$$

3. *Gaussian functions:*

$$\varphi(r) = \exp\left(-\frac{r^2}{2\sigma^2}\right) \quad \text{for some } \sigma > 0 \text{ and } r \in \mathbb{R} \tag{5.19}$$

The multiquadrics and inverse multiquadrics are both due to Hardy (1971).

For the radial-basis functions listed in Eqs. (5.17) to (5.19) to be nonsingular, the points $\{\mathbf{x}_i\}_{i=1}^{N}$ must all be different (i.e., distinct). This is all that is required for nonsingularity of the interpolation matrix $\mathbf{\Phi}$, whatever the values of size N of the data points or dimensionality m_o of the vectors (points) $\mathbf{x}_i$ happen to be.

The inverse multiquadrics of Eq. (5.18) and the Gaussian functions of Eq. (5.19) share a common property: They are both *localized* functions, in the sense that $\varphi(r) \to 0$ as $r \to \infty$. In both of these cases, the interpolation matrix $\mathbf{\Phi}$ is positive definite. By contrast, the multiquadrics of Eq. (5.17) are *nonlocal*, in that $\varphi(r)$ becomes unbounded as $r \to \infty$, and the corresponding interpolation matrix $\mathbf{\Phi}$ has $N - 1$ *negative* eigenvalues and only one positive eigenvalue, with the result that it is *not* positive definite (Micchelli, 1986). What is remarkable, however, is that an interpolation matrix $\mathbf{\Phi}$ based on Hardy's multiquadrics is nonsingular and therefore suitable for use in the design of RBF networks.

What is even more remarkable is that radial-basis functions that *grow* at infinity, such as multiquadrics, can be used to approximate a smooth input–output mapping with greater accuracy than those that yield a positive-definite interpolation matrix. This surprising result is discussed in Powell (1988).

5.4 RADIAL-BASIS-FUNCTION NETWORKS

In light of Eqs. (5.10) through (5.16), we may now envision a *radial-basis-function* (RBF) network in the form of a layered structure, as illustrated in Fig. 5.3; specifically, we have three layers:

1. *Input layer*, which consists of m_o source nodes, where m_o is the dimensionality of the input vector $\mathbf{x}$.

2. *Hidden layer*, which consists of the same number of computation units as the size of the training sample, namely, N; each unit is mathematically described by a radial-basis function

$$\varphi_j(\mathbf{x}) = \varphi(\|\mathbf{x} - \mathbf{x}_j\|), \qquad j = 1, 2, ..., N$$

The jth input data point $\mathbf{x}_j$ defines the center of the radial-basis function, and the vector $\mathbf{x}$ is the signal (pattern) applied to the input layer. Thus, unlike a multilayer perceptron, the links connecting the source nodes to the hidden units are direct connections with *no* weights.

3. *Output layer*, which, in the RBF structure of Fig. 5.3, consists of a single computational unit. Clearly, there is no restriction on the size of the output layer, except to say that typically the size of the output layer is much smaller than that of the hidden layer.

Henceforth, we focus on the use of a Gaussian function as the radial-basis function, in which case each computational unit in the hidden layer of the network of Fig. 5.3 is defined by

$$\varphi_j(\mathbf{x}) = \varphi(\mathbf{x} - \mathbf{x}_j)$$
$$= \exp\left(-\frac{1}{2\sigma_j^2}\|\mathbf{x} - \mathbf{x}_j\|^2\right), \qquad j = 1, 2, ..., N \qquad (5.20)$$

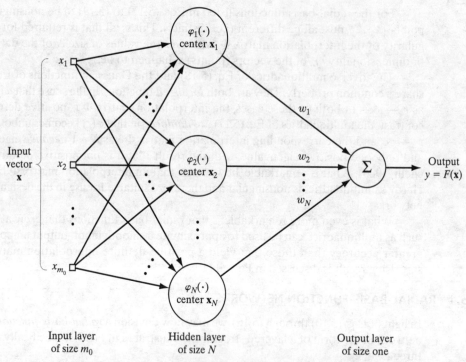

FIGURE 5.3   Structure of an RBF network, based on interpolation theory.

where σ_j is a measure of the *width* of the jth Gaussian function with center $\mathbf{x}_j$. Typically, but not always, all the *Gaussian hidden units* are assigned a common width σ. In situations of this kind, the parameter that distinguishes one hidden unit from another is the center $\mathbf{x}_j$. The rationale behind the choice of the Gaussian function as the radial-basis function in building RBF networks is that it has many desirable properties, which will become evident as the discussion progresses.

Practical Modifications to the RBF Network

Formulation of the RBF network of Fig. 5.3 via interpolation theory is rather neat. In practice, however, we find that the training sample $\{\mathbf{x}_i, d_i\}_{i=1}^{N}$ is typically *noisy*, be that in the context of pattern classification or nonlinear regression. Unfortunately, the use of interpolation based on noisy data could lead to misleading results—hence the need for a different approach to the design of an RBF network.

There is another practical issue that needs attention: Having a hidden layer of the same size as the input layer could be wasteful of computational resources, particularly when dealing with large training samples. When the hidden layer of the RBF network is specified in the manner described in Eq. (5.20), we find that any correlation existing between adjacent data points in the training sample is correspondingly transplanted into adjacent units in the hidden layer. Stated in another way, there is *redundancy* of neurons in the hidden layer when they are chosen in accordance with Eq. (5.20) by virtue of the redundancy that may inherently exist in the training sample. In situations of this kind, it is therefore good design practice to make the size of the hidden layer a fraction of the size of the training sample, as illustrated in Fig. 5.4. Note that although the RBF networks of Figs. 5.3 and 5.4 are indeed different, they do share a common feature: Unlike the case for a multilayer perceptron, the training of an RBF network does *not* involve the back propagation of error signals.

Moreover, the approximating function realized by both of these two RBF structures has the same mathematical form,

$$F(\mathbf{x}) = \sum_{j=1}^{K} w_j \varphi(\mathbf{x}, \mathbf{x}_j) \qquad (5.21)$$

where the dimensionality of the input vector $\mathbf{x}$ (and therefore that of the input layer) is m_0 and each hidden unit is characterized by the radial-basis function $\varphi(\mathbf{x}, \mathbf{x}_j)$, where $j = 1, 2, ..., K$, with K being smaller than N. The output layer, assumed to consist of a single unit, is characterized by the weight vector $\mathbf{w}$, whose dimensionality is also K. The structure of Fig. 5.3 differs from that of Fig. 5.4 in two respects:

1. In Fig. 5.3, the dimensionality of the hidden layer is N, where N is the size of the training set, whereas that of Fig. 5.4 is $K < N$.

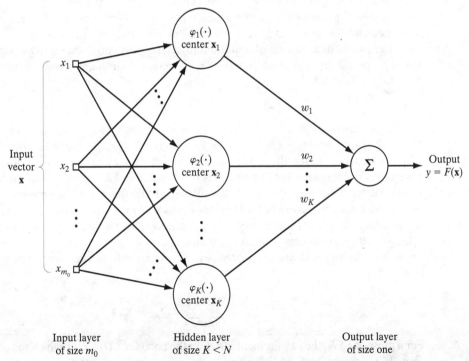

FIGURE 5.4   Structure of a practical RBF network. Note that this network is similar in structure to that of Fig. 5.3. The two networks are different, however, in that the size of the hidden layer in Fig. 5.4 is smaller than that in Fig. 5.3.

2. Assuming that the training sample $\{\mathbf{x}_i, d_i\}_{i=1}^{N}$ is noiseless, the design of the hidden layer in Fig. 5.3 is solved simply by using the input vector $\mathbf{x}_j$ to define the center of the radial-basis function $\varphi(\mathbf{x}, \mathbf{x}_j)$ for $j = 1, 2, ..., N$. On the other hand, to design the hidden layer in Fig. 5.4, we have to come up with a new procedure.

The material covered in the next section addresses this latter point in a practical way for the case when the hidden units use Gaussian functions.

5.5 K-MEANS CLUSTERING

In designing the RBF network of Fig. 5.4, a key issue that needs to be addressed is how to compute the parameters of the Gaussian units that constitute the hidden layer by using *unlabeled* data. In other words, the computation is to be performed in an unsupervised manner. In this section, we describe a solution to this problem that is rooted in *clustering*, by which we mean the following:

Clustering is a form of unsupervised learning whereby a set of observations (i.e., data points) is partitioned into natural groupings or clusters of patterns in such a way that the measure of similarity between any pair of observations assigned to each cluster minimizes a specified cost function.

There is a plethora of clustering techniques to choose from. We have chosen to focus on the so-called *K-means algorithm*,[3] because it is simple to implement, yet effective in performance, two features that have made it highly popular.

Let $\{\mathbf{x}_i\}_{i=1}^{N}$ denote a set of multidimensional observations that is to be partitioned into a proposed set of K clusters, where K is smaller than the number of observations, N. Let the relationship.

$$j = C(i), \qquad i = 1, 2, ..., N \tag{5.22}$$

denote a many-to-one mapper, called the *encoder*, which assigns the ith observation $\mathbf{x}_i$ to the jth cluster according to a rule yet to be defined. (The alert reader could wonder why it is we have chosen the index j to refer to a cluster when the logical choice would have been k; the reason for this choice is that the symbol k is used to refer to a kernel function that will be discussed later in the chapter.) To do this encoding, we need a *measure of similarity* between every pair of vectors $\mathbf{x}_i$ and $\mathbf{x}_{i'}$, which is denoted by $d(\mathbf{x}_i, \mathbf{x}_{i'})$. When the measure $d(\mathbf{x}_i, \mathbf{x}_{i'})$ is small enough, both $\mathbf{x}_i$ and $\mathbf{x}_{i'}$ are assigned to the same cluster; otherwise, they are assigned to different clusters.

To optimize the clustering process, we introduce the following cost function (Hastie et al., 2001):

$$J(C) = \frac{1}{2} \sum_{j=1}^{K} \sum_{C(i)=j} \sum_{C(i')=j} d(\mathbf{x}_i, \mathbf{x}_{i'}) \tag{5.23}$$

For a prescribed K, the requirement is to find the encoder $C(i) = j$ for which the cost function $J(C)$ is minimized. At this point in the discussion, we note that the encoder C is unknown—hence the functional dependence of the cost function J on C.

In *K*-means clustering, the squared Euclidean norm is used to define the measure of similarity between the observations $\mathbf{x}_i$ and $\mathbf{x}_{i'}$, as shown by

$$d(\mathbf{x}_i, \mathbf{x}_{i'}) = \|\mathbf{x}_i - \mathbf{x}_{i'}\|^2 \tag{5.24}$$

Hence, substituting Eq. (5.24) into Eq. (5.23), we get

$$J(C) = \frac{1}{2} \sum_{j=1}^{K} \sum_{C(i)=j} \sum_{C(i')=j} \|\mathbf{x}_i - \mathbf{x}_{i'}\|^2 \tag{5.25}$$

We now make two points:

1. The squared Euclidean distance between the observations $\mathbf{x}_i$ and $\mathbf{x}_{i'}$ is *symmetric*; that is,

$$\|\mathbf{x}_i - \mathbf{x}_{i'}\|^2 = \|\mathbf{x}_{i'} - \mathbf{x}_i\|^2$$

2. The inner summation in Eq. (5.25) reads as follows: For a given $\mathbf{x}_{i'}$, the encoder *C* assigns to cluster *j* all the observations $\mathbf{x}_{i'}$ that are closest to $\mathbf{x}_i$. Except for a scaling factor, the sum of the observations $\mathbf{x}_{i'}$ so assigned is an *estimate of the mean vector* pertaining to cluster *j*; the scaling factor in question is $1/N_j$, where N_j is the number of data points within cluster *j*.

On account of these two points, we may therefore reduce Eq. (5.25) to the simplified form

$$J(C) = \sum_{j=1}^{K} \sum_{C(i)=j} \|\mathbf{x}_i - \hat{\boldsymbol{\mu}}_j\|^2 \tag{5.26}$$

where $\hat{\boldsymbol{\mu}}_j$ denotes the "estimated" mean vector associated with cluster j.[4] In effect, the mean $\hat{\boldsymbol{\mu}}_j$ may be viewed as the *center* of cluster *j*. In light of Eq. (5.26), we may now restate the clustering problem as follows:

> *Given a set of N observations, find the encoder C that assigns these observations to the K clusters in such a way that, within each cluster, the average measure of dissimilarity of the assigned observations from the cluster mean is minimized.*

Indeed, it is because of the essence of this statement that the clustering technique described herein is commonly known as the *K-means algorithm*.

For an interpretation of the cost function $J(C)$ defined in Eq. (5.26), we may say that, except for a scaling factor $1/N_j$, the inner summation in this equation is an estimate of the *variance* of the observations associated with cluster *j* for a given encoder *C*, as shown by

$$\hat{\sigma}_j^2 = \sum_{C(i)=j} \|\mathbf{x}_i - \hat{\boldsymbol{\mu}}_j\|^2 \tag{5.27}$$

Accordingly, we may view the cost function $J(C)$ as a measure of the *total cluster variance* resulting from the assignments of all the *N* observations to the *K* clusters that are made by encoder *C*.

With encoder *C* being unknown, how do we minimize the cost function $J(C)$? To address this key question, we use an *iterative descent algorithm*, each iteration of which involves a two-step optimization. The first step uses the nearest neighbor rule to mini-mize the cost function $J(C)$ of Eq. (5.26) with respect to the mean vector $\hat{\boldsymbol{\mu}}_j$ for a given encoder C. The second step minimizes the inner summation of Eq. (5.26) with respect to the encoder C for a given mean vector $\hat{\boldsymbol{\mu}}_j$. This two-step iterative procedure is con-tinued until convergence is attained.

Thus, in mathematical terms, the K-means algorithm proceeds in two steps:[5]

Step 1.   For a given encoder C, the total cluster variance is minimized with respect to the assigned set of cluster means $\{\hat{\boldsymbol{\mu}}_j\}_{j=1}^K$; that is, we perform, the following minimization:

$$\min_{\{\hat{\boldsymbol{\mu}}_j\}_{j=1}^K} \sum_{j=i}^K \sum_{C(i)=j} \|\mathbf{x}_i - \hat{\boldsymbol{\mu}}_j\|^2 \qquad \text{for a given } C \qquad (5.28)$$

Step 2.   Having computed the optimized cluster means $\{\hat{\boldsymbol{\mu}}_j\}_{j=1}^K$ in step 1, we next opti-mize the encoder as follows:

$$C(i) = \arg \min_{1 \le j \le K} \|\mathbf{x}(i) - \hat{\boldsymbol{\mu}}_j\|^2 \qquad (5.29)$$

Starting from some initial choice of the encoder C, the algorithm goes back and forth between these two steps until there is no further change in the cluster assignments.

Each of these two steps is designed to reduce the cost function $J(C)$ in its own way; hence, convergence of the algorithm is assured. However, because the algorithm lacks a global optimality criterion, the result may converge to a local minimum, result-ing in a *suboptimal* solution to the clustering assignment. Nevertheless, the algorithm has practical advantages:

1. The K-means algorithm is computationally *efficient*, in that its complexity is *linear* in the number of clusters.
2. When the clusters are compactly distributed in data space, they are faithfully *recovered* by the algorithm.

One last comment is in order: To initialize the K-means algorithm, the recom-mended procedure is to start the algorithm with many different random choices for the means $\{\hat{\boldsymbol{\mu}}_j\}_{j=i}^K$ for the proposed size K and then choose the particular set for which the double summation in Eq. (5.26) assumes the smallest value (Hastie et al., 2001).

The *K*-Means Algorithm Fits within the Framework of Cover's Theorem

The K-means algorithm applies a *nonlinear transformation* to the input signal $\mathbf{x}$. We say so because the measure of dissimilarity—namely, the squared Euclidean distance $\|\mathbf{x} - \mathbf{x}_j\|^2$, on which it is based—is a nonlinear function of the input signal $\mathbf{x}$ for a given cluster center $\mathbf{x}_j$. Furthermore, with each cluster discovered by the K-means algorithm defining a particular computational unit in the hidden layer, it follows that if the number of clusters, K, is large enough, the K-means algorithm will satisfy the other requirement of Cover's theorem—that is, that the dimensionality of the hidden layer is high enough. We therefore conclude that the K-means algorithm is indeed computationally powerful enough to transform a set of nonlinearly separable patterns into separable ones in accordance with this theorem.

Now that this objective has been satisfied, we are ready to consider designing the linear output layer of the RBF network.

5.6   RECURSIVE LEAST-SQUARES ESTIMATION OF THE WEIGHT VECTOR

The K-means algorithm performs computation in a recursive manner. It would therefore be desirable to recast the method of least squares—discussed in Chapter 2—for computing the weight vector in the output layer of the RBF network to perform this computation in a recursive manner, too. With this objective in mind, we recast Eq. (2.33) in the form

$$\mathbf{R}(n)\hat{\mathbf{w}}(n) = \mathbf{r}(n), \qquad n = 1, 2, \dots, \tag{5.30}$$

where all three quantities are expressed as functions of discrete time n. In writing this equation, called the *normal equation* in statistics, we have introduced three terms:

1. the *K-by-K correlation function* of the hidden-unit outputs, which is defined by

$$\mathbf{R}(n) = \sum_{i=1}^{n} \boldsymbol{\phi}(\mathbf{x}_i)\boldsymbol{\phi}^T(\mathbf{x}_i) \tag{5.31}$$

where

$$\boldsymbol{\phi}(\mathbf{x}_i) = [\varphi(\mathbf{x}_i, \boldsymbol{\mu}_1), \varphi(\mathbf{x}_i, \boldsymbol{\mu}_2), \dots, \varphi(\mathbf{x}_i, \boldsymbol{\mu}_K)]^T \tag{5.32}$$

and

$$\varphi(\mathbf{x}_i, \boldsymbol{\mu}_j) = \exp\left(-\frac{1}{2\sigma_j^2}\|\mathbf{x}_i - \boldsymbol{\mu}_j\|^2\right), \qquad j = 1, 2, \dots, K \tag{5.33}$$

2. the *K-by-1 cross-correlation vector* between the desired response at the output of the RBF network and the hidden-unit outputs, which is defined by

$$\mathbf{r}(n) = \sum_{i=1}^{n} \boldsymbol{\phi}(\mathbf{x}_i)d(i) \tag{5.34}$$

3. the *unknown weight vector* $\hat{\mathbf{w}}(n)$, which is optimized in the least-squares sense.

The requirement is to solve the normal equation in Eq. (5.30) for the weight vector $\mathbf{w}(n)$. Of course, we could do this computation by first inverting the correlation matrix $\mathbf{R}(n)$ and then multiplying the resulting inverse matrix $\mathbf{R}^{-1}(n)$ by the cross-correlation vector $\mathbf{r}(n)$, which is what is done in the method of least squares. However, when the size of the hidden layer, K, is large, which is often the case, computation of the inverse matrix $\mathbf{R}^{-1}(n)$ for $n = K$ can be a demanding task. The proposed use of a recursive implementation of the method of least squares takes care of this computational difficulty. The resulting algorithm is called the *recursive least-squares (RLS) algorithm,*[6] the derivation of which is discussed next.

The RLS algorithm

We begin the derivation of the RLS algorithm by reformulating Eq. (5.34) for the cross-correlation vector $\mathbf{r}(n)$, as shown by

$$\mathbf{r}(n) = \sum_{i=1}^{n-1} \boldsymbol{\phi}(\mathbf{x}_i)d(i) + \boldsymbol{\phi}(\mathbf{x}_n)d(n)$$

$$= \mathbf{r}(n-1) + \boldsymbol{\phi}(\mathbf{x}_n)d(n)$$

$$= \mathbf{R}(n-1)\hat{\mathbf{w}}(n-1) + \boldsymbol{\phi}(\mathbf{x}_n)d(n) \tag{5.35}$$

where, in the first line, we isolated the term corresponding to $i = n$ from the summation in Eq. (5.34), and in the last line we used Eq. (5.30), replacing n with $n-1$. Next, we add the term $\boldsymbol{\phi}(n)\boldsymbol{\phi}^T(n)\hat{\mathbf{w}}(n-1)$ to the right-hand side of Eq. (5.35) in a purposeful way and subtract the same term from it in another part of the equation, leaving the equation itself unchanged; we thus write (after factoring common terms)

$$\mathbf{r}(n) = [\mathbf{R}(n-1) + \boldsymbol{\phi}(n)\boldsymbol{\phi}^T(n)]\hat{\mathbf{w}}(n-1) + \boldsymbol{\phi}(n)[d(n) - \boldsymbol{\phi}^T(n)\hat{\mathbf{w}}(n-1)] \tag{5.36}$$

The expression inside the first set of brackets on the right-hand side of Eq. (5.36) is recognized as the correlation function

$$\mathbf{R}(n) = \mathbf{R}(n-1) + \boldsymbol{\phi}(n)\boldsymbol{\phi}^T(n) \tag{5.37}$$

For the expression inside the second set of brackets on the right-hand side of Eq. (5.36), we introduce the new term

$$\alpha(n) = d(n) - \boldsymbol{\phi}^T(n)\mathbf{w}(n-1)$$

$$= d(n) - \mathbf{w}^T(n-1)\boldsymbol{\phi}(n) \tag{5.38}$$

This new term is called the *prior estimation error*, where the use of "prior" is intended to emphasize the fact that the estimation error $\alpha(n)$ is based on the old estimate $\hat{\mathbf{w}}(n-1)$ of the weight vector—that is, "before" the weight estimate was updated. The $\alpha(n)$ is also referred to as the *innovation*, because the input vector $\mathbf{x}(n)$ embedded in the $\boldsymbol{\phi}(n)$ and the corresponding desired response $d(n)$ represent "new" information available to the algorithm for estimation at time n.

Returning to Eq. (5.36), we may now make use of Eqs. (5.37) and (5.38) to simplify matters as follows:

$$\mathbf{r}(n) = \mathbf{R}(n)\hat{\mathbf{w}}(n-1) + \boldsymbol{\phi}(n)\alpha(n) \tag{5.39}$$

Accordingly, the use of this equation in Eq. (5.30) yields

$$\mathbf{R}(n)\hat{\mathbf{w}}(n) = \mathbf{R}(n)\hat{\mathbf{w}}(n-1) + \boldsymbol{\phi}(n)\alpha(n) \tag{5.40}$$

which may be expressed in the desired form for *updating* the weight vector, as shown by

$$\hat{\mathbf{w}}(n) = \hat{\mathbf{w}}(n-1) + \mathbf{R}^{-1}(n)\boldsymbol{\phi}(n)\alpha(n) \tag{5.41}$$

where we have multiplied both sides of Eq. (5.40) by the inverse matrix $\mathbf{R}^{-1}(n)$. To do the update in a computationally efficient manner, however, we need a corresponding formula for computing the inverse matrix $\mathbf{R}^{-1}(n)$, given its past value $\mathbf{R}^{-1}(n-1)$; this issue is discussed next.

Recursive Formula for Computing $\mathbf{R}^{-1}(n)$

Referring back to Eq. (5.37), we see that we do have a formula for recursively updating the correlation matrix $\mathbf{R}(n)$. We capitalize on this recursion for the purpose of a recursive formula for the inverse matrix $\mathbf{R}^{-1}(n)$ by using the matrix inverse lemma, which was discussed in Section 4.14.

To recap, consider the matrix

$$\mathbf{A} = \mathbf{B}^{-1} + \mathbf{C}\mathbf{D}\mathbf{C}^T \tag{5.42}$$

where it is assumed that matrix $\mathbf{B}$ is nonsingular and matrix $\mathbf{B}^{-1}$ therefore exists. Matrices $\mathbf{A}$ and $\mathbf{B}$ are of similar dimensions, matrix $\mathbf{D}$ is another nonsingular matrix with different dimensions, and matrix $\mathbf{C}$ is a rectangular matrix of appropriate dimensions. According to the *matrix inversion lemma*, we have

$$\mathbf{A}^{-1} = \mathbf{B} - \mathbf{B}\mathbf{C}(\mathbf{D} + \mathbf{C}^T\mathbf{B}\mathbf{C})^{-1}\mathbf{C}^T\mathbf{B} \tag{5.43}$$

For the problem at hand, we use Eq. (5.37) to make the following identifications:

$$\mathbf{A} = \mathbf{R}(n)$$
$$\mathbf{B}^{-1} = \mathbf{R}(n-1)$$
$$\mathbf{C} = \boldsymbol{\phi}(n)$$
$$\mathbf{D} = 1$$

Accordingly, the application of Eq. (5.43) to this special set of matrices yields

$$\mathbf{R}^{-1}(n) = \mathbf{R}^{-1}(n-1) - \frac{\mathbf{R}^{-1}(n-1)\boldsymbol{\phi}(n)\boldsymbol{\phi}^T(n)\mathbf{R}^{-1^T}(n-1)}{1 + \boldsymbol{\phi}^T(n)\mathbf{R}^{-1}(n-1)\boldsymbol{\phi}(n)} \tag{5.44}$$

where, in the second term on the right-hand side of the equation, we have made use of the *symmetry* property of the correlation matrix; that is,

$$\mathbf{R}^T(n-1) = \mathbf{R}(n-1)$$

To simplify the formulation of the RLS algorithm, we now introduce two new definitions:

1. $\mathbf{R}^{-1}(n) = \mathbf{P}(n)$

Hence, we may reformulate Eq. (5.44) as

$$\mathbf{P}(n) = \mathbf{P}(n-1) - \frac{\mathbf{P}(n-1)\boldsymbol{\phi}(n)\boldsymbol{\phi}^T(n)\mathbf{P}(n-1)}{\mathbf{P}(n-1)\boldsymbol{\phi}(n)\boldsymbol{\phi}^T(n)\mathbf{P}^T(n-1)} \tag{5.45}$$

where the denominator on the right-hand side of the equation is a quadratic form and therefore a scalar.

To provide an interpretation for $\mathbf{P}(n)$, consider the linear regression model

$$d(n) = \mathbf{w}^T\boldsymbol{\phi}(n) + \varepsilon(n)$$

as the *generative model* for the desired response $d(n)$, with $\boldsymbol{\phi}(n)$ as the regressor. The additive noise term $\varepsilon(n)$ is assumed to be white with zero mean and variance σ_ε^2. Then, viewing the unknown weight vector $\mathbf{w}$ as the *state* of the model and $\hat{\mathbf{w}}(n)$ as the estimate produced by the RLS algorithm, we define the *state-error covariance matrix* as follows:

$$\mathbb{E}[(\mathbf{w} - \hat{\mathbf{w}}(n))(\mathbf{w} - \hat{\mathbf{w}}(n))^T] = \sigma_\varepsilon^2\mathbf{P}(n) \qquad (5.46)$$

Verification of this result is addressed in Problem 5.5.

2. $\mathbf{g}(n) = \mathbf{R}^{-1}(n)\boldsymbol{\phi}(n)$
   $$= \mathbf{P}(n)\boldsymbol{\phi}(n) \qquad (5.47)$$

The new term $\mathbf{g}(n)$ is called the *gain vector* of the RLS algorithm, because, in light of Eq. (5.41), we may view the prior estimation error $\alpha(n)$ multiplied by $\mathbf{g}(n)$ as the correction needed for updating the old estimate $\hat{\mathbf{w}}(n-1)$ to its new value $\hat{\mathbf{w}}(n)$, as shown by

$$\hat{\mathbf{w}}(n) = \hat{\mathbf{w}}(n-1) + \mathbf{g}(n)\alpha(n) \qquad (5.48)$$

Summary of the RLS Algorithm[7]

With Eqs. (5.45), (5.47), (5.38) and (5.48) at hand, in that order, we may now summarize the RLS algorithm as follows:

Given the training sample $\{\boldsymbol{\phi}(i), d(i)\}_{i=1}^N$, do the following computations for $n = 1, 2, ..., N$:

$$\mathbf{P}(n) = \mathbf{P}(n-1) - \frac{\mathbf{P}(n-1)\boldsymbol{\phi}(n)\boldsymbol{\phi}^T(n)\mathbf{P}(n-1)}{1 + \boldsymbol{\phi}^T(n)\mathbf{P}(n-1)\boldsymbol{\phi}(n)}$$

$$\mathbf{g}(n) = \mathbf{P}(n)\boldsymbol{\phi}(n)$$
$$\alpha(n) = d(n) - \hat{\mathbf{w}}^T(n-1)\boldsymbol{\phi}(n)$$
$$\hat{\mathbf{w}}(n) = \hat{\mathbf{w}}(n-1) + \mathbf{g}(n)\alpha(n)$$

To initialize the algorithm, set

$$\hat{\mathbf{w}}(0) = \mathbf{0}$$

and

$$\mathbf{P}(0) = \lambda^{-1}\mathbf{I}, \qquad \lambda \text{ is a small positive constant}$$

Note that the λ used in the initialization of the algorithm performs the role of a regularizing parameter in the cost function

$$\mathcal{E}_{av}(\mathbf{w}) = \frac{1}{2}\sum_{i=1}^N (d(i) - \mathbf{w}^T\boldsymbol{\phi}(i))^2 + \frac{1}{2}\lambda\|\mathbf{w}\|^2$$

When λ is chosen relatively small, which is typically the case, then, indirectly, we are confirming confidence in the quality of the training sample $\{\mathbf{x}(i), d(i)\}_{i=1}^N$.

5.7 HYBRID LEARNING PROCEDURE FOR RBF NETWORKS

Equipped with the K-means clustering algorithm described in Section 5.5 and the recursive least-squares (RLS) algorithm derived in Section 5.6, we are now ready to describe a *hybrid learning procedure*[8] for the RBF network of Fig. 5.4. The K-means algorithm for training the hidden layer is applied first; it is then followed by the RLS algorithm for training the output layer. Hereafter, we refer to this hybrid learning procedure as the "K-means, RLS" algorithm, aimed at training an RBF network with the following composition:

Input layer. The size of the input layer is determined by the dimensionality of the input vector $\mathbf{x}$, which is denoted by m_0.

Hidden layer.

1. The size of the hidden layer, m_1, is determined by the proposed number of clusters, K. Indeed, the parameter K may by viewed as a *degree of freedom* under the designer's control. As such, the parameter K holds the key to the model-selection problem and thereby controls not only the performance, but also the computational complexity of the network.

2. The cluster mean $\hat{\boldsymbol{\mu}}_j$, computed by the K-means algorithm working on the unlabeled sample $\{\mathbf{x}_i\}_{i=1}^{N}$ of input vectors, determines the center $\mathbf{x}_j$ in the Gaussian function $\varphi(\cdot,\mathbf{x}_j)$ assigned to the hidden unit $j = 1, 2, ..., K$.

3. To simplify the design, the same width, denoted by σ, is assigned to all the Gaussian functions in accordance with the spread of the centers discovered by the K-means algorithm, as shown by

$$\sigma = \frac{d_{\max}}{\sqrt{2K}} \tag{5.49}$$

where K is the number of centers and $d_{\max}$ is the maximum distance between them (Lowe, 1989). This formula ensures that the individual Gaussian units are not too peaked or too flat; both extreme conditions should be avoided in practice.

Output layer. Once the training of the hidden layer is completed, the training of the output layer can begin. Let the K-by-1 vector

$$\boldsymbol{\phi}(\mathbf{x}_i) = \begin{bmatrix} \varphi(\mathbf{x}_i, \boldsymbol{\mu}_1) \\ \varphi(\mathbf{x}_i, \boldsymbol{\mu}_2) \\ \vdots \\ \varphi(\mathbf{x}_i, \boldsymbol{\mu}_K) \end{bmatrix}$$

denote the outputs of the K units in the hidden layer. This vector is produced in response to the stimulus $\mathbf{x}_i, i = 1, 2, ..., N$. Thus, insofar as the supervised training of the output layer is concerned, the training sample is defined by $\{\boldsymbol{\phi}(\mathbf{x}_i), d_i\}_{i=1}^{N}$, where d_i is the desired response at the overall output of the RBF network for input $\mathbf{x}_i$. This training is carried out using the RLS algorithm. Once the network training is completed, testing of the whole network with data not seen before can begin.

An attractive feature of the "K-means, RLS" algorithm is its computational efficiency, which follows from the fact that the K-means and RLS algorithms are both computationally efficient in their own individual ways. The only questionable feature of the algorithm is the absence of an overall optimality criterion that combines the training of the hidden and output layers, assuring the whole system of optimality in some statistical sense.

5.8   COMPUTER EXPERIMENT: PATTERN CLASSIFICATION

In this section, we use a computer experiment to evaluate the pattern-classification performance of the "K-means, RLS" algorithm used to train an RBF network. The experiment uses data obtained by randomly sampling the double-moon configuration of Fig. 1.8. A specific aim of the experiment is to compare the performance of the RBF network trained in this way with that of the multilayer perceptron (MLP) trained using the back-propagation algorithm, which was the focus of attention in the experiment performed in Section 4.7.

The hidden layer of the RBF network was chosen to consist of 20 Gaussian units, thereby making it of the same size as the hidden layer of the MLP that was investigated in Section 4.7. For training of the RBF network, 1,000 data points were used; and for testing, 2,000 data points were used. In a manner similar to that for the MLP experiments, the RBF experiments were performed for two different settings of the double-moon figure, $d = -5$ and $d = -6$, with the latter setting being the more difficult one of the two.

(a) *Vertical separation: $d = -5$*

For this vertical separation between the two moons, $K = 20$ was assigned as the number of clusters (i.e., number of hidden units). By applying the K-means algorithm to the unlabeled part of the training sample, the centers of the clusters, and therefore the centers of the Gaussian units in the hidden layer, were determined. With the spread of the centers known, the formula of Eq. (5.49) was then used to compute the common width $\sigma = 2.6$ assigned to all the Gaussian units. The design of the hidden layer of the RBF network was thus completed. Finally, the RLS algorithm was used to train the output layer and thereby compute the decision boundary, preparing the way for the testing session.

The results of the first part of the experiment are presented in Fig. 5.5. Part (a) of the figure shows the learning curve of the RLS algorithm and part (b) shows the decision boundary learned by the RBF network. As can be seen from Fig. 5.5a, within two epochs of training, the design of the output layer is completed. Part (b) of the figure confirms almost perfect separability of the two moon-shaped patterns by the RBF network.

(b) *Vertical separation: $d = -6$*

The pattern-classification experiment on the RBF network was then repeated for this more difficult setting of the double-moon configuration of Fig. 1.8. This time, the common width $\sigma = 2.4$ was assigned to the 20 Gaussian units, the assignment again being performed in accordance with the formula of Eq. (5.49).

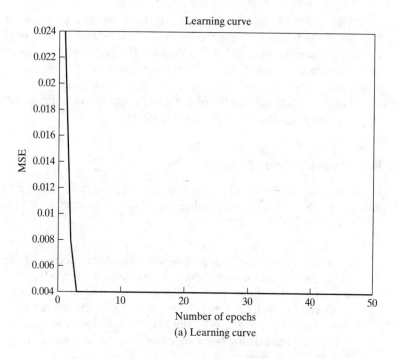

(a) Learning curve

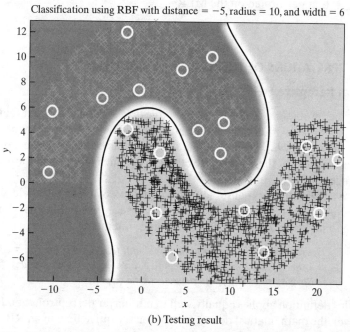

(b) Testing result

FIGURE 5.5   RBF network trained with K-means and RLS algorithms for distance $d = -5$. The MSE in part (a) of the figure stands for mean-square error.

The results of the second part of the experiment are presented in Fig. 5.6, with part (a) of the figure showing the learning curve of the RLS algorithm, and part (b) showing the decision boundary learned by the RBF network as a result of training under the "K-means, RLS" algorithm. A total of ten classification errors out of 2,000 test data points were recorded, yielding a classification error rate of 0.5%.

For both parts (a) and (b) of the experiment, the classification threshold was set at zero at the single output of the RBF network.

Comparison of the MLP and RBF Results

Comparing the results of experiments (a) and (b) performed on the RBF network in this section with those of the corresponding experiment performed on the MLP in Section 4.7, we draw the following conclusions:

1. The RBF network trained with the "K-means, RLS" algorithm outperforms the MLP trained with the back-propagation algorithm. Specifically, the MLP failed perfect classification for the setting $d = -5$ of the double moon, whereas the RBF network reported almost perfect classification. The misclassification rate of 0.5% produced by the RBF network for the difficult setting $d = -6$ was slightly greater than the 0.15% produced by the MLP for the easier setting $d = -5$. Surely, the MLP design could have been improved; however, the same thing could also be said for the RBF network.

2. The training process performed on the RBF network was significantly faster than that performed on the MLP.

5.9   INTERPRETATIONS OF THE GAUSSIAN HIDDEN UNITS

The Idea of Receptive Field

In a neurobiological context, a *receptive field* is defined as "that region of a sensory field from which an adequate sensory stimulus will elicit a response" (Churchland and Sejnowski, 1992). What is interesting to realize is that the receptive fields of cells in higher areas of the visual cortex tend to be much larger than those of cells in the earlier stages of the visual system.

Following this neurobiological definition of a receptive field, we may envision each hidden unit of a neural network to have a receptive field of its own. Indeed, we may go on to make the following corresponding statement:

> *The receptive field of a computational unit (e.g., hidden unit) in a neural network is, in general, that region of the sensory field (e.g., input layer of source nodes) from which an adequate sensory stimulus (e.g., pattern) will elicit a response.*

This definition applies equally well to multilayer perceptrons and RBF networks. However, the mathematical delineation of the receptive field in an RBF network is easier to determine than that in a multilayer perceptron.

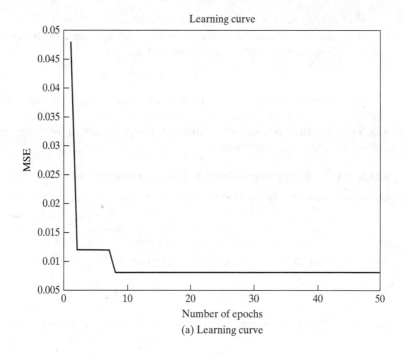

(a) Learning curve

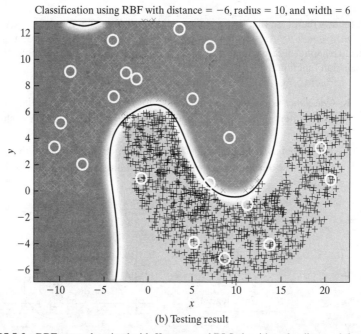

(b) Testing result

FIGURE 5.6   RBF network trained with K-means and RLS algorithms for distanced $d = -6$. The MSE in part (a) stands for mean-square error.

Let $\varphi(\mathbf{x}, \mathbf{x}_j)$ denote the functional dependence of a computational unit on the input vector $\mathbf{x}$, given that the unit is centered on the point $\mathbf{x}_j$. According to Xu et al. (1994), the receptive field of this computational unit is defined by

$$\psi(\mathbf{x}) = \varphi(\mathbf{x}, \mathbf{x}_j) - a \qquad (5.50)$$

where a is some positive constant. In words, this equation states that the receptive field of the function $\varphi(\mathbf{x}, \mathbf{x}_j)$ is that particular subset of the domain of the input vector $\mathbf{x}$ for which the function $\varphi(\mathbf{x}, \mathbf{x}_j)$ takes sufficiently large values, all of them being equal to or greater than the prescribed level a.

EXAMPLE 2   Receptive field of a Gaussian hidden unit

Consider a Gaussian computational unit defined by

$$\varphi(\mathbf{x}, \mathbf{x}_j) = \exp\left(-\frac{1}{2\sigma^2}\|\mathbf{x} - \mathbf{x}_j\|^2\right)$$

According to Eq. (5.50), the receptive field of this unit is

$$\psi(\mathbf{x}) = \exp\left(-\frac{1}{2\sigma^2}\|\mathbf{x} - \mathbf{x}_j\|^2\right) - a$$

where $a < 1$. The minimum permissible value of $\psi(\mathbf{x})$ is zero, for which this equation yields

$$\|\mathbf{x} - \mathbf{x}_j\| = \sigma\sqrt{2\log(\tfrac{1}{a})}$$

It follows therefore that the receptive field of the Gaussian function $\varphi(\mathbf{x},\mathbf{x}_j)$ is defined by a *multidimensional surface*, which is symmetrically centered around the point $\mathbf{x}_j$ in a spheroidal manner. The spheroidal symmetric property of the receptive field is inherited naturally from the Gaussian function itself.

Figure 5.7 depicts two special cases of this surface:

1. *One-dimensional receptive field,* $\psi(x)$, for which the domain of the input x is confined to the closed interval $[(x_i - \sigma\sqrt{2\log(1/a)}), (x_i + \sigma\sqrt{2\log(1/a)})]$, as shown in part (a) of the figure.

2. *Two-dimensional receptive field,* $\psi(\mathbf{x})$, for which the domain of the input x is confined to a circular disc of center $\mathbf{x}_i = [x_{i,1}, x_{i,2}]^T$ and radius $\sigma\sqrt{2\log(1/a)}$, as shown in part (b) of the figure. ∎

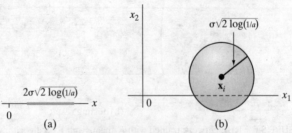

FIGURE 5.7   Illustrating the notion of receptive field for two special cases: (a) one-dimensional, and (b) two-dimensional.

Interpretation of the Gaussian Function as a Kernel

One other important facet of the Gaussian function $\varphi(\mathbf{x}, \mathbf{x}_j)$ is that it may be interpreted as a kernel, a term that is widely used in the statistics literature; it is also being increasingly used in the machine-learning literature.

Consider a function dependent on an input vector $\mathbf{x}$, with its center located at the origin of the Euclidean space. Basic to the formulation of this function as a *kernel*, denoted by $k(\mathbf{x})$, is that the function has properties similar to those associated with the probability density function of a random variable:

Property 1. *The kernel $k(\mathbf{x})$ is a continuous, bounded, and real function of $\mathbf{x}$ and symmetric about the origin, where it attains its maximum value.*

Property 2. *The total volume under the surface of the kernel $k(\mathbf{x})$ is unity; that is, for an m-dimensional vector $\mathbf{x}$, we have*

$$\int_{\mathbb{R}^m} k(\mathbf{x})d\mathbf{x} = 1$$

Except for a scaling factor, the Gaussian function $\varphi(\mathbf{x}, \mathbf{x}_j)$ satisfies both of these properties for the center $\mathbf{x}_j$ located at the origin. For a nonzero value of $\mathbf{x}_j$, properties 1 and 2 still hold except for the fact that $\mathbf{x}_j$ replaces the origin.

It is because of the interpretation of the Gaussian function as a kernel that we have used the term "kernel methods" in the title of this chapter.

5.10   KERNEL REGRESSION AND ITS RELATION TO RBF NETWORKS

The theory of RBF networks, presented in Section 5.3, is built on the notion of interpolation. In this section, we take another viewpoint—namely, *kernel regression*, which builds on the notion of density estimation.

To be specific, consider a nonlinear regression model defined by

$$y_i = f(\mathbf{x}_i) + \varepsilon(i), \qquad i = 1, 2, ..., N \tag{5.51}$$

where $\varepsilon(i)$ is an additive white-noise term of zero mean and variance σ_ε^2. To avoid confusion, we have used the symbol y_i (instead of d_i as previously) to denote the model output. As a reasonable estimate of the unknown regression function $f(\mathbf{x})$, we may take the mean of observables (i.e., values of the model output y) near a point $\mathbf{x}$. For this approach to be successful, however, the local average should be confined to observations in a small neighborhood (i.e., receptive field) around the point $\mathbf{x}$ because, in general, observations corresponding to points away from $\mathbf{x}$ will have different mean values. More precisely, we find that the unknown function $f(\mathbf{x})$ is equal to the *conditional mean of the observable y given the regressor $\mathbf{x}$*, as shown by

$$f(\mathbf{x}) = \mathbb{E}[y|\mathbf{x}]$$

$$= \int_{-\infty}^{\infty} y p_{Y|\mathbf{x}}(y|\mathbf{x})dy \tag{5.52}$$

where $p_{Y|\mathbf{X}}(y|\mathbf{x})$ is the conditional probability density function (pdf) of *the random variable Y given that the random vector $\mathbf{X}$ is assigned the value $\mathbf{x}$.*[9] From probability theory, we have

$$p_{Y|\mathbf{X}}(y|\mathbf{x}) = \frac{p_{\mathbf{X}|Y}(\mathbf{x}|y)}{p_{\mathbf{X}}(\mathbf{x})} \tag{5.53}$$

where $p_{\mathbf{X}}(\mathbf{x})$ is the pdf of $\mathbf{X}$ and $p_{\mathbf{X},Y}(\mathbf{x}, y)$ is the joint pdf of $\mathbf{X}$ and Y. Hence, using Eq. (5.53) in Eq. (5.52), we obtain the following formula for the regression function:

$$f(\mathbf{x}) = \frac{\displaystyle\int_{-\infty}^{\infty} y p_{\mathbf{X},Y}(\mathbf{x}, y) dy}{p_{\mathbf{X}}(\mathbf{x})} \tag{5.54}$$

Our particular interest is in a situation where the joint probability density function $p_{\mathbf{X},Y}(\mathbf{x}, y)$ is unknown and all that we have available is the training sample $\{(\mathbf{x}_i, y_i)\}_{i=1}^{N}$. To estimate $p_{\mathbf{X},Y}(\mathbf{x}, y)$, and therefore $p_{\mathbf{X}}(\mathbf{x})$, we may use a nonparametric estimator known as the *Parzen–Rosenblatt density estimator* (Rosenblatt, 1956, 1970; Parzen, 1962). Basic to the formulation of this estimator is the availability of a *kernel* $k(\mathbf{x})$. Assuming that the observations $\mathbf{x}_1, \mathbf{x}_2, ..., \mathbf{x}_N$ are statistically independent and identically distributed (iid), we may formally define the Parzen–Rosenblatt density estimate of $f_{\mathbf{X}}(\mathbf{x})$ as

$$\hat{p}_{\mathbf{X}}(\mathbf{x}) = \frac{1}{Nh^{m_0}} \sum_{i=1}^{N} k\left(\frac{\mathbf{x} - \mathbf{x}_i}{h}\right) \quad \text{for } \mathbf{x} \in \mathbb{R}^{m_0} \tag{5.55}$$

where the smoothing parameter h is a positive number called *bandwidth*, or simply *width*; h controls the size of the kernel. An important property of the Parzen–Rosenblatt density estimator is that it is a *consistent estimator*[10] (i.e., asymptotically unbiased) in the sense that if $h = h(N)$ is chosen as a function of N such that

$$\lim_{N \to \infty} h(N) = 0,$$

then

$$\lim_{N \to \infty} \mathbb{E}[\hat{p}_{\mathbf{X}}(\mathbf{x})] = p_{\mathbf{X}}(\mathbf{x})$$

For this latter equation to hold, $\mathbf{x}$ should be a point of continuity for $\hat{p}_{\mathbf{X}}(\mathbf{x})$.

In a manner similar to that described in Eq. (5.55), we may formulate the Parzen–Rosenblatt density estimate of the joint probability density function $p_{\mathbf{X},Y}(\mathbf{x}, y)$ as

$$\hat{p}_{\mathbf{X},Y}(\mathbf{x}, y) = \frac{1}{Nh^{m_0+1}} \sum_{i=1}^{N} k\left(\frac{\mathbf{x} - \mathbf{x}_i}{h}\right) k\left(\frac{y - y_i}{h}\right) \quad \text{for } \mathbf{x} \in \mathbb{R}^{m_0} \text{ and } y \in \mathbb{R} \tag{5.56}$$

Integrating $\hat{p}_{\mathbf{X},Y}(\mathbf{x}, y)$ with respect to y, we get the $\hat{p}_{\mathbf{X}}(\mathbf{x})$ of Eq. (5.55), as we should. Moreover,

$$\int_{-\infty}^{\infty} y \hat{p}_{\mathbf{X},Y}(\mathbf{x}, y) dy = \frac{1}{Nh^{m_0+1}} \sum_{i=1}^{N} k\left(\frac{\mathbf{x} - \mathbf{x}_i}{h}\right) \int_{-\infty}^{\infty} y k\left(\frac{y - y_i}{h}\right) dy$$

Changing the variable of integration by setting $\xi = (y - y_i)/h$, and using Property 2 of the kernel $k(\cdot)$, we obtain the result

$$\int_{-\infty}^{\infty} y\hat{p}_{X,Y}(\mathbf{x}, y)\, dy = \frac{1}{Nh^{m_0}} \sum_{i=1}^{N} y_i k\left(\frac{\mathbf{x} - \mathbf{x}_i}{h}\right) \tag{5.57}$$

Thus, using Eqs. (5.57) and (5.55) as estimates of the quantities in the numerator and denominator of Eq. (5.54), respectively, we obtain the following estimate of the regression function $f(\mathbf{x})$, after canceling common terms:

$$F(\mathbf{x}) = \hat{f}(\mathbf{x})$$

$$= \frac{\sum_{i=1}^{N} y_i k\left(\dfrac{\mathbf{x} - \mathbf{x}_i}{h}\right)}{\sum_{j=1}^{N} k\left(\dfrac{\mathbf{x} - \mathbf{x}_j}{h}\right)} \tag{5.58}$$

Here, in the denominator, for clarity of presentation, we have used j instead of i as the index of summation.

There are two ways in which the approximating function $F(\mathbf{x})$ of Eq. (5.58) may be viewed:

1. *Nadaraya–Watson regression estimator.* For the first viewpoint, define the *normalized weighting function*

$$W_{N,i}(\mathbf{x}) = \frac{k\left(\dfrac{\mathbf{x} - \mathbf{x}_i}{h}\right)}{\sum_{j=1}^{N} k\left(\dfrac{\mathbf{x} - \mathbf{x}_j}{h}\right)}, \qquad i = 1, 2, ..., N \tag{5.59}$$

with

$$\sum_{i=1}^{N} W_{N,i}(\mathbf{x}) = 1 \qquad \text{for all } \mathbf{x} \tag{5.60}$$

We may then rewrite the kernel regression estimator of Eq. (5.58) in the simplified form

$$F(\mathbf{x}) = \sum_{i=1}^{N} W_{N,i}(\mathbf{x}) y_i \tag{5.61}$$

which describes $F(\mathbf{x})$ as a *weighted average* of the observables $\{y_i\}_{i=1}^{N}$. The particular form of weighting function $W_N(\mathbf{x}, i)$ given in Eq. (5.61) was independently proposed by Nadaraya (1964) and Watson (1964). Accordingly, the approximating function of Eq. (5.61) is often called the *Nadaraya–Watson regression estimator (NWRE)*.[11]

2. *Normalized RBF network.* For the second viewpoint, we assume *spherical symmetry* of the kernel $k(\mathbf{x})$, in which case we may set

$$k\left(\frac{\mathbf{x} - \mathbf{x}_i}{h}\right) = k\left(\frac{\|\mathbf{x} - \mathbf{x}_i\|}{h}\right) \qquad \text{for all } i \tag{5.62}$$

where, as usual, $\| \cdot \|$ denotes the Euclidean norm of the enclosed vector (Krzyzak et al., 1996). Correspondingly, we define the *normalized radial basis function*

$$\psi_N(\mathbf{x}, \mathbf{x}_i) = \frac{k\left(\dfrac{\|\mathbf{x} - \mathbf{x}_i\|}{h}\right)}{\displaystyle\sum_{j=1}^{N} k\left(\dfrac{\|\mathbf{x} - \mathbf{x}_j\|}{h}\right)}, \qquad i = 1, 2, ..., N \tag{5.63}$$

with

$$\sum_{i=1}^{N} \psi_N(\mathbf{x}, \mathbf{x}_i) = 1 \qquad \text{for all } \mathbf{x} \tag{5.64}$$

The subscript N in $\psi_N(\mathbf{x}, \mathbf{x}_i)$ signifies the use of *normalization*.

For the regression problem considered under the second viewpoint, we recognize that the "linear weights," w_i, applied to the basic functions $\psi_N(\mathbf{x}, \mathbf{x}_i)$ are simply the observables, y_i of the regression model for the input data $\mathbf{x}_i$. Thus, letting

$$y_i = w_i, \qquad i = 1, 2, ..., N$$

we may reformulate the approximating function of Eq. (5.58) in the general form

$$F(\mathbf{x}) = \sum_{i=1}^{N} w_i \psi_N(\mathbf{x}, \mathbf{x}_i) \tag{5.65}$$

Equation (5.65) represents the input–output mapping of a *normalized radial-basis-function (RBF) network* (Moody and Darken, 1989; Xu et al., 1994). Note that

$$0 \leq \psi_N(\mathbf{x}, \mathbf{x}_i) \leq 1 \qquad \text{for all } \mathbf{x} \text{ and } \mathbf{x}_i \tag{5.66}$$

Accordingly, $\psi_N(\mathbf{x}, \mathbf{x}_i)$ may be interpreted as the probability of an event described by the input vector $\mathbf{x}$, conditional on $\mathbf{x}_i$.

The basic difference between the normalized radial-basis function $\psi_N(\mathbf{x}, \mathbf{x}_i)$ of Eq. (5.63) and an ordinary radial-basis function is a denominator term that constitutes the *normalization factor*. This normalization factor is an estimate of the underlying probability density function of the input vector $\mathbf{x}$. Consequently, the basis functions $\psi_N(\mathbf{x}, \mathbf{x}_i)$ for $i = 1, 2, ..., N$ sum to unity for all $\mathbf{x}$, as described in Eq. (5.64).

Multivariate Gaussian Distribution

A variety of kernel functions is possible in general. However, both theoretical and practical considerations limit the choice. A widely used kernel is the multivariate Gaussian distribution

$$k(\mathbf{x}) = \frac{1}{(2\pi)^{m_0/2}} \exp\left(-\frac{\|\mathbf{x}\|^2}{2}\right) \tag{5.67}$$

where m_0 is the dimension of the input vector $\mathbf{x}$. The spherical symmetry of the kernel $k(\mathbf{x})$ is clearly apparent in Eq. (5.67). Assuming the use of a common bandwidth σ that plays the role of smoothing parameter h for a Gaussian distribution, and centering the kernel on a data point $\mathbf{x}_i$, we may write

$$k\left(\frac{\mathbf{x} - \mathbf{x}_i}{h}\right) = \frac{1}{(2\pi\sigma^2)^{m_0/2}} \exp\left(-\frac{\|\mathbf{x} - \mathbf{x}_i\|^2}{2\sigma^2}\right), \quad i = 1, 2, ..., N \qquad (5.68)$$

Thus, using Eq. (5.68), we find that the Nadaraya–Watson regression estimator takes the form

$$F(\mathbf{x}) = \frac{\displaystyle\sum_{i=1}^{N} y_i \exp\left(-\frac{\|\mathbf{x} - \mathbf{x}_i\|^2}{2\sigma^2}\right)}{\displaystyle\sum_{j=1}^{N} \exp\left(-\frac{\|\mathbf{x} - \mathbf{x}_j\|^2}{2\sigma^2}\right)} \qquad (5.69)$$

where the denominator term, representing the Parzen–Rosenblatt density estimator, consists of the sum of N multivariate Gaussian distributions centered on the data points $\mathbf{x}_1, \mathbf{x}_2, ..., \mathbf{x}_N$ (Specht, 1991).

Correspondingly, using Eq. (5.68) in Eq. (5.63) and then Eq. (5.65), we find that the input–output mapping function of the normalized RBF network takes the form

$$F(\mathbf{x}) = \frac{\displaystyle\sum_{i=1}^{N} w_i \exp\left(-\frac{\|\mathbf{x} - \mathbf{x}_i\|^2}{2\sigma^2}\right)}{\displaystyle\sum_{j=1}^{N} \exp\left(-\frac{\|\mathbf{x} - \mathbf{x}_j\|^2}{2\sigma^2}\right)} \qquad (5.70)$$

In Eqs. (5.69) and (5.70), the centers of the normalized radial-basis functions coincide with the data points $\{\mathbf{x}_i\}_{i=1}^{N}$. As with ordinary radial-basis functions, a smaller number of normalized radial-basis functions can be used, with their centers treated as free parameters to be chosen according to some heuristic (Moody and Darken, 1989), or determined in a principled manner as discussed in Chapter 7.

5.11   SUMMARY AND DISCUSSION

In this chapter, we focused on radial-basis-function (RBF) networks as an alternative to multilayer perceptrons. Like the multilayer perceptron, discussed in Chapter 4, the RBF network is a *universal approximator* in its own right (Sandberg and Xu, 1997a, 1997b). The basic structural difference between them is summed up as follows:

> *In a multilayer perceptron, function approximation is defined by a nested set of weighted summations, whereas in an RBF network, the approximation is defined by a single weighted sum.*

Design Considerations

The design of an RBF network may follow interpolation theory, which, in mathematical terms, is elegant. However, from a practical perspective, this design approach has two shortcomings. First, the training sample may be noisy, which could yield misleading results by the RBF network. Second, when the size of the training sample is large, using an RBF network with a hidden layer of the same size as the training sample is wasteful of computational resources.

A more practical approach to the design of RBF networks is to follow the hybrid learning procedure described in Section 5.5 through 5.7. Basically, the procedure operates in two stages:

- Stage 1 applies the K-means clustering algorithm to train the hidden layer in an unsupervised manner. Typically, the number of clusters, and therefore the number of computational units in the hidden layer, is significantly smaller than the size of the training sample.
- Stage 2 applies the recursive least-squares (RLS) algorithm to compute the weight vector of the linear output layer.

This two-stage design procedure has a couple of desirable features: computational simplicity and accelerated convergence.

Experimental Results

The results of the computer experiment on the double-moon "toy" problem, presented in Section 5.8, reveal that the hybrid "K-means, RLS" classifier is capable of delivering an impressive performance. When the results of this experiment are compared with those of the same experiment using the support vector machine (SVM), to be discussed in the next chapter, we find that the two classifiers perform very similarly. However, the "K-means, RLS" classifier is much faster to converge and less demanding in computational effort than the SVM.

It is noteworthy that Rifkin (2002), in his doctoral thesis, made a detailed comparison between the RLS and the SVM for the classification of linearly separable patterns, using a collection of toy examples. Here is a summary of this part of his experimental results:

- The RLS and SVM classifiers exhibit nearly identical performance.
- They are both susceptible to the presence of outliers in the training sample.

Rifkin (2002) also performed experiments on image classification, using two different data sets:

- The U.S. Postal Service (USPS) handwritten data set, consisting of 7,291 training examples and 2,007 testing examples. The training set contains 6,639 negative examples and 652 positive ones, while the testing set contains 1,807 negative examples and 200 positive ones.
- The MIT recognition set, referred to as **faces**. The training set contains 2,429 faces and 4,548 nonfaces, and the testing set contains 572 faces and 23,573 nonfaces.

For the USPS data set, it is reported that the nonlinear RLS classifier performed as well as or better than the SVM across the entire range of the *receiver operating characteristic* (ROC) curve. The ROC curve plots the *true-positive rate* against the *false-positive rate* for a varying decision threshold when a single network output is used; the term "rate" is another way of referring to the probability of classification. The tests performed on the **faces** set produced mixed results: For one set of design parameters, the SVM performed substantially better than the nonlinear RLS classifier. For another set of design parameters, the performances were close. We should also point out that the strategy used by Rifkin (2002) for designing the hidden layer of the nonlinear RLS classifier was quite different from the K-means clustering algorithm considered in this chapter.

An important message, pertaining to our own double-moon "toy" experiments and the more extensive experiments reported in Rifkin (2002), is twofold:

1. The RLS algorithm has been thoroughly studied in the signal-processing and control literature (Haykin, 2002; Goodwin and Sin, 1984). Unfortunately, it has been almost completely ignored in the machine-learning literature, except for Rifkin's (2002) thesis and a few other publications.

2. There is a need for more extensive experiments, using real-world data sets, to come up with more definitive conclusions on how an RBF network based on the RLS algorithm (for the design of its output layer) and the SVM compare with each other, not only in terms of performance, but also with respect to rate of convergence, as well as computational complexity.

Kernel Regression

The one other important topic studied in this chapter is kernel regression, which builds on the notion of density estimation. In particular, we focused on a nonparametric estimator known as the Parzen–Rosenblatt density estimator, the formulation of which rests on the availability of a kernel. This study led us to two ways of viewing the approximating function defined in terms of a nonlinear regression model: the Nadaraya–Watson regression estimator and the normalized RBF network. For both of them, the multivariate Gaussian distribution provides a good choice for the kernel.

NOTES AND REFERENCES

1. Radial-basis functions were first introduced in the solution of the real multivariate interpolation problem. The early work on this subject is surveyed in Powell (1985). It is now one of the main fields of research in numerical analysis.

   Broomhead and Lowe (1988) were the first to exploit the use of radial-basis functions in the design of neural networks. Another major contribution to the theory and design of radial-basis function networks is due to Poggio and Girosi (1990a). This latter paper emphasizes the use of regularization theory applied to this class of networks as a method for improved generalization to new data; regularization theory is discussed in detail in Chapter 10.

2. The proof of Cover's theorem follows from two basic considerations (Cover, 1965):

   • *Schalfi's theorem*, or the *function-counting theorem*, which states that the number of homogeneously linearly separable dichotomies of N vectors, located in general position in Euclidean-m_1 space, is equal to

   $$C(N, m_1) = 2 \sum_{m=0}^{m_1-1} \binom{N-1}{m}$$

   A set of vectors $\mathcal{H} = \{\mathbf{x}_i\}_{i=1}^N$ is said to be in "general position" in Euclidean-m_1 space if every subset on m_1 or fewer vectors is linearly independent.

   • *Reflection invariance* of the joint probability distribution of $\mathcal{H}$, which implies that the probability (conditional on $\mathcal{H}$) that a random dichotomy is separable is equal to the unconditional probability that a particular dichotomy of $\mathcal{H}$ (all N vectors in one category) is separable.

The function-counting theorem has been independently proved in different forms and applied to specific configurations of perceptrons (i.e., linear threshold units) by Cameron (1960), Joseph (1960), and Winder (1961). In Cover (1968), this theorem was applied to evaluate the capacity of a network of perceptrons in terms of the total number of adjustable parameters, which is shown to be lower bounded by $N/(1 + \log_2/N)$, where N is the number of input patterns.

3. Clustering, in general, is discussed in several books, including Theodoridis and Koutroumbas (2003); Duda et al. (2001); and Fukunaga (1990).

    The K-means algorithm assumed this name after MacQueen (1967), who studied it as a statistical clustering procedure, including the convergence properties of the algorithm. The idea had been previously described in Foregey (1962) in the context of clustering.

    Ding and He (2004) present a very interesting relationship between the K-means algorithm for clustering and principal-components analysis for data reduction. In particular, it is shown that principal components represent a continuous (relaxed) solution of the cluster membership indicators in K-means clustering. In a way, these two views are consistent, in the sense that clustering of data is also a form of data reduction, both of which are, of course, performed in an unsupervised manner. The subject of principal-components analysis is presented in Chapter 8.

    In the communications literature dealing with vector quantization, the K-means algorithm is referred to as the *generalized Lloyd algorithm*, which is a generalization of Lloyd's original treatment that appeared in an unpublished 1957 report at Bell Laboratories. Much later, in 1982, Lloyd's report appeared in published form.

4. *Fisher's Linear Discriminant* The cost function defined in Eq. (5.26) is nothing but the *trace* of the so-called within-class covariance (scatter) matrix (Theodoridis and Koutroumbas, 2003).

    To understand the meaning of this statement, consider a variable y defined by an inner product as follows:

$$y = \mathbf{w}^T \mathbf{x} \tag{A}$$

The vector $\mathbf{x}$ is drawn from one of two populations $\mathcal{C}_1$ and $\mathcal{C}_2$, which differ from each other by virtue of the mean vectors $\boldsymbol{\mu}_1$ and $\boldsymbol{\mu}_2$, respectively, and $\mathbf{w}$ is a vector of adjustable parameters. The *Fisher criterion* for discriminating between these two classes is defined by

$$J(\mathbf{w}) = \frac{\mathbf{w}^T \mathbf{C}_b \mathbf{w}}{\mathbf{w}^T \mathbf{C}_t \mathbf{w}} \tag{B}$$

Where $\mathbf{C}_b$ is the *between-class covariance matrix*, defined by

$$\mathbf{C}_b = (\boldsymbol{\mu}_2 - \boldsymbol{\mu}_1)(\boldsymbol{\mu}_2 - \boldsymbol{\mu}_1)^T \tag{C}$$

and $\mathbf{C}_t$ is the total *within-class covariance matrix*, defined by

$$\mathbf{C}_t = \sum_{n \in \mathcal{C}_1} (\mathbf{x}_n - \boldsymbol{\mu}_1)(\mathbf{x}_n - \boldsymbol{\mu}_1)^T + \sum_{n \in \mathcal{C}_2} (\mathbf{x}_n - \boldsymbol{\mu}_2)(\mathbf{x}_n - \boldsymbol{\mu}_2)^T \tag{D}$$

The within-class covariance matrix $\mathbf{C}_t$ is proportional to the sample covariance matrix of the training sample. It is symmetric and nonnegative definite and is usually nonsingular if the size of the training sample is large. The between-class covariance matrix $\mathbf{C}_b$ is also symmetric and nonnegative definite, but singular. A property of particular interest is that the matrix product $\mathbf{C}_b\mathbf{w}$ is always in the direction of the difference mean vector $\boldsymbol{\mu}_1 - \boldsymbol{\mu}_2$. This property follows directly from the definition of $\mathbf{C}_b$.

The expression defining $J(\mathbf{w})$ is known as the *generalized Rayleigh quotient*. The vector $\mathbf{w}$ that maximized $J(\mathbf{w})$ must satisfy the condition

$$\mathbf{C}_b\mathbf{w} = \lambda\mathbf{C}_t\mathbf{w} \tag{E}$$

where λ is a scaling factor. Equation (E) is a generalized eigenvalue problem. Recognizing that, in our case, the matrix product $\mathbf{C}_b\mathbf{w}$ is always in the direction of the difference vector $\boldsymbol{\mu}_1 - \boldsymbol{\mu}_2$, we find that the solution for Eq. (E) is simply

$$\mathbf{w} = \mathbf{C}_t^{-1}(\boldsymbol{\mu}_1 - \boldsymbol{\mu}_2) \tag{F}$$

which is referred to as *Fisher's linear discriminant* (Duda et al., 2001).

Taking the trace of the within-class covariance matrix $\mathbf{C}_t$ of Eq. (D), we do find that the cost function of Eq. (5.26) is indeed the trace of this covariance matrix, as already stated.

5. In philosophical terms, the two-step optimization procedure described in the text for the K-means algorithm is similar to the two-step optimization involved in the *EM algorithm*, where the first step is one of expectation, denoted by "E", and the second step is one of maximization, denoted by "M". The EM algorithm was originally developed in the context of maximum-likelihood computation; it is described in Chapter 11.

6. In the literature, the acronym "RLS" is used as the abbreviation for the regularized least-squares algorithm discussed in Chapter 2 as well as the recursive least-squares algorithm discussed in this chapter. From the context of the pertinent discussion, we are usually able to discern which of these two algorithms the acroynm refers to.

7. The essence of the RLS algorithm summarized in Section 5.6, a classic, is described in the books by Diniz (2002); Haykin (2002).

8. Hybrid learning procedures for RBF networks have been variously described in the literature, using different algorithms for the two stages of the procedure; see Moody and Darken (1989) and Lippman (1989b).

9. The conditional mean estimator of Eq. (5.52) is also a minimum mean-square estimator; a proof of this statement is presented in Note 7 of Chapter 14 under the umbrella of Bayes's estimation theory.

10. For a proof of the asymptotically unbiased property of the Parzen–Rosenblatt density estimator, see Parzen (1962) and Cacoullos (1966).

11. The Nadaraya–Watson regression estimator has been the subject of extensive study in the statistics literature. In a broader context, nonparametric functional estimation occupies a central place in statistics; see Härdle (1990) and the collection of papers in Roussas (1991).

PROBLEMS

Cover's Theorem

5.1 As suggested in Section 5.2, the best way to study Eq. (5.5) is to normalize it by setting $N = \lambda m_1$. Using this normalization, plot $P(\lambda m_1, m_1)$ versus λ for $N = 1, 5, 15,$ and 25. Hence, validate the two characteristics of Eq. (5.5) described in the section.

5.2 State Cover's theorem on the separability of patterns. Discuss its two basic ingredients.

5.3 The example given in Fig. 5.1b depicts a spherically separable dictomy. Assume that the four data points outside the separating surface lie on a circle and that the only data point inside lies at the center of the separating surface. Investigate how this sample of data points is nonlinearly transformed, using

(a) the multiquadric

$$\varphi(x) = (x^2 + 1)^{1/2}$$

(b) the inverse multiquadric

$$\varphi(x) = \frac{1}{(x^2 + 1)^{1/2}}$$

K-means Clustering

5.4 Consider the following modification of the cost function defined in Eq. (5.26):

$$J(\mathbf{\mu}_j) = \sum_{j=1}^{K} \sum_{i=1}^{N} w_{ij} \|\mathbf{x}_i - \mathbf{\mu}_j\|^2$$

In this function, the weighting factor w_{ij} is defined as follows:

$$w_{ij} = \begin{cases} 1 & \text{if the data point } \mathbf{x}_i \text{ lies in cluster } j \\ 0 & \text{otherwise} \end{cases}$$

Show that the minimizing solution of this cost function is

$$\hat{\mathbf{\mu}}_j = \frac{\sum_{i=1}^{N} w_{ij} \mathbf{x}_i}{\sum_{i=1}^{N} w_{ij}}, \quad j = 1, 2, ..., K$$

How do you interpret the expressions in the numerator and denominator of this formula? Contrast the conclusion from your two answers against that we have learned in the text in the context of clustering.

Recursive Least-Squares Algorithm

5.5 In this problem, we address a statistical interpretation of the matrix $\mathbf{P}$ defined as the inverse of the correlation matrix $\mathbf{R}$.

(a) Using the linear regression model

$$d_i = \mathbf{w}^T \mathbf{\phi}_i + \varepsilon_i, \quad i = 1, 2, ..., N$$

show that the least-square optimized estimate of $\mathbf{w}$ is expressed as

$$\hat{\mathbf{w}} = \mathbf{w} + (\mathbf{\Phi}^T \mathbf{\Phi})^{-1} \mathbf{\Phi}^T \mathbf{\varepsilon}$$

where

$$\Phi = \begin{bmatrix} \phi_1^T \\ \phi_2^T \\ \vdots \\ \phi_N^T \end{bmatrix}$$

and

$$\varepsilon = [\varepsilon_1, \varepsilon_2, ..., \varepsilon_N]^T$$

Assume that the error ε_i is a sample of a white-noise process of variance σ^2.

(b) Hence, show that the covariance matrix

$$\mathbb{E}[(\mathbf{w} - \hat{\mathbf{w}})(\mathbf{w} - \hat{\mathbf{w}})^T] = \sigma^2 \mathbf{R}^{-1}$$
$$= \sigma^2 \mathbf{P}$$

where

$$\mathbf{R} = \sum_{i=1}^{N} \phi_i \phi_i^T$$

5.6 Starting with the regularized cost function

$$\mathscr{E}_{av}(\mathbf{w}) = \frac{1}{2} \sum_{i=1}^{N} (d(i) - \mathbf{w}^T \phi(i))^2 + \frac{1}{2} \lambda \|\mathbf{w}\|^2$$

do the following:

(a) Show that the addition of the regularization term $\frac{1}{2}\lambda\|\mathbf{w}\|^2$ has no effect whatsoever on the composition of the RLS algorithm, as summarized in Section 5.6.

(b) The only effect of introducing the regularization term is to modify the expression for the correlation matrix of the input data into the form

$$\mathbf{R}(n) = \sum_{i=1}^{n} \phi(i)\phi^T(i) + \lambda \mathbf{I}$$

where $\mathbf{I}$ is the identity matrix. Verify this new formulation of the correlation matrix $\mathbf{R}(n)$, and justify the practical benefit gained by introducing regularization.

5.7 How is recursive least-squares (RLS) algorithm different from least-mean-squares (LMS) algorithm for adaptive filtering discussed in Chapter 3?

Supervised Training of RBF Networks

5.8 The input–output relationship of a Gaussian-based RBF network is defined by

$$y(i) = \sum_{j=1}^{K} w_j(n) \exp\left(-\frac{1}{2\sigma^2(n)} \|\mathbf{x}(i) - \mu_j(n)\|^2\right), \qquad i = 1, 2, ..., n$$

where $\mu_j(n)$ is the center point of the jth Gaussian unit, the width $\sigma(n)$ is common to all the K units, and $w_j(n)$ is the linear weight assigned to the output of the jth unit; all these parameters are measured at time n. The cost function used to train the network is defined by

$$\mathcal{E} = \frac{1}{2}\sum_{i=1}^{n} e^2(i)$$

where

$$e(i) = d(i) - y(i)$$

The cost function $\mathcal{E}$ is a convex function of the linear weights in the output layer, but non-convex with respect to the centers and the width of the Gaussian units.

(a) Evaluate the partial derivatives of the cost function with respect to each of the network parameters $w_j(n)$, $\boldsymbol{\mu}_j(n)$, and $\sigma(n)$, for all i.

(b) Use the gradients obtained in part (a) to express the update formulas for all the network parameters, assuming the learning-rate parameters η_w, η_μ, and η_σ for the adjustable parameters of the network, respectively.

(c) The gradient vector $\partial\mathcal{E}/\boldsymbol{\mu}_j(n)$ has an effect on the input data that is similar to *clustering*. Justify this statement.

Kernel Estimation

5.9 Suppose that you are given a "noiseless" training sample $\{f(\mathbf{x}_i)\}_{i=1}^{N}$, and that the requirement is to design a network that generalizes to data samples that are corrupted by additive noise and therefore not included in the training set. Let $F(\mathbf{x})$ denote the approximating function realized by such a network, which is chosen so that the expected squared error

$$J(F) = \frac{1}{2}\sum_{i=1}^{N} \int_{\mathbb{R}^{m_0}} [f(\mathbf{x}_i) - F(\mathbf{x}_i, \boldsymbol{\xi})]^2 f_\xi(\boldsymbol{\xi})d\boldsymbol{\xi}$$

is minimum, where $f_\xi(\boldsymbol{\xi})$ is the probability density function of a noise distribution in the input space $\mathbb{R}^{m_0}$. Show that the solution of this least-squares problem is given as follows (Webb, 1994):

$$F(\mathbf{x}) = \frac{\displaystyle\sum_{i=1}^{N} f(\mathbf{x}_i)f_\xi(\mathbf{x} - \mathbf{x}_i)}{\displaystyle\sum_{i=1}^{N} f_\xi(\mathbf{x} - \mathbf{x}_i)}$$

Compare this estimator with the Nadaraya–Watson regression estimator.

Computer Experiments

5.10 The purpose of this computer experiment is to investigate the clustering process performed by the K-means algorithm. To provide insight into the experiment, we fix the number of clusters at $K = 6$, but vary the vertical separation between the two moons in Fig. 1.8. Specifically, the requirement is to do the following, using an unlabeled training sample of 1,000 data points picked randomly from the two regions of the double-moon pictured in Fig. 1.8:

(a) Experimentally, determine the mean $\hat{\boldsymbol{\mu}}_j$ and variance $\hat{\sigma}_j^2$, $j = 1, 2, ..., 6$, for the sequence of eight uniformly spaced vertical separations starting at $d = 1$ and reducing them by one till the final separation $d = -6$ is reached.

(b) In light of the results obtained in part (a), comment on how the mean $\hat{\boldsymbol{\mu}}_j$ of cluster j is affected by reducing the separation d for $j = 1, 2,$ and 3.

(c) Plot the variance $\hat{\sigma}_j^2$ versus the separation d for $j = 1, 2, ..., 6$.

(d) Compare the common σ^2 computed in accordance with the empirical formula of Eq. (5.49) with the trends exhibited in the plots obtained in part (c).

5.11 The purpose of this second experiment is to compare the classification performance of two hybrid learning algorithms: the "K-means, RLS" algorithm investigated in Section 5.8 and the "K-means, LMS" algorithm investigated in this problem.

As in Section 5.8, assume the following specifications:

Number of hidden Gaussian units: 20
Number of training samples: 1,000 data points
Number of testing samples: 2,000 data points

Let the learning-rate parameter of the LMS algorithm be annealed linearly from 0.6 down to 0.01.

(a) Construct the decision boundary computed for the "K-means, LMS" algorithm for the vertical separation between the two moons in Fig. 1.8 set at $d = -5$.

(b) Repeat the experiment for $d = -6$.

(c) Compare the classification results obtained using the "K-means, LMS" algorithm with those of the "K-means, RLS" algorithm studied in Section 5.8.

(d) Discuss how, in general, the complexity of the "K-means, LMS" algorithm compares with that of the "K-means, RLS" algorithm.

C H A P T E R   6

Support Vector Machines

ORGANIZATION OF THE CHAPTER

This chapter is devoted to the study of support vector machines: a machine-learning algorithm that is perhaps the most elegant of all kernel-learning methods. Following the introductory section, Section 6.1, the rest of the chapter is organized as follows:

1. Section 6.2 discusses the construction of an optimal hyperplane for the simple case of linearly separable patterns, which is followed by consideration of the more difficult case of nonseparable patterns in Section 6.3.

2. In Section 6.4, the idea of an inner-product kernel is introduced, thereby building the framework for viewing the learning algorithm involved in the construction of a support vector machine as a kernel method. In that section, we also introduce a widely used notion known as the "kernel trick." The design philosophy of a support vector machine is summed up in Section 6.5, followed by a revisitation of the XOR problem in Section 6.6. The second part of the chapter concludes with a computer experiment on pattern classification, presented in Section 6.7.

3. Section 6.8 introduces the concept of an ε-insensitive loss function, the use of which in solving regression problems is discussed in Section 6.9.

4. Section 6.10 deals with the representer theorem, which provides insight into the formulation of an approximating function in the context of Mercer's kernels.

The chapter concludes with a summary and discussion in Section 6.11.

6.1 INTRODUCTION

In Chapter 4, we studied multilayer perceptrons trained with the back-propagation algorithm. The desirable feature of this algorithm is its simplicity, but the algorithm converges slowly and lacks optimality. In Chapter 5, we studied another class of feedforward networks known as radial-basis function networks, which we developed from interpolation theory; we then described a suboptimal two-stage procedure for its design. In this chapter, we study another category of feedforward networks known collectively as *support vector machines* (SVMs).[1]

Basically, the support vector machine is a binary learning machine with some highly elegant properties. To explain how the machine works, it is perhaps easiest to start with the case of separable patterns that arise in the context of pattern classification. In this context, the main idea behind the machine may be summed up as follows:

Given a training sample, the support vector machine constructs a hyperplane as the decision surface in such a way that the margin of separation between positive and negative examples is maximized.

This basic idea is extended in a principled way to deal with the more difficult case of non-linearly separable patterns.

A notion that is central to the development of the support vector learning algorithm is the *inner-product kernel* between a "support vector" $\mathbf{x}_i$ and a vector $\mathbf{x}$ drawn from the input data space. Most importantly, the support vectors consist of a small subset of data points extracted by the learning algorithm from the training sample itself. Indeed, it is because of this central property that the learning algorithm, involved in the construction of a support vector machine, is also referred to as a *kernel method*. However, unlike the suboptimal kernel method described in Chapter 5, the kernel method basic to the design of a support vector machine is *optimal*, with the optimality being rooted in convex optimization. However, this highly desirable feature of the machine is achieved at the cost of increased computational complexity.

As with the design procedures discussed in Chapters 4 and 5, the support vector machine can be used to solve both pattern-classification and nonlinear-regression problems. However, it is in solving difficult pattern-classification problems where support vector machines have made their most significant impact.

6.2   OPTIMAL HYPERPLANE FOR LINEARLY SEPARABLE PATTERNS

Consider the training sample $\{(\mathbf{x}_i, d_i)\}_{i=1}^{N}$, where $\mathbf{x}_i$ *is* the input pattern for the ith example and d_i is the corresponding desired response (target output). To begin with, we assume that the pattern (class) represented by the subset $d_i = +1$ and the pattern represented by the subset $d_i = -1$ are "linearly separable." The equation of a decision surface in the form of a hyperplane that does the separation is

$$\mathbf{w}^T\mathbf{x} + b = 0 \tag{6.1}$$

where $\mathbf{x}$ is an input vector, $\mathbf{w}$ is an adjustable weight vector, and b is a bias. We may thus write

$$\begin{align}
\mathbf{w}^T\mathbf{x}_i + b \geq 0 \qquad & \text{for } d_i = +1 \\
\mathbf{w}^T\mathbf{x}_i + b < 0 \qquad & \text{for } d_i = -1
\end{align} \tag{6.2}$$

The assumption of linearly separable patterns is made here to explain the basic idea behind a support vector machine in a rather simple setting; this assumption will be relaxed in Section 6.3.

For a given weight vector $\mathbf{w}$ and bias b, the separation between the hyperplane defined in Eq. (6.1) and the closest data point is called the *margin of separation*, denoted by ρ. The goal of a support vector machine is to find the particular hyperplane for which the margin of separation, ρ, is maximized. Under this condition, the decision surface is referred to as the *optimal hyperplane*. Figure 6.1 illustrates the geometric construction of an optimal hyperplane for a two-dimensional input space.

Let $\mathbf{w}_o$ and b_o denote the optimum values of the weight vector and bias, respectively. Correspondingly, the *optimal hyperplane*, representing a multidimensional linear decision surface in the input space, is defined by

$$\mathbf{w}_o^T \mathbf{x} + b_o = 0 \tag{6.3}$$

which is a rewrite of Eq. (6.1). The discriminant function

$$g(\mathbf{x}) = \mathbf{w}_o^T \mathbf{x} + b_o \tag{6.4}$$

gives an algebraic measure of the *distance* from $\mathbf{x}$ to the optimal hyperplane (Duda and Hart, 1973). Perhaps the easiest way to see this is to express $\mathbf{x}$ as

$$\mathbf{x} = \mathbf{x}_p + r \frac{\mathbf{w}_o}{\|\mathbf{w}_o\|}$$

where $\mathbf{x}_p$ is the normal projection of $\mathbf{x}$ onto the optimal hyperplane and r is the desired algebraic distance; r is positive if $\mathbf{x}$ is on the positive side of the optimal hyperplane and negative if $\mathbf{x}$ is on the negative side. Since, by definition, $g(\mathbf{x}_p) = 0$, it follows that

$$g(\mathbf{x}) = \mathbf{w}_o^T \mathbf{x} + b_o = r\|\mathbf{w}_o\|$$

or, equivalently,

$$r = \frac{g(\mathbf{x})}{\|\mathbf{w}_o\|} \tag{6.5}$$

FIGURE 6.1 Illustration of the idea of an optimal hyperplane for linearly separable patterns: The data points shaded in red are support vectors.

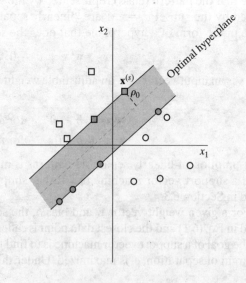

In particular, the distance from the origin (i.e., $\mathbf{x} = \mathbf{0}$) to the optimal hyperplane is given by $b_o/\|\mathbf{w}_o\|$. If $b_o > 0$, the origin is on the positive side of the optimal hyperplane; if $b_o < 0$, it is on the negative side. If $b_o = 0$, the optimal hyperplane passes through the origin. A geometric interpretation of these algebraic results is given in Fig. 6.2.

The issue at hand is to find the parameters $\mathbf{w}_o$ and b_o for the optimal hyperplane, given the training set $\mathcal{T} = \{(\mathbf{x}_i, d_i)\}$. In light of the results portrayed in Fig. 6.2, we see that the pair $(\mathbf{w}_o, b_o)$ must satisfy the following constraint:

$$\begin{aligned} \mathbf{w}_o^T \mathbf{x}_i + b_o \geq 1 && \text{for } d_i = +1 \\ \mathbf{w}_o^T \mathbf{x}_i + b_o \leq -1 && \text{for } d_i = -1 \end{aligned} \tag{6.6}$$

Note that if Eq. (6.2) holds—that is, if the patterns are linearly separable—we can always rescale $\mathbf{w}_o$ and b_o such that Eq. (6.6) holds; this scaling operation leaves Eq. (6.3) unaffected.

The particular data points $(\mathbf{x}_i, d_i)$ for which the first or second line of Eq. (6.6) is satisfied with the equality sign are called *support vectors*—hence the name "support vector machine." All the remaining examples in the training sample are completely irrelevant. Because of their distinct property, the support vectors play a prominent role in the operation of this class of learning machines. In conceptual terms, the support vectors are those data points that lie closest to the optimal hyperplane and are therefore the most difficult to classify. As such, they have a direct bearing on the optimum location of the decision surface.

Consider a support vector $\mathbf{x}^{(s)}$ for which $d^{(s)} = +1$. Then, by definition, we have

$$g(\mathbf{x}^{(s)}) = \mathbf{w}_o^T \mathbf{x}^{(s)} + b_o = \mp 1 \qquad \text{for } d^{(s)} = \mp 1 \tag{6.7}$$

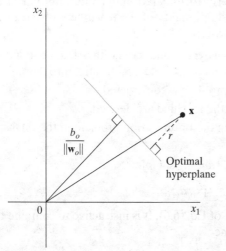

FIGURE 6.2   Geometric interpretation of algebraic distances of points to the optimal hyperplane for a two-dimensional case.

From Eq. (6.5), the *algebraic distance* from the support vector $\mathbf{x}^{(s)}$ to the optimal hyperplane is

$$r = \frac{g(\mathbf{x}^{(s)})}{\|\mathbf{w}_o\|}$$

$$= \begin{cases} \dfrac{1}{\|\mathbf{w}_o\|} & \text{if } d^{(s)} = +1 \\[2mm] -\dfrac{1}{\|\mathbf{w}_o\|} & \text{if } d^{(s)} = -1 \end{cases} \qquad (6.8)$$

where the plus sign indicates that $\mathbf{x}^{(s)}$ lies on the positive side of the optimal hyperplane and the minus sign indicates that $\mathbf{x}^{(s)}$ lies on the negative side of the optimal hyperplane. Let ρ denote the optimum value of the *margin of separation* between the two classes that constitute the training sample $\mathcal{T}$. Then, from Eq. (6.8), it follows that

$$\rho = 2r$$

$$= \frac{2}{\|\mathbf{w}_o\|} \qquad (6.9)$$

Equation (6.9) states the following:

> *Maximizing the margin of separation between binary classes is equivalent to minimizing the Euclidean norm of the weight vector* **w**.

In summary, the optimal hyperplane defined by Eq. (6.3) is *unique* in the sense that the optimum weight vector $\mathbf{w}_o$ provides the maximum possible separation between positive and negative examples. This optimum condition is attained by minimizing the Euclidean norm of the weight vector **w**.

Quadratic Optimization for Finding the Optimal Hyperplane

The support vector machine is cleverly formulated under the umbrella of *convex optimization*[2]—hence the well-defined optimality of the machine. In basic terms, the formulation proceeds along four major steps:

1. The problem of finding the optimal hyperplane starts with a statement of the problem in the primal weight space as a constrained-optimization problem.
2. The Lagrangian function of the problem is constructed.
3. The conditions for optimality of the machine are derived.
4. The stage is finally set for solving the optimization problem in the dual space of Lagrange multipliers.

To proceed then, we first note that the training sample

$$\mathcal{T} = \{\mathbf{x}_i, d_i\}_{i=1}^{N}$$

is embodied in the two-line constraint of Eq. (6.6). It is instructive to combine the two lines of this equation into the single line

$$d_i(\mathbf{w}^T\mathbf{x}_i + b) \geq 1 \qquad \text{for } i = 1, 2, ..., N \qquad (6.10)$$

With this form of the constraint at hand, we are now ready to formally state the constrained-optimization problem as follows:

Given the training sample $\{(\mathbf{x}_i, d_i)\}_{i=1}^N$, *find the optimum values of the weight vector* **w** *and bias b such that they satisfy the constraints*

$$d_i(\mathbf{w}^T\mathbf{x}_i + b) \geq 1 \qquad \text{for } i = 1, 2, ..., N$$

and the weight vector **w** *minimizes the cost function*

$$\Phi(\mathbf{w}) = \frac{1}{2}\mathbf{w}^T\mathbf{w}$$

The scaling factor $\frac{1}{2}$ is included here for convenience of presentation. This constrained-optimization problem is called the *primal problem*. It is basically characterized as follows:

- The cost function $\Phi(\mathbf{w})$ is a *convex* function of **w**.
- The constraints are *linear* in **w**.

Accordingly, we may solve the constrained-optimization problem by using the *method of Lagrange multipliers* (Bertsekas, 1995).

First, we construct the *Lagrangian function*

$$J(\mathbf{w}, b, \alpha) = \frac{1}{2}\mathbf{w}^T\mathbf{w} - \sum_{i=1}^N \alpha_i[d_i(\mathbf{w}^T\mathbf{x}_i + b) - 1] \tag{6.11}$$

where the auxiliary nonnegative variables α_i are called *Lagrange multipliers*. The solution to the constrained-optimization problem is determined by the *saddle point* of the Lagrangian function $J(\mathbf{w}, b, \alpha)$. A saddle point of a Lagrangian is a point where the roots are real, but of opposite signs; such a singularity is always unstable. The saddle point has to be *minimized* with respect to **w** and b; it also has to be *maximized* with respect to α. Thus, differentiating $J(\mathbf{w}, b, \alpha)$ with respect to **w** and b and setting the results equal to zero, we get the following two *conditions of optimality:*

$$\text{Condition 1:} \qquad \frac{\partial J(\mathbf{w}, b, \alpha)}{\partial \mathbf{w}} = \mathbf{0}$$

$$\text{Condition 2:} \qquad \frac{\partial J(\mathbf{w}, b, \alpha)}{\partial b} = 0$$

Application of optimality condition 1 to the Lagrangian function of Eq. (6.11) yields the following (after the rearrangement of terms):

$$\mathbf{w} = \sum_{i=1}^N \alpha_i d_i \mathbf{x}_i \tag{6.12}$$

Application of optimality condition 2 to the Lagrangian function of Eq. (6.11) yields

$$\sum_{i=1}^N \alpha_i d_i = 0 \tag{6.13}$$

The solution vector $\mathbf{w}$ is defined in terms of an expansion that involves the N training examples. Note, however, that although this solution is unique by virtue of the convexity of the Lagrangian, the same cannot be said about the Lagrange multipliers α_i.

It is also important to note that for all the constraints that are not satisfied as equalities, the corresponding multiplier α_i must be zero. In other words, only those multipliers that exactly satisfy the condition

$$\alpha_i[d_i(\mathbf{w}^T\mathbf{x}_i + b) - 1] = 0 \tag{6.14}$$

can assume nonzero values. This property is a statement of the *Karush–Kuhn–Tucker conditions*[3] (Fletcher, 1987; Bertsekas, 1995).

As noted earlier, the primal problem deals with a convex cost function and linear constraints. Given such a constrained-optimization problem, it is possible to construct another problem called the *dual problem*. This second problem has the same optimal value as the primal problem, but with the Lagrange multipliers providing the optimal solution. In particular, we may state the following *duality theorem* (Bertsekas, 1995):

(a) *If the primal problem has an optimal solution, the dual problem also has an optimal solution, and the corresponding optimal values are equal.*

(b) *In order for $\mathbf{w}_o$ to be an optimal primal solution and α_o to be an optimal dual solution, it is necessary and sufficient that $\mathbf{w}_o$ is feasible for the primal problem, and*

$$\Phi(\mathbf{w}_o) = J(\mathbf{w}_o, b_o, \alpha_o) = \min_{\mathbf{w}} J(\mathbf{w}, b, \alpha)$$

To postulate the dual problem for our primal problem, we first expand Eq. (6.11), term by term, obtaining

$$J(\mathbf{w}, b, \alpha) = \frac{1}{2}\mathbf{w}^T\mathbf{w} - \sum_{i=1}^{N}\alpha_i d_i\mathbf{w}^T\mathbf{x}_i - b\sum_{i=1}^{N}\alpha_i d_i + \sum_{i=1}^{N}\alpha_i \tag{6.15}$$

The third term on the right-hand side of Eq. (6.15) is zero by virtue of the optimality condition of Eq. (6.13). Furthermore, from Eq. (6.12), we have

$$\mathbf{w}^T\mathbf{w} = \sum_{i=1}^{N}\alpha_i d_i\mathbf{w}^T\mathbf{x}_i = \sum_{i=1}^{N}\sum_{j=1}^{N}\alpha_i\alpha_j d_i d_j\mathbf{x}_i^T\mathbf{x}_j$$

Accordingly, setting the objective function $J(\mathbf{w}, b, \alpha) = Q(\alpha)$, we may reformulate Eq. (6.15) as

$$Q(\alpha) = \sum_{i=1}^{N}\alpha_i - \frac{1}{2}\sum_{i=1}^{N}\sum_{j=1}^{N}\alpha_i\alpha_j d_i d_j\mathbf{x}_i^T\mathbf{x}_j \tag{6.16}$$

where the α_i are all nonnegative. Note that we have changed the notation from $J(\mathbf{w}, b, \alpha)$ to $Q(\alpha)$ so as to reflect the transformation from the primal optimization problem to its dual.

We may now state the dual problem as follows:

Given the training sample $\mathcal{T} = \{x_i, d_i\}_{i=1}^{N}$, find the Lagrange multipliers $\{\alpha_i\}_{i=1}^{N}$ that maximize the objective function

$$Q(\alpha) = \sum_{i=1}^{N} \alpha_i - \frac{1}{2} \sum_{i=1}^{N} \sum_{j=1}^{N} \alpha_i \alpha_j d_i d_j \mathbf{x}_i^T \mathbf{x}_j$$

subject to the constraints

(1) $\displaystyle\sum_{i=1}^{N} \alpha_i d_i = 0$

(2) $\alpha_i \geq 0$ for $i = 1, 2, ..., N$

Unlike the primal optimization problem based on the Lagrangian of Eq. (6.11), the dual problem defined in Eq. (6.16) is cast entirely in terms of the training data. Moreover, the function $Q(\alpha)$ to be maximized depends *only* on the input patterns in the form of a set of *dot products*

$$\{\mathbf{x}_i^T \mathbf{x}_j\}_{i,\,j=1}^{N}$$

Typically, the support vectors constitute a subset of the training sample, which means that the solution vector is *sparse*.[4] That is to say, constraint (2) of the dual problem is satisfied with the inequality sign for all the support vectors for which the α's are nonzero, and with the equality sign for all the other data points in the training sample, for which the α's are all zero. Accordingly, having determined the optimum Lagrange multipliers, denoted by $\alpha_{o,i}$, we may compute the optimum weight vector $\mathbf{w}_o$ by using Eq. (6.12) as

$$\mathbf{w}_o = \sum_{i=1}^{N_s} \alpha_{o,i} d_i \mathbf{x}_i \tag{6.17}$$

where N_s is the number of support vectors for which the Lagrange multipliers $\alpha_{o,i}$ are all nonzero. To compute the optimum bias b_o, we may use the $\mathbf{w}_o$ thus obtained and take advantage of Eq. (6.7), which pertains to a positive support vector:

$$b_o = 1 - \mathbf{w}_o^T \mathbf{x}^{(s)} \qquad \text{for } d^{(s)} = 1$$

$$= 1 - \sum_{i=1}^{N_s} \alpha_{o,i} d_i \mathbf{x}_i^T \mathbf{x}^{(s)} \tag{6.18}$$

Recall that the support vector $\mathbf{x}^{(s)}$ corresponds to any point $(\mathbf{x}_i, d_i)$ in the training sample for which the Lagrange multiplier $\alpha_{o,i}$ is nonzero. From a numerical (practical) perspective, it is better to average Eq. (6.18) over all the support vectors—that is, over all the nonzero Lagrange multipliers.

Statistical Properties of the Optimal Hyperplane

In a support vector machine, a structure is imposed on the set of separating hyperplanes by constraining the Euclidean norm of the weight vector $\mathbf{w}$. Specifically, we may state the following theorem (Vapnik, 1995, 1998):

Let D denote the diameter of the smallest ball containing all the input vectors $\mathbf{x}_1, \mathbf{x}_2, ..., \mathbf{x}_N$. The set of optimal hyperplanes described by the equation

$$\mathbf{w}_o^T \mathbf{x} + b_o = 0$$

has a VC dimension, h, bounded from above as

$$h \leq \min\left\{\left\lceil \frac{D^2}{\rho^2}\right\rceil, m_0\right\} + 1 \tag{6.19}$$

where the ceiling sign $\lceil \cdot \rceil$ *means the smallest integer greater than or equal to the number enclosed within the sign,* ρ *is the margin of separation equal to* $2/\|\mathbf{w}_o\|$, *and* m_0 *is the dimensionality of the input space.*

As mentioned previously in Chapter 4, the VC dimension, short for *Vapnik–Chervonenkis dimension*, provides a measure of the complexity of a space of functions. The theorem just stated tells us that we may exercise control over the VC dimension (i.e., complexity) of the optimal hyperplane, independently of the dimensionality m_0 of the input space, by properly choosing the margin of separation ρ.

Suppose, then, we have a nested structure made up of separating hyperplanes described by

$$S_k = \{\mathbf{w}^T\mathbf{x} + b: \|\mathbf{w}\|^2 \leq c_k\}, \qquad k = 1, 2, \ldots \tag{6.20}$$

By virtue of the upper bound on the VC dimension h defined in Eq. (6.19), the nested structure described in Eq. (6.20) may be reformulated in terms of the margin of separation in the equivalent form

$$S_k = \left\{\left\lceil \frac{r^2}{\rho^2}\right\rceil + 1: \rho^2 \geq a_k\right\}, \qquad k = 1, 2, \ldots \tag{6.21}$$

The a_k and c_k in Eqs. (6.20) and (6.21) are constants.

Equation (6.20) states that the optimal hyperplane is a hyperplane for which the margin of separation between the positive and negative examples is the largest possible. Equivalently, Eq. (6.21) states that construction of the optimal hyperplane is realized by making the squared Euclidean norm of the weight vector $\mathbf{w}$ the smallest possible. In a sense, these two equations reinforce the statement we made previously in light of Eq. (6.9).

6.3 OPTIMAL HYPERPLANE FOR NONSEPARABLE PATTERNS

The discussion thus far has focused on linearly separable patterns. In this section, we consider the more difficult case of nonseparable patterns. Given such a sample of training data, it is not possible to construct a separating hyperplane without encountering classification errors. Nevertheless, we would like to find an optimal hyperplane that minimizes the probability of classification error, averaged over the training sample.

The margin of separation between classes is said to be *soft* if a data point $(\mathbf{x}_i, d_i)$ violates the following condition (see Eq. (6.10)):

$$d_i(\mathbf{w}^T\mathbf{x}_i + b) \geq +1, \qquad i = 1, 2, \ldots, N$$

This violation can arise in one of two ways:

- The data point $(\mathbf{x}_i, d_i)$ falls inside the region of separation, but on the correct side of the decision surface, as illustrated in Fig. 6.3a.

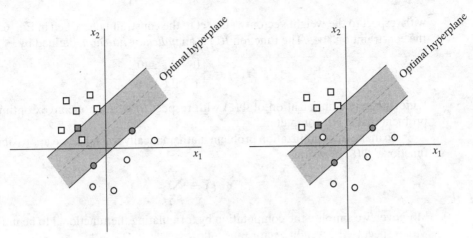

FIGURE 6.3   Soft margin hyperplane (a) Data point $\mathbf{x}_i$ (belonging to class $\mathscr{C}_1$, represented by a small square) falls inside the region of separation, but on the correct side of the decision surface. (b) Data point $\mathbf{x}_i$ (belonging to class $\mathscr{C}_2$, represented by a small circle) falls on the wrong side of the decision surface.

- The data point $(\mathbf{x}_i, d_i)$ falls on the wrong side of the decision surface, as illustrated in Fig. 6.3b.

Note that we have correct classification in the first case, but misclassification in the second.

To set the stage for a formal treatment of nonseparable data points, we introduce a new set of nonnegative scalar variables, $\{\xi_i\}_{i=1}^N$, into the definition of the separating hyperplane (i.e., decision surface), as shown here:

$$d_i(\mathbf{w}^T\mathbf{x}_i + b) \geq 1 - \xi_i, \qquad i = 1, 2, ..., N \qquad (6.22)$$

The ξ_i are called *slack variables*; they measure the deviation of a data point from the ideal condition of pattern separability. For $0 < \xi_i \leq 1$, the data point falls inside the region of separation, but on the correct side of the decision surface, as illustrated in Fig. 6.3a. For $\xi_i > 1$, it falls on the wrong side of the separating hyperplane, as illustrated in Fig. 6.3b. The support vectors are those particular data points that satisfy Eq. (6.22) precisely even if $\xi_i > 0$. Moreover, there can be support vectors satisfying the condition $\xi_i = 0$. Note that if an example with $\xi_i > 0$ is left out of the training sample, the decision surface will change. The support vectors are thus defined in exactly the same way for both linearly separable and nonseparable cases.

Our goal is to find a separating hyperplane for which the misclassification error, averaged over the training sample, is minimized. We may do this by minimizing the functional

$$\Phi(\xi) = \sum_{i=1}^{N} I(\xi_i - 1)$$

with respect to the weight vector $\mathbf{w}$, subject to the constraint described in Eq. (6.22) and the constraint on $\|\mathbf{w}\|^2$. The function $I(\xi)$ is an *indicator function*, defined by

$$I(\xi) = \begin{cases} 0 & \text{if } \xi \leq 0 \\ 1 & \text{if } \xi > 0 \end{cases}$$

Unfortunately, minimization of $\Phi(\xi)$ with respect to $\mathbf{w}$ is a nonconvex optimization problem that is NP complete.[5]

To make the optimization problem mathematically tractable, we approximate the functional $\Phi(\xi)$ by writing

$$\Phi(\xi) = \sum_{i=1}^{N} \xi_i$$

Moreover, we simplify the computation by formulating the functional to be minimized with respect to the weight vector $\mathbf{w}$ as follows:

$$\Phi(\mathbf{w}, \xi) = \frac{1}{2}\mathbf{w}^T\mathbf{w} + C \sum_{i=1}^{N} \xi_i \tag{6.23}$$

As before, minimizing the first term in Eq. (6.23) is related to the support vector machine. As for the second term, $\sum_i \xi_i$, it is an upper bound on the number of test errors.

The parameter C controls the tradeoff between complexity of the machine and the number of nonseparable points; it may therefore be viewed as the *reciprocal* of a parameter commonly referred to as the "regularization" parameter.[6] When the parameter C is assigned a large value, the implication is that the designer of the support vector machine has high confidence in the quality of the training sample $\mathcal{T}$. Conversely, when C is assigned a small value, the training sample $\mathcal{T}$ is considered to be noisy, and less emphasis should therefore be placed on it.

In any event, the parameter C has to be selected by the user. It may be determined *experimentally* via the standard use of a training (validation) sample, which is a crude form of resampling; the use of cross-validation for optimum selection of regularization parameter (i.e., $1/C$) is discussed in Chapter 7.

In any event, the functional $\Phi(\mathbf{w}, \xi)$ is optimized with respect to $\mathbf{w}$ and $\{\xi_i\}_{i=1}^{N}$, subject to the constraint described in Eq. (6.22), and $\xi_i \geq 0$. In so doing, the squared norm of $\mathbf{w}$ is treated as a quantity to be jointly minimized with respect to the nonseparable points rather than as a constraint imposed on the minimization of the number of nonseparable points.

The optimization problem for nonseparable patterns just stated includes the optimization problem for linearly separable patterns as a special case. Specifically, setting $\xi_i = 0$ for all i in both Eqs. (6.22) and (6.23) reduces them to the corresponding forms for the linearly separable case.

We may now formally state the primal problem for the nonseparable case as follows:

Given the training sample $\{(\mathbf{x}_i, d_i)\}_{i=1}^{N}$, find the optimum values of the weight vector $\mathbf{w}$ and bias b such that they satisfy the constraint

$$d_i(\mathbf{w}^T\mathbf{x}_i + b) \geq 1 - \xi_i \qquad \text{for } i = 1, 2, ..., N \tag{6.24}$$

$$\xi_i \geq 0 \qquad \text{for all } i \tag{6.25}$$

and such that the weight vector **w** *and the slack variables* ξ_i *minimize the cost functional*

$$\Phi(\mathbf{w}, \xi) = \frac{1}{2}\mathbf{w}^T\mathbf{w} + C\sum_{i=1}^{N}\xi_i \tag{6.26}$$

where C is a user-specified positive parameter.

Using the method of Lagrange multipliers and proceeding in a manner similar to that described in Section 6.2, we may formulate the dual problem for nonseparable patterns as follows (see Problem 6.3):

> *Given the training sample* $\{(\mathbf{x}_i, d_i)\}_{i=1}^{N}$, *find the Lagrange multipliers* $\{\alpha_i\}_{i=1}^{N}$ *that maximize the objective function*

$$Q(\alpha) = \sum_{i=1}^{N}\alpha_i - \frac{1}{2}\sum_{i=1}^{N}\sum_{j=1}^{N}\alpha_i\alpha_j d_i d_j \mathbf{x}_i^T\mathbf{x}_j \tag{6.27}$$

> *subject to the constraints*

> (1) $\displaystyle\sum_{i=1}^{N}\alpha_i d_i = 0$

> (2) $0 \le \alpha_i \le C$ for $i = 1, 2, ..., N$

where C is a user-specified positive parameter.

Note that neither the slack variables ξ_i nor their own Lagrange multipliers appear in the dual problem. The dual problem for the case of nonseparable patterns is thus similar to that for the simple case of linearly separable patterns, except for a minor, but important, difference. The objective function $Q(\alpha)$ to be maximized is the same in both cases. The nonseparable case differs from the separable case in that the constraint $\alpha_i \ge 0$ is replaced with the more stringent constraint $0 \le \alpha_i \le C$. Except for this modification, the constrained optimization for the nonseparable case and computations of the optimum values of the weight vector **w** and bias b proceed in the same way as in the linearly separable case. Note also that the support vectors are defined in exactly the same way as before.

Unbounded Support Vectors

For a prescribed parameter C, a data point $(\mathbf{x}_i, d_i)$ for which the condition $0 < \alpha_i < C$ holds is said to be an *unbounded*, or *free support vector*. When $\alpha_i = C$, we find that

$$d_i F(\mathbf{x}_i) \le 1, \qquad \alpha_i = C$$

where $F(\mathbf{x}_i)$ is the approximating function realized by the support vector machine for the input $\mathbf{x}_i$. On the other hand, when $\alpha_i = 0$, we find that

$$d_i F(\mathbf{x}_i) \ge 1, \qquad \alpha_i = 0$$

In light of these two arguments, it follows that for unbounded support vectors, we have

$$d_i F(\mathbf{x}_i) = 1$$

Unfortunately, the converse argument does not hold; that is, even if we know that $d_i F(\mathbf{x}_i) = 1$ for a particular data point $(\mathbf{x}_i, d_i)$, this condition does not necessarily tell us anything about the corresponding Lagrange multiplier α_i.

Consequently, there is a distinct possibility of degeneracy (i.e., reduced optimality conditions) in the solution to a pattern-classification problem computed by the support vector machine. By this statement, we mean that a point $(\mathbf{x}_i, d_i)$ that satisfies the margin requirement exactly has no constraint on the possible value of the associated α_i.

In Rifkin (2002), it is argued that the number of unbounded support vectors is the primary reason for how difficult, in a computational sense, the training of a support vector machine can be.

Underlying Philosophy of a Support Vector Machine for Pattern Classification

With the material on how to find the optimal hyperplane for nonseparable patterns at hand, we are now in a position to formally describe the construction of a support vector machine for a pattern-recognition task.

Basically, the idea of a support vector machine hinges on two mathematical operations summarized here and illustrated in Fig. 6.4:

1. nonlinear mapping of an input vector into a high-dimensional feature space that is hidden from both the input and output;

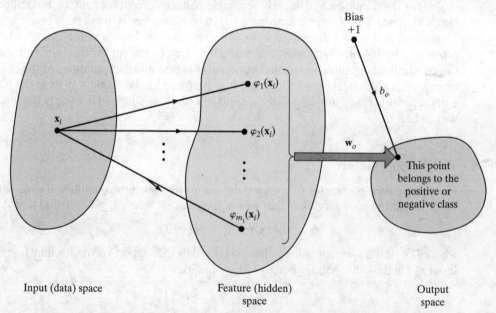

FIGURE 6.4 Illustrating the two mappings in a support vector machine for pattern classification: (i) nonlinear mapping from the input space to the feature space; (ii) linear mapping from the feature space to the output space.

2. construction of an optimal hyperplane for separating the features discovered in step 1.

The rationale for each of these two operations is explained in the upcoming text.

One last important comment is in order. The number of features constituting the hidden space in Fig. 6.4 is determined by the number of support vectors. Thus, SVM theory provides an analytic approach for determining the optimum size of the feature (hidden) space, thereby assuring optimality of the classification task.

6.4   THE SUPPORT VECTOR MACHINE VIEWED AS A KERNEL MACHINE

Inner-Product Kernel

Let $\mathbf{x}$ denote a vector drawn from the input space of dimension m_0. Let $\{\varphi_j(\mathbf{x})\}_{j=1}^{\infty}$ denote a set of nonlinear functions that, between them, transform the input space of dimension m_0 to a feature space of infinite dimensionality. Given this transformation, we may define a hyperplane acting as the decision surface in accordance with the formula

$$\sum_{j=1}^{\infty} w_j \varphi_j(\mathbf{x}) = 0 \qquad (6.28)$$

where $\{w_j\}_{j=1}^{\infty}$ denotes an infinitely large set of weights that transforms the feature space to the output space. It is in the output space where the decision is made on whether the input vector $\mathbf{x}$ belongs to one of two possible classes, positive or negative. For convenience of presentation, we have set the bias to zero in Eq. (6.28). Using matrix notation, we may rewrite this equation in the compact form

$$\mathbf{w}^T \boldsymbol{\phi}(\mathbf{x}) = 0 \qquad (6.29)$$

where $\boldsymbol{\phi}(\mathbf{x})$ is the *feature vector* and $\mathbf{w}$ is the corresponding *weight vector*.

As in Section 6.3, we seek "linear separability of the transformed patterns" in the feature space. With this objective in mind, we may adapt Eq. (6.17) to our present situation by expressing the weight vector as

$$\mathbf{w} = \sum_{i=1}^{N_s} \alpha_i d_i \boldsymbol{\phi}(\mathbf{x}_i) \qquad (6.30)$$

where the feature vector is expressed as

$$\boldsymbol{\phi}(\mathbf{x}_i) = [\varphi_1(\mathbf{x}_i), \varphi_2(\mathbf{x}_i), ...]^T \qquad (6.31)$$

and N_s is the number of support vectors. Hence, substituting Eq. (6.29) into Eq. (6.30), we may express the decision surface in the output space as

$$\sum_{i=1}^{N_s} \alpha_i d_i \boldsymbol{\phi}^T(\mathbf{x}_i) \boldsymbol{\phi}(\mathbf{x}) = 0 \qquad (6.32)$$

We now immediately see that the scalar term $\boldsymbol{\phi}^T(\mathbf{x}_i)\boldsymbol{\phi}(\mathbf{x})$ in Eq. (6.32) represents an *inner product*. Accordingly, let this inner-product term be denoted as the scalar

$$k(\mathbf{x}, \mathbf{x}_i) = \boldsymbol{\phi}^T(\mathbf{x}_i)\boldsymbol{\phi}(\mathbf{x})$$
$$= \sum_{j=1}^{\infty} \varphi_j(\mathbf{x}_i)\varphi_j(\mathbf{x}), \quad i = 1, 2, ..., N_s \tag{6.33}$$

Correspondingly, we may express the optimal decision surface (hyperplane) in the output space as

$$\sum_{i=1}^{N_s} \alpha_i d_i k(\mathbf{x}, \mathbf{x}_i) = 0 \tag{6.34}$$

The function $k(\mathbf{x}, \mathbf{x}_i)$ is called the *inner-product kernel*,[7] or simply the *kernel*, which is formally defined as follows (Shawe-Taylor and Cristianini, 2004):

> *The kernel $k(\mathbf{x}, \mathbf{x}_i)$ is a function that computes the inner product of the images produced in the feature space under the embedding $\boldsymbol{\phi}$ of two data points in the input space.*

Following the definition of a kernel introduced in Chapter 5, we may state that the kernel $k(\mathbf{x}, \mathbf{x}_i)$ is a function that has two basic properties[8]:

> *Property 1. The function $k(\mathbf{x}, \mathbf{x}_i)$ is symmetric about the center point $\mathbf{x}_i$, that is,*

$$k(\mathbf{x}, \mathbf{x}_i) = k(\mathbf{x}_i, \mathbf{x}) \quad \text{for all } \mathbf{x}_i$$

and it attains its maximum value at the point $\mathbf{x} = \mathbf{x}_i$.

Note, however, that the maximum need not exist; for example, $k(\mathbf{x}, \mathbf{x}_i) = \mathbf{x}^T\mathbf{x}_i$, as a kernel does not have a maximum.

> *Property 2. The total volume under the surface of the function $k(\mathbf{x}, \mathbf{x}_i)$ is a constant.*

If the kernel $k(\mathbf{x}, \mathbf{x}_i)$ is appropriately scaled to make the constant under property 2 equal to unity, then it will have properties similar to those of the probability density function of a random variable.

The Kernel Trick

Examining Eq. (6.34), we may now make two important observations:

1. Insofar as pattern classification in the output space is concerned, specifying the kernel $k(\mathbf{x}, \mathbf{x}_i)$ is *sufficient*; in other words, we need never explicitly compute the weight vector $\mathbf{w}_o$; it is for this reason that the application of Eq. (6.33) is commonly referred to as the *kernel trick*.
2. Even though we assumed that the feature space could be of infinite dimensionality, the linear equation of Eq. (6.34), defining the optimal hyperplane, consists of a *finite* number of terms that is equal to the number of training patterns used in the classifier.

It is in light of observation 1 that the support vector machine is also referred to as a *kernel machine*. For pattern classification, the machine is parameterized by an N-dimensional vector whose ith term is defined by the product $\alpha_i d_i$ for $i = 1, 2, ..., N$.

We may view $k(\mathbf{x}_i, \mathbf{x}_j)$ as the ij-th element of the symmetric N-by-N matrix

$$\mathbf{K} = \{k(\mathbf{x}_i, \mathbf{x}_j)\}_{i,\,j=1}^{N} \tag{6.35}$$

The matrix $\mathbf{K}$ is a nonnegative definite matrix called the *kernel matrix*; it is also referred to simply as the *Gram*. It is nonnegative definite or positive semidefinite in that it satisfies the condition

$$\mathbf{a}^T \mathbf{K} \mathbf{a} \geq 0$$

for any real-valued vector $\mathbf{a}$ whose dimension is compatible with that of $\mathbf{K}$.

Mercer's Theorem

The expansion of Eq. (6.33) for the symmetric kernel $k(\mathbf{x}, \mathbf{x}_i)$ is an important special case of *Mercer's theorem* that arises in functional analysis. This theorem may be formally stated as follows (Mercer, 1909; Courant and Hilbert, 1970):

Let $k(\mathbf{x}, \mathbf{x}')$ be a continuous symmetric kernel that is defined in the closed interval $\mathbf{a} \leq \mathbf{x} \leq \mathbf{b}$, *and likewise for $\mathbf{x}'$. The kernel $k(\mathbf{x}, \mathbf{x}')$ can be expanded in the series*

$$k(\mathbf{x}, \mathbf{x}') = \sum_{i=1}^{\infty} \lambda_i \varphi_i(\mathbf{x}) \varphi_i(\mathbf{x}') \tag{6.36}$$

with positive coefficients $\lambda_i > 0$ for all i. For this expansion to be valid and for it to converge absolutely and uniformly, it is necessary and sufficient that the condition

$$\int_b^a \int_b^a k(\mathbf{x}, \mathbf{x}') \psi(\mathbf{x}) \psi(\mathbf{x}') d\mathbf{x} d\mathbf{x}' \geq 0 \tag{6.37}$$

holds for all $\psi(\cdot)$, for which we have

$$\int_b^a \psi^2(\mathbf{x}) d\mathbf{x} < \infty \tag{6.38}$$

where $\mathbf{a}$ and $\mathbf{b}$ are the constants of integretion.

The features $\varphi_i(\mathbf{x})$ are called *eigenfunctions* of the expansion, and the numbers λ_i are called *eigenvalues*. The fact that all of the eigenvalues are positive means that the kernel $k(\mathbf{x}, \mathbf{x}')$ is *positive definite*. This property, in turn, means that we have a complex problem that can be solved efficiently for the weight vector $\mathbf{w}$, as discussed next.

Note, however, that Mercer's theorem tells us only whether a candidate kernel is actually an inner-product kernel in some space and therefore admissible for use in a support vector machine. It says nothing about how to construct the functions $\varphi_i(\mathbf{x})$; we have to do that ourselves. Nevertheless, Mercer's theorem is important because it places a limit on the number of admissible kernels. Note also that the expansion of Eq. (6.33) is a special case of Mercer's theorem, since all the eigenvalues of this expansion are unity. It is for this reason that an inner-product kernel is also referred to as a *Mercer kernel*.

6.5 DESIGN OF SUPPORT VECTOR MACHINES

The expansion of the kernel $k(\mathbf{x}, \mathbf{x}_i)$ in Eq. (6.33) permits us to construct a decision surface that is nonlinear in the input space, but whose image in the feature space is linear. With this expansion at hand, we may now state the dual form for the constrained optimization of a support vector machine as follows:

Given the training sample $\{(\mathbf{x}_i, d_i)\}_{i=1}^{N}$, find the Lagrange multipliers $\{\alpha_i\}_{i=1}^{N}$ that maximize the objective function

$$Q(\alpha) = \sum_{i=1}^{N} \alpha_i - \frac{1}{2}\sum_{i=1}^{N}\sum_{j=1}^{N} \alpha_i\alpha_j d_i d_j k(\mathbf{x}_i, \mathbf{x}_j) \tag{6.39}$$

subject to the constraints

$$(1)\quad \sum_{i=1}^{N} \alpha_i d_i = 0$$

$$(2)\quad 0 \le \alpha_i \le C \qquad \text{for } i = 1, 2, ..., N$$

where C is a user-specified positive parameter.

Constraint (1) arises from optimization of the Lagrangian $Q(\alpha)$ with respect to the bias b, which is a rewrite of Eq. (6.13). The dual problem just stated is of the same form as that for the case of nonseparable patterns considered in Section 6.3, except for the fact that the inner product $\mathbf{x}_i^T\mathbf{x}_j$ has been replaced by the Mercer kernel $k(\mathbf{x}, \mathbf{x}_i)$.

Examples of Support Vector Machines

The requirement on the kernel $k(\mathbf{x}, \mathbf{x}_i)$ is to satisfy Mercer's theorem. Within this requirement, there is some freedom in how the kernel is chosen. In Table 6.1, we summarize the kernels for three common types of support vector machines: polynomial learning machine, radial-basis-function network, and two-layer perceptron. The following points are noteworthy:

1. The Mercer kernels for polynomial and radial-basis-function types of support vector machines always satisfy Mercer's theorem. In contrast, the Mercer kernel for

TABLE 6.1 Summary of Mercer Kernels

Type of support vector machine	Mercer kernel $k(\mathbf{x}, \mathbf{x}_i), i = 1, 2, ..., N$	Comments
Polynomial learning machine	$(\mathbf{x}^T\mathbf{x}_i + 1)^p$	Power p is specified *a priori* by the user
Radial-basis-function network	$\exp\left(-\dfrac{1}{2\sigma^2}\|\mathbf{x} - \mathbf{x}_i\|^2\right)$	The width σ^2, common to all the kernels, is specified *a priori* by the user
Two-layer perceptron	$\tanh(\beta_0\mathbf{x}^T\mathbf{x}_i + \beta_1)$	Mercer's theorem is satisfied only for some values of β_0 and β_1

a two-layer perceptron type of support vector machine is somewhat restricted, as indicated in the last row of Table 6.1. This latter entry is a testament to the fact that the determination of whether a given kernel satisfies Mercer's theorem can indeed be a difficult matter.

2. For all three machine types, the dimensionality of the feature space is determined by the number of support vectors extracted from the training data by the solution to the constrained-optimization problem.

3. The underlying theory of a support vector machine avoids the need for heuristics often used in the design of conventional radial-basis-function networks and multilayer perceptrons.

4. In the radial-basis-function type of a support vector machine, the number of radial-basis functions and their centers are determined automatically by the number of support vectors and their values, respectively.

Figure 6.5 displays the architecture of a support vector machine, where m_1 denotes the size of the hidden layer (i.e., feature space).

Regardless of how a support vector machine is implemented, it differs from the conventional approach to the design of a multilayer perceptron in a fundamental way. In the conventional approach, model complexity is controlled by keeping the number of features (i.e., hidden neurons) small. On the other hand, the support vector machine offers a solution to the design of a learning machine by controlling model complexity independently of dimensionality, as summarized here (Vapnik, 1998; Schölkopf and Smola, 2002):

- *Conceptual problem.* Dimensionality of the feature (hidden) space is purposely made very large to enable the construction of a decision surface in the form of a

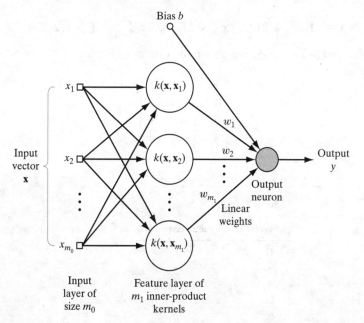

FIGURE 6.5
Architecture of support vector machine, using a radial-basis function network.

Bias b

x_1

$k(\mathbf{x}, \mathbf{x}_1)$

w_1

Input
vector
$\mathbf{x}$

x_2

$k(\mathbf{x}, \mathbf{x}_2)$

w_2

Output
y

w_{m_1}

Output
neuron

Linear
weights

x_{m_0}

$k(\mathbf{x}, \mathbf{x}_{m_1})$

Input
layer of
size m_0

Feature layer of
m_1 inner-product
kernels

hyperplane in that space. For good generalization performance, the model complexity is controlled by imposing certain constraints on the construction of the separating soft-margin hyperplane, which results in the extraction of a fraction of the training data as support vectors.

- *Computational problem.* The need to compute the weight vector and the bias in the output layer of the RBF network is avoided by using the kernel trick.

6.6   XOR PROBLEM

To illustrate the procedure for the design of a support vector machine, we revisit the XOR (Exclusive OR) problem discussed in Chapters 4 and 5. Table 6.2 presents a summary of the input vectors and desired responses for the four possible states.

To proceed, define the following kernel (Cherkassky and Mulier, 1998):

$$k(\mathbf{x}, \mathbf{x}_i) = (1 + \mathbf{x}^T\mathbf{x}_i)^2 \tag{6.40}$$

With $\mathbf{x} = [x_1, x_2]^T$ and $\mathbf{x}_i = [x_{i1}, x_{i2}]^T$, we may thus express the kernel $k(\mathbf{x}, \mathbf{x}_i)$ in terms of *monomials* of various orders as follows:

$$k(\mathbf{x}, \mathbf{x}_i) = 1 + x_1^2 x_{i1}^2 + 2x_1 x_2 x_{i1} x_{i2} + x_2^2 x_{i2}^2 + 2x_1 x_{i1} + 2x_2 x_{i2} \tag{6.41}$$

The image of the input vector $\mathbf{x}$ induced in the feature space is therefore deduced to be

$$\boldsymbol{\phi}(\mathbf{x}) = [1, x_1^2, \sqrt{2}x_1 x_2, x_2^2, \sqrt{2}x_1, \sqrt{2}x_2]^T$$

Similarly,

$$\boldsymbol{\phi}(\mathbf{x}_i) = [1, x_{i1}^2, \sqrt{2}x_{i1}x_{i2}, x_{i2}^2, \sqrt{2}x_{i1}, \sqrt{2}x_{i2}]^T, \qquad i = 1, 2, 3, 4 \tag{6.42}$$

Using the definition of Eq. (6.35), we obtain the Gram

$$\mathbf{K} = \begin{bmatrix} 9 & 1 & 1 & 1 \\ 1 & 9 & 1 & 1 \\ 1 & 1 & 9 & 1 \\ 1 & 1 & 1 & 9 \end{bmatrix}$$

TABLE 6.2   XOR Problem

Input vector x	Desired response d
(−1, −1)	−1
(−1, +1)	+1
(+1, −1)	+1
(+1, +1)	−1

The objective function for the dual form of optimization is therefore as follows (see Eq. (6.39)):

$$Q(\alpha) = \alpha_1 + \alpha_2 + \alpha_3 + \alpha_4 - \frac{1}{2}(9\alpha_1^2 - 2\alpha_1\alpha_2 - 2\alpha_1\alpha_3 + 2\alpha_1\alpha_4$$
$$+ 9\alpha_2^2 + 2\alpha_2\alpha_3 - 2\alpha_2\alpha_4 + 9\alpha_3^2 - 2\alpha_3\alpha_4 + 9\alpha_4^2)$$

(6.43)

Optimizing $Q(\alpha)$ with respect to the four Lagrange multipliers yields the following set of simultaneous equations:

$$\begin{aligned}
9\alpha_1 - \alpha_2 - \alpha_3 + \alpha_4 &= 1 \\
-\alpha_1 + 9\alpha_2 + \alpha_3 - \alpha_4 &= 1 \\
-\alpha_1 + \alpha_2 + 9\alpha_3 - \alpha_4 &= 1 \\
\alpha_1 - \alpha_2 - \alpha_3 + 9\alpha_4 &= 1
\end{aligned}$$

Hence, the optimum values of the Lagrange multipliers are

$$\alpha_{o,1} = \alpha_{o,2} = \alpha_{o,3} = \alpha_{o,4} = \frac{1}{8}$$

This result indicates that in this example, all four input vectors $\{\mathbf{x}_i\}_{i=1}^4$ are support vectors. The optimum value of $Q(\alpha)$ is

$$Q_o(\alpha) = \frac{1}{4}$$

Correspondingly, we may write

$$\frac{1}{2}\|\mathbf{w}_o\|^2 = \frac{1}{4}$$

or

$$\|\mathbf{w}_o\| = \frac{1}{\sqrt{2}}$$

From Eq. (6.30), we find that the optimum weight vector is

$$\mathbf{w}_o = \frac{1}{8}[-\varphi(\mathbf{x}_1) + \varphi(\mathbf{x}_2) + \varphi(\mathbf{x}_3) - \varphi(\mathbf{x}_4)]$$

$$= \frac{1}{8}\left[-\begin{bmatrix} 1 \\ 1 \\ \sqrt{2} \\ 1 \\ -\sqrt{2} \\ -\sqrt{2} \end{bmatrix} + \begin{bmatrix} 1 \\ 1 \\ -\sqrt{2} \\ 1 \\ -\sqrt{2} \\ \sqrt{2} \end{bmatrix} + \begin{bmatrix} 1 \\ 1 \\ -\sqrt{2} \\ 1 \\ \sqrt{2} \\ -\sqrt{2} \end{bmatrix} - \begin{bmatrix} 1 \\ 1 \\ \sqrt{2} \\ 1 \\ \sqrt{2} \\ \sqrt{2} \end{bmatrix} \right]$$

$$
= \begin{bmatrix} 0 \\ 0 \\ -1/\sqrt{2} \\ 0 \\ 0 \\ 0 \end{bmatrix}
$$

The first element of $\mathbf{w}_o$ indicates that the bias b is zero.

The optimal hyperplane is defined by

$$\mathbf{w}_o^T \boldsymbol{\phi}(\mathbf{x}) = 0$$

Expanding the inner product $\mathbf{w}_o^T \boldsymbol{\phi}(\mathbf{x})$ yields:

$$
\begin{bmatrix} 0, 0, \dfrac{-1}{\sqrt{2}}, 0, 0, 0 \end{bmatrix}
\begin{bmatrix} 1 \\ x_1^2 \\ \sqrt{2}x_1 x_2 \\ x_2^2 \\ \sqrt{2}x_1 \\ \sqrt{2}x_2 \end{bmatrix} = 0
$$

which reduces to

$$- x_1 x_2 = 0$$

The polynomial form of support vector machine for the XOR problem is therefore as shown in Fig. 6.6a. For both $x_1 = x_2 = -1$ and $x_1 = x_2 = +1$, the output $y = -1$, and for both $x_1 = -1, x_2 = +1$ and $x_1 = +1$ and $x_2 = -1$, we have $y = +1$. Thus, the XOR problem is solved as indicated in Fig. 6.6b.

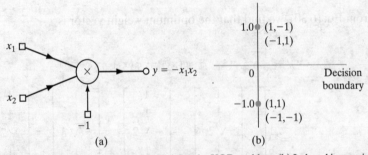

(a)   (b)

FIGURE 6.6   (a) Polynomial machine for solving the XOR problem. (b) Induced images in the feature space due to the four data points of the XOR problem.

6.7   COMPUTER EXPERIMENT: PATTERN CLASSIFICATION

In this section, we continue the sequence of pattern-classification experiments based on the double-moon problem depicted in Fig. 1.8. This time, we use the nonlinear support vector machine with a single hidden layer. The experiment was repeated for two different settings of the vertical separation between the two moons of Fig. 1.8, namely, $d = -6.0$ and $d = -6.5$. The parameter C was set equal to infinity for both parts of the experiment. The training sample consisted of 300 data points, and the test sample consisted of 2,000 data points. The training data were preprocessed in the same manner as described in Section 1.5.

The scenario corresponding to the distance $d = -6.0$ was chosen for the first part of the experiment so as to provide an illustrative way of comparing the SVM with the "K-means, RLS" algorithm used to train the RBF network in Chapter 5, for which a small number of classification errors was reported. Figure 6.7 presents the corresponding results of the experiment using the SVM with $d = -6.0$. Part (a) of the figure presents the training result, displaying the support vectors and the optimal decision boundary computed by the algorithm. For this part of the experiment, there were no classification errors when the machine was tested with data not seen before, as shown in part (b) of the figure.

Figure 6.8 presents the results of the second part of the experiment, which used the SVM for a more difficult scenario for which the vertical separation between the two moons was reduced to $d = -6.5$. Once again, part (a) of the figure presents the training result, showing the support vectors and the decision boundary computed by the algorithm. Part (b) of the figure shows the corresponding test result. This time, there were 11 classification errors in the test sample of 2,000 data points, representing a classification error of 0.55%.

As already stated, both parts of the experiment were performed using the common value $C = \infty$. In this context, the following two points are noteworthy:

1. For $d = -6.0$, the two moons are perfectly nonlinearly separable; this observation is confirmed by the complete absence of classification errors on test data, as demonstrated in Fig. 6.7b.
2. For $d = -6.5$, the two moons of Fig. 1.8 overlap slightly. Consequently, they are no longer separable, which is confirmed by the small number of classification errors that were found on test data in Fig. 6.8b. In this second part of the experiment, no attempt was made to find the optimal value of parameter C so as to minimize the classification error rate; this issue is addressed in Problem 6.24.

6.8   REGRESSION: ROBUSTNESS CONSIDERATIONS

Up to this point in the chapter, we have focused attention on the use of support vector machines for solving pattern-recognition problems. In this section, we prepare the stage for studying the use of support vector machines to solve regression problems. To do this, we will first address the issue of a suitable optimization criterion with *robustness* as a primary objective. With this objective in mind, we need a model that is insensitive to small changes in the model parameters, which is addressed next.

Classification using SVM with distance = −6, radius = 10, and width = 6

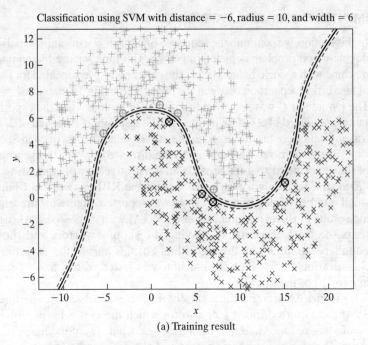

(a) Training result

Classification using SVM with distance = −6, radius = 10, and width = 6 .

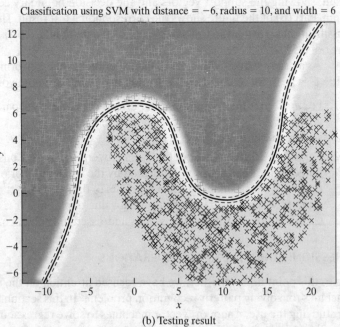

(b) Testing result

FIGURE 6.7   Experiment on SVM for the double-moon of Fig. 1.8 with distance $d = -6$.

Classification using SVM with distance $= -6.5$, radius $= 10$, and width $= 6$

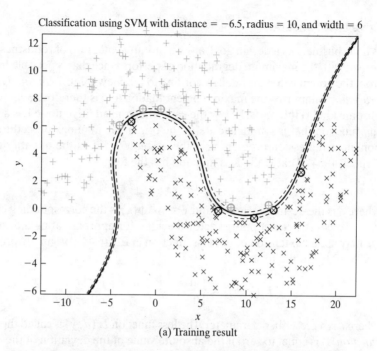

(a) Training result

Classification using SVM with distance $= -6.5$, radius $= 10$, and width $= 6$

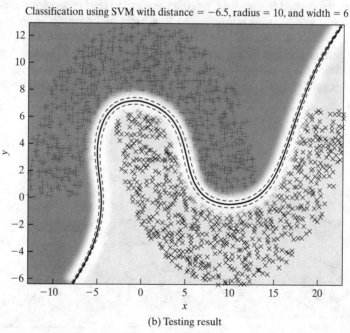

(b) Testing result

FIGURE 6.8   Experiment on SVM for the double-moon of Fig. 1.8 with distance $d = -6.5$.

ε-Insensitive Loss Function

With robustness as a design goal, any quantitative measure of robustness should be concerned with the maximum degradation of performance that is possible for an ε-deviation from the nominal noise model. According to this viewpoint, an *optimal robust estimation procedure* minimizes the maximum degradation and is therefore a *minimax* procedure[9] of some kind (Huber, 1981). For the case when the additive noise has a probability density function that is symmetric about the origin, the minimax procedure for solving the nonlinear regression problem uses the absolute error as the quantity to be minimized (Huber, 1964). That is, the loss function has the form

$$L(d, y) = |d - y| \tag{6.44}$$

where d is the desired response and $y = \mathbf{w}^T \boldsymbol{\phi}(\mathbf{x})$ is the corresponding estimator output.

To construct a support vector machine for approximating a desired response d, we may use an extension of the loss function in Eq. (6.44), originally proposed in Vapnik (1995, 1998), in the form

$$L_\varepsilon(d, y) = \begin{cases} |d - y| - \varepsilon & \text{for } |d - y| \ge \varepsilon \\ 0 & \text{otherwise} \end{cases} \tag{6.45}$$

where ε is a prescribed parameter. The loss function $L_\varepsilon(d, y)$ is called the *ε-insensitive loss function*. It is equal to zero if the absolute value of the deviation of the estimator output y from the desired response d is less than or equal to zero; otherwise, it is equal to the absolute value of the deviation minus ε. The loss function of Eq. (6.44) is a special case of the ε-insensitive loss function for $\varepsilon = 0$. Parts a and b of Figure 6.9 illustrate the *ε-insensitive tube* and the corresponding dependence of the loss $L_\varepsilon(d, y)$ on the error $(d - y)$.

With the ε-insensitive loss function of Eq. (6.45) as a basis for robustification, the stage is set for applying SVM theory to solve linear regression problems, as discussed next.

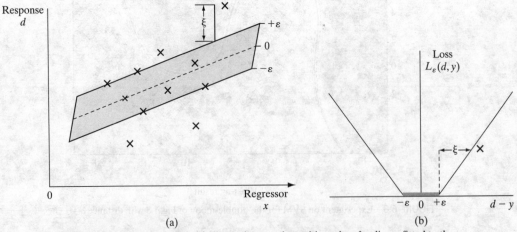

FIGURE 6.9   Linear regression (a) Illustrating an ε-insensitive tube of radius ε, fitted to the data points shown as ×'s. (b) The corresponding plot of the ε-insensitive loss function.

6.9 OPTIMAL SOLUTION OF THE LINEAR REGRESSION PROBLEM

Consider a linear regression model, in which the dependence of a scalar observable d on a regressor $\mathbf{x}$ is described by

$$d = \mathbf{w}^T \mathbf{x} + b \tag{6.46}$$

where the parameter vector $\mathbf{w}$ and the bias b are both unknown. The problem is to compute estimates of $\mathbf{w}$ and b, given the training sample $\mathcal{T} = \{\mathbf{x}_i, d_i\}_{i=1}^N$, where the data are statistically independent and identically distributed (iid).

Given the training sample $\mathcal{T}$, consider the *risk functional*

$$\frac{1}{2}\|\mathbf{w}\|^2 + C\sum_{i=1}^N |y_i - d_i|_\varepsilon \tag{6.47}$$

where the summation accounts for the ε-insensitive training error and C is a constant that determines the tradeoff between the training error and the penalizing term $\|\mathbf{w}\|^2$. The y_i is the estimator output produced in response to the input example $\mathbf{x}_i$. The requirement is to do the following:

Minimize the risk functional of Eq. (6.47) subject to the following constraints:

$$d_i - y_i \le \varepsilon + \xi_i \tag{6.48}$$
$$y_i - d_i \le \varepsilon + \xi_i' \tag{6.49}$$
$$\xi_i \ge 0 \tag{6.50}$$
$$\xi_i' \ge 0 \tag{6.51}$$

for $i = 1, 2, ..., N$. The ξ_i and ξ_i' are two sets of nonnegative slack variables that describe the ε-sensitive loss function in Eq. (6.45).

To solve this optimization problem for the Lagrange multipliers α_i and α_i', we will proceed in a manner similar to that pursued in Section 6.2 for the design of a support vector machine for linearly separable patterns. First, we construct a Lagrangian function (including the constraints), and then we go on introduce the corresponding dual set of variables. Specifically, we first to write

$$J(\mathbf{w}, \xi, \xi_i', \alpha, \alpha', \gamma, \gamma') = \frac{1}{2}\|\mathbf{w}\|^2 + C\sum_{i=1}^N (\xi_i + \xi_i') - \sum_{i=1}^N (\gamma_i \xi_i + \gamma_i' \xi_i')$$

$$- \sum_{i=1}^N \alpha_i(\mathbf{w}^T \mathbf{x}_i + b - d_i + \varepsilon + \xi_i)$$

$$- \sum_{i=1}^N \alpha_i'(d_i - \mathbf{w}^T \mathbf{x}_i - b + \varepsilon + \xi_i') \tag{6.52}$$

where, as before, the α_i and α_i' are the Lagrange multipliers. The new multipliers γ_i and γ_i' are introduced in Eq. (6.52) to ensure that the optimality constraints on the Lagrange multipliers α_i and α_i' assume variable forms. The requirement is to minimize the Lagrangian function of Eq. (6.52) with respect to the regression model's parameters $\mathbf{w}$ and b, as well as the slack variables ξ and ξ'.

Carrying out this optimization as just stated, and setting the resulting derivatives equal to zero, we respectively obtain

$$\hat{\mathbf{w}} = \sum_{i=1}^{N} (\alpha_i - \alpha_i')\mathbf{x} \qquad (6.53)$$

$$\sum_{i=1}^{N} (\alpha_i - \alpha_i') = 0 \qquad (6.54)$$

$$\alpha_i + \gamma_i = C, \qquad i = 1, 2, ..., N \qquad (6.55)$$

$$\alpha_i' + \gamma_i' = C, \qquad i = 1, 2, ..., N \qquad (6.56)$$

The *support-vector expansion* of Eq. (6.53) defines the desired parameter estimate $\hat{\mathbf{w}}$ in terms of the computed Lagrange multipliers α_i and α_i'. To find the corresponding estimate of the bias, denoted by $\hat{b}$, we exploit the *Karush–Kuhn–Tucker conditions*. From the discussion presented in Section 6.2, we infer that in order to conform to these conditions, for all the constraints that are not satisfied as equalities, the corresponding variables of the dual problem must vanish. For the problem at hand we thus have two sets of constraints:

- One set is described by the inequalities of Eqs. (6.48) and (6.49), for which the dual variables are α_i and α_i', respectively.
- The second set is described by the inequalities of Eqs. (6.50) and (6.51), for which the dual variables are γ_i and γ_i', respectively; from Eqs. (6.55) and (6.56), we find that $\gamma_i = C - \alpha_i$ and $\gamma_i' = C - \alpha_i'$.

Accordingly, applying the Karush–Kuhn–Tucker conditions to these four constraints in accordance with their pertinent dual variables, we respectively obtain

$$\alpha_i(\varepsilon + \xi_i + d_i - y_i) = 0 \qquad (6.57)$$

$$\alpha_i'(\varepsilon + \xi_i' - d_i + y_i) = 0 \qquad (6.58)$$

$$(C - \alpha_i)\xi_i = 0 \qquad (6.59)$$

$$(C - \alpha_i')\xi_i' = 0 \qquad (6.60)$$

Examining these four equations, we draw three important conclusions:

1. Equations (6.59) and (6.60) tell us that the examples $(\mathbf{x}_i, d_i)$ for which $\alpha_i = C$ and $\alpha_i' = C$ are the only ones that can lie outside the slack variables $\xi_i > 0$ and $\xi_i' > 0$; these slack variables correspond to points lying outside the ε-insensitive tube centered around the regression function $f(\mathbf{x}) = \mathbf{w}^T\mathbf{x} + b$, as depicted in Fig. 6.10a.

2. Multiplying Eq. (6.57) by α_i', multiplying Eq. (6.58) by α_i, and then adding the resulting equations, we obtain

$$\alpha_i\alpha_i'(2\varepsilon + \xi_i + \xi_i') = 0$$

Hence, for $\varepsilon > 0$, and with $\xi_i > 0$ and $\xi_i' > 0$, we have the condition

$$\alpha_i\alpha_i' = 0$$

from which it follows that there can never be a situation where the pair of Lagrange multipliers α_i and α_i' are both simultaneously nonzero.

3. From Eqs. (6.59) and (6.60), we respectively observe that

$$\xi_i = 0 \quad \text{for } 0 < \alpha_i < C$$
$$\xi_i' = 0 \quad \text{for } 0 < \alpha_i' < C$$

Under these two conditions, the respective Eqs. (6.57) and (6.58) show us that

$$\varepsilon - d_i + y_i = 0, \quad \text{for } 0 < \alpha_i < C \tag{6.61}$$
$$\varepsilon + d_i - y_i = 0, \quad \text{for } 0 < \alpha_i' < C \tag{6.62}$$

With Eqs. (6.61) and (6.62) at hand, we can now compute the bias estimate $\hat{b}$. First, we recognize that the output of the optimum estimator of the regression function is defined by

$$y = \hat{\mathbf{w}}^T \mathbf{x} + \hat{b}$$

For the example $\mathbf{x}_i$ as the input, we write

$$y = \hat{\mathbf{w}}^T \mathbf{x}_i + \hat{b} \tag{6.63}$$

Substituting Eq. (6.63) into Eqs. (6.61) and (6.62) and then solving for $\hat{b}$, we respectively obtain

$$\hat{b} = d_i - \hat{\mathbf{w}}^T \mathbf{x}_i - \varepsilon \quad \text{for } 0 < \alpha_i < C \tag{6.64}$$

and

$$\hat{b} = d_i - \hat{\mathbf{w}}^T \mathbf{x}_i + \varepsilon \quad \text{for } 0 < \alpha_i' < C \tag{6.65}$$

Hence, knowing $\hat{\mathbf{w}}$ from Eq. (6.53) and given both ε and d_i, we may compute the bias estimate $\hat{b}$.

For the computation of $\hat{b}$, in theory, we may use any Lagrange multiplier that lies inside the range $(0, C)$. However, in practice, it is prudent to use the average value computed over all the Lagrange multipliers in that range.

Sparseness of the Support Vector Expansion

From Eqs. (6.57) and (6.58), we find that for all the examples that lie inside the ε-insensitive tube, we have

$$|d_i - y_i| \geq \varepsilon$$

Under this condition, the factors inside the parentheses of both equations are nonvanishing; hence, for Eqs. (6.57) and (6.58) to hold (i.e., for the Karush–Kuhn–Tucker conditions to be satisfied), we do not need all the examples $\mathbf{x}_i$ to compute the desired estimate $\hat{\mathbf{w}}$. In other words, the computed support vector expansion of Eq. (6.53) is *sparse*.

The examples for which the Lagrange multipliers α_i and α_i' are nonvanishing define the support vectors. Insofar as the solution of Eq. (6.53) is concerned, it is geometrically plausible that the examples that lie inside the ε-insensitive tube do not contribute to this solution. The implication of this statement is that those particular examples do not contain meaningful information about the solution (Schölkopf and Smola, 2002).

6.10 THE REPRESENTER THEOREM AND RELATED ISSUES

We complete the discussion of kernel machines (inclusive of support vector machines), be they linear or nonlinear, by establishing the Representer Theorem, which adds a great deal of insight into our understanding of this important class of learning machines. To pave the way for proving this theorem, we will first describe what is meant by a Hilbert space and then by a reproducing-kernel Hilbert space.

Hilbert Space[10]

Let $\{\mathbf{x}_k\}_{k=1}^{\infty}$ be an *orthonormal basis* for an *inner-product space* $\mathcal{F}$ that is assumed to be of infinite dimensionality. As a reminder, two vectors $\mathbf{x}_j$ and $\mathbf{x}_k$ are said to be *orthonormal* if they satisfy the twofold condition

$$\mathbf{x}_j^T \mathbf{x}_k = \begin{cases} 1 & \text{for } j = k \\ 0 & \text{otherwise} \end{cases} \tag{6.66}$$

where the first part pertains to the *normalization property* and the second to the *orthogonality property*. The space $\mathcal{F}$ so defined is called a *pre-Hilbert space*. The *normed space*, in which every vector has a finite Euclidean norm (length), is a special case of the pre-Hilbert space.

Let $\mathcal{H}$ be the largest and most inclusive space of vectors for which the infinite set $\{\mathbf{x}_k\}_{k=1}^{\infty}$ is a basis. Then, vectors not necessarily lying in the space $\mathcal{F}$ represented in the form

$$\mathbf{x} = \sum_{k=1}^{\infty} a_k \mathbf{x}_k \tag{6.67}$$

are said to be spanned by the basis $\{\mathbf{x}_k\}_{k=1}^{\infty}$; the a_k are the coefficients of the representation. Define the new vector

$$\mathbf{y}_n = \sum_{k=1}^{n} a_k \mathbf{x}_k \tag{6.68}$$

Another vector $\mathbf{y}_m$ may be similarly defined. For $n > m$, we may express the squared Euclidean distance between the vectors $\mathbf{y}_n$ and $\mathbf{y}_m$ as

$$\begin{aligned} \|\mathbf{y}_n - \mathbf{y}_m\|^2 &= \left\| \sum_{k=1}^{n} a_k \mathbf{x}_k - \sum_{k=1}^{m} a_k \mathbf{x}_k \right\|^2 \\ &= \left\| \sum_{k=m+1}^{n} a_k \mathbf{x}_k \right\|^2 \\ &= \sum_{k=m+1}^{n} a_k^2 \end{aligned} \tag{6.69}$$

where, in the last line, we invoked the twofold orthonormality condition of Eq. (6.66).

In view of Eq. (6.69), we infer the following:

1. $\displaystyle\sum_{k=m+1}^{n} a_k^2 \to 0$ as both $n, m \to \infty$.

2. $\displaystyle\sum_{k=1}^{m} a_k^2 < \infty$

Moreover, for some positive ε we may pick an integer m large enough to satisfy the inequality

$$\sum_{m+1}^{\infty} a_k^2 < \varepsilon$$

Since

$$\sum_{k=1}^{\infty} a_k^2 = \sum_{k=1}^{m} a_k^2 + \sum_{k=m+1}^{\infty} a_k^2$$

it therefore follows that

$$\sum_{k=1}^{\infty} a_k^2 < \infty \tag{6.70}$$

A sequence of vectors $\{\mathbf{y}_k\}_{k=1}^{n}$ in a normed space, for which the Euclidean distance between $\mathbf{y}_n$ and $\mathbf{y}_m$ satisfies the condition

$$\|\mathbf{y}_n - \mathbf{y}_m\| < \varepsilon \quad \text{for any } \varepsilon > 0 \text{ and all } m, n > M,$$

is a convergent sequence; such a sequence is called a *Cauchy sequence.* Note that all convergent sequences are Cauchy sequences, but not all Cauchy sequences are convergent.

Consequently, a vector $\mathbf{x}$ can be expanded on the basis $\{\mathbf{x}_k\}_{k=1}^{\infty}$ if, and only if, $\mathbf{x}$ is a linear combination of the basis vectors and the associated coefficients $\{a_k\}_{k=1}^{\infty}$ are square summable. Conversely, the square summability of the set of coefficients $\{a_k\}_{k=1}^{\infty}$ implies that the squared Euclidean distance $\|\mathbf{y}_n - \mathbf{y}_m\|^2$ approaches zero as both n and m approach infinity, and the convergent sequence $\{\mathbf{y}_n\}_{n=1}^{\infty}$ is a Cauchy sequence.

From this discussion, it is apparent that the space $\mathcal{H}$ is more "complete" than the inner-product space $\mathcal{F}$. We may therefore make the following important statement:

> *An inner-product space $\mathcal{H}$ is complete if every Cauchy sequence of vectors taken from the space $\mathcal{H}$ converges to a limit in $\mathcal{H}$; a complete inner-product space is called a* Hilbert space.

Indeed, it is in view of this statement, that the inner-product space $\mathcal{F}$, in terms of which we started the discussion, is referred to as pre-Hilbert space.

Reproducing-Kernel Hilbert Space[11]

Consider a Mercer kernel $k(\mathbf{x}, \cdot)$, where the vector $\mathbf{x} \in \mathcal{X}$, and let $\mathcal{F}$ be any vector space of all real-valued functions of $\mathbf{x}$ that are generated by the kernel $k(\mathbf{x}, \cdot)$.

Suppose now two functions $f(\cdot)$ and $g(\cdot)$ are picked from the space $\mathcal{F}$ that are respectively represented by

$$f(\cdot) = \sum_{i=1}^{l} a_i k(\mathbf{x}_i, \cdot) \qquad (6.71)$$

and

$$g(\cdot) = \sum_{j=1}^{n} b_j k(\tilde{\mathbf{x}}_j, \cdot) \qquad (6.72)$$

where the a_i and the b_j are expansion coefficients and both $\mathbf{x}_i$ and $\tilde{\mathbf{x}}_j \in \mathcal{X}$ for all i and j. Given the functions $f(\cdot)$ and $g(\cdot)$, we now introduce the *bilinear form*

$$\langle f, g \rangle = \sum_{i=1}^{l} \sum_{j=1}^{n} a_i k(\mathbf{x}_i, \tilde{\mathbf{x}}_j) b_j \qquad (6.73)$$

$$= \mathbf{a}^T \mathbf{K} \mathbf{b}$$

where $\mathbf{K}$ is the Gram, or kernel matrix, and in the first line of the equation we made use of the relation

$$\langle k(\mathbf{x}_i, \cdot), k(\mathbf{x}_j, \cdot) \rangle = k(\mathbf{x}_i, \mathbf{x}_j) \qquad (6.74)$$

The first line of Eq. (6.73) may now be rewritten in the simplified form

$$\langle f, g \rangle = \sum_{i=1}^{l} a_i \sum_{j=1}^{n} b_j k(\mathbf{x}_i, \tilde{\mathbf{x}}_j)$$

$$= \sum_{i=1}^{l} a_i \underbrace{\sum_{j=1}^{n} b_j k(\tilde{\mathbf{x}}_j, \mathbf{x}_i)}_{g(\mathbf{x}_i)}$$

$$= \sum_{i=1}^{l} a_i g(\mathbf{x}_i) \qquad (6.75)$$

where, in the second line, we used the symmetric property of the Mercer kernel. Similarly, we may write

$$\langle f, g \rangle = \sum_{j=1}^{n} b_j f(\tilde{\mathbf{x}}_j) \qquad (6.76)$$

The definition of the bilinear form $\langle f, g \rangle$ introduced in Eq. (6.73) is independent of how the functions $f(\cdot)$ and $g(\cdot)$ are represented. We say so because the summation $\sum_{i=1}^{l} a_i g(\mathbf{x}_i)$ in Eq. (6.75) is invariant with respect to changes in the index n, the coefficient vector $\mathbf{b}$, and the n-dimensional vector $\tilde{\mathbf{x}}_j$. A similar statement applies to the summation $\sum_{j=1}^{n} b_j f(\tilde{\mathbf{x}}_j)$ in Eq. (6.76).

Furthermore, from the definition of Eq. (6.73), we readily derive the following three properties:

Property 1. Symmetry For all functions f and g in the space $\mathscr{F}$, the term $\langle f, g \rangle$ is symmetric, as shown by

$$\langle f, g \rangle = \langle g, f \rangle \tag{6.77}$$

Property 2. Scaling and distributive property For any pair of constants c and d and any set of functions f, g, and h in the space $\mathscr{F}$, we have

$$\langle (cf + dg), h \rangle = c \langle f, h \rangle + d \langle g, h \rangle \tag{6.78}$$

Property 3. Squared norm For any real-valued function f in the space $\mathscr{F}$, if we evaluate Eq. (6.73) for f acting all by itself, we obtain the following *squared norm*, or *quadratic metric*:

$$\|f\|^2 = \langle f, f \rangle$$

$$= \mathbf{a}^T \mathbf{K} \mathbf{a}$$

Since the Gram is nonnegative definite, the squared norm has the property

$$\|f\|^2 \geq 0 \tag{6.79}$$

By virtue of the fact that for all real-valued functions f and g in the space $\mathscr{F}$, the bilinear term $\langle f, g \rangle$ satisfies the symmetry, scaling, and distributive properties as well as the property that the norm $\|f\|^2 = \langle f, f \rangle$ is nonnegative, we may now formally state that the $\langle f, g \rangle$ introduced in Eq. (6.73) is indeed an *inner product*; moreover it is an inner product that must also satisfy the condition $\langle f, g \rangle = 0$ if, and only if, $f = 0$. In other words, the space $\mathscr{F}$ embracing the functions f and g is an inner-product space.

There is one additional property that follows directly from Eq. (6.75). Specifically, setting

$$g(\cdot) = k(\mathbf{x}, \cdot)$$

in Eq. (6.75), we obtain

$$\langle f, k(\mathbf{x}, \cdot) \rangle = \sum_{i=1}^{l} a_i k(\mathbf{x}, \mathbf{x}_i)$$

$$= \sum_{i=1}^{l} a_i k(\mathbf{x}_i, \mathbf{x}), \qquad k(\mathbf{x}, \mathbf{x}_i) = k(\mathbf{x}_i, \mathbf{x})$$

$$= f(\mathbf{x}) \tag{6.80}$$

For obvious reasons, this property of the Mercer kernel $k(\mathbf{x}, \cdot)$ is known as the *reproducing property*.

The kernel $k(\mathbf{x}, \mathbf{x}_i)$, representing a function of the two vectors $\mathbf{x}, \mathbf{x}_i \in \mathscr{X}$, is called a reproducing kernel of the vector space $\mathscr{F}$ if it satisfies the following two conditions (Aronszajn, 1950):

1. For every $\mathbf{x}_i \in \mathscr{X}$, $k(\mathbf{x}, \mathbf{x}_i)$ as a function of the vector $\mathbf{x}$ belongs to $\mathscr{F}$.

2. It satisfies the reproducing property.

These two conditions are indeed satisfied by the Mercer kernel, thereby endowing it with the designation "reproducing kernel." If the inner-product (vector) space $\mathscr{F}$, in which the reproducing kernel space is defined, is also *complete*, then we may go one step further and speak of a "reproducing-kernel Hilbert space."

To justify the property of completeness, consider a fixed input vector $\mathbf{x}$ and a pair of Cauchy sequences $\{f_n(\mathbf{x})\}_{n=1}^{\infty}$ and $\{f_m(\mathbf{x})\}_{m=1}^{\infty}$, where $n > m$. Then, applying the reproducing property of Eq. (6.80) to both $f_n(\mathbf{x})$ and $f_m(\mathbf{x})$, we may write

$$f_n(\mathbf{x}) - f_m(\mathbf{x}) = \langle f_n(\cdot) - f_m(\cdot) \rangle k(\mathbf{x}, \cdot)$$

where the right-hand side is an inner product. By invoking the *Cauchy–Schwarz inequality*,[12] we obtain

$$(f_n(\mathbf{x}) - f_m(\mathbf{x}))^2 \leq \langle f_n(\cdot) - f_m(\cdot) \rangle^2 \underbrace{k(\mathbf{x}, \cdot)k(\mathbf{x}, \cdot)}_{k(\mathbf{x}, \mathbf{x})} \tag{6.81}$$

It follows, therefore, that $f_n(\mathbf{x})$ is a bounded Cauchy sequence, which converges toward some real-valued function f in the space $\mathcal{F}$. Finally, if we define the function

$$y(\mathbf{x}) = \lim_{n \to \infty} f_n(\mathbf{x})$$

and complete the space $\mathcal{F}$ by adding to it all such convergent Cauchy sequences, we obtain the *Hilbert space* $\mathcal{H}$. We have thus demonstrated that each Mercer kernel $k(\mathbf{x}, \cdot)$ defines a Hilbert space $\mathcal{H}$, where the value of the function $f(\mathbf{x})$ is reproduced by the inner product of $f(\mathbf{x})$ with $k(\mathbf{x}, \cdot)$. The Hilbert space so defined is called a *reproducing-kernel Hilbert space*, for which we use the acronym RKHS hereafter.

The analytic power of RKHS is expressed in an important theorem considered next.

Formulation of the The Representer Theorem[13]

Define a space $\mathcal{H}$ as the RKHS induced by a Mercer kernel $k(\mathbf{x}, \cdot)$. Given any real-valued function $f(\cdot) \in \mathcal{H}$, we may decompose it into the sum of two components, both of which naturally lie in the space $\mathcal{H}$:

- One component is contained in the span of the kernel functions $k(\mathbf{x}_1, \cdot), k(\mathbf{x}_2, \cdot), ...,$ $k(\mathbf{x}_l, \cdot)$; denoting this component by $f_{\|}(\mathbf{x})$, we may use Eq. (6.71) to represent it as

$$f_{\|}(\cdot) = \sum_{i=1}^{l} a_i k(\mathbf{x}_i, \cdot)$$

- The second component is *orthogonal* to the span of the kernel functions; it is denoted by $f_{\perp}(\mathbf{x})$.

We may thus express the function $f(\cdot)$ as

$$f(\cdot) = f_{\|}(\cdot) + f_{\perp}(\cdot)$$
$$= \sum_{i=1}^{l} a_i k(\mathbf{x}_i, \cdot) + f_{\perp}(\cdot) \tag{6.82}$$

Applying the distributive property of Eq. (6.78) to Eq. (6.82), we obtain

$$f(\mathbf{x}_j) = \langle f(\cdot), k(\mathbf{x}_j, \cdot) \rangle_{\mathcal{H}}$$
$$= \left\langle \sum_{i=1}^{l} a_i k(\mathbf{x}_i, \cdot), k(\mathbf{x}_j, \cdot) \right\rangle_{\mathcal{H}} + \left\langle k(\mathbf{x}_j, \cdot), f_{\perp} \right\rangle_{\mathcal{H}}$$

With $f_\perp$ being orthogonal to the span of the kernel functions, the second term is zero; this equation therefore reduces to

$$f(\mathbf{x}_j) = \left\langle \sum_{i=1}^{l} a_i k(\mathbf{x}_i, \cdot), k(\mathbf{x}_j, \cdot) \right\rangle_{\mathcal{H}}$$

$$= \sum_{i=1}^{l} a_i k(\mathbf{x}_i, \mathbf{x}_j) \tag{6.83}$$

Equation (6.83) is a mathematical statement of the *representer theorem*:

> *Any function defined in an RKHS can be represented as a linear combination of Mercer kernel functions.*

However, there is more to be said.

Generalized Applicability of the Representer Theorem

An important property of the representer theorem is that the expansion given in Eq. (6.83) is the minimizer of the *regularized* empirical risk (cost function)

$$\mathscr{E}(f) = \frac{1}{2N} \sum_{n=1}^{N} (d(n) - f(\mathbf{x}(n)))^2 + \Omega(\|f\|_{\mathcal{H}}) \tag{6.84}$$

where $\{\mathbf{x}(n), d(n)\}_{n=1}^{N}$ is the training sample, f is the unknown function to be estimated, and $\Omega(\|f\|_{\mathcal{H}})$ is the regularizing function (Schölkopf and Smola, 2002). For the theorem to hold, the regularizing function must be a strictly monotonic increasing function of its argument; hereafter, this requirement is referred to simply as the *monotonicity condition*.

The first term on the right-hand side of Eq. (6.84) is the standard error term, which is a quadratic function in f. Hence, the expansion of Eq. (6.83) is the minimizer of this term through the use of fixed $a_i \in \mathbb{R}$.

To prove that this expansion is also the minimizer of the regularized part of the empirical risk $\mathscr{E}(f)$, we proceed in three steps as follows:

1. Let $f_\perp$ denote the orthogonal compliment to the span of the kernel functions $\{k(x_i, \cdot)\}_{i=1}^{l}$. Then, since, according to Eq. (6.82), every function can be expressed as a kernel expansion on the training data plus $f_\perp$, we may write

$$\Omega(\|f\|_{\mathcal{H}}) = \Omega\left(\left\| \sum_{i=1}^{l} a_i k(x_i, \cdot) + f_\perp(\cdot) \right\|_{\mathcal{H}}\right) \tag{6.85}$$

For mathematical convenience, we prefer to work with the new function

$$\tilde{\Omega}(\|f\|_{\mathcal{H}}^2) = \Omega(\|f\|_{\mathcal{H}}) \tag{6.86}$$

rather than the original regularizing function $\Omega(\|f\|_{\mathcal{H}})$. This move is permissible because a quadratic function is strictly monotonic on the infinite interval $[0, \infty)$. Hence, $\tilde{\Omega}(\|f\|_{\mathcal{H}}^2)$ is strictly monotonic on $[0, \infty)$ if, and only if, $\Omega(\|f\|_{\mathcal{H}})$ also satisfies the monotonicity condition. For all $f_\perp$, we may thus write

$$\tilde{\Omega}(\|f\|_{\mathcal{H}}^2) = \tilde{\Omega}\left(\left\| \sum_{i=1}^{l} a_i k(x_i, \cdot) + f_\perp(\cdot) \right\|_{\mathcal{H}}^2\right) \tag{6.87}$$

2. Applying the Pythagorean decomposition to the argument of $\tilde{\Omega}$ on the right-hand side of Eq. (6.87), we may go on to write

$$\tilde{\Omega}(\|f\|_{\mathcal{H}}^2) = \tilde{\Omega}\left(\left\|\sum_{i=1}^{l} a_i k(x_i, \cdot)\right\|_{\mathcal{H}}^2 + \|f_\perp\|_{\mathcal{H}}^2\right)$$

$$\geq \tilde{\Omega}\left(\left\|\sum_{i=1}^{l} a_i k(x_i, \cdot)\right\|_{\mathcal{H}}^2\right)$$

For the optimum condition, we must set $f_\perp = 0$, the use of which in this equation yields the equality

$$\tilde{\Omega}(\|f\|_{\mathcal{H}}^2) = \tilde{\Omega}\left(\left\|\sum_{i=1}^{l} a_i k(x_i, \cdot)\right\|_{\mathcal{H}}^2\right) \tag{6.88}$$

3. Finally, in light of the definition introduced in Eq. (6.86), we have the desired result

$$\Omega(\|f\|_{\mathcal{H}}) = \Omega\left(\left\|\sum_{i=1}^{l} a_i k(x_i, \cdot)\right\|_{\mathcal{H}}\right) \tag{6.89}$$

It follows therefore that, for fixed $a_i \in \mathbb{R}$, the representer theorem is also the minimizer of the regularizing function $\Omega(\|f\|_{\mathcal{H}})$, provided that the monotonicity condition is satisfied.

In treating the composition of the standard error and regularizing terms as one whole entity, there will be a trade-off between these two terms. In any case, for some fixed $a_i \in \mathbb{R}$, the representer theorem described by the expansion of Eq. (6.83) will serve as the minimizer of the regularized empirical risk of Eq. (6.84), thereby establishing general applicability of the representer theorem (Schölkopf and Smola, 2002).

In the next chapter, we will make extensive use of this important theorem in the study of regularization theory.

6.11   SUMMARY AND DISCUSSION

The support vector machine is an elegant and highly principled learning method for the design of a feedforward network with a single hidden layer of nonlinear units. Its derivation follows the method of structural risk minimization (SRM) that is rooted in VC dimension theory, which makes its derivation even more profound; SRM was discussed in Chapter 4. As the name implies, the design of the machine hinges on the extraction of a subset of the training data that serves as support vectors and therefore represents a stable characteristic of the data. The support vector machine includes the polynomial learning machine, radial-basis-function network, and two-layer perceptron as special cases. Thus, although these methods provide different models of intrinsic statistical regularities contained in the training data, they all stem from a common root in a support vector machine setting.

One other distinctive property of the support vector machine is that it is a kernal method of the batch-learning kind.[14]

Computational Considerations

The asymptotic behavior of a support vector machine grows linearly with the number of training examples, N. It follows therefore that the computational cost of using the machine for solving pattern recognition and regression problems has both a quadratic and a cubic component. Specifically, when the parameter C is small, the computational cost grows like N^2; and when C is large, the computational cost grows like N^3 (Bottou and Lin, 2007).

To alleviate this problem, several commercial optimization libraries have been developed to solve the quadratic-programming (QP) problem. However, these libraries are of limited use. The memory requirements of the QP problem grow with the square of the size of the training sample. Consequently, in real-life applications that may involve several thousand data points, the QP problem cannot be solved by the straightforward use of a commercial optimization library. The problem is complicated further by the fact that, in general, the solution to an SVM problem is quite *sparse*, because the weight vector $\mathbf{w}$ in the output layer of the machine consists of few nonzero elements relative to the number of data points in the training sample. Accordingly, direct attempts to solve the QP problem in a support vector machine will *not* scale to large problem sizes. To mitigate this difficulty, several innovations have been described in the literature, as summarized here:[15]

1. Osuna et al. (1997) have developed a novel decomposition algorithm that attains optimality by solving a sequence of much smaller subproblems. In particular, the decomposition algorithm takes advantage of the support vector coefficients that are active on either side of their bounds defined by $\alpha_i = 0$ or $\alpha_i = C$. It is reported therein that the decomposition algorithm performs satisfactorily in applications with as many as 100,000 data points.

2. Platt (1999) extended Osuna's methodology by introducing an algorithm called *sequential minimal optimization* (SMO), which breaks a large QP problem into a series of very small QP subproblems that are solvable analytically, thereby eliminating the need for a numerical QP library. The computation time of SMO is dominated by kernel evaluation; hence, the use of kernel optimizations can be accelerated.

3. Joachims (1999) introduced several key innovations of his own. Specifically, a large SVM problem is decomposed into a series of smaller ones, but in a more principled manner than that of Osuna. Another important innovation introduced is the notion of *shrinking*: If a point is not an unbounded support vector, has not been for a long time, and there is little evidence for it becoming one, then, with high probability, that point may be removed from further scrutiny, thereby saving computation time.

4. Rifkin (2002) developed a computational procedure called the *SvmFu algorithm*, which may be viewed as a synthesis of the ideas proposed by Osuna, Platt, and Joachims. Specifically, the advantages of each of those three procedures were combined with some new features. It is claimed that with SvmFu a large problem may be solved as a sequence of subproblems which are small enough that their associated Hessian matrices can fit in memory.

5. Drineas and Mahoney (2005) have developed an algorithm to compute an easily interpretable low-rank approximation to the N-by-N Gram, or kernel matrix, in such a way that the computation of interest may be performed more rapidly. The relationships of the new algorithm with the Nyström method from integral equation theory are discussed therein.

6. Hush et al. (2006) describe polynomial-time algorithms that produce approximate solutions with guaranteed accuracy for a class of quadratic-programming problems that arise in the design of support vector machine classifiers. The algorithms employ a two-stage process. The first stage produces an approximate solution to a dual quadratic-programming problem, and the second stage maps this approximate dual solution to an approximate primal solution.

Curse of Dimensionality

As is the case for a multilayer perceptron, the intrinsic complexity of a support vector machine as an approximating function *increases exponentially* with m_0, where m_0 denotes the dimensionality of the input space. Moreover, the intrinsic complexity of the machine decreases exponentially with s, where s denotes the smoothness index which measures the number of constraints imposed on the approximating function. Accordingly, the smoothness index of the approximating function acts as a *corrective measure* against the curse of dimensionality. We may therefore say that a support vector machine will provide a good approximation to a dimensionally high function, provided that the function of interest is correspondingly smooth.

Concluding Remarks

The support vector machine (SVM) has established itself as the most widely used kernel-learning algorithm. Indeed, we may go on to say that in the machine-learning literature, support vector machines represent the state-of-the-art by virtue of their good generlization performance, relative ease of use, and rigorous theoretical foundations. Moreover, in a practical context, they are capable of delivering robust performance in solving pattern-recognition and regression problems.

However, the major limitation of support vector machines is the fast increase in their computing and storage requirements with respect to the number of training examples. These severe requirements tend to leave many large-scale learning problems beyond the reach of support vector machines. The core of this practical limitation lies in the quadratic programming routine that is an integral part of the SVM optimization theory. To mitigate this practical difficulty, a great deal of effort has been devoted to accelerate the SVM solver through a variety of parallel-implementation techniques beyond the decomposition procedures described above (Durdanovic et al., 2007; Yom-Tov (2007).

NOTES AND REFERENCES

1. The support vector machine was pioneered by Vapnik; the first description of the machine was presented by Boser, Guyon, and Vapnik in 1992. The most comprehensive and detailed

description of this new class of learning machines appeared in Vapnik's 1998 book entitled "Statistical Learning Theory," which is already a classic in the field.

The paper entitled "On the Mathematical Foundations of Learning," by Cucker and Smale (2001), presents a mathematically rigorous treatment of supervised learning theory, with emphasis on the relationship of approximation to learning and the primary role of inductive inference.

Comprehensive treatments of kernel machines, including support vector machines, are presented in the books by Schölkopf and Smola (2002), Herbrich (2002), and Shawe-Taylor and Cristianini (2004).

2. *Convex optimization* is a special class of optimization techniques that include least-squares and linear programming, for which a complete theory is already available. Moreover, problems that lend themselves to convex optimization go beyond least-squares and linear programs. The advantages to be gained in formulating a problem as a convex-optimization problem include

- solutions that are reliable and efficient, and
- theoretical advantages, exemplified by the formulation of a dual problem, the solution of which is more computationally efficient and conceptually transparent than that of the original problem.

For a detailed treatment of convex analysis and optimization, see the books by Boyd and Vandenbergh (2004) and Bertsekas et al. (2003).

3. In any optimization problem with a differentiable objective function and constraints for which duality applies, the primal and dual solutions must satisfy the *Karush–Kuhn–Tucker (KKT) conditions*. These conditions are named for Karush (1939) and Kuhn and Tucker (1951). The survey paper by Kuhn (1976) gives a historical account of solving inequality-constrained problems, in which convex optimization plays a major role.

4. The relationship between sparse approximation and support vector expansion was first discussed in Girosi (1998) and Vapnik (1998).

Steinwart (2003) presents a detailed mathematical discussion of the *sparseness* that arises in solving pattern-recognition problems by using support vector machines; in particular, this paper establishes (asymptotically) lower bounds on the number of support vectors. Along the way, several results are proved that are of importance for the understanding of support vector machines. The paper addresses three admissible loss functions:

  i. the *hinge loss*, defined by $L(d, y) = \max(0, 1 - dy)$;
  ii. the *squared hinge loss*, defined by $L(d, y) = [\max(0, 1 - dy)]^2$;
  iii. the *least-squares loss*, defined by $L(d, y) = (1 - dy)^2$.

The corresponding SVM classifiers are denoted by L_1, L_2, and LS. The variables d and y denote the desired response and the corresponding response computed by the support vector machine for a given input example, respectively.

The design of support vector machines by using the least-squares loss is treated in a great deal of detail in the book entitled "Least-Squares Support Vector Machines," by Suykens et al. (2002).

5. With computational complexity as the issue of interest, we may identify two classes of algorithms:

- *Polynomial time algorithms*, which require a running time that a is polynomial function of the problem size. For example, the fast Fourier transform (FFT) algorithm, commonly used for spectrum analysis, is a polynomial time algorithm, as it requires a running time of order $n \log n$, where n is a measure of the problem size.

- *Exponential time algorithms*, which require a running time that is an exponential function of the problem size. For example, an exponential time algorithm may take time 2^n, where n is a measure of the problem size.

On this basis, we may view polynomial time algorithms as efficient algorithms and exponential time algorithms as inefficient algorithms.

There are many computational problems that arise in practice for which no efficient algorithms have been devised. Many, if not all, of these seemingly intractable problems are said to belong to a class of problems referred to as *NP-complete problems*. The term "NP" stands for "nondeterministic polynomial."

For more detailed discussion of NP-complete problems, see Cook (1971), Garey and Johnson (1979), and Cormen et al. (1990).

6. The reciprocal of the parameter C plays exactly the same role as the regularization parameter in regularized least-squares estimation. We have adhered to the use of the parameter C in describing the theory of support vector machines largely to be consistent with the early development of this new class of kernel machines.

7. The idea of an inner-product kernel was first described in Aizerman et al. (1964a, 1964b) in the formulation of the method of potential functions, which represents the forerunner to radial-basis-function networks. At about the same time, Vapnik and Chervonenkis (1964) developed the idea of an optimal hyperplane. The combined use of these two powerful concepts in formulating the support vector machine first appeared in Boser et al. (1992).

8. For discussions on additional properties of kernels over and above those presented in Section 6.4 under property 1 and property 2, see the books by Schölkopf and Smola (2002), Herbrich (2002), and Shawe-Taylor and Cristianini (2004).

9. To describe minimax theory, consider a function $f(x, z)$, where $x \in \mathcal{X}$ and $z \in \mathcal{Z}$. The requirement in this theory is either

$$\text{to minimize} \sup_{z \in \mathcal{Z}} f(x, z)$$

subject to $x \in \mathcal{X}$

or, alternatively,

$$\text{to maximize} \inf_{x \in \mathcal{X}} f(x, z)$$

subject to $z \in \mathcal{Z}$

The application of minimax theory arises, for example, in the study of worst-case designs, which are of engineering importance. For a discussion of this theory, see Bertsekas et al. (2003).

Huber's minimax theory is based on neighborhoods that are not global by virtue of their exclusion of asymmetric distributions. Nevertheless, this theory deals successfully with a large part of traditional statistics, particularly regression.

10. The Hilbert space is discussed in the books by Dorny (1975) and Debnath and Mikusiński (1990).

11. The original paper on reproducing-kernel Hilbert space (RKHS) is Aronszajn (1950), which is a classic; it is also discussed in the books by Shawe-Taylor and Cristianini (2004), Schölkopf and Smola (2002), and Herbrich (2002).

12. Let $\mathbf{x}$ and $\mathbf{y}$ be any two elements of an inner-product space $\mathcal{F}$. According to the *Cauchy–Schwarz inequality*, we have

$$\langle \mathbf{x}, \mathbf{y} \rangle^2 \leq \|\mathbf{x}\|^2 \cdot \|\mathbf{y}\|^2$$

the proof of which is straightforward. The inequality states that the squared inner product of **x** and **y** is less than or equal to the product of the squared Euclidean length of **x** and that of **y**. The version of the inequality presented in Eq. (6.81) is an adaptation of this statement that is made to suit the problem considered in establishing the reproducing-kernel Hilbert space.

13. In a historical context, the celebrated representer theorem was first described in Kimeldorf and Wahba (1971) for solving practical problems in statistical estimation based on squared-loss (cost) functions; see also the book by Wahba (1990). Generalized applicability of the representer theorem to regularized cost functions was addressed for the first-time in Schölkopf and Smola (2002).

14. In contrast to the support vector machine that is of a batch-learning kind, the *kernel LMS algorithm*, due to Liu et al. (2008), is of an on-line learning kind. This new algorithm embodies ideas from the least-mean-square (LMS) algorithm, discussed in Chapter 3, and the reproducting-kernel Hilbert space (RKHS), discussed in this chapter; these ideas are integrated together in a composite fashion. In particular, the kernel trick is used to permit learning on iteration-by-iteration basis.

15. An overview of quadratic programming optimization methods is presented in Bottou and Lin (2007).

PROBLEMS

Optimal separating hyperplane

6.1 Consider the case of a hyperplane for linearly separable patterns, which is defined by the equation

$$\mathbf{w}^T\mathbf{x} + b = 0$$

where **w** denotes the weight vector, b denotes the bias, and **x** denotes the input vector. The hyperplane is said to correspond to a *canonical pair* (**w**, b) if, for the set of input patterns $\{\mathbf{x}_i\}_{i=1}^{N}$, the additional requirement

$$\min_{i=1,2,\dots,N} |\mathbf{w}^T\mathbf{x}_i + b| = 1$$

is satisfied. Show that this requirement leads to a margin of separation between the two classes equal to $2/\|\mathbf{w}\|$.

6.2 In Eq. (6.3), b_o denotes the optimum value of bias. How does the value of b_o affect the origin of the optimal hyperplane?

6.3 Starting with the primal problem for the optimization of the separating hyperplane for nonseparable patterns, formulate the dual problem as described in Section 6.3.

6.4 In this problem we explore the "leave-one-out method," discussed in Chapter 4, for estimating the expected test error produced by an optimal hyperplane for the case of nonseparable patterns. Discuss the various possibilities that can arise in the use of this method by eliminating any one pattern from the training sample and constructing a solution based on the remaining patterns.

6.5 The location of the optimal hyperplane in the data space is determined by the data points selected as support vectors. If the data are noisy, one's first reaction might be to question the robustness of the margin of separation to the presence of noise. Yet careful study of the optimal hyperplane reveals that the margin of separation is actually robust to noise. Discuss the rationale for this robust behavior.

Mercer Kernels

6.6 The Mercer kernel $k(x_i, \mathbf{x}_j)$ is evaluated over a training sample $\mathcal{T}$ of size N, yielding the N-by-N matrix

$$\mathbf{K} = \{k_{ij}\}_{i,j=1}^{N}$$

where $k_{ij} = k(\mathbf{x}_i, \mathbf{x}_j)$. Assume that the matrix $\mathbf{K}$ is positive in that all of its elements have positive values. Using the similarity transformation

$$\mathbf{K} = \mathbf{Q} \mathbf{\Lambda} \mathbf{Q}^T$$

where $\mathbf{\Lambda}$ is a diagonal matrix made up of eigenvalues and $\mathbf{Q}$ is a matrix made up of the corresponding eigenvectors, formulate an expression for the Mercer kernel $k(\mathbf{x}_i, \mathbf{x}_j)$ in terms of the eigenvalues and eigenvectors of matrix $\mathbf{K}$. What conclusions can you draw from this representation?

6.7 **(a)** Demonstrate that all three Mercer kernels described in Table 6.1 satisfy the *unitary invariance property*:

$$k(\mathbf{x}, \mathbf{x}_i) = k(\mathbf{Qx}, \mathbf{Qx}_i)$$

where $\mathbf{Q}$ is a unitary matrix defined by

$$\mathbf{Q}^{-1} = \mathbf{Q}^T$$

  (b) Does this property hold in general?

6.8 **(a)** State the two basic properties of the kernel.

  (b) Name the three common types of support vector machines and the Mercer kernels used with them. Also, discuss how these Mercer kernels are different from each other.

6.9 Consider the Gaussian kernel

$$k(\mathbf{x}_i, \mathbf{x}_j) = \exp\left(-\frac{\|\mathbf{x}_i - \mathbf{x}_j\|^2}{2\sigma^2}\right), \qquad i, j = 1, 2, ..., N$$

where no $\mathbf{x}_i$ and $\mathbf{x}_j$ are the same. Show that the Gram

$$\mathbf{K} = \begin{bmatrix} k(\mathbf{x}_1, \mathbf{x}_1) & k(\mathbf{x}_1, \mathbf{x}_2) & \cdots & k(\mathbf{x}_1, \mathbf{x}_N) \\ k(\mathbf{x}_2, \mathbf{x}_1) & k(\mathbf{x}_2, \mathbf{x}_2)) & \cdots & k(\mathbf{x}_2, \mathbf{x}_N) \\ \vdots & \vdots & & \vdots \\ k(\mathbf{x}_N, \mathbf{x}_1) & k(\mathbf{x}_N, \mathbf{x}_2) & \cdots & k(\mathbf{x}_N, \mathbf{x}_N) \end{bmatrix}$$

has *full rank*—that is, any two columns of the matrix $\mathbf{K}$ are linearly independent in an algebraic sense.

6.10 The *Mahalanobis kernel* is defined by

$$k(\mathbf{x}, \mathbf{x}_i) = \exp\left(-(\mathbf{x} - \mathbf{x}_i)^T \textstyle\sum^{-1}(\mathbf{x} - \mathbf{x}_i)\right)$$

where the M-dimensional input vector $\mathbf{x} \in \mathcal{X}$, and $i = 1, 2, ..., N$, and the M-by-M matrix

$$\sum = \operatorname{diag}(\sigma_1^2, \sigma_2^2, ..., \sigma_M^2)$$

where $\sigma_1, \sigma_2, ..., \sigma_M$ are all positive. A distinct property of this kernel, compared with the Gaussian kernel, is that each axis of the M-dimensional input space $\mathcal{X}$ has a "smoothing" parameter (i.e., a particular σ) of its own.

To illustrate this property, consider the function

$$F(\mathbf{x}) = \sum_{i=1}^{N} a_i \exp\left(-\frac{\|\mathbf{x} - \mathbf{x}_i\|^2}{2\sigma_i^2}\right)$$

which may be viewed as a *density estimator* (Herbrich, 2002). Given $a_i = 1$ and $\sigma_i = \sigma$ for all i, $M = 2$, and $N = 20$, plot the function $F(\mathbf{x})$ versus the coordinates x_1 and x_2 for the following values:

(i) $\sigma = 0.5$
(ii) $\sigma = 0.7$
(iii) $\sigma = 1.0$
(iv) $\sigma = 2.0$

Comment on your results.

6.11 A joint probability density function $p_{X_1, X_2}(x_1, x_2)$ over an $\mathcal{X}$-by-$\mathcal{X}$ product space is said to be a *P-matrix* provided that it satisfies the finitely nonnegative definite (i.e., positive semidefinite) property (Shawe-Taylor and Cristianini, 2004).

By considering the simple case of a two-element set $\mathbf{X} = \{X_1, X_2\}$ of random variables, demonstrate validity of the following statement: All *P*-kernels are joint distributions, but not all joint distributions are *P*-kernels.

Pattern classification

6.12 The margin plays a key role in the design of support vector machines. Identify the important properties of the margin in solving pattern-classification problems.

6.13 Using the formula of Eq. (6.17), show that the margin of linearly separable patterns can be expressed in terms of the Lagrange multipliers as

$$\rho = \frac{2}{\left(\sum_{i=1}^{N_s} \alpha_i\right)^{1/2}}$$

where N_s is the number of support vectors.

6.14 Consider a training sample $\{\mathbf{x}_i, d_i\}_{i=1}^{N}$ that consists of positive and negative examples that are linearly separable. Justify the following statement:

The support vectors contain all the information needed to classify the positive and negative examples.

6.15 Figure P6.15 shows a data set that consists of nonlinearly separable positive and negative examples. Specifically, the decision boundary separating the positive from negative examples is an *ellipse*. Find the transformation that maps the input space into the feature space such that the positive and negative examples become linearly separable in the feature space.

6.16 The Mercer kernel for a polynomial learning machine used to solve the XOR problem is defined by

$$k(\mathbf{x}, \mathbf{x}_i) = (1 + \mathbf{x}^T\mathbf{x}_i)^p$$

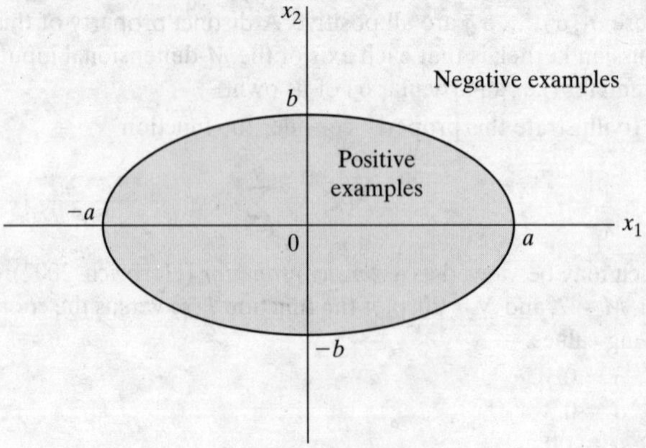

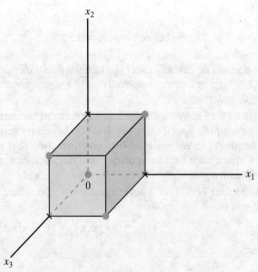

FIGURE P6.15

What is the minimum value of power p for which the XOR problem is solved? Assume that p is a positive integer. What is the result of using a value for p larger than the minimum?

6.17 Figure P6.17 shows the XOR function operating on a three-dimensional pattern **x** as described by the relationship

$$\text{XOR}(x_1, x_2, x_3) = x_1 \oplus x_2 \oplus x_3$$

where the symbol $\oplus$ denotes the exclusive-OR Boolean function operator. Design a polynomial learning machine to separate the two classes of points represented by the output of this operator.

FIGURE P6.17

Sparsity

6.18 Justify the following statement:

A support vector machine solver is sparse, but the Gram associated with the machine is rarely sparse.

6.19 The quadratic programming routine in a support vector machine solver provides the basis for splitting the training examples into three categories. Define these three categories, and use a two-dimensional figure to illustrate how the splitting is performed.

Metrics

6.20 With different algortihms being developed for accelerating support vector machine solvers, it is important that we formulate metrics for comparing the performance of these different algorithms. Develop a set of metrics that could be used for dealing with this practical issue.

Reproducing-kernel Hilbert space

6.21 Let $k(\mathbf{x}_i, \cdot)$ and $k(\mathbf{x}_j, \cdot)$ denote a pair of kernels, where $i, j = 1, 2, ..., N$. The vectors $\mathbf{x}_i$ and $\mathbf{x}_j$ have the same dimensionality. Show that

$$k(\mathbf{x}_i, \cdot)k(\mathbf{x}_j, \cdot) = k(\mathbf{x}_i, \mathbf{x}_j)$$

where the expression on the left-hand side is an inner-product kernel.

6.22 State three properties of the inner product $<f, g>$ defined in Eq. (6.75).

6.23 Under what conditions the kernel $k(x, x_i)$, representing a function of the two vectors $x, x_i \in \mathcal{H}$, is called a reproducing kernel of the vector space $\mathcal{F}$.

Computer experiments

6.24 This experiment investigates the scenario where the two moons in Fig. 1.8 overlap and are therefore nonseparable.

(a) Repeat the second part of the experiment in Fig. 6.7, for which the vertical separation between the two moons was fixed at $d = -6.5$. Experimentally, determine the value of parameter C for which the classification error rate is reduced to a minimum.

(b) Reduce the vertical separation between the two moons further by setting $d = -6.75$, for which the classification error rate is expected to be higher than that for $d = -6.5$. Experimentally, determine the value of parameter C for which the error rate is reduced to a minimum.

Comment on the results obtained for both parts of the experiment.

6.25 Among the supervised-learning algorithms studied thus far, the support vector machine stands out as the most powerful. In this problem, the performance of the support vector machine is to be challenged by using it to classify the two multicircular regions that constitute the "tightly fisted" structure shown in Fig. P6.24. The radii of the three concentric circles in this figure are $d_1 = 0.2, d_2 = 0.5$, and $d_3 = 0.8$.

(a) Generate 100 epochs, each of which consists of 200 randomly distributed training examples, and an equal number of test data for the two regions of Fig. P6.24.

(b) Train a support vector machine, assigning the value $C = 500$. Hence, construct the decision boundary computed by the machine.

(c) Test the network and thereby determine the classification error rate.

(d) Repeat the experiment for $C = 100$ and $C = 2,500$.

Comment on your results.

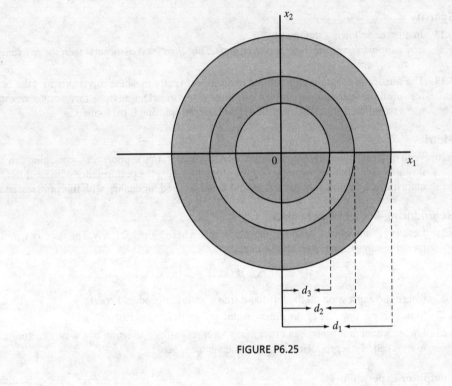

FIGURE P6.25

CHAPTER 7

Regularization Theory

ORGANIZATION OF THE CHAPTER

In this chapter, we focus attention on the many facets of regularization theory, which is at the core of all neural-network and machine-learning algorithms. Following the motivational material presented in Section 7.1, the rest of the chapter is organized as follows:

1. Section 7.2 addresses the issue of ill-posed inverse problems.
2. Section 7.3 develops Tikhonov's regularization theory, which provides the mathematical basis for the regularization of supervised-learning algorithms. This part of the chapter also includes Section 7.4, which focuses on *regularization networks* whose hidden layer has the same size as that of the training sample. Section 7.5 discusses a class of generalized radial-basis-function networks whose hidden layer is constrained to be a subset of that characterizing regularization networks. The regularized least-squares estimator is revisited in Section 7.6 as a special case of this class of generalized RBF networks. Then, in Section 7.7 we show how the insightful ideas derived from regularized least-squares estimation can be exploited in the regularization of other estimators that do not lend themselves to the application of Tikhonov's regularization theory.
3. Section 7.8 describes a procedure, based on cross-validation, for estimating the regularization parameter.
4. The last part of the chapter begins with a discussion of semisupervised learning in Section 7.9. Then, the basic ideas behind manifold regularization are discussed in Sections 7.10 through 7.12. Section 7.13 introduces spectral graph theory. Section 7.14 discusses *generalization of the representer theorem* in light of the manifold regularization theory. Section 7.15 exploits spectral graph theory on the regularized least-squares estimator (using labeled and unlabeled examples), as an illustrative application of the generalized regularization theory. In Section 7.16, we present a computer experiment on semisupervised learning, using least-squares estimation.

Section 7.17 concludes the chapter with a summary and discussion.

7.1 INTRODUCTION

In looking over the supervised-learning algorithms derived in previous chapters of the book, we find that despite the differences in their compositions, they do share a common viewpoint:

> *The training of a network by means of examples, designed to retrieve an output pattern when presented with an input pattern, is equivalent to the construction of a hypersurface (i.e., multidimensional mapping) that defines the output pattern in terms of the input pattern.*

Learning from examples as described here is an *inverse problem*, in the sense that its formulation builds on knowledge obtained from examples of the corresponding *direct problem*; the latter type of problem involves underlying physical laws that are unknown. In real-life situations, however, we usually find that the training sample suffers from a serious limitation:

> *The information content of a training sample is ordinarily not sufficient by itself to reconstruct the unknown input–output mapping uniquely—hence the possibility of overfitting by a learning machine.*

To overcome this serious problem, we may use the *method of regularization*, the aim of which is to restrict the solution of the hypersurface reconstruction problem to compact subsets by minimizing the augmented cost function:

$$\begin{pmatrix} \text{Regularized} \\ \text{cost} \\ \text{function} \end{pmatrix} = \begin{pmatrix} \text{Empirical} \\ \text{cost} \\ \text{function} \end{pmatrix} + \begin{pmatrix} \text{Regularization} \\ \text{parameter} \end{pmatrix} \times (\text{Regularizer})$$

Given a training sample, the empirical risk, or standard cost function, could, for example, be defined by a sum of error squares. The addition of the regularizer is intended to *smooth* the solution to the hypersurface reconstruction problem. Thus, through an appropriate choice of the *regularization parameter* (which is under the designer's control), the *regularized cost function* provides a tradeoff between the "fidelity" of the training sample (involved in calculating the squared errors) and "smoothness" of the solution.

In this chapter, we study two issues of fundamental importance:

1. *Classical regularization theory*, which is rooted in the regularized cost function we just described in words. This elegant theory, due to Tikhonov (1963), provides a unified mathematical basis for the regularizers discussed in previous chapters; moreover, it elaborates on them by presenting new ideas.

2. *Generalized regularization theory*, which expands the formulation of Tikhonov's classical regularization theory by including a third term; this new term, called the *manifold regularizer*, due to Belkin et al. (2006), exploits the marginal probability distribution of the input space responsible for generating *unlabeled* examples (i.e., examples without desired response). The generalized regularization theory provides a mathematical basis for *semisupervised learning* that relies on the combined use of labeled and unlabeled examples.

7.2 HADAMARD'S CONDITIONS FOR WELL-POSEDNESS

The term "well posed" was introduced by Hadamard (1902) and has been used in applied mathematics ever since. To explain this terminology, assume that we have a domain $\mathcal{X}$ and a range $\mathcal{Y}$, which are related by a fixed, but unknown, mapping f. The problem of reconstructing the mapping f is said to be *well posed* if Hadamard's three conditions are

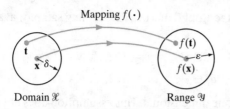

Mapping $f(\cdot)$

FIGURE 7.1   Illustration of the mapping of (input) domain $\mathcal{X}$ onto (output) range $\mathcal{Y}$.

Domain $\mathcal{X}$ Range $\mathcal{Y}$

satisfied (Tikhonov and Arsenin, 1977; Morozov, 1993; Kirsch, 1996):

1. *Existence.* For every input vector $\mathbf{x} \in \mathcal{X}$, there exists an output $y = f(\mathbf{x})$, where $y \in \mathcal{Y}$.

2. *Uniqueness.* For any pair of input vectors $\mathbf{x}, \mathbf{t} \in \mathcal{X}$, we have $f(\mathbf{x}) = f(\mathbf{t})$ if, and only if, $\mathbf{x} = \mathbf{t}$.

3. *Continuity.* The mapping f is continuous; that is, for any $\varepsilon > 0$, there exists $\delta = \delta(\varepsilon)$ such that the condition $\rho_x(\mathbf{x}, \mathbf{t}) < \delta$ implies that $\rho_y(f(\mathbf{x}), f(\mathbf{t})) < \varepsilon$, where $\rho(\cdot, \cdot)$ is the symbol for distance between the two arguments in their respective spaces. This criterion is illustrated in Fig 7.1. The property of continuity is also referred to as *stability*.

If any of these conditions is not satisfied, the problem is said to be *ill posed*. Basically, ill posedness means that large data sets may contain a surprisingly small amount of information about the desired solution.

   In the context of supervised learning, Hadamard's conditions are violated for the following reasons:[1] First, the existence criterion may be violated in that a distinct output may not exist for every input. Second, there may not be as much information in the training sample as we really need for a unique reconstruction of the input–output mapping; hence, the uniqueness criterion is likely to be violated. Third, the unavoidable presence of noise or imprecision in real-life training data adds uncertainty to the reconstruction process. In particular, if the noise level in the input is too high, it is possible for the neural network or learning machine to produce an output outside of the range $\mathcal{Y}$ for a specified input $\mathbf{x}$ in the domain $\mathcal{X}$; in other words, it is possible for the continuity criterion to be violated. If a learning problem lacks the property of continuity, then the computed input–output mapping has nothing to do with the true solution to the learning problem. There is no way to overcome these difficulties unless some prior information about the input–output mapping is available. In this context, it is rather appropriate that we remind ourselves of a statement made by Lanczos on linear differential operators (Lanczos, 1964):

   A lack of information cannot be remedied by any mathematical trickery.

7.3   TIKHONOV'S REGULARIZATION THEORY

In 1963, Tikhonov proposed a new method called *regularization* for solving ill-posed problems. In the context of a hypersurface reconstruction problem, the basic idea of regularization is to *stabilize* the solution by means of some auxiliary nonnegative functional that embeds prior information about the solution. The most common form of prior information involves the assumption that the input–output mapping function (i.e., solution to the reconstruction problem) is *smooth*, in the following sense:

   Similar inputs produce similar outputs for an input-output mapping to be smooth

To be specific, let the set of input–output data (i.e., the training sample) available for approximation be described by

$$\text{Input signal:} \qquad \mathbf{x}_i \in \mathbb{R}^m, \qquad i = 1, 2, ..., N$$
$$\text{Desired response:} \quad d_i \in \mathbb{R}, \qquad i = 1, 2, ..., N \tag{7.1}$$

Note that the output is assumed to be one dimensional. This assumption does not in any way limit the general applicability of the regularization theory being developed here. Let the approximating function be denoted by $F(\mathbf{x})$, where (for convenience of presentation) we have omitted the weight vector $\mathbf{w}$ of the network from the argument of the function F. Basically, Tikhonov's regularization theory involves two terms:

1. *Error function*, denoted by $\mathscr{E}_s(F)$, which is defined in terms of the approximating function $F(\mathbf{x}_i)$ and the training sample $\{\mathbf{x}_i, d_i\}_{i=1}^N$. For example, for the least-squares estimator, we have the standard *cost (loss) function*

$$\mathscr{E}_s(F) = \frac{1}{2} \sum_{i=1}^{N} (d_i - F(\mathbf{x}_i))^2 \tag{7.2}$$

where the subscript s in $\mathscr{E}_s$ stands for "standard." For another example that is altogether different—namely, the support vector machine—we have the *margin loss function*

$$\mathscr{E}_s(F) = \frac{1}{N} \sum_{i=1}^{N} \max(0, 1 - d_i F(\mathbf{x}_c)), \quad d_i \in \{-1, +1\}$$

We could, of course, embrace both examples under a single formula, but these two elemental loss functions are so different in their implications that their theoretical developments would have to be treated differently sooner or later. For the sake of clarity of exposition, we henceforth will focus on the error function of Eq. (7.2).

2. *Regularizer*, denoted by the term $\mathscr{E}_c(F)$, which is dependent on certain geometric properties of the approximating function $F(\mathbf{x}_i)$, as shown by

$$\mathscr{E}_c(F) = \frac{1}{2} \|\mathbf{D}F\|^2 \tag{7.3}$$

where the subscript c in $\mathscr{E}_c$ stands for "complexity." The $\mathbf{D}$ in Eq. (7.3) is a linear differential operator. Prior information about the form of the solution [i.e., the input–output mapping function $F(\mathbf{x})$] is embedded in the operator $\mathbf{D}$, which naturally makes the selection of $\mathbf{D}$ network dependent. We also refer to $\mathbf{D}$ as a *stabilizer* because it stabilizes the solution to the regularization problem, making it smooth and thereby satisfying the property of continuity. Note, however, that while smoothness implies continuity, the reverse is not necessarily true. The analytic approach used to handle the situation described in Eq. (7.3) builds on the concept of a *Hilbert space*, which was discussed in Chapter 6. In such a space, a continuous function is represented by a vector. By using this geometrical image, an insightful link is established between matrices and linear differential operators. The analysis of linear systems thereby becomes translatable to the analysis of linear differential equations (Lanczos, 1964). Thus, the symbol $\| \cdot \|$ in Eq. (7.3) denotes a norm imposed on the Hilbert space to which $\mathbf{D}F(\mathbf{x})$ belongs. With the linear differential operator $\mathbf{D}$ viewed as a map from the space of functions, to which F belongs, into a Hilbert space, it is natural to take the norm in Eq. (7.3) as the L_2 norm.

The training sample $\mathcal{T} = \{\mathbf{x}_i, d_i\}_{i=1}^N$, generated by a physical process, is represented by the regression model:

$$d_i = f(\mathbf{x}_i) + \varepsilon_i, \qquad i = 1, 2, ..., N$$

where $\mathbf{x}_i$ is the regressor, d_i is the response, and ε_i is the explanational error. Strictly speaking, we require the function $f(\mathbf{x})$ to be a member of a *reproducing-kernel Hilbert space* (RKHS) with a reproducing kernel in the form of the *Dirac delta distribution* (Tapia and Thompson, 1978); the need for this requirement will become apparent later in the discussion. The concept of RKHS was also discussed in Chapter 6.

Let $\mathcal{E}_s(F)$ denote the standard cost (loss) function and $\Omega(F)$ denote the regularizing function. Then, assuming least-squares loss, the quantity to be minimized in regularization theory is

$$\mathcal{E}(F) = \mathcal{E}_s(F) + \Omega(F)$$

$$= \frac{1}{2} \sum_{i=1}^N [d_i - F(\mathbf{x}_i)]^2 + \frac{1}{2} \lambda \, \|\mathbf{D}F\|^2 \tag{7.4}$$

where λ is a positive real number called the *regularization parameter* and $\mathcal{E}(F)$ is called the *Tikhonov functional*. A functional maps functions (defined in some suitable function space) onto the real line. The minimizer of the Tikhonov functional $\mathcal{E}(F)$ (i.e., the solution to the regularization problem) is denoted by $F_\lambda(\mathbf{x})$. It is noteworthy that Eq. (7.4) may be viewed as a constrained-optimization problem: Minimize $\mathcal{E}_s(F)$ subject to a constraint imposed on $\Omega(F)$. In so doing, we emphasize an explicit constraint on the "complexity" of the approximating function F.

Moreover, we may view the regularization parameter λ as an indicator of the sufficiency of the given training sample in specifying the solution $F_\lambda(\mathbf{x})$. In particular, the limiting case $\lambda \to 0$ implies that the problem is unconstrained, with the solution $F_\lambda(\mathbf{x})$ being completely determined from the examples. The other limiting case, $\lambda \to \infty$, on the other hand, implies that the prior smoothness constraint imposed by the differential operator $\mathbf{D}$ is by itself sufficient to specify the solution $F_\lambda(\mathbf{x})$, which is another way of saying that the examples are unreliable. In practical applications, the regularization parameter λ is assigned a value somewhere between these two limiting conditions, so that both the training-sample data and the prior information contribute to the solution $F_\lambda(\mathbf{x})$. Thus, the regularizing term $\mathcal{E}_c(F) = \frac{1}{2}\|\mathbf{D}F\|^2$ represents a *model complexity-penalty function*, the influence of which on the final solution is controlled by the regularization parameter λ.

Another way of viewing regularization is that it provides a practical solution to the bias–variance dilemma, discussed in Chapter 2. Specifically, the optimum choice of the regularization parameter λ is designed to steer the solution to the learning problem toward a satisfactory balance between model bias and model variance by incorporating the right amount of prior information into it.

Applications of Tikhonov Regularization

In the discussion on the Tikhonov regularization theory presented thus far, the emphasis has been on regression, as implied by the use of $d_i \in \mathbb{R}$ in Eq. (7.1). However, it is important to recognize that the Tikhonov regularization theory also applies to two other topics:

1. *Classification.* This may be done, for example, by simply treating binary labels as real values in standard least-squares regression. For another example, we may use empirial risk (i.e., cost) functions, such as the hinge loss, that are better suited for pattern classification, leading to support vector machines, which were discussed in Chapter 6.

2. *Structured prediction.* In some recent work, Tikhonov regularization has been applied to structural prediction, where, for example, the output space may be a sequence, a tree, or some other structured output space (Bakir et al., 2007).

The important point we wish to emphasize here is that the notion of regularization is at the heart of almost all practical settings for which the requirement is to learn from a training sample of some *finite size.*

Fréchet Differential of the Tikhonov Functional

The *principle of regularization* may now be stated as follows:

Find the approximating function $F_\lambda(\mathbf{x})$ that minimizes the Tikhonov functional $\mathcal{E}(F)$, defined by

$$\mathcal{E}(F) = \mathcal{E}_s(F) + \lambda \mathcal{E}_c(F)$$

where $\mathcal{E}_s(F)$ is the standard error term, $\mathcal{E}_c(F)$ is the regularizing term, and λ is the regularization parameter.

To proceed with the minimization of the cost functional $\mathcal{E}(F)$, we need a rule for evaluating the differential of $\mathcal{E}(F)$. We can take care of this matter by using the *Fréchet differential.* In elementary calculus, the tangent to a curve is a straight line that gives the best approximation of the curve in the neighborhood of the point of tangency. Similarly, the Fréchet differential of a functional may be interpreted as the best local linear approximation. Thus, the Fréchet differential of the functional $\mathcal{E}(F)$ is formally defined by

$$d\mathcal{E}(F, h) = \left[\frac{d}{d\beta} \mathcal{E}(F + \beta h) \right]_{\beta=0} \tag{7.5}$$

where $h(\mathbf{x})$ is a fixed function of the vector $\mathbf{x}$ (Dorny, 1975; Debnath and Mikusiński, 1990; de Figueiredo and Chen, 1993). In Eq. (7.5), the ordinary rules of differentiation apply. A necessary condition for the function $F(\mathbf{x})$ to be a relative extremum of the functional $\mathcal{E}(F)$ is that the Fréchet differential $d\mathcal{E}(F, h)$ must be zero at $F(\mathbf{x})$ for all $h \in \mathcal{H}$, as shown by

$$d\mathcal{E}(F, h) = d\mathcal{E}_s(F, h) + \lambda d\mathcal{E}_c(F, h) = 0 \tag{7.6}$$

where $d\mathcal{E}_s(F, h)$ and $d\mathcal{E}_c(F, h)$ are the Fréchet differentials of the functionals $\mathcal{E}_s(F)$ and $\mathcal{E}_c(F)$, respectively; h was used in place of $h(\mathbf{x})$ in Eq. (7.5) to simplify the presentation.

Evaluating the Fréchet differential of the standard error term $\mathcal{E}_s(F, h)$ of Eq. (7.2), we have

$$d\mathcal{E}_s(F, h) = \left[\frac{d}{d\beta} \mathcal{E}_s(F + \beta h) \right]_{\beta=0}$$

$$= \left[\frac{1}{2} \frac{d}{d\beta} \sum_{i=1}^{N} [d_i - F(\mathbf{x}_i) - \beta h(\mathbf{x}_i)]^2 \right]_{\beta=0}$$

$$= -\sum_{i=1}^{N} [d_i - F(\mathbf{x}_i) - \beta h(\mathbf{x}_i)]h(\mathbf{x}_i)|_{\beta=0} \qquad (7.7)$$

$$= -\sum_{i=1}^{N} [d_i - F(\mathbf{x}_i)]h(\mathbf{x}_i)$$

The Riesz Representation Theorem

To continue with the treatment of the Fréchet differential formulated in the Hilbert space, we find it helpful to invoke the Riesz representation theorem, which may be stated as follows (Debnath and Mikusiński, 1990):

Let f be a bounded linear functional in a Hilbert space denoted by $\mathcal{H}$. There exists one $h_0 \in \mathcal{H}$ such that

$$f(h) = \langle h, h_0 \rangle_{\mathcal{H}} \quad \text{for all } h \in \mathcal{H}$$

Moreover, we have

$$\|f\| = \|h_0\|_{\mathcal{H}}$$

where it is agreed that h_0 and f have norms in their respective spaces.

The symbol $\langle \cdot, \cdot \rangle_{\mathcal{H}}$ used here stands for the *inner (scalar) product* of two functions in the $\mathcal{H}$ space. Hence, in light of the Riesz representation theorem, we may rewrite the Fréchet differential $d\mathcal{E}_s(F, h)$ of Eq. (7.7) in the equivalent form

$$d\mathcal{E}_s(F, h) = -\left\langle h, \sum_{i=1}^{N} (d_i - F)\delta_{\mathbf{x}_i} \right\rangle_{\mathcal{H}} \qquad (7.8)$$

where $\delta_{\mathbf{x}_i}$ denotes the *Dirac delta distribution* of $\mathbf{x}$ centered at $\mathbf{x}_i$; that is,

$$\delta_{\mathbf{x}_i}(\mathbf{x}) = \delta(\mathbf{x} - \mathbf{x}_i) \qquad (7.9)$$

Consider next the evaluation of the Fréchet differential of the regularizing term $\mathcal{E}_c(F)$ of Eq. (7.3). Proceeding in a manner similar to that just described, we have (assuming that $\mathbf{D}F \in L_2(\mathbb{R}^{m_0})$)

$$d\mathcal{E}_c(F, h) = \frac{d}{d\beta}\mathcal{E}_c(F + \beta h)|_{\beta=0}$$

$$= \frac{1}{2}\frac{d}{d\beta}\int_{\mathbb{R}^{m_0}} (\mathbf{D}[F + \beta h])^2 d\mathbf{x}|_{\beta=0}$$

$$= \int_{\mathbb{R}^{m_0}} \mathbf{D}[F + \beta h]\mathbf{D}h \, d\mathbf{x}|_{\beta=0} \qquad (7.10)$$

$$= \int_{\mathbb{R}^{m_0}} \mathbf{D}F \, \mathbf{D}h \, d\mathbf{x}$$

$$= \langle \mathbf{D}h, \mathbf{D}F \rangle_{\mathcal{H}}$$

where $\langle \mathbf{D}h, \mathbf{D}F \rangle_{\mathcal{H}}$ is the inner product of the two functions $\mathbf{D}h(\mathbf{x})$ and $\mathbf{D}F(\mathbf{x})$ that results from the action of the differential operator $\mathbf{D}$ on $h(\mathbf{x})$ and $F(\mathbf{x})$, respectively.

Euler–Lagrange Equation

Given a linear differential operator $\mathbf{D}$, we can find a uniquely determined *adjoint operator*, denoted by $\tilde{\mathbf{D}}$, such that for any pair of functions $u(\mathbf{x})$ and $v(\mathbf{x})$ that are sufficiently differentiable and satisfy proper boundary conditions, we can write the following (Lanczos, 1964):

$$\int_{\mathbb{R}^m} u(\mathbf{x})\mathbf{D}v(\mathbf{x})dx = \int_{\mathbb{R}^m} v(\mathbf{x})\tilde{\mathbf{D}}u(\mathbf{x})dx \qquad (7.11)$$

Equation (7.11) is called *Green's identity*; it provides a mathematical basis for defining the adjoint operator $\tilde{\mathbf{D}}$ in terms of the given differential $\mathbf{D}$. If $\mathbf{D}$ is viewed as a matrix, the adjoint operator $\tilde{\mathbf{D}}$ plays a role similar to that of a matrix transpose.

Comparing the left-hand side of Eq. (7.11) with the fourth line of Eq. (7.10), we may make the following identifications:

$$u(\mathbf{x}) = \mathbf{D}F(\mathbf{x})$$

$$\mathbf{D}v(\mathbf{x}) = \mathbf{D}h(\mathbf{x})$$

Using Green's identity, we may rewrite Eq. (7.10) in the equivalent form

$$d\mathcal{E}_c(F, h) = \int_{\mathbb{R}^{m_0}} h(\mathbf{x})\tilde{\mathbf{D}}\mathbf{D}F(\mathbf{x})dx \qquad (7.12)$$

$$= \langle h, \tilde{\mathbf{D}}\mathbf{D}F \rangle_{\mathcal{H}}$$

where $\tilde{\mathbf{D}}$ is the adjoint of $\mathbf{D}$.

Returning to the extremum condition described in Eq. (7.6) and substituting the Fréchet differentials of Eqs. (7.8) and (7.12) into that equation, we may now express the Fréchet differential $d\mathcal{E}(F, h)$ as

$$d\mathcal{E}(F, h) = \left\langle h, \left[\tilde{\mathbf{D}}\mathbf{D}F - \frac{1}{\lambda}\sum_{i=1}^{N}(d_i - F)\delta_{\mathbf{x}_i} \right] \right\rangle_{\mathcal{H}} \qquad (7.13)$$

Since the regularization parameter λ is ordinarily assigned a value somewhere in the open interval $(0, \infty)$, the Fréchet differential $d\mathcal{E}(F, h)$ is zero for every $h(\mathbf{x})$ in $\mathcal{H}$ space if, and only if, the following condition is satisfied by $F = F_\lambda$ in the distributional sense:

$$\tilde{\mathbf{D}}\mathbf{D}F_\lambda - \frac{1}{\lambda}\sum_{i=1}^{N}(d_i - F_\lambda)\delta_{\mathbf{x}_i} = 0$$

Equivalently, we have

$$\tilde{\mathbf{D}}\mathbf{D}F_\lambda(\mathbf{x}) = \frac{1}{\lambda}\sum_{i=1}^{N}[d_i - F_\lambda(\mathbf{x}_i)]\delta(\mathbf{x} - \mathbf{x}_i) \qquad (7.14)$$

Equation (7.14) is the *Euler–Lagrange equation* for the Tikhonov functional $\mathcal{E}(F)$; it defines a necessary condition for the Tikhonov functional $\mathcal{E}(F)$ to have an extremum at $F_\lambda(\mathbf{x})$ (Debnath and Mikusiński, 1990).

Green's Function

Equation (7.14) represents a partial differential equation in the function F_λ. The solution of this equation is known to consist of the integral transformation of the right-hand side of the equation. We now digress briefly to introduce Green's function and then continue the solution to Eq. (7.14).

Let $G(\mathbf{x}, \boldsymbol{\xi})$ denote a function in which both vectors $\mathbf{x}$ and $\boldsymbol{\xi}$ appear on equal footing but for different purposes: $\mathbf{x}$ as a parameter and $\boldsymbol{\xi}$ as an argument. For a given linear differential operator $\mathbf{L}$, we stipulate that the function $G(\mathbf{x}, \boldsymbol{\xi})$ satisfies the following conditions (Courant and Hilbert, 1970):

1. For a fixed $\boldsymbol{\xi}$, $G(\mathbf{x}, \boldsymbol{\xi})$ is a function of $\mathbf{x}$ that satisfies the prescribed boundary conditions.
2. Except at the point $\mathbf{x} = \boldsymbol{\xi}$, the derivatives of $G(\mathbf{x}, \boldsymbol{\xi})$ with respect to $\mathbf{x}$ are all continuous; the number of derivatives is determined by the order of the operator $\mathbf{L}$.
3. With $G(\mathbf{x}, \boldsymbol{\xi})$ considered as a function of $\mathbf{x}$, it satisfies the partial differential equation

$$\mathbf{L}G(\mathbf{x}, \boldsymbol{\xi}) = 0 \tag{7.15}$$

everywhere, except at the point $\mathbf{x} = \boldsymbol{\xi}$, where it has a singularity. That is, the function $G(\mathbf{x}, \boldsymbol{\xi})$ satisfies the partial differential equation (taken in the sense of distributions)

$$\mathbf{L}G(\mathbf{x}, \boldsymbol{\xi}) = \delta(\mathbf{x} - \boldsymbol{\xi}) \tag{7.16}$$

where, as defined previously, $\delta(\mathbf{x} - \boldsymbol{\xi})$ is the Dirac delta function positioned at the point $\mathbf{x} = \boldsymbol{\xi}$.

The function $G(\mathbf{x}, \boldsymbol{\xi})$ is called the *influence function*, or *Green's function*, for the differential operator $\mathbf{L}$ (Courant and Hilbert, 1970). Green's function plays a role for a linear differential operator which is similar to that for the inverse matrix for a matrix equation.

Let $\varphi(\mathbf{x})$ denote a continuous or piecewise-continuous function of $\mathbf{x} \in \mathbb{R}^{m_0}$. Then the function

$$F(\mathbf{x}) = \int_{\mathbb{R}^{m_0}} G(\mathbf{x}, \boldsymbol{\xi}) \varphi(\boldsymbol{\xi}) d\boldsymbol{\xi} \tag{7.17}$$

is a solution of the differential equation

$$\mathbf{L}F(\mathbf{x}) = \varphi(\mathbf{x}) \tag{7.18}$$

where $G(\mathbf{x}, \boldsymbol{\xi})$ is Green's function for the linear differential operator $\mathbf{L}$.

To prove the validity of $F(\mathbf{x})$ as a solution of Eq. (7.18), we apply the differential operator $\mathbf{L}$ to Eq. (7.17), obtaining

$$\begin{aligned}
\mathbf{L}F(\mathbf{x}) &= \mathbf{L} \int_{\mathbb{R}^{m_0}} G(\mathbf{x}, \boldsymbol{\xi}) \varphi(\boldsymbol{\xi}) d(\boldsymbol{\xi}) \\
&= \int_{\mathbb{R}^{m_0}} \mathbf{L}G(\mathbf{x}, \boldsymbol{\xi}) \varphi(\boldsymbol{\xi}) d\boldsymbol{\xi}
\end{aligned} \tag{7.19}$$

The differential operator $\mathbf{L}$ treats $\boldsymbol{\xi}$ as a constant, acting on the kernel $G(\mathbf{x}; \boldsymbol{\xi})$ only as a function of $\mathbf{x}$. By using Eq. (7.16) in Eq. (7.19), we get

$$\mathbf{L}F(\mathbf{x}) = \int_{\mathbb{R}^{m_0}} \delta(\mathbf{x} - \boldsymbol{\xi})\varphi(\boldsymbol{\xi})d\boldsymbol{\xi}$$

Finally, using the *sifting property* of the Dirac delta function, namely,

$$\int_{\mathbb{R}^{m_0}} \varphi(\boldsymbol{\xi})\delta(\mathbf{x} - \boldsymbol{\xi})d(\boldsymbol{\xi}) = \varphi(\mathbf{x})$$

we obtain $\mathbf{L}F(\mathbf{x}) = \varphi(\mathbf{x})$, as described in Eq. (7.18).

Solution to the Regularization Problem

Returning to the issue at hand—namely, that of solving the Euler–Lagrange equation, Eq. (7.14)—we set

$$\mathbf{L} = \tilde{\mathbf{D}}\mathbf{D} \tag{7.20}$$

and

$$\varphi(\boldsymbol{\xi}) = \frac{1}{\lambda} \sum_{i=1}^{N} [d_i - F(\mathbf{x}_i)]\delta(\boldsymbol{\xi} - \mathbf{x}_i) \tag{7.21}$$

Then, we may use Eq. (7.17) to write

$$F_\lambda(\mathbf{x}) = \int_{\mathbb{R}^{m_0}} G(\mathbf{x}, \boldsymbol{\xi}) \left\{ \frac{1}{\lambda} \sum_{i=1}^{N} [d_i - F(\mathbf{x}_i)]\delta(\boldsymbol{\xi} - \mathbf{x}_i) \right\} d\boldsymbol{\xi}$$

$$= \frac{1}{\lambda} \sum_{i=1}^{N} (d_i - F(\mathbf{x}_i)) \int_{\mathbb{R}^{m_0}} G(\mathbf{x}, \boldsymbol{\xi})\delta(\boldsymbol{\xi} - \mathbf{x}_i)d\boldsymbol{\xi}$$

where, in the last line, we have interchanged the order of integration and summation. Finally, using the sifting property of the Dirac delta function, we get the desired solution to the Euler–Lagrange equation, Eq. (7.14), as shown by

$$F_\lambda(\mathbf{x}) = \frac{1}{\lambda} \sum_{i=1}^{N} [d_i - F(\mathbf{x}_i)]G(\mathbf{x}, \mathbf{x}_i) \tag{7.22}$$

Equation (7.22) states that the minimizing solution $F_\lambda(\mathbf{x})$ to the regularization problem is a linear superposition of N Green's functions. The $\mathbf{x}_i$ represent the *centers of the expansion*, and the weights $[d_i - F(\mathbf{x}_i)]/\lambda$ represent the *coefficients of the expansion*. In other words, the solution to the regularization problem lies in an N-dimensional subspace of the space of smooth functions, and the set of Green's functions $\{G(\mathbf{x}, \mathbf{x}_i)\}$ centered at $\mathbf{x}_i$, $i = 1, 2, ..., N$, constitutes a basis for this subspace (Poggio and Girosi, 1990a). Note that the coefficients of expansion in Eq. (7.22), defining the regularized function $F_\lambda(\mathbf{x})$, are

- *linear* in the estimation error, defined as the difference between the desired response d_i and the corresponding output $F(\mathbf{x}_i)$ computed by the network, and
- *inversely proportional* to the regularization parameter λ.

Determination of the Expansion Coefficients

The next issue to be resolved is the determination of the unknown coefficients in the expansion of Eq. (7.22). Let

$$w_i = \frac{1}{\lambda}[d_i - F(\mathbf{x}_i)], \qquad i = 1, 2, ..., N \tag{7.23}$$

We may then recast the minimizing solution of Eq. (7.22) simply as:

$$F_\lambda(\mathbf{x}) = \sum_{i=1}^{N} w_i G(\mathbf{x}, \mathbf{x}_i) \tag{7.24}$$

Evaluating Eq. (7.24) at $\mathbf{x}_j, j = 1, 2, ..., N$, we get a system of N simultaneous equations:

$$F_\lambda(\mathbf{x}_j) = \sum_{i=1}^{N} w_i G(\mathbf{x}_j, \mathbf{x}_i), \qquad j = 1, 2, ..., N \tag{7.25}$$

We now introduce the following matrix definitions:

$$\mathbf{F}_\lambda = [F_\lambda(\mathbf{x}_1), F_\lambda(\mathbf{x}_2), ..., F_\lambda(\mathbf{x}_N)]^T \tag{7.26}$$

$$\mathbf{d} = [d_1, d_2, ..., d_N]^T \tag{7.27}$$

$$\mathbf{G} = \begin{bmatrix} G(\mathbf{x}_1, \mathbf{x}_1) & G(\mathbf{x}_1, \mathbf{x}_2) & \cdots & G(\mathbf{x}_1, \mathbf{x}_N) \\ G(\mathbf{x}_2, \mathbf{x}_1) & G(\mathbf{x}_2, \mathbf{x}_2) & \cdots & G(\mathbf{x}_2, \mathbf{x}_N) \\ \vdots & \vdots & & \vdots \\ G(\mathbf{x}_N, \mathbf{x}_1) & G(\mathbf{x}_N, \mathbf{x}_2) & \cdots & G(\mathbf{x}_N, \mathbf{x}_N) \end{bmatrix} \tag{7.28}$$

$$\mathbf{w} = [w_1, w_2, ..., w_N]^T \tag{7.29}$$

Accordingly, we may rewrite Eqs. (7.23) and (7.25) in matrix form as follows, respectively:

$$\mathbf{w} = \frac{1}{\lambda}(\mathbf{d} - \mathbf{F}_\lambda) \tag{7.30}$$

and

$$\mathbf{F}_\lambda = \mathbf{Gw} \tag{7.31}$$

Eliminating $\mathbf{F}_\lambda$ between Eqs. (7.30) and (7.31) and rearranging terms, we get

$$(\mathbf{G} + \lambda\mathbf{I})\mathbf{w} = \mathbf{d} \tag{7.32}$$

where $\mathbf{I}$ is the N-by-N identity matrix. We call matrix $\mathbf{G}$ the *Green's matrix*.

The differential operator $\mathbf{L}$ defined in Eq. (7.20) is *self-adjoint*, in the sense that its adjoint is equal to the operator $\mathbf{L}$ itself. It follows therefore that the associated Green's function $\mathbf{G}(\mathbf{x}, \mathbf{x}_i)$ is a *symmetric function*, as shown by

$$G(\mathbf{x}_i, \mathbf{x}_j) = G(\mathbf{x}_j, \mathbf{x}_i) \qquad \text{for all } i \text{ and } j \tag{7.33}$$

Equation (7.33) states that the positions of any two points $\mathbf{x}$ and $\boldsymbol{\xi}$ can be interchanged without affecting the value of the Green's function $G(\mathbf{x}, \boldsymbol{\xi})$. Equivalently, the Green's matrix $\mathbf{G}$ defined in Eq. (7.28) is a *symmetric matrix*; that is,

$$\mathbf{G}^T = \mathbf{G} \tag{7.34}$$

We now invoke the interpolation theorem, which was described in Chapter 5 in the context of the interpolation matrix $\mathbf{\Phi}$. We first note that Green's matrix $\mathbf{G}$ plays a role in regularization theory similar to that of $\mathbf{\Phi}$ in RBF interpolation theory. Both $\mathbf{G}$ and $\mathbf{\Phi}$ are N-by-N symmetric matrices. Accordingly, we may state that the matrix $\mathbf{G}$, for certain classes of Green's functions, is positive definite provided that the data points $\mathbf{x}_1, \mathbf{x}_2, ..., \mathbf{x}_N$ are distinct. The classes of Green's functions covered by Micchelli's theorem include inverse multiquadrics and Gaussian functions, but not multiquadrics. In practice, we may always choose λ sufficiently large to ensure that the sum matrix $\mathbf{G} + \lambda \mathbf{I}$ is positive definite and therefore invertible. This, in turn, means that the linear system of equations (7.32) will have a unique solution given by the following (Poggio and Girosi, 1990a):

$$\mathbf{w} = (\mathbf{G} + \lambda \mathbf{I})^{-1} \mathbf{d} \tag{7.35}$$

Thus, having selected the differential operator $\mathbf{D}$ and therefore having identified the associated Green's function $G(\mathbf{x}_j, \mathbf{x}_i)$, where $i = 1, 2, ..., N$, we may use Eq. (7.35) to compute the weight vector $\mathbf{w}$ for a specified desired response vector $\mathbf{d}$ and an appropriate value of regularization parameter λ.

The solution to the regularization problem is thus given by the expansion

$$F_\lambda(\mathbf{x}) = \sum_{i=1}^{N} w_i G(\mathbf{x}, \mathbf{x}_i) \tag{7.36}$$

Accordingly, we may now make the following threefold statement:

1. *The approximating function $F_\lambda(\mathbf{x})$, which minimizes the regularized cost function $\xi(F)$ of Eq. (7.4), is made up of an expansion of linearly weighted Green's functions, with each Green's function depending only on the stablizer $\mathbf{D}$.*
2. *The number of Green's functions used in the expansion is equal to the size of the training sample, N.*
3. *The corresponding N weights of the expansion are defined in terms of the training sample $\{x_i, d_i\}_{i=1}^{N}$ and regularization parameter λ by Eq. (7.23).*

If the stabilizer $\mathbf{D}$ is *translationally invariant*, the Green's function $G(\mathbf{x}, \mathbf{x}_i)$ centered at $\mathbf{x}_i$ will depend only on the difference between the arguments $\mathbf{x}$ and $\mathbf{x}_i$; that is,

$$G(\mathbf{x}, \mathbf{x}_i) = G(\mathbf{x} - \mathbf{x}_i) \tag{7.37}$$

If the stabilizer $\mathbf{D}$ is both *translationally and rotationally invariant*, the Green's function $G(\mathbf{x}, \mathbf{x}_i)$ will depend only on the *Euclidean norm* of the difference vector $\mathbf{x} - \mathbf{x}_i$, as shown by

$$G(\mathbf{x}, \mathbf{x}_i) = G(\|\mathbf{x} - \mathbf{x}_i\|) \tag{7.38}$$

Under these conditions, the Green's function must be a *radial-basis function*. In such a case, the regularized solution of Eq. (7.36) takes on the special form

$$F_\lambda(\mathbf{x}) = \sum_{i=1}^{N} w_i G(\|\mathbf{x} - \mathbf{x}_i\|) \tag{7.39}$$

which constructs a linear function space that depends on the known data points according to the Euclidean distance measure.

The solution described by Eq. (7.39) is termed *strict interpolation*, since all the N data points available for training are used to generate the interpolating function $F(\mathbf{x})$. It is important, however, to realize that this solution differs from that of Eq. (5.11) of Chapter 5 in a fundamental respect: The solution of Eq. (7.39) is *regularized* by virtue of the definition given in Eq. (7.35) for the weight vector $\mathbf{w}$. It is only when we set the regularization parameter λ equal to zero that the two solutions may become one and the same.

Multivariate Gaussian Functions

The Green's function $G(\mathbf{x}, \mathbf{x}_i)$ whose linear differential operator $\mathbf{D}$ is both translationally and rotationally invariant and that satisfies the condition of Eq. (7.38) is of particular interest in practice. An example of such a Green's function is the *multivariate Gaussian function* defined by

$$G(\mathbf{x}, \mathbf{x}_i) = \exp\left(-\frac{1}{2\sigma_i^2}\|\mathbf{x} - \mathbf{x}_i\|^2\right) \tag{7.40}$$

where $\mathbf{x}_i$ denotes the center of the function and σ_i denotes its width. The self-adjoint operator $\mathbf{L} = \tilde{\mathbf{D}}\mathbf{D}$, which defines the Green's function of Eq. (7.40) in accordance with Eq. (7.16), is given by

$$\mathbf{L} = \sum_{n=0}^{\infty}(-1)^n\alpha_n\nabla^{2n} \tag{7.41}$$

where

$$\alpha_n = \frac{\sigma_i^{2n}}{n!2^n} \tag{7.42}$$

and ∇^{2n} is the *iterated Laplacian operator* in m_0 dimensions, with

$$\nabla^2 = \frac{\partial^2}{\partial x_1^2} + \frac{\partial^2}{\partial x_2^2} + \cdots + \frac{\partial^2}{\partial x_{m_0}^2} \tag{7.43}$$

With the number of terms permitted to go to infinity in Eq. (7.41), $\mathbf{L}$ ceases to be a differential operator in the standard sense. For this reason, the operator $\mathbf{L}$ in Eq. (7.41) is referred to as a *pseudodifferential operator*.

Since by definition, $\mathbf{L} = \tilde{\mathbf{D}}\mathbf{D}$, we deduce from Eq. (7.41) that the operator $\mathbf{D}$ and its adjoint $\tilde{\mathbf{D}}$ are as follows, respectively:

$$\mathbf{D} = \sum_n \alpha_n^{1/2}\left(\frac{\partial}{\partial x_1} + \frac{\partial}{\partial x_2} + \cdots + \frac{\partial}{\partial x_{m_0}}\right)^n \tag{7.44}$$

$$= \sum_{a+b+\cdots+k=n} \alpha_n^{1/2}\frac{\partial^n}{\partial x_1^a\partial x_2^b \ldots \partial x_{m_0}^k},$$

and

$$
\tilde{\mathbf{D}} = \sum_{n} (-1)^n \alpha_n^{1/2} \left(\frac{\partial}{\partial x_1} + \frac{\partial}{\partial x_2} + \cdots + \frac{\partial}{\partial x_{m_0}} \right)^n
$$

$$
= \sum_{a+b+\cdots+k=n} (-1)^n \alpha_n^{1/2} \frac{\partial^n}{\partial x_1^a \partial x_2^b \cdots \partial x_{m_0}^k}
$$

(7.45)

Thus, the regularized solution described in Eq. (7.39) is attained by using a stabilizer that includes all of its possible partial derivatives.

Using Eqs. (7.40) to (7.42) in Eq. (7.16) with $\boldsymbol{\xi}$ set equal to $\mathbf{x}_i$, we may write[2]

$$
\sum_{n=0}^{\infty} (-1)^n \frac{\sigma_i^{2n}}{n! 2^n} \nabla^{2n} \exp\left(-\frac{1}{2\sigma_i^2} \|\mathbf{x} - \mathbf{x}_i\|^2 \right) = \delta(\mathbf{x} - \mathbf{x}_i)
$$

(7.46)

With the Green's function $G(\mathbf{x}, \mathbf{x}_i)$ defined by the special form of Eq. (7.40), the regularized solution given in Eq. (7.36) takes the form of a linear superposition of multivariate Gaussian functions,

$$
F_\lambda(\mathbf{x}) = \sum_{i=1}^{N} w_i \exp\left(-\frac{1}{2\sigma_i^2} \|\mathbf{x} - \mathbf{x}_i\|^2 \right)
$$

(7.47)

where, as before, the linear weights w_i are themselves defined by Eq. (7.23).

In Eq. (7.47), the individual Gaussian members of the sum defining the approximating function $F_\lambda(\mathbf{x})$ are assigned different variances. To simplify matters, the condition $\sigma_i = \sigma$ for all i is often imposed on $F(\mathbf{x})$. Even though the RBF networks thus designed are of a somewhat restricted kind, they are still universal approximators (Park and Sandberg, 1991).

7.4   REGULARIZATION NETWORKS

The expansion of the regularized approximating function $F_\lambda(\mathbf{x})$ given in Eq. (7.36) in terms of the Green's function $G(\mathbf{x}, \mathbf{x}_i)$ centered at $\mathbf{x}_i$ suggests the network structure shown in Fig. 7.2 as a model for its implementation. For obvious reasons, this model is called a *regularization network* (Poggio and Girosi, 1990a). The network consists of three layers. The first layer is composed of input (source) nodes whose number is equal to the dimension m_0 of the input vector $\mathbf{x}$ (i.e., the number of independent variables of the problem). The second layer is a hidden layer composed of nonlinear units that are connected *directly* to all of the nodes in the input layer. There is one hidden unit for each data point $\mathbf{x}_i, i = 1, 2, ..., N$, where N is the size of the training sample. The activation functions of the individual hidden units are defined by a total of N Green's functions. Accordingly, the output of the ith hidden unit is $G(\mathbf{x}, \mathbf{x}_i)$. The output layer consists of a single linear unit, being fully connected to the hidden layer. By "linearity," we mean that the output of the network is a linearly weighted sum of the outputs of the hidden units. The weights of the output layer are the unknown coefficients of the expansion, defined in terms of the Green's functions $G(\mathbf{x}, \mathbf{x}_i)$ and the regularization parameter λ as seen in Eq. (7.23) or, equivalently, Eq. (7.35). Figure 7.2 depicts the architecture of the

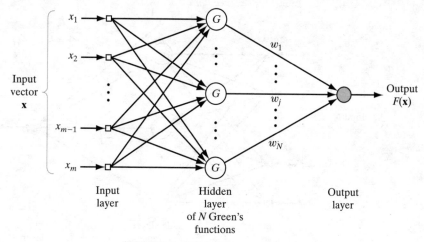

FIGURE 7.2   Regularization network.

regularization network for a single output. Clearly, such an architecture can be readily extended to accommodate any number of network outputs desired.

The regularization network shown in Fig. 7.2 assumes that Green's function $G(\mathbf{x}, \mathbf{x}_i)$ is *positive definite* for all i. Provided that this condition is satisfied, which it is in the case of the $G(\mathbf{x}, \mathbf{x}_i)$ having the Gaussian form given in Eq. (7.40), for example, then the solution produced by this network will be an "optimal" interpolant in the sense that it minimizes the functional $\mathscr{E}(F)$. Moreover, from the viewpoint of approximation theory, the regularization network has the following desirable properties (Poggio and Girosi, 1990a):

(i) The regularization network is a *universal approximator*, in that it can approximate arbitrarily well any multivariate continuous function on a compact subset of $\mathbb{R}^{m_0}$, given a sufficiently large number of hidden units.

(ii) Since the approximation scheme derived from regularization theory is linear in the unknown coefficients, it follows that the regularization network has the *best approximation property*. This means that given an unknown nonlinear function f, there always exists a choice of coefficients that approximates f better than all other possible choices. The solution computed by the regularization network is therefore *optimal*.

7.5   GENERALIZED RADIAL-BASIS-FUNCTION NETWORKS

The one-to-one correspondence between the training input vector $\mathbf{x}_i$ and the Green's function $G(\mathbf{x}, \mathbf{x}_i)$ for $i = 1, 2, ..., N$ produces a regularization network that may sometimes be considered prohibitively expensive to implement in computational terms

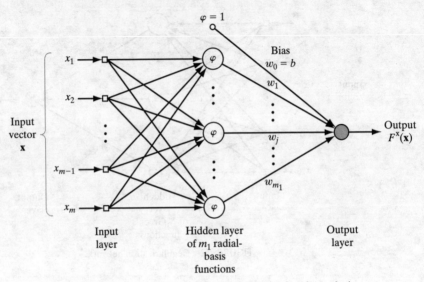

FIGURE 7.3   Radial-basis-function network of reduced complexity.

for large N. Specifically, the computation of the linear weights of the network [i.e., the coefficients of the expansion in Eq. (7.36)] requires the inversion of an N-by-N matrix, which therefore grows polynomially with N (roughly as N^3). Furthermore, the likelihood of *ill conditioning* (i.e., large conditioning number) is higher for larger matrices; the *condition number* of a matrix is defined as the ratio of the largest eigenvalue to the smallest eigenvalue of the matrix. To overcome these computational difficulties, the complexity of the network is reduced or the regularization parameter λ is increased.

The reduced complexity of the RBF network, depicted in Fig. 7.3, is based on the search for a suboptimal solution in a lower-dimensional space that approximates the regularized solution of Eq. (7.36). This is done by using a standard technique known in variational problems as *Galerkin's method*. According to this technique, the approximated solution $F^*(\mathbf{x})$ is expanded on a finite basis, as shown by

$$F^*(\mathbf{x}) = \sum_{i=1}^{m_1} w_i \varphi(\mathbf{x}, \mathbf{t}_i) \tag{7.48}$$

where $\{\varphi(\mathbf{x}, \mathbf{t}_i) | i = 1, 2, ..., m_1\}$ is a new set of basis functions that we assume to be linearly independent without loss of generality (Poggio and Girosi, 1990a). Typically, the number of basis functions is fewer than the number of data points (i.e., $m_1 < N$), and the w_i constitute a new set of weights. With radial-basis functions in mind, we set

$$\varphi(\mathbf{x}, \mathbf{t}_i) = G(\|\mathbf{x} - \mathbf{t}_i\|), \qquad i = 1, 2, ..., m_1 \tag{7.49}$$

This particular choice of basis functions is the only one which guarantees that in the case of $m_1 = N$ and

$$\mathbf{t}_i = \mathbf{x}_i, \qquad i = 1, 2, ..., N \tag{7.49}$$

the correct solution of Eq. (7.39) is consistently recovered. Thus, using Eq. (7.49) in Eq. (7.48), we may redefine $F^*(\mathbf{x})$ as

$$
\begin{aligned}
F^*(\mathbf{x}) &= \sum_{i=1}^{m_1} w_i G(\mathbf{x}, \mathbf{t}_i) \\
&= \sum_{i=1}^{m_1} w_i G(\|\mathbf{x} - \mathbf{t}_i\|)
\end{aligned}
\tag{7.50}
$$

Given the expansion of Eq. (7.50) for the approximating function $F^*(\mathbf{x})$, the problem we now address is the determination of the new set of weights $\{w_i\}_{i=1}^{m_1}$ so as to minimize the new cost functional $\mathscr{E}(F^*)$ defined by

$$
\mathscr{E}(F^*) = \sum_{i=1}^{N}\left(d_i - \sum_{j=1}^{m_1} w_j G(\|\mathbf{x}_i - \mathbf{t}_j\|)\right)^2 + \lambda\|\mathbf{D}F^*\|^2
\tag{7.51}
$$

The first term on the right-hand side of Eq. (7.51) may be expressed as the squared Euclidean norm $\|\mathbf{d} - \mathbf{G}\mathbf{w}\|^2$, where

$$
\mathbf{d} = [d_1, d_2, \ldots, d_N]^T
\tag{7.52}
$$

$$
\mathbf{G} = \begin{bmatrix}
G(\mathbf{x}_1, \mathbf{t}_1) & G(\mathbf{x}_1, \mathbf{t}_2) & \cdots & G(\mathbf{x}_1, \mathbf{t}_{m_i}) \\
G(\mathbf{x}_2, \mathbf{t}_1) & G(\mathbf{x}_2, \mathbf{t}_2) & \cdots & G(\mathbf{x}_2, \mathbf{t}_{m_i}) \\
\vdots & \vdots & & \vdots \\
G(\mathbf{x}_N, \mathbf{t}_1) & G(\mathbf{x}_N, \mathbf{t}_2) & \cdots & G(\mathbf{x}_N, \mathbf{t}_{m_i})
\end{bmatrix}
\tag{7.53}
$$

$$
\mathbf{w} = [w_1, w_2, \ldots, w_{m_1}]^T
\tag{7.54}
$$

The desired-response vector $\mathbf{d}$ is N dimensional as before. However, the matrix $\mathbf{G}$ of Green's functions and the weight vector $\mathbf{w}$ have different dimensions; the matrix $\mathbf{G}$ is now N by m_1 and therefore no longer symmetric, and the vector $\mathbf{w}$ is m_1 by 1. From Eq. (7.50), we note that the approximating function F^* is a linear combination of the Green's functions for the stabilizer $\mathbf{D}$. Accordingly, in light of the material covered previously, we may express the second term on the right-hand side of Eq. (7.51) as

$$
\begin{aligned}
\|\mathbf{D}F^*\|^2 &= <\mathbf{D}F^*, \mathbf{D}F^*>_{\mathscr{H}} \\
&= \left[\sum_{i=1}^{m_1} w_i G(\mathbf{x}, \mathbf{t}_i), \tilde{\mathbf{D}}\mathbf{D}\sum_{i=1}^{m_1} w_i G(\mathbf{x}; \mathbf{t}_i)\right]_{\mathscr{H}} \\
&= \left[\sum_{i=1}^{m_1} w_i G(\mathbf{x}, \mathbf{t}_i), \sum_{i=1}^{m_1} w\delta_{\mathbf{t}_i}\right]_{\mathscr{H}} \\
&= \sum_{j=1}^{m_1}\sum_{i=1}^{m_1} w_j w_i G(\mathbf{t}_j, \mathbf{t}_i) \\
&= \mathbf{w}^T \mathbf{G}_0 \mathbf{w}
\end{aligned}
\tag{7.55}
$$

where, in the second and third lines, we made use of the definition of an adjoint operator and Eq. (7.16), respectively. The new matrix $\mathbf{G}_0$ is a symmetric m_1-by-m_1 matrix, defined by

$$\mathbf{G}_0 = \begin{bmatrix} G(\mathbf{t}_1, \mathbf{t}_1) & G(\mathbf{t}_1, \mathbf{t}_2) & \cdots & G(\mathbf{t}_1, \mathbf{t}_{m_1}) \\ G(\mathbf{t}_2, \mathbf{t}_1) & G(\mathbf{t}_2, \mathbf{t}_2) & \cdots & G(\mathbf{t}_2, \mathbf{t}_{m_1}) \\ \vdots & \vdots & \vdots & \vdots \\ G(\mathbf{t}_{m_1}, \mathbf{t}_1) & G(\mathbf{t}_{m_1}, \mathbf{t}_2) & \cdots & G(\mathbf{t}_{m_1}, \mathbf{t}_{m_1}) \end{bmatrix} \tag{7.56}$$

Thus, the minimization of Eq. (7.51) with respect to the weight vector $\mathbf{w}$ yields the following result (see Problem 7.4):

$$(\mathbf{G}^T\mathbf{G} + \lambda \mathbf{G}_0)\hat{\mathbf{w}} = \mathbf{G}^T\mathbf{d}$$

Solving this equation for the weight vector $\hat{\mathbf{w}}$, we obtain

$$\hat{\mathbf{w}} = (\mathbf{G}^T\mathbf{G} + \lambda \mathbf{G}_0)^{-1}\mathbf{G}^T\mathbf{d} \tag{7.57}$$

As the regularization parameter λ approaches zero, the optimized weight vector $\hat{\mathbf{w}}$ converges to the pseudoinverse (minimum-norm) solution to the underdetermined least-squares data-fitting problem for $m_1 < N$, as shown by

$$\mathbf{w} = \mathbf{G}^+\mathbf{d}, \qquad \lambda = 0 \tag{7.58}$$

where $\mathbf{G}^+$ is the *pseudoinverse* of matrix $\mathbf{G}$ (Golub and Van Loan, 1996); that is,

$$\mathbf{G}^+ = (\mathbf{G}^T\mathbf{G})^{-1}\mathbf{G}^T \tag{7.59}$$

Weighted Norm

The norm in the approximated solution of Eq. (7.50) is ordinarily intended to be a Euclidean norm. When, however, the individual elements of the input vector $\mathbf{x}$ belong to different classes, it is more appropriate to consider a general *weighted norm*, the squared form of which is defined by

$$\begin{aligned} \|\mathbf{x}\|_C^2 &= (\mathbf{C}\mathbf{x})^T(\mathbf{C}\mathbf{x}) \\ &= \mathbf{x}^T\mathbf{C}^T\mathbf{C}\mathbf{x} \end{aligned} \tag{7.60}$$

where $\mathbf{C}$ is an m_0-by-m_0 *norm-weighting matrix* and m_0 is the dimension of the input vector $\mathbf{x}$.

Using the definition of weighted norm, we may now rewrite the approximation to the regularized solution given in Eq. (7.50) in the following more generalized form (Lowe, 1989; Poggio and Girosi, 1990a):

$$F^*(\mathbf{x}) = \sum_{i=1}^{m_1} w_i G(\|\mathbf{x} - \mathbf{t}_i\|_C) \tag{7.61}$$

The use of a weighted norm may be interpreted in two ways. We may simply view it as applying an *affine transformation* to the original input space. In principle, allowing for such a transformation cannot degrade results from the default case, since it actually corresponds to an identity norm-weighting matrix. On the other hand, the weighted norm follows directly from a slight generalization of the m_0-dimensional Laplacian in the definition of the pseudodifferential operator $\mathbf{D}$ in Eq. (7.44). The use of a weighted norm may also be justified in the context of Gaussian radial-basis functions on the following grounds: A Gaussian radial-based function $G(\|\mathbf{x} - \mathbf{t}_i\|_C)$ centered at $\mathbf{t}_i$ and with norm-weighting matrix $\mathbf{C}$ may be expressed as

$$G(\|\mathbf{x} - \mathbf{t}_i\|_C = \exp[-(\mathbf{x} - \mathbf{t}_i)^T \mathbf{C}^T \mathbf{C}(\mathbf{x} - \mathbf{t}_i)]$$

$$= \exp\left[-\frac{1}{2}(\mathbf{x} - \mathbf{t}_i)^T \mathbf{\Sigma}^{-1}(\mathbf{x} - \mathbf{t}_i)\right] \qquad (7.62)$$

where the inverse matrix $\mathbf{\Sigma}^{-1}$ is defined by

$$\frac{1}{2}\mathbf{\Sigma}^{-1} = \mathbf{C}^T \mathbf{C}$$

The generalized multivariate Gaussian distribution of Eq. (7.62) has an exponent equal to the Mahalanobis distance; see Eq. (27) of the introductory chapter. It is for this reason that a kernel defined by Eq. (7.62) is referred to as the *Mahalanobis kernel*. This kernel was also discussed in Problem 6.10 of Chapter 6.

The solution to the approximation problem given in Eq. (7.51) provides the framework for the *generalized radial-basis-function (RBF) network's* having the structure shown in Fig. 7.3. In this network, provision is made for a bias (i.e., data-independent variable) applied to the output unit. This is done simply by setting one of the linear weights in the output layer of the network equal to the bias and treating the associated radial-basis function as a constant equal to +1.

In structural terms, the generalized RBF network of Fig. 7.3 is similar to the regularization RBF network of Fig. 7.2. However, they differ from each other in two important ways:

1. The number of nodes in the hidden layer of the generalized RBF network of Fig. 7.3 is m_1, where m_1 is ordinarily smaller than the number N of examples available for training. On the other hand, the number of hidden nodes in the regularization RBF network of Fig. 7.2 is exactly N.

2. In the generalized RBF network of Fig. 7.3, the linear weights associated with the output layer, the positions of the centers of the radial-basis functions, and the norm-weighting matrix associated with the hidden layer are all unknown parameters that have to be learned. However, the activation functions of the hidden layer in the regularization RBF network of Fig. 7.2 are known, being defined by a set of Green's functions centered at the training data points; the linear weights of the output layer are the only unknown parameters of the network.

7.6   THE REGULARIZED LEAST-SQUARES ESTIMATOR: REVISITED

We first studied the *least-squares estimator* in Chapter 2, and then we made use of it in Chapter 5 for computing the output layer of a suboptimal RBF network. In this section, we revisit this relatively simple, yet effective, estimator one more time, with two points in mind: First, we will show that the formula of Eq. (7.57) includes the regularized least-squares estimator as a special case. Second, we will show that, like any other kernel method, regularized least-squares estimation is also governed by the *Representer Theorem*.

The Least-Squares Estimator Viewed as a Special Case of Eq. (7.57)

Given the training sample $\{\mathbf{x}_i, d_i\}_{i=1}^{N}$, the regularized cost function of a least-squares estimator is defined by (see Chapter 2)

$$\mathscr{E}(\mathbf{w}) = \frac{1}{2} \sum_{i=1}^{N} (d_i - \mathbf{w}^T \mathbf{x}_i)^2 + \frac{1}{2} \lambda \|\mathbf{w}\|^2 \tag{7.63}$$

where the weight vector $\mathbf{w}$ is fixed throughout the training interval and λ is the regularization parameter. Comparing this cost function with that of Eq. (7.4), we readily see that the regularizer is defined in terms of $\mathbf{w}$ simply as

$$\|\mathbf{D}F\|^2 = \|\mathbf{w}\|^2$$
$$= \mathbf{w}^T \mathbf{w}$$

in light of which we may immediately set the symmetric matrix $\mathbf{G}_0$ in Eq. (7.57) equal to the identity matrix. Correspondingly, the line preceding Eq. (7.57) reduces to

$$(\mathbf{G}^T \mathbf{G} + \lambda \mathbf{I})\hat{\mathbf{w}} = \mathbf{G}^T \mathbf{d}$$

Next, noting that since the least-squares estimator is linear and also lacks a hidden layer, we may go on to express the transpose of the remaining matrix $\mathbf{G}$ of Eq. (7.53) simply as

$$\mathbf{G}^T = [\mathbf{x}_1, \mathbf{x}_2, ..., \mathbf{x}_N] \tag{7.64}$$

Then, using this expression for $\mathbf{G}^T$ and the expression of Eq. (7.52) for the desired response d in the regularized solution of Eq. (7.57) for the weight vector $\hat{\mathbf{w}}$, we get (after some algebraic manipulations)

$$\hat{\mathbf{w}} = (\mathbf{R}_{xx} + \lambda \mathbf{I})^{-1} \mathbf{r}_{dx} \tag{7.65}$$

where

$$\mathbf{R}_{xx} = \sum_{i=1}^{N} \mathbf{x}_i \mathbf{x}_i^T$$

and

$$\mathbf{r}_{dx} = \sum_{i=1}^{N} \mathbf{x}_i d_i$$

Equation (7.65) is a repeat of the formula defined in Eq. (2.29) for the *maximum a posteriori (MAP) estimator*, which, as pointed out previously, also applies to the *regularized least-squares (RLS) estimator*.

Using the expressions for the correlation matrix $\mathbf{R}_{xx}$ and the cross-correlation vector $\mathbf{r}_{dx}$, we may restate the formula of Eq. (7.65) directly in terms of the training sample $\{\mathbf{x}_i, d_i\}_{i=1}^{N}$ as

$$\hat{\mathbf{w}} = (\mathbf{X}^T\mathbf{X} + \lambda\mathbf{I})^{-1}\mathbf{X}^T\mathbf{d} \tag{7.66}$$

where $\mathbf{X}$ is the input data matrix

$$\mathbf{X} = \begin{bmatrix} x_{11} & x_{12} & \cdots & x_{1M} \\ x_{21} & x_{22} & \cdots & x_{2M} \\ \vdots & \vdots & & \vdots \\ x_{N1} & x_{N2} & \cdots & x_{NM} \end{bmatrix} \tag{7.67}$$

where the subscript N is the size of the training sample and the subscript M is the dimension of the weight vector $\hat{\mathbf{w}}$. The vector $\mathbf{d}$ is the *desired-response vector*, defined in Eq. (7.52); it is reproduced here for convenience of presentation:

$$\mathbf{d} = [d_1, d_2, ..., d_N]^T$$

The Least-Squares Estimator Viewed in Light of the Representer Theorem

Next, viewing the least-squares estimator as a "kernel machine," we may express its kernel as the inner product

$$k(\mathbf{x}, \mathbf{x}_i) = \langle \mathbf{x}, \mathbf{x}_i \rangle$$
$$= \mathbf{x}^T\mathbf{x}_i, \quad i = 1, 2, ..., N \tag{7.68}$$

Then, invoking the *Representer Theorem*, discussed in Chapter 6, we may express the approximating function realized by the regularized least-squares estimator as

$$F_\lambda(\mathbf{x}) = \sum_{i=1}^{N} a_i k(\mathbf{x}, \mathbf{x}_i) \tag{7.69}$$

where the *expansion coefficients* $\{a_i\}_{i=1}^{N}$ are uniquely defined by the training sample $\{\mathbf{x}_i, d_i\}_{i=1}^{N}$; the question is, how?

To address this question, we first use the identity

$$\mathbf{X}^T(\mathbf{X}\mathbf{X}^T + \lambda\mathbf{I}_N)^{-1}\mathbf{d} = (\mathbf{X}^T\mathbf{X} + \lambda\mathbf{I}_M)^{-1}\mathbf{X}^T\mathbf{d} \tag{7.70}$$

where $\mathbf{X}$ is the N-by-M input data matrix, $\mathbf{d}$ is the N-by-1 desired-response vector, λ is the regularization parameter, and $\mathbf{I}_N$ and $\mathbf{I}_M$ are respective identity matrices of sizes N and M; as a reminder, M is the size of the weight vector $\mathbf{w}$. A proof of the matrix identity of Eq. (7.70) is addressed in Problem 7.11. The right-hand side of this equation is recognized as the formula for the optimized weight vector $\hat{\mathbf{w}}$; see Eq. (7.66). Using the identity of Eq. (7.70), we may therefore express the approximating function realized by the regularized least-squares estimator in terms of the weight vector $\hat{\mathbf{w}}$ and the input vector $\mathbf{x}$ as

$$F_\lambda(\mathbf{x}) = \mathbf{x}^T\hat{\mathbf{w}}$$
$$= \mathbf{x}^T\mathbf{X}^T(\mathbf{X}\mathbf{X}^T + \lambda\mathbf{I}_N)^{-1}\mathbf{d} \tag{7.71}$$

which is now formulated as the inner product

$$F_\lambda(\mathbf{x}) = \mathbf{k}^T(\mathbf{x})\mathbf{a}$$
$$= \mathbf{a}^T\mathbf{k}(\mathbf{x}) \tag{7.72}$$

This formula is the matrix version of the representer theorem of Eq. (7.69), with the following interpretations:

1. The row vector of kernels is defined in terms of the input vector $\mathbf{x}$ and the data matrix $\mathbf{X}$, as shown by

$$
\begin{aligned}
\mathbf{k}^T(\mathbf{x}) &= [k(\mathbf{x}, \mathbf{x}_1), k(\mathbf{x}, \mathbf{x}_2), ..., k(\mathbf{x}, \mathbf{x}_N)] \\
&= \mathbf{x}^T \mathbf{X}^T = (\mathbf{X}\mathbf{x})^T
\end{aligned}
\tag{7.73}
$$

which is a 1-by-N row vector, as it should be.

2. The vector of expansion coefficients, $\mathbf{a}$, is defined in terms of the estimator's N-by-N kernel matrix, or Gram, $\mathbf{K}$, the regularization parameter λ, and the desired-response vector $\mathbf{d}$, as shown by

$$
\begin{aligned}
\mathbf{a} &= [a_1, a_2, ..., a_N]^T \\
&= (\mathbf{K} + \lambda \mathbf{I}_N)^{-1} \mathbf{d}
\end{aligned}
\tag{7.74}
$$

where

$$
\begin{aligned}
\mathbf{K} &= \mathbf{X}\mathbf{X}^T \\
&= \begin{bmatrix}
\mathbf{x}_1^T \mathbf{x}_1 & \mathbf{x}_1^T \mathbf{x}_2 & \cdots & \mathbf{x}_1^T \mathbf{x}_N \\
\mathbf{x}_2^T \mathbf{x}_1 & \mathbf{x}_2^T \mathbf{x}_2 & \cdots & \mathbf{x}_2^T \mathbf{x}_1 \\
\vdots & \vdots & & \vdots \\
\mathbf{x}_N^T \mathbf{x}_1 & \mathbf{x}_N^T \mathbf{x}_2 & \cdots & \mathbf{x}_N^T \mathbf{x}_N
\end{bmatrix}
\end{aligned}
\tag{7.75}
$$

Two Equivalent Ways of Describing the Regularized Least-Squares Estimator

From the discussion presented in this section, we see that, in fact, there are two ways of describing the approximating function $F_\lambda(\mathbf{x})$ realized by a regularized least-squares estimator:

1. The formula of Eq. (7.71), which is defined in terms of the weight vector $\hat{\mathbf{w}}$ for a given input vector $\mathbf{x}$. Basically, this formulation is traced back to the normal equation for least-squares estimation, as discussed in Chapter 2.
2. The formula of Eq. (7.72), which is defined in terms of the estimator's kernel. This second formulation follows from the Representer Theorem derived in Chapter 6. The important virtue of this formula is that it bypasses the need for computing the weight vector of the RLS algorithm, which is the essence of the "kernel trick," discussed in Chapter 6.

The first viewpoint on regularized least-squares estimation, formulated in terms of the normal equation, is well known in the statistics literature. However, the second viewpoint formulated in terms of the representer theorem (well-known in the kernel-learning literature) is new.

7.7   ADDITIONAL NOTES OF INTEREST ON REGULARIZATION

An attribute of Gaussian-based RBF networks is that they do lend themselves to rigorous application of Tikhonov's regularization theory, as demonstrated in Sections 7.4 and 7.5. The same remark also applies to least-squares estimators, as shown in Section 7.6.

The aim of this section is to capitalize on lessons learned from least-squares estimation and extend them to situations where the application of Tikhonov's regularization theory is a difficult undertaking.

Regression

Referring back to Eq. (7.63), it is insightful to reproduce this equation in the form:

$$\mathscr{E}(\mathbf{w}) = \underbrace{\frac{1}{2} \sum_{i=1}^{N} (d_i - \mathbf{w}^T \mathbf{x}_i)^2}_{\substack{\text{Regularized} \\ \text{cost function}}} \;\;\;\; \underbrace{\phantom{\frac{1}{2} \sum}}_{\substack{\text{Empirical} \\ \text{risk}}} + \underbrace{\frac{1}{2} \lambda \|\mathbf{w}\|^2}_{\substack{\text{Regularization} \\ \text{term}}} \tag{7.76}$$

Viewed in the context of regression, the term $\frac{1}{2} \|\mathbf{w}\|^2$ has a certain intuitive appeal. Geometrically speaking, in minimizing the cost function $\mathscr{E}(\mathbf{w})$, it turns out that inclusion of the regularizer $\frac{1}{2} \|\mathbf{w}\|^2$ is helpful in finding the flattest function with desirable approximation properties. Indeed, it was with this aim in mind that in Section 4.14, we proposed minimizing the cost function

$$\mathscr{E}(\mathbf{w}) = \underbrace{\frac{1}{2} \sum_{i=1}^{N} (d_i - F(\mathbf{x}_i, \mathbf{w}))^2}_{\substack{\text{Regularized} \\ \text{cost function}}} \;\;\;\; \underbrace{\phantom{\frac{1}{2} \sum}}_{\substack{\text{Empirical} \\ \text{risk}}} + \underbrace{\frac{1}{2} \lambda \|\mathbf{w}\|^2}_{\substack{\text{Regularization} \\ \text{term}}}$$

as a plausible method for the regularization of a multilayer perceptron as a function approximator. The fact of the matter is that it is mathematically diffcult to apply Tikhonov's regularization theory to a multilayer perceptron. Unlike a radial-basis function network, the adjustable synaptic weights of a multilayer perceptron are distrubuted across the hidden layer(s) as well as the output layer of the network. In practical terms, the adoption of $\frac{1}{2} \|\mathbf{w}\|^2$ as the regularizer is therefore a sensible option.

Maximum-Likelihood Estimation

Referring back to Chapter 2 dealing with the method of least-squares and Bayesian estimation, therein we showed that the objective function of the maximum a posterior (MAP) parameter estimator, operating in a Gaussian enviornment, may be expressed as follows (see Eqs. (2.22) and (2.28)):

$$L(\mathbf{w}) = \underbrace{-\frac{1}{2} \sum_{i=1}^{N} (d_i - \mathbf{w}^T \mathbf{x}_i)^2}_{\substack{\text{Log-} \\ \text{posterior}}} \;\;\;\; \underbrace{}_{\substack{\text{Log-} \\ \text{likelihood}}} - \underbrace{\frac{1}{2} \lambda \|\mathbf{w}\|^2}_{\substack{\text{Log} \\ \text{prior}}} \tag{7.77}$$

We may therefore view the term $\dfrac{1}{2}\|\mathbf{w}\|^2$ as prior information about the underlying structure of the MAP parameter estimator. The two equations, Eqs. (7.76) and (7.77), respectively defining $\mathscr{E}(\mathbf{w})$ and $L(\mathbf{w})$ have exactly the same mathematical structure, except for the log-posterior $L(\mathbf{w})$ being the negative of the regularized cost function $\mathscr{E}(\mathbf{w})$. It follows therefore that the terms "regularization" and "prior information" play the same role insofar as least-squares estimation, or equivalently, maximum-likehood estimation in a Gaussian environment, is concerned.

Generalizing this insightful observation, on least-squares estimation, we may now postulate a *regularized maximum-likelihood estimator* as the estimator whose objective function is expressed as follows:

$$L(\mathbf{w}) = \underbrace{\log l(\mathbf{w})}_{\substack{\text{Log-}\\\text{likelihood}}} \underbrace{- \frac{1}{2}\lambda\|\mathbf{w}\|^2}_{\substack{\text{Regularization}\\\text{(penalty)}}}$$

$$\underbrace{\phantom{L(\mathbf{w})}}_{\substack{\text{Regularized}\\\text{Log-likelihood}}}$$

where $\mathbf{w}$ is the parameter vector to be optimized. Basically, what is being said here is that when it is hard to formulate the prior for a maximum-likelihood estimation algorithm aimed at estimating an unknown parameter vector $\mathbf{w}$, subtraction of the penalty term $\dfrac{\lambda}{2}\|\mathbf{w}\|^2$ from the logarithm of the likelihood function $l(\mathbf{w})$ may provide a sensible option for stabilizing the maximum-likelihood estimator.

7.8   ESTIMATION OF THE REGULARIZATION PARAMETER

The regularization parameter λ plays a central role in the regularization theory of radial-basis function networks, least-squares estimators, and support vector machines. To derive the full benefit of this theory, we need an equally principled approach to the estimation of λ.

To fix ideas, consider a *nonlinear regression problem*, described by a model whose observable output y_i at time-step i in response to an input vector $\mathbf{x}_i$ is defined by

$$d_i = f(\mathbf{x}_i) + \varepsilon_i, \qquad i = 1, 2, ..., N \tag{7.78}$$

where $f(\mathbf{x}_i)$ is a "smooth curve" and ε_i is a sample drawn from a white-noise process of zero mean with covariance defined by

$$\mathbb{E}[\varepsilon_i\varepsilon_k] = \begin{cases} \sigma^2 & \text{for } k = i \\ 0 & \text{otherwise} \end{cases} \tag{7.79}$$

The problem is to reconstruct the underlying function of the model, $f(\mathbf{x}_i)$, given the training sample $\{(\mathbf{x}_i, y_i)\}_{i=1}^{N}$.

Let $F_\lambda(\mathbf{x})$ be the regularized estimate of $f(\mathbf{x})$ for some value of the regularization parameter λ. That is, $F_\lambda(\mathbf{x})$ is the minimizer of the Tikhonov functional formulated for the nonlinear-regression problem as follows (see Eq. (7.4))

$$\mathscr{E}(F) = \frac{1}{2}\sum_{i=1}^{N}[d_i - F(\mathbf{x}_i)]^2 + \frac{\lambda}{2}\|\mathbf{D}F(\mathbf{x})\|^2$$

It is a nontrivial matter to choose a suitable value for λ, which controls the trade off between two conflicting issues:

- "fidelity" to the data, measured by the empirical cost function $\sum_{i=1}^{N}[d_i - F(\mathbf{x}_i)]^2$;

- "smoothness" of the solution, measured by the regularizer $\|\mathbf{D}F(\mathbf{x})\|^2$.

A good choice for the regularization parameter λ is the subject matter of this section.

Average Squared Error

Let $R(\lambda)$ denote the average squared error over a given data set between two functions—the regression function $f(\mathbf{x})$ pertaining to the model and the approximating function $F_\lambda(\mathbf{x})$ representing the solution for some λ—evaluated over the entire training sample. That is,

$$R(\lambda) = \frac{1}{N}\sum_{i=1}^{N}[f(\mathbf{x}_i) - F_\lambda(\mathbf{x}_i)]^2 \tag{7.80}$$

The *optimum* λ is the particular value of λ that minimizes $R(\lambda)$.

Let $F_\lambda(\mathbf{x}_k)$ be expressed as a linear combination of the given set of observables as follows:

$$F_\lambda(\mathbf{x}_k) = \sum_{i=1}^{N} a_{ki}(\lambda)d_i \tag{7.81}$$

In matrix form, we may equivalently write

$$\mathbf{F}_\lambda = \mathbf{A}(\lambda)\mathbf{d} \tag{7.82}$$

where $\mathbf{d}$ is the desired-response vector (i.e., the regression model's response vector),

$$\mathbf{F}_\lambda = [F_\lambda(\mathbf{x}_1), F_\lambda(\mathbf{x}_2), ..., F_\lambda(\mathbf{x}_N)]^T$$

and

$$\mathbf{A}(\lambda) = \begin{bmatrix} a_{11} & a_{12} & \cdots & a_{1N} \\ a_{21} & a_{22} & \cdots & a_{2N} \\ \vdots & \vdots & & \vdots \\ a_{N1} & a_{N2} & \cdots & a_{NN} \end{bmatrix} \tag{7.83}$$

The N-by-N matrix $\mathbf{A}(\lambda)$ is called the *influence matrix*.

Using this matrix notation, we may rewrite Eq. (7.80) in the form

$$R(\lambda) = \frac{1}{N}\|\mathbf{f} - \mathbf{F}_\lambda\|^2$$

$$= \frac{1}{N}\|\mathbf{f} - \mathbf{A}(\lambda)\mathbf{d}\|^2 \tag{7.84}$$

where the N-by-1 vector $\mathbf{f}$ is given by

$$\mathbf{f} = [f(\mathbf{x}_1), f(\mathbf{x}_2), ..., f(\mathbf{x}_N)]^T$$

We can go one step further in our matrix formalism by rewriting Eq. (7.78) in the form

$$\mathbf{d} = \mathbf{f} + \boldsymbol{\epsilon} \tag{7.85}$$

where

$$\boldsymbol{\epsilon} = [\varepsilon_1, \varepsilon_2, ..., \varepsilon_N]^T$$

Hence, using Eq. (7.85) in Eq. (7.84) and then expanding terms, we obtain

$$
\begin{aligned}
R(\lambda) &= \frac{1}{N} \| (\mathbf{I} - \mathbf{A}(\lambda))\mathbf{f} - \mathbf{A}(\lambda)\,\boldsymbol{\epsilon} \|^2 \\
&= \frac{1}{N} \| (\mathbf{I} - \mathbf{A}(\lambda))\mathbf{f} \|^2 - \frac{2}{N}\, \boldsymbol{\epsilon}^T \mathbf{A}^T(\lambda)(\mathbf{I} - \mathbf{A}(\lambda))\mathbf{f} \\
&\quad + \frac{1}{N} \| \mathbf{A}(\lambda)\boldsymbol{\epsilon} \|^2
\end{aligned} \tag{7.86}
$$

where $\mathbf{I}$ is the N-by-N identity matrix. To find the expected value of $R(\lambda)$, we note the following four points:

1. The first term on the right-hand side of Eq. (7.86) is a constant; it is therefore unaffected by the expectation operator.
2. The expectation of the second term is zero, by virtue of the fact that the expectational error ε_i in Eq. (7.78) has zero mean for all i.
3. The expectation of the scalar $\| \mathbf{A}(\lambda)\,\boldsymbol{\epsilon} \|^2$ is

$$
\begin{aligned}
\mathbb{E}[\| \mathbf{A}(\lambda)\boldsymbol{\epsilon} \|^2] &= \mathbb{E}[\boldsymbol{\epsilon}^T \mathbf{A}^T(\lambda)\mathbf{A}(\lambda)\boldsymbol{\epsilon}] \\
&= \mathrm{tr}(\mathbb{E}[\boldsymbol{\epsilon}^T \mathbf{A}^T(\lambda)\mathbf{A}(\lambda)\boldsymbol{\epsilon}]) \\
&= \mathbb{E}[\mathrm{tr}(\boldsymbol{\epsilon}^T \mathbf{A}^T(\lambda)\mathbf{A}(\lambda)\boldsymbol{\epsilon})]
\end{aligned} \tag{7.87}
$$

where we first used the fact that the trace of a scalar is the same as the scalar itself and then interchanged the order of expectation and trace operation.
4. We next use the following rule in matrix algebra: Given two matrices $\mathbf{B}$ and $\mathbf{C}$ of compatible dimensions, the trace of $\mathbf{BC}$ is equal to the trace of $\mathbf{CB}$. Thus, setting $\mathbf{B} = \boldsymbol{\epsilon}^T$ and $\mathbf{C} = \mathbf{A}^T(\lambda)\,\mathbf{A}(\lambda)\,\boldsymbol{\epsilon}$, we may rewrite Eq. (7.87) in the equivalent form

$$
\begin{aligned}
\mathbb{E}[\| \mathbf{A}(\lambda)\mathbf{f} \|^2] &= \mathbb{E}\{\mathrm{tr}[\mathbf{A}^T(\lambda)\mathbf{A}(\lambda)\,\boldsymbol{\epsilon}\,\boldsymbol{\epsilon}^T]\} \\
&= \sigma^2 \mathrm{tr}[\mathbf{A}^T(\lambda)\mathbf{A}(\lambda)]
\end{aligned} \tag{7.88}
$$

where in the last line we have made use of Eq. (7.79). Finally, noting that the trace of $\mathbf{A}^T(\lambda)\mathbf{A}(\lambda)$ is the same as the trace of $\mathbf{A}^2(\lambda)$, we may write

$$\mathbb{E}[\| \mathbf{A}(\lambda)\mathbf{f} \|^2] = \sigma^2 \mathrm{tr}[\mathbf{A}^2(\lambda)] \tag{7.89}$$

Putting the results of these four points together, we may now express the expected value of $R(\lambda)$ as

$$\mathbb{E}[R(\lambda)] = \frac{1}{N} \| \mathbf{I} - \mathbf{A}(\lambda)\mathbf{f} \|^2 + \frac{\sigma^2}{N} \mathrm{tr}[\mathbf{A}^2(\lambda)] \tag{7.90}$$

The average squared error over a given training sample, $R(\lambda)$, however, is not a practical measure, because it requires knowledge of the regression function $f(\mathbf{x})$, the function that is to be reconstructed. As an estimate of $\mathbb{E}[R(\lambda)]$, we introduce the following definition (Craven and Wahba, 1979):

$$\hat{R}(\lambda) = \frac{1}{N}\|(\mathbf{I} - \mathbf{A}(\lambda))\mathbf{d}\|^2 + \frac{\sigma^2}{N}\,\mathrm{tr}[\mathbf{A}^2(\lambda)] - \frac{\sigma^2}{N}\,\mathrm{tr}[(\mathbf{I} - \mathbf{A}(\lambda))^2] \quad (7.91)$$

Subtraction of the last term in this formula is intended to make the estimate $\hat{R}(\lambda)$ *unbiased*. Specifically, following a procedure similar to that described for deriving Eq. (7.90) we may show the following:

$$\mathbb{E}[\hat{R}(\lambda)] = \mathbb{E}[R(\lambda)] \quad (7.92)$$

Accordingly, the minimizer of the estimate $\hat{R}(\lambda)$ can be taken as a good choice for the regularization parameter λ.

Generalized Cross-Validation

A drawback of the estimate $\hat{R}(\lambda)$ is that it requires knowledge of the noise variance σ^2. In situations encountered in practice, σ^2 is usually not known. To deal with situations of this kind, we may use the concept of generalized cross-validation that was originated by Craven and Wahba (1979).

We begin by adapting the *leave-one-out* form of cross-validation to the problem at hand. Specifically, let $F_\lambda^{[k]}(\mathbf{x})$ be the minimizer of the new functional

$$\mathscr{E}_{\text{modified}}(F) = \frac{1}{2}\sum_{\substack{i=1 \\ i \neq k}}^{N} [d_i - F_\lambda(\mathbf{x}_i)]^2 + \frac{\lambda}{2}\|DF(\mathbf{x})\|^2 \quad (7.93)$$

In this equation, the kth term $[d_k - F_\lambda(\mathbf{x}_k)]$ has been left out of the standard error function; by leaving out this term, we may use the ability of $F_\lambda^{[k]}(\mathbf{x})$, to "predict" the missing data point d_k as a measure of the goodness of λ; that is, the cross-validation is tested on the single data point that is left out. Accordingly, we may introduce the measure of goodness

$$V_0(\lambda) = \frac{1}{N}\sum_{k=1}^{N}[d_k - F_\lambda^{[k]}(\mathbf{x}_k)]^2 \quad (7.94)$$

which depends on the data alone. The *ordinary cross-validation estimate* of λ is thus defined to be the minimizer of $V_0(\lambda)$ (Wahba, 1990).

A useful property of $F_\lambda^{[k]}(\mathbf{x}_k)$ is that if the data point d_k is replaced by the prediction $F_\lambda^{[k]}(\mathbf{x}_k)$, and the original Tikhonov functional $\mathscr{E}(F)$ of Eq. (7.4) is minimized using the data points $d_1, d_2, \ldots, d_{k-1}, d_k, d_{k+1}, \ldots, d_N$, we get $F_\lambda^{[k]}(\mathbf{x}_k)$ for the solution, since d_k contributes zero loss. This property, together with the fact that for each input vector $\mathbf{x}$, the minimizer $F_\lambda(\mathbf{x})$, of $\mathscr{E}(F)$ depends linearly on d_k, allows us to write

$$F_\lambda^{[k]}(\mathbf{x}_k) = F_\lambda(\mathbf{x}_k) + (F_\lambda^{[k]}(\mathbf{x}_k) - d_k)\frac{\partial F_\lambda(\mathbf{x}_k)}{\partial d_k} \quad (7.95)$$

From Eq. (7.81), which defines the entries of the influence matrix $\mathbf{A}(\lambda)$, we readily see that

$$\frac{\partial F_\lambda(\mathbf{x}_k)}{\partial d_k} = a_{kk}(\lambda) \tag{7.96}$$

where $a_{kk}(\lambda)$ is the kth diagonal element of $\mathbf{A}(\lambda)$. Hence, using Eq. (7.96) in Eq. (7.95) and solving the resulting equation for $F_\lambda^{[k]}(\mathbf{x}_k)$, we obtain

$$F_\lambda^{[k]}(\mathbf{x}_k) = \frac{F_\lambda(\mathbf{x}_k) - a_{kk}(\lambda)d_k}{1 - a_{kk}(\lambda)}$$

$$= \frac{F_\lambda(\mathbf{x}_k) - d_k}{1 - a_{kk}(\lambda)} + d_k \tag{7.97}$$

Substituting Eq. (7.97) into Eq. (7.94), we may redefine $V_0(\lambda)$ as

$$V_0(\lambda) = \frac{1}{N}\sum_{k=1}^{N}\left(\frac{d_k - F_\lambda(\mathbf{x}_k)}{1 - a_{kk}(\lambda)}\right)^2 \tag{7.98}$$

Typically, $a_{kk}(\lambda)$ is different for different k, which means that the data points in $V_0(\lambda)$ are not treated equally. To circumvent this undesirable feature of ordinary cross-validation, Craven and Wahba (1979) introduced the *generalized cross-validation* (GCV), using a rotation of coordinates.[4] Specifically, the ordinary cross-validation function $V_0(\lambda)$ of Eq. (7.98) is modified to

$$V(\lambda) = \frac{1}{N}\sum_{k=1}^{N}\omega_k\left(\frac{d_k - F_\lambda(\mathbf{x}_k)}{1 - a_{kk}(\lambda)}\right)^2 \tag{7.99}$$

where the weights, ω_k, are themselves defined by

$$\omega_k = \left(\frac{1 - a_{kk}(\lambda)}{\dfrac{1}{N}\text{tr}[\mathbf{I} - \mathbf{A}(\lambda)]}\right)^2 \tag{7.100}$$

Then, the generalized cross-validation function $V(\lambda)$ becomes

$$V(\lambda) = \frac{\dfrac{1}{N}\displaystyle\sum_{k=1}^{N}(d_k - F_\lambda(\mathbf{x}_k))^2}{\left(\dfrac{1}{N}\text{tr}[\mathbf{I} - \mathbf{A}(\lambda)]\right)^2} \tag{7.101}$$

Finally, using Eq. (7.81) in Eq. (7.101) yields the desired formula

$$V(\lambda) = \frac{\dfrac{1}{N}\|(\mathbf{I} - \mathbf{A}(\lambda))\mathbf{d}\|^2}{\left(\dfrac{1}{N}\text{tr}[\mathbf{I} - \mathbf{A}(\lambda)]\right)^2} \tag{7.102}$$

which relies solely on quantities related to the training sample for its computation.

An Optimal Property of the Generalized Cross-Validation Function $V(\lambda)$

The *expectation inefficiency* of the method of generalized cross-validation is defined by

$$I^* = \frac{\mathbb{E}[R(\lambda)]}{\min_{\lambda} \mathbb{E}[R(\lambda)]} \qquad (7.103)$$

where $R(\lambda)$ is the average squared error over the training sample, given in Eq. (7.80). Naturally, the asymptotic value of I^* satisfies the condition

$$\lim_{N \to \infty} I^* = 1 \qquad (7.104)$$

In other words, for large N, the average squared error $R(\lambda)$ with λ estimated by minimizing the generalized cross-validation function $V(\lambda)$ should be close to the minimum possible value of $R(\lambda)$, which makes $V(\lambda)$ a good method for estimating λ.

Summarizing Comments

The general idea of cross-validation is to choose the regularization parameter λ so as to minimize the average squared error over the training sample, $R(\lambda)$. Unfortunately, this cannot be accomplished directly, since $R(\lambda)$ involves the unknown regression function $f(\mathbf{x})$. With this being so, there are two possibilities that may be pursued in practice:

- If the noise variance σ^2 is known, we may use the minimizer of the estimate $\hat{R}(\lambda)$ of Eq. (7.91) as the optimum choice of λ; it is optimum in the sense that it also minimizes $R(\lambda)$.
- If σ^2 is not known, we may use the minimizer of the generalized cross-validation function $V(\lambda)$ of Eq. (7.102) as a good choice of λ, which produces an expected mean-square error that approaches its minimum possible value as the sample size $N \to \infty$.

The important point to note here is that the theory justifying the use of generalized cross-validation for estimating λ is an asymptotic one. Good results can therefore be expected only when the available training sample is large enough for the signal to be distinguishable from noise.

Practical experience with generalized cross-validation appears to show that it is robust against nonhomogeneity of variances and non-Gaussian noise (Wahba, 1990). However, the method is quite likely to produce unsatisfactory estimates of the regularization parameter λ if the noise process is highly correlated.

Some comments pertaining to the computation of the generalized cross-validation function $V(\lambda)$ are in order. For given trial values of the regularization parameter λ, finding the denominator term $[\text{tr}[\mathbf{I} - \mathbf{A}(\lambda)]/N]^2$ in the formula of Eq. (7.102) is the most expensive part of the work involved in computing $V(\lambda)$. The "randomized trace method" described in Wahba et al. (1995) may be used to compute $\text{tr}[\mathbf{A}(\lambda)]$; it is feasible to apply this method to large-scale learning problems.

The material presented in this section has focused on cross-validation applied to supervised learning for the purpose of estimating the regularization parameter λ.

When we discuss semisupervised learning in Section 7.12, we find ourselves faced with the estimation of two different regularization parameters. It would make for an interesting study to extend the cross-validation theory covered herein to semisupervised learning.

7.9   SEMISUPERVISED LEARNING

Starting from Chapter 1 on the perceptron and moving along up to this point in the book, we have focused attention on supervised learning whose goal is to learn an input–output mapping, given the training sample $\{\mathbf{x}_i\, d_i\}_{i=1}^N$. Such a data set is said to be *labeled*, in the sense that each input vector $\mathbf{x}_i$ is paired with a desired response or label d_i for all i. From a practical perspective, the manual labeling of examples for the supervised training of a network is not only a time-consuming and expensive undertaking, but also a process that is prone to errors. In contrast, the collection of *unlabeled* examples (i.e., examples without a desired response) is relatively inexpensive, and usually there is a wealth of such examples readily available. Given these practical realities, how do we exploit the availability of both labeled and unlabeled examples in the training of networks? The answer to this challenging question lies in the use of *semisupervised learning*.

In this new approach to learning, the input data set $\{\mathbf{x}_i\}_{i=1}^N$ is divided into two subsets:

1. a subset of data points denoted by $\{\mathbf{x}_i\}_{i=1}^l$, for which a corresponding set of labels denoted by $\{d_i\}_{i=1}^l$ is supplied;

2. another subset of data points denoted by $\{\mathbf{x}_i\}_{i=l+1}^N$, for which the labels are unknown.

On this basis, we may view semisupervised learning as a new form of learning that resides midway between supervised and unsupervised learning, which makes it a more difficult learning task than supervised learning, but perhaps easier than unsupervised learning.

As a subject with many potential applications, semisupervised learning uses a wide range of learning algorithms. In this chapter, we pursue the kernel approach based on *manifold regularization*. By "manifold," we mean a k-dimensional topological space embedded in an n-dimensional Euclidean space where n is greater than k. If the functions describing the manifold are partially differentiable, then the manifold is called a *differentiable manifold*. We may thus view the concept of a manifold as the generalization of the concept of a surface in $\mathbb{R}^3$ and, by the same token, view the concept of a differentiable manifold as the generalization of a differentiable surface in $\mathbb{R}^3$.

The rationale for focusing on the kernel approach based on manifold regularization is threefold:

1. The kernel approach for semisupervised learning fits naturally within the scope of this chapter on regularization theory.

2. Manifold regularization provides a principled approach for the formulation of a data-dependent, nonparametric kernel for semisupervised learning.

3. The use of manifold regularization has contributed encouraging results on some classification tasks.

Simply put, kernel-based manifold regularization has the potential to make a significant difference in semisupervised learning theory.

7.10   MANIFOLD REGULARIZATION: PRELIMINARY CONSIDERATIONS

A model of the semisupervised learning process is depicted in Fig. 7.4. To simplify the presentation in this figure and the material to follow in the rest of the chapter, the term "distribution" is used to refer to a "probability density function." To proceed with the discussion, the model of Fig. 7.4 is abstracted in mathematical terms as follows:

1. The *input space* is denoted by $\mathcal{X}$ and assumed to be *stationary*; it supplies two sets of inputs, one denoted by $\{\mathbf{x}_i\}_{i=1}^{l}$ and the other denoted by $\{\mathbf{x}_i\}_{i=l+1}^{N}$, both of which are governed by a fixed distribution $p_{\mathbf{X}}(\mathbf{x})$, which is assumed to pertain to a stationary process.

2. The *teacher* provides the label d_i as the desired response for every input vector $\mathbf{x}$ in the set $\{\mathbf{x}_i\}_{i=1}^{l}$ received from the input space $\mathcal{X}$ in accordance with the conditional distribution $p_{D|\mathbf{X}}(d|\mathbf{x})$, which is also fixed, but unknown.

3. The *learning machine* produces an output in response to the combined action of the two subsets of data:

    *   Labeled data $\{\mathbf{x}_i, d_i\}_{i=1}^{l}$, received from the input space via the teacher, with the joint distribution

$$p_{\mathbf{X},D}(\mathbf{x}, d) = p_{D|\mathbf{X}}(d|\mathbf{x})p_{\mathbf{X}}(\mathbf{x}) \qquad (7.105)$$

According to this definition, $p_{\mathbf{X}}(\mathbf{x})$ is the *marginal distribution*, obtained by integrating out the dependence of the joint distribution $p_{\mathbf{X},D}(\mathbf{x}, d)$ on the desired response d.

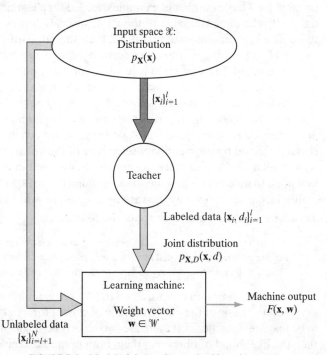

FIGURE 7.4   Model of the semisupervised learning process.

- Unlabeled data $\{\mathbf{x}_i\}_{i=l+1}^{N}$, received *directly* from the input data space $\mathcal{X}$, with the distribution $p_{\mathbf{X}}(\mathbf{x})$.

Unlike supervised learning, the training sample in semisupervised learning is therefore made-up as follows:

$$(\text{Training sample}) = (\{\mathbf{x}_i, d_i\}_{i=1}^{l}; \{\mathbf{x}_i\}_{i=l+1}^{N}) \qquad (7.106)$$
$$\underbrace{\phantom{\{\mathbf{x}_i, d_i\}_{i=1}^{l}}}_{\text{Labeled}} \quad \underbrace{\phantom{\{\mathbf{x}_i\}_{i=l+1}^{N}}}_{\text{Unlabeled}}$$

Henceforth, it is assumed that there exists an identifiable relationship between the distribution $p_{\mathbf{X}}(\mathbf{x})$ and the conditional distribution $p_{\mathbf{X}|D}(\mathbf{x}|d)$ for the principle of manifold regularization to make a difference in improved function learning, be that in the context of pattern classification or regression. Possible connections between these two distributions may be formulated as two important assumptions (Chapelle et al., 2006);

1. *The manifold assumption*, which states the following:

   > *The marginal distribution $p_{\mathbf{X}}(\mathbf{x})$ underlying the input space $\mathcal{X}$ is supported on a low-dimensional manifold.*

   The implication of this first assumption is that the conditional distribution function $p_{\mathbf{X}|D}(\mathbf{x}|d)$ varies *smoothly* (as a function of $\mathbf{x}$) with respect to the underlying structure of the manifold.

   A good question to raise here is: How can the manifold assumption be of practical use? To answer this question, we have to remind ourselves of the curse-of-dimensionality problem, discussed at some length in Chapter 4. Simply put, the demand for a large number of examples needed for a learning task grows exponentially with the dimensionality of the input space. If, however, the data are known to lie in a low-dimensional manifold, then the curse-of-dimensionality can be avoided by operating in a space of correspondingly low dimension.

   The manifold assumption is justified for many physical processes. Consider, for example, the speech production process, which may be viewed as a form of filtering when seen as *a sound source exciting a vocal tract filter*. The vocal tract consists of a tube of nonuniform cross-sectional area, beginning at the glottis and ending at the lips. As the sound propagates along the local tract, the spectrum of the sound signal is shaped by the frequency selectivity of the vocal tract; this effect is somewhat similar to the resonance phenomenon observed in organ pipes. The important point to note here is that the space of sound (voice) signals is a low-dimensional manifold, parameterized by the varying lengths and widths of the vocal tract.

2. *The cluster assumption*, which states the following:

   > *The marginal distribution $p_{\mathbf{X}}(\mathbf{x})$, according to which the examples for function learning are generated, is defined in such a way that if certain points are located in the same "cluster," then they are likely to have the same class or label.*

   This second assumption is considered to be a reasonable assumption to make. We say so on the basis of the very existence of classes for a pattern-classification task to be feasible. Specifically, if there are two objects belonging to two different classes, then the likelihood of observing them both in the same cluster is relatively low.

7.11   DIFFERENTIABLE MANIFOLDS

We begin the discussion on differentiable manifolds with the following intuitive notion:

> *A manifold is an abstract mathematical space in which every point has a local neighborhood that resembles Euclidean space, but, in a global sense, has an underlying structure that is more complicated than Euclidean space.*

We may thus think of manifolds as an abstraction of the idea of *smooth surfaces* embedded in Euclidean space.

In describing manifolds, the idea of dimension is extremely important. In general, we may speak of a *manifold of dimension n*, or *n-manifold*, if the local neighborhood of a point on the manifold is Euclidean of dimension n.

The local resemblance of a manifold to Euclidean space is typically assumed to be close enough to permit the application of the customary rules of calculus to manifolds, which makes the study of manifolds that much simpler. Expanding on this statement, let $\mathbb{R}$ denote the real numbers and $\mathbb{R}^n$ denote their Cartesian product. In the study of manifolds, the space $\mathbb{R}^n$ is used in several senses: Sometimes $\mathbb{R}^n$ merely means a topological space; Sometimes $\mathbb{R}^n$ denotes an n-dimensional vector space where operations are performed in a *continuous* manner with respect to the topology; and sometimes $\mathbb{R}^n$ is identified simply with the Euclidean space.

Roughly speaking, a topological space is a geometric object. For a more precise definition, we have to invoke *set theory*:

> *Let X be any set, and let $\mathcal{T}$ be a family of subsets of X. Then $\mathcal{T}$ is a topology on the set X provided that three conditions are satisfied:*
>
> **(i)**   *Both the set X and the empty set (i.e., a set with no elements) belong to $\mathcal{T}$.*
> **(ii)** *The intersection of any finite number of elements of $\mathcal{T}$ is an element of $\mathcal{T}$.*
> **(iii)** *The union of any collection of elements of $\mathcal{T}$ is an element of $\mathcal{T}$.*
>
> *If $\mathcal{T}$ is a topology as just defined, then the set X (involved in the definition) together with $\mathcal{T}$ constitutes a topological space.*

The elements of $\mathcal{T}$ are called the "open sets" of X. The essence of this definition is that it enables us to define "continuous" mappings: A mapping (or function) $f : X \rightarrow Y$ between topological spaces is said to be continuous if the *preimage* $f^{-1}(A)$ of any open set A of Y is itself an open set of X. The mapping $f^{-1}(A)$ means that the set of points x in X maps to A in Y.

With "differentiability" being an issue of special interest, let X, a subset of $\mathbb{R}^n$, be an open set. An *open set* is defined as a set where *the distance between any point in the set and its edge is always greater than zero*. Let $\mathbf{x} \in X$, with the ith component of the vector $\mathbf{x}$ being denoted by x_i, and let the function $f(\mathbf{x})$ map X onto $\mathbb{R}$. We may then make the following statement:

> *The function $f(\mathbf{x})$ is differentiable and said to be of class C^k on the open set X, or simply f is C^k for a nonnegative integer k, if all the partial derivatives $\partial^\alpha f / \partial x_i^\alpha$ exist and are continuous on X for $1 \leq i \leq n$ and $0 \leq \alpha \leq k$.*

On this basis, for example, we may say that the function f is C^∞ (i.e., infinitely differentiable and therefore *smooth*) if it is C^k for all $k \geq 0$.

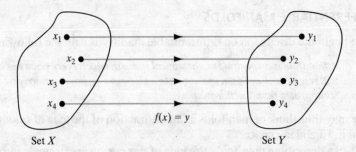

FIGURE 7.5   A bijection $f : X \rightarrow Y$.

We are still not quite ready for a formal definition of differentiable manifolds. Rather, we need to introduce some other concepts, described as follows:

1. Homeomorphism

Consider a mapping $f : X \rightarrow Y$ between sets X and Y. If f has the property that for every y in Y, there is exactly one x in X such that

$$f(x) = y$$

as illustrated in Fig. 7.5, then f is called a *bijection*.

A bijection $f : X \rightarrow Y$ between two topological spaces X and Y is called a *homeomorphism* if both f and its inverse f^{-1} are continuous mappings. Whenever such an f can be found, X and Y are said to be *homeomorphic* to each other.

In physical terms, we may view homeomorphism as a continuous *stretching and bending* of a topological space such that it is deformed into a new shape. For example, a coffee mug and a doughnut are homeomorphic with respect to each other in that the coffee mug can be continuously deformed into the doughnut, and vice versa.[5] On the other hand, a doughnut can never be deformed into a sphere, no matter what forms of continuous stretching and bending are applied to it.

Intuitively, we may thus say that a homeomorphism maps points in one topological space that are *close together* into an entirely different topological space such that the corresponding points *remain close together* in the new topological space.

2. Diffeomorphism

For the definition of this concept, we require X and Y to be open sets in $\mathbb{R}^n$ for some n. Then, we say that $f : X \rightarrow Y$ is a *diffeomorphism* if the following two conditions hold:

(i) f is a homeomorphism, and
(ii) both f and f^{-1} are continuously differentiable.

In this case, X and Y are said to be *diffeomorphic* to each other. If f and f^{-1} are both k-times continuously differentiable, then f is called a C^k-diffeomorphism.

3. Charts and Atlas

In studying the geography of the world, we find it convenient to use geographic maps and charts as a substitute for examining the world as one whole entity. For a complete picture of the world, we use an atlas—namely, a family of geographic maps that covers all the different parts of the world.

This nonmathematical view of geography of the world leads us to the following intuitive procedure for constructing a topological manifold $\mathcal{M}$:

(i) A family of overlapping "simple" spaces that covers the whole topological space $\mathcal{M}$ is picked.

(ii) Each simple space is homeomorphic to an open set in $\mathbb{R}^n$. Each such homeomorphism is called a *chart*.

(iii) The charts are pieced together in a smooth manner.

Each chart therefore consists of a triple (X, Y, f), where X is an open set in $\mathcal{M}$, Y is an open set in $\mathbb{R}^n$ and $f : X \rightarrow Y$ is a homeomorphism.

A family of overlapping charts that covers all of $\mathcal{M}$ is called, for obvious reasons, an *atlas*. Clearly, there is no unique way of constructing a manifold using this procedure.

In mathematical terms, we may follow up the definitions of charts and atlas with the following pair of statements:

(i) Let the ith chart be denoted by the pair (X_i, f_i); then the atlas is the intersection of all the charts.

(ii) Any two charts (X_i, f_i) and (X_j, f_j) in the atlas must be *compatible* in the following sense, as illustrated in Fig. 7.6:

• The part common to the two charts, shown as the shaded area in Fig. 7.6, must be open.

• The shaded *overlap map*, denoted by f_{ji}, must be a C^k diffeomorphism.

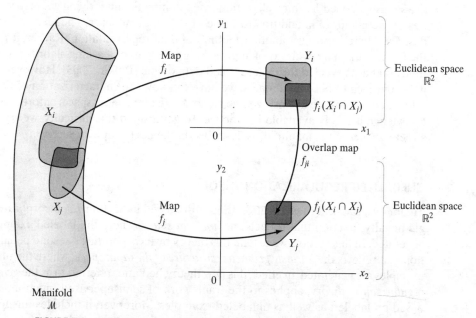

FIGURE 7.6 Illustrating the relationship between an atlas and its constituent charts. [This figure is adapted from Abraham et al. (1988).]

Note that f_{ji} is a mapping from the image set $f_i(X_i \cap X_j)$ to the set $f_j(X_i \cap X_j)$, where the symbol $\cap$ denotes the *product*, or *intersection*, of two sets of interest. By requiring each f_{ji} to be a C^k-diffeomorphism, we are able to decide what is meant by a C^k-differentiable function on $\mathcal{M}$.

Differentiable Manifolds

At long last, we are now ready to define what we mean by a differentiable manifold:

> *A C^k-differentiable manifold $\mathcal{M}$ of dimension n with atlas $(X_i, Y_i, f_i), i = 1, ..., I$, is a topological set where each Y_i is an open set in $\mathbb{R}^n$, and such that the overlap mappings f_{ji} are all C^k-diffeomorphisms.*

The implication of this definition is that for every n-dimensional point $\mathbf{x} \in \mathcal{M}$, there is an admissible chart (X, Y, f), where $\mathbf{x} \in X$ and f maps the open set X onto the open subset Y of $\mathbb{R}^n$.

Why Be Interested in Manifolds for Learning?

To appreciate why the study of manifolds is important in the study of learning theory, suppose we have a set of unlabeled examples denoted by $\mathbf{x}_1, \mathbf{x}_2, ...$, where the dimensionality of each example is n. These examples are represented as a set of data points in an n-dimensional Euclidean space. Most unsupervised-learning algorithms operate only on the *ambient space*, represented by the examples, $\mathbf{x}_1, \mathbf{x}_2, ...$ Suppose, however, that we are able to construct a manifold of *lower dimensionality* than n, such that the true data may reside on or around that manifold. Then, it may be possible to design a more *effective* semisupervised-learning algorithm by exploiting the underlying geometric properties of the manifold in addition to those of the ambient space. The idea we have just described here is not just another method of data representation. Rather, it provides the framework of a novel way of approaching problems of learning algorithms on manifolds that are revealed through sampled data points (Belkin, 2003). However, for this new approach to become a reality, we have to know the characterization of the manifold that describes the intrinsic geometric structure of the input space; unfortunately, this knowledge is rarely available in practice. To get around this difficulty, we try to construct a *model* of the manifold, as described in the next couple of sections.

7.12 GENERALIZED REGULARIZATION THEORY

Tikhonov's classical regularization theory, discussed in Section 7.3, incorporates a single penalty function that reflects the *ambient space*, where the labeled examples are generated. In this section, we extend this theory by incorporating a second penalty function that reflects the *intrinsic geometric structure of the input space*, where the unlabeled examples are generated. In effect, this new theory, hereafter referred to as the *generalized regularization theory*, applies to the framework of semisupervised function learning, based on labeled as well as unlabeled examples. Moreover, it includes unsupervised function learning, based on unlabeled examples alone, as a special case.

Appearing in pairs denoted by $(\mathbf{x}, d)$, the labeled examples are generated in accordance with the joint distribution function $p_{\mathbf{X},D}(\mathbf{x}, d)$, defined in Eq. (7.105). The unlabeled examples, $\mathbf{x} \in X$, are generated in accordance with the marginal distribution function $p_{\mathbf{X}}(\mathbf{x})$. The underlying premise of the generalized regularization theory is the existence of an identifiable relationship between these two distribution functions. Otherwise, it is unlikely that the knowledge of the marginal $p_{\mathbf{X}}(\mathbf{x})$ would be of practical use. Henceforth, we make the following assumption:

> *If two input data points $\mathbf{x}_i, \mathbf{x}_j \in X$ are close to each other in the intrinsic geometry of the marginal distribution function $p_{\mathbf{X}}(\mathbf{x})$, then the conditional distribution function $p_{\mathbf{X}|D}(\mathbf{x}|d)$, evaluated at the data points $\mathbf{x} = \mathbf{x}_i$ and $\mathbf{x} = \mathbf{x}_j$, behaves similarly.*

To recast this assumption in a more tangible way that would lead to a practical solution, we say the following:

> *If two data points $\mathbf{x}_i$ and $\mathbf{x}_j$ are very close to each other in the input space, the goal of semisupervised function learning is to find a mapping, denoted by the function $F(\mathbf{x})$, that forces the corresponding output points $F(\mathbf{x}_i)$ and $F(\mathbf{x}_j)$ to lie on a real line in very close proximity to each other with high likelihood.*

To attain this goal, we need to introduce a new penalty term, over and above the penalty term considered in the classical regularization theory.

To be specific, we extend the cost functional for the regularization of semisupervised learning so a to include a new penalty term, giving us

$$\mathscr{E}_\lambda(F) = \frac{1}{2}\sum_{i=1}^{l}(d_i - F(\mathbf{x}_i))^2 + \frac{1}{2}\lambda_A\|F\|_K^2 + \frac{1}{2}\lambda_I\|F\|_I^2 \qquad (7.107)$$

where the two penalty terms are as follows:

1. The penalty term $\|F\|_K^2$, under the control of the *ambient regularization parameter* λ_A, reflects the complexity of the approximating function F in the ambient space. In particular, this penalty term is expressed in terms of the reproducing-kernel Hilbert space (RKHS) representation of the feature space—hence the subscript K.

2. The penalty term $\|F\|_I^2$, under the control of the *intrinsic regularization parameter* λ_I, reflects the intrinsic geometric structure of the input space—hence the subscript I.

The subscript λ in $\mathscr{E}_\lambda(F)$ stands for the two regularization parameters, λ_A and λ_I. Note also that in the first term on the right-hand side of Eq. (7.107), we have used l to denote the number of labeled examples.

In the absence of the intrinsic penalty term $\|F\|_I^2$, the minimizer of the cost functional $\mathscr{E}_\lambda(F)$ over the RKHS is defined by the *classical representer theorem* as

$$F_\lambda^*(\mathbf{x}) = \sum_{i=1}^{l} a_i k(\mathbf{x}, \mathbf{x}_i) \qquad \text{for } \lambda_I = 0 \qquad (7.108)$$

according to which the problem is reduced to that of optimizing over a finite dimensional space defined by the expansion coefficients $\{a_i\}_{i=1}^{l}$. We would like to extend this theorem so as to include the intrinsic penalty term $\|F\|_I^2$ as well.

With this aim in mind, we propose to *model* the intrinsic geometric structure of the input space by a *graph*, for whose construction the unlabeled examples are sufficient, as discussed next.

7.13 SPECTRAL GRAPH THEORY

Consider the training sample

$$X = \{\mathbf{x}_i\}_{i=1}^{N}$$

which embodies N input data points, labeled as well as unlabeled. Given this training sample, we proceed by constructing a *weighted undirected graph* consisting of N *nodes* or *vertices*, one for each input data point, and a set of *edges* connecting adjacent nodes. Any two nodes i and j are connected, provided that the Euclidean distance between their respective data points $\mathbf{x}_i$ and $\mathbf{x}_j$ is small enough to satisfy the condition

$$\|\mathbf{x}_i - \mathbf{x}_j\| < \varepsilon \qquad (7.109)$$

for some prescribed constant ε. The attractive feature of this *adjancy criterion* is twofold: geometric insight and a naturally symmetric metric. However, we have to bear in mind that the choice of a satisfactory value for the constant ε may give rise to difficulty due to the possibility of the graph having a multiplicity of connected components.

Let w_{ij} denote the *weight* of an undirected edge connecting nodes i and j. The weights in the graph as a whole are usually real numbers, the selection of which must satisfy three conditions:

1. *symmetry*, by which we mean

$$w_{ij} = w_{ji} \qquad \text{for all } (i, j) \text{ pairs}$$

2. *connectivity*, which means that the weight w_{ij} is nonzero if the pertinent nodes i and j are connected, and zero otherwise;

3. *nonnegativity*, that is,

$$w_{ij} \geq 0 \qquad \text{for all } (i, j) \text{ pairs}$$

It follows therefore that the N-by-N weight matrix

$$\mathbf{W} = \{w_{ij}\}$$

is a symmetric, nonnegative-definite matrix, with all of its elements being nonnegative. The rows and columns of the matrix $\mathbf{W}$ are indexed by the nodes of the graph, but their ordering is unimportant. Hereafter, we refer to the undirected graph, characterized by the weight matrix $\mathbf{W}$, as graph G.

Let $\mathbf{T}$ denote an N-by-N *diagonal matrix* whose ii-th element is defined by

$$t_{ii} = \sum_{j=1}^{N} w_{ij} \qquad (7.110)$$

which is called the *degree* of node i. In words, the degree of a node i is equal to the sum of all the elements in the ith row of the weight matrix $\mathbf{W}$. The larger the degree t_{ii} is, the more important the node i is. In the limiting case when t_{ii} is zero, the node i is said to be *isolated*.

In terms of the weight matrix $\mathbf{W}$ and the diagonal matrix $\mathbf{T}$, we now define the *Laplacian* of the graph G as

$$\mathbf{L} = \mathbf{T} - \mathbf{W} \tag{7.111}$$

If we assume that there are no self-loops—that is, $w_{ii} = 0$ for all i—then for the ij-th element of the Laplacian $\mathbf{L}$, we have

$$l_{ij} = \begin{cases} t_{ii} & \text{for } j = i \\ -w_{ij} & \text{for adjacent nodes } i \text{ and } j \\ 0 & \text{otherwise} \end{cases} \tag{7.112}$$

It follows therefore that the Laplacian $\mathbf{L}$ is a symmetric matrix.

The graph Laplacian holds the key for the formulation of a suitable smoothing functional to deal with the intrinsic penalty term $\|F\|_I^2$, as described next.

Since the Laplacian $\mathbf{L}$ is a symmetric matrix, it has *real* eigenvalues. The subject of eigendecomposition, involving the computation of the eigenvalues of a symmetric matrix and their associated eigenvectors, is discussed in detail in Chapter 8. For now, we find it adequate to focus on the Rayleigh coefficient of a symmetric matrix to evaluate the variational characteristics of the eigenvalues of the Laplacian $\mathbf{L}$. To this end, let $\mathbf{f}$ denote an arbitrary vector-valued function of the input vector $\mathbf{x}$, which assigns a real value to each node of the graph G. We may then define the *Rayleigh quotient* of the Laplace operator $\mathbf{L}$ as the ratio

$$\lambda_{\text{Rayleigh}} = \frac{\mathbf{f}^T \mathbf{L} \mathbf{f}}{\mathbf{f}^T \mathbf{f}} \tag{7.113}$$

which expresses the ratio of two inner products:

1. the inner product of the function $\mathbf{f}$ and the matrix product $\mathbf{Lf}$, where the Laplacian $\mathbf{L}$ acts as an *operator* on the function $\mathbf{f}$;
2. the inner product of the function $\mathbf{f}$ with itself, which is the squared Euclidean norm of $\mathbf{f}$.

Note that according to Eq. (7.113), the Laplacian $\mathbf{L}$ is a nonnegative-definite matrix, which follows from Eq. (7.111).

With $\mathbf{L}$ being a N-by-N matrix, the Laplacian will have N real-valued *eigenvalues*, arranged in increasing order, as shown by the set

$$\lambda_0 \leq \lambda_1 \leq \cdots \leq \lambda_{N-1}$$

which is called the *eigenspectrum* of the *Laplacian* $\mathbf{L}$, or the *eigenspectrum of the associated graph G*. It is not hard to show that the smallest eigenvalue λ_0 is zero and that the associated eignvector is the vector $\mathbf{1}$ whose N elements all have the value of 1. The second smallest eigenvalue λ_1 plays a critical part in spectral graph theory.

Notwithstanding the importance of λ_1 and the other eigenvalues of the Laplacian $\mathbf{L}$, our primary interest in this chapter is to find a suitable measure for dealing with the intrinsic penalty term $\|F\|_I^2$. As we examine Eq. (7.113), the measure we are looking for is to be found in the numerator of the Rayleigh quotient—namely, the quadratic term $\mathbf{f}^T\mathbf{L}\mathbf{f}$. Accordingly, we introduce the *smoothness functional*

$$S_G(F) = \mathbf{f}^T\mathbf{L}\mathbf{f} \tag{7.114}$$

which is not only reasonable, but also intuitively satisfying. The vector-valued function $\mathbf{f}$ is defined in terms of the training sample X as follows:

$$\mathbf{f} = [F(\mathbf{x}_1), F(\mathbf{x}_2), ..., F(\mathbf{x}_N)]^T \tag{7.115}$$

Hence, using Eqs. (7.112) and (7.115) in Eq. (7.114), we may also express the smoothness functional by a double summation, as shown by

$$S_G(F) = \sum_{i=1}^{N} \sum_{j=1}^{N} w_{ij}(F(\mathbf{x}_i) - F(\mathbf{x}_j))^2 \tag{7.116}$$

where w_{ij} is the weight of the edge connecting nodes i and j.

To complete the description of the smoothing function $S_G(f)$, we need a formula for evaluating the edge weights of the graph G. In the spirit of kernel methods, we define the weight w_{ij}, connecting nodes i and j, as a kernel function; that is,

$$w_{ij} = k(\mathbf{x}_i, \mathbf{x}_j) \tag{7.117}$$

This definition satisfies the symmetry, connectivity, and nonnegativity-preserving conditions on the weight w_{ij}. An example of such a kernel is the Gaussian function

$$k(\mathbf{x}_i, \mathbf{x}_j) = \exp\left(-\frac{\|\mathbf{x}_i - \mathbf{x}_j\|^2}{2\sigma^2}\right) \tag{7.118}$$

where σ^2, the parameter under the designer's control, is assumed to be the same for all i, that is, all the kernels in the spectral graph.

The important point to note here in the context of semisupervised learning is summed up as follows:

> *Application of spectral graph theory, through the combined use of Eqs. (7.117) and (7.118), makes the learning machine for semisupervised learning into a kernel machine, whose hidden layer is determined by exploiting the intrinsic geometric structure of the input space that is responsible for generating the unlabelled examples.*

7.14 GENERALIZED REPRESENTER THEOREM

With the smoothing functional of Eq. (7.114) at hand, we are now ready to recast the cost functional of Eq. (7.107) in the desired form

$$\mathcal{E}_\lambda(F) = \frac{1}{2}\sum_{i=1}^{l}(d_i - F(\mathbf{x}_i))^2 + \frac{1}{2}\lambda_A\|F\|_K^2 + \frac{1}{2}\lambda_I\mathbf{f}^T\mathbf{L}\mathbf{f} \tag{7.119}$$

where the optimization is performed over a reproducing-kernel Hilbert space (i.e., F is in the RKHS). Optimization of the cost functional $\mathcal{E}_\lambda(F)$ admits an expansion of the form

$$F_\lambda^*(\mathbf{x}) = \sum_{i=1}^{N} a_i^* k(\mathbf{x}, \mathbf{x}_i) \tag{7.120}$$

which incorporates both labeled and unlabeled examples (Belkin et al., 2006). As such, this expansion may be viewed as the *semisupervised generalization* of the classical representer theorem.

To prove this theorem, we proceed by first recognizing that any function $F(\mathbf{x})$ belonging to the reproducing-kernel Hilbert space may be decomposed into the sum of two components: one component, $F_{\|}(\mathbf{x})$, is contained in the span of the kernel functions $k(\cdot, \mathbf{x}_1), k(\cdot, \mathbf{x}_2), ..., k(\cdot, \mathbf{x}_N)$, and the other component, $F_{\perp}(\mathbf{x})$, is contained in the orthogonal complement. That is to say, we write

$$F(\mathbf{x}) = F_{\|}(\mathbf{x}) + F_{\perp}(\mathbf{x})$$

$$= \sum_{i=1}^{N} a_i\, k(\mathbf{x}, \mathbf{x}_i) + F_{\perp}(\mathbf{x}) \tag{7.121}$$

where the a_i are real coefficients. By invoking the *reproducing property* discussed in Chapter 6, we find that the evaluation of the function $F(\mathbf{x})$ at any data point $\mathbf{x}_j, 1 \leq j \leq N$, is independent of the orthogonal component, as shown by

$$F(\mathbf{x}_j) = \langle F, k(\cdot, \mathbf{x}_j)\rangle$$

$$= \left\langle \sum_{i=1}^{N} a_i k(\cdot, \mathbf{x}_i), k(\cdot, \mathbf{x}_j)\right\rangle + \langle F_{\perp}, k(\cdot, \mathbf{x}_j)\rangle$$

$$= \sum_{i=1}^{N} a_i \langle k(\cdot, \mathbf{x}_i), k(\cdot, \mathbf{x}_j)\rangle + \langle F_{\perp}, k(\cdot, \mathbf{x}_j)\rangle \tag{7.122}$$

We now note two points:

1. In the first term of Eq. (7.122), we have

$$\langle k(\cdot, \mathbf{x}_i), k(\cdot, \mathbf{x}_j)\rangle = k(\mathbf{x}_i, \mathbf{x}_j)$$

2. The second term, $\langle F_{\perp}, k(\cdot, \mathbf{x}_j)\rangle$, is zero.

We may therefore go on to write

$$F(\mathbf{x}_j) = \sum_{i=1}^{N} a_i k(\mathbf{x}_i, \mathbf{x}_j) \tag{7.123}$$

which shows that the empirical terms involving the standard regularized cost function and the intrinsic norm in the minimization of Eq. (7.119) depend only on the expansion coefficients $\{a_i\}_{i=1}^{N}$ and the Gram of the kernel function.

Next, we note that for all $F_{\perp}$, this orthogonal component tends only to increase the norm of the function in the reproducing-kernel Hilbert space—that is to say,

$$\|F\|_K^2 = \left\|\sum_{i=1}^{N} a_i k(\cdot, \mathbf{x}_i)\right\|_K^2 + \|F_{\perp}\|_K^2$$

$$\geq \left\|\sum_{i=1}^{N} a_i k(\cdot, \mathbf{x}_i)\right\|_K^2$$

where the lower subscript K refers to the reproducing-kernel Hilbert space.

It follows, therefore, that for the minimization of the cost functional $\mathscr{E}_{\lambda}(F)$ to be realized, we must have $F_{\perp} = 0$, proving the generalized representer theorem presented in Eq. (7.120), where the use of a signifies the optimum setting.

This simple form of the generalized representer theorem makes it possible to translate an extrinsic-intrinsic regularization framework into a corresponding optimization problem formulated over the finite-dimensional space of coefficients $\{a_i^*\}_{i=1}^N$, where N is the total number of labeled and unlabeled examples (Belkin et al., 2006). In so doing, we are enabled to invoke the machinery of kernel methods for solving difficult semi-supervised learning problems, as illustrated in the next section.

7.15 LAPLACIAN REGULARIZED LEAST-SQUARES ALGORITHM

In Section 7.12, we introduced the concept of the smoothing functional, the formulation of which embodies the Laplacian operator under the umbrella of spectral graph theory. In particular, the defining formula of the smoothing functional is *kernelized*, which makes the functional nonlinearly dependent on the input vector **x**, as shown in Eqs. (7.116) through (7.118). Next we generalized the representer theorem so as to accommodate the employment of both labeled and unlabeled examples. With these tools at our disposal, the stage is now set for formulation of the *Laplacian regularized least-squares (LapRLS) algorithm* (Belkin et al., 2006; Sindhwani et al., 2006). The practical virtue of this new algorithm is twofold:

1. The training of the algorithm uses both labeled and unlabeled examples, thereby enhancing applicability of the algorithm to a range of problems broader than that attainable under supervised training alone.

2. Through kernelization, the algorithm can handle the recognition of nonlinearly separable patterns, thereby broadening the applicability of least-squares estimation.

Basically, the LapRLS algorithm is derived by minimizing the cost functional of Eq. (7.119) with respect to the function $F(\mathbf{x})$. Using the representer theorem (for both labeled and unlabeled examples), we have

$$F(\mathbf{x}) = \sum_{i=1}^N a_i k(\mathbf{x}, \mathbf{x}_i)$$

in Eq. (7.119) and using matrix notations, we get

$$\mathscr{E}_\lambda(\mathbf{a}) = \frac{1}{2}(\mathbf{d} - \mathbf{JKa})^T(\mathbf{d} - \mathbf{JKa}) + \frac{1}{2}\lambda_A \mathbf{a}^T \mathbf{Ka} + \frac{1}{2}\lambda_I \mathbf{a}^T \mathbf{KLKa} \quad (7.124)$$

where we have introduced the following notations:

$\mathbf{d}$ = l-by-1 desired-response vector
= $[d_1, d_2, ..., d_l]^T$

$\mathbf{a}$ = N-by-1 expansion-coefficient vector
= $[a_1, a_2, ..., a_N]^T$

$\mathbf{J}$ = N-by-N diagonal matrix, partially filled with l unity terms
= diag$[1, 1, ..., 1, 0, 0, ..., 0]$

The l-by-l matrix $\mathbf{K}$ is the *Gram*, and $\mathbf{L}$ is the *Laplacian graph matrix*. Note that the expression on the right-hand side of Eq. (7.124) is a quadratic function of the unknown vector $\mathbf{a}$—hence the designation of the cost function as $\mathscr{E}_\lambda(\mathbf{a})$. Differentiating this equation with respect to the vector $\mathbf{a}$, collecting and simplifying terms, and then solving for the minimizer $\mathbf{a}^*$, we get

$$\mathbf{a}^* = (\mathbf{JK} + \lambda_A \mathbf{I} + \lambda_I \mathbf{LK})^{-1} \mathbf{J}^T \mathbf{d} \tag{7.125}$$

where we have used the symmetry of the Gram matrix $\mathbf{K}$ and the diagonal matrix $\mathbf{J}$, and $\mathbf{I}$ is the identity matrix; see Problem 7.16.

When we set the intrinsic regularization parameter λ_I equal to zero (i.e., $l = N$) and note that under this condition the matrix $\mathbf{J}$ assumes the form of a standard diagonal matrix, the formula of Eq. (7.125) reduces to that of Eq. (7.74) for the ordinary regularized least-squares algorithm.

Table 7.1 presents a summary of the LapRLS algorithm, where we have four parameters under the designer's control:

1. two regularization parameters λ_A and λ_I;
2. two graph parameters normal ε and σ^2, where ε is needed in the adjacency matrix of Eq. (7.109) and σ^2 is needed for the Gaussian kernel weight of Eq. (7.118).

Note that the algorithm does *not* require computation of the weight vector of the RLS algorithm. Rather, we bypass the need for this computation by focusing on the parameter vector $\mathbf{a}$ in accordance with the representer theorem.

A distinguishing feature of the semisupervised-learning algorithm summarized in Table 7.1 is the need to know the two regularization parameters λ_A and λ_I. As pointed out previously, there is merit in extending the cross-validation theory of Section 7.8 to cater to the estimation of λ_A and λ_I.

TABLE 7.1   Summary of the Laplacian Regularized Least-Squares Algorithm

Given quantities

Training samples $\{\mathbf{x}_i, d_i\}_{i=1}^{l}$ and $\{\mathbf{x}_i\}_{i=l+1}^{N}$, which are respectively labeled and unlabeled.
l is the number of the labeled examples and $(N - l)$ is the number of unlabeled examples

Design parameters

ε and σ^2:	spectral graph parameters
λ_A and λ_I:	regularization parameters, ambient and intrinsic

Computation

1. Construct the weighted undirected graph G with N nodes, using
    *   Eq. (7.109) for identifying the adjacent nodes of the graph, and
    *   Eqs. (7.117 and 7.118) for computing the edge weights.
2. Choose a kernel function $k(\mathbf{x}, \cdot)$ and, using the training sample, compute the Gram
    $\mathbf{K} = \{k(\mathbf{x}_i, \mathbf{x}_j)\}_{i,j=1}^{N}$
3. Compute the Laplacian matrix $\mathbf{L}$ of the graph G, using Eqs. (7.110) and (7.112).
4. Compute the optimum coefficient vector $\mathbf{a}^*$, using Eq. (7.125).
5. Finally, use the representer theorem of Eq. (7.120) to compute the optimized approximating function $F_\lambda^*(\mathbf{x})$.

7.16   EXPERIMENTS ON PATTERN CLASSIFICATION USING SEMISUPERVISED LEARNING

Pattern Classification Using Synthetic Data

To illustrate the pattern-classification capability of the Laplacian RLS algorithm, we performed a toy experiment based on synthetic data extracted from the double-moon configuration of Fig. 1.8. Specifically, two parameters of the experiment were held constant:

$$\text{Vertical separation between the two moons, } d = -1.$$

$$\text{Ambient regularization parameter, } \lambda_A = 0.001.$$

The only variable parameter in the experiment was the intrinsic regularization parameter λ_I.

When λ_I is set equal to zero exactly, the Laplacian RLS algorithm reduces to the conventional RLS algorithm, for which the labeled data provide the only source of information for learning. From an experimental point of view, the issue of interest is therefore to see how the incorporation of unlabeled data in the semisupervised learning process affects the decision boundary constructed by the Laplacian RLS algorithm by varying λ_I. To this end, the first part of the experiment explored what happens to the decision boundary when the intrinsic regularization parameter λ_I is assigned a very small value. In the second part of the experiment, λ_I was assigned a large enough value to permit the unlabeled data sample to have its full impact on the algorithm.

For both parts of the experiment, only two labeled data points were supplied to the algorithm for each of the two classes, one class representing the top moon in Fig. 1.8 and the other class representing the bottom moon. The total size of the training sample, consisting of both labeled and unlabeled data, was $N = 1000$ data points; the size of the testing sample was also 1000 data points.

(a) *Intrinsic regularization parameter, $\lambda_I = 0.0001$.* For this setting, Fig. 7.7 shows the decision boundary constructed by the Laplacian RLS algorithm. Despite the very small value assigned to λ_I, it is still enough to markedly change the decision boundary from that of the RLS algorithm (i.e., $\lambda_I = 0$). Recall from Figs. 2.2 and 2.3 that the RLS algorithm is characterized by a decision boundary in the form of a straight line with a positive slope.

In terms of performance, there were a total of 107 misclassifications out of a total of 1000 test data points; that is, the classification error rate was 10.7 percent.

(b) *Intrinsic regularization parameter, $\lambda_I = 0.1$.* In the second part of the experiment, the intrinsic regularization parameter λ_I was assigned the value 0.1, thereby enabling the Laplacian RLS algorithm to fully exploit the intrinsic information content of the unlabeled data. The locations of the labeled data points were exactly the same as in the first part of the experiment.

To implement the Laplacian RLS algorithm, an RBF kernel for which we set $2\sigma^2 = 3$ in Eq. (7.118). For construction of the Laplacian itself, a 20-nearest neighbor graph was employed. In effect, the RBF network for implementing the Laplacian RLS algorithm had a hidden layer of 20 computational nodes.

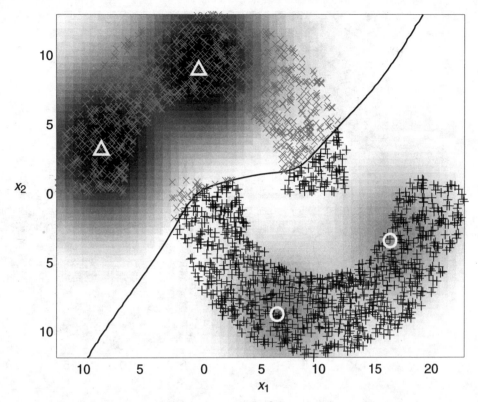

FIGURE 7.7   Lapacian RLS classification of the double-moon of Fig. 1.8 with distance $d = -1$ and two labeled data points per class that are denoted by the markers Δ and $\bigcirc$. Intrinsic regularization parameter $\lambda_I = 0.0001$.

The results of the second part of the experiment, using this network configuration, are shown in Fig. 7.8. Comparing this figure with Fig. 7.7, we see a dramatic difference in the decision boundary constructed by the Laplacian RLS algorithm for $\lambda_I = 0.1$ compared with $\lambda_I = 0.0001$. In particular, the two classes (i.e., the top and bottom moons) are now separated from each other with no classification error. This result is all the more impressive when it is recognized that for the setting $d = -1$, the two classes are not linearly separable, yet the Laplacian RLS algorithm was able to separate them successfully with only two labeled data points per class. This impressive performance of the Laplacian RLS algorithm is attributed to its ability to fully use the intrinsic information contained about the two classes in the unlabeled data.

The two parts of the experiment clearly demonstrate the tradeoffs between the ambient and intrinsic forms of regularization, whereby a semisupervised-learning process, exemplified by the Laplacian RLS algorithm, is enabled to generalize from unlabeled examples with the aid of relatively few labeled examples.

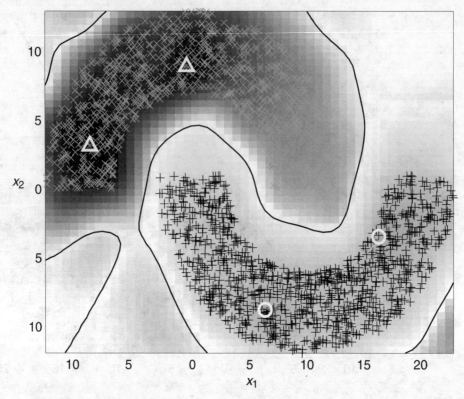

FIGURE 7.8 Laplacian RLS classification of the double-moon of Fig. 1.8 with distance $d = -1$ and two labeled data points that are denoted by the markers Δ and $\bigcirc$. The intrinsic regularization parameter $\lambda_I = 0.1$.

Case Study: Pattern Classification Using USPS Data

Figure 7.9 shows learning curves for the RLS and Laplacian RLS algorithms for a real-world image classification problem, using the *United States Postal Service (USPS) data set*. The data set consists of 2,007 images of 10 classes of handwritten digits, each of which is represented by a pixel vector of 256 dimensions. For each of the 10 classes, a separate binary classifier was trained using the RLS and Laplacian RLS algorithms. Multiway classification was performed by taking the class with maximum output, by which we mean: one-versus-rest multiclass classification. Figure 7.9 plots the mean classification error rate and standard deviations of the two algorithms as a function of the number of labels provided in the training set of 2,007 examples. Each point in Fig. 7.9 was obtained by randomizing over ten choices of labels. A Gaussian RBF kernel was used, for which, again referring to the exponent in Eq. (7.118), we set $2\sigma^2$ equal to the mean pairwise Euclidean distance between examples picked at random from the training sample. For the Laplacian RLS, a ten-nearest-neighbor graph was used to construct the Laplacian; $\lambda_A = 10^{-6}$ and $\lambda_I = 0.01$ were used as the regularization parameters. For the RLS, λ_A was tuned over a grid of values to return the optimized learning curve in Fig. 7.9. The results

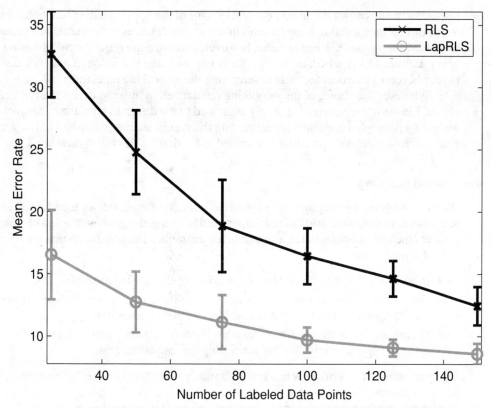

FIGURE 7.9   USPS data classification using (a) RLS algorithm and (b) Laplician RLS algorithm. (Reproduced with the permission of Dr. Vikas Sindhwani.)

presented in Fig. 7.9 demonstrate further that the use of unlabeled data significantly boosts the performance of the Laplacian RLS as compared with the RLS algorithm.

7.17   SUMMARY AND DISCUSSION

Regularization theory is at the core of all learning algorithms. In this chapter, we presented a detailed study of regularization theory, starting with Tikhonov's classical regularization theory for supervised learning using labeled examples, and finishing with the generalized regularization theory for semisupervised learning using labeled as well as unlabeled examples.

Tikhonov's Regularization Theory

In its most basic form, the functional for Tikhonov's regularization theory consists of two terms, one being the empirical cost function, defined in terms of the labeled training sample, and the other being the regularizing term, defined in terms of a differential operator applied to the approximating function. The differential operator acts as a *smoothing constraint* imposed on the solution obtained by minimizing the cost functional with respect to the unknown parameter (weight) vector of the approximating function. Central to this optimal solution is the Green's function, which serves as the kernel of a radial-basis-function network. Keep in mind, however, that once the requirement of having a fewer number of kernels than data points is imposed, the reduction in network complexity becomes a critical factor in determining the smoothing regularizer.

Whatever the choice of the smoothing regularizer, in order to derive the full benefits of Tikhonov's regularization theory as applied to the design of regularized networks, we need a principled approach for estimating the regularization parameter λ. The generalized cross-validation procedure described in Section 7.8 fills this special need.

Semisupervised Learning

With the study of regularization of supervised learning completed, we then turned our attention to the regularization of semisupervised learning, the implementation of which involves the use of both labeled and unlabeled examples. The cost functional now consists of three terms:

- the *empirical cost function*, defined in terms of the labeled examples;
- the *ambient regularization term*, which reflects the complexity of the approximating function that requires the availability of labeled examples;
- the *intrinsic regularization term*, which reflects the intrinsic geometric structure of the input space responsible for generating the unlabeled examples.

Correspondingly, there are now two regularization parameters, one for the ambient term and the other for the intrinsic term.

As an important instance of the generalized regularization theory, we considered the least-squares estimation problem, using labeled and unlabeled examples. Through the use of a kernelized smoothing function that embodies a Laplacian operator and the application of a generalized form of the representer theorem, we derived an algorithm for the semisupervised version of regularized least-squares estimation; the algorithm, called the Laplacian regularized least-squares algorithm, has two important practical virtues:

1. For its training, the algorithm can handle both labeled and unlabeled examples, which therefore broadens its application to more difficult pattern-recognition problems.
2. Through kernelization of the smoothing function, basic to the formulation of the algorithm, the recognition of nonlinearly separable patterns becomes feasible with least-squares estimation.

The practical feasibility of this algorithm was demonstrated by way of two insightful computer experiments, one involving synthetic data and the other involving real-life data.

In Belkin et al. (2006), a semisupervised-learning algorithm is derived for *Laplacian support vector machines* (LapSVM). The capability of this algorithm has been successfully tested on some real-life data sets. However, the algorithm requires the inversion of a dense Gram, which, in turn, leads to a computational complexity on the order of N^3, where N is the size of the complete training sample (labeled as well as unlabeled); moreover, as with the standard support vector machine, we still have the quadratic-programming problem to solve, the complexity of which is also of the order of N^3. The LapRLS algorithm is computationally simpler than the LapSVM, as there is no quadratic programming involved in its formulation. Most importantly, experimental results appear to show that the performances of these two semisupervised-learning machines are fairly close. From a practical perspective, it therefore appears that the LapRLS is the better choice for solving semisupervised-learning problems.

Nevertheless, the computational complexity of the LapRLS is also of the order of N^3, which arises because of the inclusion of the intrinsic term in the cost functional. This exceptionally high computational complexity could make it impractical to apply the LapRLS to real-life problems involving large data sets. The development of *scalable* semisupervised-learning machines is an active area of current research.

NOTES AND REFERENCES

1. *Learning from Examples as an Ill-posed Inverse Problem.* The fact that the task of machine learning through examples would typically violate one or more of Hadamard's conditions of well-posedness may prompt us to view the learning process as an "ill-posed" inverse problem. However, from a rigorous mathematical perspective, the connection between learning theory and the theory of ill-posed inverse problems, is not that straightforward. The mathematical foundations of these two theories are different; basically, learning theory is intrinsically probabilistic in nature (regardless of whether we explicitly bring probability theory into its formulation), while on the other hand, the theory of inverse problems could be viewed as mostly deterministic. DeVito et al. (2005) present an insightful exposition of learning from examples viewed as an ill-posed inverse problem.

2. *Validation of Eq. (7.46).* In basic terms, we may justify the validation of Eq. (7.46) by starting with the *unit Gaussian function*

$$G(x) = \exp(-\pi x^2) \tag{A}$$

which is one-dimensional with $\sigma^2 = 1/2\pi$. Basically, then, the requirement is to show that

$$\sum_{n=0}^{\infty} (-1)^n \frac{(2\pi)^{-n}}{n!2^n} \frac{\partial^{2n}}{\partial x^{2n}} G(x) = \delta(x) \tag{B}$$

where $\delta(x)$ is the Dirac delta function centered at the origin $x = 0$.

To justify Eq. (B), the most expedient way is to exploit the fundamental properties of the Fourier transform (Kammler, 2000). In particular, the *differentiation property* states

Differentiation of $G(x)$ in the x-domain is equivalent to multiplication of $\hat{G}(s)$, the Fourier transform of $G(x)$, by $i2\pi s$, where s is the spatial frequency and i is the square root of -1.

From Fourier-transform theory we also know that in mathematical terms, the unit Gaussian function is its own Fourier transform. Specifically, for the $G(x)$ of Eq. (A), we have

$$\hat{G}(s) = \exp(-\pi s^2) \tag{C}$$

Therefore, taking the Fourier transform of the infinite summation on the left-hand side of Eq. (B) yields (after the simplification of terms)

$$\sum_{p=0}^{\infty} (-1)^p \frac{(2\pi)^{-p}}{p!2^p} (i2\pi s)^{2p} \exp(-\pi s^2) = \exp(-\pi s^2) \sum_{p=0}^{\infty} \frac{(\sqrt{\pi}s)^{2p}}{p!} \tag{D}$$

The new infinite summation on the right-hand side of Eq. (D) is now recognized to be the series expansion of the exponential $\exp(\pi s^2)$. It follows therefore that the right-hand side of Eq. (D) is equal to unity, the inverse transform of which is indeed the Dirac delta function $\delta(x)$. Justification of Eq. (B) is thereby established.

With Eq. (B) justified for the one-dimensional case, we may continue the justification of Eq. (7.46) by invoking the method of induction by considering the two-dimensional case, and so on.

3. *Regularized Strict Interpolation.* In Yee and Haykin (2001), a method for designing RBF networks is described, combining elements of two rigorous theories:
   - the regularization theory of strict interpolation presented in Section 7.3, and
   - the kernel regressive estimation theory presented in Chapter 5.

With respect to the latter theory, attention is focused on the Nadaraya-Watson regression estimator. This method offers a principled approach for solving regression and pattern-classification problems in a way that is simple to encode and effective in performance. However, it is computationally demanding, particularly when the size of the training sample is large.

4. *Generalized Cross-validation.* To obtain generalized cross-validation from ordinary cross-validation, we may consider a *ridge regression problem* described in Wahba (1990) as

$$\mathbf{y} = \mathbf{X}\boldsymbol{\alpha} + \boldsymbol{\epsilon} \tag{A}$$

where $\mathbf{X}$ is an N-by-N matrix of inputs, and the noise vector $\boldsymbol{\epsilon}$ has a mean vector of zero and a covariance matrix equal to $\sigma^2 \mathbf{I}$. Using the singular-value decomposition of $\mathbf{X}$, we may write

$$\mathbf{X} = \mathbf{U}\mathbf{D}\mathbf{V}^T$$

where $\mathbf{U}$ and $\mathbf{V}$ are orthogonal matrices and $\mathbf{D}$ is a diagonal matrix. Let

$$\tilde{\mathbf{y}} = \mathbf{U}^T\mathbf{y}$$
$$\boldsymbol{\beta} = \mathbf{V}^T\boldsymbol{\alpha}$$

and

$$\tilde{\boldsymbol{\epsilon}} = \mathbf{U}^T\boldsymbol{\epsilon} \tag{B}$$

We may then use $\mathbf{U}$ and $\mathbf{V}$ to transform Eq. (A) into the new form

$$\tilde{\mathbf{y}} = \mathbf{D}\boldsymbol{\beta} + \tilde{\boldsymbol{\epsilon}}$$

The diagonal matrix $\mathbf{D}$ (not to be confused with a differential operator) is chosen to have its singular values come in pairs. Then, there is an orthogonal matrix $\mathbf{W}$ for which $\mathbf{W}\mathbf{D}\mathbf{W}^T$ is a circulant matrix; that is,

$$
\begin{aligned}
\mathbf{A} &= \mathbf{W}\mathbf{D}\mathbf{W}^T \\
&= \begin{bmatrix}
a_0 & a_1 & \cdots & a_{N-1} \\
a_{N-1} & a_0 & \cdots & a_{N-2} \\
a_{N-2} & a_{N-1} & \cdots & a_{N-3} \\
\vdots & \vdots & \vdots & \vdots \\
a_1 & a_2 & \cdots & a_0
\end{bmatrix}
\end{aligned}
$$

which is constant along the main diagonal. Let

$$\mathbf{z} = \mathbf{W}\tilde{\mathbf{y}}$$
$$\boldsymbol{\gamma} = \mathbf{W}\boldsymbol{\beta}$$

and

$$\xi = W\tilde{\epsilon}$$

We may then use W to transform Eq. (B) into

$$z = A\gamma + \xi \tag{C}$$

The diagonal matrix D has "maximally uncoupled" rows, while the circulant matrix A has "maximally coupled" rows.

   With these transformations at hand, we may now state that generalized cross-validation is equivalent to transforming the ridge regression problem of Eq. (A) into the maximally coupled form of Eq. (C), then doing ordinary cross-validation on z, and finally transforming the result back to the original coordinate system (Wahba, 1990).

5. *Wikipedia Demonstration.* To see the continuous deformation of a coffee mug into a doughnut and vice versa, visit the *Wikipedia* web site and search for "homeomorphism."

PROBLEMS

Green's Functions

7.1 The *thin-plate-spline function* is described by

$$\varphi(r) = \left(\frac{r}{\sigma}\right)^2 \log\left(\frac{r}{\sigma}\right).$$

for some $\sigma > 0$ and $r \in \mathbb{R}$.

Justify the use of this function as a translationally and rotationally invariant Green's function.

7.2 Let $\varphi(x)$ denotes a continuous function of $x \in \mathbb{R}^{m_0}$ then prove that the function

$$F(x) = \int_{\mathbb{R}^{m_0}} G(x, \xi)\varphi(\xi)d\xi$$

is a solution of the differential equation

$$LF(x) = \varphi(x)$$

where, $G(x, \xi)$ is a Green's function for the linear differential operator L.

7.3 In Chapter 5, we identified three radial-basis functions—the Gaussian function, the inverse multiquadric, and the multiquadric—all of which satisfy Micchelli's theorem. However, the class of Green's functions includes only the first two radial-basis functions. Explain why the multiquadric is excluded from the class of Green's functions.

Regularized Networks

7.4 Consider the cost functional

$$\mathscr{E}(F^*) = \sum_{i=1}^{N}\left[d_i - \sum_{j=1}^{m_1} w_i G(\|x_j - t_i\|)\right]^2 + \lambda\|DF^*\|^2$$

which refers to the approximating function

$$F^*(x) = \sum_{i=1}^{m_1} w_i G(\|x - t_i\|)$$

Using the Fréchet differential, show that the cost functional $\mathscr{E}(F^*)$ is minimized when

$$(G^T G + \lambda G_0)\hat{w} = G^T d$$

where the N-by-m_1 matrix $\mathbf{G}$, the m_1-by-m_1 matrix $\mathbf{G}_0$, the m_1-by-1 vector $\hat{\mathbf{w}}$, and the N-by-1 vector $\mathbf{d}$ are defined by Eqs. (7.53), (7.56), (7.54), and (7.27), respectively.

7.5 Consider a regularizing term defined by

$$\int_{\mathbb{R}^{m_o}} \|\mathbf{D}F(\mathbf{x})\|^2 d\mathbf{x} = \sum_{k=0}^{\infty} a_k \int_{\mathbb{R}^{m_o}} \|D^k F(\mathbf{x})\|^2 d\mathbf{x}$$

where

$$a_k = \frac{\sigma^{2k}}{k! 2^k}$$

and the linear differential operator D is defined in terms of the gradient operator ∇ and the Laplacian operator ∇^2 as

$$D^{2k} = (\nabla^2)^k$$

and

$$D^{2k+1} = \nabla(\nabla^2)^k$$

Show that

$$\mathbf{D}F(\mathbf{x}) = \sum_{k=0}^{\infty} \frac{\sigma^{2k}}{k! 2^k} \nabla^{2k} F(\mathbf{x})$$

7.6 In Section 7.3, we derived the approximating function $F_\lambda(\mathbf{x})$ of Eq. (7.47) by using the relationship of Eq. (7.46). In this problem, we wish to start with the relationship of Eq. (7.46) and use the multidimensional Fourier transformation to derive Eq. (7.47). Perform this derivation by using

$$G(\mathbf{s}) = \int_{\mathbb{R}^{m_o}} G(\mathbf{x}) \exp(-i\mathbf{s}^T\mathbf{x}) d\mathbf{x}$$

as the definition of the multidimensional Fourier transform of the Green's function $G(\mathbf{x})$, where $i = \sqrt{-1}$ and $\mathbf{s}$ is the m_0-dimensional transform variable. Reference may be made to a book on properties of the Fourier transform.

7.7 Consider the nonlinear regression problem described in Eq. (7.78). Let a_{ik} denote the ik-th element of the inverse matrix $(\mathbf{G} + \lambda\mathbf{I})^{-1}$. Hence, starting with Eq. (7.39), show that the estimate of the regression function $f(\mathbf{x})$ may be expressed as

$$\hat{f}(\mathbf{x}) = \sum_{k=1}^{N} \psi(\mathbf{x}, \mathbf{x}_k) d_k$$

where d_k is the model output for the input $\mathbf{x}_k$, and

$$\psi(\mathbf{x}, \mathbf{x}_k) = \sum_{i=1}^{N} G(\|\mathbf{x} - \mathbf{x}_i\|) a_{ik}, \qquad k = 1, 2, ..., N$$

where $G(\|\cdot\|)$ is the Green's function.

7.8 *Spline functions* are examples of piecewise polynomial approximators (Schumaker, 1981). The basic idea behind the method of splines is as follows: An approximation region of interest is broken up into a finite number of subregions via the use of *knots*; the knots can be fixed, in which case the approximators are *linearly* parameterized, or they can be variable, in which case the approximators are *nonlinearly* parameterized. In both cases, in each region of the approximation a polynomial of at most degree n is used, with the additional requirement that the overall function be $n-1$ times differentiable. Polynomial splines are relatively smooth functions that are easy to store, manipulate, and evaluate on a computer.

Among spline functions used in practice, *cubic splines* are perhaps the most popular. The cost functional for a cubic spline, pertaining to a one-dimensional input, is defined by

$$\mathscr{E}(f) = \frac{1}{2}\sum_{i=1}^{N}[d_i - f(x_i)]^2 + \frac{\lambda}{2}\int_{x_1}^{x_N}\left[\frac{d^2f(x)}{dx^2}\right]^2 dx$$

where, in the language of splines, λ denotes a *smoothing* parameter.

(a) Justify the following properties of the solution $f_\lambda(x)$ to this problem:
   (1) $f_\lambda(x)$ is a cubic polynomial between two successive values of x.
   (2) $f_\lambda(x)$ and its first two derivatives are all continuous, except at the boundary points, where the second derivative of $f_\lambda(x)$ is zero.

(b) Since $\mathscr{E}(f)$ has a unique minimum, we must have

$$\mathscr{E}(f_\lambda + \alpha g) \geq \mathscr{E}(f_\lambda)$$

for any g drawn from the same class of twice-differentiable functions as f_λ and for any real-valued constant α. This means that $\mathscr{E}(f_\lambda + \alpha g)$, interpreted as a function of α, must have a local minimum at $\alpha = 0$. Hence, show that

$$\int_{x_1}^{x_N}\left(\frac{d^2f_\lambda(x)}{dx^2}\right)\left(\frac{d^2g(x)}{dx^2}\right)dx = \frac{1}{2}\sum_{i=1}^{N}[d - f_\lambda(x_i)]g(x_i)$$

which is the Euler–Lagrange equation for the cubic-spline problem.

7.9 Discuss how the generalized RBF network shown in Fig. 7.3 is different from the regularization RBF network shown in Fig. 7.2.

Regularized Least-Squares Estimation

7.10 Starting from Eq. (7.57), derive the normal equation of Eq. (7.65) for the regularized least-squares estimator.

7.11 Justify the identity of Eq. (7.70), which involves the data matrix $\mathbf{X}$ and desired response vector $\mathbf{d}$.

Semisupervised Learning

7.12 How can we exploit the availability of both labeled and unlabeled examples in the training of networks?

Spectral Graph Theory

7.13 In Section 7.13, we made the statement that the smallest eigenvalue of the Laplacian $\mathbf{L}$ is zero. Using the Rayleigh quotient of Eq. (7.113), justify this statement.

Generalized Representer Theorem

7.14 In the last line of Eq. (7.122), we used the following property of the representer theorem:

$$\left\langle \sum_{i=1}^{N} a_i k(\cdot, \mathbf{x}_i), k(\cdot, \mathbf{x}_j)\right\rangle = \sum_{i=1}^{N} a_i k(\mathbf{x}_i; \mathbf{x}_j)$$

Prove this property.

7.15 The representer theorem of Eq. (7.120) for both labeled and unlabeled examples and that of Eq. (6.83) for labeled examples have the same mathematical form. Explain how the representer theorem for semisupervised learning includes the representer theorem for supervised learning as a special case.

Laplacian Regularized Least-Squares Algorithm

7.16 **(a)** Derive the cost functional of Eq. (7.124). Then use this functional to derive the optimized $\mathbf{a}^*$ of Eq. (7.125).

(b) Show the details of how this minimizer includes that of Eq. (7.74) for labeled examples as a special case.

7.17 The computational complexity of both LapRLS and LapSVM algorithms for semisupervised learning is of the order of N^3. Which algorithm do you think is a better choice for solving semisupervised-learning problems?

7.18 In solving the method of least squares, we have the option of using either the normal equation or the representer theorem, as discussed in Section 7.6. However, in solving the semisupervised extension of this method, the representer theorem is the right choice. Explain the rationale for this statement.

7.19 Implementation of the Laplacian RLS algorithm uses an RBF network. Discuss the distinctive roles of unlabeled and labeled examples in designing the hidden and output layers of this network.

Computer Experiment

7.20 The small set of labeled data points may be viewed as the initializing condition of the Laplacian RLS algorithm. As such, for a given unlabeled training sample, we would expect the decision boundary constructed by the algorithm to depend on the locations of the labeled data points. In this experiment, we explore this dependence, using synthetic data extracted from the double-moon configuration of Fig. 1.8.

(a) *One labeled data point per class.* Repeat the computer experiment of Section 7.16 using exactly the same specifications as before, but this time explore how the decision boundary is affected by the locations of the two labeled data points, one per class.

(b) *Two labeled data points per class.* For the same settings as in part (a), repeat the experiment using a pair of labeled data points per class.

Comment on the results of your experiments.

C H A P T E R   8

Principal-Components Analysis

ORGANIZATION OF THE CHAPTER

The purpose of this chapter is to describe how the implementation of principal-components analysis can be accomplished through the use of unsupervised learning. The chapter is organized as follows:

1. The introductory section, Section 8.1, highlights the essence of unsupervised learning.
2. Section 8.2 describes the four principles of self-organization: self-reinforcement, competition, cooperation, and structural information. These principles are particularly important in the study of neural networks. The roles of these principles in the formation of self-organized features in the visual system are illustrated in Section 8.3.
3. Section 8.4 develops the mathematical background of principal-components analysis (PCA), using a perturbation-theoretic approach.
4. The next two sections address the formulation of two Hebbian-based on-line learning algorithms, with Section 8.5 focusing on Oja's rule for maximum eigenfiltering (i.e., extraction of the strongest principal component), followed by Section 8.6 on the generalization of Oja's rule. In Section 8.7, this generalized rule is applied to image compression.
5. Section 8.8 discusses the kernelization of PCA, which makes it possible to extract higher-order statistics of the input signal. Higher-order statistics constitute an intrinsic property of natural images, an issue discussed in Section 8.9. In order to tackle the modeling of natural images in a computationally efficient manner, Section 8.10 describes an adaptive modification of kernelized PCA by building on the generalized Hebbian algorithm. A case study on the denoising of a multipatch image is presented in Section 8.10.

The chapter concludes with a summary and discussion in Section 8.11.

8.1   INTRODUCTION

An important property of neural networks is their ability to learn from their environment and, through training, to improve their performance in some statistical sense. Except for the discussion on semisupervised learning in Chapter 7, the focus in previous chapters has been on algorithms for supervised learning, for which a training sample is provided. In supervised learning, the training sample embodies a set of examples on a desired input–output mapping, which the network is required to approximate. In this and the next three chapters, we take a new direction: We study algorithms for unsupervised learning.

In *unsupervised learning*, the requirement is to *discover* significant patterns, or features, of the input data through the use of *unlabeled examples*. That it to say, the network operates in accordance with the rule:

Learn from examples without a teacher.

The study of unsupervised learning may be pursued from two different perspectives:

(i) *Self-organized learning*, the formulation of which is motivated by neurobiological considerations. In particular, the unsupervised-learning algorithm is supplied with a set of *rules of local behavior*, and the requirement is to use the rules to compute an input–output mapping with desirable properties. Here, the term "local" means that the adjustments applied to the synaptic weights of each neuron in the network are confined to the immediate local neighborhood of the neuron. In this context, the modeling of a neural network used for self-organized learning tends to follow neurobiological structures, recognizing that network organization is fundamental to the brain.

(ii) *Statistical learning theory*, which is the approach that is traditionally pursued in machine learning. The notion of locality of learning that is emphasized in neural networks plays a lesser role in machine learning. Instead, in statistical learning theory, a much greater emphasis is placed on well-established mathematical tools.

In this chapter, we study *principal-components analysis* (PCA)[1] from both of these two perspectives. PCA is a standard technique that is widely used for dimensionality reduction is statistical pattern recognition and signal processing.

8.2 PRINCIPLES OF SELF-ORGANIZATION

Principle 1. Self-amplification

This first principle of self-organization states the following:

> *Modifications in the synaptic weights of a neuron tend to self-amplify in accordance with Hebb's postulate of learning, which is made possible by synaptic plasticity.*

In a single neuron, the process of *self-amplification*, or *self-reinforcement*, is constrained by the requirement that modifications in the synaptic weights of the neuron must be based on presynaptic and postsynaptic signals available at the *local* level. Basically, the requirements of self-reinforcement and locality specify a feedback mechanism, by means of which a strong synapse leads to the coincidence of presynaptic and postsynaptic signals. In turn, the synapse is increased in strength by such a coincidence. The mechanism described here is the very essence of Hebbian learning.

Hebb's postulate of learning is the oldest and most famous of all learning rules; it is named in honor of the neuropsychologist Hebb (1949). Hebb's book *The Organization of Behavior* (1949) states the following (p. 62):

When an axon of cell A is near enough to excite a cell B and repeatedly or persistently takes part in firing it, some growth process or metabolic changes take place in one or both cells such that A's efficiency as one of the cells firing B is increased.

Hebb proposed this change on the basis of associative learning (at the cellular level), which would result in an enduring modification in the activity pattern of a spatially distributed "assembly of nerve cells."

The statement on Hebb's postulate of learning is made in a neurobiological context. We may expand and rephrase it as a two-part rule (Stent, 1973; Changeux and Danchin, 1976):

1. *If two neurons on either side of a synapse (connection) are activated simultaneously (i.e., synchronously), then the strength of that synapse is selectively increased.*
2. *If two neurons on either side of a synapse are activated asynchronolusly, then that synapse is selectively weakened or eliminated.*

Such a synapse is called a *Hebbian synapse.*[2] (The original Hebbian rule did not contain part 2.) More precisely, we define a Hebbian synapse as a synapse that uses a *time-dependent, highly local, and strongly interactive mechanism to increase synaptic efficiency as a function of the correlation between the presynaptic and postsynaptic activities.* From this definition, we may deduce the following four key mechanisms (properties) that characterize Hebbian learning (Brown et al., 1990):

1. *Time-dependent mechanism.* This mechanism refers to the fact that the modifications in a Hebbian synapse depend on the exact time of occurrence of the presynaptic and postsynaptic signals.
2. *Local mechanism.* By its very nature, a synapse is the transmission site where information-bearing signals (representing ongoing activity in the presynaptic and postsynaptic units) are in *spatiotemporal* contiguity. This locally available information is used by a Hebbian synapse to produce a local synaptic modification that is input specific.
3. *Interactive mechanism.* The occurrence of a change in a Hebbian synapse depends on signals on both sides of the synapse. That is, the Hebbian form of learning depends on "true interaction" between presynaptic and postsynaptic signals in the sense that we cannot make a prediction from either one of these two activities by itself. Note also that this dependence or interaction may be deterministic or statistical in nature.
4. *Conjunctional or correlational mechanism.* One interpretation of Hebb's postulate of learning is that the condition for a change in synaptic efficiency is the conjunction of presynaptic and postsynaptic signals. Thus, according to this interpretation, the co-occurrence of presynaptic and postsynaptic signals (within a short interval of time) is sufficient to produce the synaptic modification. It is for this reason that a Hebbian synapse is sometimes referred to as a *conjunctional synapse.* For another interpretation of Hebb's postulate of learning, we may think of the interactive mechanism characterizing a Hebbian synapse in statistical terms. In particular, the correlation over time between presynaptic and postsynaptic signals is viewed as being responsible for a synaptic change. Accordingly, a Hebbian synapse is also referred to as a *correlational synapse.* Correlation is indeed the basis of learning (Chen et al., 2007).

To formulate Hebbian learning in mathematical terms, consider a synaptic weight w_{kj} of neuron k with presynaptic and postsynaptic signals denoted by x_j and y_k, respectively. The adjustment applied to the synaptic weight w_{kj} at time-step n is expressed in the general form

$$\Delta w_{kj}(n) = f(y_k(n), x_j(n)) \qquad (8.1)$$

where $f(\cdot,\cdot)$ is a function of both postsynaptic and presynaptic signals. The signals $x_j(n)$ and $y_k(n)$ are often treated as dimensionless. The formula of Eq. (8.1) admits many forms,[3] all of which qualify as Hebbian. In what follows, we consider the simplest form of Hebbian learning, described by

$$\Delta w_{kj}(n) = \eta y_k(n)x_j(n) \qquad (8.2)$$

where η is a positive constant that determines the *rate of learning*. Equation (8.2) clearly emphasizes the correlational nature of a Hebbian synapse. It is sometimes referred to as the *activity product rule*. From the representation of Eq. (8.2), we see that the repeated application of the input signal (presynaptic activity) x_j leads to an increase in y_k and, therefore, *exponential growth* that finally drives the synaptic connection into saturation. At that point, no new information will be stored in the synapse, and selectivity is lost. Some mechanism is therefore needed to stabilize the self-organized behavior of the neuron, which is taken care of by the second principle.

Principle 2. Competition

This second principle of self-organization states the following:

> *The limitation of available resources, in one form or another, leads to competition among the synapses of a single neuron or an assembly of neurons, with the result that the most vigorously growing (i.e., fittest) synapses or neurons, respectively, are selected at the expense of the others.*

This second principle is made possible by synaptic *plasticity* (i.e., adjustability of a synaptic weight).

For a given single neuron to *stabilize*, for example, there must be competition among its synapses for limited resources (e.g., energy) in such a way that the increase in strength of some synapses in the neuron is compensated for by a decrease in strength in others. Accordingly, only the "successful" synapses can grow in strength, while the less successful synapses tend to weaken and may eventually disappear altogether.

At the network level, a similar competitive process may prevail, by proceeding as follows (Rumelhart and Zipser, 1985):

- To begin with, the neurons in the network are all the same, except for some randomly distributed synaptic weights; hence, the neurons respond differently to a given set of input patterns.
- A specific limit is imposed on the "strength" (e.g., the sum of synaptic weights) of each neuron in the network.
- The neurons compete with each other in accordance with a prescribed rule for the right to respond to a given subset of inputs; consequently, only one output neuron,

or one neuron per group, is active at a time. The neuron that wins the competition is called a *winner-takes-all neuron*.

We thus find that, through this *competitive-learning process*, the individual neurons of the network assume the role of *feature detectors* for different classes of input patterns.

Whereas in Hebbian learning, several output neurons of a neural network may be active simultaneously, in competitive learning only a single output neuron, or one output neuron per group, is active at any one time. It is this characteristic of competitive learning that makes it highly suited to discovering statistically salient features that could be used to classify a set of input patterns.

Principle 3. Cooperation

The third principle of self-organization states the following:

> *Modifications in synaptic weights at the neural level and in neurons at the network level tend to cooperate with each other.*

The cooperation may arise because of synaptic plasticity or because of simultaneous stimulation of presynaptic neurons brought on by the existence of the right conditions in the external environment.

Consider first the case of a single neuron: A single synapse on its own cannot efficiently produce favorable events. Rather, there has to be cooperation among the neuron's synapses, making it possible to carry coincident signals strong enough to activate that neuron.

At the network level, cooperation may take place through *lateral interaction* among a group of *excited* neurons. In particular, a neuron that is firing tends to excite the neurons in its immediate neighborhood more so than those farther away from it. Over the course of time, we typically find that a cooperative system evolves through a sequence of small changes from one configuration to another, until an equilibrium condition is established.

It is also important to note that in a self-organizing system that involves both competition and cooperation, *competition always precedes cooperation*.

Principle 4. Structural Information

The fourth, and last, principle of self-organization states the following:

> *The underlying order and structure that exist in an input signal represent redundant information, which is acquired by a self-organizing system in the form of knowledge.*

Structural information contained in the input data is therefore a prerequisite to self-organized learning. It is also noteworthy that whereas self-amplification, competition, and cooperation are processes that are carried out within a neuron or a neural network, structural information, or redundancy, is an inherent characteristic of the input signal.

Consider, for example, a voice or video signal. When such a signal is sampled at a high rate, the resulting sampled signal is correspondingly found to exhibit a higher degree of *correlation* between adjacent samples. The meaning of this high correlation is that, on average, the signal does not change rapidly from one sample to the next, which, in turn, means that the signal contains *structured*, or *redundant*, information. In other words, correlation is synonomous with structure and redundancy.

To appreciate the importance of structure, suppose that all the redundant information contained in a signal is completely removed. What we are then left with is a completely nonredundant signal that is unpredictable and may therefore be indistinguishable from noise. Given this kind of an input, no self-organizing or unsupervised-learning system can function.

Summarizing Remarks

The neurobiologically motivated rules of self-organization hold for the unsupervised training of neural networks, but not necessarily for more general learning machines that are required to perform unsupervised-learning tasks. In any event, the goal of unsupervised learning is to fit a *model* to a set of unlabeled input data in such a way that the underlying *structure* of the data is well represented. For the model to be realizable, however, it is essential that the data be structured.

8.3   SELF-ORGANIZED FEATURE ANALYSIS

To illustrate the principles of self-organization just described, consider information processing in the visual system, which is performed in stages. In particular, simple features such as contrast and edge orientation are analyzed in the early stages of the system, whereas more elaborate, complex features are analyzed in later stages. Figure 8.1 shows the gross structure of a modular network that resembles the visual system. In *Linsker's model* of the mammalian visual system (Linsker, 1986), the neurons of the network in Fig. 8.1 are organized into two-dimensional layers, with local forward connections from one layer to the next; the layers are labeled A, B, and C in Fig. 8.1. Each neuron receives information from a limited number of neurons located in an overlying region of the previous layer, which constitutes the *receptive field* of that neuron. The receptive fields of the network play a crucial role in the synaptic development process because they make it possible for neurons in one layer to respond to *spatial correlations* of the neuronal activities (i.e., structural information) in the previous layer. Two assumptions of a structural nature are made in Linsker's model:

1. The positions of the synaptic connections are fixed for the entire neural development process once they have been chosen.
2. Each neuron acts as a linear combiner.

The model combines aspects of Hebb-like synaptic modification with competitive and cooperative learning in such a way that the network's outputs optimally discriminate among an ensemble of inputs, with the self-organized learning proceeding on a *layer-by-layer basis*. That is, the learning process permits the self-organized feature-analyzing properties of each layer to develop fully before proceeding to the next layer; this form of learning is an example of *learning features of features*.

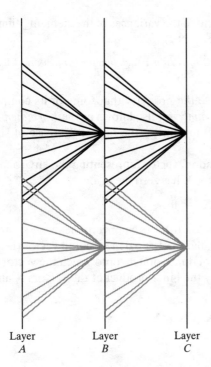

FIGURE 8.1   Layout of modular self-adaptive Linsker's model, with overlapping receptive fields.

Layer
A

Layer
B

Layer
C

In Linsker's model, simulation results are presented that are qualitatively similar to properties found in the early stages of visual processing in cats and monkeys. In light of the highly complex nature of the visual system, it is indeed remarkable that the simple model considered by Linsker is capable of developing similar feature-analyzing neurons. The point is not to imply that feature-analyzing neurons in the mammalian visual system develop in exactly the manner described in Linsker's model. Rather, such structures may be produced by a relatively simple layered network whose synaptic connections develop in accordance with a Hebbian form of learning, combined with competition and cooperation, thereby providing practical justification for the principles of self-organization.

8.4   PRINCIPAL-COMPONENTS ANALYSIS: PERTURBATION THEORY

A common problem in statistical pattern recognition is that of feature selection, or feature extraction. *Feature selection* refers to a process whereby a *data space* is transformed into a *feature space* that, in theory, has exactly the same dimension as the original data space. However, the transformation is designed in such a way that the data set may be represented by a reduced number of "effective" features, yet retain most of the intrinsic information content of the original data; in other words, the data set undergoes a *dimensionality reduction*. To be specific, suppose we have an m-dimensional vector $\mathbf{x}$ and wish to transmit it using l numbers, where $l < m$, which implies that *data compression* is an intrinsic part of feature mapping. If we simply truncate the vector $\mathbf{x}$, we will cause a mean-square error equal to the sum of the variances of the elements eliminated from **x**, so we ask the following question:

> *Does there exist an invertible linear transformation* **T** *such that the truncation of* **Tx** *is optimum in the mean-square-error sense?*

Clearly, the transformation **T** should have the property that some of its components have low variance. *Principal-components analysis* (also known as the *Karhunen–Loève transformation* in communication theory) maximizes the rate of decrease of variance and is therefore a right choice.

Let **X** denote an m-dimensional random vector representing the environment of interest. We assume that the random vector **X** has zero mean, or

$$\mathbb{E}[\mathbf{X}] = \mathbf{0}$$

where $\mathbb{E}$ is the statistical expectation operator. If **X** has a nonzero mean, we subtract the mean from it before proceeding with the analysis. Let **q** denote a unit vector (i.e., a vector with a Euclidean norm of unity), also of dimension m, onto which the vector **X** is to be *projected*. This projection is defined by the inner product of the vectors **X** and **q**, as shown by

$$A = \mathbf{X}^T\mathbf{q} = \mathbf{q}^T\mathbf{X} \tag{8.3}$$

subject to the constraint

$$\|\mathbf{q}\| = (\mathbf{q}^T\mathbf{q})^{1/2} = 1 \tag{8.4}$$

The projection A is a *random variable* with a mean and variance related to the statistics of the random vector **X**. Under the assumption that the random vector **X** has zero mean, it follows that the mean value of the projection A is zero, too:

$$\mathbb{E}[A] = \mathbf{q}^T\mathbb{E}[\mathbf{X}] = 0$$

The variance of A is therefore the same as its mean-square value, so we may write

$$\begin{aligned}
\sigma^2 &= \mathbb{E}[A^2] \\
&= \mathbb{E}[(\mathbf{q}^T\mathbf{X})(\mathbf{X}^T\mathbf{q})] \\
&= \mathbf{q}^T\mathbb{E}[\mathbf{X}\mathbf{X}^T]\mathbf{q} \\
&= \mathbf{q}^T\mathbf{R}\mathbf{q}
\end{aligned} \tag{8.5}$$

The m-by-m matrix **R** is the *correlation matrix* of the random vector **X**, formally defined as the expectation of the outer product of the vector **X** with itself, as shown by

$$\mathbf{R} = \mathbb{E}[\mathbf{X}\mathbf{X}^T] \tag{8.6}$$

We observe that the correlation matrix **R** is *symmetric*, which means that

$$\mathbf{R}^T = \mathbf{R}$$

From this property, it follows that if **a** and **b** are any m-by-1 vectors, then

$$\mathbf{a}^T\mathbf{R}\mathbf{b} = \mathbf{b}^T\mathbf{R}\mathbf{a} \tag{8.7}$$

From Eq. (8.5), we see that the variance σ^2 of the projection A is a function of the unit vector $\mathbf{q}$; we may thus write

$$\psi(\mathbf{q}) = \sigma^2$$

$$= \mathbf{q}^T \mathbf{R} \mathbf{q} \tag{8.8}$$

on the basis of which we may think of $\psi(\mathbf{q})$ as a *variance probe*.

Eigenstructure of Principal-Components Analysis

The next issue to be considered is that of finding those unit vectors $\mathbf{q}$ along which $\psi(\mathbf{q})$ has *extremal* or *stationary* values (i.e., local maxima or minima), subject to a constraint on the Euclidean norm of $\mathbf{q}$. The solution to this problem lies in the *eigenstructure* of the correlation matrix $\mathbf{R}$. If $\mathbf{q}$ is a unit vector such that the variance probe $\psi(\mathbf{q})$ has an extremal value, then for any small perturbation $\delta\mathbf{q}$ of the unit vector $\mathbf{q}$, we find that, to a first order in $\delta\mathbf{q}$,

$$\psi(\mathbf{q} + \delta\mathbf{q}) = \psi(\mathbf{q})$$

Now, from the definition of the variance probe given in Eq. (8.8), we have

$$\psi(\mathbf{q} + \delta\mathbf{q}) = (\mathbf{q} + \delta\mathbf{q})^T \mathbf{R} (\mathbf{q} + \delta\mathbf{q})$$

$$= \mathbf{q}^T \mathbf{R} \mathbf{q} + 2(\delta\mathbf{q})^T \mathbf{R} \mathbf{q} + (\delta\mathbf{q})^T \mathbf{R} \delta\mathbf{q}$$

where in the second line, we have made use of Eq. (8.7). Ignoring the second-order term $(\delta\mathbf{q})^T \mathbf{R} \, \delta\mathbf{q}$ and invoking the definition of Eq. (8.8), we may therefore write

$$\psi(\mathbf{q} + \delta\mathbf{q}) = \mathbf{q}^T \mathbf{R} \mathbf{q} + 2(\delta\mathbf{q})^T \mathbf{R} \mathbf{q}$$

$$= \psi(\mathbf{q}) + 2(\delta\mathbf{q})^T \mathbf{R} \mathbf{q} \tag{8.9}$$

But $\psi(\mathbf{q} + \delta\mathbf{q})$ is equal to $\psi(\mathbf{q})$ to a first-order of approximation; it therefore follows that we must have

$$(\delta\mathbf{q})^T \mathbf{R} \mathbf{q} = 0 \tag{8.10}$$

Just any perturbations $\delta\mathbf{q}$ of $\mathbf{q}$ are not admissible; rather, we are restricted to use only those perturbations for which the Euclidean norm of the perturbed vector $\mathbf{q} + \delta\mathbf{q}$ remains equal to unity; that is,

$$\|\mathbf{q} + \delta\mathbf{q}\| = 1$$

or, equivalently,

$$(\mathbf{q} + \delta\mathbf{q})^T (\mathbf{q} + \delta\mathbf{q}) = 1$$

Hence, in light of Eq. (8.4), to a first order in $\delta\mathbf{q}$, we require that

$$(\delta\mathbf{q})^T \mathbf{q} = 0 \tag{8.11}$$

This means that the perturbations $\delta\mathbf{q}$ must be *orthogonal* to $\mathbf{q}$, and therefore only a change in the direction of $\mathbf{q}$ is permitted.

By convention, the elements of the unit vector $\mathbf{q}$ are dimensionless in a physical sense. If, therefore, we are to combine Eqs. (8.10) and (8.11), we must introduce a scaling factor λ into the latter equation with the same dimensions as the entries in the corelation matrix $\mathbf{R}$. We may then write

$$(\delta \mathbf{q})^T \mathbf{R} \mathbf{q} - \lambda (\delta \mathbf{q})^T \mathbf{q} = 0$$

or, equivalently,

$$(\delta \mathbf{q})^T (\mathbf{R} \mathbf{q} - \lambda \mathbf{q}) = 0 \tag{8.12}$$

For the condition of Eq. (8.12) to hold, it is necessary and sufficient to have

$$\mathbf{R} \mathbf{q} = \lambda \mathbf{q} \tag{8.13}$$

This is the equation that governs the unit vectors $\mathbf{q}$ for which the variance probe $\psi(\mathbf{q})$ has extremal values.

Equation (8.13) is recognized as the *eigenvalue problem*, commonly encountered in linear algebra (Strang, 1980). The problem has nontrivial solutions (i.e., $\mathbf{q} \neq \mathbf{0}$) only for special values of λ that are called the *eigenvalues* of the correlation matrix $\mathbf{R}$. The associated values of $\mathbf{q}$ are called *eigenvectors*. Being symmetric, a correlation matrix is characterized by real, nonnegative eigenvalues. The associated eigenvectors are unique, assuming that the eigenvalues are distinct. Let the eigenvalues of the m-by-m matrix $\mathbf{R}$ be denoted by $\lambda_1, \lambda_2, ..., \lambda_m$, and the associated eigenvectors be denoted by $\mathbf{q}_1, \mathbf{q}_2, ..., \mathbf{q}_m$, respectively. We may then write

$$\mathbf{R} \mathbf{q}_j = \lambda_j \mathbf{q}_j, \qquad j = 1, 2, ..., m \tag{8.14}$$

Let the corresponding eigenvalues be arranged in decreasing order as

$$\lambda_1 > \lambda_2 > \cdots > \lambda_j > \cdots > \lambda_m \tag{8.15}$$

so that $\lambda_1 = \lambda_{\max}$. Let the associated eigenvectors be used to construct the m-by-m matrix,

$$\mathbf{Q} = [\mathbf{q}_1, \mathbf{q}_2, ..., \mathbf{q}_j, ..., \mathbf{q}_m] \tag{8.16}$$

We may then combine the set of m equations represented in Eq. (8.14) into the single equation

$$\mathbf{R} \mathbf{Q} = \mathbf{Q} \boldsymbol{\Lambda} \tag{8.17}$$

where $\boldsymbol{\Lambda}$ is a diagonal matrix defined by the eigenvalues of matrix $\mathbf{R}$, that is,

$$\boldsymbol{\Lambda} = \text{diag}[\lambda_1, \lambda_2, ..., \lambda_j, ..., \lambda_m] \tag{8.18}$$

The matrix $\mathbf{Q}$ is an *orthogonal (unitary) matrix* in the sense that its column vectors (i.e., the eigenvectors of $\mathbf{R}$) satisfy the *conditions of orthonormality*:

$$\mathbf{q}_i^T \mathbf{q}_j = \begin{cases} 1, & j = i \\ 0, & j \neq i \end{cases} \tag{8.19}$$

Equation (8.19) requires distinct eigenvalues. Equivalently, we may write

$$\mathbf{Q}^T \mathbf{Q} = \mathbf{I}$$

from which we deduce that the inverse of matrix $\mathbf{Q}$ is the same as its transpose, as shown by

$$\mathbf{Q}^T = \mathbf{Q}^{-1} \tag{8.20}$$

This means that we may rewrite Eq. (8.17) in a form known as the *orthogonal similarity transformation*:

$$\mathbf{Q}^T \mathbf{R} \mathbf{Q} = \Lambda \tag{8.21}$$

In the expanded form, it is written as

$$\mathbf{q}_j^T \mathbf{R} \mathbf{q}_k = \begin{cases} \lambda_j, & k = j \\ 0, & k \neq j \end{cases} \tag{8.22}$$

The orthogonal similarity transformation of Eq. (8.21) transforms the correlation matrix $\mathbf{R}$ into a diagonal matrix of eigenvalues. The correlation matrix $\mathbf{R}$ may itself be expressed in terms of its eigenvalues and eigenvectors as

$$\begin{aligned} \mathbf{R} &= \sum_{i=1}^{m} \lambda_i \mathbf{q}_i \mathbf{q}_i^T \\ &= \mathbf{Q}\Lambda\mathbf{Q}^T \end{aligned} \tag{8.23}$$

which is referred to as the *spectral theorem*. The outer product $\mathbf{q}_i\mathbf{q}_i^T$ is of *rank* 1 for all i. Equations (8.21) and (8.23) are two equivalent representations of the *eigendecomposition* of the correlation matrix $\mathbf{R}$.

Principal-components analysis and eigendecomposition of matrix $\mathbf{R}$ are basically one and the same, just different ways of viewing the problem. This equivalence follows from Eqs. (8.8) and (8.22), where we see that the variance probes and eigenvalues are indeed equal, as shown by

$$\psi(\mathbf{q}_j) = \lambda_j, \quad j = 1, 2, ..., m \tag{8.24}$$

We may now summarize the two important findings we have made from the eigenstructure of principal-components analysis:

- The eigenvectors of the correlation matrix $\mathbf{R}$ pertaining to the zero-mean random vector $\mathbf{X}$ define the unit vectors $\mathbf{q}_j$, representing the principal directions along which the variance probes $\psi(\mathbf{q}_j)$ have their extremal values.
- The associated eigenvalues define the extremal values of the variance probes $\psi(\mathbf{u}_j)$.

Basic Data Representations

Let the *data vector* $\mathbf{x}$ denote a realization (i.e., sample value) of the random vector $\mathbf{X}$. Let a denote a realization of the random variable A.

With m possible solutions for the unit vector $\mathbf{q}$, we find that there are m possible projections of the data vector $\mathbf{x}$ to be considered. Specifically, from Eq. (8.3), we note that

$$a_j = \mathbf{q}_j^T \mathbf{x} = \mathbf{x}^T \mathbf{q}_j, \quad j = 1, 2, ..., m \tag{8.25}$$

where the a_j are the projections of $\mathbf{x}$ onto the principal directions represented by the unit vectors $\mathbf{q}_j$. The a_j are called the *principal components*; they have the same physical dimensions as the data vector $\mathbf{x}$. The formula in Eq. (8.25) may be viewed as one of *analysis*.

To reconstruct the original data vector $\mathbf{x}$ exactly from the projections a_j, we proceed as follows: First, we combine the set of projections $\{a_j | j = 1, 2, ..., m\}$ into a single vector, as shown by

$$\begin{aligned}
\mathbf{a} &= [a_1, a_2, ..., a_m]^T \\
&= [\mathbf{x}^T \mathbf{q}_1, \mathbf{x}^T \mathbf{q}_2, ..., \mathbf{x}^T \mathbf{q}_m]^T \\
&= \mathbf{Q}^T \mathbf{x}
\end{aligned} \tag{8.26}$$

Next, we premultiply both sides of Eq. (8.26) by the matrix $\mathbf{Q}$ and then use the relation $\mathbf{Q}\mathbf{Q}^T = \mathbf{I}$. Accordingly, the original data vector $\mathbf{x}$ may be reconstructed as

$$\begin{aligned}
\mathbf{x} &= \mathbf{Q}\mathbf{a} \\
&= \sum_{j=1}^{m} a_j \mathbf{q}_j
\end{aligned} \tag{8.27}$$

which may be viewed as the formula for *synthesis*. In this sense, the unit vectors $\mathbf{q}_j$ represent a *basis* of the data space. Indeed, Eq. (8.27) is nothing but a coordinate transformation, according to which a point $\mathbf{x}$ in the data space is transformed into a corresponding point $\mathbf{a}$ in the feature space.

Dimensionality Reduction

From the perspective of statistical pattern recognition, the practical value of principal-components analysis is that it provides an effective technique for *dimensionality reduction*. In particular, we may reduce the number of features needed for effective data representation by discarding those linear combinations in Eq. (8.27) that have small variances and retain only those terms that have large variances. Let $\lambda_1, \lambda_2, ..., \lambda_l$ denote the largest l eigenvalues of the correlation matrix $\mathbf{R}$. We may then approximate the data vector $\mathbf{x}$ by *truncating* the expansion of Eq. (8.27) after l terms as follows:

$$\begin{aligned}
\hat{\mathbf{x}} &= \sum_{j=1}^{l} a_j \mathbf{q}_j \\
&= [\mathbf{q}_1, \mathbf{q}_1, ..., \mathbf{q}_j] \begin{bmatrix} a_1 \\ a_2 \\ \vdots \\ a_l \end{bmatrix}, \quad l \leq m
\end{aligned} \tag{8.28}$$

Given the original data vector $\mathbf{x}$, we may use Eq. (8.25) to compute the set of principal components retained in Eq. (8.28) as follows:

$$\begin{bmatrix} a_1 \\ a_2 \\ \vdots \\ a_l \end{bmatrix} = \begin{bmatrix} \mathbf{q}_1^T \\ \mathbf{q}_2^T \\ \vdots \\ \mathbf{q}_l^T \end{bmatrix} \mathbf{x}, \quad l \leq m \tag{8.29}$$

The linear projection of Eq. (8.29) from $\mathbb{R}^m$ to $\mathbb{R}^l$ (i.e., the mapping from the data space to the feature space) represents an *encoder* for the approximate representation of the

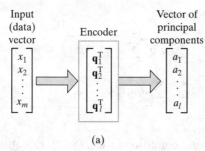

FIGURE 8.2   Illustration of two phases of principal-components analysis: (a) Encoding. (b) Decoding.

(a)

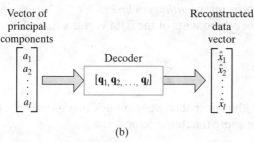

(b)

data vector $\mathbf{x}$, as illustrated in Fig. 8.2a. Correspondingly, the linear projection of Eq. (8.28) from $\mathbb{R}^l$ to $\mathbb{R}^m$ (i.e., the mapping from the feature space back to the data space) represents a *decoder* for the approximate reconstruction of the original data vector $\mathbf{x}$, as illustrated in Fig. 8.2b. Note that the *dominant* (i.e., largest) eigenvalues $\lambda_1, \lambda_2, ..., \lambda_l$ do not enter the computations described in Eqs. (8.28) and (8.29); they merely determine the number of principal components used for encoding and decoding, respectively.

The *approximation error vector* $\mathbf{e}$ equals the difference between the original data vector $\mathbf{x}$ and the approximating data vector $\hat{\mathbf{x}}$, as shown by

$$\mathbf{e} = \mathbf{x} - \hat{\mathbf{x}} \tag{8.30}$$

Substituting Eqs. (8.27) and (8.28) into Eq. (8.30) yields

$$\mathbf{e} = \sum_{i=l+1}^{m} a_i \mathbf{q}_i \tag{8.31}$$

The error vector $\mathbf{e}$ is orthogonal to the approximating data vector $\hat{\mathbf{x}}$, as illustrated in Fig. 8.3. In other words, the inner product of the vectors $\hat{\mathbf{x}}$ and $\mathbf{e}$ is zero. This property is shown

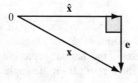

FIGURE 8.3   Illustration of the relationship between vector $\mathbf{x}$, its reconstructed version $\hat{\mathbf{x}}$, and error vector $\mathbf{e}$.

by using Eqs. (8.28) and (8.31) to obtain:

$$\mathbf{e}^T \hat{\mathbf{x}} = \sum_{i=l+1}^{m} a_i \mathbf{q}_i^T \sum_{j=1}^{l} a_j \mathbf{q}_j \quad \text{for } l < m$$

$$= \sum_{i=l+1}^{m} \sum_{j=1}^{l} a_i a_j \mathbf{q}_i^T \mathbf{q}_j \tag{8.32}$$

$$= 0$$

where we have made use of the second condition in Eq. (8.19). Equation (8.32) is a mathematical statement of the *principle of orthogonality*.

The total variance of the m components of the data vector $\mathbf{x}$ is, via Eq. (8.8) and the first line of Eq. (8.22),

$$\sum_{j=1}^{m} \sigma_j^2 = \sum_{j=1}^{m} \lambda_j \tag{8.33}$$

where σ_j^2 is the variance of the jth principal component a_j. Correspondingly, the total variance of the l elements of the approximating vector $\hat{\mathbf{x}}$ is

$$\sum_{j=1}^{l} \sigma_j^2 = \sum_{j=1}^{l} \lambda_j \tag{8.34}$$

The total variance of the $(l-m)$ elements in the approximation error vector $\mathbf{x} - \hat{\mathbf{x}}$ is therefore the difference between Eqs. (8.33) and (8.34):

$$\sum_{j=l+1}^{m} \sigma_j^2 = \sum_{j=l+1}^{m} \lambda_j \tag{8.35}$$

The eigenvalues $\lambda_{l+1}, ..., \lambda_m$ are the *smallest* $(m-l)$ eigenvalues of the correlation matrix $\mathbf{R}$; they correspond to the terms discarded from the expansion of Eq. (8.28) used to construct the approximating vector $\hat{\mathbf{x}}$. The closer all these eigenvalues are to zero, the more effective the dimensionality reduction (resulting from the application of principal-components analysis to the data vector $\mathbf{x}$) will be in preserving the information content of the original input data. Thus, to perform dimensionality reduction on some input data, we do the following:

> *Compute the eigenvalues and eigenvectors of the correlation matrix of the input data vector, and then project the data orthogonally onto the subspace spanned by the eigenvectors belonging to the dominant eigenvalues.*

This method of data representation is commonly referred to as *subspace decomposition* (Oja, 1983).

EXAMPLE 1   Bivariate Data Set

To illustrate the application of principal-components analysis, consider the example of a bivariate (two-dimensional) data set depicted in Fig. 8.4, where it is assumed that both feature axes are approximately of the same scale. The horizontal and vertical axes of the diagram represent the natural coordinates of the data set. The rotated axes labeled 1 and 2 result from the application of

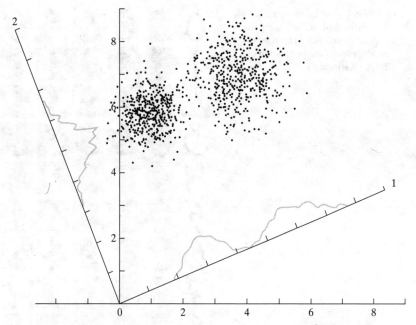

FIGURE 8.4   A cloud of data points is shown in two dimensions, and the density plots formed by projecting this cloud onto each of two axes, 1 and 2, are indicated. The projection onto axis 1 has maximum variance and clearly shows the bimodal, or clustered, character of the data.

principal-components analysis to this data set. From Fig. 8.4, we see that projecting the data set onto axis 1 captures the salient feature of the data—namely, the fact that the data set is bimodal (i.e., there are two clusters in its structure). Indeed, the variance of the projections of the data points onto axis 1 is greater than that for any other projection axis in the figure. By contrast, the inherent bimodal nature of the data set is completely obscured when it is projected onto the orthogonal axis 2.

The important point to note from this simple example is that although the cluster structure of the data set is evident from the two-dimensional plot of the raw data displayed in the framework of the horizontal and vertical axes, this is not always the case in practice. In the more general case of high-dimensional data sets, it is quite conceivable to have the intrinsic cluster structure of the data concealed, and to see it we must perform a statistical analysis similar to principal-components analysis (Linsker, 1988a). ■

Case Study   Digital Image Compression

Principal-components analysis provides a simple, yet efficient, method for compressing digital images. A practical requirement for the storage, transmission, and feature extraction of digital images is that the images be compressed. The PCA application of Fig. 8.5, using real-life data, validates this statement (Holmström et al., 1997; Hyvärinen et al., 2001).

The leftmost column of Fig. 8.5 shows a set of 10 handwritten characters, namely, 0 to 9, each of which is represented by a binary image consisting of a 32-by-32 matrix. When each of these images is scanned on a row-by-row basis, a 1,024-by-1 vector is produced. For each one of the 10 characters, a set of about 1,700 handwritten samples was collected. The sample means (1,024-by-1 vectors)

FIGURE 8.5 Digital compression of handwritten digits using principal-components analysis. (This figure is reproduced with the permission of Dr. Juha Karhunen.)

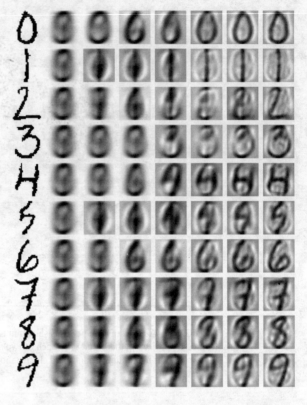

and the covariance matrices (1,024-by-1,024 matrices) were estimated with the use of standard procedures. For each of the 10 classes represented by a handwritten character, the first 64 principal eigenvectors (components) of the covariance matrix were computed. The second column of the figure presents the computed sample means. The remaining six columns show reconstructed images for increasing values of the index l, which denotes the number of principal components in the reconstruction formula of Eq. (8.28). In these images, the respective computed sample means were added so as to properly scale the images for display.

Three important observations follow from the PCA results presented in Fig. 8.5:

- As the reconstruction size l is progressively increased from 1 to 2, 5, 16, 32, and 64, the reconstructed images increasingly resemble the original 10 handwritten characters.
- By the time the reconstruction size $l = 64$ is reached, every one of the reconstructed characters is perfectly legible.
- With a total of 1,024 possible principal components, the largest reconstruction size $l = 64$ is a small percentage of the total.

Estimation of the Number of Principal Components

In the case study on digital image compression just presented, the number of principal components (i.e., the size of the reduction in dimensionality) was determined experimentally. For an analytical approach to this estimation problem, we may view it as a *model-selection problem*. The *minimum-description-length (MDL) criterion*, discussed in Chapter 2, provides a well-tested method for solving the problem.

In Wax and Kailath (1985), the MDL criterion was applied to array-signal processing, in which the primary motivation is that of *ascertaining a signal's direction of arrival* in the presence of additive noise. To solve this problem, the MDL criterion was used to decompose the input data space into two subspaces, one representing the *signal subspace* and the other representing the *noise subspace*. In basic terms, decomposing the input data space into the sum of a signal subspace and a noise subspace is nothing more than solving the dimensionality reduction problem, with the dimension of the signal subspace defining the underlying number of principal eigenvectors (components) associated with the dominant eigenvalues.

8.5   HEBBIAN-BASED MAXIMUM EIGENFILTER

There is a close correspondence between the behavior of self-organized neural networks and the statistical method of principal-components analysis. In this section, we demonstrate this correspondence by establishing a remarkable result (Oja, 1982):

> *A single linear neuron with a Hebbian-type adaptation rule for its synaptic weights can evolve into a filter for the first principal component of the input distribution.*

To proceed with the demonstration, consider the simple neural model depicted in Fig. 8.6a. The model is *linear* in the sense that the model's output is a linear combination of its inputs. The neuron receives a set of m input signals $x_1, x_2, ..., x_m$ through a corresponding set of m synapses with weights $w_1, w_2, ..., w_m$, respectively. The resulting output y of the model is thus defined by

$$y = \sum_{i=1}^{m} w_i x_i \tag{8.36}$$

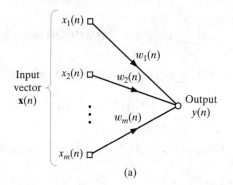

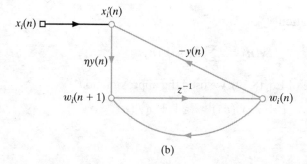

FIGURE 8.6   Signal-flow graph representation of maximum eigenfilter. (a) Graph of Eq. (8.36). (b) Graph of Eqs. (8.41) and (8.42).

Note that in the situation described here, we have a single neuron to deal with, so there is no need to use double subscripts to identify the synaptic weights of the neuron.

Derivation of the Maximum Eigenfilter

In accordance with Hebb's postulate of learning, a synaptic weight w_i varies with time, growing strong when the presynaptic signal x_i and postsynaptic signal y coincide with each other. Specifically, we write

$$w_i(n + 1) = w_i(n) + \eta y(n)x_i(n), \qquad i = 1, 2, ..., m \qquad (8.37)$$

where n denotes discrete time and η is the *learning-rate parameter*. However, as pointed out in Section 8.2, this learning rule in its basic form leads to unlimited growth of the synaptic weight w_i, which is unacceptable on physical grounds. We may overcome this problem by incorporating some form of *normalization* in the learning rule for the adaptation of synaptic weights. The use of normalization has the effect of introducing competition among the synapses of the neuron over limited resources, which, from Principle 2 of self-organization, is essential for stabilization. From a mathematical point of view, a convenient form of normalization is to recast Eq. (8.37) in the new form:

$$w_i(n + 1) = \frac{w_i(n) + \eta y(n)x_i(n)}{\left(\sum_{i=1}^{m} (w_i(n) + \eta y(n)x_i(n))^2 \right)^{1/2}} \qquad (8.38)$$

where the summation in the denominator extends over the complete set of synapses associated with the neuron. Assuming that the learning-rate parameter η is small, we may expand the denominator of Eq. (8.38) as a power series, obtaining

$$\left(\sum_{i=1}^{m} (w_i(n) + \eta y(n)x_i(n))^2 \right)^{1/2} = \left(\sum_{i=1}^{m} (w_i^2(n) + 2\eta w_i(n)y(n)x_i(n)) \right)^{1/2} + O(\eta^2)$$

$$= \left(\sum_{i=1}^{m} w_i^2(n) + 2\eta y(n) \sum_{i=1}^{m} w_i(n)x_i(n) \right)^{1/2} + O(\eta^2)$$

$$= (1 + 2\eta y^2(n))^{1/2} + O(\eta^2)$$

$$= 1 + \eta y^2(n) + O(\eta^2) \qquad (8.39)$$

In the third line of the right-hand side of Eq. (8.39), we used the constraint

$$\sum_{i=1}^{m} w_i^2(n) = \|\mathbf{w}(n)\|^2 = 1 \qquad \text{for all } n$$

and the input–output relation

$$y(n) = \sum_{i=1}^{m} w_i(n)x_i(n)$$

Moreover, in the last line of Eq. (8.39), we used the approximation

$$(1 + 2\eta y^2(n))^{1/2} \approx 1 + \eta y^2(n)$$

assuming small η.

Next, dividing the numerator of Eq. (8.38) by the approximate expression for the denominator given in Eq. (8.39), and again assuming small η, we may go on to write

$$
\begin{aligned}
w_i(n + 1) &= \frac{w_i(n) + \eta y(n)x_i(n)}{1 + \eta y^2(n) + O(\eta^2)} \\
&= (w_i(n) + \eta y(n)x_i(n))(1 + \eta y^2(n) + O(\eta^2))^{-1} \\
&= (w_i(n) + \eta y(n)x_i(n))(1 - \eta y^2(n)) + O(\eta^2) \\
&= w_i(n) + \eta y(n)x_i(n) - \eta y^2(n)w_i(n) + O(\eta^2)
\end{aligned}
$$

Collecting common terms and ignoring second-order terms, we finally write

$$
w_i(n + 1) = w_i(n) + \eta y(n)(x_i(n) - y(n)w_i(n)) \tag{8.40}
$$

The term $y(n)x_i(n)$ on the right-hand side of Eq. (8.40) represents the usual Hebbian modifications to synaptic weight w_i and therefore accounts for the self-amplification effect dictated by Principle 1 of self-organization. The inclusion of the negative term $-y(n)w_i(n)$ is responsible for stabilization in accordance with Principle 2, which requires competition among the synapses of the neurons. The inclusion of this term modifies the input $x_i(n)$ into a form that is dependent on the associated synaptic weight $w_i(n)$ and the output $y(n)$, as shown by

$$
x_i'(n) = x_i(n) - y(n)w_i(n) \tag{8.41}
$$

which may be viewed as the *effective input* of the ith synapse. We may now use the definition given in Eq. (8.41) to rewrite the learning rule of Eq. (8.40) simply as

$$
w_i(n + 1) = w_i(n) + \eta y(n)x_i'(n) \tag{8.42}
$$

The overall operation of the neuron is represented by a combination of two signal-flow graphs, as shown in Fig. 8.6. The signal-flow graph of Fig. 8.6a shows the dependence of the output $y(n)$ on the weights $w_1(n), w_2(n), ..., w_m(n)$, in accordance with Eq. (8.36). The signal-flow graph of Fig. 8.6b provides a portrayal of Eqs. (8.41) and (8.42); the transmittance z^{-1} in the middle portion of the graph represents a unit-time delay operator. The output signal $y(n)$ produced in Fig. 8.6a acts as a transmittance in Fig. 8.6b. The graph of Fig. 8.6b clearly exhibits the following two forms of internal feedback acting on the neuron:

- *positive feedback for self-amplification and therefore growth of the synaptic weight $w_i(n)$, influenced by the external input $x_i(n)$;*
- *negative feedback due to $-y(n)$ for controlling the growth, thereby resulting in stabilization of the synaptic weight $w_i(n)$ as it evolves across time.*

The product term $-y(n)w_i(n)$ is related to a *forgetting*, or *leakage factor*, that is frequently used in learning rules, but with a difference: The forgetting factor becomes more pronounced with a stronger response $y(n)$. This kind of control appears to have neurobiological support (Stent, 1973).

Matrix Formulation of the Maximum Eigenfilter

For convenience of presentation, let

$$\mathbf{x}(n) = [x_1(n), x_2(n), ..., x_m(n)]^T \tag{8.43}$$

and

$$\mathbf{w}(n) = [w_1(n), w_2(n), ..., w_m(n)]^T \tag{8.44}$$

The input vector $\mathbf{x}(n)$ and the synaptic weight vector $\mathbf{w}(n)$ are typically both realizations of random vectors. Using this vector notation, we may rewrite Eq. (8.36) in the form of an inner product as follows:

$$y(n) = \mathbf{x}^T(n)\mathbf{w}(n) = \mathbf{w}^T(n)\mathbf{x}(n) \tag{8.45}$$

Similarly, we may rewrite Eq. (8.40) as

$$\mathbf{w}(n + 1) = \mathbf{w}(n) + \eta y(n)[\mathbf{x}(n) - y(n)\mathbf{w}(n)] \tag{8.46}$$

Hence, substituting Eq. (8.45) into Eq. (8.46) yields

$$\mathbf{w}(n + 1) = \mathbf{w}(n) + \eta[\mathbf{x}(n)\mathbf{x}^T(n)\mathbf{w}(n) - \mathbf{w}^T(n)(\mathbf{x}(n)\mathbf{x}^T(n))\mathbf{w}(n)\mathbf{w}(n)] \tag{8.47}$$

The self-organized learning algorithm of Eq. (8.47) represents a *nonlinear stochastic difference equation*, which makes convergence analysis of the algorithm mathematically difficult. To pave the way for this convergence analysis, we will digress briefly to introduce a general tool for convergence analysis of stochastic approximation algorithms, assuming that the learning-rate parameter η is small.

Kushner's Direct-Averaging Method

Examining the right-hand side of the self-organized learning algorithm of Eq. (8.47), we make two observations:

1. The input vector $\mathbf{x}(n)$ appears in the form of an outer product $\mathbf{x}(n)\mathbf{x}^T(n)$, which represents the *instantaneous value of the correlation matrix* $\mathbf{R}$—that is, Eq. (8.6) without the expectation operator and with $\mathbf{x}(n)$ used as a realization of the random vector $\mathbf{X}(n)$. Indeed, it is the term $\mathbf{x}(n)\mathbf{x}^T(n)$ that is responsible for the stochastic behavior of the equation.
2. Since the algorithm is unsupervised, there is *no* external force acting on the algorithm.

From Eq. (8.47), it therefore follows that the *characteristic matrix* of the algorithm is defined by

$$\mathbf{I} + \eta[(\mathbf{x}(n)\mathbf{x}^T(n)) - \mathbf{w}^T(n)(\mathbf{x}(n)\mathbf{x}^T(n))\mathbf{w}(n)\mathbf{I}] \tag{8.48}$$

where $\mathbf{I}$ is the identity matrix. Post-multiplication of this characteristic matrix by the old weight vector $\mathbf{w}(n)$ yields the updated weight vector $\mathbf{w}(n + 1)$ of Eq. (8.47). Note that since the term $\mathbf{w}^T(n)(\mathbf{x}(n)\mathbf{x}^T(n))\mathbf{w}(n)$ is an inner product and therefore a scalar, we must multiply it by the identity matrix $\mathbf{I}$ for matrix compatibility with the rest of the expression in Eq. (8.48).

Now, recall *Kushner's direct-averaging method* from Chapter 3 on the least-mean-square (LMS) algorithm, according to which we replace the characteristic matrix of Eq. (8.48) by its expected value

$$\mathbf{I} + \eta[\mathbf{R} - \mathbf{w}^T(n)\mathbf{Rw}(n)\mathbf{I}] \tag{8.49}$$

This replacement is justified, provided that the learning-rate parameter η is small. In effect, over the course of time the outer product $\mathbf{x}(n)\mathbf{x}^T(n)$ assumes the role of the correlation matrix $\mathbf{R}$.

We may thus state that the solution of the stochastic equation of Eq. (8.47) is effectively close to the solution of the much simplified deterministic difference equation

$$\mathbf{w}(n + 1) = \mathbf{w}(n) + \eta[\mathbf{R} - \mathbf{w}^T(n)\mathbf{Rw}(n)\mathbf{I}]\mathbf{w}(n) \tag{8.50}$$

for small η.

Let

$$\Delta\mathbf{w}(n) = \mathbf{w}(n + 1) - \mathbf{w}(n)$$

Then, using t to denote continuous time, we may now say that the incremental weight change $\Delta\mathbf{w}(n)$ in discrete time n is proportional to the rate of change of the weight $\mathbf{w}(t)$ in continuous time t, as shown by the proportionality relationship

$$\frac{d\mathbf{w}(t)}{dt} \propto \Delta\mathbf{w}(n) \tag{8.51}$$

Thus, absorbing the learning-rate parameter η into the proportionality factor in Eq. (8.51), and normalizing time t, accordingly, we may describe the evolution of the maximum eigenfilter over time t by the *ordinary nonlinear differential equation*

$$\frac{d\mathbf{w}(t)}{dt} = \mathbf{Rw}(t) - (\mathbf{w}^T(t)\mathbf{Rw}(t))\mathbf{w}(t) \tag{8.52}$$

where the quadratic term $\mathbf{w}^T(t)\mathbf{Rw}(t)$, being a scalar, makes the equation dimensionally correct in matrix terms.

Asymptotic Stability of the Maximum Eigenfilter

Let $\mathbf{w}(t)$ be expanded in terms of the *complete orthonormal set of eigenvectors* of the correlation matrix $\mathbf{R}$, as shown by

$$\mathbf{w}(t) = \sum_{k=1}^{m} \theta_k(t)\mathbf{q}_k \tag{8.53}$$

where $\mathbf{q}_k$ is the kth normalized eigenvector of the matrix $\mathbf{R}$, and the coefficient $\theta_k(t)$ is the time-varying projection of the vector $\mathbf{w}(t)$ onto $\mathbf{q}_k$. Substituting Eq. (8.53) into Eq. (8.52), and using the basic definitions from Section 8.4—namely,

$$\mathbf{Rq}_k = \lambda_k\mathbf{q}_k$$

and

$$\mathbf{q}_k^T\mathbf{Rq}_k = \lambda_k$$

where λ_k is the eigenvalue associated with $\mathbf{q}_k$—we finally get

$$\sum_{k=1}^{m} \frac{d\theta_k(t)}{dt} \mathbf{q}_k = \sum_{k=1}^{m} \lambda_k \theta_k(t) \mathbf{q}_k - \left[\sum_{l=1}^{m} \lambda_l \theta_l^2(t) \right] \sum_{k=1}^{m} \theta_k(t) \mathbf{q}_k \qquad (8.54)$$

which, in turn, simplifies to

$$\frac{d\theta_k(t)}{dt} = \lambda_k \theta_k(t) - \theta_k(t) \sum_{l=1}^{m} \lambda_l \theta_l^2(t), \qquad k = 1, 2, ..., m \qquad (8.55)$$

We have thus reduced the convergence analysis of the stochastic approximation algorithm of Eq. (8.47) to the stability analysis of a *nonlinear* system of ordinary differential equations given by Eq. (8.55) involving the *principal modes* $\theta_k(t)$.

Modified Langevin Equation

In light of the discussion presented in Chapter 3 on the adaptive LMS filter, we may view Eq. (8.55), pertaining to the maximum eigenfilter, as a *nonlinear modified form of the Langevin equation without a driving force*, as explained here:

(i) The Langevin equation is "modified" in the sense that we have the positive term $\lambda_k \theta_k(t)$ on the right-hand side of the equation, which provides amplification rather than friction; this amplification term is Hebbian in origin.

(ii) The Langevin equation is "nonlinear" because of the second term $-\theta_k(t) \sum_l \lambda_l \theta_l^2(t)$, which is attributed to competition among the synapses of the maximum eigenfilter.

(iii) The Langevin equation has *no driving force* because the maximum eigenfilter is self-organized.

With no driving force, we therefore expect that, unlike the LMS filter, the maximum eigenfilter will be absolutely convergent in an asymptotic sense. However, the nonlinearity of the maximum eigenfilter will make the study of its convergence behavior more difficult in mathematical terms.

Convergence Analysis of the Langevin Equation

There are two cases to be considered in the convergence analysis, depending on the value assigned to the index k. Case I corresponds to $1 < k \leq m$, and case II corresponds to $k = 1$; m is the dimension of both $\mathbf{x}(n)$ and $\mathbf{w}(n)$. These two cases are considered in turn.

Case I. $1 < k \leq m$.
For the treatment of this case, define

$$\alpha_k(t) = \frac{\theta_k(t)}{\theta_1(t)}, \qquad 1 < k \leq m \qquad (8.56)$$

Hence, it is assumed that $\theta_1(t) \neq 0$, which is true with probability 1 provided that *the initial values* $\mathbf{w}(0)$ *are chosen at random*. Then, differentiating both sides of Eq. (8.56) with respect to time t, we get

$$\frac{d\alpha_k(t)}{dt} = \frac{1}{\theta_1(t)}\frac{d\theta_k(t)}{dt} - \frac{\theta_k(t)}{\theta_1^2(t)}\frac{d\theta_1(t)}{dt}$$

$$= \frac{1}{\theta_1(t)}\frac{d\theta_k(t)}{dt} - \frac{\alpha_k(t)}{\theta_1(t)}\frac{d\theta_1(t)}{dt}, \qquad 1 < k \le m \tag{8.57}$$

Next, using Eq. (8.55) in Eq. (8.57), applying the definition of Eq. (8.56), and then simplifying the result, we get

$$\frac{d\alpha_k(t)}{dt} = -(\lambda_1 - \lambda_k)\alpha_k(t), \qquad 1 < k \le m \tag{8.58}$$

With the eigenvalues of the correlation matrix $\mathbf{R}$ assumed to be distinct and arranged in decreasing order, we have

$$\lambda_1 > \lambda_2 > \cdots > \lambda_k > \cdots > \lambda_m > 0 \tag{8.59}$$

It follows therefore that the eigenvalue difference $\lambda_1 - \lambda_k$, representing the reciprocal of a time constant in Eq. (8.58), is positive, so we find that for case I,

$$\alpha_k(t) \to 0 \qquad \text{as } t \to \infty \qquad \text{for } 1 < k \le m \tag{8.60}$$

Case II. $k = 1$.
From Eq. (8.57), this second case is described by the differential equation

$$\frac{d\theta_1(t)}{dt} = \lambda_1\theta_1(t) - \theta_1(t)\sum_{l=1}^{m}\lambda_l\theta_l^2(t)$$

$$= \lambda_1\theta_1(t) - \lambda_1\theta_1^3(t) - \theta_1(t)\sum_{l=2}^{m}\lambda_l\theta_l^2(t) \tag{8.61}$$

$$= \lambda_1\theta_1(t) - \lambda_1\theta_1^3(t) - \theta_1^3(t)\sum_{l=2}^{m}\lambda_l\alpha_l^2(t)$$

Where in the last line we have used Eq. (8.56). However, from case I, we know that $\alpha_l \to 0$ for $l \ne 1$ as $t \to \infty$. Hence, the last term on the right-hand side of Eq. (8.61) approaches zero as time t approaches infinity. Ignoring this term, we find that Eq. (8.61) simplifies to

$$\frac{d\theta_1(t)}{dt} = \lambda_1\theta_1(t)[1 - \theta_1^2(t)] \qquad \text{for } t \to \infty \tag{8.62}$$

It must be emphasized, however, that Eq. (8.62) holds only in an asymptotic sense.

Equation (8.62) represents an *autonomous system* (i.e., a system with no explicit time dependence). The stability of such a system is best handled using a positive-definite function called the *Lyapunov function*, a detailed treatment of which is deferred to Chapter 13. Let $\mathbf{s}$ denote the state vector of an autonomous system and $V(t)$ denote a Lyapunov function of the system. An equilibrium state $\bar{\mathbf{s}}$ of the system is asymptotically stable if

$$\frac{d}{dt}V(t) < 0 \qquad \text{for } \mathbf{s} \in \mathcal{U} - \bar{\mathbf{s}}$$

where $\mathcal{U}$ is a small neighborhood around $\bar{\mathbf{s}}$.

For the problem at hand, we assert that the differential equation of Eq. (8.62) has a Lyapunov function defined by

$$V(t) = [\theta_1^2(t) - 1]^2 \tag{8.63}$$

To validate this assertion, we must show that $V(t)$ satisfies two conditions:

1. $\dfrac{dV(t)}{dt} < 0 \qquad$ for all t $\hfill$ (8.64)

2. $V(t)$ has a minimum $\hfill$ (8.65)

Differentiating Eq. (8.63) with respect to time, we get

$$\frac{dV(t)}{dt} = 4\theta_1(t)[\theta_1(t) - 1]\frac{d\theta_1(t)}{dt} \tag{8.66}$$

$$= -4\lambda_1\theta_1^2(t)[\theta_1^2(t) - 1]^2 \qquad \text{as } t \to \infty$$

where in the second line we have made use of Eq. (8.62). Since the eigenvalue λ_1 is positive, we find from Eq. (8.66) that the condition of Eq. (8.64) is true for t approaching infinity. Furthermore, from Eq. (8.66) we note that $V(t)$ has minima [i.e., $dV(t)/dt$ is zero] at $\theta_1(t) = \pm1$, so the condition of Eq. (8.65) is also satisfied. We may therefore conclude the analysis of case II by stating that

$$\theta_1(t) \to \pm1 \qquad \text{as } t \to \infty \tag{8.67}$$

In light of the result described in Eq. (8.67) and the definition of Eq. (8.66), we may restate the result of case I given in Eq. (8.60) in its final form:

$$\theta_k(t) \to 0 \qquad \text{as } t \to \infty \qquad \text{for } 1 < k \le m \tag{8.68}$$

The overall conclusion drawn from the analysis of cases I and II is twofold:

- The only principal mode of the stochastic approximation algorithm described in Eq. (8.47) that will converge is $\theta_1(t)$; all the other modes of the algorithm will decay to zero.
- The mode $\theta_1(t)$ will converge to ±1.

Hence, in light of the expansion described in Eq. (8.53), we may formally state that

$$\mathbf{w}(t) \to \mathbf{q}_1, \qquad \text{as } t \to \infty \tag{8.69}$$

where $\mathbf{q}_1$ is the normalized eigenvector associated with the largest eigenvalue λ_1 of the correlation matrix $\mathbf{R}$.

Finally, to establish that the solution of Eq. (8.69) is a locally asymptotically stable (in the sense of Lyapunov) solution to the ordinary nonlinear differential equation of Eq. (8.52), we have to satisfy the following condition, formulated in the discrete-time domain:

Let $\mathcal{B}(\mathbf{q})$ denote the basin of attraction surrounding the solution to Eq. (8.52); then the parameter vector $\mathbf{w}(n)$ enters a compact subset $\mathcal{A}$ of the basin of attraction $\mathcal{B}(\mathbf{q})$ infinitely often, with probability 1.

(The basin of attraction is defined in Chapter 13.)

To satisfy this condition, we have to show that there exists a subset $\mathcal{A}$ of the set of all possible vectors such that

$$\lim_{n \to \infty} \mathbf{w}(n) = \mathbf{q}_1 \quad \text{infinitely often with probability 1} \qquad (8.70)$$

To do so, we must first show that the sequence of parameter vectors $\mathbf{w}(n)$ is bounded with probability 1. We do so by *hard-limiting* the entries of $\mathbf{w}(n)$ so that their magnitudes remain below some threshold a. We may then define the norm of $\mathbf{w}(n)$ by writing

$$\|\mathbf{w}(n)\| = \max_j |w_j(n)| \leq a \qquad (8.71)$$

Let $\mathcal{A}$ be the compact subset of $\mathbb{R}^m$ defined by the set of vectors with norm less than or equal to a. It is straightforward to show the following (Sanger, 1989b):

> If $\|\mathbf{w}(n)\| \leq a$, and the constant a is sufficiently large, then $\|\mathbf{w}(n+1)\| < \|\mathbf{w}(n)\|$ with probability 1.

Thus, as the number of iterations n increases, $\mathbf{w}(n)$ will eventually be within $\mathcal{A}$, and it will remain inside $\mathcal{A}$ (infinitely often) with probability 1. Since the basin of attraction $\mathcal{B}(\mathbf{q}_1)$ includes all vectors with a bounded norm, we have $\mathcal{A} \in \mathcal{B}(\mathbf{q}_1)$. In other words, the aforementioned condition for locally asymptotic stability, concerning the basin of attraction, is satisfied.

We have thus shown that, subject to the use of a small learning-rate parameter η, the stochastic approximation algorithm of Eq. (8.47) will cause the parameter weight vector $\mathbf{w}(n)$ to converge with probability 1 to the eigenvector $\mathbf{q}_1$ associated with the largest eigenvalue λ_1 of the correlation matrix $\mathbf{R}$ of the input vector $\mathbf{x}(n)$. Moreover, this solution is not the only fixed point of the algorithm, but it is the only one that is asymptotically stable.

Summarizing Properties of the Hebbian-Based Maximum Eigenfilter

The convergence analysis just presented shows that a single linear neuron governed by the self-organized learning rule of Eq. (8.40)—or equivalently, that of Eq. (8.46)—adaptively extracts the first principal component of a stationary input. This first principal component corresponds to the largest eigenvalue λ_1 of the correlation matrix of the random vector $\mathbf{X}(n)$, a sample realization of which is denoted by $\mathbf{x}(n)$; in fact, λ_1 is related to the variance of the model output $y(n)$, as shown next.

Let $\sigma^2(n)$ denote the variance of random variable $Y(n)$, with a realization of it denoted by $y(n)$—that is,

$$\sigma^2(n) = \mathbb{E}[Y^2(n)] \qquad (8.72)$$

where the random variable $Y(n)$ has zero mean for a zero-mean input. Letting $n \to \infty$ in Eq. (8.46) and using the fact that, in a corresponding way, $\mathbf{w}(n)$ approaches $\mathbf{q}_1$, we obtain

$$\mathbf{x}(n) = y(n)\mathbf{q}_1 \quad \text{for } n \to \infty$$

Using this relation, we can show that the variance $\sigma^2(n)$ approaches λ_1 as the number of iterations n approaches infinity; see Problem 8.6.

In summary, a Hebbian-based linear neuron whose operation is described by Eq. (8.46) converges with probability 1 to a fixed point, which is characterized as follows (Oja, 1982):

1. The variance of the model output approaches the largest eigenvalue of the correlation matrix **R**, as shown by

$$\lim_{n \to \infty} \sigma^2(n) = \lambda_1 \qquad (8.73)$$

2. The synaptic-weight vector of the model approaches the associated eigenvector, as shown by

$$\lim_{n \to \infty} \mathbf{w}(n) = \mathbf{q}_1 \qquad (8.74)$$

with

$$\lim_{n \to \infty} \|\mathbf{w}(n)\| = 1 \qquad (8.75)$$

These results assume that the correlation matrix **R** is positive definite, with the largest eigenvalue λ_1 having multiplicity 1. They also hold for a nonnegative definite correlation matrix **R** provided that $\lambda_1 > 0$ with multiplicity 1.

EXAMPLE 2   Matched Filter

Consider a random vector **X**, a realization of which is denoted by the sample vector **x**. Let

$$\mathbf{X} = \mathbf{s} + \mathbf{V} \qquad (8.76)$$

where the vector **s**, representing the *signal component*, is fixed with a Euclidean norm of one. The random vector **V**, representing the *additive noise* component, has zero mean and covariance matrix $\sigma^2 \mathbf{I}$. The correlation matrix of **X** is given by

$$\begin{aligned} \mathbf{R} &= \mathbb{E}[\mathbf{X}(n)\mathbf{X}^T(n)] \\ &= \mathbf{s}\,\mathbf{s}^T + \sigma^2 \mathbf{I} \end{aligned} \qquad (8.77)$$

The largest eigenvalue of the correlation matrix **R** is therefore

$$\lambda_1 = 1 + \sigma^2 \qquad (8.78)$$

The associated eigenvector $\mathbf{q}_1$ is equal to **s**. It is readily shown that this solution satisfies the eigenvalue problem

$$\mathbf{R}\mathbf{q}_1 = \lambda_1 \mathbf{q}_1$$

Hence, for the situation described in this example, the self-organized linear neuron (upon convergence to its stable condition) acts as a *matched filter* in the sense that its impulse response (represented by the synaptic weights) is matched to the signal component **s**. ∎

8.6   HEBBIAN-BASED PRINCIPAL-COMPONENTS ANALYSIS

The Hebbian-based maximum eigenfilter discussed in the previous section extracts the first principal component of the input. This single linear neural model may be expanded into a feedforward network with a single layer of linear neurons for the purpose of principal-components analysis of arbitrary size on the input (Sanger, 1989b).

Generalized Hebbian Algorithm

Consider the feedforward network shown in Fig. 8.7, for the operation of which the following two assumptions of a structural nature are made:

1. Each neuron in the output layer of the network is *linear*.
2. The network has m inputs and l outputs, both of which are specified. Moreover, the network has fewer outputs than inputs (i.e., $l < m$).

The only aspect of the network that is subject to training is the set of synaptic weights $\{w_{ji}\}$ connecting source nodes i in the input layer to computational nodes j in the output layer, where $i = 1, 2, ..., m$ and $j = 1, 2, ..., l$.

The output $y_j(n)$ of neuron j at time n produced in response to the set of inputs $\{x_i(n)|i = 1, 2, ..., m\}$ is given as follows (see Fig 8.8a):

$$y_j(n) = \sum_{i=1}^{m} w_{ji}(n)x_i(n), \qquad j = 1, 2, ..., l \tag{8.79}$$

The synaptic weight $w_{ji}(n)$ is adapted in accordance with a generalized form of Hebbian learning, as shown by

$$\Delta w_{ji}(n) = \eta\left(y_j(n)x_i(n) - y_j(n)\sum_{k=1}^{j} w_{ki}(n)y_k(n) \right), \qquad \begin{matrix} i = 1, 2, ..., m \\ j = 1, 2, ..., l \end{matrix} \tag{8.80}$$

where $\Delta w_{ji}(n)$ is the change applied to the synaptic weight $w_{ji}(n)$ at time n and η is the learning-rate parameter (Sanger, 1989b). Note that in Eq. (8.80), the index i refers to the input of the network in Fig. 8.7 and the index j refers to its output. The *generalized Hebbian algorithm* (GHA)[4] of Eq. (8.80) for a layer of l neurons includes the algorithm of Eq. (8.40) for a single neuron as a special case—that is, $j = 1$.

To develop insight into the behavior of the generalized Hebbian algorithm, we rewrite Eq. (8.80) in the form

$$\Delta w_{ji}(n) = \eta y_j(n)[x_i'(n) - w_{ji}(n)y_j(n)], \qquad \begin{matrix} i = 1, 2, ..., m \\ j = 1, 2, ..., l \end{matrix} \tag{8.81}$$

where $x_i'(n)$ is a modified version of the ith element of the input vector $\mathbf{x}(n)$; it is a function of the index j, as shown by

$$x_i'(n) = x_i(n) - \sum_{k=1}^{j-1} w_{ki}(n)y_k(n) \tag{8.82}$$

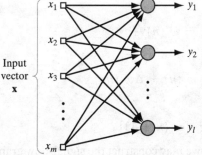

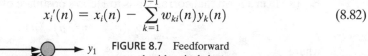

FIGURE 8.7   Feedforward network with a single layer of computational nodes.

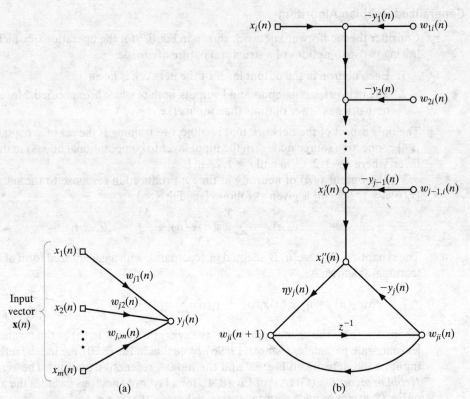

FIGURE 8.8 The signal-flow graph representation of generalized Hebbian algorithm. (a) Graph of Eq. (8.79). (b) Graph of Eqs. (8.80) through (8.81), where $x_i'(n)$ and $x_i''(n)$ are defined in Eqs. (8.82) and (8.84).

For a specified neuron j, the algorithm described in Eq. (8.81) has exactly the same mathematical form as that of Eq. (8.40), except for the fact that the input signal $x_i(n)$ is replaced by its modified value $x_i'(n)$ defined in Eq. (8.82). We may go one step further and rewrite Eq. (8.81) in a form that corresponds to Hebb's postulate of learning, as shown by

$$\Delta w_{ji}(n) = \eta y_j(n) x_i''(n) \tag{8.83}$$

where

$$x_i''(n) = x_i' - w_{ji}(n) y_j(n) \tag{8.84}$$

Thus, noting that

$$w_{ji}(n+1) = w_{ji}(n) + \Delta w_{ji}(n) \tag{8.85}$$

and

$$w_{ji}(n) = z^{-1}[w_{ji}(n+1)] \tag{8.86}$$

where z^{-1} is the unit-time delay operator, we may construct the signal-flow graph of Fig. 8.8b for the generalized Hebbian algorithm. From this graph, we see that the algorithm lends itself to a *local* form of implementation, provided that it is formulated as in Eq. (8.85). Note also that $y_j(n)$, responsible for feedback in the signal-flow graph of Fig. 8.8b, is itself determined by Eq. (8.79); signal-flow graph representation of this latter equation is shown in Fig. 8.8a.

For a heuristic understanding of how the generalized Hebbian algorithm actually operates, we first use matrix notation to rewrite the version of the algorithm defined in Eq. (8.81) as

$$\Delta \mathbf{w}_j(n) = \eta y_j(n)\mathbf{x}'(n) - \eta y_j^2(n)\mathbf{w}_j(n), \qquad j = 1, 2, ..., l \tag{8.87}$$

where $\mathbf{w}_j(n)$ is the synaptic weight vector of neuron j, and

$$\mathbf{x}'(n) = \mathbf{x}(n) - \sum_{k=1}^{j-1} \mathbf{w}_k(n) y_k(n) \tag{8.88}$$

The vector $\mathbf{x}'(n)$ represents a modified form of the input vector $\mathbf{x}(n)$. Based on the representation given in Eq. (8.87), we make the following observations (Sanger, 1989b):

1. For the first neuron of the feedforward network shown in Fig. 8.7, we have

$$j = 1: \qquad \mathbf{x}'(n) = \mathbf{x}(n)$$

In this case, the generalized Hebbian algorithm reduces to that of Eq. (8.46) for a single neuron. From the material presented in Section 8.5, we already know that this neuron will discover the first principal component of the input vector $\mathbf{x}(n)$.

2. For the second neuron of the network in Fig. 8.7, we write

$$j = 2: \qquad \mathbf{x}'(n) = \mathbf{x}(n) - \mathbf{w}_1(n) y_1(n)$$

Provided that the first neuron has already converged to the first principal component, the second neuron sees an input vector $\mathbf{x}'(n)$ from which the first eigenvector of the correlation matrix $\mathbf{R}$ has been removed. The second neuron therefore extracts the first principal component of $\mathbf{x}'(n)$, which is equivalent to the second principal component of the original input vector $\mathbf{x}(n)$.

3. For the third neuron, we write

$$j = 3: \qquad \mathbf{x}'(n) = \mathbf{x}(n) - \mathbf{w}_1(n) y_1(n) - \mathbf{w}_2(n) y_2(n)$$

Suppose that the first two neurons have already converged to the first and second principal components, as explained in steps 1 and 2. The third neuron now sees an input vector $\mathbf{x}'(n)$, from which the first two eigenvectors have been removed. Therefore, it extracts the first principal component of the vector $\mathbf{x}'(n)$, which is equivalent to the third principal component of the original input vector $\mathbf{x}(n)$.

4. Proceeding in this fashion for the remaining neurons of the feedforward network in Fig. 8.7, it is now apparent that each output of the network trained in accordance with the generalized Hebbian algorithm of Eq. (8.81) represents the response to a particular eigenvector of the correlation matrix of the input vector, and that the individual outputs are ordered by decreasing eigenvalue.

This method of computing eigenvectors is similar to a technique known as *Hotelling's deflation technique* (Kreyszig, 1988); it follows a procedure similar to Gram–Schmidt orthogonalization (Strang, 1980).

Convergence Considerations

Let $\mathbf{W}(n) = \{w_{ji}(n)\}$ denote the l-by-m synaptic-weight matrix of the feedforward network shown in Fig. 8.7; that is,

$$\mathbf{W}(n) = [\mathbf{w}_1(n), \mathbf{w}_2(n), ..., \mathbf{w}_l(n)]^T \tag{8.89}$$

Let the learning-rate parameter of the generalized Hebbian algorithm of Eq. (8.81) take a time-varying form $\eta(n)$ such that in the limit, we have

$$\lim_{n\to\infty} \eta(n) = 0 \quad \text{and} \quad \sum_{n=0}^{\infty} \eta(n) = \infty \tag{8.90}$$

We may then rewrite this algorithm in the matrix form

$$\Delta\mathbf{W}(n) = \eta(n)\{\mathbf{y}(n)\mathbf{x}^T(n) - \text{LT}[\mathbf{y}(n)\mathbf{y}^T(n)]\mathbf{W}(n)\} \tag{8.91}$$

where

$$\mathbf{y}(n) = \mathbf{W}(n)\mathbf{x}(n)$$

and the operator LT[·] sets all the elements above the diagonal of its matrix argument to zero, thereby making that matrix *lower triangular*. Under these conditions, and invoking the assumptions made in Section 8.5, convergence of the GHA algorithm is proved by following a procedure similar to that presented in the previous section for the maximum eigenfilter. Thus, we may state the following theorem (Sanger, 1989b):

> *If the synaptic-weight matrix* $\mathbf{W}(n)$ *is assigned random values at time-step* n = 0, *then with probability 1, the generalized Hebbian algorithm of Eq. (8.91) will converge to a fixed point, with* $\mathbf{W}^T(n)$ *approaching a matrix whose columns are the first l eigenvectors of the m-by-m correlation matrix* $\mathbf{R}$ *of the m-by-1 input vector, ordered by decreasing eigenvalue.*

The practical significance of this theorem is that it guarantees the generalized Hebbian algorithm to find the first l eigenvectors of the correlation matrix $\mathbf{R}$, assuming that the associated eigenvalues are distinct. Equally important is the fact that we do not need to compute the correlation matrix $\mathbf{R}$. Rather, the first l eigenvectors of $\mathbf{R}$ are computed by the algorithm directly from the input data. The resulting computational savings can be enormous, especially if the dimensionality m of the input space is very large and the required number of the eigenvectors associated with the l largest eigenvalues of the correlation matrix $\mathbf{R}$ is a small fraction of m. Just as importantly, the algorithm has a built-in capability for adaptation; in other words, the algorithm can *track* statistical variations in a nonstationary environment.

The convergence theorem is formulated in terms of a time-varying learning-rate parameter $\eta(n)$. In practice, the learning-rate parameter is chosen to be a small constant η, in which case convergence is guaranteed with mean-square error in synaptic weights of order η.

In Chatterjee et al. (1998), the convergence properties of the GHA algorithm described in Eq. (8.91) are investigated. The analysis presented therein shows that increasing η leads to faster convergence and larger asymptotic mean-square error, which is intuitively satisfying. In that paper, the tradeoff between the accuracy of computation and speed of learning is made explicit.

Optimality of the Generalized Hebbian Algorithm

Suppose that in the limit we write

$$\Delta\mathbf{w}_j(n) \to \mathbf{0} \quad \text{and} \quad \mathbf{w}_j(n) \to \mathbf{q}_j \quad \text{as } n \to \infty \quad \text{for } j = 1, 2, ..., l \qquad (8.92)$$

and that we have

$$\|\mathbf{w}_j(n)\| = 1 \quad \text{for all } j \qquad (8.93)$$

Then the limiting values $\mathbf{q}_1, \mathbf{q}_2, ..., \mathbf{q}_l$ of the synaptic-weight vectors of the neurons in the feedforward network of Fig. 8.6 represent the *normalized eigenvectors* associated with l dominant eigenvalues of the correlation matrix $\mathbf{R}$, and which are ordered in descending eigenvalue. At equilibrium, we may therefore write

$$\mathbf{q}_j^T\mathbf{R}\mathbf{q}_k = \begin{cases} \lambda_j, & k = j \\ 0, & k \neq j \end{cases} \qquad (8.94)$$

where $\lambda_1 > \lambda_2 > \cdots > \lambda_l$.

For the output of neuron j, we have the limiting value

$$\lim_{n\to\infty} y_j(n) = \mathbf{x}^T(n)\mathbf{q}_j = \mathbf{q}_j^T\mathbf{x}(n) \qquad (8.95)$$

Let $Y_j(n)$ denote a random variable with a realization denoted by the output $y_j(n)$. The cross-correlation between the random variables $Y_j(n)$ and $Y_k(n)$, at equilibrium, is given by

$$\lim_{n\to\infty} \mathbb{E}[Y_j(n)Y_k(n)] = \mathbb{E}[\mathbf{q}_j^T\mathbf{X}(n)\mathbf{X}^T(n)\mathbf{q}_k]$$
$$= \mathbf{q}_j^T\mathbf{R}\mathbf{q}_k \qquad (8.96)$$
$$= \begin{cases} \lambda_j, & k = j \\ 0, & k \neq j \end{cases}$$

Hence, we may state that at equilibrium the generalized Hebbian algorithm of Eq. (8.91) acts as an *eigenanalyzer* of the input data.

Let $\hat{\mathbf{x}}(n)$ denote the particular value of the input vector $\mathbf{x}(n)$ for which the limiting conditions of Eq. (8.92) are satisfied for $j = l - 1$. Hence, from the matrix form of Eq. (8.80), we find that in the limit

$$\hat{\mathbf{x}}(n) = \sum_{k=1}^{l} y_k(n)\mathbf{q}_k \qquad (8.97)$$

This means that given two sets of quantities, the limiting values $\mathbf{q}_1, \mathbf{q}_2, ..., \mathbf{q}_l$ of the synaptic-weight vectors of the neurons in the feedforward network of Fig. 8.6 and the corresponding outputs $y_1(n), y_2(n), ..., y_l(n)$, we may construct a *linear least-squares estimate* $\hat{\mathbf{x}}(n)$ of the input vector $\mathbf{x}(n)$. In effect, the formula of Eq. (8.97) may be viewed as one of *data reconstruction*, as depicted in Fig. 8.9. Note that in light of the discussion presented in Section 8.4, this method of data reconstruction is subject to an approximation error vector that is orthogonal to the estimate $\hat{\mathbf{x}}(n)$.

FIGURE 8.9   Signal-flow
graph representation of how
the reconstructed vector $\hat{\mathbf{x}}$ is
computed in the GHA.

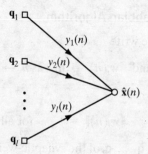

Summary of the GHA

The computations involved in the generalized Hebbian algorithm (GHA) are simple;
they may be summarized as follows:

1. Initialize the synaptic weights of the network, w_{ji}, to small random values at time
   $n = 1$. Assign a small positive value to the learning-rate parameter η.
2. For $n = 1, j = 1, 2, ..., l$, and $i = 1, 2, ..., m$, compute

$$y_j(n) = \sum_{i=1}^{m} w_{ji}(n)x_i(n), \qquad j = 1, 2, ..., l$$

$$\Delta w_{ji}(n) = \eta\left(y_j(n)x_i(n) - y_j(n)\sum_{k=1}^{j} w_{ki}(n)y_k(n) \right), \qquad \begin{array}{l} j = 1, 2, ..., l \\ i = 1, 2, ..., m \end{array}$$

where $x_i(n)$ is the ith component of the m-by-1 input vector $\mathbf{x}(n)$ and l is the desired
number of principal components.

3. Increment n by 1, go back to step 2, and continue until the synaptic weights w_{ji}
   reach their steady-state values. For large n, the synaptic weight w_{ji} of neuron j converges to the ith component of the eigenvector associated with the jth eigenvalue
   of the correlation matrix of the input vector $\mathbf{x}(n)$.

8.7   CASE STUDY: IMAGE CODING

We continue our discussion of the generalized Hebbian learning algorithm by examining its use for solving an *image-coding* problem.

Figure 8.10a shows an image of Lena used for training; this image emphasizes *edge*
information. It was digitized to form a 256 × 256 image with 256 gray levels. The image
was coded using a linear feedforward network with a single layer of 8 neurons, each
with 64 inputs. To train the network, 8 × 8 nonoverlapping blocks of the image were
used. The experiment was performed with 2,000 scans of the picture and a small learning-
rate parameter $\eta = 10^{-4}$.

Figure 8.10b shows the 8 × 8 masks representing the synaptic weights learned by
the network. Each of the eight masks displays the set of synaptic weights associated with
a particular neuron of the network. Specifically, excitatory synapses (positive weights)
are shown in white, whereas inhibitory synapses (negative weights) are shown in black;

Original Image

Weights

Using First 8 Components

11 to 1 compression

FIGURE 8.10   (a) An image of Lena used in the image-coding experiment. (b) 8×8 masks representing the synaptic weights learned by the GHA. (c) Reconstructed image of Lena obtained using the dominant 8 principal components without quantization. (d) Reconstructed image of Lena with an 11-to-1 compression ratio using quantization.

gray indicates zero weights. In our notation, the masks represent the columns of the 64×8 synaptic-weight matrix $\mathbf{W}^T$ after the generalized Hebbian algorithm has converged. To code the image, the following procedure was used:

- Each 8×8 block of the image was multiplied by each of the 8 masks shown in Fig. 8.10b, thereby generating 8 coefficients for image coding; Fig. 8.10c shows the reconstructed image based on the dominant 8 principal components without quantization.

- Each coefficient was uniformly quantized with a number of bits approximately proportional to the logarithm of the variance of that coefficient over the image. Thus, the first three masks were assigned 6 bits each, the next two masks 4 bits each, the next two masks 3 bits each, and the last mask 2 bits. Based on this representation, a total of 34 bits were needed to code each 8×8 block of pixels, resulting in a data rate of 0.53 bits per pixel.

To reconstruct the image from the quantized coefficients, all the masks were weighted by their quantized coefficients and then added to reconstitute each block of the image. The reconstructed Lena's image with 11-to-1 compression ratio is shown in Fig. 8.10d.

For a variation on the first image, we next applied the generalized Hebbian algorithm to the image of peppers shown in Fig. 8.11a. This second image emphasizes *textural*

Original Image

Weights

Using First 8 Components

12 to 1 compression

12 to 1 compression

Weights From Lena

FIGURE 8.11 (a) Image of peppers. (b) 8×8 masks representing the synaptic weights learned by the GHA applied to the peppers. (c) Reconstructed image of the peppers, using 8 dominant principal components. (d) Reconstructed image of the peppers with 12-to-1 compression ratio, using masks of part (b) with quantization. (e) Reconstructed image of the peppers, using the masks of Fig. 8.10(b) for encoding, with quantization for a compression ratio of 12 to 1, the same as that in part (d). Part (f) reproduces the Lena mask (i.e., weights) of Fig. 8.10b.

information. Figure 8.11b shows the 8×8 masks of synaptic weights learned by the network by proceeding in the same manner described for Fig. 8.10; note the difference between these masks and those of Fig. 8.10b. Figure 8.11c shows the reconstructed image of the peppers based on the dominant 8 principal components without quantization. To study the effect of quantization, the outputs of the first 2 masks were quantized using 5 bits each, the third using 3 bits, and the remaining 5 masks using 2 bits each. Thus, a total of 23 bits were needed to code each 8×8 block of pixels, resulting in a bit rate of 0.36 bits per pixel. Figure 8.11d shows the reconstructed image of the peppers, using its own masks quantized in the manner just described. The compression ratio of this image was 12 to 1.

To test the "generalization" performance of the GHA, we finally used the masks of Fig. 8.10b to decompose the peppers of Fig. 8.11a and then applied the same quantization procedure that was used to generate the reconstructed image of Fig. 8.11d. The result of this image reconstruction is shown in Fig. 8.11e with a compression ratio of 12 to 1, the same as that in Fig. 8.11d. While the reconstructed images in Figs. 8.11d and 8.11e do bear a striking resemblance to each other, it can be seen that the image in Fig. 8.11d possesses a greater amount of "true" textural information and thus looks less "blocky" than that in Fig. 8.11e. The reason for this behavior lies in the network weights. Comparing the masks (i.e., weights) of Fig. 8.11b for the peppers image with those of Fig. 8.10b for the Lena image, reproduced in Fig. 8.11f for convenience of presentation, we make two observations:

(i) The first four weights of these two masks are very similar.

(ii) The final four weights for the Lena image encode edge information; but in the case of the peppers image, the final four weights encode textural information.

It is therefore the cited differences under point (ii) that explain the blocky appearance of the peppers image in part (e) compared with the corresponding image in part (d).

8.8   KERNEL PRINCIPAL-COMPONENTS ANALYSIS

The underlying theory of principal-components analysis, as presented thus far in this chapter, is based on second-order statistics (i.e., correlations) of the input data; it is for this reason that the standard PCA is referred to as a *linear method* of dimensionality reduction. From a practical perspective, however, it would be highly desirable to expand the data-reduction capability of PCA to encompass input data whose structure contains higher-order statistics. This expanded capability requires that we make the PCA *nonlinear*. To that end, Schölkopf et al. (1998) have developed a nonlinear PCA called *kernel PCA*. This new technique builds on the notion of a *reproducing-kernel Hilbert space* (RKHS) studied previously in Chapter 6.

It is informative to compare the GHA and the kernel PCA in implementational terms:

1. The GHA uses a feedforward network composed simply of an input layer and an output layer; the network is made up entirely of linear neurons. Kernel PCA also uses a feedforward network, but the network includes a nonlinear hidden layer and a linear output layer.

2. GHA is an on-line learning algorithm, whereas kernel PCA is a batch-learning algorithm.

Insofar as the hidden layer is concerned, kernel PCA follows the theory embodied in the design of support vector machines studied in Chapter 6. With regard to the output layer, kernel PCA follows the dimensionality-reduction theory embodied in standard PCA— hence the name "kernel PCA."

Derivation of Kernel PCA

Let the vector $\boldsymbol{\phi}: \mathbb{R}^{m_0} \to \mathbb{R}^{m_1}$ denote the nonlinear mapping from the input space of dimensionality m_0 to the feature space of dimensionality m_1. Correspondingly, let the vector $\boldsymbol{\phi}(\mathbf{x}_i)$ denote the image of an input vector $\mathbf{x}_i$ induced in the feature space. Then, given the set of examples $\{\mathbf{x}_i\}_{i=1}^{N}$, we have a corresponding set of feature vectors $\{\boldsymbol{\phi}(\mathbf{x}_i)\}_{i=1}^{N}$. Accordingly, we may define an m_1-by-m_1 correlation matrix in the feature space, denoted by $\tilde{\mathbf{R}}$, in terms of the outer product $\boldsymbol{\phi}(\mathbf{x}_i)\boldsymbol{\phi}^T(\mathbf{x}_i)$ as

$$\tilde{\mathbf{R}} = \frac{1}{N} \sum_{i=1}^{N} \boldsymbol{\phi}(\mathbf{x}_i)\boldsymbol{\phi}^T(\mathbf{x}_i) \tag{8.98}$$

As with ordinary PCA, the first thing we have to do is to ensure that the set of feature vectors $\{\boldsymbol{\phi}(\mathbf{x}_i)\}_{i=1}^{N}$ has zero mean, that is,

$$\frac{1}{N} \sum_{i=1}^{N} \boldsymbol{\phi}(\mathbf{x}_i) = \mathbf{0}$$

To satisfy this condition in the feature space is a more difficult proposition than it is in the input space; in Problem 8.15 we describe a procedure for catering to this requirement. Proceeding, then, on the assumption that the feature vectors have been centered, we may adapt the use of Eq. (8.14) to our present situation by writing

$$\tilde{\mathbf{R}}\tilde{\mathbf{q}} = \tilde{\lambda}\tilde{\mathbf{q}} \tag{8.99}$$

where $\tilde{\lambda}$ is an eigenvalue of the correlation matrix $\tilde{\mathbf{R}}$ and $\tilde{\mathbf{q}}$ is the associated eigenvector. Now we note that all eigenvectors that satisfy Eq. (8.99) for $\tilde{\lambda} \neq 0$ lie in the span of the set of feature vectors $\{\boldsymbol{\phi}(\mathbf{x}_j)\}_{j=1}^{N}$. Consequently, there does exist a corresponding set of coefficients $\{\alpha_j\}_{j=1}^{N}$ for which we can write

$$\tilde{\mathbf{q}} = \sum_{j=1}^{N} \alpha_j \boldsymbol{\phi}(\mathbf{x}_j) \tag{8.100}$$

Thus, substituting Eqs. (8.98) and (8.100) into Eq. (8.99), we obtain

$$\sum_{i=1}^{N} \sum_{j=1}^{N} \alpha_j \boldsymbol{\phi}(\mathbf{x}_i) k(\mathbf{x}_i, \mathbf{x}_j) = N\tilde{\lambda} \sum_{j=1}^{N} \alpha_j \boldsymbol{\phi}(\mathbf{x}_j) \tag{8.101}$$

where $k(\mathbf{x}_i, \mathbf{x}_j)$ is a *Mercer kernel* defined in terms of the feature vectors by an inner product, as shown by

$$k(\mathbf{x}_i, \mathbf{x}_j) = \boldsymbol{\phi}^T(\mathbf{x}_i)\boldsymbol{\phi}(\mathbf{x}_j) \tag{8.102}$$

We need to go one step further with Eq. (8.101) so that the relationship is expressed entirely in terms of the kernel. To do so, we premultiply both sides of Eq. (8.101) by the transposed vector $\boldsymbol{\phi}^T(\mathbf{x}_s)$, thereby obtaining

$$\sum_{i=1}^{N}\sum_{j=1}^{N}\alpha_j k(\mathbf{x}_s,\mathbf{x}_i)k(\mathbf{x}_i,\mathbf{x}_j) = N\tilde{\lambda}\sum_{j=1}^{N}\alpha_j k(\mathbf{x}_s,\mathbf{x}_j), \quad s=1,2,...,N \quad (8.103)$$

where the definitions of $k(\mathbf{x}_s,\mathbf{x}_i)$ and $k(\mathbf{x}_s,\mathbf{x}_j)$ follow Eq. (8.102)

We now introduce two matrix definitions:

- the N-by-N kernel matrix $\mathbf{K}$, or *Gram*, whose ij-th element is the Mercer kernel $k(\mathbf{x}_i,\mathbf{x}_j)$;
- the N-by-1 vector $\boldsymbol{\alpha}$, whose jth element is the coefficient α_j.

Accordingly, we may recast Eq. (8.103) in the compact matrix form

$$\mathbf{K}^2\boldsymbol{\alpha} = N\tilde{\lambda}\mathbf{K}\boldsymbol{\alpha} \quad (8.104)$$

where the squared matrix $\mathbf{K}^2$ denotes the product of $\mathbf{K}$ with itself. Since premultiplication by $\mathbf{K}$ is common to both sides of Eq. (8.104), all the solutions of this eigenvalue problem that are of interest are equally well represented in the dual eigenvalue problem

$$\mathbf{K}\boldsymbol{\alpha} = N\tilde{\lambda}\boldsymbol{\alpha} \quad (8.105)$$

Let $\lambda_1 \geq \lambda_2 \geq \cdots \geq \lambda_N$ denote the eigenvalues of the Gram matrix $\mathbf{K}$; that is,

$$\lambda_j = N\tilde{\lambda}_j, \quad j=1,2,...,N \quad (8.106)$$

where $\tilde{\lambda}_j$ is the jth eigenvalue of the correlation matrix $\tilde{\mathbf{R}}$. Then Eq. (8.105) takes the standard form

$$\mathbf{K}\boldsymbol{\alpha} = \lambda\boldsymbol{\alpha} \quad (8.107)$$

where the coefficient vector $\boldsymbol{\alpha}$ plays the role of the eigenvector associated with the eigenvalue λ of the Gram $\mathbf{K}$. The vector $\boldsymbol{\alpha}$ is normalized by requiring that the eigenvector $\tilde{\mathbf{q}}$ of the correlation matrix $\tilde{\mathbf{R}}$ is normalized to unit length; that is,

$$\tilde{\mathbf{q}}_k^T\tilde{\mathbf{q}}_k = 1 \quad \text{for } k=1,2,...,l \quad (8.108)$$

where it is assumed that the eigenvalues of $\mathbf{K}$ are arranged in decreasing order, with λ_l being the smallest nonzero eigenvalue of the Gram matrix $\mathbf{K}$. Using Eq. (8.100) and then invoking Eq. (8.107), we may show that the normalization condition of Eq. (8.108) is equivalent to

$$\boldsymbol{\alpha}_r^T\boldsymbol{\alpha}_r = \frac{1}{\lambda_k}, \quad r=1,2,...,l \quad (8.109)$$

For the extraction of principal components, we need to compute the projections onto the eigenvectors $\tilde{\mathbf{q}}_k$ in feature space, as shown by

$$\tilde{\mathbf{q}}_k^T\boldsymbol{\phi}(\mathbf{x}) = \sum_{j=1}^{N}\alpha_{k,j}\boldsymbol{\phi}^T(\mathbf{x}_j)\boldsymbol{\phi}(\mathbf{x})$$
$$= \sum_{j=1}^{N}\alpha_{k,j}k(\mathbf{x}_j,\mathbf{x}), \quad k=1,2,...,l \quad (8.110)$$

where the vector $\mathbf{x}$ is a "test" point and $\alpha_{k,j}$ is the jth coefficient of eigenvector $\boldsymbol{\alpha}_k$ associated with the kth eigenvalue of the Gram $\mathbf{K}$. The projections of Eq. (8.110) define the *nonlinear principal components* in the m_1-dimensional feature space.

Figure 8.12 illustrates the basic idea of kernel PCA, where the feature space is nonlinearly related to the input space via the transformation $\boldsymbol{\phi}(\mathbf{x})$. Parts (a) and (b) of the figure refer to the input space and feature space, respectively. The contour lines shown in Fig. 8.12b represent constant projections onto a principal eigenvector, which is shown as a red arrow. In this figure, it is assumed that the transformation $\boldsymbol{\phi}(\mathbf{x})$ has been chosen in such a way that the images of the data points induced in the future space congregate themselves essentially along the eigenvector. Figure 8.11a shows the *nonlinear* contour lines in the input space that correspond to those in the feature space. Note that we purposely have not shown a preimage of the eigenvector in the input space, as it may not even exist (Schölkopf et al., 1998).

For kernels defined in accordance with Mercer's theorem, we are basically performing ordinary PCA in an m_1-dimensional feature space, where the dimension m_1 is a design parameter. All the properties of ordinary PCA that are described in Section 8.4 carry over to kernel PCA. In particular, kernel PCA is linear in the feature space, but nonlinear in the input space.

In Chapter 6, we presented three methods for constructing Mercer kernels that were based on the use of polynomials, radial-basis functions, and hyperbolic functions; see Table 6.1. The question of how to select the optimal kernel for a given task (i.e., the appropriate feature space) remains an open problem.

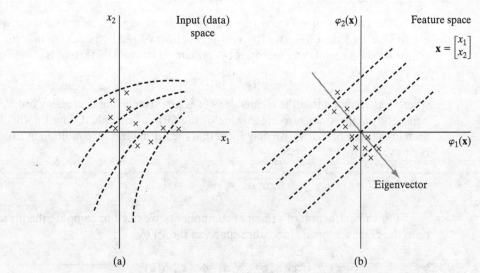

(a)   (b)

FIGURE 8.12 Illustration of kernel PCA. (a) Two-dimensional input space, displaying a set of data points. (b) Two-dimensional feature space, displaying the induced images of the data points congregating around a principal eigenvector. The uniformly spaced dashed lines in part (b) represent contours of constant projections onto the eigenvector; the corresponding contours are nonlinear in the input space.

Summary of the Kernel PCA

1. Given the unlabeled training sample $\{\mathbf{x}_i\}_{i=1}^{N}$, compute the N-by-N Gram $\mathbf{K} = \{k(\mathbf{x}_i, \mathbf{x}_j)\}$, where

$$k(\mathbf{x}_i, \mathbf{x}_j) = \boldsymbol{\phi}^T(\mathbf{x}_i)\boldsymbol{\phi}(\mathbf{x}_j), \qquad i, j = 1, 2, ..., N$$

where it is assumed that preprocessing has been performed to satisfy the zero-mean condition of all feature vectors over the training sample, that is

$$\frac{1}{N} \sum_{i=1}^{N} \boldsymbol{\phi}(\mathbf{x}_i) = \mathbf{0}$$

2. Solve the eigenvalue problem

$$\mathbf{K}\boldsymbol{\alpha} = \lambda\boldsymbol{\alpha}$$

where λ is an eigenvalue of the Gram $\mathbf{K}$ and $\boldsymbol{\alpha}$ is the associated eigenvector.

3. Normalize the eigenvectors so computed by requiring that

$$\boldsymbol{\alpha}_r^T\boldsymbol{\alpha}_r = \frac{1}{\lambda_r}, \qquad r = 1, 2, ..., l$$

where λ_l is the smallest nonzero eigenvalue of Gram $\mathbf{K}$, assuming that the eigenvalues are arranged in decreasing order.

4. For the extraction of principal components of a test point $\mathbf{x}$, compute the projections

$$a_k = \tilde{\mathbf{q}}_r^T\boldsymbol{\phi}(\mathbf{x})$$
$$= \sum_{j=1}^{N} \alpha_{r,j}k(\mathbf{x}_j, \mathbf{x}), \qquad r = 1, 2, ..., l$$

where $\alpha_{r,j}$ is the jth element of eigenvector $\boldsymbol{\alpha}_r$.

EXAMPLE 3   ILLUSTRATIVE EXPERIMENT ON KERNEL PCA

To provide some intuitive understanding for the operation of kernel PCA, we show in Fig. 8.13 the results of a simple experiment described in Schölkopf et al. (1998). The two-dimensional data, consisting of components x_1 and x_2, used in this experiment were generated as follows: The x_1-values have a uniform distribution in the interval $[-1, 1]$. The x_2-values are nonlinearly related to the x_1-values by the formula

$$x_2 = x_1^2 + v$$

where v is additive Gaussian noise of zero mean and variance 0.04.

The results of kernel PCA shown in Fig. 8.13 were obtained using kernel polynomials

$$k(\mathbf{x}, \mathbf{x}_i) = (\mathbf{x}^T\mathbf{x}_i)^d, \qquad d = 1, 2, 3, 4$$

where $d = 1$ corresponds to linear PCA, and $d = 2, 3$, and 4 correspond to kernel PCA. Linear PCA, shown on the left-hand side of Fig. 8.13, results in only two eigenvalues, since the dimensionality of the input space is two. In contrast, kernel PCA permits the extraction of higher-order components, as shown by the results depicted in columns 2, 3, and 4 of Fig. 8.13, corresponding to polynomial degree $d = 2, 3$, and 4, respectively. The contour lines shown in each part of the figure (except for the zero eigenvalue in the case of linear PCA) represent constant principal values (i.e., constant projections onto the eigenvector associated with the eigenvalue in question).

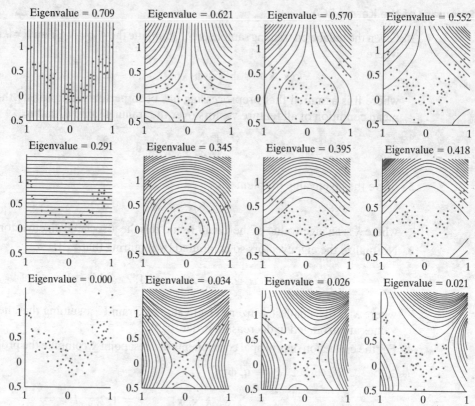

FIGURE 8.13   Two-dimensional example illustrating kernel PCA. From left to right, the polynomial degree of the kernel is $d = 1, 2, 3$, and 4, respectively. From top to bottom, the first three eigenvectors in the feature space are shown. The first column corresponds to linear PCA, and the other three columns correspond to kernel PCA with polynomial degree $d = 2$, 3, and 4, respectively. (Reproduced with permission from Dr. Klaus-Robert Müller.)

Based on the results shown in Fig. 8.13, we make the following observations:

- As expected, linear PCA fails to provide an adequate representation of the nonlinear input data.
- In all cases, the first principal component varies monotonically along a parabola that underlies the input data.
- In kernel PCA, the second and third principal components exhibit a behavior that appears somewhat similar for different values of polynomial degree d.
- In the case of polynomial degree $d = 2$, the third principal component of kernel PCA appears to pick up the variance caused by the additive Gaussian noise v. By removing the contribution from this component, we would in effect be performing some form of noise reduction. ∎

8.9   BASIC ISSUES INVOLVED IN THE CODING OF NATURAL IMAGES

In the coding of natural images, there are basically two strategies, both of which, in their own ways, exploit the inherent redundancy that characterizes the underlying structure of such images so as to produce effective representations of the underlying scenes. The two strategies are as follows:

1. *Compact coding.* In this coding strategy, the image is transformed in such a way that it is represented with a reduced number of vectors, subject to a prescribed level of root-mean-square error. Principal-components analysis is a well-studied example of compact coding.

2. *Sparse-distributed coding.* In this second coding strategy, the dimensionality of the natural image is *not* reduced. Rather, the redundancy contained in the input image is transformed in a special way that matches the redundancy of the firing patterns of neuronal cells in the visual system.

In a classic paper (Field, 1994), these two coding strategies are contrasted. In particular, it is pointed out that the signature of a sparse-distributed code is found in the *fourth-order moment* (i.e., *kurtosis*) of the underlying distribution of a natural image. PCA is a linear coding scheme, relying on second-order statistics for its functionality; it is therefore incapable of capturing the fourth-order statistics of a natural image, which appears to be essential for an efficient coding strategy. Another important point made in Field's paper is that sparse-distributed-coding schemes, exemplified by the *wavelet transform*,[5] are effective because the response histograms of such codes exhibit a high kurtosis when they are applied to natural images. Furthermore, the paper points out that, to a first-order degree of approximation, natural images may be considered as a sum of *self-similar local functions* (i.e., the inverse of a wavelet transform).

Nowadays, it is generally agreed that the process involved in the generation of natural images is nonlinear (Ruderman, 1997). One of the contributing factors is *occlusion*, which is highly nonlinear. There are four primary sources of image contours, which are responsible for occlusion in natural images (Richards, 1988):

- external occluding edges;
- crease or fold;
- shadow or illumination effects;
- surface markings or texture.

All four types of image contours provide information about surface shapes in their own individual ways. However, the rules for inference as to what type of edge created the image contour are quite different, which makes the encoding and decoding of natural images a research challenge.

To capture higher-order statistics of a natural image, it is therefore apparent that we must somehow introduce nonlinearity into PCA.[6] In the next section, we discuss an adaptive method of achieving this objective in a computationally efficient manner.

8.10   KERNEL HEBBIAN ALGORITHM

The discussion presented in the preceding section has taught us an important lesson:

> *Higher-order statistics are particularly important in the structural coding (i.e., modeling) of natural images.*

Moreover, natural images are highly *complex*, in the sense that the number of pixels contained in the digital representation of a natural image can be arbitrarily high; this number of pixels defines the dimensionality of the *image space*, in which a sample image is represented merely as a point. Hence, if a machine is required to learn the model of a natural image, then it usually would take a large number of examples to train the machine.

Now, recalling that the kernel PCA is a batch-learning algorithm, we find that the storage and manipulation of the Gram will occupy a size equal to N^2, where N is the number of training examples. Accordingly, the computational complexity of kernel PCA can become unmanageable when it is required to model a natural image.

To alleviate this computational difficulty, Kim et al. (2005) have devised an iterative method for computing the kernel PCA by exploiting the on-line unsupervised-learning capability of the generalized Hebbian algorithm (GHA), studied in Section 8.6. The resulting algorithm, called the *kernel Hebbian algorithm* (*KHA*), is capable of estimating the kernel principal components with a memory complexity that is *linear* in the number of training examples. Unlike the kernel PCA, the KHA is therefore applicable to large-scale learning problems of an unsupervised kind.

Derivation of the KHA

Consider a training sample, denoted by $\{\mathbf{x}_i\}_{i=1}^N$. We may reformulate the update rule of GHA, described in Eqs. (8.79) and (8.80) in the *feature space*, as

$$y_j(n) = \mathbf{w}_j^T(n)\boldsymbol{\phi}(\mathbf{x}(n)), \quad j = 1, 2, ..., l \tag{8.111}$$

and

$$\Delta \mathbf{w}_j(n) = \eta \left[y_j(n)\boldsymbol{\phi}(\mathbf{x}(n)) - y_j(n) \sum_{p=1}^{j} \mathbf{w}_p(n)y_p(n) \right], \quad j = 1, 2, ..., l \tag{8.112}$$

We have chosen p as a new index in place of k so as to avoid confusion with the symbol k for kernel. As before, $\Delta \mathbf{w}_j(n)$ and $\mathbf{x}(n)$ are, respectively, the changes applied to the synaptic weight vector and the input vector selected from the training sample at time n; η is the learning-rate parameter. The index l denotes the number of outputs. Due to the possible high dimensionality of the feature space, we may not be able to apply Eq. (8.112) directly. However, from the kernel PCA solution, it is known that $\mathbf{w}_j$ is expanded in the training sample in the feature space, as shown by

$$\mathbf{w}_j = \sum_{i=1}^{N} \alpha_{ji}\boldsymbol{\phi}(\mathbf{x}_i) \tag{8.113}$$

where α_{ji} are the coefficients of the expansion. The use of this formula in Eqs. (8.111) and (8.112) leads to the following reformulation of the two update rules:

$$y_j(n) = \sum_{i=1}^{N} \alpha_{ji}(n)\boldsymbol{\phi}^T(\mathbf{x}_i)\boldsymbol{\phi}(\mathbf{x}(n)), \quad j = 1, 2, ..., l \tag{8.114}$$

and

$$\sum_{i=1}^{N} \Delta\alpha_{ji}(n)\boldsymbol{\phi}(\mathbf{x}_i) = \eta \left[y_j(n)\boldsymbol{\phi}(\mathbf{x}(n)) - y_j(n)\sum_{i=1}^{N}\sum_{p=1}^{j} y_p(n)\alpha_{pi}\boldsymbol{\phi}(\mathbf{x}_i) \right], \quad j = 1, 2, ..., l \tag{8.115}$$

Invoking the definition of the Mercer kernel, we write

$$k(\mathbf{x}_i, \mathbf{x}(n)) = \boldsymbol{\phi}^T(\mathbf{x}_i)\boldsymbol{\phi}(\mathbf{x}(n)), \qquad i = 1, 2, ..., N$$

Moreover, we may identify two possible conditions:

(i) The index of the input vector $\mathbf{x}(n)$ in the training sample is i, in which case $\mathbf{x}(n) = \mathbf{x}_i$.

(ii) Condition (i) does not hold, in which case $\mathbf{x}(n) \neq \mathbf{x}_i$.

Accordingly, by removing the outer summation in Eq. (8.115) with respect to index i, we finally obtain the update rule for the coefficients $\{\alpha_{ji}\}$ to be as follows (Kim et al., 2005):

$$y_j(n) = \sum_{i=1}^{N} \alpha_{ji}(n)k(\mathbf{x}_i, \mathbf{x}(n)), \qquad j = 1, 2, ..., l \qquad (8.116)$$

and

$$\Delta\alpha_{ji}(n) = \begin{cases} \eta y_j(n) - \eta y_j(n)\sum_{p=1}^{j}\alpha_{pi}(n)y_p(n) & \text{if } \mathbf{x}(n) = \mathbf{x}_i \\ -\eta y_j(n)\sum_{p=1}^{j}\alpha_{pi}(n)y_p(n), & \text{if } \mathbf{x}(n) \neq \mathbf{x}_i \end{cases} \qquad (8.117)$$

where $j = 1, 2, ..., l$ and $i = 1, 2, ..., N$. As with any other kernel method, implementations of the KHA are performed in the reproducing-kernel Hilbert space (RKHS).

With kernel PCA, we have to ensure that the set of feature vectors $\{\boldsymbol{\phi}(\mathbf{x}_i)\}_{i=1}^{N}$ has a zero mean. Problem 8.15 address a procedure for catering to this requirement for batch processing. For on-line processing, which pertains to KHA, we would have to use a sliding mean to adapt to changes in the input distribution.

One other comment concerning convergence of the KHA is in order: Since the KHA builds on the GHA, we may say, in light of the convergence considerations presented in Section 8.6, that the KHA is *locally convergent*, provided that the learning-rate parameter η is small enough.

Case Study: Denoising of Multipatch Image

When we speak of a complex image, a good example to consider is that of a patch taken from the image of a natural scene. Modeling such an image becomes all the more challenging when the image has multiple patches. Indeed, the *Lena image* studied in Section 8.7 has multiple patches and therefore provides the basis of an insightful case study on image denoising.

This case study is reported in Kim et al. (2005),[7] who tested the KHA against six other denoising algorithms. Specifically, two different versions of the Lena image were constructed as follow:

(i) *White Gaussian noise* was added to the 256-by-256 Lena image, producing a signal-to-noise ratio (SNR) of 7.72 dB.

(ii) *Salt-and-pepper noise* was added to the same image, producing an SNR of 4.94 dB.

From each of these two images, 12-by-12 overlapping images patches were then sampled at a regular interval of two pixels.

The image model based on the kernel PCA, assuming a Gaussian kernel of fixed width $\sigma = 1$, was obtained by applying the KHA (with a learning-rate parameter $\eta = 0.05$) to each training sample for around 800 sweeps through the noisy Lena image data. Denoised reconstructions of the original Lena image were then obtained by retaining the first r principal components from each kernel PCA model for varying r.

For comparison purposes, the denoised kernel PCA models were tested against the median filter,[8] Matlab's Wiener filter,[9] Wavelet-based methods, and the linear PCA. Moreover, two state-of-the art methods were included in the comparative evaluations:

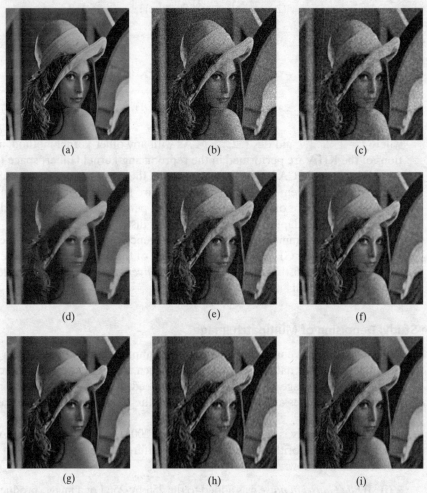

FIGURE 8.14 Denoising an image corrupted by white Gaussian noise: (a) Original image of Lena. (b) Input noisy image. (c) Median filter. (d) Matlab's wavelet denoising. (e) Matlab's Wiener filter. (f) Choi and Baraniuk's method. (g) Pižurica and Philips's method. (h) PCA ($r = 20$). (i) KHA ($r = 40$). (This figure is reproduced with the permission of Dr. K. I. Kim.)

- the Pizurica and Philips algorithm (Pizurica and Philips, 2006), which, assuming additive Gaussian noise, estimates the probability that a given coefficient in the wavelet subspace contains a noise-free component;
- the Choi and Baraniuk algorithm (Choi and Baraniuk, 1999), according to which an estimate of the original signal is obtained by projecting the noisy signal onto the *Besov space*[10] in the wavelet domain.

The results of the experiments are reproduced in Figs. 8.14 and 8.15, in light of which the following observations may be made Kim et al. (2005):

(i) The superior denoising performance produced by the Pižurica and Philips algorithm for the case of additive white Gaussian noise (AWGN) in Fig. 8.14 and the

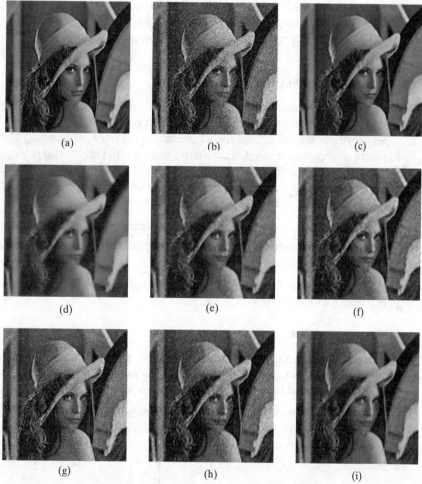

FIGURE 8.15 Denoising an image corrupted by salt and pepper type noise. (a) Original image of Lena. (b) Input noisy image. (c) Median filter. (d) Matlab's wavelet denoising. (e) Matlab's Wiener filter. (f) Choi and Baraniuk's method. (g) Pižurica and Philips's method. (h) PCA ($r = 20$). (i) KHA ($r = 20$).(This figure is reproduced with the permission of Dr. K. I. Kim.)

median filter for the case of salt-and-pepper noise in Fig. 8.15 are attributed to the use of prior knowledge of the statistics of the pertinent noise sources.

(ii) The somewhat degraded performance of these two denoising methods, when tested against the other type of noise (i.e., salt and pepper noise in the Pižurica and Philips algorithm, and the AWGN in the median filter) demonstrates the risk of relying on prior knowledge.

(iii) The KHA performs well for both types of noise, as shown in Figs. 8.14 and 8.15; this result indicates that if we have no information about the additive noise characteristics, then the KHA could be viewed as an alternative to existing methods.

Last, but by no means least, the KHA is an on-line unsupervised learning algorithm, hence offering two additional advantages:

- Being of an on-line learning kind, it is computationally efficient.
- Being unsupervised, it avoids the need for labeled examples, the collection of which (for supervised learning) can be costly in both time and effort.

8.11 SUMMARY AND DISCUSSION

An important issue in unsupervised learning is how to formulate a performance measure or cost function for the learning process to generate an *internal signal* that plays a supervisory role such that the network is enabled to predict or reconstruct its own input. In principal-components analysis, the cost function is the mean-square value of the *error vector*, defined as the difference between the input vector (assumed to be of zero mean) and its reconstructed version that is to be minimized with respect to a set of adjustable coefficients, subject to two *orthonormality constraints*:

(i) *normalization*, according to which each eigenvector has unit length;

(ii) *orthogonality*, according to which any two different eigenvectors are orthogonal to each other.

Problem 8.3 explores this approach to the derivation of PCA, as a complement to the perturbation theory presented in Section 8.4.

Dimensionality Reduction

The one notion that most aptly provides the motivation for using PCA is dimensionality reduction, the essence of which is summarized in Eqs. (8.28) and (8.29). These two equations are reproduced here for convenience of the discussion:

(i) *Representation of Data.* Given an m-dimensional data vector $\mathbf{x}$, Eq. (8.29) states that $\mathbf{x}$ can be represented by an l-dimensional vector of *principal components*, denoted by

$$\mathbf{a} = \begin{bmatrix} a_1 \\ a_2 \\ \vdots \\ a_l \end{bmatrix} = \begin{bmatrix} \mathbf{q}_1^T \\ \mathbf{q}_2^T \\ \vdots \\ \mathbf{q}_l^T \end{bmatrix} \mathbf{x}, \qquad l \leq m$$

where $\mathbf{q}_i$ is the ith eigenvector of the m-by-m correlation matrix

$$\mathbf{R} = \mathbb{E}[\mathbf{x}\mathbf{x}^T]$$

and a_i, the ith component of the vector $\mathbf{a}$, is the projection of the data vector $\mathbf{x}$ onto the ith eigenvector $\mathbf{q}_i$. If $l = m$, then the new vector $\mathbf{a}$ is a rotated version of the original data vector $\mathbf{x}$; the real difference between them is that $\mathbf{a}$ has uncorrelated components, whereas $\mathbf{x}$ does not. If $l < m$, then only a subset of the eigenvectors is retained, which makes the representation of data approximate. In the latter case, we speak of *dimensionality reduction*.

(ii) *Reconstruction of Data.*   Given the vector of principal components, $\mathbf{a}$, Eq. (8.28) states that the original data vector $\mathbf{x}$ may be reconstructed by a linear combination of the eigenvectors, as shown by the estimate

$$\hat{\mathbf{x}} = \sum_{i=1}^{l} a_i\mathbf{q}_i, \quad l \le m$$

where the principal components $a_1, a_2, ..., a_l$ are coefficients of the expansion. Here again, the reconstruction is exact if $l = m$, and approximate if $l < m$. The resulting error vector

$$\mathbf{e} = \mathbf{x} - \hat{\mathbf{x}}$$

satisfies the *principle of orthogonality*, which states that the error vector $\mathbf{e}$ is *orthogonal* to the estimate $\hat{\mathbf{x}}$. A consequence of this principle is that the estimator $\hat{\mathbf{x}}$ is optimal in the *minimum mean-square error* sense (Haykin, 2002). An optimal method for determining the reduced dimension l is the *minimum-description-length* (MDL) criterion discussed in Chapter 2.

One application of PCA, with an emphasis on the principle of dimensionality reduction, is in *denoising*. In one such application, the data vector $\mathbf{x}$ consists of a signal component $\mathbf{s}$ and additive white Gaussian noise $\mathbf{v}$; the objective is to minimize the effect of the noise in some optimal sense. Let $\mathscr{X}$ denote the m-dimensional *data space* in which the vector $\mathbf{x}$ lies. Given $\mathbf{x}$, PCA decomposes the space $\mathscr{X}$ into two orthogonal subspaces:

- The *signal subspace* S. An estimate of the signal component, denoted by $\hat{\mathbf{s}}$, lies in S; the estimate $\hat{\mathbf{s}}$ plays a role similar to that of $\hat{\mathbf{x}}$ in dimensionality reduction.
- The *noise subspace* $\mathscr{N}$. An estimate of the noise component, denoted by $\hat{\mathbf{v}}$, lies in $\mathscr{N}$; the estimate $\hat{\mathbf{v}}$ plays a role similar to that of the error $\mathbf{e}$ in dimensionality reduction.

Another application of PCA is in *data compression*. In this application, the objective is to preserve as much information about an input set of data as possible. Given a data vector $\mathbf{x}$ of dimension m, PCA achieves this objective through *subspace decomposition* of the input data, whereby the first l (less than m) principal components of the input data provides a *linear mapping*. The mapping is optimal in the sense that it permits reconstruction of the original input data in the minimum mean-square error sense. Moreover, a representation based on the first l principal components is preferable to an arbitrary subspace representation, because the principal components of the input data are naturally ordered in decreasing eigenvalue or, equivalently, decreasing variance. Accordingly, we may optimize the use of principal components analysis for data compression by employing the greatest numerical precision to encode the first principal component of the input and progressively less precision to encode the remaining $l - 1$ components, as illustrated in the image-coding case study presented in Section 8.7.

Two Views of Unsupervised Learning

1. *The Bottom-up View.* The notion of *locality* plays an essential role in the first three principles of self-organization, namely, self-amplification, competition, and cooperation, as described in Section 8.2. These three principles represent *bottom-up learning*, the motivation for which is to formulate a *model* of the learning process. Such an approach to modeling is pursued in unsupervised neural networks, exemplified by the Hebbian maximum eigenfilter and the generalized Hebbian algorithm studied in Sections 8.5 and 8.6, respectively.

   On the other hand, as pointed out previously in the introductory section, locality is not emphasized in machine learning. This lack of emphasis on self-organization, in turn, means that the bottom-up view of computational intelligence may play no role in unsupervised machine learning.

2. *The Top-down View.* Having formulated a model of an unsupervised learning problem by following the principles of self-organization, we next *tune* the adjustable parameters (i.e., weights) of the model in an analytical manner. Specifically, given a set of *unlabeled examples*, we minimize the cost function subject to constraints imposed on the learning process. The underlying theory of this second phase represents *top-down learning*, as pursued in neural networks. Iterative formulations of the maximum eigenfiltering algorithm and generalized Hebbian algorithm (GHA) are examples of this view of unsupervised learning.

   On the other hand, machine learning confines itself essentially to the top-down view of unsupervised learning. To make up for the lack of emphasis on self-organization, effective use is made of analytical tools in *statistical learning theory*. This approach to unsupervised learning is exemplified by the kernel PCA discussed in Section 8.9.

   Irrespective of how the unsupervised learning is performed, it is in the top-down learning where the intrinsic structural information contained in the input data (i.e., Principle 4 of self-organization) is actually exploited.

Kernelization of Neurobiologically Inspired Algorithms

Kernel methods, exemplified by the kernel PCA, are computationally effective in that they have a built-in capability to account for certain higher-order information contained in the input data. Typically, however, these methods suffer from the *curse of dimensionality*, which means that the computational complexity of the methods (for one reason or another) increases exponentially with linearly increasing dimensionality of the input data space.

Consider, for example, the problem of *image denoising*. Unfortunately, the computational complexity of the original form of kernel PCA severely limits its application to real-life images (e.g., faces and natural scenes). However, by *kernelizing* the generalized Hebbian algorithm (GHA), as in the kernel Hebbian algorithm (KHA) discussed in Section 8.10, we have an iterative unsupervised algorithm that estimates the kernel principal components with only *linear* computational (i.e., memory) complexity. Just as important, the denoised images, presented in Section 8.10, demonstrate a performance comparable to that of supervised-learning algorithms currently in use. It may therefore be argued that, through the kernelization of an iterative PCA algorithm, we have not only circumvented the curse-of-dimensionality problem in some measurable way, but also solved an image denoising problem, using unlabeled examples only.

The message to take away from this discussion is indeed a profound one:

> *There is much to be gained by kernelizing (rooted in statistical learning theory) neurobiologically motivated unsupervised learning algorithms.*

In the next chapter, on self-organizing maps that are motivated by neurobiological considerations, we will describe another application of kernelization that does make a difference in its own right.

NOTES AND REFERENCES

1. Principal-components analysis (PCA) is perhaps the oldest and best known technique in multivariate analysis (Jolliffe, 1986; Preisendorfer, 1988). It was first introduced by Pearson (1901), who used it in a biological context to recast linear regression analysis into a new form. It was then developed by Hotelling (1933) in work done on psychometry. It appeared once again and quite independently in the setting of probability theory, as considered by Karhunen (1947), and was subsequently generalized by Loève (1963).

2. *Synaptic Enhancement and Depression.* We may generalize the concept of a Hebbian modification by recognizing that positively correlated activity produces synaptic strengthening, and that either uncorrelated or negatively correlated activity produces synaptic weakening (Stent, 1973). Synaptic depression may also be of a noninteractive type. Specifically, the interactive condition for synaptic weakening may simply be noncoincident presynaptic or postsynaptic activity.

   We may go one step further by classifying synaptic modifications as *Hebbian*, *anti-Hebbian*, and *non-Hebbian* (Palm, 1982). According to this scheme, a Hebbian synapse increases its strength with positively correlated presynaptic and postsynaptic signals and decreases its strength when these signals are either uncorrelated or negatively correlated. Conversely, an anti-Hebbian synapse weakens positively correlated presynaptic and postsynaptic signals and strengthens negatively correlated signals. In both Hebbian and anti-Hebbian synapses, however, the modification of synaptic efficiency relies on a mechanism that is time dependent, highly local, and strongly interactive in nature. In that sense, an anti-Hebbian synapse is still Hebbian in nature, though not in function. A non-Hebbian synapse, on the other hand, does not involve a Hebbian mechanism of either kind.

3. *Covariance Hypothesis.* One way of overcoming the limitation of Hebb's hypothesis is to use the *covariance hypothesis* introduced in Sejnowski (1977a, b). In this hypothesis, the presynaptic and postsynaptic signals in Eq. (8.2) are replaced by the departure of presynaptic and postsynaptic signals from their respective average values over a certain time interval. Let $\bar{x}$ and $\bar{y}$ denote the *time-averaged values* of the presynaptic signal x_j and postsynaptic signal y_k, respectively. According to the covariance hypothesis, the adjustment applied to the synaptic weight w_{kj} is defined by

$$\Delta w_{kj} = \eta(x_j - \bar{x})(y_k - \bar{y}) \tag{A}$$

where η is the learning-rate parameter. The average values $\bar{x}$ and $\bar{y}$ constitute respective presynaptic and postsynaptic thresholds, which determine the sign of synaptic modification. In particular, the covariance hypothesis allows for the following:

- convergence to a nontrivial state, which is reached when $x_k = \bar{x}$ or $y_j = \bar{y}$;
- prediction of both synaptic *potentiation* (i.e., increase in synaptic strength) and synaptic *depression* (i.e., decrease in synaptic strength).

Figure A illustrates the difference between Hebb's hypothesis and the covariance hypothesis. In both cases, the dependence of Δw_{kj} on y_k is linear; however, the intercept with the y_k-axis in Hebb's hypothesis is at the origin, whereas in the covariance hypothesis it is at $y_k = \bar{y}$.

We make the following important observations from Eq. (A):

1. The synaptic weight w_{kj} is enhanced if there are sufficient levels of presynaptic and postsynaptic activities—that is, the conditions $x_j > \bar{x}$ and $y_k > \bar{y}$ are both satisfied.
2. The synaptic weight w_{kj} is depressed if there is either
    - a presynaptic activation (i.e., $x_j > \bar{x}$) in the absence of sufficient postsynaptic activation (i.e., $y_k < \bar{y}$), or
    - a postsynaptic activation (i.e., $y_k > \bar{y}$) in the absence of sufficient presynaptic activation (i.e., $x_j < \bar{x}$).

This behavior may be regarded as a form of temporal competition between the incoming patterns.

4. *Historical Note.* Long before the publication of Sanger's GHA in 1989, Karhunen and Oja (1982) published a conference paper that described a new algorithm, called the *stochastic gradient algorithm (SGA)*, derived for the purpose of computing the eigenvectors of PCA. It turns out that the SGA is very close in its composition to the GHA.

5. *Wavelets.* The preface to the book by Mallat (1998) states the following:

> *Wavelets are based not on a "bright new idea," but on concepts that already existed under various forms in many different fields. The formalization and emergence of this "wavelet theory" is the result of a multidisciplinary effort that brought together mathematicians, physicists and engineers, who recognized that they were independently*

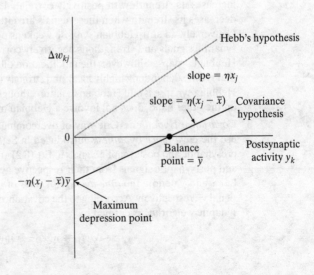

FIGURE A Illustration of Hebb's hypothesis and the covariance hypothesis.

developing similar ideas. For signal processing, this connection has created a flow of ideas that goes well beyond the construction of new bases or transforms.

Let $\psi(t)$ denote a function of zero mean, as shown by

$$\int_{-\infty}^{\infty} \psi(t)dt = 0$$

The function $\psi(t)$ represents the impulse response of a band-pass filter; such a function is called a *wavelet*. The wavelet is *dilated* with a *scale* parameter s and *shifted* in position by a *time* parameter u; we thus write

$$\psi_{u,s}(t) = \frac{1}{\sqrt{s}} \psi\left(\frac{t-u}{s}\right)$$

Given a real-valued signal $g(t)$ with Fourier transform $G(f)$, the *continuous wavelet transform* of $g(t)$ is defined by the inner product in integral form:

$$W_g(u,s) = \langle \psi_{u,s}(t), g(t) \rangle$$

$$= \int_{-\infty}^{\infty} g(t)\psi_{u,s}(t)dt$$

According to this formula, the wavelet transform *correlates* the signal $g(t)$ with $\psi_{u,s}(t)$. Equivalently, we may write

$$W_g(u,s) = \langle \Psi_{u,s}(f), G(f) \rangle$$

$$= \int_{-\infty}^{\infty} G(f)\Psi_{u,s}^*(f)df$$

where $\Psi_{u,s}(f)$ is the Fourier transform of $\psi_{u,s}(t)$ and the asterisk denotes complex conjugation. We thus see that the wavelet transform $W_g(u,s)$ depends on the values of the signal $g(t)$ and its Fourier transform $G(f)$ in the time–frequency domain, where the energy of $\psi_{u,s}(t)$ and that of its Fourier transform $\Psi_{u,s}(f)$ are concentrated.

For authoritative treatment of the wavelet transform, the reader is referred to the books by Mallat (1998) and Daubechies (1992, 1993). The introductory book by Meyer (1993) includes a historical perspective of the wavelet transform.

6. *Nonlinear PCA methods.*

These methods may be categorized into four classes:

(i) **Hebbian networks**, where the linear neurons in the generalized Hebbian algorithms, for example, are replaced with nonlinear neurons (Karhunen and Joutsensalo, 1995).

(ii) **Replicator networks** or **autoencoders**, which are built around multilayer perceptrons containing three hidden layers (Kramer, 1991):

- mapping layer;
- bottleneck layer;
- demapping layer.

Replicator networks were discussed in Chapter 4.

(iii) **Principal curves**, which are based on an iterative estimation of a curve or a surface capturing the structure of the input data (Hastie and Stuetzle, 1989). The self-organizing maps, studied in Chapter 9, may be viewed as a computational procedure for finding a discrete approximation of principal curves.

(iv) **Kernel PCA**, originated by Schölkopf et al. (1998), was studied in Section 8.8 of this chapter.

7. In Kim et al. (2005), the results of image-denoising experiments involving the KHA are also presented for the following scenarios:
   - superresolution and denoising of face (single-patch) images;
   - multipatch superresolution images of natural scenes.

8. The *median filter* is a filter (estimator) that minimizes the Bayes risk for the absolute error cost function

$$R(e(n)) = |e(n)|$$

where $e(n)$ is the *error signal*, defined as the difference between a desired response and the actual response of the filter. It turns out that the result of this minimization is the median of the posterior probability density function—hence the name of the filter.

9. *Adaptive Wiener filters.* The Wiener filter was studied in Chapter 3. In the adaptive Wiener filter, the training sample $\{\mathbf{x}_i(n), \mathbf{d}_i(n)\}_{i=1}^N$ is split into a successive sequence of windowed batches of labeled data, and the filter parameters are computed using the normal equations (or discrete form of the Wiener–Hopf equation) on a batch-by-batch basis. In effect, within each batch, the data are viewed as pseudostationary, and the statistical variations in the training sample show up in the corresponding changes in the filter parameters as the computation proceeds from one batch to the next.

10. The *Sobolev space* is the space of all functions that contains all m derivatives in the space L^m and in which the mth derivative is absolutely integrable (Vapnik, 1998). The *Besov space* refines the condition for *smoothness* by including a third parameter for $m = 1$ and $m = \infty$.

PROBLEMS

Competition and Cooperation

8.1 Explain the competitive process and cooperation among neurons at the network level.

Principal-Components Analysis: Constrained-Optimization Approach

8.2 In Section 8.4, we used perturbation theory to derive the PCA. In this problem, we address this same issue from the perspective of a constrained-optimization approach.

Let $\mathbf{x}$ denote an m-dimensional zero-mean data vector and $\mathbf{w}$ denote an adjustable parameter vector of the same dimension m. Let σ^2 denote the variance of the projection of the data vector $\mathbf{x}$ onto the parameter vector $\mathbf{w}$.

(a) Show that the Lagrangian for maximizing the variance σ^2, subject to the normalizing condition $\|\mathbf{w}\| = 1$, is defined by

$$J(\mathbf{w}) = \mathbf{w}^T \mathbf{R} \mathbf{w} - \lambda(\mathbf{w}^T \mathbf{w} - 1)$$

where $\mathbf{R}$ is the correlation matrix of the data vector $\mathbf{x}$ and λ is the Lagrangian multiplier.

(b) Using the result of part (a), show that maximization of the Lagrangian $J(\mathbf{w})$ with respect to $\mathbf{w}$ yields the defining *eigenequation*

$$\mathbf{R}\mathbf{w} = \lambda \mathbf{w}$$

Hence, show that $\sigma^2 = \mathbb{E}[(\mathbf{w}^T \mathbf{x})^2] = \lambda$. In the eigendecomposition terminology, $\mathbf{w}$ is the eigenvector and λ is the associated eigenvalue.

(c) Let the Lagrange multiplier λ_i represent the *normalizing condition* $\|\mathbf{w}_i\| = 1$ for the ith eigenvector, and let the Lagrange multiplier λ_{ij} represent the *orthogonality condition* $\mathbf{w}_i^T \mathbf{w}_j = 0$. Show that the Lagrangian now assumes the expanded form

$$J(\mathbf{w}_i) = \mathbf{w}_i^T \mathbf{R} \mathbf{w}_i - \lambda_{ii}(\mathbf{w}_i^T \mathbf{w} - 1) - \sum_{j=1}^{i-1} \lambda_{ij} \mathbf{w}_i^T \mathbf{w}_j, \qquad i = 1, 2, ..., m$$

Hence, show that the maximization of $J(\mathbf{w}_i)$ yields a set of m equations for which the optimal solution is the eigenvalue λ_i associated with the eigenvector $\mathbf{w}_i$.

8.3 Let the estimator of an m-dimensional zero-mean data vector $\mathbf{x}$ be defined by the expansion

$$\hat{\mathbf{x}}_l = \sum_{i=1}^{l} a_i \mathbf{q}_i, \qquad l \leq m$$

where $\mathbf{q}_i$ is the ith eigenvector of the correlation matrix

$$\mathbf{R} = \mathbb{E}[\mathbf{x}\mathbf{x}^T]$$

and $a_1, a_2, ..., a_l$ are the coefficients of the expansion, subject to the condition

$$\mathbf{q}_i^T \mathbf{q}_j = \begin{cases} 1 & \text{for } j = i \\ 0 & \text{otherwise} \end{cases}$$

Show that minimization of the mean-square error

$$J(\hat{\mathbf{x}}_l) = \mathbb{E}[\|\mathbf{x} - \hat{\mathbf{x}}_l\|^2]$$

with respect to the adjustable coefficients $a_1, a_2, ..., a_l$ yields the defining formula

$$a_i = \mathbf{q}_i^T \mathbf{x}, \quad i = 1, 2, ..., l$$

as the ith principal component—that is, the projection of the data vector $\mathbf{x}$ onto the eigenvector $\mathbf{q}_i$.

8.4 Following on the constrained-optimization problem considered in Problem 8.2, consider the Lagrangian

$$J(\mathbf{w}) = (\mathbf{w}^T \mathbf{x})^2 - \lambda(\mathbf{w}^T \mathbf{w} - 1)$$

where $(\mathbf{w}^T \mathbf{x})^2$ denotes the instantaneous value of the variance of a zero-mean data vector $\mathbf{x}$ projected onto the weight vector $\mathbf{w}$.

(a) Evaluating the gradient of the Lagrangian $J(\mathbf{w})$ with respect to the adjustable weight vector $\mathbf{w}$, show that

$$g(\mathbf{w}) = \frac{\partial J(\mathbf{w})}{\partial \mathbf{w}}$$
$$= 2(\mathbf{w}^T \mathbf{x})\mathbf{x} - 2\lambda \mathbf{w}$$

(b) With the stochastic gradient ascent in mind for on-line learning, we may express the weight-update formula as

$$\hat{\mathbf{w}}(n + 1) = \hat{\mathbf{w}}(n) + \frac{1}{2}\eta g(\hat{\mathbf{w}}(n))$$

where η is the learning-rate parameter. Hence, derive the iterative equation

$$\hat{\mathbf{w}}(n + 1) = \hat{\mathbf{w}}(n) + \eta[(\mathbf{x}(n)\mathbf{x}^T(n))\hat{\mathbf{w}}(n) - \hat{\mathbf{w}}^T(n)(\mathbf{x}(n)\mathbf{x}^T(n))\hat{\mathbf{w}}(n)\hat{\mathbf{w}}(n)]$$

which is a rewrite of Eq. (8.47) defining the evolution of the maximum eigenfilter across discrete time n, with $\hat{\mathbf{w}}(n)$ written in place of $\mathbf{w}(n)$.

Hebbian-Based Maximum Eigenfilter

8.5   For the matched filter considered in Example 2, the eigenvalue λ_1 and associated eigenvector $\mathbf{q}_1$ are respectively defined by

$$\lambda_1 = 1 + \sigma^2$$

and

$$\mathbf{q}_1 = s$$

Show that these parameters satisfy the basic relation

$$\mathbf{R}\mathbf{q}_1 = \lambda_1 \mathbf{q}_1$$

where $\mathbf{R}$ is the correlation matrix of the input vector.

8.6   Eq. (8.37) shows that a synaptic weight w_i varies with time, growing strong when the presynaptic signal x_i and postsynaptic signal y coincide with each other. This learning rule in basic form leads to unlimited growth of the synaptic weight w_i, which is unacceptable on physical grounds. How can you overcome this problem?

8.7   *Minor-components analysis* (MCA) is the opposite of principal-components analysis. In MCA, we seek to find those directions that *minimize* the projection variance. The directions so found are the eigenvectors corresponding to the smallest (minimum) eigenvalues of the correlation matrix $\mathbf{R}$ of the input random vector $\mathbf{X}(n)$.

In this problem, we explore how to modify the single neuron of Section 8.4 so as to find the minor component of $\mathbf{R}$. In particular, we make a change of sign in the learning rule of Eq. (8.40), obtaining the following (Xu et al., 1992):

$$w_i(n + 1) = w_i(n) - \eta y(n)(x_i(n) - y(n)w_i(n))$$

Show that if the smallest eigenvalue of the correlation matrix $\mathbf{R}$ is λ_m with multiplicity 1, then

$$\lim_{n\to\infty} \mathbf{w}(n) = \eta \mathbf{q}_m$$

where $\mathbf{w}(n)$ is the weight vector whose ith component is $w_i(n)$ and $\mathbf{q}_m$ is the eigenvector associated with λ_m.

Hebbian-Based Principal-Components Analysis

8.8   Construct a signal-flow graph to represent the vector-valued Eqs. (8.87) and (8.88).

8.9   The ordinary differential equation approach to convergence analysis described in Section 8.5 does not apply directly to the generalized Hebbian-learning algorithm (GHA). However, by expressing the synaptic-weight matrix $\mathbf{W}(n)$ in Eq. (8.91) as a vector made up of the individual columns of $\mathbf{W}(n)$, we may build on the asymptotic stability theory of the maximum eigenfilter. Hence, in light of what has been said here, explore the convergence behavior of the generalized Hebbian-learning algorithm.

8.10   In this problem, we explore the use of the generalized Hebbian-learning algorithm to study two-dimensional receptive fields produced by a random input (Sanger, 1990). The random input consists of a two-dimensional field of independent Gaussian noise with zero mean and unit variance, which is convolved with a Gaussian mask (filter) and then multiplied by a Gaussian window. The Gaussian mask has a standard deviation of 2 pixels, and the Gaussian window has a standard deviation of 8 pixels. The resulting random input $x(r, s)$ at position (r, s) may thus be written as

$$x(r, s) = m(r, s)[g(r, s) * w(r, s)]$$

where $w(r, s)$ is the field of independent and identically distributed Gaussian noise, $g(r, s)$ is the Gaussian mask, and $m(r, s)$ is the Gaussian window function. The circular convolution of $g(r, s)$ and $w(r, s)$ is defined by

$$g(r, s) * w(r, s) = \sum_{p=0}^{N-1} \sum_{q=0}^{N-1} g(p, q)w(r - p, s - q)$$

where $g(r, s)$ and $w(r, s)$ are both assumed to be periodic.

Use 2,000 samples of the random input $x(r, s)$ to train a single-layer feedforward network by means of the generalized Hebbian-learning algorithm. The network has 4,096 inputs arranged as a 64×64 grid of pixels and 16 outputs. The resulting synaptic weights of the trained network are represented as 64×64 arrays of numbers. Perform the computations described herein and display the 16 arrays of synaptic weights as two-dimensional masks. Comment on your results.

8.11 In situations where only the *principal subspace* (i.e., the space of the principal eigenvectors) is required, we may use the symmetric algorithm, which is defined by

$$\hat{\mathbf{w}}_j(n + 1) = \hat{\mathbf{w}}_j(n) + \eta y_j[\mathbf{x}(n) - \hat{\mathbf{x}}_j(n)]$$

$$\hat{\mathbf{x}}(n) = \sum_{j=1}^{t} \hat{\mathbf{w}}_j(n)\mathbf{y}_j(n)$$

(a) Discuss the similarity and difference between the symmetric algorithm and the GHA.
(b) The principal subspace may be viewed as a generalization of Oja's rule, defined in Eq. (8.46). Explain the rationale for this generalization.

Feature Extraction: Preamble for Problems 8.12 and 8.13

In the presentation of a data set made up of an aggregate of several clusters, we may say that, for the clusters to be individually visible, the separation between them has to be larger than the internal scatter of the clusters. If it happens that there are only a few clusters in the data set, then the leading principal axes found by PCA are to pick projections of the clusters with good separation, thereby providing an effective basis for *feature extraction*.

8.12 In Section 4.19 of Chapter 4, we described *structural risk minimization* as a method of systematically realizing the best generalization performance by matching the capacity of a learning machine to the available size of the training sample.

Given the principal-components analyzer as a *preprocessor* aimed at reducing the dimension of the input data space, discuss how such a processor can embed structure into the learning process by ranking a family of pattern classifiers.

8.13 Another application of the principal-components analyzer as a preprocessor is in the supervised training of a multilayer perceptron using the back-propagation algorithm.

The aim in this application is to speed up the convergence of the learning process by decorrelating the input data. Discuss how this aim is realized.

Adaptive Principal-Components Extraction

8.14 The generalized Hebbian-learning algorithm (GHA) relies on the exclusive use of feedforward connections for principal-components analysis. In this problem, we address another algorithm called the *adaptive principal-components extraction* (APEX) (Kung and Diamantaras, 1990; Diamantaras and Kung, 1996).

The APEX algorithm uses both feedforward and feedback connections, as depicted in Fig. P8.14. The input vector $\mathbf{x}$ is m dimensional, and each neuron in the network is linear.

FIGURE P8.14   Network with feedforward and lateral connections for deriving the APEX algorithm.

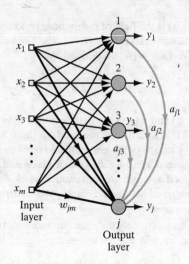

There are two kinds of synaptic connections in the network:

(i) *Feedforward connections* from the input nodes to each of the neurons $1, 2, ..., j$, with $j < m$. These connections are represented by the feedforward weight vector

$$\mathbf{w}_j(n) = [w_{j1}(n), w_{j2}(n), ..., w_{jm}(n)]^T$$

where n denotes discrete time.

(ii) *Lateral connections* from the individual neural outputs $1, 2, ..., j - 1$ to neuron j; these connections are represented by the feedback weight vector

$$\mathbf{a}_j(n) = [a_{j1}(n), a_{j2}(n), ..., a_{j, j-1}(n)]^T$$

The feedforward synaptic connections are *Hebbian*, but the feedback synaptic connections are *anti-Hebbian* and therefore *inhibitory*. The output of neuron j is given by

$$y_j(n) = \mathbf{w}_j^T(n)\mathbf{x}(n) + \mathbf{a}_j^T(n)\mathbf{y}_{j-1}(n)$$

For the analysis to follow, assume that all the neurons in the network have already converged to their respective stable conditions, given as

$$\mathbf{w}_k(0) = \mathbf{q}_k, \qquad k = 1, 2, ..., j - 1$$
$$\mathbf{a}_k(0) = \mathbf{0}, \qquad k = 1, 2, ..., j - 1$$

where $\mathbf{q}_k$ is the eigenvector associated with the kth eigenvalue of the correlation matrix

$$\mathbf{R} = \mathbb{E}[\mathbf{x}(n)\mathbf{x}^T(n)] \text{ at time step } n = 0.$$

(a) Building on Eq. (8.40), write the update equations for $\mathbf{w}_j(n)$ and $\mathbf{a}_j(n)$ pertaining to neuron j.

(b) Assume that the eigenvalues of the correlation matrix $\mathbf{R}$ are arranged in decreasing order, with λ_1 being the largest. Let $\mathbf{q}_k$ be the eigenvector associated with the eigenvalue λ_k. To express the time-varying behavior of the feedforward weight vector $\mathbf{w}_j(n)$, you may use the expansion

$$\mathbf{w}_j(n) = \sum_{k=1}^{m} \theta_{jk}(n)\mathbf{q}_k$$

where $\theta_{jk}(n)$ is a time-varying coefficient. Hence, show that

(i) $\sum_{k=1}^{m} \theta_{jk}(n+1)\mathbf{q}_k = \sum_{k=1}^{m} \{1 + \eta[\lambda_k - \sigma_j^2(n)]\}\theta_{jk}(n)\mathbf{q}_k + \eta \sum_{k=1}^{j-1} \lambda_k a_{jk}(n)\mathbf{q}_k$

where η is the learning-rate parameter, $a_{jk}(n)$ is the kth element of the feedback weight vector $\mathbf{a}_j$, and $\sigma_j^2(n) = \mathbb{E}[y_j^2(n)]$ is the average output power of neuron j.

(ii) $\mathbf{a}_j(n+1) = -\eta \lambda_k \theta_{jk}(n)\mathbf{1}_k + \{1 - \eta[\lambda_k + \sigma_j^2(n)]\}\mathbf{a}_j(n)$

where $\mathbf{1}_k$ is a vector whose j elements are all zero, except for the kth element, which is equal to 1.

(c) To proceed further, there are two cases to be considered:

Case I: $1 \le k \le j - 1$

For this case, show that

$$\begin{bmatrix} \theta_{jk}(n+1) \\ a_{jk}(n+1) \end{bmatrix} = \begin{bmatrix} 1 + \eta(\lambda_k - \sigma_j^2(n)) & \eta\lambda_k \\ -\eta\lambda_k & 1 - \eta(\lambda_k + \sigma_j^2(n)) \end{bmatrix} \begin{bmatrix} \theta_{jk}(n) \\ a_{jk}(n) \end{bmatrix}$$

This two-by-two matrix has the double eigenvalue

$$\rho_{jk} = [1 - \eta\sigma_j^2(n)]^2$$

Given that $\rho_{jk} < 1$, show that $\theta_{jk}(n)$ and $a_{jk}(n)$ approach zero asymptotically for increasing n. Explain the rationale for this asymptotic behavior.

Case II: $j \le k \le m$

For this second case, the feedback weights $a_{jk}(n)$ have no influence on the modes of the network; thus,

$$a_{jk}(n) = 0 \quad \text{for } j \le k \le m$$

Hence, for every principal mode $k \ge j$, show that

$$\theta_{jk}(n+1) = \{1 + \eta[\lambda_k - \sigma_j^2(n)]\}\theta_{jk}(n)$$

and $\theta_{jk}(n)$ will therefore asymptotically converge to zero for increasing n.

Expressing the average output power of neuron j as

$$\sigma_j^2(n) = \sum_{k=j}^{m} \lambda_k \theta_{jk}^2(n)$$

finally show that

$$\lim_{n \to \infty} \sigma_j^2(n) = \lambda_j$$

and

$$\lim_{n \to \infty} \mathbf{w}_j(n) = \mathbf{q}_j$$

Kernel PCA

8.15 Let $\bar{k}_{ij}$ denote the centered counterpart of the ij-th element k_{ij} of the Gram **K**. Derive the following formula (Schölkopf, 1997):

$$\bar{k}_{ij} = k_{ij} - \frac{1}{N}\sum_{m=1}^{N}\boldsymbol{\phi}^T(\mathbf{x}_m)\boldsymbol{\phi}(\mathbf{x}_j) - \frac{1}{N}\sum_{n=1}^{N}\boldsymbol{\phi}^T(\mathbf{x}_i)\boldsymbol{\phi}(\mathbf{x}_n)$$

$$+ \frac{1}{N^2}\sum_{m=1}^{N}\sum_{n=1}^{N}\boldsymbol{\phi}^T(\mathbf{x}_m)\boldsymbol{\phi}(\mathbf{x}_n)$$

Suggest a compact representation of this relation in matrix form.

8.16 The computational complexity of kernel PCA can become unmanageable when it is required to model a natural image. Justify the rationale of this statement. Is there any algorithm that can overcome this difficult?

Computer Experiments

8.17 This problem continues with the computer experiment on image coding presented in Section 8.7. Specifically, there are two issues of interest:

(a) Plot the learning curve of the GHA, where the algorithm is trained on the Lena image (i.e., the mean-square error is plotted versus the number of epochs used for training).

(b) Correspondingly, plot the learning curve of the algorithm on the peppers image.

Hence, determine the number of epochs for the algorithm to converge in both cases (a) and (b).

8.18 In this experiment, we revisit Example 3 on kernel PCA. The requirement is to compute the kernel PCA components for the two-dimensional data described by the formula

$$x_2 = x_1^2 + v$$

where v is an additive Gaussian noise of zero mean and variance 0.04. However, this time the requirement is to perform the computation with the kernel Hebbian algorithm. Compare the results of the experiment with those described in Example 3.

C H A P T E R   9

Self-Organizing Maps

ORGANIZATION OF THE CHAPTER

This chapter studies the generation of "topographic maps" using principles of self-organization. Treatment of the subject is organized as follows:

1. The introductory section, Section 9.1, motivates interest in the use of self-organizing maps.

2. Section 9.2 describes two basic feature models, both of which, in their own ways, are motivated by neurobiological considerations.

3. Sections 9.3 and 9.4 deal with the highly popular and widely used self-organizing (feature) map (SOM) and its properties. Section 9.5 presents computer experiments, highlighting distinguishing features of the SOM. Section 9.6 illustrates application of the SOM for constructing contextual maps.

4. Section 9.7 discusses hierarchical vector quantization, whose implementation is simplified through the use of the self-organizing map.

5. Section 9.8 describes the kernel-based self-organizing map (kernal SOM), followed by a computer experiment in Section 9.9 illustrating the improved topographic mapping capability of this new algorithm. Section 9.10 discusses the relationship between kernel SOM and Kullback-Leibler divergence.

Section 9.10 concludes the chapter with a summary and discussion of the material covered in the chapter.

9.1 INTRODUCTION

In this chapter, we continue our study of self-organizing systems by considering a special class of artificial neural networks known as self-organizing maps. These networks are based on *competitive learning*; the output neurons of the network compete among themselves to be activated or fired, with the result that only *one* output neuron, or one neuron per group, is on at any one time. An output neuron that wins the competition is called a *winner-takes-all neuron*, or simply a *winning neuron*.[1] One way of inducing a winner-takes-all competition among the output neurons is to use lateral inhibitory connections (i.e., negative feedback paths) between them; such an idea was originally proposed by Rosenblatt (1958).

In a *self-organizing map*, the neurons are placed at the nodes of a *lattice* that is usually one or two dimensional. Higher-dimensional maps are also possible but not as common. The neurons become *selectively tuned* to various input patterns (stimuli) or classes of input patterns in the course of a competitive-learning process. The locations of the neurons so tuned (i.e., the winning neurons) become ordered with respect to each other in such a way that a meaningful coordinate system for different input *features* is created over the lattice. A self-organizing map is therefore characterized by the formation of a *topographic map* of the input patterns, in which the *spatial locations (i.e., coordinates) of the neurons in the lattice are indicative of intrinsic statistical features contained in the input patterns*—hence, the name "self-organizing map."

As a neural model, the self-organizing map provides a bridge between two levels of adaptation:

- adaptation rules formulated at the microscopic level of a single neuron;
- formation of experientially better and physically accessible patterns of feature selectivity at the microscopic level of neural layers.

The self-organizing map is inherently *nonlinear*.

The development of self-organizing maps as a neural model is motivated by a distinct feature of the human brain:

> The brain is organized in many places in such a way that different sensory inputs are represented by topologically ordered computational maps.

In particular, sensory inputs such as tactile (Kaas et al., 1983), visual (Hubel and Wiesel, 1962, 1977), and acoustic (Suga, 1985) inputs are mapped onto different areas of the cerebral cortex in a topologically ordered manner. Thus, the computational map constitutes a basic building block in the information-processing infrastructure of the nervous system. A computational map is defined by an array of neurons representing slightly differently tuned processors or filters, which operate on the sensory information-bearing signals in parallel. Consequently, the neurons transform input signals into a *place-coded probability distribution* that represents the computed values of parameters by sites of maximum relative activity within the map (Knudsen et al., 1987). The information so derived is of such a form that it can be readily accessed by higher-order processors using relatively simple connection schemes.

9.2 TWO BASIC FEATURE-MAPPING MODELS

Anyone who examines a human brain cannot help but be impressed by the extent to which the brain is dominated by the cerebral cortex, which obscures the other parts. In terms of sheer complexity, the cerebral cortex probably exceeds any other known structure in the universe (Hubel and Wiesel, 1977). What is equally impressive is the way in which different sensory inputs (motor, somatosensory, visual, auditory, etc.) are *mapped* onto corresponding areas of the cerebral cortex in an *orderly* fashion; to appreciate this point, see the cyto-architectural maps of the cerebral cortex in Fig. 4 of the introductory chapter. Computational maps offer four properties (Knudsen et al., 1987; Durbin and Michison, 1990):

1. *In each map, neurons act in parallel and process pieces of information that are similar in nature, but originate from different regions in the sensory input space.*
2. *At each stage of representation, each incoming piece of information is kept in its proper context.*

3. *Neurons dealing with closely related pieces of information are close together so that they can interact via short synaptic connections.*

4. *Contextual maps can be understood in terms of decision-reducing mappings from higher-dimensional parameter spaces onto the cortical surface.*

Our interest lies in building artificial topographic maps that learn through self-organization in a neurobiologically inspired manner. In this context, the one important point that emerges from this very brief discussion of computational maps of the brain is the *principle of topographic map formation*, stated as follows (Kohonen, 1990):

> *The spatial location of an output neuron in a topographic map corresponds to a particular domain or feature of data drawn from the input space.*

This principle has provided the neurobiological motivation for two different *feature-mapping models*[2], described herein.

Figure 9.1 displays the layout of the two models. In both cases, the output neurons are arranged in a two-dimensional lattice. This kind of topology ensures that each neuron has a set of neighbors. The models differ from each other in the manner in which the input patterns are specified.

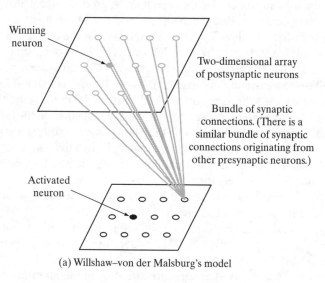

Winning neuron

Two-dimensional array of postsynaptic neurons

Bundle of synaptic connections. (There is a similar bundle of synaptic connections originating from other presynaptic neurons.)

Activated neuron

(a) Willshaw–von der Malsburg's model

FIGURE 9.1   Two self-organized feature maps.

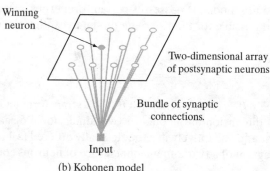

Winning neuron

Two-dimensional array of postsynaptic neurons

Bundle of synaptic connections.

Input

(b) Kohonen model

The model in Fig. 9.1a was originally proposed by Willshaw and von der Malsburg (1976) on biological grounds to explain the problem of retinotopic mapping from the retina to the visual cortex (in higher vertebrates). Specifically, there are two separate two-dimensional lattices of neurons connected together, one projecting onto the other. One lattice represents presynaptic (input) neurons, and the other lattice represents postsynaptic (output) neurons. The postsynaptic lattice uses a *short-range excitatory mechanism* as well as a *long-range inhibitory mechanism*. These two mechanisms are *local* in nature and critically important for self-organization. The two lattices are interconnected by modifiable synapses of a Hebbian type. Strictly speaking, therefore, the postsynaptic neurons are not winner-takes-all neurons; rather, a threshold is used to ensure that only a few postsynaptic neurons will fire at any one time. Moreover, to prevent a steady buildup in the synaptic weights that may lead to network instability, the total weight associated with each postsynaptic neuron is limited by an upper-boundary condition.[3] Thus, for each neuron some synaptic weights increase, while others decrease. The basic idea of the *Willshaw–von der Malsburg model* is for the geometric proximity of presynaptic neurons to be coded in the form of correlations in their electrical activity, and to use these correlations in the postsynaptic lattice so as to connect neighboring presynaptic neurons to neighboring postsynaptic neurons. A topologically ordered mapping is thereby produced through a process of self-organization. Note, however, that the Willshaw–von der Malsburg model is specialized to mappings for which the input dimension is the same as the output dimension.

The second model of Fig. 9.1b, introduced by Kohonen (1982), is not meant to explain neurobiological details. Rather, the model captures the essential features of computational maps in the brain and yet remains computationally tractable. It appears that the *Kohonen model* is more general than the Willshaw–von der Malsburg model in the sense that it is capable of performing data compression (i.e., dimensionality reduction on the input).

In reality, the Kohonen model belongs to the class of *vector-coding algorithms*. The model provides a topological mapping that optimally places a fixed number of vectors (i.e., code words) into a higher-dimensional input space, thereby facilitating data compression. The Kohonen model may therefore be derived in two ways. First, we may use basic ideas of self-organization, motivated by neurobiological considerations, to derive the model, which is the traditional approach (Kohonen, 1982, 1990, 1997). Alternatively, we may use a vector quantization approach that uses a model involving an encoder and a decoder; this way is motivated by considerations of communication theory (Luttrell, 1989b, 1991a). In this chapter, we consider both approaches.

The Kohonen model has received much more attention in the literature than the Willshaw–von der Malsburg model. It possesses certain properties, discussed later in the chapter, that make it possible for the Kohonen model to capture the essential features of cortical maps.

9.3 SELF-ORGANIZING MAP

The principal goal of the *self-organizing map* (SOM) is to transform an incoming signal pattern of arbitrary dimension into a one- or two-dimensional discrete map, and to perform this transformation adaptively in a topologically ordered fashion. Figure 9.2 shows the schematic diagram of a two-dimensional lattice of neurons commonly used

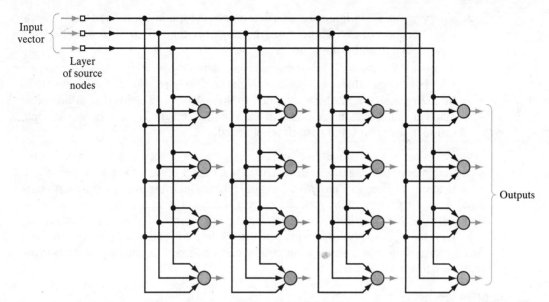

FIGURE 9.2   Two-dimensional lattice of neurons, illustrated for a three-dimensional input and four-by-four dimensional output (all shown in red).

as a discrete map. Each neuron in the lattice is fully connected to all the source nodes in the input layer. This network represents a feedforward structure with a single computational layer consisting of neurons arranged in rows and columns. A one-dimensional lattice is a special case of the configuration depicted in Fig. 9.2: in this special case, the computational layer consists simply of a single column or row of neurons.

Each input pattern presented to the network typically consists of a localized region or "spot" of activity against a quiet background. The location and nature of such a spot usually varies from one realization of the input pattern to another. All the neurons in the network should therefore be exposed to a sufficient number of different realizations of the input pattern in order to ensure that the self-organization process has a chance to develop properly.

The algorithm responsible for the formation of the self-organizing map proceeds first by *initializing* the synaptic weights in the network. This can be done by assigning them *small values picked from a random-number generator*; in so doing, no prior order is imposed on the feature map. Once the network has been properly initialized, there are three essential processes involved in the formation of the self-organizing map, as summarized here:

1. *Competition.* For each input pattern, the neurons in the network compute their respective values of a discriminant function. This discriminant function provides the basis for competition among the neurons. The particular neuron with the largest value of discriminant function is declared winner of the competition.

2. *Cooperation.* The winning neuron determines the spatial location of a topological neighborhood of excited neurons, thereby providing the basis for cooperation among such neighboring neurons.

3. *Synaptic Adaptation.* This last mechanism enables the excited neurons to increase their individual values of the discriminant function in relation to the input pattern through suitable adjustments applied to their synaptic weights. The adjustments made are such that the response of the winning neuron to the subsequent application of a similar input pattern is enhanced.

The processes of competition and cooperation are in accordance with two of the four principles of self-organization described in Chapter 8. As for the principle of self-amplification, it comes in a modified form of Hebbian learning in the adaptive process. As explained in Chapter 8, the presence of redundancy in the input data, though not mentioned explicitly in describing the SOM algorithm, is essential for learning, since it provides knowledge about the underlying structure of the input activation patterns. Detailed descriptions of the processes of competition, cooperation, and synaptic adaptation are presented in what follows.

Competitive Process

Let m denote the dimension of the input (data) space. Let an input pattern (vector) selected at random from the input space be denoted by

$$\mathbf{x} = [x_1, x_2, ..., x_m]^T \tag{9.1}$$

The synaptic-weight vector of each neuron in the network has the same dimension as the input space. Let the synaptic-weight vector of neuron j be denoted by

$$\mathbf{w}_j = [w_{j1}, w_{j2}, ..., w_{jm}]^T, \qquad j = 1, 2, ..., l \tag{9.2}$$

where l is the total number of neurons in the network. To find the best match of the input vector $\mathbf{x}$ with the synaptic-weight vectors $\mathbf{w}_j$, we compare the inner products $\mathbf{w}_j^T \mathbf{x}$ for $j = 1, 2, ..., l$ and select the largest. This method assumes that the same threshold is applied to all the neurons; the threshold is the negative of bias. Thus, by selecting the neuron with the largest inner product $\mathbf{w}_j^T \mathbf{x}$, in effect we will have determined the location where the topological neighborhood of excited neurons is to be centered.

From the introductory chapter, we recall that the best-matching criterion, based on maximizing the inner product $\mathbf{w}_j^T \mathbf{x}$, is mathematically equivalent to minimizing the Euclidean distance between the vectors $\mathbf{x}$ and $\mathbf{w}_j$, provided that $\mathbf{w}_j$ has unit length for all j. If we use the index $i(\mathbf{x})$ to identify the neuron that best matches the input vector $\mathbf{x}$, we may then determine $i(\mathbf{x})$ by applying the following condition, which sums up the essence of the competition process among the neurons.[4]

$$i(\mathbf{x}) = \arg \min_j \|\mathbf{x} - \mathbf{w}_j\|, \qquad j \in \mathcal{A} \tag{9.3}$$

where $\mathcal{A}$ denotes the lattice of neurons. According to Eq. (9.3), $i(\mathbf{x})$ is the subject of attention because we want to find the identity of neuron i. The particular neuron i that satisfies this condition is called the *best-matching*, or *winning, neuron* for the input vector $\mathbf{x}$. Equation (9.3) leads to the following observation:

A continuous input space of activation patterns is mapped onto a discrete output space of neurons by a process of competition among the neurons in the network.

Depending on the application of interest, the response of the network could be either the index of the winning neuron (i.e., its position in the lattice) or the synaptic-weight vector that is closest to the input vector in a Euclidean sense.

Cooperative Process

The winning neuron locates the center of a topological neighborhood of cooperating neurons. The key question is: How do we define a topological neighborhood that is neurobiologically correct?

To answer this basic question, remember that there is neurobiological evidence for *lateral interaction* among a set of excited neurons in the human brain. In particular, a neuron that is firing tends to excite the neurons in its immediate neighborhood *more* than those farther away from it, which is intuitively satisfying. This observation leads us to introduce a topological neighborhood around the winning neuron i and make it decay smoothly with lateral distance (Lo et al., 1991, 1993; Ritter et al., 1992).[5] To be specific, let $h_{j,i}$ denote the *topological neighborhood* centered on winning neuron i and encompassing a set of excited (cooperating) neurons, a typical one of which is denoted by j. Let $d_{j,i}$ denote the *lateral* distance between the winning neuron i and the excited neuron j. Then, we may assume that the topological neighborhood $h_{j,i}$ is a unimodal function of the lateral distance $d_{j,i}$, such that it satisfies two distinct requirements:

1. The topological neighborhood $h_{j,i}$ is symmetric about the maximum point defined by $d_{j,i} = 0$; in other words, it attains its maximum value at the winning neuron i for which the distance $d_{j,i}$ is zero.

2. The amplitude of the topological neighborhood $h_{j,i}$ decreases monotonically with increasing lateral distance $d_{j,i}$, decaying to zero for $d_{j,i} \to \infty$; this is a necessary condition for convergence.

A good choice of $h_{j,i}$ that satisfies these requirements is the *Gaussian* function[6]

$$h_{j,i(\mathbf{x})} = \exp\left(-\frac{d_{j,i}^2}{2\sigma^2}\right), \qquad j \in \mathcal{A} \qquad (9.4)$$

which is *translation invariant* (i.e., independent of the location of winning neuron i). The parameter σ is the "effective width" of the topological neighborhood, as illustrated in Fig. 9.3; it measures the degree to which excited neurons in the vicinity of the winning neuron participate in the learning process. In a qualitative sense, the Gaussian topological neighborhood of Eq. (9.4) is more biologically appropriate than a rectangular one that was used in the past. The use of a Gaussian topological neighborhood also makes the SOM algorithm converge more quickly than a rectangular topological neighborhood would (Lo et al., 1991, 1993; Erwin et al., 1992a).

For cooperation among neighboring neurons to hold, it is necessary that topological neighborhood $h_{j,i}$ be dependent on the lateral distance $d_{j,i}$ between the winning neuron i and excited neuron j in the output space, rather than on some distance measure in the original input space. This is precisely what we have in Eq. (9.4). In the case

FIGURE 9.3 Gaussian
neighborhood function.

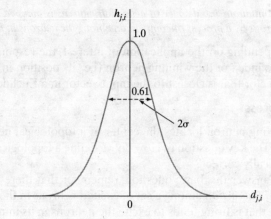

of a one-dimensional lattice, $d_{j,i}$ is an integer equal to $|j - i|$. On the other hand, in the case of a two-dimensional lattice, it is defined by

$$d_{j,i}^2 = \|\mathbf{r}_j - \mathbf{r}_i\|^2 \tag{9.5}$$

where the discrete vector $\mathbf{r}_j$ defines the position of excited neuron j and $\mathbf{r}_i$ defines the position of the winning neuron i, both of which are measured in the discrete output space.

Another unique feature of the SOM algorithm is that the size of the topological neighborhood is permitted to shrink with time. This requirement is satisfied by making the width σ of the topological neighborhood function $h_{j,i}$ decrease with time. A popular choice for the dependence of σ on discrete time n is the *exponential decay* described by

$$\sigma(n) = \sigma_0 \exp\left(-\frac{n}{\tau_1}\right) \qquad n = 0, 1, 2, ..., \tag{9.6}$$

where σ_0 is the value of σ at the initiation of the SOM algorithm and τ_1 is a *time constant* to be chosen by the designer (Ritter et al., 1992; Obermayer et al., 1991). Correspondingly, the topological *neighborhood function* assumes a time-varying form of its own, as shown by

$$h_{j,i(\mathbf{x})}(n) = \exp\left(-\frac{d_{j,i}^2}{2\sigma^2(n)}\right), \qquad n = 0, 1, 2, ..., \tag{9.7}$$

where $\sigma(n)$ is defined by Eq. (9.6). Thus, as discrete time n (i.e., the number of iterations) increases, the width $\sigma(n)$ decreases at an exponential rate, and the topological neighborhood shrinks in a corresponding manner. It is important to note, however, that the neighborhood function will eventually still have a unity value for the winning neuron i, since the distance $d_{j,i}$ for neuron j is calculated in the lattice space and compared to the winning neuron i.

There is another useful way of viewing the variation of the neighborhood function $h_{j,i(\mathbf{x})}(n)$ around a winning neuron $i(\mathbf{x})$ across time n. The purpose of a wide $h_{j,i(\mathbf{x})}(n)$ is essentially to *correlate* the directions of the weight updates of a large number of excited neurons in the lattice. As the width of $h_{j,i(\mathbf{x})}(n)$ is decreased, so is the number of neurons whose update directions are correlated. This phenomenon becomes particularly obvious when the training of a self-organizing map is played out on a computer screen. It is rather wasteful of computer resources to move a large number of degrees of freedom around a winning neuron in a correlated fashion, as in the usual implementation of the SOM algorithm. Instead, it is much better to use a *renormalized* SOM form of training, according to which we work with a much smaller number of *normalized degrees of freedom*. This operation is easily performed in discrete form by having a neighborhood function $h_{j,i(\mathbf{x})}(n)$ of *constant* width, but gradually *increasing* the total number of neurons that lie inside the neighborhood function. The new neurons are inserted halfway between the old ones, and the smoothness properties of the SOM algorithm guarantee that the new ones join the synaptic adaptation in a graceful manner (Luttrell, 1989a). A summary of the renormalized SOM algorithm is presented in Problem 9.15.

Adaptive Process

Now we come to the last process, the synaptic adaptive process, in the self-organized formation of a feature map. For the network to be self-organizing, the synaptic-weight vector $\mathbf{w}_j$ of neuron j in the network is required to change in relation to the input vector $\mathbf{x}$. The question is how to make the change. In Hebb's postulate of learning, a synaptic weight is increased with a simultaneous occurrence of presynaptic and postsynaptic activities. The use of such a rule is well suited for associative learning (e.g., principal-components analysis). For the type of unsupervised learning being considered here, however, the Hebbian hypothesis in its basic form is unsatisfactory for the following reason: Changes in connectivities occur in one direction only, finally driving all the synaptic weights into saturation. To overcome this problem, we modify the Hebbian hypothesis by including the *forgetting term* $g(y_j)\mathbf{w}_j$, where $\mathbf{w}_j$ is the synaptic-weight vector of neuron j and $g(y_j)$ is some positive scalar function of the response y_j. The only requirement imposed on the function $g(y_j)$ is that the constant term in the Taylor series expansion of $g(y_j)$ be zero, so that we may write

$$g(y_j) = 0 \quad \text{for } y_j = 0 \tag{9.8}$$

The significance of this requirement will become apparent momentarily. Given such a function, we may then express the change to the weight vector of neuron j in the lattice as:

$$\Delta\mathbf{w}_j = \eta y_j \mathbf{x} - g(y_j)\mathbf{w}_j \tag{9.9}$$

where η is the *learning-rate parameter* of the algorithm. The first term on the right-hand side of Eq. (9.9) is the Hebbian term, and the second term is the forgetting term. To satisfy the requirement of Eq. (9.8), we choose a linear function for $g(y_j)$, as shown by

$$g(y_j) = \eta y_j \tag{9.10}$$

For a winning neuron $i(\mathbf{x})$, we may further simplify Eq. (9.9) by setting the response

$$y_j = h_{j,i(\mathbf{x})} \tag{9.11}$$

Using Eqs. (9.10) and (9.11) in Eq. (9.9), we obtain

$$\Delta\mathbf{w}_j = \eta h_{j,i(\mathbf{x})}(\mathbf{x} - \mathbf{w}_j), \qquad \begin{cases} i: & \text{winning neuron} \\ j: & \text{excited (activated) neuron} \end{cases} \tag{9.12}$$

Finally, using discrete-time formalism, given the synaptic-weight vector $\mathbf{w}_j(n)$ of neuron j at time n, we define the updated weight vector $\mathbf{w}_j(n + 1)$ at time $n + 1$ by

$$\mathbf{w}_j(n + 1) = \mathbf{w}_j(n) + \eta(n)h_{j,i(\mathbf{x})}(n)(\mathbf{x}(n) - \mathbf{w}_j(n)) \tag{9.13}$$

which is applied to all the neurons in the lattice that lie inside the topological neighborhood of winning neuron i (Kohonen, 1982; Ritter et al., 1992; Kohonen, 1997). Equation (9.13) has the effect of moving the synaptic-weight vector $\mathbf{w}_i$ of winning neuron i toward the input vector $\mathbf{x}$. Upon repeated presentations of the training data, the synaptic-weight vectors tend to follow the distribution of the input vectors because of the neighborhood updating. The algorithm therefore leads to a *topological ordering* of the feature map in the input space in the sense that neurons that are adjacent in the lattice will tend to have similar synaptic-weight vectors. We have more to say on this issue in Section 9.4.

Equation (9.13) is the desired formula for computing the synaptic weights of the feature map. In addition to this equation, however, we need the heuristic of Eq. (9.7) for selecting the neighborhood function $h_{j,i(\mathbf{x})}(n)$.

The learning-rate parameter $\eta(n)$ should also be time varying, as indicated in Eq. (9.13), which is how it should be for stochastic approximation. In particular, it should start at some initial value η_0 and then decrease gradually with increasing time n. This requirement can be satisfied by the following heuristic:

$$\eta(n) = \eta_0 \exp\left(-\frac{n}{\tau_2}\right), \qquad n = 0, 1, 2, ..., \tag{9.14}$$

where τ_2 is another time constant of the SOM algorithm. According to this second heuristic, the learning-rate parameter decays exponentially with time n. Even though the exponential-decay formulas described in Eqs. (9.6) and (9.14) for the width of the neighborhood function and the learning-rate parameter, respectively, may not be optimal, they are usually adequate for the formation of the feature map in a self-organized manner.

Two Phases of the Adaptive Process: Ordering and Convergence

Starting from an initial state of complete disorder, it is amazing how the SOM algorithm gradually leads to an organized representation of activation patterns drawn from the input space, provided that the parameters of the algorithm are selected properly. We may decompose the adaptation of the synaptic weights in the network, computed in accordance with Eq. (9.13), into two phases: an ordering or self-organizing phase, followed by a convergence phase. These two phases of the adaptive process are described as follows (Kohonen, 1982, 1997a):

1. *Self-organizing or ordering phase.* It is during this first phase of the adaptive process that the topological ordering of the weight vectors takes place. The ordering phase may take as many as 1,000 iterations of the SOM algorithm, and possibly even

more. Careful consideration must therefore be given to the choice of the learning-rate parameter and neighborhood function, as described here:

- The learning-rate parameter $\eta(n)$ should begin with a value close to 0.1; thereafter it should decrease gradually, but remain above 0.01 (i.e., it should never be allowed to get to zero). These desirable values are satisfied by the following choices in the formula of Eq. (9.14):

$$\eta_0 = 0.1$$
$$\tau_2 = 1000$$

- The neighborhood function $h_{j,i}(n)$ should initially include almost all neurons in the network centered on the winning neuron i and then shrink slowly with time.

Specifically, during the ordering phase—which, again, may occupy 1,000 iterations or more—$h_{j,i}(n)$ is permitted to reduce to a small value of only a couple of neighboring neurons around the winning neuron or to the winning neuron by itself. Assuming the use of a two-dimensional lattice of neurons for the discrete map, we may thus set the initial size σ_0 of the neighborhood function equal to the "radius" of the lattice. Correspondingly, we may set the time constant τ_1 in the formula of Eq. (9.6) as:

$$\tau_1 = \frac{1000}{\log\sigma_0}$$

2. *Convergence phase.* This second phase of the adaptive process is needed to fine-tune the feature map and therefore provide an accurate statistical quantification of the input space. Moreover, the number of iterations needed for convergence depends strongly on the dimensionality of the input space. As a general rule, the number of iterations constituting the convergence phase must be at least 500 times the number of neurons in the network. Thus, the convergence phase may have to go on for thousands, and possibly even tens of thousands, of iterations. The choice of learning-rate parameter and neighborhood function should be made as follows:

- For good statistical accuracy, the learning-rate parameter $\eta(n)$ should be maintained during the convergence phase at a small value, on the order of 0.01. As stated previously, $\eta(n)$ must not be allowed to decrease to zero; otherwise, it is possible for the network to get stuck in a metastable state. A *metastable state* belongs to a configuration of the feature map with a topological defect. The exponential decay of Eq. (9.14) guarantees against the possibility of metastable states.
- The neighborhood function $h_{j,i(x)}$ should contain only the nearest neighbors of a winning neuron, which may eventually reduce to one or zero neighboring neurons.

One other comment is in order: In discussing the issues of ordering and convergence, we have stressed the numbers of iterations needed to achieve them. In some software packages, however, epochs (rather than iterations) are used to describe these two issues.

Summary of the SOM Algorithm

The essence of Kohonen's SOM algorithm is that it substitutes a simple geometric computation for the more detailed properties of the Hebb-like rule and lateral interactions. The essential ingredients and parameters of the algorithm are as follows:

- a continuous input space of activation patterns that are generated in accordance with a certain probability distribution;
- a topology of the network in the form of a lattice of neurons, which defines a discrete output space;
- a time-varying neighborhood function $h_{j,i(\mathbf{x})}(n)$ that is defined around a winning neuron $i(\mathbf{x})$;
- a learning-rate parameter $\eta(n)$ that starts at an initial value η_0 and then decreases gradually with time n, but never goes to zero.

For the neighborhood function and learning-rate parameter, we may use Eqs. (9.7) and (9.14), respectively, for the ordering phase (i.e., the first 1,000 iterations or so). For good statistical accuracy, $\eta(n)$ should be maintained at a small value (0.01 or less) during the convergence for a fairly long period of time, which is typically thousands of iterations. As for the neighborhood function, it should contain only the nearest neighbors of the winning neuron at the start of the convergence phase and may eventually shrink to one or zero neighboring neurons.

There are three basic steps involved in the application of the algorithm after initialization: sampling, similarity matching, and updating. These three steps are repeated until formation of the feature map has been completed. The algorithm is summarized as follows:

1. *Initialization.* Choose random values for the initial weight vectors $\mathbf{w}_j(0)$. The only restriction here is that the $\mathbf{w}_j(0)$ be different for $j = 1, 2, ..., l$, where l is the number of neurons in the lattice. It may be desirable to keep the magnitude of the weights small.

   Another way of initalizing the algorithm is to select the weight vectors $\{\mathbf{w}_j(0)\}_{j=1}^{l}$ from the available set of input vectors $\{\mathbf{x}_i\}_{i=1}^{N}$ in a random manner. The advantage of this alternative choice is that the initial map will be in the range of the final map.

2. *Sampling.* Draw a sample $\mathbf{x}$ from the input space with a certain probability; the vector $\mathbf{x}$ represents the activation pattern that is applied to the lattice. The dimension of vector $\mathbf{x}$ is equal to m.

3. *Similarity matching.* Find the best-matching (winning) neuron $i(\mathbf{x})$ at time-step n by using the minimum-distance criterion

$$i(\mathbf{x}) = \arg\min_{j} \|\mathbf{x}(n) - \mathbf{w}_j\|, \qquad j = 1, 2, ..., l$$

4. *Updating.* Adjust the synaptic-weight vectors of all excited neurons by using the update formula

$$\mathbf{w}_j(n + 1) = \mathbf{w}_j(n) + \eta(n)h_{j,i(\mathbf{x})}(n)(\mathbf{x}(n) - \mathbf{w}_j(n))$$

where $\eta(n)$ is the learning-rate parameter and $h_{j,i(x)}(n)$ is the neighborhood function centered around the winning neuron $i(\mathbf{x})$; both $\eta(n)$ and $h_{j,i(x)}(n)$ are varied dynamically during learning for best results.

5. *Continuation.* Continue with step 2 until no noticeable changes in the feature map are observed.

9.4 PROPERTIES OF THE FEATURE MAP

Once the SOM algorithm has converged, the *feature map* computed by the algorithm displays important statistical characteristics of the input space.

To begin with, let $\mathcal{X}$ denote a *spatially continuous input (data) space*, the topology of which is defined by the metric relationship of the vectors $\mathbf{x} \in \mathcal{X}$. Let $\mathcal{A}$ denote a *spatially discrete output space*, the topology of which is endowed by arranging a set of neurons as the computation nodes of a lattice. Let Φ denote a nonlinear transformation called a *feature map*, which maps the input space $\mathcal{X}$ onto the output (i.e., lattice) space $\mathcal{A}$, as shown by

$$\Phi: \mathcal{X} \to \mathcal{A} \tag{9.15}$$

Equation (9.15) may be viewed as an abstraction of Eq. (9.3), which defines the location of a winning neuron $i(\mathbf{x})$ developed in response to an input vector $\mathbf{x}$. For example, in a neurobiological context, the input space $\mathcal{X}$ may represent the coordinate set of somatosensory receptors distributed densely over the entire body surface. Correspondingly, the output space $\mathcal{A}$ represents the set of neurons located in that layer of the cerebral cortex to which the somatosensory receptors are projecting.

Given an input vector $\mathbf{x}$, the SOM algorithm proceeds by first identifying a best-matching, or winning neuron, $i(\mathbf{x})$ in the output space $\mathcal{A}$, in accordance with the feature map Φ. The synaptic-weight vector $\mathbf{w}_i$ of neuron $i(\mathbf{x})$ may then be viewed as a *pointer* for that neuron into the input space $\mathcal{X}$.

Thus, as depicted in Fig. 9.4, the SOM algorithm embodies two ingredients that define the algorithm:

- A *projection* from the continuous input data space $\mathcal{X}$ onto the discrete output neural space $\mathcal{A}$. In this way, an input vector is mapped onto a "winning neuron" in the lattice structure in accordance with the similarity matching step (i.e., step 3) in the algorithmic summary presented in Section 9.3.
- A *pointer* from the output space back to the input space. In effect, the pointer defined by the weight vector of the winning neuron identifies a particular point in the input data space as the "image" of the winning neuron; this operation is iteratively carried out in accordance with the updating step (i.e., step 4) in the algorithmic summary.

In other words, there is communication, back and forth, between the output space where the lattice of neurons resides and the input space where the examples are generated.

The SOM algorithm has some important properties that are discussed next.

Property 1. Approximation of the Input Space

The feature map Φ, represented by the set of synaptic weight vectors $\{\mathbf{w}_j\}$ in the output space $\mathcal{A}$, provides a good approximation to the input space $\mathcal{X}$.

FIGURE 9.4   Illustration of
the relationship between
feature map Φ and weight
vector $\mathbf{w}_i$ of winning neuron i.

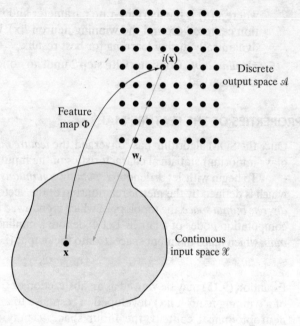

The basic aim of the SOM algorithm is to store a large set of input vectors $\mathbf{x} \in \mathcal{X}$ by finding a smaller set of prototypes $\mathbf{w}_j \in \mathcal{A}$ so as to provide a good approximation to the original input space $\mathcal{X}$. The theoretical basis of the idea just described is rooted in *vector quantization theory*, the motivation for which is dimensionality reduction or data compression (Gersho and Gray, 1992). It is therefore appropriate to present a brief discussion of this theory.

Consider Fig. 9.5, where $\mathbf{c}(\mathbf{x})$ acts as an *encoder* of the input vector $\mathbf{x}$ and $\mathbf{x}'(\mathbf{c})$ acts as a *decoder* of $\mathbf{c}(\mathbf{x})$. The vector $\mathbf{x}$ is selected at random from a training sample (i.e., input space $\mathcal{X}$), subject to an underlying probability density function $p_{\mathbf{X}}(\mathbf{x})$. The optimum encoding–decoding scheme is determined by varying the functions $\mathbf{c}(\mathbf{x})$ and $\mathbf{x}'(\mathbf{c})$ so as to minimize the *expected distortion*, defined by

$$D = \frac{1}{2} \int_{-\infty}^{\infty} p_{\mathbf{X}}(\mathbf{x}) d(\mathbf{x}, \mathbf{x}') d\mathbf{x} \tag{9.16}$$

FIGURE 9.5   Encoder–decoder
model for describing Property 1
of the SOM model.

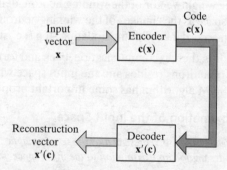

where the factor $\frac{1}{2}$ has been introduced for convenience of presentation and $d(\mathbf{x}, \mathbf{x}')$ is a *distortion* measure. The integration is performed over the entire input space $\mathcal{X}$, assumed to be of dimensionality m, hence, the use of the differential variable $d\mathbf{x}$ in Eq. (9.16). A popular choice for the distortion measure $d(\mathbf{x}, \mathbf{x}')$ is the square of the Euclidean distance between the input vector $\mathbf{x}$ and the reconstruction vector $\mathbf{x}'$; that is,

$$d(\mathbf{x}, \mathbf{x}') = \|\mathbf{x} - \mathbf{x}'\|^2 \tag{9.17}$$
$$= (\mathbf{x} - \mathbf{x}')^T(\mathbf{x} - \mathbf{x}')$$

Thus, we may rewrite Eq. (9.16) as

$$D = \frac{1}{2}\int_{-\infty}^{\infty} p_\mathbf{X}(\mathbf{x})\|\mathbf{x} - \mathbf{x}'\|^2 d\mathbf{x} \tag{9.18}$$

The necessary conditions for the minimization of the expected distortion D are embodied in the *generalized Lloyd algorithm*[7] (Gersho and Gray, 1992). The conditions are twofold:

Condition 1. Given the input vector $\mathbf{x}$, choose the code $\mathbf{c} = \mathbf{c}(\mathbf{x})$ to minimize the squared-error distortion $\|\mathbf{x} - \mathbf{x}'(\mathbf{c})\|^2$.

Condition 2. Given the code $\mathbf{c}$, compute the reconstruction vector $\mathbf{x}' = \mathbf{x}'(\mathbf{c})$ as the centroid of those input vectors $\mathbf{x}$ that satisfy condition 1.

Condition 1 is recognized as a *nearest-neighbor* encoding rule. Both conditions imply that the average distortion D is stationary (i.e., at a local minimum) with respect to variations in the encoder $\mathbf{c}(\mathbf{x})$ and decoder $\mathbf{x}'(\mathbf{c})$, respectively. To implement vector quantization, the generalized Lloyd algorithm operates in a *batch* training mode. Basically, the algorithm consists of alternately optimizing the encoder $\mathbf{c}(\mathbf{x})$ in accordance with condition 1 and then optimizing the decoder $\mathbf{x}'(\mathbf{c})$ in accordance with condition 2 until the expected distortion D reaches a minimum. In order to overcome the local-minimum problem, it may be necessary to run the generalized Lloyd algorithm several times with different initial code vectors.

The generalized Lloyd algorithm is closely related to the SOM algorithm, as shown in Luttrell (1989b). We may delineate the form of this relationship by considering the scheme shown in Fig. 9.6, where we have introduced an additive signal-independent "noise-term" following the encoder $\mathbf{c}(\mathbf{x})$. The noise, denoted by $\mathbf{v}$, is associated with a fictitious "communication channel" between the encoder and the decoder, the purpose of which is to account for the possibility that the output code $\mathbf{c}(\mathbf{x})$ may be distorted. On the basis of the model shown in Fig. 9.6, we may consider a *modified* form of the expected distortion given as

$$D_1 = \frac{1}{2}\int_{-\infty}^{\infty} p_\mathbf{X}(\mathbf{x}) \int_{-\infty}^{\infty} \pi(\mathbf{v})\|\mathbf{x} - \mathbf{x}'(\mathbf{c}(\mathbf{x}) + \mathbf{v})\|^2 d\mathbf{v} \, d\mathbf{x} \tag{9.19}$$

where $\pi(\mathbf{v})$ is the probability density function (pdf) of the additive noise $\mathbf{v}$. The inner integration is over all possible realizations of this noise, hence the use of the incremental variable $d\mathbf{v}$ in Eq. (9.19).

In accordance with the strategy described for the generalized Lloyd algorithm, there are two separate optimizations to be considered for the model of Fig. 9.6, one pertaining to the encoder and the other pertaining to the decoder. To find the optimum

FIGURE 9.6 Noisy encoder–
decoder model.

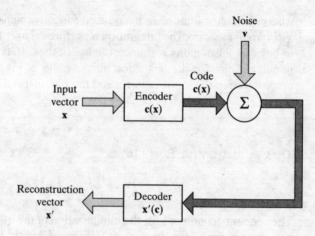

encoder for a fixed $\mathbf{x}$, we need the partial derivative of the expected distortion measure D_1 with respect to the decoded vector $\mathbf{c}$. Using Eq. (9.19), we thus obtain

$$\frac{\partial D_1}{\partial \mathbf{c}} = \frac{1}{2} p_{\mathbf{X}}(\mathbf{x}) \int_{-\infty}^{\infty} \pi(\mathbf{v}) \frac{\partial}{\partial \mathbf{c}} \|\mathbf{x} - \mathbf{x}'(\mathbf{c})\|^2 \big|_{\mathbf{c}=\mathbf{c}(\mathbf{x})+\mathbf{v}} d\mathbf{v} \qquad (9.20)$$

To find the optimum decoder for a fixed $\mathbf{c}$, we need the partial derivative of the expected distortion measure D_1 with respect to the decoded vector $\mathbf{x}'(\mathbf{c})$. Using Eq. (9.19), we thus obtain

$$\frac{\partial D_1}{\partial \mathbf{x}'(\mathbf{c})} = - \int_{-\infty}^{\infty} p_{\mathbf{X}}(\mathbf{x}) \pi(\mathbf{c} - \mathbf{c}(\mathbf{x}))(\mathbf{x} - \mathbf{x}'(\mathbf{c})) d\mathbf{x} \qquad (9.21)$$

Hence, in light of Eqs. (9.20) and (9.21), conditions 1 and 2 stated earlier for the generalized Lloyd algorithm are modified as follows (Luttrell, 1989b):

Condition I. Given the input vector $\mathbf{x}$, choose the code $\mathbf{c} = \mathbf{c}(\mathbf{x})$ to minimize the distortion measure

$$D_2 = \int_{-\infty}^{\infty} \pi(\mathbf{v}) \|\mathbf{x} - \mathbf{x}'(\mathbf{c}(\mathbf{x}) + \mathbf{v})\|^2 d\mathbf{v} \qquad (9.22)$$

Condition II. Given the code $\mathbf{c}$, compute the reconstruction vector $\mathbf{x}'(\mathbf{c})$ to satisfy the condition

$$\mathbf{x}'(\mathbf{c}) = \frac{\int_{-\infty}^{\infty} p_{\mathbf{X}}(\mathbf{x}) \pi(\mathbf{c} - \mathbf{c}(\mathbf{x})) \mathbf{x} d\mathbf{x}}{\int_{-\infty}^{\infty} p_{\mathbf{X}}(\mathbf{x}) \pi(\mathbf{c} - \mathbf{c}(\mathbf{x})) d\mathbf{x}} \qquad (9.23)$$

Equation (9.23) is obtained by setting the partial derivative $\partial D_1/\partial \mathbf{x}'(\mathbf{c})$ in Eq. (9.21) equal to zero and then solving for $\mathbf{x}'(\mathbf{c})$.

The encoder-decoder model described in Fig. 9.5 may now be viewed as a special case of that shown in Fig. 9.6. In particular, if we set the probability density function $\pi(\mathbf{v})$ of the noise $\mathbf{v}$ equal to a Dirac delta function $\delta(\mathbf{v})$, conditions I and II reduce to conditions 1 and 2, respectively, for the generalized Lloyd algorithm.

To simplify condition I, we assume that $\pi(\mathbf{v})$ is a smooth function of $\mathbf{v}$. It may then be shown that, to a second-order of approximation, the distortion measure D_2 defined in Eq. (9.22) consists of two components (Luttrell, 1989b):

- the *conventional* distortion term, defined by the squared-error distortion $\|\mathbf{x} - \mathbf{x}'(\mathbf{c})\|^2$;
- a *curvature* term that arises from the noise model $\pi(\mathbf{v})$.

Assuming that the curvature term is small, condition I for the model in Fig. 9.6 may be approximated by condition 1 for the noiseless model in Fig. 9.5. This approximation, in turn, reduces condition I to a nearest-neighbor encoding rule as before.

As for condition II, we may realize it by using stochastic descent learning. In particular, we choose input vectors $\mathbf{x}$ at random from the input space $\mathcal{X}$, in accordance with the $p_{\mathbf{X}}(\mathbf{x})$, and then update the reconstruction vector $\mathbf{x}'(\mathbf{c})$ as

$$\mathbf{x}'_{\text{new}}(\mathbf{c}) \leftarrow \mathbf{x}'_{\text{old}}(\mathbf{c}) + \eta\pi(\mathbf{c} - \mathbf{c}(\mathbf{x}))[\mathbf{x} - \mathbf{x}'_{\text{old}}(\mathbf{c})] \qquad (9.24)$$

where η is the learning-rate parameter and $\mathbf{c}(\mathbf{x})$ is the nearest-neighbor encoding approximation to condition 1. The update equation of Eq. (9.24) is obtained by inspection of the partial derivative in Eq. (9.21). This update is applied to all $\mathbf{c}$, for which we have

$$\pi(\mathbf{c} - \mathbf{c}(\mathbf{x})) > 0 \qquad (9.25)$$

We may think of the gradient descent procedure described in Eq. (9.24) as a way of minimizing the distortion measure D_1 of Eq. (9.19). That is, Eqs. (9.23) and (9.24) are essentially of the same type, except for the fact that Eq. (9.23) is batch and Eq. (9.24) is continuous (i.e., in flowthrough form).

The update equation of Eq. (9.24) is identical to the (continuous) SOM algorithm of Eq. (9.13), bearing in mind the correspondences listed in Table 9.1. Accordingly, we may state that the generalized Lloyd algorithm for vector quantization is the batch training version of the SOM algorithm with zero neighborhood size; for zero neighborhood, $\pi(0) = 1$. Note that in order to obtain the generalized Lloyd algorithm from the batch version of the SOM algorithm, we do *not* need to make any approximations, because

TABLE 9.1   Correspondence between the SOM Algorithm and the Model of Fig. 9.6

Encoding–Decoding Model of Fig. 9.6	SOM Algorithm
Encoder $\mathbf{c}(\mathbf{x})$	Best-matching neuron $i(\mathbf{x})$
Reconstruction vector $\mathbf{x}'(\mathbf{c})$	Synaptic-weight vector $\mathbf{w}_j$
Probability density function $\pi(\mathbf{c} - \mathbf{c}(\mathbf{x}))$	Neighborhood function $h_{j,i(\mathbf{x})}$

the curvature terms (and all higher-order terms) make no contribution when the neighborhood has zero width.

The important points to note from the discussion presented here are as follows:

1. The SOM algorithm is a vector quantization algorithm, which provides a good approximation to the input space $\mathcal{X}$. This viewpoint provides another approach for deriving the SOM algorithm, as exemplified by Eq. (9.24).

2. According to this viewpoint, the neighborhood function $h_{j,i(\mathbf{x})}$ in the SOM algorithm has the form of a probability density function. In Luttrell (1991a), a zero-mean Gaussian model is considered appropriate for the noise $\mathbf{v}$ in the model of Fig. 9.6. We thus also have theoretical justification for adopting the Gaussian neighborhood function of Eq. (9.4).

The *batch SOM*[8] is merely a rewrite of Eq. (9.23), with summations used to approximate the integrals in the numerator and denominator of the right-hand side of the equation. Note that in this version of the SOM algorithm, the order in which the input patterns are presented to the network has no effect on the final form of the feature map, and there is no need for a learning-rate schedule. But the algorithm still requires the use of a neighborhood function.

Property 2. Topological Ordering

> *The feature map Φ computed by the SOM algorithm is topologically ordered in the sense that the spatial location of a neuron in the lattice corresponds to a particular domain or feature of input patterns.*

The topological ordering property[9] is a direct consequence of the update equation of Eq. (9.13), which forces the synaptic-weight vector $\mathbf{w}_i$ of the winning neuron $i(\mathbf{x})$ to move toward the input vector $\mathbf{x}$. It also has the effect of moving the synaptic-weight vectors $\mathbf{w}_j$ of the closest excited neurons j along with the winning neuron $i(\mathbf{x})$. We may therefore visualize the feature map Φ as an *elastic* or *virtual net* with the topology of a one- or two-dimensional lattice as prescribed in the output space $\mathcal{A}$, and whose nodes have weights as coordinates in the input space $\mathcal{X}$ (Ritter, 2003). The overall aim of the algorithm may thus be stated as follows:

> *Approximate the input space $\mathcal{X}$ by pointers or prototypes in the form of synaptic-weight vectors $\mathbf{w}_j$ in such a way that the feature map Φ provides a faithful representation of the important features that characterize the input vectors $\mathbf{x} \in \mathcal{X}$ in terms of a certain statistical criterion.*

The feature map Φ is usually displayed in the input space $\mathcal{X}$. Specifically, all the pointers (i.e., synaptic-weight vectors) are shown as dots, and the pointers of neighboring neurons are connected with lines in accordance with the topology of the lattice. Thus, by using a line to connect two pointers $\mathbf{w}_i$ and $\mathbf{w}_j$, we are indicating that the corresponding neurons i and j are neighboring neurons in the lattice.

Property 3. Density Matching

> *The feature map Φ reflects variations in the statistics of the input distribution: Regions in the input space $\mathcal{X}$ from which sample vectors $\mathbf{x}$ are drawn with a high probability of occurrence*

are mapped onto larger domains of the output space , and therefore with better resolution than regions in $\mathcal{X}$ from which sample vectors $\mathbf{x}$ are drawn with a low probability of occurrence.

Let $p_{\mathbf{X}}(\mathbf{x})$ denote the multidimensional pdf of the random input vector $\mathbf{X}$, a sample realization of which is denoted by $\mathbf{x}$. This pdf, integrated over the entire input space $\mathcal{X}$, must by definition, equal unity:

$$\int_{-\infty}^{\infty} p_{\mathbf{X}}(\mathbf{x})d\mathbf{x} = 1$$

Let $m(\mathbf{x})$ denote the map *magnification factor*, defined as the number of neurons in a small volume $d\mathbf{x}$ of the input space $\mathcal{X}$. The magnification factor, integrated over the input space $\mathcal{X}$, must contain the total number l of neurons in the network, as shown by

$$\int_{-\infty}^{\infty} m(\mathbf{x})d\mathbf{x} = l \tag{9.26}$$

For the SOM algorithm to *match the input density* exactly, we therefore require the following proportionality relationship (Amari, 1980):

$$m(\mathbf{x}) \propto p_{\mathbf{X}}(\mathbf{x}) \tag{9.27}$$

This property implies that if a particular region of the input space contains frequently occurring stimuli, it will be represented by a larger area in the feature map than a region of the input space where the stimuli occur less frequently.

Generally speaking, in two-dimensional feature maps, the magnification factor $m(\mathbf{x})$ is not expressible as a simple function of the probability density function $p_{\mathbf{X}}(\mathbf{x})$ of the input vector $\mathbf{x}$. It is only in the case of a one-dimensional feature map that it is possible to derive such a relationship. For this special case, we find that, contrary to an earlier supposition (Kohonen, 1982), the magnification factor $m(\mathbf{x})$ is *not* proportional to $p_{\mathbf{X}}(\mathbf{x})$. Two different results are reported in the literature, depending on the encoding method advocated:

1. *Minimum-distortion encoding*, according to which the curvature terms and all higher-order terms in the distortion measure of Eq. (9.22) due to the noise model $\pi(\mathbf{v})$ are retained. This encoding method yields the result

$$m(\mathbf{x}) \propto p_{\mathbf{X}}^{1/3}(\mathbf{x}) \tag{9.28}$$

   which is the same as the result obtained for the standard vector quantizer (Luttrell, 1991a).

2. *Nearest-neighbor encoding*, which emerges if the curvature terms are ignored, as in the standard form of the SOM algorithm. This second encoding method yields the following result (Ritter, 1991):

$$m(\mathbf{x}) \propto p_{\mathbf{X}}^{2/3}(\mathbf{x}) \tag{9.29}$$

Our earlier statement that a cluster of frequently occurring input stimuli is represented by a larger area in the feature map still holds, albeit in a distorted version of the ideal condition described in Eq. (9.27).

As a general rule (confirmed by computer simulations), the feature map computed by the SOM algorithm tends to overrepresent regions of low input density and to underrepresent regions of high input density. In other words, the SOM algorithm fails to provide a faithful representation of the probability distribution that underlies the input space.[10]

Property 4. Feature Selection

Given data from an input space, the self-organizing map is able to select a set of best features for approximating the underlying distribution.

This property is a natural culmination of Properties 1 through 3. In a loose sense, Property 4 brings to mind the idea of principal-components analysis that was discussed in the previous chapter, but with an important difference, as illustrated in Fig. 9.7. Figure 9.7a shows a two-dimensional distribution of zero-mean data points resulting from a linear

FIGURE 9.7 (a) Two-dimensional distribution produced by a linear input–output mapping. (b) Two-dimensional distribution produced by a nonlinear input–output mapping.

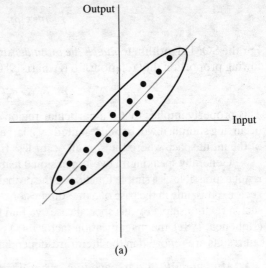

(a)

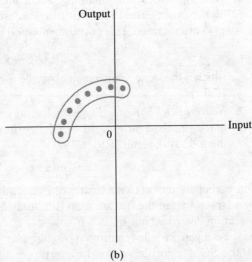

(b)

input–output mapping corrupted by additive noise. In such a situation, principal-components analysis works perfectly fine: It tells us that the best description of the "linear" distribution in Fig. 9.7a is defined by a straight line (i.e., one-dimensional "hyperplane") that passes through the origin and runs parallel to the eigenvector associated with the largest eigenvalue of the correlation matrix of the data. Consider next the situation described in Fig. 9.7b, which is the result of a nonlinear input–output mapping corrupted by additive noise of zero mean. In this second situation, it is impossible for a straight-line approximation computed from principal-components analysis to provide an acceptable description of the data. On the other hand, the use of a self-organizing map built on a one-dimensional lattice of neurons is able to overcome this approximation problem by virtue of its topological-ordering property. This latter approximation, illustrated in Fig. 9.7b, works well only when the dimensionality of the lattice matches the intrinsic dimensionality of the distribution.

9.5 COMPUTER EXPERIMENTS: DISENTANGLING LATTICE DYNAMICS USING SOM

I. Two-dimensional lattice driven by two-dimensional stimulus

We illustrate the behavior of the SOM algorithm by using computer simulations to study a network with 576 neurons, arranged in the form of a two-dimensional lattice with 24 rows and 24 columns. The network is trained with a two-dimensional input vector $\mathbf{x}$, whose elements x_1 and x_2 are uniformly distributed in the region $\{x_1, x_2 \text{ in } (-1, 1)\}$. To initialize the network, randomly chosen values are assigned to the synaptic weights.

Figure 9.8 shows three stages of training as the network learns to represent the input distribution, starting with Fig. 9.8a that shows the uniform distribution of data used to train the feature map. Figure 9.8b shows the initial values of the synaptic weights, randomly chosen. Figures 9.8c and 9.8d display the 24-by-24 maps computed by the SOM algorithm, after completion of the ordering and convergence phases, respectively. The lines drawn in Fig. 9.8 connect neighboring neurons (across rows and columns) in the network, as discussed previously under Property 2.

The results shown in Fig. 9.8 demonstrate the ordering phase and the convergence phase that characterize the learning process of the SOM algorithm. During the ordering phase, the map *unfolds* to form a mesh, as shown in Fig. 9.8c. The neurons are mapped in the correct order at the end of this phase. During the convergence phase, the map spreads out to fill the input space. At the end of this second phase, shown in Fig. 9.8d, the statistical distribution of the neurons in the map approaches that of the input vectors, except for some distortion. Comparing the final state of the feature map in Fig. 9.8d with the uniform distribution of the input in Fig. 9.8a, we see that the tuning of the map during the convergence phase has captured the local irregularities that can be seen in the input distribution.

The topological-ordering property of the SOM algorithm is well illustrated in Fig. 9.8d. In particular, we observe that the algorithm (after convergence) captures the underlying topology of the uniform distribution at the input. In the computer simulations presented in Fig. 9.8, the input space $\mathcal{X}$ and output space $\mathcal{A}$ are both two-dimensional.

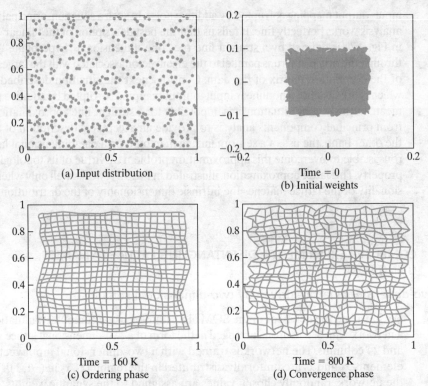

(a) Input distribution

Time = 0
(b) Initial weights

Time = 160 K
(c) Ordering phase

Time = 800 K
(d) Convergence phase

FIGURE 9.8   (a) Distribution of the input data. (b) Initial condition of the two-dimensional lattice. (c) Condition of the lattice at the end of the ordering phase. (d) Condition of the lattice at the end of the convergence phase. The times indicated under maps (b), (c), and (d) represent the numbers of iterations.

II. One-dimensional lattice driven by two-dimensional stimulus

We now examine the case for which the dimension of the input space $\mathscr{X}$ is greater than the dimension of the output space $\mathscr{A}$. In spite of this mismatch, the feature map Φ is often able to form a topological representation of the input distribution. Figure 9.9 shows three different stages in the evolution of a feature map initialized as in Fig. 9.9b and trained with input data drawn from a uniform distribution inside a square as in Fig. 9.9a, but this time the computation is performed with a one-dimensional lattice of 100 neurons. Figures 9.9c and 9.9d show the feature map after the completion of the ordering and convergence phases, respectively. Here, we see that the feature map computed by the algorithm is very distorted in order to fill the square as densely as possible and thereby provide a reasonably good approximation to the underlying topology of the two-dimensional input space $\mathscr{X}$. The approximating curve shown in Fig. 9.9d resembles a *Peano curve* (Kohonen, 1990a). An operation of the kind exemplified by the feature map of Fig. 9.9, where an input space $\mathscr{X}$ is represented by projecting it onto a lower-dimensional output space $\mathscr{A}$, is referred to as *dimensionality reduction*.

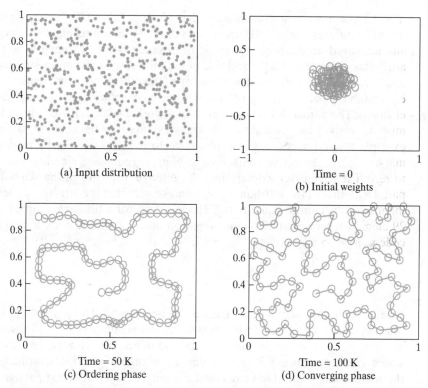

FIGURE 9.9   (a) Distribution of the two-dimensional input data. (b) Initial condition of the one-dimensional lattice. (c) Condition of the one-dimensional lattice at the end of the ordering phase. (d) Condition of the lattice at the end of the convergence phase. The times included under maps (b), (c), and (d) represent the numbers of iterations.

9.6   CONTEXTUAL MAPS

There are two fundamentally different ways of visualizing a self-organizing feature map. In one method of visualization, the feature map is viewed as an elastic net, with the synaptic-weight vectors treated as pointers for the respective neurons, which are directed into the input space. This method of visualization is particularly useful for displaying the topological-ordering property of the SOM algorithm, as illustrated by the results of the computer simulation experiments presented in Section 9.5.

In the second method of visualization, class labels are assigned to neurons in a two-dimensional lattice (representing the output layer of the network), depending on how each *test pattern* (not seen before) excites a particular neuron in the self-organized network. As a result of this second stage of stimulation, the neurons in the two-dimensional lattice are partitioned into a number of *coherent regions*, coherent in the sense that each grouping of neurons represents a distinct set of contiguous symbols or labels (Ritter, 2003). This method assumes that the right conditions have been followed for the development of a well-ordered feature map in the first place.

Consider, for example, the set of data given in Table 9.2, which pertains to a number of 16 different animals. Each column of the table is a schematic description of an animal, based on the presence (= 1) or absence (= 0) of some of the 13 different attributes given on the left-hand side of the table. Some attributes, such as "feathers" and "two legs," are correlated, while many of the other attributes are uncorrelated. For each animal given at the top of the table, we have an *attribute code* $\mathbf{x}_a$ made up of 13 elements. The animal is itself specified by a *symbol code* $\mathbf{x}_s$, the composition of which must *not* convey any information or known similarities between the animals. For the example at hand, $\mathbf{x}_s$ consists of a column vector whose kth element, representing animal $k = 1, 2, ..., 16$, is given a fixed value of a; the remaining elements are all set equal to zero. The parameter a determines the relative influence of the symbol code compared with that of the attribute code. To make sure that the attribute code is the dominant one, a is chosen equal to 0.2. The input vector $\mathbf{x}$ for each animal is a vector of 29 elements, representing a concatenation of the attribute code $\mathbf{x}_a$ and the symbol code $\mathbf{x}_s$, as shown by

$$\mathbf{x} = \begin{bmatrix} \mathbf{x}_s \\ \mathbf{x}_a \end{bmatrix} = \begin{bmatrix} \mathbf{x}_s \\ \mathbf{0} \end{bmatrix} + \begin{bmatrix} \mathbf{0} \\ \mathbf{x}_a \end{bmatrix}$$

Finally, each data vector is normalized to unit length. The patterns of the data set thus generated are presented to a two-dimensional lattice of 10×10 neurons, and the synaptic weights of the neurons are adjusted in accordance with the SOM algorithm summarized in Section 9.3. The training is continued for 2,000 iterations, after which the feature map should have reached a steady state. Next, a test pattern defined by

TABLE 9.2   Animal Names and Their Attributes

Animal		Dove	Hen	Duck	Goose	Owl	Hawk	Eagle	Fox	Dog	Wolf	Cat	Tiger	Lion	Horse	Zebra	Cow
is	small	1	1	1	1	1	1	0	0	0	0	1	0	0	0	0	0
	medium	0	0	0	0	0	0	1	1	1	1	0	0	0	0	0	0
	big	0	0	0	0	0	0	0	0	0	0	0	1	1	1	1	1
has	2 legs	1	1	1	1	1	1	1	0	0	0	0	0	0	0	0	0
	4 legs	0	0	0	0	0	0	0	1	1	1	1	1	1	1	1	1
	hair	0	0	0	0	0	0	0	1	1	1	1	1	1	1	1	1
	hooves	0	0	0	0	0	0	0	0	0	0	0	0	0	1	1	1
	mane	0	0	0	0	0	0	0	0	0	1	0	0	1	1	1	0
	feathers	1	1	1	1	1	1	1	0	0	0	0	0	0	0	0	0
likes to	hunt	0	0	0	0	1	1	1	1	0	1	1	1	1	0	0	0
	run	0	0	0	0	0	0	0	0	1	1	0	1	1	1	1	0
	fly	1	0	0	1	1	1	1	0	0	0	0	0	0	0	0	0
	swim	0	0	1	1	0	0	0	0	0	0	0	0	0	0	0	0

$\mathbf{x} = [\mathbf{x}_s, 0]^T$ containing the symbol code of only one of the animals is presented to the self-organized network, and the neuron with the strongest response is identified. This procedure is repeated for all 16 animals.

Proceeding in the manner just described, we obtain the map shown in Fig. 9.10, where the labeled neurons represent those with the strongest responses to their respective test patterns; the unoccupied rectangular spaces in the figure represent neurons with weaker responses.

Figure 9.11 shows the result of *simulated electrode penetration mapping* for the same self-organized network. This time, however, each neuron in the network has been marked by the particular animal for which it produces the best response. Figure 9.11 clearly shows that the feature map has essentially captured the "family relationships" among the 16 different animals. There are three distinct clusters: the white (unshaded) area representing "birds," the grey shaded area representing "peaceful species," and the red area shaded representing animals that are "hunters."

A feature map of the type illustrated in Fig. 9.11 is referred to as a *contextual map* or *semantic map* (Ritter, 2003). Such a map resembles cortical maps (i.e., the computational maps formed in the cerebral cortex), which were discussed briefly in Section 9.2. Contextual maps, which result from the use of the SOM algorithm, find applications in such diverse fields as unsupervised categorization of phonemic classes from text, remote sensing (Kohonen, 1997a), and data exploration or data mining (Kohonen, 1997b).

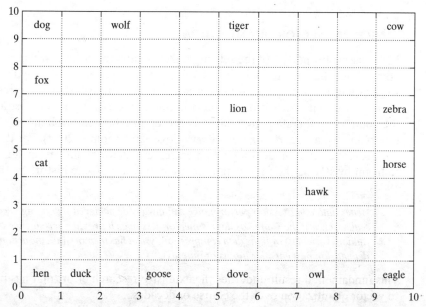

FIGURE 9.10   Feature map containing labeled neurons with strongest responses to their respective inputs.

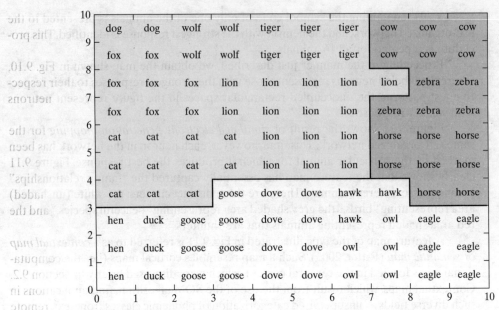

FIGURE 9.11 Semantic map obtained through the use of simulated electrode penetration mapping. The map is divided into three regions, representing birds (white), peaceful species (grey), and hunters (red).

9.7 HIERARCHICAL VECTOR QUANTIZATION

In discussing property 1 of the self-organizing feature map discussed in Section 9.4, we pointed out that this map is closely related to the generalized Lloyd algorithm for vector quantization. Vector quantization is a form of *lossy* data compression—lossy in the sense that some information contained in the input data is lost as a result of the compression. Data compression is rooted in a branch of Shannon's information theory known as *rate distortion theory* (Cover and Thomas, 2002). For the purpose of our present discussion dealing with hierarchical vector quantization, it is appropriate to begin by stating the following fundamental result of rate distortion theory (Gray, 1984):

> *Better data compression performance can always be achieved by coding vectors instead of scalars, even if the source of data is memoryless (e.g., it provides a sequence of independent random variables) or if the data compression system has memory (i.e., the action of an encoder depends on past encoder inputs or outputs).*

This fundamental result underlies the extensive research effort that has been devoted to vector quantization over the course of decades.

However, conventional vector quantization algorithms require a prohibitive amount of computation. The most time-consuming part of vector quantization is the encoding operation. For encoding, the input vector must be compared with each code vector in the code book in order to determine which particular code yields the minimum distortion. For a code book containing N code vectors, for example, the time taken for encoding is on the order of N, which can therefore be large for large N. In Luttrell (1989a), a *multistage hierarchical vector quantizer* is described that trades off accuracy for speed of encoding. The multistage hierarchical vector quantizer attempts to factorize the overall vector quantization into a number of suboperations, each of which requires very little computation. Desirably, the factorization is reduced to a single table lookup per suboperation. By clever use of the SOM algorithm to train each stage of the quantizer, the loss in accuracy can be small (as low as a fraction of a decibel), while the gain in speed of computation can be large.

Consider two vector quantizers VQ_1 and VQ_2, with VQ_1 feeding its output into VQ_2. The output from VQ_2 is the final encoded version of the original input signal applied to VQ_1. In performing its quantization, it is inevitable for VQ_2 to discard some information. As far as VQ_1 is concerned, the sole effect of VQ_2 is therefore to distort the information output by VQ_1. It thus appears that the appropriate training method for VQ_1 is the SOM algorithm, which accounts for the signal distortion induced by VQ_2 (Luttrell, 1989a). In order to use the generalized Lloyd algorithm to train VQ_2, we need only assume that the output of VQ_2 is not corrupted before we do the reconstruction. Then we do not need to introduce any noise model (at the output of VQ_2) with its associated finite-width neighborhood function.

We can generalize this heuristic argument to a multistage vector quantizer. Each stage must be designed to account for the distortion induced by all *subsequent* stages and to model this distortion as noise. To do so, the SOM algorithm is used to train all the stages of the quantizer, except for the last stage, for which the generalized Lloyd algorithm is adequate.

Hierarchical vector quantization is a special case of multistage vector quantization. As an illustration, consider the quantization of 4-by-1 input vector

$$\mathbf{x} = [x_1, x_2, x_3, x_4]^T$$

In Fig. 9.12a, we show a single-stage vector quantizer for $\mathbf{x}$. Alternatively, we may use a two-stage hierarchical vector quantizer, as depicted in Fig. 9.12b. The significant difference between these two schemes is that the input dimension of the quantizer in Fig. 9.12a is four, whereas for the quantizer in Fig. 9.12b it is two. Accordingly, the quantizer of Fig. 9.12b requires a lookup table of smaller size and is therefore simpler to implement than that of Fig. 9.12a. This is the advantage of a hierarchical quantizer over a conventional quantizer.

Case Study. First-Order Autoregressive Model

Luttrell (1989a) has demonstrated the performance of a multistage hierarchical vector quantizer applied to various stochastic time series, with little loss in encoding accuracy. In Fig. 9.13, we have reproduced Luttrell's results for the case of a correlated Gaussian noise process generated using a *first-order autoregressive (AR) model*, given as

$$x(n + 1) = \rho x(n) + v(n) \tag{9.30}$$

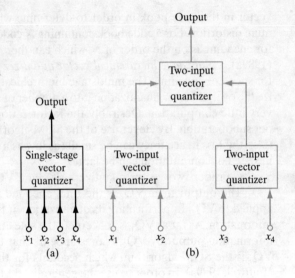

FIGURE 9.12 (a) Single-stage vector quantizer with four-dimensional input. (b) Two-stage hierarchical vector quantizer using two-input vector quantizers. (From S.P. Luttrell, 1989a, British Crown copyright.)

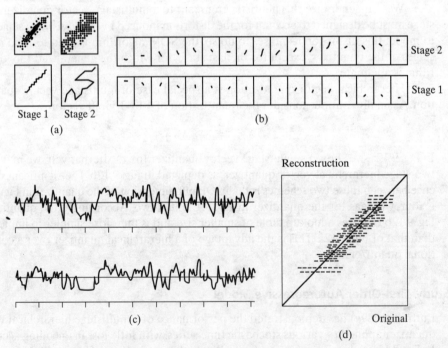

FIGURE 9.13 Two-stage encoding–decoding results, using the binary tree shown in red in Fig. 9.12, for the compression of correlated Gaussian noise input. Correlation coefficient $\rho = 0.85$. (From S.P. Luttrell, 1989a, British Crown copyright.)

where ρ is the AR coefficient and $v(n)$ is drawn from a set of statistically independent and identically distributed (iid) Gaussian random variables of zero mean and unit variance. Hence, we may show that $x(n)$ is statistically characterized as follows:

$$\mathbb{E}[x(n)] = 0 \tag{9.31}$$

$$\mathbb{E}[x^2(n)] = \frac{1}{1 - \rho^2} \tag{9.32}$$

$$\frac{\mathbb{E}[x(n + 1)x(n)]}{\mathbb{E}[x^2(n)]} = \rho \tag{9.33}$$

Thus, ρ may also be viewed as the *correlation coefficient* of the time series $\{x(n)\}$. To initiate the generation of the time series according to Eq. (9.30), a Gaussian random variable of zero mean and variance $1/(1 - \rho^2)$ was used for $x(0)$, and the value $\rho = 0.85$ was used for the correlation coefficient.

For the vector quantization a hierarchical encoder with a four-dimensional input space, like the binary tree, shown in red in Fig. 9.12b, was used. For the AR time series $\{x(n)\}$, translational symmetry implies that only *two* distinct lookup tables are needed. The size of each table depends exponentially on the number of input bits and linearly on the number of output bits. During training, a large number of bits is needed to represent numbers for a correct computation of the updates described in Eq. (9.24); as a result, the lookup tables are not used during training. Once training is complete, however, the number of bits may be reduced to their normal level and the table entries filled in as required. For the encoder shown in Fig. 9.12b, the input samples were approximated by using four bits per sample. For all stages of the encoder, $N (= 17)$ code vectors were used, so the number of output bits from each lookup table was approximately four, too. Thus, the address-space size of both the first-stage and second-stage lookup tables is $256 (= 2^{4 + 4})$, which means that the overall memory requirements for representing the tables are modest.

Figure 9.13 shows the encoding–decoding results obtained with $x(n)$ as the input. The lower half of Fig 9.13a shows the code vectors for each of the two stages as a curve embedded in a two-dimensional input space; the upper half of Fig. 9.13a presents estimates of the corresponding co-occurrence matrices using 16×16 bins. Figure 9.13b presents, as fragments of the time series, the following:

- the code vector computed by the first encoder stage;
- the reconstruction vector computed by the second stage that minimizes the mean-square distortion while keeping all other variables fixed.

Figure 9.13c presents 512 samples of both the original time series (top curve) and its reconstruction (bottom curve) from the output of the last encoder stage; the horizontal scale in Fig. 9.13c is half that in Fig. 9.13b. Finally, Fig. 9.13d presents a co-occurrence matrix created from a pair of samples: an original time-series sample and its corresponding reconstruction. The width of the band in Fig. 9.13d indicates the extent of the distortion produced by the hierarchical vector quantization.

Examining the waveforms in Fig. 9.13c, we see that the reconstruction is a good representation of the original time series, except for some positive and negative peaks that were clipped. According to Luttrell (1989a), the normalized mean-square distortion was computed to be almost as good as the corresponding result obtained with a single-stage four-sample block encoder using one bit per sample that was reported in Jayant and Noll (1984).

9.8 KERNEL SELF-ORGANIZING MAP

Kohonen's self-organizing map algorithm is a powerful tool for exploring large amounts of high-dimensional data, exemplified by many large-scale visualization and data-mining applications. However, from a theoretical perspective, the self-organizing map algorithm has two fundamental limitations:

1. The estimate of the probability density function of the input space provided by the algorithm lacks accuracy. Indeed, this shortcoming of the algorithm shows itself up in the experimental results presented in Fig. 9.8. This shortcoming is also found theoretically, be that in Eq. (9.28) or Eq. (9.29), in either one of which the density-matching property of the algorithm is imperfect.

2. The formulation of the algorithm has *no* objective function that could be optimized. Considering the nonlinear stochastic characterization of the algorithm, the lack of an objective function makes the problem of developing a proof of convergence that much more difficult.

Indeed, it is largely these two limitations of the self-organizing map, particularly the latter one, that have prompted many investigators to devise different ways of approaching the formulation of feature-mapping models. In this section, we describe a kernel-based formulation of the self-organizing map developed by Van Hulle (2002b), the motivation of which is improved topographic mapping.

Objective Function

In applications of the kernel method we have discussed previously, exemplified by the support vector machine (SVM) and kernel principal-components analysis, the kernel parameters are usually fixed. In contrast, in a kernel *self-organizing map* (*SOM*), each neuron in the lattice structure of the map acts as a kernel. As such, the kernel parameters are adjusted individually in accordance with a prescribed *objective function*, which is maximized iteratively so as to facilitate the formation of a satisfactory topographic map.

In this section, we focus attention on the *joint entropy* of the kernel (i.e., neural) outputs as the objective function. The notion of entropy is discussed in detail in Chapter 10. For the present, it suffices to start with the definition of this new concept. Consider a continuous random variable Y_i, whose probability density function is denoted by $p_{Y_i}(y_i)$, where the sample value y_i lies in the range $0 \le y_i < \infty$. The *differential entropy* of Y_i is defined by

$$H(Y_i) = -\int_{-\infty}^{\infty} p_{Y_i}(y_i) \log p_{y_i}(y_i) dy_i \qquad (9.34)$$

where we have used log to denote the logarithm to be consistent with the terminology of Chapter 10. For the kernel SOM, the random variable Y_i refers to the output of the ith kernel in the lattice, and y_i refers to a sample value of Y_i.

In what follows, we will proceed in a bottom-up manner:

- The differential entropy of a given kernel is first maximized.
- Then, when this maximization has been attained, the kernel parameters are adjusted so as to maximize the "mutual information" between the kernel's output and input. We will have more to say on this second new concept later on.

Definition of the Kernel

Let the kernel be denoted by $k(\mathbf{x}, \mathbf{w}_i, \sigma_i)$, where $\mathbf{x}$ is the *input vector* of dimensionality m, $\mathbf{w}_i$ is the *weight (parameter) vector* of the ith kernel, and σ_i is its width; the index $i = 1, 2, ..., l$, where l is the total number of neurons constituting the lattice structure of the map. The rationale for assigning the index i to the kernel width, in addition to the weight vector, is that both parameters will be iteratively adjusted. With the kernel being radially *symmetric* around its center, defined by $\mathbf{w}_i$, we have

$$k(\mathbf{x}, \mathbf{w}_i, \sigma_i) = k(\|\mathbf{x} - \mathbf{w}_i\|, \sigma_i), \qquad i = 1, 2, ..., l \tag{9.35}$$

where $\|\mathbf{x} - \mathbf{w}_i\|$ is the Euclidean distance between the input vector $\mathbf{x}$ and the weight vector $\mathbf{w}_i$, both of which naturally have the same dimension.

Now, just as in the case of SVM and kernel PCA, we look to a probability distribution— namely, a Gaussian one—for the kernel definition. We will also look for a probability distribution but adopt a different definition for the kernel, as explained next.

Suppose the kernel output y_i has "bounded" support. Then the differential entropy $H(Y_i)$, defined in Eq. (9.34), will be maximized when Y_i is uniformly distributed. (The justification for this statement is that entropy is a measure of randomness, and a uniform distribution is the extreme form of randomness.) The optimality condition just stated occurs when the output distribution matches the cumulative distribution function of the input space. For a Gaussian-distributed input vector $\mathbf{x}$, we find that the cumulative distribution function of the corresponding Euclidean distance $\mathbf{x} - \mathbf{w}_i$ is the *incomplete gamma distribution*. This distribution, to be defined, is the desired kernel definition.

Let the m elements of the input vector $\mathbf{x}$ be statistically independent and identically distributed (iid), with the jth element being Gaussian distributed with mean μ_j and variance σ^2. Let v denote the squared Euclidean distance between the input vector $\mathbf{x}$ and the mean vector $\boldsymbol{\mu} = [\mu_1, \mu_2, ..., \mu_m]^T$, as shown by

$$v = \|\mathbf{x} - \boldsymbol{\mu}\|^2$$
$$= \sum_{j=1}^{m} (x_j - \mu_j)^2 \tag{9.36}$$

The random variable V, represented by the sample value v, has a *chi-square distribution*, as shown by (Abramowitz and Stegun, 1965)

$$p_V(v) = \frac{1}{\sigma^m 2^{m/2} \Gamma(m/2)} v^{(m/2)-1} \exp\left(-\frac{v}{2\sigma^2}\right), \qquad v \geq 0 \tag{9.37}$$

where m is the *number of degrees of freedom* of the distribution and $\Gamma(\cdot)$ is the *gamma function*, defined by

$$\Gamma(\alpha) = \int_0^\infty z^{\alpha-1}\exp(-z)dz \qquad (9.38)$$

Let r denote the radial distance to the center of the kernel, defined by

$$r = v^{1/2} = \|\mathbf{x} - \boldsymbol{\mu}\| \qquad (9.39)$$

which represents the sample value of a new random variable R. Then, using the rule for the transformation of the random V into the random variable R, we write

$$p_R(r) = \frac{p_V(v)}{\left|\dfrac{\partial r}{\partial v}\right|} \qquad (9.40)$$

Using this transformation, we find after some appropriate algebraic manipulations that the probability density function of the random variable R, represented by the sample value r, is given by the following (see Problem 9.8):

$$p_R(r) = \begin{cases} \dfrac{1}{2^{(m/2)-1}\Gamma(m/2)}\left(\dfrac{r}{\sigma}\right)^{m-1}\exp\left(-\dfrac{r^2}{2\sigma^2}\right), & r \geq 0 \\ 0, & r < 0 \end{cases} \qquad (9.41)$$

The continuous curves (printed in black) in Fig. 9.14 are plots of the probability density function $p_R(r)$ versus the distance r for unit variance and increasing $m = 1, 2, 3, \ldots$. From these plots we see that as the input-space dimensionality m increases, $p_R(r)$ approaches a Gaussian function rather rapidly. To be more specific, the second-order statistical parameters of the approximating Gaussian function are defined by (Van Hulle, 2002b)

$$\left. \begin{array}{c} \mathbb{E}(R) \approx \sqrt{m}\,\sigma \\[2mm] \mathrm{Var}[R] \approx \dfrac{\sigma^2}{2} \end{array} \right\} \quad \text{for large } m \qquad (9.42)$$

Determination of the cumulative distribution function of the random variable R is addressed in part (a) of Problem 9.9, the solution for which is defined by the *incomplete gamma distribution* (Abramowitz and Stegun, 1965):

$$P_R(r|m) = 1 - \underbrace{\frac{\Gamma\left(\dfrac{m}{2}, \dfrac{r^2}{2\sigma^2}\right)}{\Gamma\left(\dfrac{m}{2}\right)}}_{\substack{\text{Complement of incomplete} \\ \text{gamma distribution}}} \qquad (9.43)$$

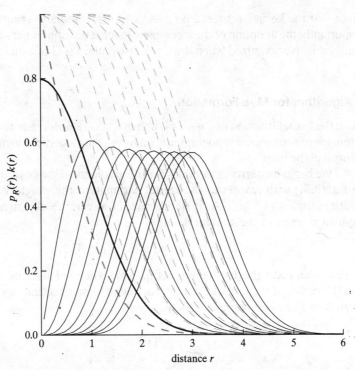

FIGURE 9.14   Two different sets of plots versus the distance r are shown in the figure for unit variance and increasing dimensionality $m = 1, 2, 3, ...$:

- The continuous curves (printed in black) are plots of the probability density function of Eq. (9.41).
- The dashed curves (printed in red) are plots of the complement of the incomplete gamma distribution or, equivalently, kernel $k(r)$ of Eq. (9.44) with $r = \|\mathbf{x} - \mathbf{w}\|$.

(This figure is reproduced with the permission of Dr. Marc Van Hulle.)

The factor $\Gamma\left(\dfrac{m}{2}, \dfrac{r^2}{2\sigma^2}\right) \Big/ \Gamma\left(\dfrac{m}{2}\right)$ is the *complement of the incomplete gamma distribution*, plots of which versus the distance r are also included as the dashed curves (printed in red) in Fig. 9.14 for unit variance and increasing m. These curves also provide graphical plots of the desired kernel. Specifically, viewing r^2 as the squared Euclidean distance between the input vector $\mathbf{x}$ and the weight vector $\mathbf{w}_i$ for the ith neuron, the corresponding kernel $k(\mathbf{x}, \mathbf{w}_i, \sigma_i)$ is finally defined as follows (Van Hulle, 2002b):

$$k(\mathbf{x}, \mathbf{w}_i, \sigma_i) = \frac{1}{\Gamma\left(\dfrac{m}{2}\right)} \Gamma\left(\frac{m}{2}, \frac{\|\mathbf{x} - \mathbf{w}_i\|^2}{2\sigma_i^2}\right), \qquad i = 1, 2, ..., l \qquad (9.44)$$

Note that the kernel, centered on $r = \|\mathbf{x} - \mathbf{w}_i\|$, is radially symmetric for all i. Most importantly, the adoption of the incomplete gamma distribution ensures that the kernel's differential is maximized when the input distribution is Gaussian.

Learning Algorithm for Map Formation

With the kernel function of Eq. (9.44) at hand, we are now ready to formulate the algorithm for self-organized topographic formation, using a kernel function to describe each neuron in the map.

We begin by deriving formulas for the gradients of the objective function defined in Eq. (9.34) with respect to the kernel parameters: the weight vector $\mathbf{w}_i$ and kernel width σ_i for $i = 1, 2, ..., l$. As it stands now, however, the objective function $H(Y_i)$ is defined in terms of the ith neural output

$$y_i = k(\mathbf{x}, \mathbf{w}_i, \sigma_i), \qquad i = 1, 2, ..., l \tag{9.45}$$

On the other hand, the distribution of Eq. (9.41) is defined in terms of the radial distance r to the center of the kernel. We therefore need to make a change of random variables from R to Y_i, and correspondingly we write

$$p_{Y_i}(y_i) = \frac{p_R(r)}{\left|\dfrac{dy_i}{dr}\right|} \tag{9.46}$$

where the denominator on the right-hand side accounts for the dependence of y_i on r. Hence, substituting Eq. (9.46) into Eq. (9.34), we may redefine the objective function $H(Y_i)$ as

$$H(Y_i) = -\int_0^\infty p_R(r)\log p_R(r)dr + \int_0^\infty p_R(r)\log\left|\frac{\partial y_i(r)}{\partial r}\right|dr \tag{9.47}$$

To proceed further, consider first the gradient of $H(Y_i)$ with respect to the weight vector $\mathbf{w}_i$. The first term on the right-hand side of this equation is independent of $\mathbf{w}_i$. The second term is the expectation of the partial derivative $\log|(\partial y_i(r))/dr|$. We may therefore express the derivative of $H(Y_i)$ with respect to $\mathbf{w}_i$ as

$$\frac{\partial H(Y_i)}{\partial \mathbf{w}_i} = \frac{\partial}{\partial \mathbf{w}_i}\mathbb{E}\left[\log\left|\frac{\partial y_i(r)}{\partial r}\right|\right] \tag{9.48}$$

Suppose now that for each kernel we start with a training sample of r's to approximate the probability density function $p_R(r)$ so as to maximize the differential entropy of the kernel output $y_i(r)$. We may then replace the expectation on the right-hand side of Eq. (9.48) with a deterministic quantity, as shown by

$$\mathbb{E}\left[\log\left|\frac{\partial y_i(r)}{\partial r}\right|\right] = \log\left|\frac{\partial \bar{y}_i(r)}{\partial r}\right| \tag{9.49}$$

where $\bar{y}_i(r)$ is the value of $y_i(r)$ averaged over the training sample of r's. Accordingly, we may rewrite Eq. (9.48) in the simplified form

$$\frac{\partial H(\bar{y}_i)}{\partial \mathbf{w}_i} = \frac{\partial}{\partial \mathbf{w}_i}\left(\log\left|\frac{\partial \bar{y}_i(r)}{\partial r}\right|\right)$$

$$= \frac{\partial r}{\partial \mathbf{w}_i}\frac{\partial}{\partial r}\left(\log\left|\frac{\partial \bar{y}_i(r)}{\partial r}\right|\right) \qquad (9.50)$$

The avereged $\bar{y}_i(r)$ has the form of complement of incomplete gamma distribution defined in Eq. (9.43), the use of which yields (see part (b) of Problem 9.9)

$$\frac{\partial \bar{y}_i(r)}{\partial r} = \frac{-\sqrt{2}}{\Gamma(m/2)(\sqrt{2}\sigma_i)^m} r^{m-1}\exp\left(-\frac{r^2}{2\sigma^2}\right) \qquad (9.51)$$

Recall that the kernel is symmetrically centered on the point

$$r = \|\mathbf{x} - \mathbf{w}_i\|$$

Thus, performing the partial differentiation $\partial \bar{y}_i(r)/\partial r$ of Eq. (9.51) with respect to $\mathbf{w}_i$ and substituting the result into Eq. (9.50), we obtain (after simplifying)

$$\frac{\partial H(\bar{y}_i)}{\partial \mathbf{w}_i} = \frac{\mathbf{x} - \mathbf{w}_i}{\sigma_i^2} - (m - 1)\left(\frac{\mathbf{x} - \mathbf{w}_i}{\|\mathbf{x} - \mathbf{w}_i\|^2}\right) \qquad (9.52)$$

The following two remarks about Eq. (9.52) are noteworthy:

(i) Both terms on the right-hand side of the equation converge to the centroid of the input vector $\mathbf{x}$ for a large number of iterations.

(ii) For a Gaussian-distributed input vector $\mathbf{x}$ of dimensionality m, we know from previous discussion that the expectation

$$\mathbb{E}[\|\mathbf{x} - \mathbf{w}_i\|^2] = m\sigma_i^2 \qquad (9.53)$$

The second term on the right-hand side of the equation is therefore expected to be smaller than the first term for all m.

From a computational point of view, it would be highly desirable to simplify Eq. (9.52) so that we end up with a single learning-rate parameter for the update rule pertaining to the weight vector $\mathbf{w}_i$.[11] To this end, we opt for a heuristic proposition: Replace the squared Euclidean term $\|\mathbf{x} - \mathbf{w}_i\|^2$ with the expected value of Eq. (9.53), thereby approximating Eq. (9.52) as follows:

$$\frac{\partial H(\bar{y}_i)}{\partial \mathbf{w}_i} \approx \frac{\mathbf{x} - \mathbf{w}_i}{m\sigma_i^2} \qquad \text{for all } i \qquad (9.54)$$

With the objective function being maximized, the weight update is naturally applied in the same direction as the gradient vector of Eq. (9.54), in accordance with *gradient ascent*. We may thus write

$$\Delta\mathbf{w}_i = \eta_w\left(\frac{\partial H(\bar{y}_i)}{\partial \mathbf{w}_i}\right)$$

where η_w is a small learning-rate parameter. Absorbing the fixed dimensionality m of the input vector $\mathbf{x}$ in η_w, we may finally express the weight adjustment as

$$\Delta\mathbf{w}_i \approx \eta_w\left(\frac{\mathbf{x} - \mathbf{w}_i}{\sigma_i^2}\right) \tag{9.55}$$

The first update formula of the kernel SOM algorithm is therefore

$$\mathbf{w}_i^+ = \mathbf{w}_i + \Delta\mathbf{w}_i$$

$$= \mathbf{w}_i + \eta_w\left(\frac{\mathbf{x} - \mathbf{w}_i}{\sigma_i^2}\right) \tag{9.56}$$

where $\mathbf{w}_i$ and $\mathbf{w}_i^+$ denote the old and updated values of the weight vector of neuron i, respectively.

Consider next the gradient vector of the objective function $H(\bar{y}_i)$ with respect to the kernel width σ_i. Proceeding in a manner similar to that described for the gradient vector $\partial H(\bar{y}_i)/(\partial\mathbf{w}_i)$, we obtain

$$\frac{\partial H(\bar{y}_i)}{\partial\sigma_i} = \frac{1}{\sigma_i}\left(\frac{\|\mathbf{x} - \mathbf{w}_i\|^2}{m\sigma_i^2} - 1\right) \tag{9.57}$$

We may thus define the kernel-width adjustment as

$$\Delta\sigma_i = \eta_\sigma\frac{\partial H(\bar{y}_i)}{\partial\sigma_i}$$

$$= \frac{\eta_\sigma}{\sigma_i}\left(\frac{\|\mathbf{x} - \mathbf{w}_i\|^2}{m\sigma_i^2} - 1\right) \tag{9.58}$$

where η_σ is the second learning-rate parameter. For the second update formula of the kernel SOM algorithm, we therefore have

$$\sigma_i^+ = \sigma_i + \Delta\sigma_i$$

$$= \sigma_i + \frac{\eta_\sigma}{\sigma_i}\left(\frac{\|\mathbf{x} - \mathbf{w}_i\|^2}{m\sigma_i^2} - 1\right) \tag{9.59}$$

The two update rules given by Eqs. (9.56) and (9.59) work well for a single neuron. We next consider their extensions for a network of multiple neurons.

Joint Maximization of the Objective Function

The maximization of the objective function $H(\bar{y}_i)$ on a neuron-by-neuron basis is not sufficient for a workable algorithm. To see why this is so, consider a lattice made up of two neurons whose respective kernel outputs are denoted by y_1 and y_2. When the update equations of Eqs. (9.56) and (9.59) are used, assuming a Gaussian input distribution, for example, the two neural kernels will eventually coincide; in other words, the two kernel outputs y_1 and y_2 become statistically dependent. To guard against this unsatisfactory eventuality (i.e., to maintain the statistical independence of y_1 and y_2 as much as possible), we should maximize the objective function $H(\bar{y}_i)$ by putting the mechanism of kernel adaptation in a *competitive-learning framework*, which is exactly what we did in deriving Kohonen's SOM algorithm.

Then the kernel of the neuron winning the competition will decrease its range of interaction with neighboring neurons, particularly when the winning neuron is strongly active; thus, the overlap with neighboring neurons is diminished. Moreover, as we did with Kohonen's SOM algorithm, we impose a neighborhood function on the learning process in order to topologically preserve the neural lattice with respect to the data distribution of the input space. Accordingly, the combined use of competitive learning and a neighborhood function enables us to use the two update rules with multiple neurons, as discussed next.

Topographic Map Formation

Consider a lattice $\mathcal{A}$ consisting of l neurons characterized by a corresponding set of (complement of incomplete gamma distribution) kernels

$$k(\mathbf{x}, \mathbf{w}_i, \sigma_i), \qquad i = 1, 2, ..., l \tag{9.60}$$

With topographic map formation as the objective, we introduce an activity-based competition among the l neurons in the lattice $\mathcal{A}$, with the *winning neuron* being defined by

$$i(\mathbf{x}) = \arg\max_i y_j(\mathbf{x}), \qquad \text{for } j \in \mathcal{A} \tag{9.61}$$

Note that this *similarity-matching criterion* is different from that of Eq. (9.3), which is based on a minimum distance-based neuronal competition. The two criteria of Eqs. (9.3) and (9.61) are equivalent only when all the neural kernels have equal widths (radii).

To supply the information needed for topological map formation, as in Kohonen's SOM, we introduce a *neighborhood function* $h_{j,i(\mathbf{x})}$, centered on the winning neuron $i(\mathbf{x})$. Moreover, following the discussion in Section 9.3, we adopt a monotonically decreasing function of the lattice distance from the winning neuron $i(\mathbf{x})$. In particular, we opt for the Gaussian function of Eq. (9.4), reproduced here in the form

$$h_{j,i(\mathbf{x})} = \exp\left(-\frac{\|\mathbf{x}_j - \mathbf{w}_i\|^2}{2\sigma^2}\right), \qquad j \in \mathcal{A} \tag{9.62}$$

where σ denotes the range of the neighborhood function $h_{j,i(\mathbf{x})}$; the neighborhood range σ should not be confused with the kernel width σ_i.

Summary of the Kernel SOM Algorithm

We are now ready to describe the steps involved in the kernel self-organizing map:

1. *Initialization.* Choose random values for the initial weight vectors $\mathbf{w}_i(0)$ and kernel widths $\sigma_i(0)$ for $i = 1, 2, ..., l$, where l is the total number of neurons in the lattice structure. The only restriction here is that the $\mathbf{w}_i(0)$ and $\sigma_i(0)$ be different for the different neurons.

2. *Sampling.* Draw a sample $\mathbf{x}$ from the input distribution with a certain probability.

3. *Similarity matching.* At time-step n of the algorithm, identify the winning neuron $i(\mathbf{x})$, using the criterion:

$$i(\mathbf{x}) = \arg\max_i y_j(\mathbf{x}), \qquad j = 1, 2, ..., l$$

4. *Adaptation.* Adjust the weight vector and width of each kernel, using the respective update formulas

$$
\mathbf{w}_j(n+1) =
\begin{cases}
\mathbf{w}_j(n) + \dfrac{\eta_w h_{j,i(\mathbf{x})}}{\sigma_j^2}(\mathbf{x}(n) - \mathbf{w}_j(n)), & j \in \mathcal{A} \\[2ex]
\mathbf{w}_j(n), & \text{otherwise}
\end{cases}
\tag{9.63}
$$

$$
\sigma_j(n+1) =
\begin{cases}
\sigma_j(n) + \dfrac{\eta_\sigma h_{j,i(\mathbf{x})}}{\sigma_j(n)}\left[\dfrac{\|\mathbf{x}(n) - \mathbf{w}_j(n)\|^2}{m\sigma_j^2(n)} - 1\right], & j \in \mathcal{A} \\[2ex]
\sigma_j(n), & \text{otherwise}
\end{cases}
\tag{9.64}
$$

where η_w and η_σ are the two learning-rate parameters of the algorithm and $h_{j,i(\mathbf{x})}$ is the neighborhood function centered on the winning neuron $i(\mathbf{x})$, defined in accordance with Eq. (9.61). As in Kohonen's SOM, the neighborood range σ is permitted to decay exponentially over time.

9.9 COMPUTER EXPERIMENT II: DISENTANGLING LATTICE DYNAMICS USING KERNEL SOM

In this experiment, we revisit a two-dimensional lattice, which was studied in part I of the computer experiment of Section 9.5, except that this time we use the kernel SOM in the experiment. The two learning-rate parameters of the algorithm were chosen to be

$$\eta_w = 0.01$$

and

$$\eta_\sigma = 10^{-4}\eta_w$$

The two-dimensional lattice is a square lattice made up of 24-by-24 neurons, and the input data are uniformly distributed. The weights were initialized by sampling from the same input distribution, and the radii were initialized by sampling the uniform distribution $[0, 0.1]$. The neighborhood function used a Gaussian function with the width

$$\sigma(n) = \sigma_0 \exp\left(-2\sigma_0\left(\frac{n}{n_{\max}}\right)\right) \tag{9.64}$$

where $n_{\max}$ denotes the maximum number of time-steps and σ_0 denotes the range spanned by the neighborhood function at time $n = 0$. The values used in the experiment are

$$n_{\max} = 2 \times 10^6$$

and

$$\sigma_0 = 12$$

These choices were made to ensure that the neighborhood function will vanish at the end of the learning process, at which point it assumes the approximate value 4.5×10^{-10},

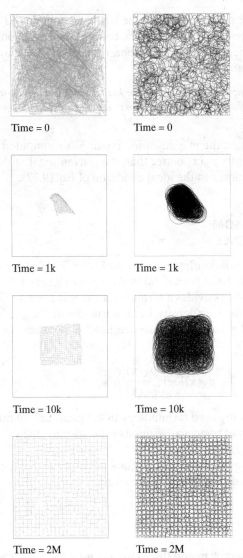

Time = 0   Time = 0

Time = 1k   Time = 1k

Time = 10k   Time = 10k

Time = 2M   Time = 2M

FIGURE 9.15   The evolution of a 24-by-24 lattice over time, the values of which (in terms of the number of iterations) are given below each picture. Left column: Evolution of the kernel weights. Right column: Evolution of the kernel widths. Each box in the figure outlines the result of a uniform input distribution. The time given below each map represents the number of iterations. (This figure is reproduced with the permission of Dr. Marc Van Hulle.)

which is practically zero. When this condition is finally reached, the neighborhood function encompasses the winning neuron alone.

Figure 9.15 presents two sequences illustrating the disentanglement of the topographic maps produced by the kernel SOM algorithm. Note that

- the pictures displayed in the left-hand column of the figure show the evolution of the kernel weights over time n;
- the pictures displayed in the right-half column of the figure show the corresponding evolution of the kernel widths over time n.

Comparing the final form of the topographic map on the left-hand column of Fig. 9.15 with that of Fig. 9.8, computed by the kernel SOM and the conventional SOM on 24-by-24 lattices and for roughly the same number of iterations, respectively, we may make the following significant observation:

> *The distribution of the topographic map computed by the kernel SOM is much closer to the uniform distribution assigned to the input data space than that of the topographic map computed by the conventional SOM.*

Accordingly, we may go on to say that the magnification factor $m(\mathbf{x})$ computed by the kernel SOM matches the input density $p_{\mathbf{X}}(\mathbf{x})$ better than the conventional SOM does; that is, the kernel SOM may come closer to the ideal condition of Eq. (9.27).

9.10 RELATIONSHIP BETWEEN KERNEL SOM AND KULLBACK–LEIBLER DIVERGENCE

We find it informative to discuss the relationship between the kernel SOM (using incomplete gamma distribution kernels) and *Kullback–Leibler divergence* (KLD). KLD, to be discussed in detail in the next chapter, provides a formula for assessing the quality of a density estimate measured against the true density. Let the true density be denoted by $p_{\mathbf{X}}(\mathbf{x})$ and its estimate be denoted by $\hat{p}_{\mathbf{X}}(\mathbf{x})$. Then we define KLD between these two densities as

$$D_{p_{\mathbf{X}}\|\hat{p}_{\mathbf{X}}} = \int_{-\infty}^{\infty} p_{\mathbf{X}}(\mathbf{x})\log\left(\frac{p_{\mathbf{X}}(\mathbf{x})}{\hat{p}_{\mathbf{X}}(\mathbf{x})}\right)d\mathbf{x} \tag{9.65}$$

where we have followed the commonly used terminology in the literature on information theory. So defined, KLD is always a nonnegative number that assumes the value zero if, and only if, $\hat{p}_{\mathbf{X}}(\mathbf{x})$ matches $p_{\mathbf{X}}(\mathbf{x})$ exactly.

For the present discussion, suppose the density estimate is expressed as a *mixture of Gaussian density functions* with equal mixings, as shown by

$$\hat{p}_{\mathbf{X}}(\mathbf{x}|\mathbf{w}_i,\sigma_i) = \frac{1}{l}\sum_{i=1}^{l}\frac{1}{(2\pi)^{m/2}\sigma_i^m}\exp\left(-\frac{1}{2\sigma_i^2}\|\mathbf{x}-\mathbf{w}_i\|^2\right) \tag{9.66}$$

which is conditional on the weight vector $\mathbf{w}_i$ and the width σ_i, for $i = 1, 2, ..., l$. The optimal density estimate, $p_{\mathbf{X}}(\mathbf{x})$, is obtained by minimizing the KLD between it and the density estimate $\hat{p}_{\mathbf{X}}(\mathbf{x}|\mathbf{w}_i, \sigma_i)$, In effect, the optimal density estimate $p_{\mathbf{X}}(\mathbf{x})$ is viewed as the true density. With optimality as the issue of interest, we need to differentiate the KLD of Eq. (9.66) with respect to the adjustable parameters, $\mathbf{w}_i$ and σ_i. To this end, we obtain the following pair of partial derivatives with respect to $\mathbf{w}_i$:

$$\frac{\partial}{\partial \mathbf{w}_i}(D_{p_{\mathbf{X}}\|\hat{p}_{\mathbf{X}}}) = \frac{\partial}{\partial \mathbf{w}_i}\int_{-\infty}^{\infty}p_{\mathbf{X}}(\mathbf{x})\log\left(\frac{p_{\mathbf{X}}(\mathbf{x})}{\hat{p}_{\mathbf{X}}(\mathbf{x}|\mathbf{w}_i,\sigma_i)}\right)d\mathbf{x}$$

$$= \int_{-\infty}^{\infty}\frac{\partial}{\partial \mathbf{w}_i}(p_{\mathbf{X}}(\mathbf{x})\log p_{\mathbf{X}}(\mathbf{x}) - p_{\mathbf{X}}(\mathbf{x})\log \hat{p}_{\mathbf{X}}(\mathbf{x}|\mathbf{w}_i,\sigma_i))d\mathbf{x}$$

$$= -\int_{-\infty}^{\infty} p_{\mathbf{X}}(\mathbf{x}) \frac{\partial}{\partial \mathbf{w}_i} (\log \hat{p}_{\mathbf{X}}(\mathbf{x}|\mathbf{w}_i, \sigma_i)) d\mathbf{x}$$

$$= -\int_{-\infty}^{\infty} p_{\mathbf{X}}(\mathbf{x}) \left(\frac{1}{\hat{p}_{\mathbf{X}}(\mathbf{x}|\mathbf{w}_i, \sigma_i)} \frac{\partial}{\partial \mathbf{w}_i} \hat{p}_{\mathbf{X}}(\mathbf{x}|\mathbf{w}_i, \sigma_i) \right) d\mathbf{x} \qquad (9.67)$$

Similarly, we may express the partial derivative with respect to σ_i as

$$\frac{\partial}{\partial \sigma_i} (D_{p_{\mathbf{X}} \| \hat{p}_{\mathbf{X}}}) = -\int_{-\infty}^{\infty} p_{\mathbf{X}}(\mathbf{x}) \left(\frac{1}{\hat{p}_{\mathbf{X}}(\mathbf{x}|\mathbf{w}_i, \sigma_i)} \frac{\partial}{\partial \sigma_i} \hat{p}_{\mathbf{X}}(\mathbf{x}|\mathbf{w}_i, \sigma_i) \right) d\mathbf{x} \qquad (9.68)$$

Setting these two partial derivatives of the KLD equal to zero and then invoking stochastic approximation theory (Robbins and Monro, 1951), we obtain the pair of learning rules (Van Hulle, 2002b)

$$\Delta \mathbf{w}_i = \eta_{\mathbf{w}} \hat{p}_{\mathbf{X}}(\mathbf{x}|\mathbf{w}_i, \sigma_i) \left(\frac{\mathbf{x} - \mathbf{w}_i}{\sigma_i^2} \right), \qquad (9.69)$$

and

$$\Delta \sigma_i = \eta_{\mathbf{w}} \hat{p}_{\mathbf{X}}(\mathbf{x}|\mathbf{w}_i, \sigma_i) \cdot \frac{m}{\sigma_i} \left(\frac{\|\mathbf{x} - \mathbf{w}_i\|^2}{m \sigma_i^2} - 1 \right) \qquad (9.70)$$

for $i = 1, 2, ..., l$; the term $\hat{p}_{\mathbf{X}}(\mathbf{x}|\mathbf{w}_i, \sigma_i)$ is the conditional posterior density of the ith neuron characterized by the weight vector $\mathbf{w}_i$ and width σ_i.

Suppose we set the conditional posterior density

$$\hat{p}_{\mathbf{X}}(\mathbf{x}_j|\mathbf{w}_i, \sigma_i) = \delta_{ji} \quad \text{for } j = 1, 2, ..., l \qquad (9.71)$$

where

$$\delta_{ji} = \begin{cases} 1 \text{ for } j = i \\ 0 \text{ for } j \neq i \end{cases}$$

When this ideal condition is satisfied, we say that neuron i is the winning neuron in the competition among the neurons $j = 1, 2, ..., l$. We may therefore view the conditional posterior density function $\hat{p}_{\mathbf{X}}(\mathbf{x}|\mathbf{w}_j, \sigma_j)$ as playing the role of the topological neighborhood function $h_{j, i(\mathbf{x})}$ introduced in the formulation of the kernel SOM. Indeed, setting

$$\hat{p}_{\mathbf{X}}(\mathbf{x}|\mathbf{w}_j, \sigma_j) = h_{j, i(\mathbf{x})} \qquad (9.72)$$

we find that the pair of update rules derived from the Kullback–Leibler divergence, namely, Eqs. (9.69) and (9.70), has a mathematical form similar to the corresponding pair of update rules, Eqs. (9.63) and (9.64), derived in Section 9.9 for the kernel SOM.

We may therefore make the following statement (Van Hulle, 2002b):

> *Minimization of the Kullback–Leibler divergence, assuming a Gaussian mixture model, is equivalent to maximization of the joint entropy defined in terms of incomplete gamma distribution kernels and an activity-based neighborhood function, which are at the core of kernel SOM.*

This statement is particularly important in the context of *density estimation*, where we are given a data set $\{\mathbf{x}_i\}_{i=1}^{N}$ and the requirement is to compute an estimate of the underlying distribution intrinsic to generation of the data.

9.11 SUMMARY AND DISCUSSION

Self-Organizing Map

The self-organizing map due to Kohonen (1982) is a simple, yet powerful, algorithm that is typically built around a one- or two-dimensional lattice of neurons for capturing the important features contained in an input (data) space of interest. In so doing, it provides a structural representation of the input data by the neurons' weight vectors as prototypes. The SOM algorithm is neurobiologically inspired, incorporating the mechanisms that are basic to self-organization, as discussed in Chapter 8: competition, cooperation, self-amplification, and structural information. It may therefore serve as a generic, though degenerate, model for describing the emergent behavior of collective-ordering phenomena in complex systems after starting from total disorder. In other words, the SOM has a built-in capability of producing "order out of disorder" in an evolutionary process over the course of time.

The self-organizing map may also be viewed as a vector quantizer, thereby providing an analytic approach for deriving the update rule used to adjust the weight vectors (Luttrell, 1989b). This latter approach clearly emphasizes the role of the neighborhood function as a probability density function.

It should, however, be emphasized that this latter approach, based on the use of average distribution D_1 in Eq. (9.19) as the cost function to be minimized, can be justified only when the feature map is already well ordered. In Erwin et al. (1992b), it is shown that the learning dynamics of a self-organizing map during the ordering phase of the adaptive process (i.e., during the topological ordering of a feature map that is initially highly disordered) *cannot* be described by a stochastic gradient descent on a *single* cost function. But in the case of a one-dimensional lattice, it may be described using a set of cost functions, one for each neuron in the network, that are independently minimized following a stochastic gradient descent.

Convergence Considerations of Self-Organizing Map

What is remarkable about Kohonen's SOM algorithm is that it is so simple to implement, yet mathematically so difficult to analyze its properties in a general setting. Some fairly powerful methods have been used to analyze it by several investigators, but they have only produced results of limited applicability. In Cottrell et al. (1997), a survey of results on theoretical aspects of the SOM algorithm is given. In particular, the survey highlights a result given by Forte and Pagés (1995, 1996) which states that in the case of a one-dimensional lattice, we have a rigorous proof of the "almost sure" convergence of the SOM algorithm to a unique state after completion of the self-organization phase. This important result has been shown to hold for a general class of neighborhood functions. However, the same cannot be said in a multidimensional setting.

Neurobiological Considerations

With the self-organizing map being inspired by ideas derived from cortical maps in the brain, it seems natural to enquire whether such a model could actually explain the formation of cortical maps. Erwin et al. (1995) have performed such an investigation. They have shown that the self-organizing map is able to explain the formation of computational maps in the primary visual cortex of the macaque monkey. The input space used in this study had five dimensions: two dimensions for representing the position of a receptive field in retinotopic space, and the remaining three dimensions for respectively representing orientation preference, orientation selectivity, and ocular dominance. The cortical surface is divided into small patches that are considered as computational units (i.e., artificial neurons) of a two-dimensional square lattice. Under certain assumptions, it is shown that Hebbian learning leads to spatial patterns of orientation and ocular dominance that are remarkably similar to those found in the macaque monkey.

Applications of The Self-Organizing Map

The combination of the simplicity of the SOM algorithm and its powerful capability for insightful visualization has prompted the algorithm's use for many large-scale applications. Typically, the algorithm is trained in an unsupervised mode, using a large training sample of data. In particular, if the data contain *semantically related object groupings* (*classes*), the subsets of vectors belonging to the user-defined classes are mapped by the SOM in such a way that the distribution of the data vectors over the map computed by the algorithm provides a two-dimensional discrete approximation of the underlying distribution of the original data space. Building on this idea, in Laaksonen et al. (2004) and Laaksonen and Viitaniemi (2007), the SOM is successfully used to detect and describe *ontological relations* between semantic objects and object classes in a visual database containing 2,618 images, each of which belongs to one or more predefined semantic classes. The ontological relations used in the study include the following:

- simultaneous existence of objects from two or more object classes in one image;
- taxonomy of visual similarity;
- spatial relationships between different object types in one image.

In another application altogether different, Honkela et al. (1995) have used the SOM algorithm to study the semantic roles of words in natural languages, where the roles are reflected by the contexts in which they occur. The objective of the study was to compute a *contextual map* for the explicit visualization of these roles. In the experiments carried out in the study, the source database consisted of English translations of fairy tales by the Brothers Grimm, without any prior syntactic or semantic categorization of the words; the number of words was almost 250,000 in total, and the size of the vocabulary was over 7,000 words. The SOM algorithm was able to create a contextual map that seemed to comply reasonably well with the traditional syntactical categorizations and human intuition about the semantics of the words. The analysis of textual content has been extended to collections of millions of documents; in this kind of application, the number of neurons in the lattice may reach hundreds of thousands, and the dimensionality of the input data space may be as high as thousands (Honkela, 2007). It is large-scale applications of this kind that make the self-organizing map such a powerful tool.

The Kernel SOM

In the latter part of the chapter, we described Van Hulle's (2002b) kernel SOM algorithm, the primary aim of which is to provide improved topographic mappings and approximate distribution capabilities. A distinctive feature of the kernel SOM is that its derivation begins with the formulation of an entropic objective function. Most importantly, the kernel SOM is an *on-line, stochastic-gradient-based algorithm.*

Comparing the two self-organizing maps studied in the chapter, we may say that the standard SOM and kernel SOM have similar update rules for the weight vectors in the neural lattice. Also, they make the weight updates in the same direction, but use different learning-rate parameters. Unlike the standard SOM, the kernel SOM has the built-in capability to automatically adjust the kernel with σ_i for each neuron i in the lattice, so as to maximize the joint entropy of the kernel (neuron) outputs.

However, the kernel SOM requires careful tuning of the two learning-rate parameters η_w and η_σ, in order to keep the weight and width updates from exploding. This explosion happens if, and when, the inverse of the kernel-width variance σ_i^2 becomes greater than the learning-rate parameter η_w or η_σ. Such undesirable behavior is attributed to the fact that in the update rules of Eqs. (9.56) and (9.59), the learning-rate parameters η_w and η_σ are divided by σ_i^2 and σ_i, respectively. To avoid the possibility of explosive growth in $\mathbf{w}_i$ and σ_i, we may replace σ_i^2 by the sum term $\sigma_i^2 + \alpha$, where α is a prescribed small constant.

NOTES AND REFERENCES

1. There are other types of competitive learning where there is no winner, such as those discussed in Heskes (2001) and Van Hulle (2005).

2. The two feature-mapping models of Fig. 9.1 were inspired by the pioneering self-organizing studies of von der Malsburg (1973), who noted that a model of the visual cortex could not be entirely genetically predetermined; rather, a self-organizing process involving synaptic learning may be responsible for the *local* ordering of feature-sensitive cortical cells. However, global topographic ordering was *not* achieved in von der Malsburg's model, because the model used a fixed (small) neighborhood. The computer simulation by von der Malsburg was perhaps the first to demonstrate self-organization.

3. Amari (1980) relaxes this restriction on the synaptic weights of the postsynaptic neurons somewhat. The mathematical analysis presented by Amari elucidates the dynamic stability of a cortical map formed by self-organization.

4. The competitive-learning rule described in Eq. (9.3) was first introduced into the neural network literature in Grossberg (1969).

5. In the original form of the SOM algorithm derived by Kohonen (1982), the topological neighborhood is assumed to have a constant amplitude. Let $d_{j,i}$ denote the *lateral distance* between winning neuron i and excited neuron j inside the neighborhood function. The topological neighborhood for the case of a one-dimensional lattice was defined by

$$h_{j,i} = \begin{cases} 1, & -K \le d_{j,i} \le K \\ 0, & \text{otherwise} \end{cases} \tag{A}$$

where $2K$ is the overall size of the one-dimensional neighborhood of excited neurons. Contrary to neurobiological considerations, the implication of the model described in Eq. (A) is that all the neurons located inside the topological neighborhood fire at the same rate, and the interaction among those neurons is independent of their lateral distance from the winning neuron i.

6. In Erwin et al. (1992b), it is shown that metastable states, representing topological defects in the configuration of a feature map, arise when the SOM algorithm uses a neighborhood

function that is not convex. A broad, convex neighborhood function, such as a broad Gaussian, leads to relatively shorter topological ordering times than a nonconvex one, due to the absence of metastable states.

7. In Note 3 of Chapter 5, it was pointed out that the communications and information theory literature, an early method known as the *Lloyd algorithm* was proposed for scalar quantization. The algorithm was first described by Lloyd in an unpublished 1957 report at Bell Laboratories (Lloyd, 1957) and then much later appeared in published form (Lloyd, 1982). The Lloyd algorithm is also sometimes referred to as the "Max quantizer." The *generalized Lloyd algorithm* (GLA) for vector quantization is a direct generalization of Lloyd's original algorithm. The generalized Lloyd algorithm is sometimes referred to as the *k-means algorithm*, after McQueen (1967), who used it as a tool for statistical clustering, as discussed in Chapter 5. In that previous chapter, we did point out that the k-means algorithm operates in a manner similar to the *expectation-maximization (EM) algorithm*; the only basic difference between them is that the objective function of the k-means algorithm, and likewise that of the GLA, is minimized, whereas the objective function of the EM algorithm is maximized. The EM algorithm is discussed in Chapter 11. For a historical account of the Lloyd algorithm and generalized Lloyd algorithm, see Gersho and Gray (1992).

8. In Kohonen (1993), experimental results are presented showing that the batch version of the SOM algorithm is faster than its on-line version. However, the adaptive capability of the SOM algorithm is lost when using the batch version.

9. The topological property of a self-organizing map may be assessed quantitavely in different ways. One such quantitative measure, called the *topographic product*, is described in Bauer and Pawelzik (1992). It may be used to compare the faithful behavior of different feature maps pertaining to different dimensionalities. However, the measure is quantitative only when the dimension of the lattice matches that of the input space.

10. The inability of the SOM algorithm to provide a faithful representation of the distribution that underlies the input data has prompted modifications to the algorithm and the development of new self-organizing algorithms that are faithful to the input.

    Two types of modifications to the SOM algorithm have been reported in the literature:

    (i) *Modification to the competitive process.*   In DeSieno (1988), a form of memory is used to track the cumulative activities of individual neurons in the lattice. Specifically, a "conscience" mechanism is added to bias the competitive-learning process of the SOM algorithm. This is done in such a way that each neuron, regardless of its location in the lattice, has the chance to win competition with a probability close to the ideal of $1/l$, where l is the total number of neurons. A description of the SOM algorithm with conscience is presented in Problem 9.7.

    (ii) *Modification to the adaptive process.*   In this second approach, the update rule for adjusting the weight vector of each neuron under the neighborhood function is modified to control the magnification properties of the feature map. In Bauer et al. (1996), it is shown that through the addition of an adjustable step-size parameter to the update rule, it is possible for the feature map to provide a faithful representation of the input distribution. Lin et al. (1997) follow a similar path by introducing two modifications to the SOM algorithm:

    - The update rule is modified to extract direct dependence on the input vector **x** and weight vector $\mathbf{w}_j$ of neuron j in question.
    - The Voronoi partition is replaced with an equivariant partition designed specially for separable input distributions.

This second modification enables the SOM algorithm to perform blind source separation. (Blind source separation is explained in detail in Chapter 10.)

The modifications mentioned build on the standard SOM algorithm in one form or another. In Linsker (1989b), a completely different approach is taken. Specifically, a global learning rule for topographic map formation is derived by maximizing the mutual information between the output signal and the signal part of the input corrupted by additive noise. (The notion of mutual information, rooted in Shannon's information theory, is discussed in Chapter 10.) Linsker's model yields a distribution of neurons that matches the input distribution exactly. The use of an information-theoretic approach to topographic map formation in a self-organized manner is also pursued in Van Hulle (1996, 1997).

11. In Van Hulle (2002), ignoring the second term on the right-hand side of Eq. (9.52) is based on the following arguments:

- The expected value of $\|\mathbf{x} - \mathbf{w}_i\|^2$ obtained for a Gaussian-distributed input vector $\mathbf{x}$ is defined in Eq. (9.53).
- In an m-dimensional radially symmetric Gaussian distribution, the distribution can be built up by taking m samples, with one sample for each input dimension. Then, in a one-dimensional Gaussian distribution with the same radius, when the weight updates Δw_{ij} are small (which presumes the use of a small learning-rate parameter η_w) and when the update is performed along each input dimension separately (i.e., in random order), the second term of Eq. (9.52) may be ignored.

PROBLEMS

SOM algorithm

9.1 The algorithm responsible for the formation of the self-organizing maps first initializes the synaptic weights in the network. Once the network has been properly initialized, three essential processes are performed for the formation of the self-organizing map. Explain these three processes.

9.2 Assume that $\pi(\mathbf{v})$ is a smooth function of the noise $\mathbf{v}$ in the model of Fig. 9.6. Using a Taylor expansion of the distortion measure of Eq. (9.19), determine the curvature term that arises from the noise model $\pi(\mathbf{v})$.

9.3 It is sometimes said that the SOM algorithm *preserves* the topological relationships that exist in the input space. Strictly speaking, this property can be guaranteed only for an input space of equal or lower dimensionality than that of the neural lattice. Discuss the validity of this latter statement.

9.4 It is said that the SOM algorithm based on competitive learning lacks any tolerance against hardware failure. However, the algorithm is error-tolerant in that a small perturbation applied to the input vector causes the output to jump from the winning neuron to a neighboring one. Discuss the implications of these two statements.

9.5 Consider the batch version of the SOM algorithm obtained by expressing Eq. (9.23) in its discrete form, leading to the formula

$$\mathbf{w}_j = \frac{\sum_i \pi_{j,i} \mathbf{x}_i}{\sum_i \pi_{j,i}}, \qquad j = 1, 2, ..., l$$

Show that this version of the SOM algorithm can be expressed in a form similar to the Nadaraya–Watson regression estimator (Cherkassky and Mulier, 1995); this estimator was discussed in Chapter 5.

TABLE P9.7   Summary of the Conscience Algorithm

1. Find the synaptic-weight vector $\mathbf{w}_i$ closest to the input vector $\mathbf{x}$:

$$\|\mathbf{x} - \mathbf{w}_i\| = \min_j \|\mathbf{x} - \mathbf{w}_j\|, \quad j = 1, 2, ..., N$$

2. Keep a running total of the fraction of time, p_j, that neuron j wins the competition, given as

$$p_j^{new} = p_j^{old} + B(y_j - p_j^{old})$$

where B is a small positive number, and

$$y_j = \begin{cases} 1 & \text{if neuron } j \text{ is the winning neuron} \\ 0 & \text{otherwise} \end{cases}$$

The p_j are initialized to zero at the beginning of the algorithm.

3. Find the new winning neuron, using the conscience mechanism

$$\|\mathbf{x} - \mathbf{w}_i\| = \min_j (\|\mathbf{x} - \mathbf{w}_j\| - b_j)$$

where b_j is a *bias term* introduced to modify the competition; it is defined as

$$b_j = C\left(\frac{1}{N} - p_j\right)$$

where C is a bias factor and N is the total number of neurons in the network.

4. Update the synaptic-weight vector of the winning neuron to obtain

$$\mathbf{w}_i^{new} = \mathbf{w}_i^{old} + \eta(\mathbf{x} - \mathbf{w}_i^{old})$$

where η is the usual learning-rate parameter used in the SOM algorithm.

Learning vector quantization

9.6 Why is vector quantization considered as lossy data compression technique? Compare the computational speed of conventional vector quantization algorithms with that of multi-stage hierarchical vector quantization.

9.7 The *conscience algorithm* is a modification of the SOM algorithm that forces the density matching to be exact (DeSieno, 1988). In the conscience algorithm, summarized in Table P9.7, each neuron keeps track of how many times it has won the competition (i.e., how many times its synaptic-weight vector has been the neuron closest to the input vector in Euclidean distance). The notion used here is that if a neuron wins too often, it "feels guilty" and therefore pulls itself out of the competition.

To investigate the improvement produced in density matching by the use of the conscience algorithm, consider a one-dimensional lattice (i.e., linear array) made up of 20 neurons that is trained with the linear input density plotted in Fig. P9.7.

(a) Using computer simulations, compare the density matching produced by the conscience algorithm with that produced by the SOM algorithm. For the SOM algorithm use $\eta = 0.05$, and for the conscience algorithm use $B = 0.0001$, $C = 1.0$, and $\eta = 0.05$.

(b) As frames of reference for this comparison, include the "exact" match to the input density. Discuss the results of your computer simulations.

Kernel self-organizing map

9.8 Using the transformation formula of Eq. (9.40) applied to Eq. (9.37), derive the probability density function of Eq. (9.41).

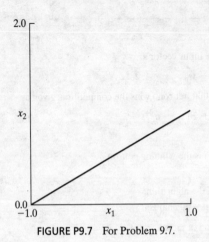

FIGURE P9.7 For Problem 9.7.　　　　　　**FIGURE P9.11** For Problem 9.11.

9.9 This problem is in two parts, addressing the issues involved in deriving couple of equations that pertain to the kernel SOM algorithm:

(a) The *incomplete gamma distribution* of a random variable X, with sample value x, is defined by (Abramowitz and Stegun, 1965, p. 260):

$$P_X(x|\alpha) = \frac{1}{\Gamma(\alpha)} \int_0^x t^{\alpha-1} \exp(-t)dt$$

where $\Gamma(\alpha)$ is the gamma function. The *complement* of the incomplete gamma distribution is correspondingly defined by

$$\Gamma(\alpha, x) = \frac{1}{\Gamma(\alpha)} \int_x^\infty t^{\alpha-1} \exp(-t)dt$$

Using these two formulas, derive the cumulative distribution function of random variable R that is defined in Eq. (9.43).

(b) Using the formula of the incomplete gamma distribution as the definition of the averaged neural output $\bar{y}_i$, derive Eq. (9.51) for the partial derivative $\partial \bar{y}_i(r)/\partial r$.

9.10 In developing the approximate update formula of Eq. (9.55) for the weight vector of the kernel SOM algorithm, we justified ignoring the second term in Eq. (9.52). Yet, in deriving the update formula of Eq. (9.58) for the kernel width σ_i, no approximation was made. Justify this latter choice.

Computer Experiments

9.11 In this experiment, we use computer simulations to investigate the SOM algorithm applied to a one-dimensional lattice with a two-dimensional input. The lattice consists of 65 neurons. The inputs consist of random points uniformly distributed inside the triangular area shown in Fig. P9.11. Compute the map produced by the SOM algorithm after 0, 20, 100, 1,000, 10,000, and 25,000 iterations.

9.12 Consider a two-dimensional lattice of neurons trained with a three-dimensional input distribution. The lattice consists of 10×10 neurons.

(a) The input is uniformly distributed in a thin volume defined by

$$\{(0 < x_1 < 1), (0 < x_2 < 1), (0 < x_3 < 0.2)\}$$

Use the SOM algorithm to compute a two-dimensional projection of the input space after 50, 1,000, and 10,000 iterations of the algorithm.

(b) Repeat your computations for the case when the input is uniformly distributed inside a wider parallelepiped volume defined by

$$\{(0 < x_1 < 1), (0 < x_2 < 1), (0 < x_3 < 0.4)\}$$

(c) Repeat your computations one more time for the case when the input is uniformly distributed inside a cube defined by

$$\{(0 < x_1 < 1), (0 < x_2 < 1), (0 < x_3 < 1)\}$$

Discuss the implications of the results of your computer simulations.

9.13 A problem that occasionally arises in the application of the SOM algorithm is the failure of topological ordering by creating a "folded" map. This problem arises when the neighborhood size is permitted to decay too rapidly. The creation of a folded map may be viewed as some form of a "local minimum" of the topological-ordering process.

To investigate this phenomenon, consider a two-dimensional lattice of a 10×20 network of neurons trained on a two-dimensional input uniformly distributed inside the square $\{(-1 < x_1 < +1), (-1 < x_2 < +1)\}$. Compute the map produced by the SOM algorithm, permitting the neighborhood function around the winning neuron to decay much faster than that normally used. You may have to repeat the experiment several times in order to see a failure of the ordering process.

9.14 The topological-ordering property of the SOM algorithm may be used to form an abstract two-dimensional representation of a high-dimensional input space. To investigate this form of a representation, consider a two-dimensional lattice consisting of a 10×10 network of neurons that is trained with an input consisting of four Gaussian clouds $\mathscr{C}_1$, $\mathscr{C}_2$ $\mathscr{C}_3$, and $\mathscr{C}_4$ in an eight-dimensional input space. All the clouds have unit variance, but different centers. The centers are located at the points $(0, 0, 0, ..., 0)$, $(4, 0, 0, ..., 0)$, $(4, 4, 0, ..., 0)$, and $(0, 4, 0, ..., 0)$. Compute the map produced by the SOM algorithm, with each neuron in the map being labeled with the particular class most frequently represented by the input points around it.

9.15 Table P9.15 presents a summary of the *renormalized SOM algorithm*; a brief description of the algorithm is given in Section 9.3. Compare the conventional and renormalized SOM algorithms, keeping in mind the following two issues:

1. the coding complexity involved in algorithmic implementation;
2. the computer time taken to do the training.

Illustrate the comparison between these two algorithms using data drawn from a uniform distribution inside a square and the following two network configurations:

(a) a one-dimensional lattice of 257 neurons;
(b) a one-dimensional lattice of 2,049 neurons.

In both cases, start with an initial number of code vectors equal to two.

9.16 Consider the signal-space diagram shown in Fig. P9.16 corresponding to *M-level pulse-amplitude modulation* (PAM) with $M = 8$. The signal points correspond to Gray-encoded data blocks. Each signal point is represented by a rectangular pulse signal with appropriate amplitude scaling

$$p(t) = \pm\frac{7}{2}, \ \pm\frac{5}{2}, \ \pm\frac{3}{2}, \ \pm\frac{1}{2}, \quad 0 \le t \le T$$

TABLE P9.15 Summary of Renormalized Training Algorithm (One-Dimensional Version)

1. *Initialization.* Set the number of code vectors to be some small number (e.g., use two for simplicity, or some other value more representative of the problem at hand). Initialize their positions to be those of a corresponding number of training vectors chosen randomly from the training sample.

2. *Selection of an input vector.* Choose an input vector randomly from the training sample.

3. *Encoding of the input vector.* Determine the "winning" code vector (i.e., the synaptic-weight vector of the winning neuron). To do this, use either the nearest-neighbor or the minimum-distortion encoding prescription as required.

4. *Updating of the code book.* Do the usual "winner and its topological neighbors" update. You may find it sufficient to keep the learning-rate parameter η fixed (at 0.125, say) and to update the winning neuron by using η and its nearest neighbors by using $\eta/2$, for example.

5. *Splitting of the code book.*[a] Continue with the code-book update (step 4), each time using a new input vector chosen randomly from the training sample, until the number of code-book updates is about 10–30 times the number of code vectors. When this number is reached, the code book has probably settled down, and it is time to split the code book. You may do so by taking the Peano string of code vectors that you have and interpolating their positions to generate a finer grained approximation to the Peano string; you may simply put an extra code vector halfway between each two existing code vectors.

6. *Completion of training.* The code-book update and the code-book splitting are continued until the total number of code vectors has reached some predetermined value (e.g., 100), at which time the training is all over.

---

[a]The splitting of the code book approximately doubles the number of code vectors after each epoch, so it does not take too many epochs to get to any prescribed number of code vectors.

where T is the signaling interval. At the receiver input, white Gaussian noise of zero mean is added to the transmitted signal with varying signal-to-noise ratio (SNR). The SNR is defined as the ratio of the "average" transmitted signal power to the average noise power.

(a) Using a random binary sequence as the transmitter input, generate data representing the received signal for SNR = 10, 20, and 30 dB.

(b) For each of these SNRs, set up a self-organizing map. For typical values, you may use the following:

- An input vector made up of eight elements obtained by sampling the received signal at a rate equal to eight times the signaling rate (i.e., eight samples per signaling interval). Do not assume knowledge of timing information.
- A one-dimensional lattice of 64 neurons (i.e., eight times the size of the input vector).

(c) Display the feature maps for each of the three SNRs, and thereby demonstrate the topological-ordering property of the SOM algorithm.

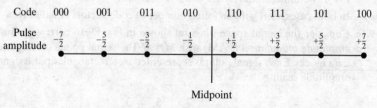

Code	000	001	011	010	110	111	101	100
Pulse amplitude	$-\frac{7}{2}$	$-\frac{5}{2}$	$-\frac{3}{2}$	$-\frac{1}{2}$	$+\frac{1}{2}$	$+\frac{3}{2}$	$+\frac{5}{2}$	$+\frac{7}{2}$

Midpoint

FIGURE P9.16 For Problem 9.16.

CHAPTER 10

Information-Theoretic Learning Models

ORGANIZATION OF THE CHAPTER

The theme of this chapter is the study of unsupervised learning models whose formulations, in one way or another, are rooted in information theory.

The chapter is organized as follows:

1. Section 10.1 presents motivational material on information theory and its profound impact on neural processing.

2. Section 10.2 to 10.6 review fundamental concepts in Shannon's information theory. The review begins with Section 10.2 on the concept of entropy, followed by Section 10.3 on the maximum-entropy principle. Section 10.4 discusses the concept of mutual information between a pair of continuous random variables and examines the associated properties. The related concept of Kullback–Leibler divergence, providing a measure of how closely a pair of different probability density functions are matched with each other, is discussed in Section 10.5, which also discusses the relationship between mutual information and Kullback–Leibler divergence. Section 10.6 completes the review by describing copulas, which is a useful concept that has been known for several decades but largely overlooked.

3. Section 10.7 discusses the role of mutual information as an objective function for unsupervised learning, thereby paving the way for discussions of the following five principles and some of their applications, set forth in Sections 10.8 to 10.12.
   - Maximum mutual information (Infomax) principle
   - Principle of minimum redundancy
   - Imax principle for dealing with spatially coherent features
   - Imin principle for dealing with spatially incoherent features
   - Principle of independent-components analysis (ICA)

4. Section 10.13 addresses the issue of sparseness, which is an inherent characteristic of natural images; the section also motivates ICA theory by demonstrating its relationship to sparseness.

5. Section 10.14 to 10.17 describe different ICA algorithms, emphasizing their practical virtues and limitations:
   - Natural-gradient learning algorithm
   - Maximum-likelihood estimation

- • Maximum-entropy learning algorithm
- • FastICA through maximization of a non-Gaussian criterion known as negentropy

6. Section 10.18 discusses a relatively new concept known as coherent ICA, the development of which builds on the use of copulas.

7. Section 10.19 introduces another new and fascinating method known as the information-bottleneck (IB) method, which builds on another concept in Shannon's information theory: rate distortion theory. The IB method paves the way for the description of an optimal manifold representation of data, which is discussed in Section 10.20, followed by a computer experiment in Section 10.21.

The chapter concludes with a summary and discussion in Section 10.22.

10.1 INTRODUCTION

In a classic paper published in 1948, Claude Shannon laid down the foundations of *information theory*. Shannon's original work on information theory,[1] and its refinement by other researchers, was in direct response to the need of electrical engineers to design communication systems that are both *efficient* and *reliable*. In spite of its practical origins, information theory as we know it today is a deep mathematical theory concerned with the very essence of the *communication process*. The theory provides a framework for the study of fundamental issues such as the efficiency of information representation and the limitations involved in the reliable transmission of information over a communication channel. Moreover, the theory encompasses a multitude of powerful theorems for computing ideal *bounds* on the optimum representation and transmission of information-bearing signals. These bounds are important because they provide benchmarks for the improved design of information-processing systems.

The main purpose of this chapter is to discuss *information-theoretic models* that lead to self-organization in a principled manner. In this context, a model that deserves special mention is the *maximum mutual information principle* due to Linsker (1988a,b). This principle states the following:

> *The synaptic connections of a multilayered neural network develop in such a way as to* maximize the amount of information that is preserved when signals are transformed at each processing stage of the network, subject to certain constraints.

The idea that information theory may offer an explanation for perceptual processing is not new.[2] For instance, in an early paper by Attneave (1954), the following information-theoretic function is proposed for perceptual systems:

> *A major function of the perceptual machinery is to strip away some of the redundancy of stimulation, to describe or encode information in a form more economical than that in which it impinges on the receptors.*

The main idea behind Attneave's paper is the recognition that encoding of data from a scene for the purpose of redundancy reduction is related to the identification of specific features in the scene. This important insight is related to a view of the brain described in Craik (1943), where a model of the external world is constructed so as to incorporate the regularities and constraints of the world.

10.2   ENTROPY

Consider a random variable X, each realization (presentation) of which may be regarded as a *message*. Strictly speaking, if the random variable X is continuous in its amplitude range, then it carries an infinite amount of information. However, on physical and biological grounds, we recognize that it is meaningless to think in terms of amplitude measurements with infinite precision, which suggests that the value of X may be uniformly *quantized* into a finite number of discrete levels. Accordingly, we may view X as a *discrete* random variable, modeled as

$$X = \{x_k | k = 0, \pm 1, ..., \pm K\} \tag{10.1}$$

where the sample value x_k is a discrete number and $(2K + 1)$ is the total number of discrete levels. The separation δx between the discrete levels is assumed to be small enough for the model of Eq. (10.1) to provide an adequate representation for the random variable X. We may, of course, pass to the continuum limit by letting δx approach zero and K approach infinity, in which case we have a continuous random variable; then sums become integrals.

To complete the model, let the event $X = x_k$ occur with *probability*

$$p_k = P(X = x_k) \tag{10.2}$$

with the requirement that

$$0 \le p_k \le 1 \quad \text{and} \quad \sum_{k=-K}^{K} p_k = 1 \tag{10.3}$$

Suppose that the event $X = x_k$ occurs with probability $p_k = 1$, which therefore requires that $p_i = 0$ for all $i \neq k$. In such a situation, there is no "surprise," and therefore no "information" is conveyed by the occurrence of the event $X = x_k$, since we know what the message must be. If, on the other hand, the various discrete levels were to occur with different probabilities and, in particular, if the probability p_k is low, then there is more "surprise" and therefore "information" when X takes the value x_k rather than another value x_i with higher probability $p_i, i \neq k$. Thus, the concepts "uncertainty," "surprise," and "information" are all related. Before the occurrence of the event $X = x_k$, there is an amount of uncertainty. When the event $X = x_k$ occurs, there is an amount of surprise. After the occurrence of the event $X = x_k$, there is an increase in the amount of information. These three amounts are obviously the same. Moreover, the amount of information is related to the *inverse* of the probability of occurrence.

We define the amount of information gained after observing the event $X = x_k$ with probability p_k as the logarithmic function

$$I(x_k) = \log\left(\frac{1}{p_k}\right) = -\log p_k \tag{10.4}$$

where the base of the logarithm is arbitrary. When the natural logarithm is used, the units for information are called *nats*, and when the base-2 logarithm is used, the units are called *bits*. In any case, the definition of information given in Eq. (10.4) exhibits the following properties:

1.
$$I(x_k) = 0 \qquad \text{for } p_k = 1 \tag{10.5}$$

Obviously, if we are absolutely certain of the outcome of an event, there is *no* information gained by its occurrence.

2.
$$I(x_k) \geq 0 \qquad \text{for } 0 \leq p_k \leq 1 \tag{10.6}$$

That is, the occurrence of an event $X = x_k$ either provides some or no information, but it never results in a loss of information.

3.
$$I(x_k) > I(x_i) \qquad \text{for } p_k < p_i \tag{10.7}$$

That is, the less probable an event is, the more information we gain through its occurrence.

The amount of information $I(x_k)$ is a discrete random variable with probability p_k. The mean value of $I(x_k)$ over the complete range of $2K + 1$ discrete values is given by

$$
\begin{aligned}
H(X) &= \mathbb{E}[I(x_k)] \\
&= \sum_{k=-K}^{K} p_k I(x_k) \\
&= -\sum_{k=-K}^{K} p_k \log p_k
\end{aligned}
\tag{10.8}
$$

The quantity $H(X)$ is called the *entropy* of a random variable X permitted to take a finite set of discrete values; it is so called in recognition of the analogy between the definition given in Eq. (10.8) and that of entropy in statistical thermodynamics.[3] The entropy $H(X)$ is a measure of the *average amount of information conveyed per message*. Note, however, that the X in $H(X)$ is not an argument of a function, but rather a label for a random variable. Note also that in the definition of Eq. (10.8), we take $0 \log 0$ to be 0.

The entropy $H(X)$ is bounded as

$$0 \leq H(X) \leq \log (2K + 1) \tag{10.9}$$

where $(2K + 1)$ is the total number of discrete levels. Furthermore, we may make two statements:

1. $H(X) = 0$ if, and only if, the probability $p_k = 1$ for some k and the remaining probabilities in the set are all zero; this lower bound on entropy corresponds to *no uncertainty*.

2. $H(X) = \log(2K + 1)$, if, and only if, $p_k = 1/(2K + 1)$ for all k (i.e., all the discrete levels are equiprobable); this upper bound on entropy corresponds to *maximum uncertainty*.

Differential Entropy of Continuous Random Variables

The discussion of information-theoretic concepts has thus far involved ensembles of random variables that are discrete in their amplitude values. We now extend some of these concepts to continuous random variables.

Consider next a continuous random variable X with the probability density function $p_X(x)$. By analogy with the entropy of a discrete random variable, we introduce the definition:

$$h(X) = -\int_{-\infty}^{\infty} p_X(x) \log p_X(x)\, dx$$

$$= -\mathbb{E}[\log p_X(x)]$$

(10.10)

We refer to $h(X)$ as the *differential entropy* of X to distinguish it from the ordinary entropy, or *absolute entropy*.

We justify the use of Eq. (10.10) as follows: We begin by viewing the continuous random variable X as the limiting form of a discrete random variable that assumes the value $x_k = k\,\delta x$, where $k = 0, \pm 1, \pm 2, \ldots$, and δx approaches zero. By definition, the continuous random variable X assumes a value in the interval $[x_k, x_k + \delta x]$ with probability $p_X(x_k)\,\delta x$. Hence, permitting δx to approach zero, the ordinary entropy of the continuous random variable X may be written in the limit as

$$H(X) = -\lim_{\delta x \to 0} \sum_{k=-\infty}^{\infty} p_X(x_k)\,\delta x \log(p_X(x_k)\,\delta x)$$

$$= -\lim_{\delta x \to 0} \left[\sum_{k=-\infty}^{\infty} p_X(x_k)(\log p_X(x_k))\,\delta x + \log \delta x \sum_{k=-\infty}^{\infty} p_X(x_k)\,\delta x \right]$$

(10.11)

$$= -\int_{-\infty}^{\infty} p_X(x) \log p_X(x)\, dx - \lim_{\delta x \to 0} \log \delta x \int_{-\infty}^{\infty} p_X(x)\, dx$$

$$= h(X) - \lim_{\delta x \to 0} \log \delta x$$

where, in the last line, we have made use of the first line of Eq. (10.10) and the fact that the total area under the curve of the probability density function $p_X(x)$ is unity. In the limit as δx approaches zero, the term $-\log \delta x$ approaches infinity. This means that the entropy of a continuous random variable is infinitely large. Intuitively, we would expect this to be true because a continuous random variable may assume a value anywhere in the open interval $(-\infty, \infty)$ and the uncertainty associated with the variable is on the order of infinity. We avoid the problem associated with the term $\log \delta x$ by adopting $h(X)$ as the *differential entropy*, with the term $-\log \delta x$ serving as a reference. Moreover, since the information processed by a stochastic system as an entity of interest is actually the difference between two entropy terms that have a common reference, the information will be the same as the difference between the corresponding differential entropy terms. We are therefore justified in using the term $h(X)$, defined in Eq. (10.11), as the differential entropy of the continuous random variable X.

When we have a continuous random vector $\mathbf{X}$ consisting of n random variables $X_1, X_2, \ldots, X_n$, we define the differential entropy of $\mathbf{X}$ as the *n-fold integral*

$$h(\mathbf{X}) = -\int_{-\infty}^{\infty} p_{\mathbf{X}}(\mathbf{x}) \log p_{\mathbf{X}}(\mathbf{x}) \, d\mathbf{x}$$

$$= -\mathbb{E}[\log p_{\mathbf{X}}(\mathbf{x})]$$

(10.12)

where $p_{\mathbf{X}}(\mathbf{x})$ is the joint probability density function of $\mathbf{X}$ and $\mathbf{x}$ is a sample value of $\mathbf{X}$.

EXAMPLE 1   Uniform Distribution

Consider a random variable X uniformly distributed inside the interval $[0, a]$ such that the probability density function

$$p_X(x) = \begin{cases} \dfrac{1}{a}, & 0 \le x \le a \\ 0, & \text{otherwise} \end{cases}$$

The differential entropy of X is

$$h(X) = -\int_0^a \frac{1}{a} \log\left(\frac{1}{a}\right) dx$$

$$= \log a$$

For $a < 1$, $\log a$ is negative, which means that the entropy $h(X)$ is negative. We may therefore state that, unlike the differential entropy of a discrete random variable, the differential entropy of a continuous random variable can assume a negative value.

For $a = 1$, the differential entropy $h(X)$ assumes the value zero. We may therefore say that a uniformly distributed random variable contains the *least amount of information* among all random variables. ∎

Properties of Differential Entropy

From the definition of differential entropy $h(X)$ given in Eq. (10.10), we readily see that translation does not change its value; that is,

$$h(X + c) = h(X)$$

(10.14)

where c is constant.

Another useful property of $h(X)$ is described by

$$h(aX) = h(X) + \log|a|$$

(10.15)

where a is a scaling factor. To prove this property, we first recognize that since the area under the curve of a probability density function is unity, then

$$p_Y(y) = \frac{1}{|a|} p_Y\left(\frac{y}{a}\right)$$

(10.16)

Next, using the formula of Eq. (10.10), we may write

$$h(Y) = -\mathbb{E}[\log p_Y(y)]$$

$$= -\mathbb{E}\left[\log\left(\frac{1}{|a|} p_Y\left(\frac{y}{a}\right)\right)\right]$$

(10.17)

$$= -\mathbb{E}\left[\log p_Y\left(\frac{y}{a}\right)\right] + \log|a|$$

By putting $Y = aX$ in this equation, we obtain

$$h(aX) = -\int_{-\infty}^{\infty} p_X(x) \log p_X(x) dx + \log |a| \tag{10.17}$$

from which Eq. (10.15) follows immediately.

Equation (10.15) applies to a scalar random variable. It may be generalized to the case of a random vector $\mathbf{X}$ premultiplied by matrix $\mathbf{A}$ to yield

$$h(\mathbf{AX}) = h(\mathbf{X}) + \log |\det(\mathbf{A})| \tag{10.18}$$

where $\det(\mathbf{A})$ is the determinant of matrix $\mathbf{A}$.

10.3 MAXIMUM-ENTROPY PRINCIPLE

Suppose that we are given a stochastic system with a set of known states, but unknown probabilities, and that somehow we learn some *constraints* on the probability distribution of the states. The constraints can be certain ensemble average values or bounds on these values. The problem is to choose a probability model that is optimum in some sense, given this *prior knowledge* about the model. We usually find that there is an infinite number of possible models that satisfy the constraints. Which model should we choose?

The answer to this fundamental question lies in the *maximum-entropy (Max Ent) principle*[4] given by Jaynes (1957). The Max Ent principle may be stated as follows (Jaynes, 1957, 2003):

> *When an inference is made on the basis of incomplete information, it should be drawn from the probability distribution that maximizes the entropy, subject to constraints on the distribution.*

In effect, the notion of entropy defines a kind of measure on the space of probability distributions such that those distributions of high entropy are favored over others.

From this statement, it is apparent that the Max Ent principle is a constrained-optimization problem. To illustrate the procedure for solving such a problem, consider the maximization of the differential entropy

$$h(X) = -\int_{-\infty}^{\infty} p_X(x) \log p_X(x) \, dx$$

over all probability density functions $p_X(x)$ of a random variable X, subject to the following three constraints:

1. $p_X(x) \geq 0$, with equality outside the support of x

2. $\displaystyle\int_{-\infty}^{\infty} p_X(x) \, dx = 1$

3. $\displaystyle\int_{-\infty}^{\infty} p_X(x) g_i(x) \, dx = \alpha_i$ for $i = 1, 2, ..., m$

where $g_i(x)$ is some function of x. Constraints 1 and 2 simply describe two fundamental properties of a probability density function. Constraint 3 defines the moments of X, depending on how the function $g_i(x)$ is formulated. In effect, constraint 3 sums up the prior knowledge available about the random variable X. To solve this constrained-optimization problem, we use the *method of Lagrange multipliers,* discussed in Chapter 6. Specifically, we first formulate the Lagrangian

$$J(p) = \int_{-\infty}^{\infty}\left[-p_X(x)\log p_X(x) + \lambda_0 p_X(x) + \sum_{i=1}^{m}\lambda_i g_i(x)p_X(x)\right]dx \quad (10.19)$$

where $\lambda_0, \lambda_1, ..., \lambda_m$ are the *Lagrange multipliers.* Differentiating the integrand of Eq. (10.19) with respect to $p_X(x)$ and then setting the result equal to zero, we get

$$-1 - \log p_X(x) + \lambda_0 + \sum_{i=1}^{m}\lambda_i g_i(x) = 0$$

Solving this equation for the unknown $p_X(x)$ yields

$$p_X(x) = \exp\left(-1 + \lambda_0 + \sum_{i=1}^{m}\lambda_i g_i(x)\right) \quad (10.20)$$

The Lagrange multipliers in Eq. (10.20) are chosen in accordance with constraints 2 and 3. Equation (10.20) defines the maximum-entropy distribution for this problem.

EXAMPLE 2   One-Dimensional Gaussian Distribution

Suppose the prior knowledge available to us is made up of the mean μ and variance σ^2 of a random variable X. By definition, the variance of the random variable X is given by

$$\int_{-\infty}^{\infty}(x - \mu)^2 p_X(x)dx = \sigma^2 = \text{constant}$$

Comparing this equation with constraint 3, we readily see that

$$g_1(x) = (x - \mu)^2$$

and

$$\alpha_1 = \sigma^2$$

Hence, the use of Eq. (10.20) yields

$$p_X(x) = \exp[-1 + \lambda_0 + \lambda_1(x - \mu)^2]$$

Note that λ_1 has to be negative if the integrals of $p_X(x)$ and $(x - \sigma)^2 p_X(x)$ with respect to x are to converge. Substituting this equation in equality constraints 2 and 3 and then solving for λ_0 and λ_1, we get

$$\lambda_0 = 1 - \log(2\pi\sigma^2)$$

and

$$\lambda_1 = -\frac{1}{2\sigma^2}$$

The desired form for $p_X(x)$ is therefore described by

$$p_X(x) = \frac{1}{\sqrt{2\pi}\sigma} \exp\left(-\frac{(x-\mu)^2}{2\sigma^2}\right) \tag{10.21}$$

which is recognized as the probability density of a *Gaussian random variable X of mean* μ *and variance* σ^2. The maximum value of the differential entropy of such a random variable is given by

$$h(X) = \frac{1}{2}[1 + \log(2\pi\sigma^2)] \tag{10.22}$$

We may summarize the results of this example as follows:

1. *For a given variance* σ^2, *the Gaussian random variable has the largest differential entropy attainable by any random variable.* That is, if X is a Gaussian random variable and Y is any other random variable with the same mean and variance, then for all Y we have

$$h(X) \geq h(Y)$$

   with the equality holding only if the second random variable Y is also Gaussian.
2. *The entropy of a Gaussian random variable X is uniquely determined by the variance of X* (i.e., it is independent of the mean of X). ∎

EXAMPLE 3   Multidimensional Gaussian Distribution

In this second example, we want to build on the results of Example 2 to evaluate the differential entropy of a *multidimensional Gaussian distribution*. Since the entropy of a Gaussian random variable X is independent of the mean of X, we may justifiably simplify the discussion in this example by considering an m-dimensional vector $\mathbf{X}$ of zero mean. Let the second-order statistics of $\mathbf{X}$ be described by the covariance matrix $\mathbf{\Sigma}$, defined as the expectation of the outer product of $\mathbf{X}$ with itself. The joint probability density function of the random vector $\mathbf{X}$ is given by

$$p_{\mathbf{X}}(\mathbf{x}) = \frac{1}{(2\pi)^{m/2}(\det(\mathbf{\Sigma}))^{1/2}} \exp\left(-\frac{1}{2}\mathbf{x}^T\mathbf{\Sigma}^{-1}\mathbf{x}\right) \tag{10.23}$$

where $\det(\mathbf{\Sigma})$ is the determinant of $\mathbf{\Sigma}$ (Wilks, 1962). Equation (10.12) defines the differential entropy of $\mathbf{X}$. Therefore, substituting Eq. (10.23) into Eq. (10.12), we obtain the result

$$h(\mathbf{X}) = \frac{1}{2}[m + m\log(2\pi) + \log|\det(\mathbf{\Sigma})|] \tag{10.24}$$

which includes Eq. (10.22) as a special case. In light of the Max Ent principle, we may thus state the following:

> *For a given covariance matrix* $\mathbf{\Sigma}$, *the multivariate Gaussian distribution of Eq. (10.23) has the largest differential entropy attainable by any random vector of zero mean, and that maximum differential entropy is defined by Eq. (10.24); the term "variate" is another way of referring to a component of random vector* $\mathbf{X}$. ∎

10.4   MUTUAL INFORMATION

Consider a pair of continuous random variables X and Y, which are correlated. From probability theory, we may express the joint probability density function of X and Y as

$$p_{X,Y}(x, y) = p_Y(y|x)p_X(x) \tag{10.25}$$

Hence, invoking the definition of differential entropy, we may write

$$h(X, Y) = h(X) + h(Y|X) \tag{10.26}$$

where $h(X, Y)$ is called the *joint differential entropy* of X and Y, and $h(Y|X)$ is called the *conditional differential entropy* of Y given X. In words, we may say that the uncertainty about X and Y is equal to the uncertainty about X plus the uncertainty about Y given X. Similarly, we may say that the uncertainty about X and Y is equal to the uncertainty about Y plus the uncertainty about X given Y, as shown by

$$h(X, Y) = h(Y) + h(X|Y) \tag{10.27}$$

Consider next a more structured situation that involves a stochastic neural system, where the application of a continuous random variable X to the input of the system produces a continuous random variable Y at the output of the system. By definition, the differential entropy $h(X)$ is the uncertainty about the system input X before observation of the system output Y, and the conditional differential entropy $H(X|Y)$ is the uncertainty about the system input X *after* observation of the system output Y. The difference, $H(X) - H(X|Y)$, is therefore the uncertainty about the system input X that is *resolved* by observing the system output Y. This entropic difference is called the *mutual information* between the system input X and the system output Y; denoting it by $I(X; Y)$, we may thus write

$$
\begin{aligned}
I(X; Y) &= h(X) - h(X|Y) \\
&= \int_{-\infty}^{\infty} \int_{-\infty}^{\infty} p_{X,Y}(x, y) \log \left(\frac{p_{X,Y}(x, y)}{p_X(x)p_Y(y)} \right) dx\,dy \\
&= \int_{-\infty}^{\infty} \int_{-\infty}^{\infty} \underbrace{p_{X|Y}(x|y)p_Y(y)}_{p_{X,Y}(x, y)} \log \left(\frac{p_{X|Y}(x|y)}{p_Y(y)} \right) dx\,dy
\end{aligned} \tag{10.28}
$$

For the transition from line 1 to line 2 of Eq. (10.28), see Problem 10.2. The differential entropy $h(X)$ is a special case of the mutual information, since we have

$$h(X) = I(X; X)$$

The formula for the mutual information $I(X; Y)$ in Eq. (10.28) is expressed in terms of the differential entropy $h(X)$. In a corresponding way, the mutual information $I(Y; X)$ may be expressed in terms of the differential entropy $h(Y)$ as

$$I(Y; X) = h(Y) - h(Y|X) \tag{10.29}$$

where $h(Y|X)$ is the conditional differential entropy of Y given X. The mutual information $I(Y; X)$ is the uncertainty about the system output Y by observing the system input X.

The mutual information between two continuous random variables X and Y has three important properties:

Property 1. Nonnegativity
The mutual information $I(X; Y)$ is always nonnegative; that is,

$$I(X; Y) \geq 0 \tag{10.30}$$

This property states that, on average, we cannot lose information about the system input X by observing the system output Y. Moreover, the mutual information $I(X; Y)$ is zero if, and only if, the input and output of the system are statistically independent.

Property 2. Symmetry
This second property states that

$$I(Y; X) = I(X; Y) \tag{10.31}$$

Properties 1 and 2 follow directly from the defining equation of Eq. (10.28).

Summing up Eqs. (10.26) to (10.31), we write

$$
\begin{aligned}
I(X; Y) &= h(X) - h(X|Y) \\
&= h(Y) - h(Y|X) \\
&= (h(X) + h(Y)) - h(X, Y)
\end{aligned}
\tag{10.32}
$$

in light of which we may construct the picture presented in Fig. 10.1 (MacKay, 2003). The differential entropy of the system input X is represented by the second rectangle in the figure, and the differential entropy of the system output Y is represented by the third rectangle. The mutual information between X and Y, shown as the shaded area in the figure, is represented by the overlap between these two rectangles. The figure also includes representations of the joint entropy $h(X, Y)$, and the two conditional entropies $h(X|Y)$ and $h(Y|X)$.

Property 3. Invariance
The mutual information is invariant under invertible transformations of random variables.

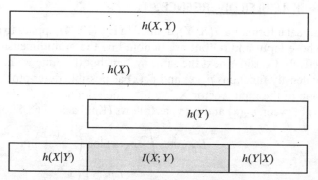

FIGURE 10.1   Relationships embodied in the three lines of Eq. (10.32), involving the mutual information $I(X; Y)$.

Consider the invertible transformations

$$u = f(x)$$

and

$$v = g(y)$$

where x and y are sample values of the random variables X and Y, and u and v are sample values of the transformed random variables U and V. The invariance property of mutual information states that

$$I(X; Y) = I(U; V) \tag{10.33}$$

Since the transformations from x to u and from y to v are both invertible, there is no loss of information in the course of these two transformations. Intuitively, this result validates the invariance property of mutual information.

Generalization of Mutual Information

The definition of mutual information $I(X; Y)$ given in Eq. (10.28) applies to scalar random variables X and Y. This definition may be readily extended to random vectors $\mathbf{X}$ and $\mathbf{Y}$, and we may thus write $I(\mathbf{X}; \mathbf{Y})$. Specifically, we define the mutual information $I(\mathbf{X}; \mathbf{Y})$ as

$$
\begin{aligned}
I(\mathbf{X}; \mathbf{Y}) &= h(\mathbf{X}) - h(\mathbf{X}|\mathbf{Y}) \\
&= \int_{-\infty}^{\infty} \int_{-\infty}^{\infty} p_{\mathbf{X},\mathbf{Y}}(\mathbf{x}, \mathbf{y}) \log \left(\frac{p_{\mathbf{X},\mathbf{Y}}(\mathbf{x}, \mathbf{y})}{p_{\mathbf{X}}(\mathbf{x}) p_{\mathbf{Y}}(\mathbf{y})} \right) d\mathbf{x}\, d\mathbf{y} \\
&= \int_{-\infty}^{\infty} \int_{-\infty}^{\infty} \underbrace{p_{\mathbf{X}|\mathbf{Y}}(\mathbf{x}|\mathbf{y})\, P_{\mathbf{Y}}(\mathbf{y})}_{p_{\mathbf{X},\mathbf{Y}}(\mathbf{x}, \mathbf{y})} \log \left(\frac{p_{\mathbf{X}|\mathbf{Y}}(\mathbf{x}|\mathbf{y})}{p_{\mathbf{Y}}(\mathbf{y})} \right) d\mathbf{x}\, d\mathbf{y}
\end{aligned} \tag{10.34}
$$

The mutual information $I(\mathbf{X}; \mathbf{Y})$ has properties that parallel those given in Eqs. (10.30) and (10.31) for scalar random variables, which is intuitively satisfying.

10.5 KULLBACK–LEIBLER DIVERGENCE

The mutual information $I(\mathbf{X}; \mathbf{Y})$, defined in Eq. (10.34), applies to a stochastic neural system whose input and output are denoted by the multidimensional vectors $\mathbf{X}$ and $\mathbf{Y}$, respectively. Consider next the same system, but this time we have two different probability density functions $p_{\mathbf{X}}(\mathbf{x})$ and $g_{\mathbf{X}}(\mathbf{x})$ as possible descriptors of the underlying distribution of the input vector $\mathbf{X}$. We may then define the *Kullback–Leibler divergence* (KLD) between $p_{\mathbf{X}}(\mathbf{x})$ and $g_{\mathbf{X}}(\mathbf{x})$ as follows (Kullback, 1968; Shore and Johnson, 1980):

$$
\begin{aligned}
D_{p\|g} &= \int_{-\infty}^{\infty} p_{\mathbf{X}}(\mathbf{x}) \log \left(\frac{p_{\mathbf{X}}(\mathbf{x})}{g_{\mathbf{X}}(\mathbf{x})} \right) d\mathbf{x} \\
&= \mathbb{E} \left[\log \left(\frac{p_{\mathbf{X}}(\mathbf{x})}{g_{\mathbf{X}}(\mathbf{x})} \right) \right]
\end{aligned} \tag{10.35}
$$

where the expectation is with respect to the probability density function $p_{\mathbf{X}}(\mathbf{x})$.

The KLD has two unique properties of its own:

Property 1. Nonnegativity
This property states that

$$D_{p\|g} \geq 0 \tag{10.36}$$

For the special case when $g_X(x) = p_X(x)$, we have a perfect match between these two distributions, in that the KLD between them is exactly zero.

Property 2. Invariance
Consider the invertible transformation

$$\mathbf{y} = \mathbf{f}(\mathbf{x})$$

where $\mathbf{x}$ and $\mathbf{y}$ are samples of the random vectors $\mathbf{X}$ and $\mathbf{Y}$, respectively. Correspondingly, the KLD is invariant under this transformation, which means that

$$D_{p_X\|g_X} = D_{p_Y\|g_Y}$$

The $D_{p_X\|g_X}$ is the KLD referring to the input vector $\mathbf{X}$ and the $D_{p_Y\|g_Y}$ is the corresponding KLD referring to the transformed output vector $\mathbf{Y}$.

Relationship between the Kullback–Leibler Divergence and Mutual Information

The mutual information $I(\mathbf{X}; \mathbf{Y})$ between a pair of vectors $\mathbf{X}$ and $\mathbf{Y}$ has an interesting interpretation in terms of the Kullback–Leibler divergence. Reproducing the second line of Eq.(10.34) for convenience of presentation, we write

$$I(\mathbf{X}; \mathbf{Y}) = \int_{-\infty}^{\infty} \int_{-\infty}^{\infty} p_{\mathbf{X},\mathbf{Y}}(\mathbf{x}, \mathbf{y}) \log\left(\frac{p_{\mathbf{X},\mathbf{Y}}(\mathbf{x}, \mathbf{y})}{p_{\mathbf{X}}(\mathbf{x})p_{\mathbf{Y}}(\mathbf{y})}\right) d\mathbf{x}\, d\mathbf{y}$$

and comparing this formula with that of Eq. (10.35), we immediately deduce the following result:

$$I(\mathbf{X}; \mathbf{Y}) = D_{p_{\mathbf{X},\mathbf{Y}}\|p_{\mathbf{X}}p_{\mathbf{Y}}} \tag{10.37}$$

In words, the mutual information $I(\mathbf{X}; \mathbf{Y})$ between $\mathbf{X}$ and $\mathbf{Y}$ is equal to the Kullback–Leibler divergence between the joint probability density function $p_{\mathbf{X},\mathbf{Y}}(\mathbf{x}, \mathbf{y})$ and the product of the marginal probability density functions $p_{\mathbf{X}}(\mathbf{x})$ and $p_{\mathbf{Y}}(\mathbf{y})$.

Entropic Interpretation of the Kulback–Leibler Divergence

A special case of this latter result described in Eq. (10.37) is the Kullback–Leibler divergence between the probability density function $p_{\mathbf{X}}(\mathbf{x})$ of an m-by-1 random vector $\mathbf{X}$ and the product of its m marginal probability density functions. Let $\tilde{p}_{X_i}(x_i)$ denote the ith marginal probability density function of component X_i, which is defined by

$$\tilde{p}_{X_i}(x_i) = \int_{-\infty}^{\infty} p_{\mathbf{X}}(\mathbf{x}) d\mathbf{x}^{(i)}, \quad i = 1, 2, ..., m \tag{10.38}$$

where $\mathbf{x}^{(i)}$ is the $(m-1)$-by-1 vector left after removing the ith element from vector $\mathbf{x}$.

Define the *factorial distribution*

$$\tilde{p}_{\mathbf{X}}(\mathbf{x}) = \prod_{i=1}^{m} \tilde{p}_{X_i}(x_i)$$

which represents an independent set of random variables; the distribution of the *i*th component X_i in this set is the same as the *i*th marginal distribution of the original random vector $\mathbf{X}$. The KLD between the ordinary probability density function $p_{\mathbf{X}}(\mathbf{x})$ and its factorial counterpart $\tilde{p}_{\mathbf{X}}(\mathbf{x})$ is given by

$$D_{p_{\mathbf{X}}\|\tilde{p}_{\mathbf{X}}} = \int_{-\infty}^{\infty} p_{\mathbf{X}}(\mathbf{x}) \log\left(\frac{p_{\mathbf{X}}(\mathbf{x})}{\prod_{i=1}^{m}\tilde{p}_{X_i}(x_i)}\right) d\mathbf{x}$$

$$= \int_{-\infty}^{\infty} p_{\mathbf{X}}(\mathbf{x}) \log p_{\mathbf{X}}(\mathbf{x}) d\mathbf{x} - \sum_{i=1}^{m} \int_{-\infty}^{\infty} p_{\mathbf{X}}(\mathbf{x}) \log \tilde{p}_{X_i}(x_i) d\mathbf{x} \qquad (10.39)$$

The first integral on the right-hand in the second line of side of Eq. (10.39) is, by definition, equal to $-h(\mathbf{X})$, where $h(\mathbf{X})$ is the differential entropy of $\mathbf{X}$. To deal with the second term on the right-hand side of the equation, we first note that the differential $d\mathbf{x}$ may be expressed as

$$d\mathbf{x} = d\mathbf{x}^{(i)} dx_i$$

Hence, we may write

$$\int_{-\infty}^{\infty} p_{\mathbf{X}}(\mathbf{x}) \log \tilde{p}_{X_i}(x_i) d\mathbf{x} = \int_{-\infty}^{\infty} \log \tilde{p}_{X_i}(x_i) \int_{-\infty}^{\infty} p_{\mathbf{X}}(\mathbf{x}) d\mathbf{x}^{(i)} dx_i \qquad (10.40)$$

where the inner integral on the right-hand side is with respect to the $(m-1)$-by-1 vector $\mathbf{x}^{(i)}$ and the outer integral is with respect to the scalar x_i. But from Eq. (10.38), we see that the inner integral is in fact equal to the marginal probability density function $\tilde{p}_{X_i}(x_i)$. Accordingly, we may rewrite Eq. (10.40) in the equivalent form

$$\int_{-\infty}^{\infty} p_{\mathbf{X}}(\mathbf{x}) \log \tilde{p}_{X_i}(x_i) d\mathbf{x} = \int_{-\infty}^{\infty} \tilde{p}_{X_i}(x_i) \log \tilde{p}_{X_i}(x_i) dx_i \qquad (10.41)$$

$$= -\tilde{h}(X_i), \qquad i = 1, 2, ..., m$$

where $\tilde{h}(X_i)$ is the *i*th *marginal entropy* (i.e., the differential entropy based on the marginal probability density function $\tilde{f}_{X_i}(x_i)$). Finally, using Eq. (10.41) in Eq. (10.39) and noting that the first integral in Eq. (10.39) is equal to $-h(\mathbf{X})$, we may simplify the Kullback–Leibler divergence of Eq. (10.39) to

$$D_{p_{\mathbf{X}}\|\tilde{p}_{\mathbf{X}}} = -h(\mathbf{X}) + \sum_{i=1}^{m} \tilde{h}(X_i) \qquad (10.42)$$

Later in the chapter, we will use this formula in the study of independent-components analysis.

Pythagorean Decomposition

Next, we consider the Kullback–Leibler divergence between the probability density functions $p_X(\mathbf{x})$ and $p_U(\mathbf{x})$, where the vector $\mathbf{x}$ is a sample value common to both random vectors $\mathbf{X}$ and $\mathbf{U}$, and x_i is the ith component of $\mathbf{x}$. The m-by-1 random vector $\mathbf{U}$ consists of independent variables, as shown by

$$p_U(\mathbf{x}) = \prod_{i=1}^{m} p_{U_i}(x_i)$$

The m-by-1 random vector $\mathbf{X}$ is defined in terms of $\mathbf{U}$ as

$$\mathbf{X} = \mathbf{AU}$$

where $\mathbf{A}$ is a nondiagonal matrix. Let $\tilde{p}_{X_i}(x_i)$ denote the marginal probability density function of each X_i that is derived from $p_X(\mathbf{x})$. Then the Kullback–Leibler divergence between $p_X(\mathbf{x})$ and $p_U(\mathbf{x})$ admits the following *Pythagorean decomposition*:

$$D_{p_X \| p_U} = D_{p_X \| \tilde{p}_X} + D_{p_X \| \tilde{p}_U} \tag{10.43}$$

We refer to this classic relation as a *Pythagorean decomposition* because it has an information-geometric interpretation (Amari, 1985).[5]

10.6 COPULAS

The mutual information $I(X; Y)$ provides a measure of the statistical dependence between two random variables X and Y. For a graphical interpretation of this dependence, we may look to the picture depicted in Fig. 10.1, based on Eq. (10.32). However, this equation lacks mathematical insight. Specifically, if the mutual information $I(X; Y)$ is zero, it tells us that the random variables X and Y are statistically independent. But, if $I(X; Y)$ is greater than zero, confirming statistical dependence between X and Y, it does *not* provide us with a statistical measure of the dependence.

To elaborate, consider a pair of random variables X and Y whose sample values are denoted by x and y, respectively. The issue of interest is to formulate a measure of *statistical dependence* between X and Y that is not disturbed by their scaled versions or their variances. In order to achieve this objective, we transform X and Y into two new random variables U and V, respectively, such that the distributions of both U and V are uniform over the interval $[0, 1]$. This transformation is one of nonlinear scaling expressed in terms of the cumulative distribution functions $P_X(x)$ and $P_Y(y)$; it is performed by setting

$$u = P_X(x)$$

and

$$v = P_Y(y)$$

where u and v are sample values of the random variables U and V, respectively. The joint distribution of the pair (U, V) is spread over the unit square $[0, 1] \times [0, 1]$; the distribution is uniform if, and only if, the original random variables X and Y (or, equivalently, the new random variables U and V) are statistically independent. The joint distribution of X and Y is thus transformed to that of U and V on the unit square, where the marginal distributions are uniform.

The new pair of random variables (U, V) is uniquely determined, and it is called a *copula*.[6] Formally,

> *The copula, involving the pair of random variables (U, V), is a function that models the statistical dependence between U and V in a distribution-free manner.*

We may go on to state *Sklar's theorem* on copulas as follows (Sklar, 1959):

> *Given the cumulative distribution functions $P_{X,Y}(x, y)$, $P_X(x)$, and $P_Y(y)$, there exists a unique copula $C_{U,V}(u, v)$ that satisfies the pair of relationships*

$$P_{X,Y}(x, y) = C_{U,V}(P_X(x), P_Y(y)) \tag{10.44}$$

and

$$C_{U,V}(u, v) = P(P_X^{-1}(x), P_Y^{-1}(y)) \tag{10.45}$$

where the two new random variables U and V are nonlinearly transformed versions of the original random variables X and Y, respectively, and their sample values, u and v, are themselves defined by

$$u = P_X(x) \tag{10.46}$$

and

$$v = P_Y(y) \tag{10.47}$$

The joint distribution of the pair of random variables (U, V) is spread over the unit square.

Properties of Copulas

Property 1. Limiting values of copulas
With both sample values u and v limited to the range $[0, 1]$, the copula values are themselves limited as

$$C_{U,V}(u, 0) = C_{U,V}(0, v) = 0$$
$$C_{U,V}(u, 1) = u$$
$$C_{U,V}(1, v) = v$$

Property 2. Joint density $p_{X,Y}(x, y)$ expressed using the copula
The joint probability density function $p_{X,Y}(x, y)$ is informatively expressed in terms of the copula as the product of three terms:

- the marginal probability density functions $p_X(x)$ and $p_Y(y)$, and
- the copula's joint probability density function $c_{U,V}(u,v)$.

To establish this relationship, we start with the basic definition of the joint probability density function:

$$p_{X,Y}(x, y) = \frac{\partial^2}{\partial x \partial y} P_{X,Y}(x, y)$$

Then, using Eq. (10.44), we write

$$p_{X,Y}(x, y) = \frac{\partial^2}{\partial x \partial y} C_{U,V}(P_X(x), P_Y(y))$$

$$= \frac{\partial}{\partial x} \frac{\partial}{\partial y} C_{U,V}(P_X(x), P_Y(y))$$

$$= \frac{\partial}{\partial x} \left[\frac{\partial P_Y(y)}{\partial y} \frac{\partial}{\partial P_Y(y)} C_{U,V}(P_X(x), P_Y(y)) \right]$$

$$= \frac{\partial}{\partial x} \left[p_Y(y) C'_{U,V}(P_X(x), v) \right]$$

where, in the last line, we used the definition $P_Y(y) = v$, and the prime in $C'_{U,V}(P_X(x), P_Y(y))$ denotes differentiation of the copula with respect to $P_Y(y)$. With the marginal $P_Y(y)$ being independent of x, we go on to write

$$p_{X,Y}(x, y) = p_Y(y) \frac{\partial}{\partial x} C'_{U,V}(P_X(x), v)$$

$$= p_Y(y) \frac{\partial P_X(x)}{\partial x} \frac{\partial}{\partial P_X(x)} C'_{U,V}(P_X(x), v)$$

$$= p_Y(y) p_X(x) C''_{U,V}(P_X(x), v)$$

where the second prime in $C''_{U,V}(P_X(x), v)$ denotes differentiation of the derivative $C'_{U,V}(P_X(x), v)$ with respect to $P_X(x)$. Finally, recognizing that $P_X(x) = u$ and that, by definition, the joint probability density function of the copula is expressed as

$$c_{U,V}(u, v) = \frac{\partial^2}{\partial u \partial v} C_{U,V}(u, v) \tag{10.48}$$

we obtain the following relationship:

$$p_{X,Y}(x, y) = p_X(x) p_Y(y) c_{U,V}(u, v) \tag{10.49}$$

Equation (10.49) now leads us to make the following insightful statement:

> If two random variables X and Y are statistically dependent, then the copula's joint density $c_{U,V}(u, v)$ distinctly accounts for the statistical dependence between X and Y.

This statement highlights the very essence of the copula.

EXAMPLE 4   The Copula of Two Statistically Independent Random Variables

Let the random variables X and Y be statistically independent. We then have

$$p_{X,Y}(x, y) = p_X(x) p_Y(y)$$

Under this condition, Eq. (10.49) reduces to

$$c_{U,V}(u,v) = 1, \quad \text{for } 0 \le u, v \le 1$$

Correspondingly, we have

$$C_{U,V}(u,v) = \int_0^u \int_0^v c_{U,V}(u,v)\,du\,dv$$

$$= \int_0^u \int_0^v 1 \, du \, dv$$

$$= uv$$

Thus, the product copula's density $C_{U,V}(u,v) = uv$ joins U and V together when the corresponding random variables X and Y are statistically independent. ∎

Relationship between Mutual Information and the Copula's Entropy

With the background just presented on the copula, we are now ready to make another statement:

> *The mutual information between two random variables X and Y is the negative of the copula's joint entropy of the corresponding nonlinearly transformed pair of random variables U and V.*

To demonstrate this relationship, we may proceed as follows:

(i) Since the random variables U and V are the results of invertible transformations applied to the original random variables X and Y, the invariance property of mutual information, described in Section 10.4, immediately yields

$$I(X;Y) = I(U;V)$$

(ii) Applying the last line of Eq. (10.32) to the mutual information $I(U;V)$ gives

$$I(U;V) = h_C(U) + h_C(V) - h_C(U,V)$$

Since the random variables U and V are both uniformly distributed over the interval $[0, 1]$, it follows that the differential entropies $h(U)$ and $h(V)$ are both zero. Hence, the formula for $I(U;V)$ reduces to

$$I(U;V) = -h_C(U,V)$$
$$= \mathbb{E}[\log c_{U,V}(u,v)] \tag{10.50}$$

which is the desired relationship.

The definition of mutual information in Eq. (10.50) is intuitively more satisfying than any of the three standard formulas presented in Eq. (10.32), for two reasons:

1. Given a pair of random variables, the mutual information between them is expressed directly as a function of the copula, which is part and parcel of the underlying distribution that matches the dependency between the two random variables.

2. The mutual information is not a function of the marginal distributions of the two random variables.

Furthermore, following on Eq. (10.49), we may make two more insightful remarks:

$$I(X; Y) = 0 \text{ corresponds to } c_{U, V}(u, v) = 1.$$
$$I(X; Y) > 0 \text{ corresponds to } c_{U, V}(u, v) > 1.$$

10.7 MUTUAL INFORMATION AS AN OBJECTIVE FUNCTION TO BE OPTIMIZED

Now that we have developed an adequate understanding of Shannon's information theory, we are ready to discuss its role in the study of self-organizing systems.

To proceed with the discussion, consider a neural system with multiple inputs and multiple outputs. The primary objective here is for the system to be self-organizing, designed for a specific task (e.g., modeling, extraction of statistically salient features, or signal separation). This requirement can be satisfied by choosing the mutual information between certain variables of the system as the *objective function* to be optimized. This particular choice is justified by two considerations:

1. The mutual information has some unique properties, as discussed in Sections 10.4 to 10.6.
2. The mutual information can be determined without the need for a teacher, so the provision for self-organization is naturally met.

The problem thus becomes one of adjusting the free parameters (i.e., synaptic weights) of the system so as to optimize the mutual information.

Depending on the application of interest, we may identify the four different scenarios illustrated in Fig. 10.2. These scenarios are described as follows:

- In scenario 1, depicted in Fig. 10.2a, the input vector X is composed of the elements $X_1, X_2, ..., X_m$, and the output vector Y is composed of the elements $Y_1, Y_2, ..., Y_l$. The requirement is to *maximize the information conveyed to the system output Y about the system input X* (i.e., the information flow across the system).
- In scenario 2, depicted in Fig. 10.2b, a pair of input vectors X_a and X_b is derived from adjacent, but nonoverlapping, regions of an image. The inputs X_a and X_b produce scalar outputs Y_a and Y_b, respectively. The requirement is to *maximize the information conveyed to Y_b about Y_a and vice versa.*
- In scenario 3, depicted in Fig. 10.2c, the input vectors X_a and X_b are derived from a corresponding pair of regions belonging to two separate, but related, images. The outputs produced by these two input vectors are denoted by Y_a and Y_b, respectively. The objective is to *minimize the information conveyed to Y_b about Y_a and vice versa.*
- In scenario 4, depicted in Fig. 10.2d, the input vector X and the output vector Y are defined in a manner similar to those in Fig. 10.2a, but with equal dimensionality

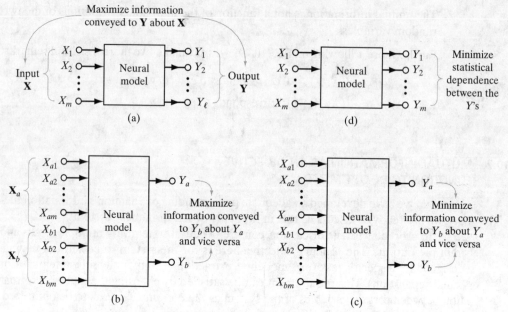

FIGURE 10.2   Four basic scenarios that lend themselves to the application of information maximization and its three variants.

(i.e., $l = m$). The objective here is for the *statistical dependence between the components of the output vector* **Y** *to be minimized.*

In all four situations, mutual information plays a central role. However, the way in which it is formulated depends on the particular situation being considered. In what follows, the issues involved in these scenarios and their practical implications are discussed in the same order just presented. Most importantly, it should be noted that scenario 4 encompasses much of the material presented in the chapter in terms of theory, computing algorithms, and applications, which reflect the practical realities of information-theoretic models.

10.8   MAXIMUM MUTUAL INFORMATION PRINCIPLE

The idea of designing a neural processor to maximize the mutual information $I(\mathbf{Y}; \mathbf{X})$ is appealing as the basis for statistical signal processing. This method of optimization is embodied in the *maximum mutual information (Infomax) principle* due to Linsker (1987, 1988a, 1989a), which may be stated formally as follows:

> *The transformation of a random vector* **X** *observed in the input layer of a neural system to a random vector* **Y** *produced in the output layer of the system should be so chosen that the activities of the neurons in the output layer jointly maximize information about the activities in the input layer. The objective function to be maximized is the mutual information $I(\mathbf{Y}; \mathbf{X})$ between the vectors* **X** *and* **Y**.

The Infomax principle provides a mathematical framework for self-organization of the signal transmission system described in Fig. 10.2a, assuming that the number of components l in the output vector Y is smaller than the number of components m in the input vector **x**. Also, this principle may be viewed as the neural network counterpart of the concept of *channel capacity*, which defines the Shannon limit on the rate of information transmission through a communication channel.

Next, we illustrate applications of the Infomax principle with two examples involving a single noisy neuron. In one example the noise appears at the output, and in the other example it appears at the input.

EXAMPLE 5   Single Neuron Corrupted by Processing Noise

Consider the simple case of a linear neuron that receives its inputs from a set of m source nodes. Let the output of this neuron in the presence of *processing noise* be expressed as

$$Y = \left(\sum_{i=1}^{m} w_i X_i \right) + N \tag{10.51}$$

where w_i is the ith synaptic weight and the random N is processing noise, as modeled in Fig. 10.3. It is assumed that

- the output Y of the neuron is a Gaussian random variable with zero mean and variance σ_Y^2;
- the processing noise N is also a Gaussian random variable with zero mean and variance σ_N^2;
- the processing noise is uncorrelated with any of the input components; that is,

$$\mathbb{E}[NX_i] = 0 \qquad \text{for all } i$$

The Gaussianity of the output Y can be satisfied in one of two ways. First, we start with $X_1, X_2, ..., X_m$ that are all Gaussian distributed. Then, with the additive noise N assumed to be Gaussian, too, the Gaussianity of Y is assured by virtue of the fact that it is the weighted sum of a number of Gaussian-distributed random variables. Alternatively, the inputs $X_1, X_2, ..., X_m$ are statistically independent, and, under mild conditions, their weighted sum approaches a Gaussian distribution for large m by the central limit theorem of probability theory.

To proceed with the analysis, we first note from the second line of Eq. (10.32) that the mutual information $I(Y; \mathbf{X})$ between the output Y of the neuron and the input vector $\mathbf{X}$ is

$$I(Y; \mathbf{X}) = h(Y) - h(Y|\mathbf{X}) \tag{10.52}$$

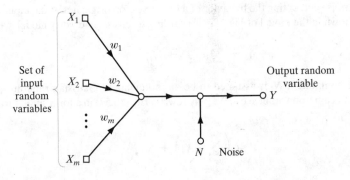

FIGURE 10.3   Signal-flow graph of a noisy neuron.

In view of Eq. (10.51), we find that the probability density function of Y, given the input vector $\mathbf{X}$, is the same as the probability density function of a constant plus a Gaussian-distributed random variable. Accordingly, the conditional entropy $h(Y|\mathbf{X})$ is the "information" that the output neuron conveys about the processing noise N rather than about the signal vector $\mathbf{X}$. We may thus set

$$h(Y|\mathbf{X}) = h(N)$$

and therefore rewrite Eq. (10.52) simply as

$$I(Y; \mathbf{X}) = h(Y) - h(N) \tag{10.53}$$

By applying Eq. (10.22) for the differential entropy of a Gaussian random variable to the problem at hand, we obtain

$$h(Y) = \frac{1}{2}[1 + \log(2\pi\sigma_Y^2)] \tag{10.54}$$

and

$$h(N) = \frac{1}{2}[1 + \log(2\pi\sigma_N^2)] \tag{10.55}$$

After simplification, the use of Eqs. (10.54) and (10.55) in Eq. (10.53) yields

$$I(Y; \mathbf{X}) = \frac{1}{2}\log\left(\frac{\sigma_Y^2}{\sigma_N^2}\right) \tag{10.56}$$

where σ_Y^2 depends on σ_N^2.

The ratio σ_Y^2/σ_N^2 may be viewed as a *signal-to-noise ratio*. Imposing the constraint that the noise variance σ_N^2 is fixed, we see from Eq. (10.56) that the mutual information $I(Y; \mathbf{X})$ is maximized by maximizing the variance σ_Y^2 of the neuron output Y. We may therefore state that under the condition that noise produced at the output of a neuron is due to a source independent of the neural inputs, maximizing the output variance of the neuron maximizes the mutual information between the output signal of that neuron and its inputs.

Lastly, the treatment of a single neuron corrupted by additive processing noise, based on minimizing the output's variance, yields a solution that is just the PCA neuron trained on Oja's rule, which was described in Chapter 8. ∎

EXAMPLE 6 Single Neuron Corrupted by Additive Input Noise

Suppose that the noise corrupting the behavior of a linear neuron originates at the input ends of the synapses as shown in the model of Fig. 10.4. According to this second noisy model, we have

$$Y = \sum_{i=1}^{m} w_i(X_i + N_i) \tag{10.57}$$

where each noise component N_i is assumed to be an independent Gaussian random variable with zero mean and common variance σ_N^2. We may rewrite Eq. (10.57) in a form similar to that of Eq. (10.51), as shown by

$$Y = \left(\sum_{i=1}^{m} w_i X_i\right) + N'$$

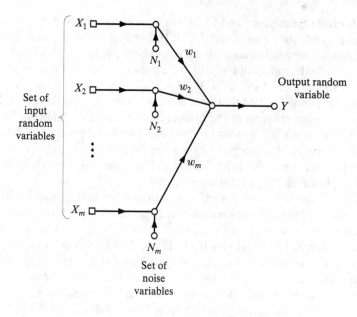

FIGURE 10.4   Another noisy model of the neuron.

where N' is a composite noise component defined by

$$N' = \sum_{i=1}^{m} w_i N_i$$

The noise N' has a Gaussian distribution with zero mean and a variance equal to the sum of the variances of its independent noise components; that is,

$$\sigma_{N'}^2 = \sum_{i=1}^{m} w_i^2 \sigma_N^2$$

As before, we assume that the output Y of the neuron has a Gaussian distribution with variance σ_Y^2. The mutual information $I(Y; \mathbf{X})$ between Y and $\mathbf{X}$ is still given by Eq. (10.52). This time, however, the conditional entropy $h(Y|\mathbf{X})$ is defined by

$$h(Y|\mathbf{X}) = h(N')$$

$$= \frac{1}{2}(1 + 2\pi\sigma_{N'}^2) \tag{10.58}$$

$$= \frac{1}{2}\left[1 + 2\pi\sigma_N^2 \sum_{i=1}^{m} w_i^2\right]$$

Thus, using Eqs. (10.54) and (10.58) in (10.52) and then simplifying terms, we get

$$I(Y; \mathbf{X}) = \frac{1}{2}\log\left(\frac{\sigma_Y^2}{\sigma_N^2 \sum_{i=1}^{m} w_i^2}\right) \tag{10.59}$$

Under the constraint that the noise variance σ_N^2 is maintained constant, the mutual information $I(Y; \mathbf{X})$ is now maximized by maximizing the ratio $\sigma_Y^2 / \sum_{i=1}^{m} w_i^2$ where σ_Y^2 is a function of w_i. ∎

What can we infer from Examples 5 and 6? First, we see from the material presented in these two examples that the result of applying the Infomax principle is problem dependent. The equivalence between maximizing the mutual information $I(Y; \mathbf{X})$ and output variance that applies to the model of Fig. 10.3, for a prescribed noise variance σ_N^2, does not carry over to the model of Fig. 10.4. It is only when we impose the constraint $\sum_i w_i^2 = 1$ on the model of Fig. 10.4 that both models behave in a similar manner.

In general, the determination of the mutual information $I(Y; \mathbf{X})$ between input vector $\mathbf{X}$ and output vector $\mathbf{Y}$ is a difficult task. In Examples 5 and 6, we made the analysis mathematically tractable by assuming that the noise distributions in a system with one or more sources of noise are *multivariate Gaussian*. This assumption needs to be justified in practical applications of the Infomax principle.

In adopting a Gaussian noise model, we are in essence invoking a "surrogate" mutual information computed on the premise that the output vector $\mathbf{Y}$ of a neuron has a multivariate Gaussian distribution with the same mean vector and covariance matrix as the actual distribution. In Linsker (1993), the Kullback–Leibler divergence is employed to provide a principled justification for the use of such surrogate mutual information, under the condition that the network has stored information about the mean vector and covariance matrix of the output vector $\mathbf{Y}$, but not about higher-order statistics.

Finally, the analysis presented in both Examples 5 and 6 was carried out in the context of a single neuron. This was done purposely with a specific point in mind: For the Infomax principle to be mathematically tractable, the optimization should be performed at the local neural level; such optimization is consistent with the essence of self-organization.

EXAMPLE 7   Noiseless Network

In Examples 5 and 6, we considered noisy neurons. In this example, we consider a noiseless network that transforms a random vector $\mathbf{X}$ of arbitrary distribution to a new random vector $\mathbf{Y}$ of different distribution. Recognizing that $I(\mathbf{X}; \mathbf{Y}) = I(\mathbf{Y}; \mathbf{X})$ and extending the second line of Eq. (10.32) to the situation described here, we may express the mutual information between the input vector $\mathbf{X}$ and output vector $\mathbf{Y}$ as

$$I(\mathbf{Y}; \mathbf{X}) = h(\mathbf{Y}) - h(\mathbf{Y}|\mathbf{X})$$

where $h(\mathbf{Y})$ is the entropy of $\mathbf{Y}$ and $h(\mathbf{Y}|\mathbf{X})$ is the conditional entropy of $\mathbf{Y}$ given $\mathbf{X}$. With the mapping from $\mathbf{X}$ to $\mathbf{Y}$ assumed to be noiseless, the conditional differential entropy $h(\mathbf{Y}|\mathbf{X})$ attains its lowest possible value: It diverges to $-\infty$. This result is due to the differential nature of the entropy of a continuous random variable, discussed in Section 10.2. However, this difficulty is of no consequence when we consider the *gradient* of the mutual information $I(\mathbf{Y}; \mathbf{X})$ with respect to a weight matrix $\mathbf{W}$ that parameterizes the input–output mapping network. Specifically, we may write

$$\frac{\partial I(\mathbf{Y}; \mathbf{X})}{\partial \mathbf{W}} = \frac{\partial h(\mathbf{Y})}{\partial \mathbf{W}} \tag{10.60}$$

because the conditional entropy $h(\mathbf{Y}|\mathbf{X})$ is independent of $\mathbf{W}$. Equation (10.60) states the following:

> *For a noiseless mapping network, maximizing the differential entropy of the network output* $\mathbf{Y}$ *is equivalent to maximizing the mutual information between* $\mathbf{Y}$ *and the network input* $\mathbf{X}$, *with both maximizations being performed with respect to the weight matrix* $\mathbf{W}$ *of the mapping network.* ∎

10.9   INFOMAX AND REDUNDANCY REDUCTION

In Shannon's framework of information theory, order and structure represent *redundancy*, which diminishes uncertainty via the receipt of information. The more order and structure we have in the underlying process, the less information we receive by observing that process. Consider for example, the highly structured and redundant sequence of examples *aaaaaa*. On receiving the first example, *a*, we can immediately say that the remaining five examples are all the same. The information conveyed by such a sequence of examples is limited to that contained in a single example. In other words, the more redundant a sequence of examples is, the smaller is the information content of that sequence, but the greater is the structure of that information content.

From the definition of mutual information $I(\mathbf{Y}; \mathbf{X})$, we know mutual information is a measure of the uncertainty about the output $\mathbf{Y}$ of a system that is resolved by observing the system input $\mathbf{X}$. The Infomax principle operates by maximizing the mutual information $I(\mathbf{Y}; \mathbf{X})$, as a result of which we are more certain about the system output $\mathbf{Y}$ by observing the system input $\mathbf{X}$. In light of the previously mentioned relationship between information and redundancy, we may therefore say the following:

> *The Infomax principle leads to a reduction in redundancy in the output* $\mathbf{Y}$ *compared with that in the input* $\mathbf{X}$.

The presence of noise is a factor that prompts the use of redundancy and the related method of diversity, which we define as follows: By "diversity," we mean the use of two or more outputs with different properties being produced by a processor. More to the point, when the additive noise in the input signal is high, we may use redundancy to combat the degrading effects of the noise. In such an environment, more of the (correlated) components of the input signal are combined by the processor to provide an accurate representation of the input. Also, when the output noise (i.e., processor noise) is high, more of the output components are directed by the processor to provide redundant information. The number of independent properties observed at the output of the processor is thereby reduced, but the representation accuracy of each property is increased. We may thus state that *a high level of noise favors redundancy of representation*. When, however, the *noise level is low, diversity of representation is favored* over redundancy.

Modeling of a Perceptual System

Since the early days of information theory, it has been suggested that the redundancy of sensory messages (stimuli) is important for understanding perception (Attneave, 1954; Barlow, 1959). Indeed, the redundancy of sensory messages provides the *knowledge* that enables the brain to build up its "cognitive maps" or "working models" of the environment around it. Regularities in the sensory messages must somehow be recoded by the brain for it to know what usually happens. However, *redundancy reduction* is the more specific form of *Barlow's hypothesis*, which states the following:

> *The purpose of early processing is to transform the highly redundant sensory input into a more efficient* factorial code.

In other words, the neural outputs become *statistically independent* when conditioned on the input.

Inspired by Barlow's hypothesis, Atick and Redlich (1990) postulated the *principle of minimum redundancy* as the basis for an information-theoretic model of the perceptual system shown in Fig. 10.5. The model consists of three components: *input channel*, *recoding system*, and *output channel*. The output of the input channel is described by

$$\mathbf{X} = \mathbf{S} + \mathbf{N}_i$$

where $\mathbf{S}$ is an ideal signal received by the input channel and $\mathbf{N}_i$ is assumed to be the source of all noise in the input. The signal $\mathbf{X}$ is subsequently transformed (recoded) by a linear matrix operator $\mathbf{A}$. It is then transmitted through the optic nerve, or output channel, producing the output $\mathbf{Y}$, as shown by

$$\mathbf{Y} = \mathbf{A}\mathbf{X} + \mathbf{N}_o$$

where $\mathbf{N}_o$ denotes the postencoding intrinsic noise. In the approach taken by Atick and Redlich, it is observed that light signals arriving at the retina contain useful sensory information in a highly redundant form. Moreover, it is hypothesized that the purpose of retinal signal processing is to reduce or eliminate the redundant bits of data caused by both correlations and noise before sending the signal along the optic nerve. To quantify this notion, a *redundancy measure* is defined by

$$R = 1 - \frac{I(\mathbf{Y}; \mathbf{S})}{C(\mathbf{Y})} \tag{10.61}$$

where $I(\mathbf{Y}; \mathbf{S})$ is the mutual information between $\mathbf{Y}$ and $\mathbf{S}$ and $C(\mathbf{Y})$ is the channel capacity of the optic nerve (output channel). Equation (10.61) is justified on the grounds that the information the brain is interested in is the ideal signal $\mathbf{S}$, while the physical channel through which this information must pass is in reality the optic nerve. It is assumed that there is no dimensionality reduction in the input–output mapping performed by the perceptual system, which means that $C(\mathbf{Y}) > I(\mathbf{Y}; \mathbf{S})$. The requirement is to find an input–output mapping (i.e., matrix $\mathbf{A}$) that minimizes the redundancy measure R, subject to the constraint of no information loss, as shown by

$$I(\mathbf{Y}; \mathbf{X}) = I(\mathbf{X}; \mathbf{X}) - \epsilon$$

where ϵ is some small positive parameter. The *channel capacity* $C(\mathbf{Y})$ in Eq. (10.61) is defined as the maximum rate of information flow possible through the optic nerve, ranging over all probability distributions of inputs applied to it, with the average input power fixed.

FIGURE 10.5 Model of a perceptual system. The signal vector **s** and noise vectors $\mathbf{v}_i$ and $\mathbf{v}_o$ are values of the random vectors **S**, $\mathbf{N}_i$, and $\mathbf{N}_o$, respectively.

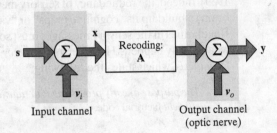

When the signal vector $\mathbf{S}$ and the output vector $\mathbf{Y}$ have the same dimensionality and there is noise in the system, the principle of minimum redundancy and the Infomax principle are mathematically equivalent, provided that a similar constraint is imposed on the computational capability of the output neurons in both cases. To be specific, suppose that the channel capacity is measured in terms of the dynamic range of the output of each neuron in the model of Fig. 10.5. Then, according to the principle of minimum redundancy, the quantity to be minimized is

$$1 - \frac{I(\mathbf{Y}; \mathbf{S})}{C(\mathbf{Y})}$$

for a given permissible information loss, and therefore for a given $I(\mathbf{Y}; \mathbf{S})$. Thus, for some parameter λ, the quantity to be minimized is essentially

$$F_1(\mathbf{Y}; \mathbf{S}) = C(\mathbf{Y}) - \lambda I(\mathbf{Y}; \mathbf{S}) \tag{10.62}$$

On the other hand, according to the Infomax principle, the quantity to be maximized in the model of Fig. 10.5 is

$$F_2(\mathbf{Y}; \mathbf{S}) = I(\mathbf{Y}; \mathbf{S}) + \lambda C(\mathbf{Y}) \tag{10.63}$$

Although the functions $F_1(\mathbf{Y}; \mathbf{S})$ and $F_2(\mathbf{Y}; \mathbf{S})$ are different, their optimizations yield identical results: They are both formulations of the method of Lagrange multipliers, with the roles of $I(\mathbf{Y}; \mathbf{S})$ and $C(\mathbf{Y})$ being simply interchanged.

The important point to take from this discussion is that despite the difference in formulations, these two information-theoretic principles lead to similar results[7]:

> *Maximization of the mutual information between the output and input of a neural system does indeed lead to redundancy reduction.*

10.10   SPATIALLY COHERENT FEATURES

The Infomax principle, as postulated in Section 10.8, applies to a situation where the mutual information $I(\mathbf{Y}; \mathbf{X})$ between the output vector $\mathbf{Y}$ of a neural system and the input vector $\mathbf{X}$ is the objective function to be maximized, as illustrated in Fig. 10.2a. With appropriate changes in terminology, we may extend this principle to deal with the unsupervised processing of the image of a natural scene (Becker and Hinton, 1992). An unprocessed pixel of such an image contains a wealth of information about the scene of interest, albeit in complex structural form. In particular, the intensity of each pixel is affected by such intrinsic parameters as depth, reflectance, and surface orientation, as well as background noise and illumination. The goal is to design a self-organizing system that is capable of learning to encode this complex information in a simpler form. To be more specific, the objective is to extract higher-order features that exhibit *coherence across space* in such a way that the representation of information in one spatially localized region of the image makes it easy to produce the representation of information in neighboring regions; a region refers to a collection of pixels in the image. The situation described herein pertains to the second scenario illustrated in Fig. 10.2b.

We may thus formulate the *Imax principle* for scenario 2 as follows (Becker, 1996; Becker and Hinton, 1992):

> *The transformation of a pair of vectors $\mathbf{X}_a$ and $\mathbf{X}_b$ (representing adjacent, nonoverlapping regions of an image by a neural system) should be so chosen that the scalar output Y_a of the*

system due to the input $\mathbf{X}_a$ maximizes information about the second scalar output Y_b due to $\mathbf{X}_b$, and vice versa. The objective function to be maximized is the mutual information $I(Y_a; Y_b)$ between the outputs Y_a and Y_b.

Although the Imax principle is not equivalent to or derived from the Infomax principle, it certainly functions in a similar spirit.

EXAMPLE 8   Coherent Image Processing

Consider the example of Fig. 10.6, which shows two neural networks (modules) a and b receiving respective inputs $\mathbf{X}_a$ and $\mathbf{X}_b$ from adjacent, nonoverlapping regions of an image. The scalars Y_a and Y_b denote the outputs of these two modules due to the respective input vectors $\mathbf{X}_a$ and $\mathbf{X}_b$, respectively. Let S denote a random signal component common to both Y_a and Y_b, which is representative of the spatial coherence across the two pertinent regions of the original image. We may express Y_a and Y_b as noisy versions of the common signal S, as shown by

$$Y_a = S + N_a$$

and

$$Y_b = S + N_b$$

The N_a and N_b are additive noise components, assumed to be statistically independent, zero-mean, Gaussian-distributed random variables. The signal component S is also assumed to be Gaussian with a distribution of its own. According to these two equations, the two modules a and b in Fig. 10.6 make consistent assumptions about each other.

Using the last line of Eq. (10.32), we find that the mutual information between Y_a and Y_b is defined by

$$I(Y_a; Y_b) = h(Y_a) + h(Y_b) - h(Y_a, Y_b) \tag{10.64}$$

According to the formula of Eq. (10.22) for the differential entropy of a Gaussian random variable, the differential entropy $h(Y_a)$ of Y_a is given by

$$h(Y_a) = \frac{1}{2}[1 + \log(2\pi\sigma_a^2)] \tag{10.65}$$

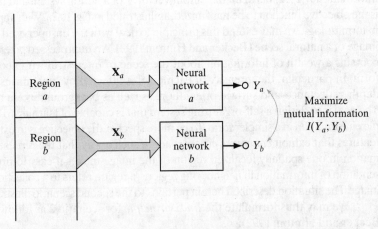

FIGURE 10.6   Processing of two neighboring regions of an image in accordance with the Imax principle.

where σ_a^2 is the variance of Y_a. Similarly, the differential entropy of Y_b is given by

$$h(Y_b) = \frac{1}{2}[1 + \log(2\pi\sigma_b^2)] \tag{10.66}$$

where σ_b^2 is the variance of Y_b. As for the joint differential entropy $h(Y_a, Y_b)$, we use the formula of Eq. (10.24) with a value of two for the number m of outputs to write

$$h(Y_a; Y_b) = 1 + \log(2\pi) + \frac{1}{2}\log|\det(\mathbf{\Sigma})|$$

The two-by-two matrix $\mathbf{\Sigma}$, denoting the covariance matrix of Y_a and Y_b, is defined by

$$\mathbf{\Sigma} = \begin{bmatrix} \sigma_a^2 & \rho_{ab}\sigma_a\sigma_b \\ \rho_{ab}\sigma_a\sigma_b & \sigma_b^2 \end{bmatrix} \tag{10.67}$$

and

$$\det(\mathbf{\Sigma}) = \sigma_a^2\sigma_b^2(1 - \rho_{ab}^2)$$

The parameter ρ_{ab} is the *correlation coefficient* of Y_a and Y_b; that is,

$$\rho_{ab} = \frac{\mathbb{E}[(Y_a - \mathbb{E}[Y_a])(Y_b - \mathbb{E}[Y_b])]}{\sigma_a\sigma_b}.$$

Hence, we may reformulate the joint differential entropy of Y_a and Y_b as

$$h(Y_a; Y_b) = 1 + \log(2\pi) + \frac{1}{2}\log[\sigma_a^2\sigma_b^2(1 - \rho_{ab}^2)] \tag{10.68}$$

Using Eqs. (10.65), (10.66), and (10.68) in Eq. (10.64) and then simplifying terms, we get

$$I(Y_a; Y_b) = -\frac{1}{2}\log(1 - \rho_{ab}^2) \tag{10.69}$$

From Eq. (10.69), we immediately deduce that maximizing the mutual information $I(Y_a; Y_b)$ is equivalent to maximizing the correlation coefficient ρ_{ab}, which is intuitively satisfying. Note that, by definition, $|\rho_{ab}| \leq 1$. ∎

The result described in Eq. (10.69) was derived for the example of two random variables Y_a and Y_b produced at the outputs of the stochastic system in Fig. 10.6, both of which are assumed to be both Gaussian distributed. In the more general case of non-Gaussian distribution, however, the use of the correlation coefficient ρ_{ab} does not serve as an appropriate measure for the Imax principle. To generalize the utility of Imax, we propose the use of copula, inspired by the formula of Eq. (10.50). To be more specific, consider the scenario depicted in Fig. 10.2b. Let $\mathbf{W}$ denote the weight matrix of the system responsible for generating the outputs Y_a and Y_b in response to the combined influence of the respective input vectors $\mathbf{X}_a$ and $\mathbf{X}_b$. We may then use the first line of Eq. (10.50) to formulate the Imax principle simply as

$$\max_{\mathbf{W}} I(Y_a; Y_b) = \min_{\mathbf{W}} h_C(U_a, U_b; \mathbf{W}) \tag{10.70}$$

where, in terms of the pertinent cumulative probability distributions, we write

$$u_a = P_{Y_a}(y_a)$$

and

$$u_b = P_{Y_b}(y_b)$$

and $h_C(U_a, U_b; \mathbf{W})$ is the joint differential entropy of the random variables U_a and U_b, whose respective sample values are u_a and u_b. Equivalently, in light of the second line of Eq. (10.50), we may also write

$$\max_{\mathbf{W}} I(Y_a; Y_b) = \max_{\mathbf{W}} \mathbb{E}[\log c_{U_a, U_b}(u_a, u_b; \mathbf{W})] \tag{10.71}$$

where $c_{U_a, U_b}(u_a, u_b; \mathbf{W})$ is the copula's joint probability density function of the random variables U_a and U_b. The formula of Eq. (10.71) includes the result of Eq. (10.69) as a special case; the importance of this formula will be demonstrated later on in the chapter.

Relationship Between Imax and Canonical Correlation Analysis

Consider again the two input vectors $\mathbf{X}_a$ and $\mathbf{X}_b$, which are not necessarily of the same dimensionality. Let there be two corresponding weight (basis) vectors, denoted by $\mathbf{w}_a$ and $\mathbf{w}_b$, that are of similar dimensionality to $\mathbf{X}_a$ and $\mathbf{X}_b$, respectively. The objective of *canonical correlation analysis* (CCA), commonly used in statistics, is to find two linear combinations

$$Y_a = \mathbf{w}_a^T \mathbf{X}_a$$

and

$$Y_b = \mathbf{w}_b^T \mathbf{X}_b$$

that have *maximum correlation* between them. Comparing the problem stated herein with that of Imax, we readily see that Imax is indeed the nonlinear counterpart of CCA. For a more detailed treatment of CCA, the reader is referred to Note 8 under Notes and References.

10.11 SPATIALLY INCOHERENT FEATURES

The unsupervised processing of an image considered in the previous section deals with the extraction of spatially coherent features from an image. We now consider the opposite scenario. To be specific, consider the third scenario of Fig. 10.2c, where the objective is to enhance the *spatial differences* between a pair of corresponding regions derived from two separate, but correlated, images. Whereas we maximized the mutual information between the outputs of the modules in Fig. 10.2b, we do the exact opposite in Fig. 10.2c.

We may thus state the *Imin principle*[9] for scenario 3 as follows (Ukrainec and Haykin, 1992, 1996):

> *The transformation of a pair of input vectors, $\mathbf{X}_a$ and $\mathbf{X}_b$, representing data derived from corresponding regions in a pair of separate images, by a neural system should be so chosen that the scalar output Y_a of the system due to the input $\mathbf{X}_a$ minimizes information about the second scalar output Y_b due to $\mathbf{X}_b$ and vice versa. The objective function to be minimized is the mutual information $I(Y_a; Y_b)$ between the outputs Y_a and Y_b.*

Case Study: Radar Polarimetry

The Imin principle finds application in *radar polarimetry*, for example, where a surveillance radar system produces a pair of images of an environment of interest by transmitting on one polarization and receiving the backscatter from the environment on the same or a different polarization. The polarization can be vertical or horizontal. For example, we may have a pair of radar images, one image representing like polarization (horizontal–horizontal, say), and the other image representing cross-polarization (horizontal on transmit and vertical on receive). Such an application is described in Ukrainec and Haykin (1992, 1996), which pertains to the *enhancement of a polarization target* in a dual-polarized radar system. The sample radar scene used in the study is described as follows: An incoherent radar transmits in a horizontally polarized fashion and receives radar returns on both horizontal and vertical polarization channels. The target of interest is a *cooperative, polarization-twisting reflector* designed to rotate the incident polarization through 90 degrees. In the normal operation of a radar system, the detection of such a target is made difficult by imperfections in the system as well as reflections from unwanted polarimetric targets on the ground (i.e., radar clutter). We perceive that a nonlinear mapping is needed to account for the non-Gaussian distribution common to radar returns. The target-enhancement problem is cast as a variational problem, the objective of which is to minimize a quadratic cost functional with constraints. The net result is a processed cross-polarized image that exhibits a significant improvement in target visibility, this improvement is expected to be far more pronounced than that attainable through the use of a linear technique such as principal-components analysis. The model used by Ukrainec and Haykin assumes Gaussian statistics for the transformed data, since a model-free estimate of the probability density function is a computationally challenging task. The mutual information between two Gaussian variables Y_a and Y_b is defined by Eq. (10.69). To learn the synaptic weights of the two modules, a variational approach is taken. The requirement is to suppress the radar clutter that is common to the horizontally polarized and vertically polarized radar images. To satisfy this requirement, the mutual information $I(Y_a; Y_b)$ is minimized, subject to a constraint imposed on the synaptic weights as shown by

$$C = (\text{tr}[\mathbf{W}^T\mathbf{W}] - 1)^2$$

where $\mathbf{W}$ is the overall weight matrix of the network and $\text{tr}[\cdot]$ is the trace of the enclosed matrix product. A stationary point is reached when we have

$$\nabla_{\mathbf{W}}I(Y_a; Y_b) + \lambda\nabla_{\mathbf{W}}C = 0 \tag{10.72}$$

where $\nabla_{\mathbf{W}}$ is the gradient operator with respect to the matrix $\mathbf{W}$ and λ is the Lagrange multiplier. A quasi-Newton optimization routine was used to find the minimum; quasi-Newton's methods were discussed in Chapters 3 and 4.

Figure 10.7 shows the architecture of the neural network used in Ukrainec and Haykin (1992, 1996). A Gaussian radial-basis function (RBF) network was chosen for each of the two modules because it has the advantage of providing a set of fixed-basis functions (i.e., a nonadaptive hidden layer). The input data were expanded onto the basis functions and then combined using layers of *linear* weights; the dashed lines shown in Fig. 10.7 represent the cross-coupling connections between the two modules. The centers of the Gaussian functions were chosen at evenly spaced intervals to cover the entire

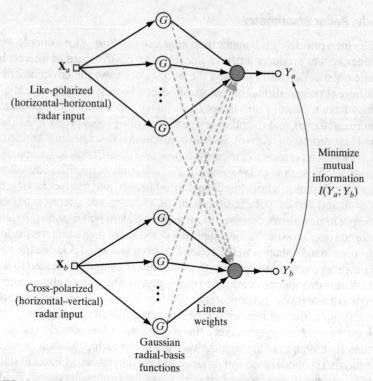

FIGURE 10.7 Block diagram of a neural processor, the goal of which is to suppress background clutter using a pair of polarimetric, noncoherent radar inputs; clutter suppression is attained by minimizing the mutual information between the outputs of the two modules.

input domain, and their widths were chosen using a heuristic. Figure 10.8a shows the raw horizontally polarized and vertically polarized (both on receive) radar images of a parklike setting on the shore of Lake Ontario. The range coordinate is along the horizontal axis of each image, increasing from left to right; the azimuth coordinate is along the vertical axis, increasing down the image. Figure 10.8b shows the combined image obtained by minimizing the mutual information between the horizontally and vertically polarized radar images, in accordance with the Imin principle. The bright spot clearly visible in this image corresponds to the radar return from a cooperative, polarization-twisting reflector placed along the lakeshore. The case study discussed herein demonstrates the practical benefit of applying the Imin principle to the processing of spatially incoherent images.[10]

Generalizations of the Imax and Imin Principles

In formulating the Imax principle in Section 10.10 and the Imin principle in this section, we treated the maximization or minimization of the mutual information $I(Y_a; Y_b)$ for a pair of output terminals. Both the Imax and Imin principles may be generalized for any number of terminals, the outputs of which are denoted by $Y_a, Y_b, Y_c, ...$, by maximizing or minimizing the multivariate mutual information $I(Y_a; Y_b; Y_c; ...)$, respectively.

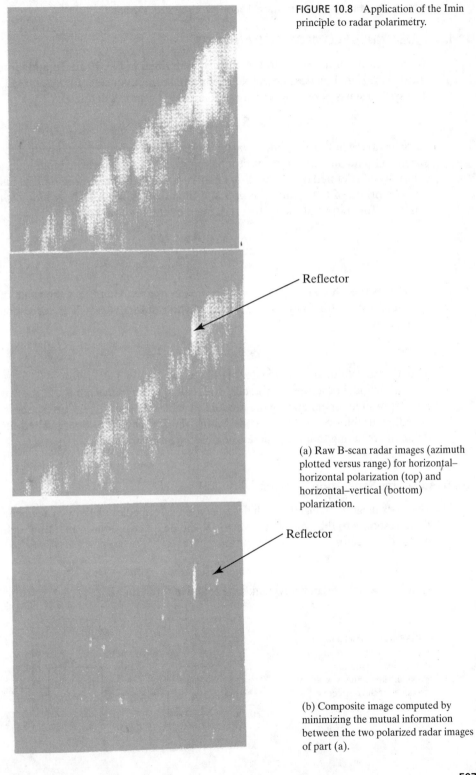

FIGURE 10.8 Application of the Imin principle to radar polarimetry.

Reflector

(a) Raw B-scan radar images (azimuth plotted versus range) for horizontal–horizontal polarization (top) and horizontal–vertical (bottom) polarization.

Reflector

(b) Composite image computed by minimizing the mutual information between the two polarized radar images of part (a).

507

10.12 INDEPENDENT-COMPONENTS ANALYSIS

We now turn our attention to the scenario described in Fig. 10.2d. To add more specificity to the signal-processing problem depicted therein, consider the system of Fig. 10.9. The system starts operating with a random source vector **S** defined by

$$\mathbf{S} = [S_1, S_2, ..., S_m]^T$$

Sample values of the m random variables constituting **S** are respectively denoted by $s_1, s_2, ..., s_m$. The random source vector **S** is applied to a *mixer*, whose input–output characterization is defined by a nonsingular matrix **A** called the *mixing matrix*. The linear system comprised of the source vector **S** and the mixer **A** is completely *unknown* to the observer. The output of the system is defined by the random vector

$$\mathbf{X} = \mathbf{AS}$$
$$= \sum_{i=1}^{m} \mathbf{a}_i S_i \qquad (10.73)$$

where $\mathbf{a}_i$ is the ith column vector of the mixing matrix **A** and S_i is the random signal produced by the ith source, $i = 1, 2, ..., m$. The random vector **X** is correspondingly denoted by

$$\mathbf{X} = [X_1, X_2, ..., X_m]^T$$

with a sample value of X_j being denoted by x_j, where $j = 1, 2, ..., m$.

The model described in Eq. (10.73) is called a *generative model*, in the sense that it is responsible for generating the random variables $X_1, X_2, ..., X_m$. Correspondingly, the random variables $S_1, S_2, ..., S_m$, constituting the source vector **S**, are called the *latent variables*, meaning that they cannot be observed directly.

The Blind Source Separation Problem[11]

The block diagram of Fig. 10.9 includes a *demixer*, described by an m-by-m *demixing matrix* **W**. In response to the observation vector **X**, the demixer produces an output defined by the random vector

$$\mathbf{Y} = \mathbf{WX}$$

in light of which we may now make the following statement:

FIGURE 10.9 Block diagram of the processor for solving the blind source separation problem. The vectors **s**, **x**, and **y** are values of the respective random vectors **S**, **X**, and **Y**.

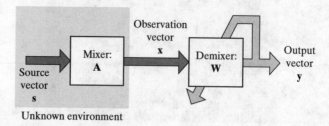

Given a set of independent realizations of the observation vector **X** *resulting from an unknown linear mixing of the latent (source) variables* $S_1, S_2, ..., S_m$, *estimate the demixing matrix* **W** *such that the components of the resulting output vector* **Y** *are as statistically independent as possible; here, the term "independence" should be understood in its strong statistical sense.*

This statement describes the essence of the *blind source separating problem*. The problem is said to be blind to signify the fact that the estimation of the demixing matrix **W** is carried out in an *unsupervised* manner. Moreover, the only information used to recover the original source vector **S** is contained in the observation vector **X**. The underlying principle involved in solving the blind source separation (BSS) problem is called *independent-components analysis* (Comon, 1994). Independent-components analysis (ICA) may be viewed as an extension of principal-components analysis (PCA), with the following basic difference between them: Whereas PCA can only impose statistical independence up to the second order while constraining the direction vectors to be orthogonal, ICA imposes statistical independence on *all* the individual components of the output vector **Y** and involves no orthogonality constraint.

Basic Assumptions

To simplify the study of principal-components analysis, the following four basic assumptions are made:

1. *Statistical independence.* The latent variables constituting the source vector **S** are assumed to be statistically independent, Note, however, that since the observation vector **X** is made up of a linear combination of the latent variables, the individual components of the observation vector **X** are statistically *dependent* on each other.

2. *Dimensionalities of the Mixing Matrix.* The mixing matrix is a square matrix, which means that the number of observations is the same as the number of sources.

3. *Noise-free model.* The generative model is assumed to be noise free, which means that the only source of stochasicity in the model is the source vector **S**.

4. *Zero mean.* It is assumed that the source vector **S** has zero mean, which, in turn, implies that the observation vector **X** has zero mean too. If not, then the mean vector $\mathbb{E}[\mathbf{X}]$ is subtracted from **X** to make it assume a zero-mean value.

One other assumption is sometimes invoked:

5. *Whitening.* It is also assumed that the observation vector **X** has been "whitened," which means that its individual components are *uncorrelated*, but not necessarily *independent*. Whitening is achieved by *linearly transforming* the observation vector so that the correlation matrix $\mathbb{E}[\mathbf{XX}^T]$ is equal to the identity matrix.

It is also important to recognize that the solution of a BSS problem is feasible except for an *arbitrary scaling of the estimate of each source output (i.e., latent variable) and permutation of indices.* To elaborate, it is possible to find a demixing matrix **W** whose individual rows are a rescaling and permutation of the mixing matrix **A**. In other words, the solution to the BSS problem produced by the ICA algorithm may be expressed in the form

$$\mathbf{y} = \mathbf{Wx} = \mathbf{WAs} = \mathbf{DPs}$$

where $\mathbf{D}$ is a nonsingular diagonal matrix and $\mathbf{P}$ is a permutation matrix; $\mathbf{s}$, $\mathbf{x}$, and $\mathbf{y}$ are respective realizations of the random vectors $\mathbf{S}$, $\mathbf{X}$, and $\mathbf{Y}$.

Non-Gaussianity of Sources: A Necessary Requirement for ICA, Except Possibly for One Source

For an ICA algorithm to be capable of separating a given set of source signals as independently as possible at the demixer output, it is a requirement that there be *sufficient information* in the observable vector $\mathbf{X}$ produced at the output of the generative model. The key question is as follows:

> *How should the information content in the observation vector $\mathbf{X}$ manifest itself for the separability of source signals to be feasible?*

We will address this basic question by way of a simple, yet insightful, example.

EXAMPLE 9 Two Different Characterizations of a Pair of Independent Sources

Consider a generative model involving a pair of independent random source signals S_1 and S_2, both of which have zero mean and unit variance. The mixing matrix is defined by the nonsingular matrix

$$A = \begin{bmatrix} 1 & -1 \\ 1 & 2 \end{bmatrix}$$

The example is in two parts: In the first part, both sources are Gaussian distributed; in the second part of the example, one source is Gaussian distributed and the other is uniformly distributed.

From probability theory, we know the following two properties of Gaussian distributions (Bertsekas and Tsitsiklis, 2002):

1. The higher-order moments of a zero-mean Gaussian random variable are all even and uniquely defined by the variance (i.e., the second-order moment for the special case of zero mean).
2. The sum of two linearly scaled (weighted) Gaussian random variables is also Gaussian.

It follows therefore that when the source signals S_1 and S_2 are both Gaussian with zero mean, the observables X_1 and X_2 are also both Gaussian with zero mean. Moreover, for the prescribed mixing matrix, X_1 has a variance

$$(1)^2\sigma_1^2 + (-1)^2\sigma_2^2 = 17,$$

and X_2 has the variance

$$(1)^2\sigma_1^2 + (2)^2\sigma_2^2 = 65,$$

where $\sigma_1^2 = 1$ and $\sigma_2^2 = 16$.

Part (a) of Fig. 10.10 plots the histograms of the source signals S_1 and S_2, while part (b) of the figure plots the corresponding two-dimensional distribution of the observables X_1 and X_2. Examining Fig. 10.10b, we find that the two-dimensional distribution is *symmetric* about the origin, and its information content is *insufficient* to discriminate between the individual directions of the original source signals S_1 and S_2.

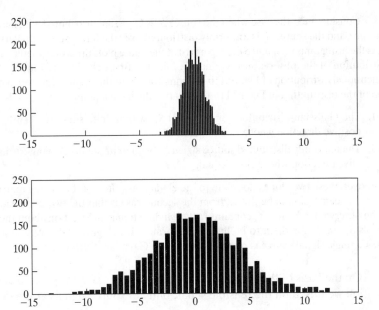

(a) Histograms of the two processes: The top histogram refers to Gaussian signal source S_1 of zero mean and veriance $\sigma_1^2 = 1$; the bottom one refers to Gaussian source signal S_2 of zero mean and variance $\sigma_2^2 = 16$.

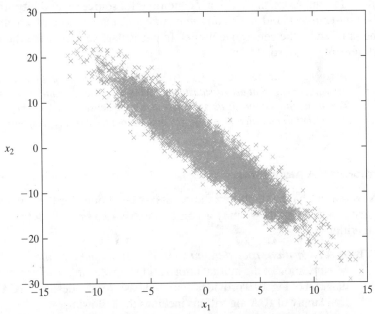

(b) Two-dimensional distribution of the linearly mixed signals X_1 and X_2.

FIGURE 10.10   Two Gaussian distributed processes.

Consider next the case when the source S_1 is Gaussian distributed with zero mean and unit variance, and the source S_2 is uniformly distributed over the interval $[-2, 2]$. Part (a) of Fig. 10.11 plots the histograms of S_1 and S_2, and part (b) of the figure plots the corresponding two-dimensional distribution of the observables X_1 and X_2. Like the first case depicted in Fig. 10.10b, the two-dimensional distribution of Fig. 10.11b is symmetric about the origin. However, a deeper examination of the distribution in Fig. 10.11b reveals two distinctive points:

1. The Gaussian-distributed source signal S_1 (with infinite support) manifests itself along a positive direction whose slope equals $+1$.
2. The uniformly distributed source signal S_2 (with finite support) manifests itself along a negative direction whose slope equals -2.

Moreover, these two slopes do relate to the elemental values of the mixing matrix.

The conclusion to be drawn from the second case is that the two-dimensional distribution of the observables X_1 and X_2 contains *sufficient* directional information about the original source signals S_1 and S_2 for them to be linearly separable. This highly desirable condition arises only when a single signal source is permitted to have a Gaussian distribution. ∎

On the basis of the results of this example, we may now go on to answer the basic question we raised on the feasible separability of source signals at the demixer output:

1. The observables $X_1, X_1, ..., X_m$ must have higher-order moments that are unrelated to their respective second-order moments. Accordingly, the source signals $S_1, S_1, ..., S_m$ must be non-Gaussian.
2. At the very most, only a single source is permitted to have a Gaussian distribution.

To summarize, the necessary conditions for source separability are that the sources be *non-Gaussian* and the *mixing matrix be nonsinguar*, both of which conditions must be satisfied by the generative model. In particular, we may make the following succint statement (Cardoso, 2003):

> *Independent components analysis (ICA) is the decomposition of a random vector into linear components that are as statistically independent as possible, where the term "independence" is understood in its strongest statistical sense; ICA goes beyond (second-order) decorrelation and therefore requires that the observations representing the data vector be non-Gaussian.*

Classification of ICA Algorithms

Now that we have established the necessary conditions for the separability of linearly mixed source signals, we may go on to identify two broadly defined families of ICA algorithms:

1. *ICA Algorithms rooted in minimization of mutual information*
   Minimization of the mutual information between the demixer outputs in the block diagram of Fig. 10.9 provides a natural basis for the design of ICA algorithms. This first family of ICA algorithms includes the following:
   1.1 The algorithm developed by Amari et al. (1996), which is based on the Kullback–Leibler divergence. This algorithm is described in Section 10.14.

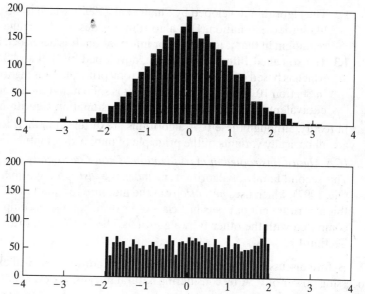

(a) Histograms of the two processes: The top histogram refers to Gaussian source signal S_1 of zero mean and veriance σ_1^2; the bottom one refers to uniformly distributed source signal S_2 uniformly distributed over the interval $[-2, 2]$.

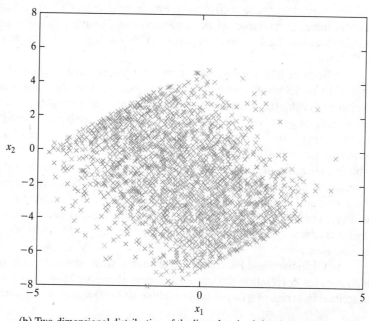

(b) Two-dimensional distribution of the linearly mixed signals X_1 and X_2.

FIGURE 10.11   Gaussian- and uniformly-distributed processes.

1.2 The algorithm developed by Pham et al. (1992), which is based on maximum-likelihood estimation. This algorithm resides on the fringe of the Bayesian paradigm in that it ignores prior information. It is described in Section 10.15.

1.3 The so-called Infomax algorithm, developed by Bell and Sejnowski (1995), which is based on the maximum-entropy principle. This algorithm is described in Section 10.16. In Cardoso (1997), it is shown that the Infomax algorithm is equivalent to the maximum-likelihood-estimation algorithm.

In reality, although these ICA algorithms are different in their formulations, they are all basically variants of the principle of minimizing mutual information.

2. *ICA Algorithms rooted in maximization of non-Gaussianity*
This second family of algorithms includes the *fastICA algorithm* (Hyvärinen and Oja, 1997), which uses *negentropy* as the measure for non-Gaussianity. Moreover, this algorithm not only sits in a class of its own, but also is computationally faster compared with the other ICA algorithms. The fastICA algorithm is described in Section 10.18.

Before discussing the aforementioned ICA algorithms, we will explore the signal-processing power of ICA by considering natural images, as described next.

10.13 SPARSE CODING OF NATURAL IMAGES AND COMPARISON WITH ICA CODING

In Chapter 8, we emphasized the importance of higher-order statistics of natural images and the impact of those statistics on image modeling. In this section, we emphasize another important characteristic of natural images—namely, *sparseness*—and the role of ICA in capturing it. In so doing, we provide motivation for the practical importance of ICA.

In Section 10.9, we discussed how the *principle of minimum redundancy* may be applied to model visual systems (Atick and Redlich, 1990). In Dong and Atick (1995) and Dan et al. (1996), the application of this principle was extended to see how the properties of retinal ganglion cells in the visual system may be explained by whitening, or decorrelating, a set of outputs produced by these cells in response to the $1/f$ amplitude power spectra of natural images. Subsequently, Olshausen and Field (1997) pointed out a basic limitation of the model studied by Atick and collaborators: The reduction of redundancy considered therein was limited to linear pairwise correlations among the pixels of a natural image; these correlations can be captured by principal-components analysis. In reality, however, natural images exhibit higher-order correlations due to oriented lines and edges—especially those of the curved variety—all of which are prevalent in natural images.

In Olshausen and Field (1997) a probabilistic model is described for capturing the higher-order correlation structure of a natural image. Most importantly, the model is described in terms of a *linear superposition of basis functions*, as illustrated by

$$I(\mathbf{x}) = \sum_i a_i \psi_i(\mathbf{x}) \tag{10.74}$$

where the vector $\mathbf{x}$ denotes a discrete *spatial position* within the two-dimensional images $I(\mathbf{x})$, the $\psi_i(\mathbf{x})$ denote the *basis functions*, and the a_i denote the *mixing amplitudes*. The computed values of the a_i constitute the output of the coding strategy. Moreover, the basis functions were chosen to be *adaptive*, so as to account for the underlying structure of the image in terms of a collection of *statistically independent events* in the best manner possible. Thus, building on some prior work by Field (1994), Olshausen and Field (1997) made the following conjecture:

> *Sparseness is an appropriate prior for the mixing amplitudes a_i in Eq. (10.74), which is based on the intuition that natural images may be described in terms of a relatively small number of structural primitives exemplified by edges, lines, and other elementary features.*

To validate this conjecture, Olshausen and Field carried out the following two tasks:

1. Formulation of a *sparse-coding algorithm*, aimed at maximization of spareseness that is rooted in image processing and information theory. The algorithm was designed to *learn* a set of *basis functions* for the image model based on Eq. (10.74) that would best account for natural images in terms of *sparse, statistically independent components*; the sparse-coding algorithm was shown to minimize the same objective function as ICA, but by making an approximation due to the intractability introduced by overcomplete representations.

2. Generation of data, taken from ten 512-by-512 pixel images of natural surroundings (trees, rocks, mountains, and so on); the data were applied to train the algorithm.

A stable solution computed by the sparse-coding algorithm was usually obtained after approximately 2,000 updates (i.e., approximately 200,00 image presentations). The result of the training process is shown in Fig. 10.12, in which the vast majority of basis functions have become localized within individual pixels.

In an independent study, Bell and Sejnowski (1997) applied ICA to four natural scenes involving trees, leaves, and so on, which were converted to greyscale byte values ranging between 0 and 255. The Infomax algorithm for ICA, to be described in Section 10.16, was used in the study. The resulting solution is shown in Fig. 10.13.

Comparing the solution of Fig. 10.12, using the sparse-coding algorithm, and that of Fig. 10.13, using the Infomax algorithm for ICA, it is remarkable to see how similar these two solutions are. The similarity is all the more remarkable when we recognize that entirely different natural image data were used to train the two algorithms independently.

The results of these two completely independent studies teach us the following two important lessons:

1. Natural images are inherently sparse, in the sense that they may be described by a relatively small number of distinctive structural primitives, examples of which include edges and lines.

2. By its very essence, an algorithm for independent-components analysis has a built-in capability of capturing these structural primitives.

So, indeed, the results presented in Figs. 10.12 ands 10.13 do provide the motivation to study learning algorithms for ICA, which we do in the next four sections.

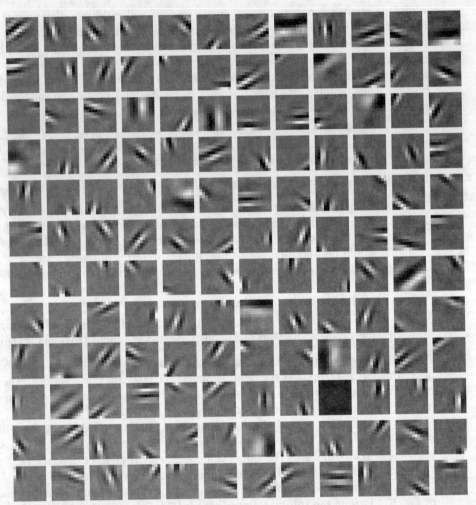

FIGURE 10.12   The result of applying the sparse-coding algorithm to a natural image. (The figure is reproduced with the permission of Dr. Bruno Olshausen.)

10.14   NATURAL-GRADIENT LEARNING FOR INDEPENDENT-COMPONENTS ANALYSIS

Consider the input–output relationship

$$\mathbf{Y} = \mathbf{WX} \tag{10.75}$$

where the random vector $\mathbf{X}$ denotes the observables (i.e., the demixer input), $\mathbf{W}$ denotes the demixing matrix, and the random vector $\mathbf{Y}$ denotes the resulting response (i.e., the demixer output). With statistical independence among the individual components of the output $\mathbf{Y}$ as the desired property for blind source separation, what is a practical

FIGURE 10.13   The result of applying the Infomax algorithm for ICA to another natural image. (The figure is reproduced with the permission of Dr. Anthony Bell.)

measure that we can use to achieve that property? To prepare ourselves for the answer to this fundamental question, let $p_{\mathbf{Y}}(\mathbf{y}, \mathbf{W})$ denote the probability density function of the output $\mathbf{Y}$, *parameterized* by the demixing matrix $\mathbf{W}$, and let the corresponding *factorial distribution* be defined by

$$\tilde{p}_{\mathbf{Y}}(\mathbf{y}) = \prod_{i=1}^{m} \tilde{p}_{Y_i}(y_i) \tag{10.76}$$

where $\tilde{p}_{Y_i}(y_i)$ is the marginal probability density function of the random variable Y_i (i.e., the ith component of $\mathbf{Y}$); for obvious reasons, the factorial distribution $\tilde{p}_{\mathbf{Y}}(\mathbf{y})$ is *not* parameterized. In effect, Eq. (10.76) may be viewed as a *constraint* imposed on the learning rule (to be developed), forcing it to contrast $p_Y(\mathbf{y}, \mathbf{W})$ against the factorial distribution $\tilde{p}_Y(\mathbf{y})$, which, ideally, should match that of the original sources. Focusing on the distributions $p_Y(\mathbf{y}, \mathbf{W})$ and $\tilde{p}_Y(\mathbf{y})$ as the only two distributions at our disposal, we may now state the answer to our question, embodied in the principle of *independent-components analysis* (ICA) which states (Comon, 1994),

> Given an m-by-1 random vector **X** representing a linear combination of m independent source signals, the transformation of the observation vector **X** into a new random vector **Y** should be carried out in such a way that the Kullback–Leibler divergence between the parameterized probability density function $p_Y(\mathbf{y}, \mathbf{W})$ and the corresponding factorial distribution $\tilde{p}_Y(\mathbf{y})$ is minimized with respect to the unknown parameter matrix **W**.

From this statement, it is clear that the Kullback–Leibler divergence is a natural basis for the *expected contrast function*, the formulation of which constitutes the very first step in deriving a learning algorithm for ICA. With the demixing matrix **W** being the unknown parameter in ICA, the expected contrast function is a function of **W**. Hereafter, we use $R(\mathbf{W})$ to denote that contrast function, which, in light of the formula for the Kullback–Leibler divergence presented in the first line of Eq. (10.39), may now be formally defined as follows:

$$R(\mathbf{W}) = \int_{-\infty}^{\infty} p_Y(\mathbf{y}, \mathbf{W}) \log\left(\frac{p_Y(\mathbf{y}, \mathbf{W})}{\prod_{i=1}^{m} \tilde{p}_{Y_i}(y_i)}\right) dy \tag{10.77}$$

What is truly remarkable about this formula is the fact that it appears to be the inspirational framework used to derive many of the learning algorithms proposed in the literature for ICA and blind source separation (Cichocki and Amari, 2002).

Following the discussion of the Kullback–Leibler divergence presented in Section 10.5, we may reformulate the expected contrast function $R(\mathbf{W})$ in terms of the two entropies at our disposal, as shown by

$$R(\mathbf{W}) = -h(\mathbf{Y}) + \sum_{i=1}^{m} \tilde{h}(Y_i) \tag{10.78}$$

where $h(\mathbf{Y})$ is the entropy of the random vector **Y** at the output of the demixer and $\tilde{h}(Y_i)$ is the marginal entropy of the ith element of **Y**. $R(\mathbf{W})$ is the objective function to be minimized with respect to **W**.

Determination of the Differential Entropy h(Y)

The output vector **Y** is related to the input vector **X** by Eq. (10.75), where **W** is the demixing matrix. In light of Eq. (10.18), we may express the differential entropy of **Y** as

$$h(\mathbf{Y}) = h(\mathbf{WX})$$
$$= h(\mathbf{X}) + \log|\det(\mathbf{W})| \tag{10.79}$$

where $h(\mathbf{X})$ is the differential entropy of **X** and $\det(\mathbf{W})$ is the determinant of **W**. Using this expression in Eq. (10.77), we may reformulate the expected contrast function one more time, as

$$R(\mathbf{W}) = -h(\mathbf{X}) - \log|\det(\mathbf{W})| + \sum_{i=1}^{m} \tilde{h}(Y_i)$$

$$= -h(\mathbf{X}) - \log|\det(\mathbf{W})| - \sum_{i=1}^{m} \mathbb{E}[\log \tilde{p}_{Y_i}(y_i)] \qquad (10.80)$$

where, for the rightmost term in the second line of the equation, we used Eq. (10.10) and the expectation in that term is with respect to Y_i. Note that the entropy $h(\mathbf{X})$ is independent of the demixing matrix $\mathbf{W}$; henceforth, we are justified to ignore this term in deriving the learning algorithm for ICA.

Derivation of Stochastic Gradient Algorithm for ICA

With stochastic gradient descent in mind, it is the usual practice to ignore the expectation operator $\mathbb{E}$ and focus attention on instantaneous values only. For the problem at hand, there is only one instantaneous value to be considered, namely, $\log \tilde{p}_{Y_i}(y_i)$. Let $\rho(\mathbf{W})$ denote the instantaneous value of the expected contrast function $R(\mathbf{W})$, which, henceforth, we refer to simply as the *contrast function*; that is to say,

$$R(\mathbf{W}) = \mathbb{E}[\rho(\mathbf{W})]$$

Thus, ignoring the entropy $h(\mathbf{X})$, we may use Eq. (10.80) to write

$$\rho(\mathbf{W}) = -\log|\det(\mathbf{W})| - \sum_{i=1}^{m} \log \tilde{p}_{Y_i}(y_i) \qquad (10.81)$$

The stochastic gradient matrix is defined by

$$\nabla\rho(\mathbf{W}) = -\frac{\partial}{\partial \mathbf{W}} \log|\det(\mathbf{W})| - \frac{\partial}{\partial \mathbf{W}} \sum_{i=1}^{m} \log \tilde{p}_{Y_i}(y_i) \qquad (10.82)$$

where ∇ is the gradient operator with respect to the demixing matrix $\mathbf{W}$. The two contributions to this gradient matrix are considered separately:

1. The first contribution is defined by

$$\frac{\partial}{\partial \mathbf{W}} \log|\det(\mathbf{W})| = \mathbf{W}^{-T} \qquad (10.83)$$

   where $\mathbf{W}^{-T}$ is the transpose of the inverse matrix $\mathbf{W}^{-1}$.

2. The ith component of the second contribution to the stochastic gradient matrix is defined by

$$\frac{\partial}{\partial \mathbf{w}_i} \log \tilde{p}_{Y_i}(y_i) = \frac{\partial y_i}{\partial \mathbf{w}_i} \frac{\partial}{\partial y_i} \log \tilde{p}_{Y_i}(y_i) \qquad (10.84)$$

   where $\mathbf{w}_i$ is the ith column vector of the demixing matrix $\mathbf{W}$ and y_i is a sample value of the output vector Y_i. Thus, taking sample values of the ith components in Eq. (10.75), we have

$$y_i = \mathbf{w}_i^T \mathbf{x}, \quad i = 1, 2, ..., m \qquad (10.85)$$

where $\mathbf{x}$ is a sample value of the input vector $\mathbf{X}$ and y_i is a sample value of Y_i. Differentiating Eq. (10.85) with respect to $\mathbf{w}_i$, we obtain

$$\frac{\partial y_i}{\partial \mathbf{w}_i} = \mathbf{x} \tag{10.86}$$

Moreover,

$$\frac{\partial}{\partial y_i} \log \tilde{p}_{Y_i}(y_i) = \frac{1}{\tilde{p}_{Y_i}(y_i)} \frac{\partial}{\partial y_i} \tilde{p}_{Y_i}(y_i)$$

$$= \frac{\tilde{p}'_{Y_i}(y_i)}{\tilde{p}_{Y_i}(y_i)} \tag{10.87}$$

where the partial derivative

$$\tilde{p}'_{Y_i}(y_i) = \frac{\partial}{\partial y_i} \tilde{p}_{Y_i}(y_i)$$

At this point in the discussion, we find it convenient to introduce the *activation function* φ for the *i*th neuron used in constructing the demixer; specifically, we define

$$\varphi_i(y_i) = -\frac{\tilde{p}'_{Y_i}(y_i)}{\tilde{p}_{Y_i}(y_i)}, \quad i = 1, 2, ..., m \tag{10.88}$$

Accordingly, using Eqs. (10.85) to (10.88), we may write

$$\frac{\partial}{\partial \mathbf{w}_i} \log \tilde{p}_{Y_i}(y_i) = -\varphi_i(y_i)\mathbf{x}, \quad i = 1, 2, ..., m \tag{10.89}$$

From this expression, we may express the contribution of the summation term in Eq. (10.82) to the stochastic gradient matrix as

$$\frac{\partial}{\partial \mathbf{W}} \sum_{i=1}^{m} \log \tilde{p}_{Y_i}(y_i) = -\boldsymbol{\phi}(\mathbf{y})\mathbf{x}^T = -\mathbf{x}\boldsymbol{\phi}^T(\mathbf{y}) \tag{10.90}$$

where the vector of activation functions, expressed as a function of the output vector $\mathbf{y}$, is

$$\boldsymbol{\phi}(\mathbf{y}) = [\varphi_1(y_1), \varphi_2(y_2), ..., \varphi_m(y_m)]^T$$

Next, substituting Eqs. (10.83) and (10.90) into Eq.(10.82), we get the desired stochastic gradient matrix:

$$\nabla\rho(\mathbf{W}) = -\mathbf{W}^{-T} + \boldsymbol{\phi}(\mathbf{y})\mathbf{x}^T \tag{10.91}$$

Now, let η denote the learning-rate parameter, assumed to be a small positive constant. Then, given the gradient matrix of Eq. (10.91), the incremental adjustment made to the demixing matrix $\mathbf{W}$ is

$$\Delta\mathbf{W} = -\eta\nabla\rho(\mathbf{W})$$

$$= \eta[\mathbf{W}^{-T} - \boldsymbol{\phi}(\mathbf{y})\mathbf{x}^T] \tag{10.92}$$

For reasons that will become apparent momentarily, we find it convenient to reformulate Eq. (10.92) by first taking the transpose of Eq. (10.85), which yields

$$\mathbf{y}^T = \mathbf{x}^T \mathbf{W}^T$$

Hence, we may rewrite Eq. (10.92) in the new, equivalent form

$$\Delta \mathbf{W} = \eta[\mathbf{I} - \boldsymbol{\phi}(\mathbf{y})\mathbf{x}^T\mathbf{W}^T]\mathbf{W}^{-T}$$
$$= \eta[\mathbf{I} - \boldsymbol{\phi}(\mathbf{y})\mathbf{y}^T\mathbf{W}^{-T} \tag{10.93}$$

where $\mathbf{I}$ is the identity matrix. Correspondingly, the on-line learning rule for adapting the demixing matrix takes the form

$$\mathbf{W}(n + 1) = \mathbf{W}(n) + \eta(n)\underbrace{[\mathbf{I} - \boldsymbol{\phi}(\mathbf{y}(n))\mathbf{y}^T(n)]\mathbf{W}^{-T}(n)}_{\text{Correction term}} \tag{10.94}$$

where the parameters are all shown in their time-varying forms.

An undesirable property of this algorithm is postmultiplication of the adjustment term by the inverse of the transposed weight matrix $\mathbf{W}$. Our next task is to find a method for eliminating the computation of the inverse.

Equivariant Property

The purpose of the ICA algorithm is to update the demixing matrix $\mathbf{W}(n)$ such that the output vector

$$\mathbf{y}(n) = \mathbf{W}(n)\mathbf{x}(n) = \mathbf{W}(n)\mathbf{A}\mathbf{s}(n)$$

is as close as possible to the original source vector $\mathbf{s}(n)$ in some statistical sense. To be more specific, consider a *global system* characterized by the *system matrix* $\mathbf{C}(n)$ that is obtained by multiplying the mixing matrix $\mathbf{A}$ and demixing matrix $\mathbf{W}(n)$; that is,

$$\mathbf{C}(n) = \mathbf{W}(n)\mathbf{A} \tag{10.95}$$

Ideally, this global system satisfies two conditions:

1. The algorithm responsible for adjusting $\mathbf{C}(n)$ converges to an optimum value equal to the permutation matrix. (Note, however, that a signed permutation matrix, which has +1 or −1 in each row and column only once, is also optimal.)
2. The algorithm is itself described by

$$\mathbf{C}(n + 1) = \mathbf{C}(n) + \eta(n)\mathbf{G}(\mathbf{C}(n)\mathbf{s}(n))\mathbf{C}(n) \tag{10.96}$$

where $\mathbf{G}(\mathbf{C}(n)\mathbf{s}(n))$ is a matrix-valued function of the matrix product $\mathbf{C}(n)\mathbf{s}(n)$. The performance of the algorithm is completely characterized by the system matrix $\mathbf{C}(n)$, *not* by the individual values of the mixing matrix $\mathbf{A}$ and demixing matrix $\mathbf{W}(n)$. Such an adaptive system is said to be *equivariant* (Cardoso and Laheld, 1996).

The on-line learning algorithm of Eq. (10.94) is certainly capable of satisfying the first condition approximately. However, as it stands, it cannot satisfy the second condition. To see that this is so, we multiply Eq. (10.94) by the mixing matrix $\mathbf{A}$ and then use Eq. (10.95) to write

$$\mathbf{C}(n + 1) = \mathbf{C}(n) + \eta(n)\mathbf{G}(\mathbf{C}(n)\mathbf{s}(n))\mathbf{W}^{-T}(n)\mathbf{A} \tag{10.97}$$

where

$$G(C(n)s(n)) = I - \phi(C(n)s(n))(C(n)s(n))^T \tag{10.98}$$

Clearly, the algorithm of Eq. (10.94) falls short of the equivariant condition described in Eq. (10.96) in that the matrix-valued function $G(C(n)s(n))$ is postmultiplied by $W^{-T}(n)A$, which, in general, is different from $C(n)$. To correct this situation, we interpose the matrix product $W^T(n)W(n)$ between the function $G(C(n)s(n))$ and the matrix product $W^{-T}(n)A$ in Eq. (10.97). The term W^TW, being made up of the product of matrix W and its transpose, is always positive definite. This is the reason that multiplication by W^TW does not change the sign of the minima of the learning algorithm.

The important question is: What is the implication of this modification that is made in order to achieve the equivariant condition? The answer lies in how the gradient descent in parameter space is formulated. Ideally, we should use the *natural gradient*[12] of the contrast function $\rho(W)$, defined in terms of the usual gradient $\nabla\rho(W)$ as

$$\nabla^*\rho(W) = (\nabla\rho(W))W^TW \tag{10.99}$$

The ordinary gradient matrix is itself defined by Eq. (10.91). In an implicit sense, the gradient $\nabla\rho(W)$ is the optimum direction for descent only when the parameter space $\mathcal{W} \in \{W\}$ is Euclidean with an orthonormal coordinate system. In a typical situation involving neural networks, however, the parameter space $\mathcal{W}$ has a coordinate system that is not orthonormal. The natural gradient $\nabla^*\rho(W)$ will provide the *steepest descent* in this latter situation—hence the preference for using it instead of the usual gradient in formulating the stochastic gradient algorithm for ICA. For the natural gradient space to be definable, two conditions must be satisfied:

1. The parameter space $\mathcal{W}$ is *Riemannian*.[13] The Riemannian structure is a differentiable manifold. (The notion of a differentiable manifold was discussed in Chapter 7.)
2. The matrix W is nonsingular (i.e., invertible).

Both of these conditions are satisfied for the problem at hand.

Accordingly, the stage is set for us to modify the algorithm of Eq. (10.94) in the manner just described, permitting us to write

$$W(n + 1) = W(n) + \eta(n)[I - \phi(y(n))y^T(n)]W(n)(W^T(n)W^{-T}(n))$$

Finally, recognizing that the matrix product $W^T(n) W^{-T}(n)$ equals the identity matrix, we finally write

$$W(n + 1) = W(n) + \eta(n)[I - \phi(y(n))y^T(n)]W(n) \tag{10.100}$$

which leads to blind source separation with the desired equivariant property. Since the derivation of the on-line learning algorithm of Eq. (10.100) is based on the natural gradient, this algorithm is commonly referred to in the literature as the *natural-gradient learning algorithm for independent-components analysis* (Cichocki and Amari, 2002). Obviously, a complete picture of this algorithm must also include the matrix representation of the input-output relationship of Eq. (10.85) over the complete set of outputs:

$$\mathbf{y} = \{y_i\}_{i=1}^{M}$$
$$= \mathbf{Wx}$$

This complete input-output picture of the algorithm is depicted in the signal-flow graph of Fig. 10.14.

Important Virtues of the Natural-Gradient Learning Algorithm

In addition to possessing the equivariant property, the natural-gradient learning algorithm, described in Eq. (10.100), has four important virtues:

1. The algorithm is *computationally efficient*, since it avoids the need for inverting the demixing matrix $\mathbf{W}$.
2. The convergence rate of the algorithm is relatively *fast*.
3. The algorithm lends itself to implementation in the form of an adaptive neural system.
4. Being a stochastic gradient algorithm, the algorithm has a built-in capability to track statistical variations of a nonstationary environment.

Robustness of ICA Theory

The natural-gradient learning algorithm of Eq. (10.100) requires knowledge of the activation function $\varphi(y)$ defined in Eq. (10.88), which shows that $\varphi(y)$ is dependent on the marginal distribution $\tilde{p}_Y(y)$. Accordingly, for the algorithm to provide a satisfactory

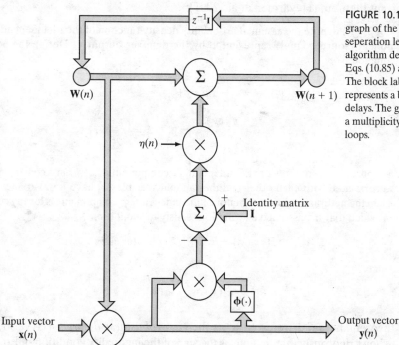

FIGURE 10.14 Signal-flow graph of the blind source seperation learning algorithm described in Eqs. (10.85) and (10.104): The block labeled $z^{-1}\mathbf{I}$ represents a bank of uni-time delays. The graph embodies a multiplicity of feedback loops.

solution to the blind source separation problem, any mathematical description of the marginal distribution $\tilde{p}_Y(y)$ must be close to the *true* distribution of the original independent component (i.e., source); otherwise, we have a serious model mismatch.

In practice, however, we find that it is sufficient to consider only *two* possible approximations of the underlying probability distribution of each independent component:[14]

1. **Super-Gaussian distribution.** This distribution has a form similar to the *Laplacian distribution*, defined by

$$p_Y(y) = \frac{\alpha}{2} \exp(-\alpha|y|), \quad -\infty < \alpha < \infty$$

which decays exponentially with respect to the absolute value $|y|$ at a rate α. For example, samples of the amplitude of a speech signal tend to follow the Laplacian distribution.

2. **Sub-Gaussian distribution.** This second distribution is like a log-Gaussian distribution that is somewhat flattened around the origin.

The preceding statement on *approximations* is testimony to the *robustness of ICA theory*:

(i) *Simple models* of the underlying distributions are adequate for estimating the independent components.

(ii) *Small modeling errors* are tolerated in testing the super-Gaussian and sub-Gaussian approximations for each independent component.

More specifically, the robustness of ICA theory is substantiated by the following important theorem (Hyvärinen et al., 2001):

Let $\tilde{p}_{Y_i}(y_i)$ denote the assumed probability density function of the ith independent component (source signal) represented by the demixer output y_i. Define the activation function

$$\varphi(y_i) = -\frac{\partial}{\partial y_i} \log \tilde{p}_{Y_i}(y_i)$$

$$= -\frac{\tilde{p}'_{Y_i}(y_i)}{\tilde{p}_{Y_i}(y_i)}, \qquad \tilde{p}'_{Y_i}(y_i) = \frac{\partial}{\partial y_i} \tilde{p}_{Y_i}(y_i)$$

Suppose that estimates of the independent components $\{y_i\}_{i=1}^m$ are constrained to be uncorrelated with each other and the random variables Y_i have unit variance for all i. Then the natural-gradient estimator of the independent components is locally consistent, provided that the assumed distributions satisfy the condition

$$\mathbb{E}[y_i\varphi(y_i) - \varphi'(y_i)] > 0 \qquad \text{for all } i \tag{10.101}$$

where

$$\varphi'(y_i) = \frac{\partial}{\partial y_i} \varphi(y_i)$$

This theorem, hereafter referred to as the *ICA robustness theorem* (Hyvärinen et al., 2001), shows rigorously that, so long as the sign of the inequality condition of Eq. (10.101) remains unchanged for all i, small discrepancies in the approximate distributions $\tilde{p}_{Y_i}(y_i)$ do not affect the local consistency of estimates of the independent components computed with the use of the natural-gradient learning algorithm.[15]

The ICA robustness theorem described for natural-gradient learning applies equally well to the maximum-likelihood estimation procedure described in the next section. Moreover, the ICA robustness theorem teaches us how to construct a family of functions based on the inequality of Eq. (10.101), with each pair in the family consisting of the log-probability density function pertaining to a super-Gaussian distribution and its sub-Gaussian counterpart. In practice, we therefore have a simple binary choice between two candidate distributions. The next example illustrates such a choice.

EXAMPLE 10   Super-Gaussian and Sub-Gaussian Functions

Consider the pair of log-density functions

$$\log p_Y^+(y) = \alpha_1 - 2 \log \cosh(y)$$
$$\log p_Y^-(y) = \alpha_2 - \left(\frac{1}{2}y^2 - \log \cosh(y)\right)$$

where α_1 and α_2 are positive constants included to make sure that each function satisfies the basic properties of a probability density function. The plus and minus superscripts are intended to signify whether the function in question refers to a super-Gaussian or sub-Gaussian probability density function, respectively.

Applying the formula of Eq. (10.88) for the activation function to $p_Y^+(y)$, we get the hyperbolic tangent function

$$\varphi^+(y) = \tanh(y)$$

where we have ignored the multiplying factor 2 for mathematical convenience. Differentiating this result with respect to y one more time, we get the gradient of the activation function:

$$\varphi^{+\prime} = \mathrm{sech}^2(y)$$

Hence, for the super-Gaussian function, the left-hand side of Eq. (10.101) yields the result (except for the scaling factor 2)

$$\mathbb{E}[y \tanh(y) - \mathrm{sech}^2(y)]$$

Performing the same two operations for $p_Y^-(y)$, we get

$$\varphi^-(y) = y - \tanh(y)$$
$$\varphi^{-\prime}(y) = 1 - \mathrm{sech}^2(y)$$

Hence, for the sub-Gaussian function, the left-hand side of Eq. (10.101) yields

$$\mathbb{E}[y^2 - y\tanh(y) - 1 + \mathrm{sech}^2(y)] = \mathbb{E}[-y\tanh(y) + \mathrm{sech}^2(y)]$$

where we have invoked the assumption that the variance of the zero-mean random variable Y (represented by sample value y) is unity—that is, $\mathbb{E}[Y^2] = 1$.

Examining the results just obtained for the pair of super-Gaussian and sub-Gaussian functions, we see that they indeed have opposite algebraic signs. Accordingly, only one of them satisfies the inequality of Eq. (10.101); the particular activation function that satisfies this inequality for the dataset under the ICA study is the one that should be used for the class of algorithms rooted in the principle of independent-components analysis (e.g., the natural-gradient learning algorithm). ∎

10.15 MAXIMUM-LIKELIHOOD ESTIMATION FOR INDEPENDENT-COMPONENTS ANALYSIS

The principle of independent-components analysis described in the previous section is just one of many methods that have been proposed in the literature for blind source separation. In the context of this principle, however, there are two other methods for performing the task of source separation in an unsupervised manner: maximum likelihood and maximum entropy. In this section, we discuss maximum likelihood, followed by maximum entropy in the next section.

Maximum likelihood is a well-established procedure for statistical estimation with some nice properties.[16] In this procedure, we first formulate a log-likelihood function and then optimize it with respect to the parameter vector of the probabilistic model under consideration. From the discussion presented in Chapter 2, we recall that the likelihood function is the probability density function of a data set in a given model, but viewed as a function of the unknown parameters of the model. Referring to Fig. 10.9, let $p_S(s)$ denote the probability density function of the random source vector $\mathbf{S}$ whose sample value is $\mathbf{s}$. Then the probability density function of the observation vector $\mathbf{X} = \mathbf{A}\mathbf{S}$ at the output of the mixer is defined by

$$p_{\mathbf{X}}(\mathbf{x}, \mathbf{A}) = |\det(\mathbf{A})|^{-1} p_S(\mathbf{A}^{-1}\mathbf{x}) \tag{10.102}$$

where $\det(\mathbf{A})$ is the determinant of the mixing matrix $\mathbf{A}$. Let $\mathcal{T} = \{\mathbf{x}_k\}_{k=1}^N$ denote a training sample consisting of N independent realizations of the random vector $\mathbf{X}$. We may then write

$$p_{\mathbf{X}}(\mathcal{T}, \mathbf{A}) = \prod_{k=1}^N p_{\mathbf{X}}(\mathbf{x}_k, \mathbf{A}) \tag{10.103}$$

We find it more convenient to work with the *normalized* (divided by the sample size N) version of the log-likelihood function, as shown by

$$\frac{1}{N} \log p_{\mathbf{X}}(\mathcal{T}, \mathbf{A}) = \frac{1}{N} \sum_{k=1}^N \log p_{\mathbf{X}}(\mathbf{x}_k, \mathbf{A})$$

$$= \frac{1}{N} \sum_{k=1}^N \log p_S(\mathbf{A}^{-1}\mathbf{x}_k) - \log|\det(\mathbf{A})|$$

Let $\mathbf{y} = \mathbf{A}^{-1}\mathbf{x}$ be a realization of the random vector $\mathbf{Y}$ at the demixer output, and thus we write

$$\frac{1}{N} \log p_{\mathbf{X}}(\mathcal{T}, \mathbf{A}) = \frac{1}{N} \sum_{k=1}^N \log p_S(\mathbf{y}_k) - \log|\det(\mathbf{A})| \tag{10.104}$$

Let $\mathbf{A}^{-1} = \mathbf{W}$ and let $p_{\mathbf{Y}}(\mathbf{y}, \mathbf{W})$ denote the probability density function of $\mathbf{Y}$ parameterized by $\mathbf{W}$. Then, recognizing that the summation in Eq. (10.104) is the sample average of $\log p_S(\mathbf{y}_k)$ and invoking the law of large numbers that, with probability 1, as the sample size N approaches infinity, we may introduce the function

$$L(\mathbf{W}) = \lim_{N \to \infty} \frac{1}{N} \sum_{k=1}^{N} \log p_S(\mathbf{y}_k) + \log|\det(\mathbf{W})|$$

$$= \mathbb{E}[\log p_S(\mathbf{y})] + \log|\det(\mathbf{W})|$$

$$= \int_{-\infty}^{\infty} p_Y(\mathbf{y}, \mathbf{W})\log p_S(\mathbf{y})d\mathbf{y} + \log|\det(\mathbf{W})| \qquad (10.105)$$

where the expectation in the second line is with respect to $\mathbf{Y}$. The function $L(\mathbf{W})$ is the desired log-likelihood function. By writing

$$p_S(\mathbf{y}) = \left(\frac{p_S(\mathbf{y})}{p_Y(\mathbf{y}, \mathbf{W})} \right) p_Y(\mathbf{y}, \mathbf{W})$$

we may express $L(\mathbf{W})$ in the equivalent form

$$L(\mathbf{W}) = \int_{-\infty}^{\infty} p_Y(\mathbf{y}, \mathbf{W})\log\left(\frac{p_S(\mathbf{y})}{p_Y(\mathbf{y}, \mathbf{W})} \right)d\mathbf{y}$$

$$+ \int_{-\infty}^{\infty} p_Y(\mathbf{y}, \mathbf{W})\log p_Y(\mathbf{y}, \mathbf{W})d\mathbf{y} + \log|\det(\mathbf{W})|$$

$$= -R(\mathbf{W}) - h(\mathbf{Y}, \mathbf{W}) + \log|\det(\mathbf{W})| \qquad (10.106)$$

where we have used the following definitions:

- the expected contrast function $R(\mathbf{w})$ with the same formula as the Kullback-Leibler divergence, as defined in Eq. (10.77);
- the differential entropy $h(\mathbf{Y},\mathbf{w})$ as defined in the first line of Eq. (10.12)

Next, using the formula of Eq. (10.78), we finally rewrite Eq. (10.79), in the desired form:

$$L(\mathbf{W}) = -R(\mathbf{W}) - h(\mathbf{X}) \qquad (10.107)$$

where $h(\mathbf{X})$ is the differential entropy of the random vector $\mathbf{X}$ at the demixer input (Cardoso, 1998a). The only quantity in Eq. (10.107) that depends on the weight vector $\mathbf{W}$ of the demixer is the expected contrast function $R(\mathbf{W})$. We therefore conclude from Eq. (10.107) that maximizing the log-likelihood function $L(\mathbf{W})$ is equivalent to minimizing $R(\mathbf{W})$, which requires matching the probability distribution of the demixer output $\mathbf{Y}$ to that of the original source vector $\mathbf{S}$.

Relationship between Maximum-Likelihood Estimation and the Principle of Independent-Components Analysis

Applying the Pythagorean decomposition described in Eq. (10.43) to the problem at hand, we may express the expected contrast function for maximum likelihood as follows:

$$R(\mathbf{W}) = D_{p_Y \| \tilde{p}_Y} + D_{\tilde{p}_Y \| p_S} \qquad (10.108)$$

The first Kullback–Leibler divergence, $D_{p_Y \| \tilde{p}_Y}$, on the right-hand side of Eq. (10.108) is a measure of *structural mismatch* that characterizes the method of independent-components analysis. The second Kullback–Leibler divergence, $D_{\tilde{p}_Y \| p_S}$, is a measure of the *marginal mismatch* between the marginal distribution of the demixer output $\mathbf{Y}$ and the distribution of the original source vector **S**. In words, we may express the "global" distribution-matching criterion for maximum likelihood as follows:

$$\begin{pmatrix} \text{Total} \\ \text{mismatch} \end{pmatrix} = \underbrace{\begin{pmatrix} \text{Structural} \\ \text{mismatch} \end{pmatrix}}_{D_{p_Y \| \tilde{p}_Y}} + \underbrace{\begin{pmatrix} \text{Marginal} \\ \text{mismatch} \end{pmatrix}}_{D_{\tilde{p}_Y \| p_S}} \qquad (10.109)$$

Insofar as the right-hand side of Eq. (10.109) is concerned, "structural mismatch" refers to the structure of a distribution pertaining to the set of independent variables, whereas "marginal mismatch" refers to the mismatch between the individual marginal distributions.

Under the ideal condition $\mathbf{W} = \mathbf{A}^{-1}$ (i.e., perfect blind source separation), both the structural mismatch and marginal mismatch vanish. At that point, the maximum-likelihood method and the principle of independent-components analysis yield exactly the same solution. The idealized relationship between the maximum-likelihood method and the principle of independent-components analysis is depicted in Fig. 10.15. In this figure, $\mathcal{S}$ is the set

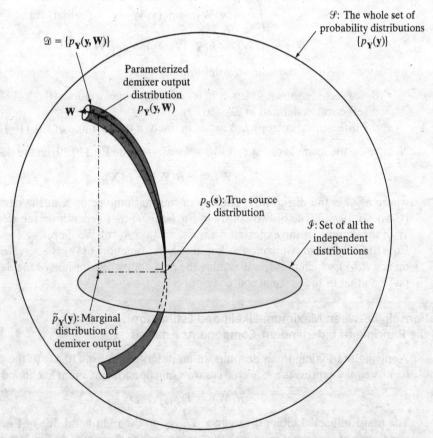

FIGURE 10.15 Illustration of the relationship between the maximum-likelihood method and independent-components analysis for blind source separation. The maximum-likelihood method minimizes $D_{p_Y \| p_S}$ whereas independent-components analysis minimizes $D_{p_Y \| \tilde{p}_Y}$.

of *all* probability density functions $p_{\mathbf{Y}}(\mathbf{y})$ of the random vector $\mathbf{Y}$ at the demixer output; $\mathscr{I}$ is the set of all independent probability distributions—that is, those of the product form. Both $\mathscr{S}$ and $\mathscr{I}$ are of infinite dimension. The set $\mathscr{D} = \{p_{\mathbf{Y}}(\mathbf{y}, \mathbf{W})\}$ is the finite set of probability distributions measured at the demixer output. The set $\mathscr{D}$ is m^2 dimensional, where m is the dimension of $\mathbf{Y}$, and the weight matrix $\mathbf{W}$ is a coordinate system in it. From Fig. 10.15, we clearly see that both $D_{p_{\mathbf{Y}}\|\tilde{p}_{\mathbf{Y}}}$ and $D_{p_{\mathbf{Y}}\|p_{\mathbf{S}}}$ are minimized at $\mathbf{W} = \mathbf{A}^{-1}$. Moreover, as indicated in Fig 10.15, the sets $\mathscr{D}$ and $\mathscr{I}$ are indeed orthogonal at their intersection point, defined by the true probability density function $p_{\mathbf{S}}(\mathbf{s})$.

A blind source separation algorithm based on the maximum-likelihood method must include a provision for estimating the underlying source distributions when they are unknown, which is typically the case. The parameters for this estimation can be adapted just as we adapt the demixing weight matrix W. In other words, we should perform a *joint estimation* of the mixing matrix and (some characteristics of) the source distributions (Cardoso, 1997, 1998); an elegant and well-developed approach for this joint estimation is presented in Pham et al. (1992, 1997).

10.16   MAXIMUM-ENTROPY LEARNING FOR BLIND SOURCE SEPARATION

In this section, we look to the maximum-entropy principle discussed in Section 10.3, for another method for blind source separation. To this end, consider Fig. 10.16, which shows the block diagram of the system based on this method. As before, the demixer operates on the observation vector $\mathbf{x}$ to produce an output $\mathbf{y} = \mathbf{W}\mathbf{x}$ that is an estimate of the original source vector $\mathbf{s}$. The vector $\mathbf{y}$ is transformed into a vector $\mathbf{z}$ by passing it through a componentwise nonlinearity denoted by $\mathbf{G}(\cdot)$, which is monotonic and invertible. Thus, unlike $\mathbf{y}$, the vector $\mathbf{z}$ is assured of a bounded differential entropy $h(\mathbf{Z})$ for an arbitrarily large demixer. For a prescribed nonlinearity $\mathbf{G}(\cdot)$, the principle of maximum entropy produces an estimate of the original source vector $\mathbf{s}$ by maximizing the entropy $h(\mathbf{z})$ with respect to $\mathbf{W}$. In light of Eq. (10.60), derived in Example 7, for a noiseless network, we recall that the maximum-entropy principle is closely related to the Infomax principle. Indeed, it is for this reason that the algorithm based on the scheme of Fig. 10.16 is referred to in the literature as the *Infomax algorithm for ICA* (Bell and Sejnowski, 1995).

The nonlinearity $\mathbf{G}$ is a *diagonal map* described by

$$\mathbf{G}: \begin{bmatrix} y_1 \\ y_2 \\ \vdots \\ y_m \end{bmatrix} \to \begin{bmatrix} g_1(y_1) \\ g_2(y_2) \\ \vdots \\ g_m(y_m) \end{bmatrix} = \begin{bmatrix} z_1 \\ z_2 \\ \vdots \\ z_m \end{bmatrix} \tag{10.110}$$

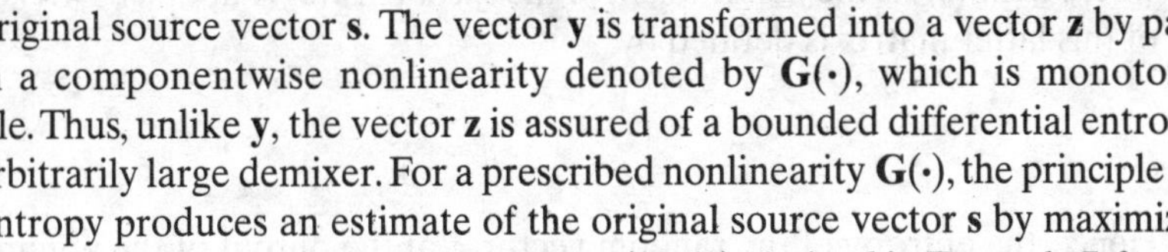

Unknown environment

FIGURE 10.16   Block diagram of the maximum-entropy principle for blind source separation. The vectors $\mathbf{s}$, $\mathbf{x}$, $\mathbf{y}$, and $\mathbf{z}$ are sample values of the random vectors $\mathbf{S}$, $\mathbf{X}$, $\mathbf{Y}$, and $\mathbf{Z}$, respectively.

We may thus write

$$\mathbf{z} = \mathbf{G}(\mathbf{y})$$
$$= \mathbf{G}(\mathbf{WAs}) \tag{10.111}$$

Since the nonlinearity $\mathbf{G}(\cdot)$ is invertible, we may express the original source vector $\mathbf{s}$ in terms of the demixer output vector $\mathbf{z}$ as

$$\mathbf{s} = \mathbf{A}^{-1}\mathbf{W}^{-1}\mathbf{G}^{-1}(\mathbf{z})$$
$$= \mathbf{\Psi}(\mathbf{z}) \tag{10.112}$$

where $\mathbf{G}^{-1}$ is the *inverse nonlinearity*:

$$\mathbf{G}^{-1} : \begin{bmatrix} z_1 \\ z_2 \\ \vdots \\ z_m \end{bmatrix} \rightarrow \begin{bmatrix} g_1^{-1}(z_1) \\ g_2^{-1}(z_2) \\ \vdots \\ g_m^{-1}(z_m) \end{bmatrix} = \begin{bmatrix} y_1 \\ y_2 \\ \vdots \\ y_m \end{bmatrix} \tag{10.113}$$

The probability density function of the output vector $\mathbf{z}$ is defined in terms of that of the source vector $\mathbf{s}$ by

$$p_{\mathbf{Z}}(\mathbf{z}) = \left. \frac{p_{\mathbf{S}}(\mathbf{s})}{|\det(\mathbf{J}(\mathbf{s}))|} \right|_{\mathbf{s}=\mathbf{\Psi}(\mathbf{z})} \tag{10.114}$$

where $\det(\mathbf{J}(\mathbf{s}))$ is the determinant of the Jacobian $\mathbf{J}(\mathbf{s})$ (Papoulis, 1984). The ij-th element of this latter matrix is defined by

$$J_{ij} = \frac{\partial z_i}{\partial s_j} \tag{10.115}$$

Hence, the entropy of the random vector $\mathbf{Z}$ at the output of the nonlinearity $\mathbf{G}$ is

$$h(\mathbf{Z}) = -\mathbb{E}[\log p_{\mathbf{Z}}(\mathbf{z})]$$
$$= -\mathbb{E}\left[\log \left(\frac{p_{\mathbf{S}}(\mathbf{s})}{|\det(\mathbf{J}(\mathbf{s}))|} \right) \right]_{\mathbf{s}=\mathbf{\Psi}(\mathbf{z})}$$
$$= -D_{p_{\mathbf{S}}\||\det\mathbf{J}|} \qquad \text{evaluated at } \mathbf{s} = \mathbf{\Psi}(\mathbf{z}) \tag{10.116}$$

We thus see that maximizing the differential entropy $h(\mathbf{Z})$ is equivalent to minimizing the Kullback–Leibler divergence between $p_{\mathbf{S}}(\mathbf{s})$ and a probability density function of $\mathbf{s}$ defined by $|\det(\mathbf{J}(\mathbf{s}))|$; see the last line of Eq. (10.35).

Suppose now the random variable Z_i (i.e., the ith element of $\mathbf{Z}$) is *uniformly distributed* inside the interval $[0, 1]$ for all i. According to Example 1, the entropy $h(\mathbf{Z})$ is then equal to zero. Correspondingly, we find from Eq. (10.116) that

$$p_{\mathbf{S}}(\mathbf{s}) = |\det(\mathbf{J}(\mathbf{s}))| \tag{10.117}$$

Under the ideal condition $\mathbf{W} = \mathbf{A}^{-1}$, this relationship reduces to

$$p_{S_i}(s_i) = \left. \frac{\partial z_i}{\partial y_i} \right|_{z_i=g(s_i)} \qquad \text{for all } i \tag{10.118}$$

Conversely, we can say that if Eq. (10.118) is satisfied, then maximizing $h(\mathbf{Z})$ yields $\mathbf{W} = \mathbf{A}^{-1}$, and blind source separation is thereby achieved.

We may now summarize the idea of the maximum-entropy principle for blind source separation as follows (Bell and Sejnowski, 1995):

Let the nonlinearity at the demixer output in Fig. 10.16 be defined in terms of the original source distribution as

$$z_i = g_i(y_i)$$

$$= \int_{-\infty}^{z_1} p_{S_i}(s_i)ds_i \qquad \text{for } i = 1, 2, ..., m \qquad (10.119)$$

Maximizing the differential entropy of the random vector $\mathbf{Z}$ (the ith element of which has the sample value z_i) at the output of the nonlinearity $\mathbf{G}$ is then equivalent to $\mathbf{W} = \mathbf{A}^{-1}$, which yields perfect blind source separation.

Equivalence of the Maximum-Entropy and Maximum-Likelihood Methods

The maximum-entropy and maximum-likelihood methods for blind source separation are indeed equivalent under the condition that the random variable Z_i is uniformly distributed inside the interval $[0, 1]$ for all i (Cardoso, 1997). To prove this relationship, we first use the chain rule of calculus to rewrite Eq. (10.115) in the equivalent form

$$J_{ij} = \sum_{k=1}^{m} \frac{\partial z_i}{\partial y_i} \frac{\partial y_i}{\partial x_k} \frac{\partial x_k}{\partial s_j}$$

$$= \sum_{k=1}^{m} \frac{\partial z_i}{\partial y_i} w_{ik} a_{kj} \qquad (10.120)$$

where the partial derivative $\partial z_i/\partial y_i$ is to be defined. The Jacobian $\mathbf{J}$ may therefore be expressed as

$$\mathbf{J} = \mathbf{DWA}$$

where $\mathbf{D}$ is the diagonal matrix

$$\mathbf{D} = \text{diag}\left(\frac{\partial z_1}{\partial y_1}, \frac{\partial z_2}{\partial y_2}, ..., \frac{\partial z_m}{\partial y_m} \right)$$

Hence,

$$|\det(\mathbf{J})| = |\det(\mathbf{WA})| \prod_{i=1}^{m} \frac{\partial z_i}{\partial y_i} \qquad (10.121)$$

In light of Eq. (10.121), an estimate of the probability density function $p_S(s)$ parameterized by the weight matrix $\mathbf{W}$ and the nonlinearity $\mathbf{G}$ may be written formally as follows (Roth and Baram, 1996):

$$p_S(s|\mathbf{W}, \mathbf{G}) = |\det(\mathbf{WA})| \prod_{i=1}^{m} \frac{\partial g_i(y_i)}{\partial y_i} \qquad (10.122)$$

We thus see that under this condition, maximizing the log-likelihood function $\log p_{\mathbf{s}}(\mathbf{s}|\mathbf{W},\mathbf{G})$ is equivalent to maximizing the entropy $h(\mathbf{Z})$ for blind source separation. That is, the methods of maximum entropy and maximum likelihood are indeed equivalent.

The Learning Algorithm for Blind Source Separation

Referring to the second line of Eq. (10.116), we note that since the source distribution is typically fixed, maximizing the entropy $h(\mathbf{Z})$ requires maximizing the expectation of the denominator term $\log|\det(\mathbf{J}(\mathbf{s}))|$ with respect to the weight matrix $\mathbf{W}$. With an adaptive algorithm for doing this computation as our goal, we may thus consider the instantaneous objective function

$$\Phi = \log|\det(\mathbf{J})| \tag{10.123}$$

Substituting Eq. (10.121) into Eq. (10.123) yields

$$\Phi = \log|\det(\mathbf{A})| + \log|\det(\mathbf{W})| + \sum_{i=1}^{m}\log\left(\frac{\partial z_i}{\partial y_i}\right) \tag{10.124}$$

Hence, differentiating Φ with respect to the weight matrix $\mathbf{W}$ of the demixer, we get the following (see Problem 10.20):

$$\frac{\partial \Phi}{\partial \mathbf{W}} = \mathbf{W}^{-T} + \sum_{i=1}^{m}\frac{\partial}{\partial \mathbf{W}}\log\left(\frac{\partial z_i}{\partial y_i}\right) \tag{10.125}$$

To proceed further with this formula, we need to specify the nonlinearity fed by the demixer output. A simple form of nonlinearity that may be used here is the logistic function

$$z_i = g(y_i)$$
$$= \frac{1}{1 + e^{-y_i}}, \qquad i = 1, 2, ..., m \tag{10.126}$$

Figure 10.17 presents plots of this nonlinearity and its inverse. The figure shows that the logistic function satisfies the basic requirements of monotonicity and invertibility for blind source separation. Substituting Eq. (10.126) into Eq. (10.125) yields

$$\frac{\partial \Phi}{\partial \mathbf{W}} = \mathbf{W}^{-T} + (\mathbf{1} - 2\mathbf{z})\mathbf{x}^{T}$$

where $\mathbf{x}$ is the received signal vector, $\mathbf{z}$ is the nonlinear transformed output vector of the demixer, and $\mathbf{1}$ is a corresponding vector of ones.

The objective of the learning algorithm is to maximize the differential entropy $h(\mathbf{Z})$. Accordingly, invoking the method of steepest ascent, we find that the change applied to the weight matrix $\mathbf{W}$ is[17]

$$\Delta \mathbf{W} = \eta \frac{\partial \Phi}{\partial \mathbf{W}}$$
$$= \eta(\mathbf{W}^{-T} + (\mathbf{1} - 2\mathbf{z})\mathbf{x}^{T}) \tag{10.127}$$

where η is the learning-rate parameter. As with the ICA natural gradient learning algorithm described in Section 10.14, we may eliminate the need for inverting the

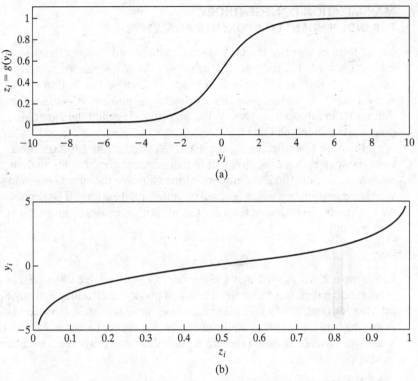

FIGURE 10.17   (a) Logistic function: $z_i = g(y_i) = \dfrac{1}{1 + e^{-y_i}}$. (b) Inverse of logistic function: $y_i = g^{-1}(z_i)$.

transposed weight matrix $\mathbf{W}^T$ by using the natural gradient, which is equivalent to multiplying Eq. (10.127) by the matrix product $\mathbf{W}^T\mathbf{W}$. This optimal rescaling yields the desired formula for weight adjustment as

$$\begin{aligned}
\Delta\mathbf{W} &= \eta(\mathbf{W}^{-T} + (1 - 2\mathbf{z})\mathbf{x}^T)\mathbf{W}^T\mathbf{W} \\
&= \eta(\mathbf{I} + (1 - 2\mathbf{z})(\mathbf{Wx})^T)\mathbf{W} \qquad (10.128) \\
&= \eta(\mathbf{I} + (1 - 2\mathbf{z})\mathbf{y}^T)\mathbf{W}
\end{aligned}$$

where $\mathbf{I}$ is the identity matrix and the vector $\mathbf{y}$ is the demixer output. The learning algorithm for computing the weight matrix $\mathbf{W}$ is therefore described by

$$\mathbf{W}(n + 1) = \mathbf{W}(n) + \eta(\mathbf{I} + (1 - 2\mathbf{z}(n))\mathbf{y}^T(n))\mathbf{W}(n) \qquad (10.129)$$

The algorithm is initiated with $\mathbf{W}(0)$ selected from a uniformly distributed set of small numbers. Referring to the block diagram of Fig. 10.16, we readily see that at time n the output $\mathbf{y}(n)$ is defined in terms of the input $\mathbf{x}(n)$ by the matrix product $\mathbf{W}(n)\,\mathbf{x}(n)$. Thus, every time the demixing matrix $\mathbf{W}(n)$ is updated, we may correspondingly compute the updated value of the demixer output $\mathbf{y}(n)$.

10.17   MAXIMIZATION OF NEGENTROPY
FOR INDEPENDENT-COMPONENTS ANALYSIS

In one form or another, the ICA algorithm discussed in Sections 10.14, 10.15, and 10.16 is basically rooted in the *principle of statistical independent components*, which is itself based on the *Kullback–Leibler divergence*, as discussed in Section 10.14. In this section, we will depart from that principle by describing another ICA algorithm that is rooted differently in information theory. The algorithm is called the *FastICA algorithm* and is due to Hyvärinen and Oja (1997).

In more specific terms, the FastICA algorithm exploits the notion of non-Gaussianity, which is a requirement of independent-components analysis, discussed previously in Section 10.12. An important measure for the non-Gaussianity of a random variable is negentropy, which is based on differential entropy. It is therefore *a propos* that we begin our discussion of the FastICA algorithm by describing what is meant by this new concept.

Negentropy

In Example 2, we showed that a Gaussian random variable distinguishes itself from all other random variables by having the largest possible differential entropy. Specifically, the information content of a Gaussian random variable is confined to second-order statistics, from which all higher-order statistics can be computed. To assess the non-Gaussianity of a random variable, it would therefore be desirable to postulate a measure that satisfies two properties:

1. The measure is nonnegative, assuming the limiting value of zero for a Gaussian random variable.

2. For all other random variables, the measure is greater than zero.

The concept of negentropy satisfies both of these properties.

Consider a random vector $\mathbf{X}$ that is known to be non-Gaussian. The *negentropy* of $\mathbf{X}$ is formally defined by

$$N(\mathbf{X}) = H(\mathbf{X}_{\text{Gaussian}}) - H(\mathbf{X}) \qquad (10.130)$$

where $H(\mathbf{X})$ is the differential entropy of $\mathbf{X}$, and $H(\mathbf{X}_{\text{Gaussian}})$ is the differential entropy of a Gaussian random vector whose covariance matrix is equal to that of $\mathbf{X}$.

In information-theoretic terms, negentropy is an elegant measure of non-Gaussianity. But it is highly demanding in computational terms, which limits its practical use. To overcome this computational difficulty, we have to seek a simple approximation to negentropy. Consider, then, a non-Gaussian random variable V of zero mean and unit variance. Hyvärinen and Oja (2000) have proposed the approximation

$$N(V) = \mathbb{E}[\Phi(V)] - \mathbb{E}[\Phi(U)]^2 \qquad (10.131)$$

where U is a Gaussian random variable also of zero mean and unit variance (i.e., it is standardized). For all practical purposes, $\Phi(\cdot)$ is a nonquadratic function; desirably, this function does not grow rapidly, so as to robustify the estimation procedure. According to Hyvärinen and Oja (2000) two choices have proven their usefulness, given as

1. $\Phi(v) = \log(\cosh(v))$ (10.132)

2. $\Phi(v) = -\exp\left(-\dfrac{v^2}{2}\right)$ (10.133)

where v is a sample value of the random variable V. We may therefore look to Eq. (10.131) as the "contrast function" to be maximized for the purpose of independent-components analysis. Except for scaling factors, the function $\Phi(v)$ may be viewed as a probability density function. Note that the function $\Phi(\cdot)$ used in Eqs. (10.132) and (10.133) should not be confused with the matrix $\mathbf{\Phi}$ used in Eq. (10.123).

Basic Learning Rule of the FastICA Algorithm

To pave the way for the development of the FastICA algorithm, we first consider a single-unit version of the algorithm. The term "unit" refers to a neuron with an adjustable-weight vector $\mathbf{w}$. The neuron is to be designed in such a way that we develop the basic learning rule of the FastICA algorithm.

Let $\mathbf{x}$ be the sample value of a prewhitened random vector of zero mean, $\mathbf{X}$, that is applied to the input of the neuron. We start the development of the basic learning rule by doing the following:

Maximize the negentropy of the projection of the adjustable-weight vector $\mathbf{w}$ on to the random vector $\mathbf{X}$, subject to the constraint $\|\mathbf{w}\| = 1$.

The projection is defined by the inner product $\mathbf{w}^T\mathbf{X}$. With the random vector $\mathbf{X}$ prewhitened, the constraint $\|\mathbf{w}\| = 1$ is equivalent to constraining the projection to have a variance equal to unity, as shown by

$$
\begin{aligned}
\text{var}[\mathbf{w}^T\mathbf{X}] &= \mathbb{E}[(\mathbf{w}^T\mathbf{X})^2] \\
&= \mathbb{E}[\mathbf{w}^T\mathbf{X}\mathbf{X}^T\mathbf{w}] \\
&= \mathbf{w}^T\mathbb{E}[\mathbf{X}\mathbf{X}^T]\mathbf{w} \\
&= \mathbf{w}^T\mathbf{w} \\
&= \|\mathbf{w}\|^2 \\
&= 1
\end{aligned}
$$
(10.134)

In the first line of Eq. (10.134), we made use of the zero-mean assumption imposed on $\mathbf{X}$, and in the third line, we made use of the prewhiteneing assumption also imposed on $\mathbf{X}$.

For the basic learning rule to be computationally efficient, we look to the approximation of Eq. (10.131) as the formula for computing the negentropy $N(V)$, where $V = \mathbf{w}^T\mathbf{X}$. Since U is a standard Gaussian random variable of zero mean and unit variance, and therefore independent of $\mathbf{w}$, it follows that maximizing $N(V)$ with respect to $\mathbf{w}$ is equivalent to maximizing the nonquadratic function $\Phi(V) = \Phi(\mathbf{w}^T\mathbf{X})$. We may thus reformulate the optimization problem of interest as follows:

Maximize the expectation $\mathbb{E}[\Phi(\mathbf{w}^T\mathbf{x})]$, subject to the constraint $\|\mathbf{w}\| = 1$.

According to the *Karush–Kuhn–Tucker conditions* of optimization theory (discussed in Chapter 6), the solution to this constrained maximization problem is to be found in the equation

$$\frac{\partial}{\partial \mathbf{w}} \mathbb{E}[\Phi(\mathbf{w}^T \mathbf{x})] - \lambda \mathbf{w} = 0 \tag{10.135}$$

where $\mathbf{x}$ is the sample value of the random vector $\mathbf{X}$. The gradient vector of the expectation $\mathbb{E}[\Phi(\mathbf{w}^T \mathbf{x})]$ with respect to the weight vector $\mathbf{w}$ is evaluated as

$$\frac{\partial}{\partial \mathbf{w}} \mathbb{E}[\Phi(\mathbf{w}^T \mathbf{x})] = \mathbb{E}\left[\frac{\partial}{\partial \mathbf{w}} \Phi(\mathbf{w}^T \mathbf{x})\right]$$

$$= \mathbb{E}\left[\frac{\partial(\mathbf{w}^T \mathbf{x})}{\partial \mathbf{w}} \frac{\partial}{\partial \mathbf{w}^T \mathbf{x}} \Phi(\mathbf{w}^T \mathbf{x})\right]$$

$$= \mathbb{E}[\mathbf{x}\varphi(\mathbf{w}^T \mathbf{x})] \tag{10.136}$$

where $\varphi(\cdot)$ is the first derivative of the nonquadratic function $\Phi(\cdot)$ with respect to its argument—that is,

$$\varphi(v) = \frac{d\Phi(v)}{dv}$$

For example, for the function $\Phi(\cdot)$ defined in Eq. (10.132), we have

$$\varphi(v) = \frac{d}{dv} \log(\cosh(v))$$

$$= \tanh(v)$$

and for the function $\Phi(v)$ defined in Eq. (10.33), we have

$$\varphi(v) = \frac{d}{dv}\left(-\exp\left(-\frac{v^2}{2}\right)\right)$$

$$= v \exp\left(-\frac{v^2}{2}\right)$$

Thus, we may rewrite Eq. (10.135) in the equivalent form

$$\mathbb{E}[\mathbf{x}\varphi(\mathbf{w}^T \mathbf{x})] - \lambda \mathbf{w} = 0 \tag{10.137}$$

What we are interested in is finding a computationally efficient iterative procedure for implementing a basic learning rule whereby the optimized weight vector $\mathbf{w}$ points along the direction of an independent component. To this end, we propose the application of *Newton's method* to the expression on the left-hand side of Eq. (10.137).

Let this expression be denoted by the vector-valued function

$$\mathbf{f}(\mathbf{w}) = \mathbb{E}[\mathbf{x}\varphi(\mathbf{w}^T \mathbf{x})] - \lambda \mathbf{w} \tag{10.138}$$

Newton's method was discussed in Chapters 3 and 4. For the application of this method, we need the *Jacobian* of the function $\mathbf{f}(\mathbf{w})$, which is defined by

$$J(\mathbf{w}) = \frac{\partial}{\partial \mathbf{w}} \mathbf{f}(\mathbf{w})$$

$$= \frac{\partial}{\partial \mathbf{w}} \{\mathbb{E}[\mathbf{x}\varphi(\mathbf{w}^T\mathbf{x})] - \lambda\mathbf{w}\}$$

$$= \frac{\partial}{\partial \mathbf{w}} \mathbb{E}[\mathbf{x}\varphi(\mathbf{w}^T\mathbf{x})] - \frac{\partial}{\partial \mathbf{w}}(\lambda\mathbf{w})$$

$$= \mathbb{E}\left[\frac{\partial}{\partial \mathbf{w}} \mathbf{x}\varphi(\mathbf{w}^T\mathbf{x})\right] - \lambda\mathbf{I}$$

$$= \mathbb{E}[\mathbf{x}\mathbf{x}^T\varphi'(\mathbf{w}^T\mathbf{x})] - \lambda\mathbf{I} \tag{10.139}$$

where $\mathbf{I}$ is the identity matrix. The prime in $\varphi'(\cdot)$ signifies differentiation of the function $\varphi(\cdot)$ with respect to its argument. In other words, $\varphi'(\cdot)$ is the second-order derivative of the original function $\Phi(\cdot)$ with respect to its argument. Now we can see why, earlier on, we stated that $\varphi(\cdot)$ must be a nonquadratic function; otherwise, we would have ended up with $\varphi'(\cdot)$ equal to a constant in Eq. (10.139), which is clearly unacceptable.

Before proceeding, however, we wish to simplify development of the basic learning rule further. Since the input vector $\mathbf{x}$ has been prewhitened, it is reasonable to assume that the outer product $\mathbf{x}\mathbf{x}^T$ is statistically independent of the term $\varphi'(\mathbf{w}^T\mathbf{x})$ in Eq. (10.139). Under this assumption, we may go on to write

$$\mathbb{E}[\mathbf{x}\mathbf{x}^T\varphi'(\mathbf{w}^T\mathbf{x})] \approx \mathbb{E}[\mathbf{x}\mathbf{x}^T]\mathbb{E}[\varphi'(\mathbf{w}^T\mathbf{x})]$$

$$= \mathbb{E}[\varphi'(\mathbf{w}^T\mathbf{x})]\mathbf{I} \tag{10.140}$$

where, in the last line, we have made use of the whitening property of the input $\mathbf{x}$—that is, $\mathbb{E}[\mathbf{x}\mathbf{x}^T] = \mathbf{I}$. Accordingly, we now find that the whole expression for the Jacobian $J(\mathbf{w})$ in Eq. (10.139) takes the form of a scalar multiplied by the identity matrix $\mathbf{I}$, as shown by

$$J(\mathbf{w}) \approx (\mathbb{E}[\varphi'(\mathbf{w}^T\mathbf{x})] - \lambda)\mathbf{I} \tag{10.141}$$

which is readily invertible. With this approximate formula at hand, we may express the *Newton iterative step* as

$$\mathbf{w}^+ = \mathbf{w} - J^{-1}(\mathbf{w})\mathbf{f}(\mathbf{w}) \tag{10.142}$$

where $\mathbf{w}$ is the old value of the weight vector and $\mathbf{w}^+$ is its updated value. Note also that we have used a minus sign in the iterative step, since we are seeking the maxima of the function $\mathbf{f}(\mathbf{w})$. Thus, substituting Eq. (10.141) into Eq. (10.142), we obtain

$$\mathbf{w}^+ = \mathbf{w} - (\mathbb{E}[\varphi'(\mathbf{w}^T\mathbf{x})] - \lambda)^{-1}(\mathbb{E}[\mathbf{x}\varphi(\mathbf{w}^T\mathbf{x})] - \lambda\mathbf{w})$$

We may simplify this iterative step by multiplying both sides of this equation by the scalar $(\mathbb{E}[\varphi'(\mathbf{w}^T\mathbf{x})] - \lambda)$, which yields

$$\mathbf{w}^+ = (\mathbb{E}[\varphi'(\mathbf{w}^T\mathbf{x})] - \lambda)\mathbf{w} - (\mathbb{E}[\mathbf{x}\varphi(\mathbf{w}^T\mathbf{x})] - \lambda\mathbf{w})$$

$$= \mathbb{E}[\varphi'(\mathbf{w}^T\mathbf{x})]\mathbf{w} - \mathbb{E}[\mathbf{x}\varphi(\mathbf{w}^T\mathbf{x})] \tag{10.143}$$

where, on the left-hand side, we have absorbed the scaling factor $(\mathbb{E}[\varphi'(\mathbf{w}^T\mathbf{x})] - \lambda)$ in the new value of $\mathbf{w}^+$. Note also that we do not need to know the value of the Lagragian multiplier λ, as it has been eliminated algebraically from the iterative step of Eq. (10.143).

Equation (10.143) is at the core of the basic learning rule that we have been seeking. Indeed, in light of this equation, we may now model the single neuron, around which this equation is built, as shown in Fig. 10.18. According to this figure, we may view the nonlinear function $\varphi(\cdot)$ as the activation function of the neuron.

With the iterative step of Eq. (10.143) at our disposal, we are finally ready to summarize the Newton-based learning rule of the fastICA algorithm as follows:

1. Choose an initial value of the weight vector $\mathbf{w}$, using a random-number generator, subject to the constraint that the Euclidean norm of $\mathbf{w}$ is unity.

2. Using the old value of the weight vector $\mathbf{w}$, compute the updated value

$$\mathbf{w}^+ = \mathbb{E}[\varphi'(\mathbf{w}^T\mathbf{x})]\mathbf{w} - \mathbb{E}[\mathbf{x}\varphi(\mathbf{w}^T\mathbf{x})]$$

3. Normalize the updated weight vector $\mathbf{w}^+$ so that its Euclidean norm is equal to unity, as shown by

$$\mathbf{w} = \frac{\mathbf{w}^+}{\|\mathbf{w}^+\|}$$

4. If the algorithm has not converged, go back to step 2 and repeat the computation.

To compute the expectations in step 2 of the learning rule, we may invoke *ergodicity* and replace the expectations by *time averages*, based on a sequence of independent samples (realizations) of the input vector $\mathbf{x}$.

The learning rule is said to have *converged*—that is, the rule has reached an *equilibrium point*—when the updated weight vector $\mathbf{w}^+$ and the old weight vector $\mathbf{w}$ point along a common direction. That is, the absolute value of the inner product $\mathbf{w}^T\mathbf{w}^+$ is close to unity. However, since an ICA algorithm can extract an independent component only to within a multiplicative scaling factor, it is not necessary to seek an equilibrium point where the weight vectors $\mathbf{w}^+$ and $\mathbf{w}$ point in exactly the same direction. In other words, it is acceptable for $\mathbf{w}^+$ to be the negative of $\mathbf{w}$.

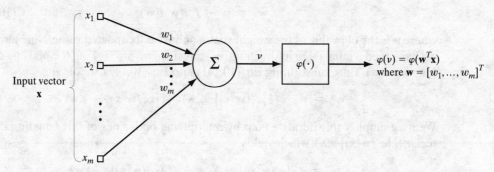

FIGURE 10.18 Model of the neuron featuring in the basic learning rule of the FastICA algorithm.

One last comment is in order: Derivation, and therefore application, of the algorithm is based on the premise that the mixer output has been prewhitened; the issue of prewhitening was discussed in Section 10.12.

Multiunit Version of the FastICA Algorithm

Naturally, the Newton-based learning rule, built around a single neuron, can estimate only one of the m independent components (sources) responsible for generating the observation vector $\mathbf{x}$. To expand this rule so as to estimate all the m independent components, we obviously need a network of m neurons or its equivalent.

To explore the conditions that this network must satisfy, let $\mathbf{w}_1, \mathbf{w}_2, ..., \mathbf{w}_m$ denote the weight vectors produced by m individual neurons of the network. For this set of vectors to represent a *correct* solution to the blind source separation (BSS) problem, we require two conditions:

1. *Orthogonality.* Suppose the random observation vector $\mathbf{X}$ is applied simultaneously to the m neurons, producing the set of outputs

$$\{V_i\}_{i=1}^m, \qquad \text{where } V_i = \mathbf{w}_i^T \mathbf{X}$$

   In order to prevent all the m weight vectors from converging into the same independent components, we require that the neural outputs be uncorrelated with each other—that is,

$$\mathbb{E}[V_i V_j] = 0 \qquad \text{for } j \neq i \tag{10.144}$$

   Thus, with $V_i = \mathbf{w}_i^T \mathbf{X}$ and $V_j = \mathbf{w}_j^T \mathbf{X} = \mathbf{X}^T \mathbf{w}_j$, we write

$$\begin{aligned}
\mathbb{E}[V_i V_j] &= \mathbb{E}[\mathbf{w}_i^T \mathbf{X} \mathbf{X}^T \mathbf{w}_j] \\
&= \mathbf{w}_i^T \mathbb{E}[\mathbf{X} \mathbf{X}^T] \mathbf{w}_j \\
&= \mathbf{w}_i^T \mathbf{w}_j \qquad \text{for } j \neq i
\end{aligned}$$

   where, in the last line, we made use of the whitening property of the observation vector $\mathbf{X}$. It follows, therefore, that for the decorrelation property of Eq. (10.144) to be satisfied, the weight vectors $\mathbf{w}_1, \mathbf{w}_2, ..., \mathbf{w}_m$ must form an *orthogonal set*, as shown by

$$\mathbf{w}_i^T \mathbf{w}_j = 0 \qquad \text{for } j \neq i \tag{10.145}$$

2. *Normalization.* To be in line with the Newton-based learning rule, we require that each weight vector be *normalized* for its Euclidean norm to equal unity, as shown by

$$\|\mathbf{w}_i\| = 1 \qquad \text{for all } i \tag{10.146}$$

Putting conditions 1 and 2 together, we may now make the following formal statement:

For the weight vectors $\mathbf{w}_1, \mathbf{w}_2, ..., \mathbf{w}_m$ to provide estimates of the m independent components (sources) responsible for the generation of the observation vector $\mathbf{x}$, they must form an orthonormal set, as shown by

$$\mathbf{w}_i^T \mathbf{w}_j = \begin{cases} 1 & \text{for } j = i \\ 0 & \text{otherwise} \end{cases} \tag{10.147}$$

The Gram–Schmidt Orthogonalization Procedure

The twofold necessary condition of Eq. (10.147) imposed on the weight vectors leads us to think in terms of a simple *deflational method*, based on the *Gram–Schmidt orthogonalization procedure*,[18] for estimating all the m independent components, one by one, as originally proposed by Hyvärinen and Oja (1997, 2000). To be specific, suppose that we first run the single-neuron, Newton-based learning rule on N independent realizations (samples) of the observation vector $\mathbf{x}$, obtaining the weight vector $\mathbf{w}_1$ as the estimate of one of the m independent components. When running this rule on the next set of N independent realizations of $\mathbf{x}$, suppose the resulting weight vector is denoted by $\boldsymbol{\alpha}_2$. The reason for using a different symbol for this second weight vector is that the vector $\boldsymbol{\alpha}_2$ is unlikely to be orthogonal to $\mathbf{w}_1$. To correct for this deviation from the necessary condition of orthogonality, we apply the Gram–Schmidt orthogonalization procedure, obtaining

$$\boldsymbol{\theta}_2 = \boldsymbol{\alpha}_2 - (\boldsymbol{\alpha}_2^T \mathbf{w}_1)\mathbf{w}_1$$

where we have subtracted from $\boldsymbol{\alpha}_2$ the "projection" $(\boldsymbol{\alpha}_2^T \mathbf{w}_1)\mathbf{w}_1$. By recognizing that $\|\mathbf{w}_1\| = 1$, it is a straightforward matter to show that $\boldsymbol{\theta}_2$ is indeed orthogonal to $\mathbf{w}_1$—that is, $\boldsymbol{\theta}_2^T \mathbf{w}_1 = 0$. All that remains to be done is to normalize $\boldsymbol{\theta}_2$ by setting

$$\mathbf{w}_2 = \frac{\boldsymbol{\theta}_2}{\|\boldsymbol{\theta}_2\|}$$

Proceeding in this manner, suppose that on the next set of N samples of the observation vector $\mathbf{x}$, the Newton-based learning rule yields the weight vector $\boldsymbol{\alpha}_3$, where again it is unlikely for $\boldsymbol{\alpha}_3$ to be orthogonal to $\mathbf{w}_2$ and $\mathbf{w}_1$. To correct for these deviations, we apply the Gram–Schmidt orthogonalization procedure one more time, obtaining

$$\boldsymbol{\theta}_3 = \boldsymbol{\alpha}_3 - (\boldsymbol{\alpha}_3^T \mathbf{w}_1)\mathbf{w}_1 - (\boldsymbol{\alpha}_3^T \mathbf{w}_2)\mathbf{w}_2$$

where we have subtracted from $\boldsymbol{\alpha}_3$ the projections $(\boldsymbol{\alpha}_3^T \mathbf{w}_j)\mathbf{w}_j$, $j = 1, 2$. By recognizing that $\|\mathbf{w}_1\| = \|\mathbf{w}_2\| = 1$ and $\mathbf{w}_1^T \mathbf{w}_2 = 0$, it is a straightforward matter to show that $\boldsymbol{\theta}_3$ is orthogonal to both $\mathbf{w}_1$ and $\mathbf{w}_2$. Hence, all that remains is to normalize $\boldsymbol{\theta}_3$ by setting

$$\mathbf{w}_3 = \frac{\boldsymbol{\theta}_3}{\|\boldsymbol{\theta}_3\|}$$

We may continue in this manner until all the m independent components have been accounted for.

We may now summarize the Gram–Schmidt orthogonalization procedure for computing the desired set of m weight vectors as follows:

1. Given that $\mathbf{w}_1$ is the normalized weight vector produced by the single-unit Newton-based learning rule on its first complete iteration, and given that $\boldsymbol{\alpha}_2, ..., \boldsymbol{\alpha}_{i+1}$ are the weight vectors produced by the rule on the next i complete iterations, compute

$$\boldsymbol{\theta}_{i+1} = \boldsymbol{\alpha}_{i+1} - \sum_{j=1}^{i} (\boldsymbol{\theta}_{i+1}^T \mathbf{w}_j)\mathbf{w}_j, \qquad i = 1, 2, ..., m - 1$$

where the "projections" $(\boldsymbol{\theta}_{i+1}^T \mathbf{w}_j)\mathbf{w}_j$ have been subtracted from $\boldsymbol{\alpha}_{i+1}$ for $j = 1, 2, ..., i$.

2. Normalize θ_{i+1} by setting

$$\mathbf{w}_{i+1} = \frac{\theta_{i+1}}{\|\theta_{i+1}\|}, \qquad i = 1, 2, ..., m - 1$$

The FastICA algorithm based on this procedure represents the *single-unit defla-tion* version of the algorithm.[19]

Properties of the FastICA Algorithm

Compared with other ICA algorithms, the fast ICA algorithm has some desirable prop-erties (Hyvärinen and Oja, 2000; Tichavsky et al., 2006):

1. Under the assumption of a noise-free, linear generative model, the convergence of the FastICA algorithm is relatively *fast*—hence the name of the algorithm. Whereas the gradient-based ICA algorithms discussed in Sections 10.14, 10.15, and 10.16, tend to con-verge in a linear manner, convergence of the FastICA is cubic (or at least quadratic).
2. Unlike the gradient-based ICA algorithms, the FastICA algorithm does *not* require the use of a learning-rate parameter, making it simpler to design.
3. The FastICA algorithm has a built-in capability to find the independent components of practically any non-Gaussian distributions, using any nonquadratic form of nonlinearity $\varphi(v)$. This versatility of the algorithm is to be contrasted against gradient-based ICA algorithms, where applicability is confined to sub-Gaussian or super-Gaussian distrib-utions, and careful attention is given to the choice of nonlinearity.
4. Through proper selection of the nonquadratic function $\varphi(\cdot)$, exemplified by Eqs. (10.132) and (10.133), robustness of the FastICA algorithm may be assured, even with large data sets and under somewhat noisy conditions.
5. The independent components are computed by the FastICA algorithm sytematically, one by one. This feature of the algorithm makes it a useful tool for *exploratory data analysis*, where the estimation of a limited number of independent components may be all that is required for the application of interest. The computational load of the analysis is thereby reduced.
6. The FastICA algorithm has many attributes usually associated with neural networks: parallelism, distributed computation, simplicity, and small memory requirement. On the other hand, stochastic gradient-based ICA algorithms—exemplified by the natural-gradient algorithm discussed in Section 10.14 —are the preferred choice for blind source separation problems involving nonstationary environments, where there is a definite need for fast adaptivity.

10.18 COHERENT INDEPENDENT-COMPONENTS ANALYSIS

Looking back at the material we have thus far covered in this chapter on the impact of information theory on the development of learning models, we find that the maximization of the mutual information principle—or the Infomax principle, for short—stands out promi-nently. Not only does the Infomax principle play a significant role in our understanding of redundancy reduction, the modeling of perception, and the extraction of independent com-ponents, but also its relative the Imax principle plays a role of its own in the extraction of spatially coherent features. In reality, Infomax and Imax play complementary roles:

> *Infomax deals with information flow across a network, whereas Imax deals with spatial coher-ence across a pair of network outputs.*

Figure 10.19 depicts a scenario where these two principles are embodied together. Specif-ically, we have two separate, but dimensionally similar neural networks: Network a is characterized by the weight matrix $\mathbf{W}_a$, and network b is characterized by the weight matrix $\mathbf{W}_b$. Both networks are assumed to be *noiseless*. The goal is to combine the Infomax and Imax principles in such a way that the two aforementioned properties—information flow in each network in accordance with the Infomax principle, and spatial coherence across the neural outputs of the two networks treated on a *pair-by-pair* basis in accordance with the Imax principle—are integrated into a composite learning principle.

Contributions of the Infomax Principle

Consider first the Infomax principle applied across the input–output of each network in Fig. 10.19. Then, in light of Eq. (10.60), pertaining to the noiseless Example 7, the network characterized by the weight matrix $\mathbf{W}_a$ may be described by the mutual information

$$I(\mathbf{Y}_a; \mathbf{X}_a) = -\mathbb{E}[\log p_{\mathbf{Y}_a}(\mathbf{y}_a)]$$

where, to simplify the presentation, we have ignored an additive constant that is indepen-dent of the weight matrix $\mathbf{W}_a$; moreover, we have made use of Eq. (10.60) in a way that involves the entropy of a random vector. With the elements constituting the output random vector $\mathbf{Y}_a$ being "independent," we may express the probability density function of $\mathbf{Y}_a$ as

$$p_{\mathbf{Y}_a}(\mathbf{y}_a) = \prod_{i=1}^{l} p_{Y_{a,i}}(y_{a,i})$$

where l is the number of output terminals. We may therefore go on to write

$$
\begin{aligned}
I(\mathbf{Y}_a; \mathbf{X}_a) &= -\mathbb{E}\left[\log \prod_{i=1}^{l} p_{Y_{a,i}}(y_{a,i})\right] \\
&= -\mathbb{E}\left[\sum_{i=1}^{l} \log p_{Y_{a,i}}(y_{a,i})\right], \quad i = 1, 2, ..., l
\end{aligned}
\tag{10.148}
$$

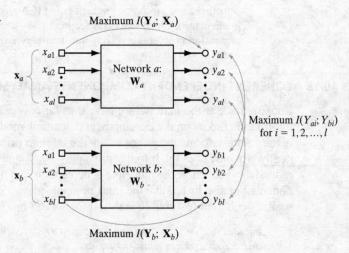

FIGURE 10.19   The coupled-network layout for coherent ICA.

Maximum $I(\mathbf{Y}_a; \mathbf{X}_a)$

x_{a1} Network a: $\mathbf{W}_a$ y_{a1}
x_{a2} y_{a2}
$\mathbf{x}_a$ x_{al} y_{al}

Maximum $I(Y_{ai}; Y_{bi})$
for $i = 1, 2, ..., l$

x_{a1} Network b: $\mathbf{W}_b$ y_{b1}
x_{a2} y_{b2}
$\mathbf{x}_b$ x_{bl} y_{bl}

Maximum $I(\mathbf{Y}_b; \mathbf{X}_b)$

Similarly, for the second network, characterized by the weight matrix $\mathbf{W}_b$, we may write

$$I(\mathbf{Y}_b; \mathbf{X}_b) = -\mathbb{E}\left[\sum_{i=1}^{l} \log p_{Y_{b,i}}(y_{b,i})\right], \qquad i = 1, 2, ..., l \qquad (10.149)$$

Contributions of the Imax Principle

Consider next the Imax principle applied across the outputs of these two networks, treated on a pair-by-pair basis. In light of the second line of Eq. (10.50), we may express the mutual information between the outputs $Y_{a,i}$ and $Y_{b,i}$ in terms of the copula as

$$I(Y_{a,i}; Y_{a,b}) = \mathbb{E}[\log c_{Y_{a,i}; Y_{b,i}}(\mathbf{y}_{a,i}; \mathbf{y}_{b,i})] \qquad \text{for } i = 1, 2, ..., l$$

Again, because the l outputs of each network in Fig. 10.19 are independent, these individual mutual contributions are additive, yielding the sum

$$\sum_{i=1}^{l} I(Y_{a,i}; Y_{b,i}) = \mathbb{E}\left[\sum_{i=1}^{l} \log c_{Y_{a,i}; Y_{b,i}}(y_{a,i}; y_{b,i})\right] \qquad (10.150)$$

Overall Cost Function

Let $J(\mathbf{W}_a, \mathbf{W}_b)$ denote the ensemble-averaged objective function, accounting for the combined actions of the Infomax and Imax principles. Then, combining the mutual information contributions of Eqs. (10.148) to (10.150), we write

$$J(\mathbf{W}_a, \mathbf{W}_b) = -\mathbb{E}\left[\sum_{i=1}^{l} \log p_{Y_{a,i}}(y_{a,i})\right] - \mathbb{E}\left[\sum_{i=1}^{l} \log p_{Y_{b,i}}(y_{b,i})\right] - \mathbb{E}\left[\sum_{i=1}^{l} \log c_{Y_{a,i}Y_{b,i}}(y_{a,i}y_{b,i})\right]$$

$$= -\mathbb{E}\left[\sum_{i=1}^{l} \log \left(p_{Y_{a,i}}(y_{a,i}) p_{Y_{b,i}}(y_{b,i}) c_{Y_{a,i}, Y_{b,i}}(y_{a,i}, y_{b,i})\right)\right]$$

$$= -\mathbb{E}\left[\sum_{i=1}^{l} \log p_{Y_{a,i}Y_{b,i}}(y_{a,i}, y_{b,i})\right] \qquad (10.151)$$

where, in the last line, we have made use of Eq. (10.49), expressing the joint probability density function of the output random variables $Y_{a,i}$ and $Y_{b,i}$. The objective function $J(\mathbf{W}_a, \mathbf{W}_b)$ defines the sum of the joint entropies of the two sets of network outputs $\{Y_{a,i}\}_{i=1}^{l}$ and $\{Y_{b,i}\}_{i=1}^{l}$, which are treated on an orderly pair-by-pair basis; these outputs are respectively dependent on the weight matrices $\mathbf{W}_a$ and $\mathbf{W}_b$. Indeed, it is precisely with this definition in mind that we introduced the minus sign in combining the contribution of copulas into the first line of Eq. (10.151). In so doing, the desired orderly statistical dependence between the two sets of network outputs has been enforced, and hence we can make the following formal statement:

> *The coherent ICA principle maximizes the overall sum of the joint entropies of the two sets of network outputs $\{Y_{a,i}\}_{i=1}^{l}$ and $\{Y_{b,i}\}_{i=1}^{l}$, treated on an orderly pair-by-pair basis, with the maximization being performed with respect to the weight matrices $\mathbf{W}_a$ and $\mathbf{W}_b$ of the two constituent networks.*

To proceed further, we make two reasonable assumptions:

1. The two neural networks in Fig. 10.19 are both *linear*, as shown by

$$\mathbf{y}_i = \begin{bmatrix} y_{a,i} \\ y_{b,i} \end{bmatrix}$$

$$= \begin{bmatrix} \mathbf{w}_{a,i}^T \mathbf{x}_{a,i} \\ \mathbf{w}_{b,i}^T \mathbf{x}_{b,i} \end{bmatrix}, \qquad i = 1, 2, ..., l \qquad (10.152)$$

where $\mathbf{w}_{a,i}^T$ and $\mathbf{w}_{b,i}^T$ are the ith row vectors of the weight matrices $\mathbf{W}_a$ and $\mathbf{W}_b$, respectively.

2. With data drawn from natural scenes being typically sparse as discussed in Section 10.13, the distributions of the composite output vector $\mathbf{y}_i$ may be described by the *zero-mean generalized Gaussian bivariate distribution* with a two-by-two covariance matrix Σ, as shown by

$$p_{\mathbf{Y}_i}(\mathbf{y}_i) = \frac{1}{2\pi \det^{1/2}(\Sigma)} \exp\left(-\frac{1}{2}(\mathbf{y}_i^T \Sigma^{-1} \mathbf{y}_i)^{\alpha/2}\right), \qquad i = 1, 2, ..., l \quad (10.153)$$

where the parameter α *controls the shape and sparseness of the copula.* The covariance matrix Σ is itself defined by

$$\Sigma = \begin{bmatrix} 1 & \rho \\ \rho & 1 \end{bmatrix} \qquad (10.154)$$

which is the variance-*normalized* form of the covariance matrix defined in Eq. (10.67) for Imax. The correlation coefficient ρ controls the extent of correlation between the paired network outputs $y_{a,i}$ and $y_{b,i}$ for all i. Increasing ρ does not affect the shape or skew of the copula; rather, it affects the relative importance of Imax over Infomax by favoring a greater coherence in learning across the two networks.

For $\alpha = 2$, the distribution of Eq. (10.153) reduces to the Gaussian bivariate distribution. For α less than 2, Eq. (10.153) begins to take on the form of a super-Gaussian distribution, as illustrated in Fig. 10.20 for three different values of α. In particular, for $\alpha = 1.3$, the distribution of Eq. (10.153) assumes a form more like that of the Laplacian distribution of a speech signal.

The vector $\mathbf{y}_i$ embodies the two elements $y_{a,i}$ and $y_{b,i}$. Hence, substituting Eq. (10.153) into Eq. (10.151) and ignoring the constant term $2\pi\det^{1/2}(\Sigma)$, we get

$$J(\mathbf{W}_a, \mathbf{W}_b) = \frac{1}{2} \mathbb{E}\left[\sum_{i=1}^{l} (\mathbf{y}_i^T \Sigma^{-1} \mathbf{y}_i)^{\alpha/2}\right] \qquad (10.155)$$

where the ensemble averaging is performed with respect to $\mathbf{y}_i$. To simplify computational complexity, we bypass the need for ensemble averaging by using the *instantaneous values* of the quadratic form $\mathbf{y}_i^T \Sigma^{-1} \mathbf{y}_i$, for all i. Thus, using the definition in Eq. (10.154) for the covariance matrix Σ, we may go on to write

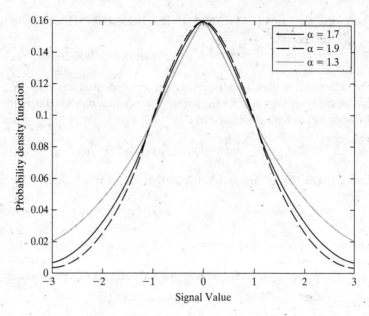

FIGURE 10.20   Generalized Gaussian distributions for varying values of parameter α.

$$\hat{J}(\mathbf{W}_a, \mathbf{W}_b) = \frac{1}{2}\left[\sum_{i=1}^{l}(\mathbf{y}_i^T\mathbf{\Sigma}^{-1}\mathbf{y}_i)^{\alpha/2}\right]$$

$$= \frac{1}{2(1-\rho^2)}\sum_{i=1}^{l}(y_{i,a}^2 - 2\rho y_{i,a}y_{i,b} + y_{i,b}^2)^{\alpha/2} \qquad (10.156)$$

where the hat in $\hat{J}(\mathbf{W}_a, \mathbf{W}_b)$ distinguishes it from its ensemble-averaged counterpart.

Formulation of the Learning Rules for the Two Networks

To formulate the adaption rule for the weight vector $\mathbf{W}_{a,i}$, we start by differentiating $\hat{J}(\mathbf{W}_a, \mathbf{W}_b)$ with respect to $\mathbf{w}_{a,i}$. Using the chain rule of calculus, we write

$$\frac{\partial \hat{J}(\mathbf{W}_a, \mathbf{W}_b)}{\partial \mathbf{w}_{a,i}} = \frac{\partial \hat{J}(\mathbf{W}_a, \mathbf{W}_b)}{\partial y_{a,i}}\frac{\partial y_{a,i}}{\partial \mathbf{w}_{a,i}} \qquad (10.157)$$

Differentiating Eq. (10.156) with respect to $y_{i,a}$ yields

$$\frac{\partial \hat{J}(\mathbf{W}_a, \mathbf{W}_b)}{\partial y_{a,i}} = \frac{\alpha}{(1-\rho^2)}(y_{a,i} - \rho y_{b,i})(y_{a,i}^2 - 2\rho y_{a,i}y_{b,i} + y_{b,i}^2)^{(\alpha/2)-1} \quad (10.158)$$

Using Eq. (10.152), we find that differentiating $y_{a,i} = \mathbf{w}_{a,i}^T\mathbf{x}_a$ with respect to $\mathbf{w}_{a,i}$ yields

$$\frac{\partial y_{a,i}}{\partial \mathbf{w}_{a,i}} = \mathbf{x}_a \qquad (10.159)$$

Therefore, using Eqs. (10.158) and (10.159) in Eq. (10.157), we obtain the gradient vector

$$\frac{\partial \hat{J}(\mathbf{W}_a, \mathbf{W}_b)}{\partial \mathbf{w}_{a,i}} = \frac{\alpha}{(1 - \rho^2)} (y_{a,i} - \rho y_{b,i})(y_{a,i}^2 - 2\rho y_{a,i} y_{b,i} + y_{b,i}^2)^{(\alpha/2)-1} \mathbf{x}_a \quad (10.160)$$

The objective is to maximize the instantaneous objective function $\hat{J}(\mathbf{W}_a, \mathbf{W}_b)$, which means that we use *gradient ascent* for the iterative computation. Accordingly, the change applied to the weight vector $\mathbf{w}_{a,i}$ is defined by

$$\Delta \mathbf{w}_{a,i} = \frac{\alpha \eta}{(1 - \rho^2)} (y_{a,i} - \rho y_{b,i})(y_{a,i}^2 - 2\rho y_{a,i} y_{b,i} + y_{b,i}^2)^{(\alpha/2)-1} \mathbf{x}_a \quad (10.161)$$

Similarly, the change applied to the weight vector $\mathbf{w}_{b,i}$ is defined by

$$\Delta \mathbf{w}_{b,i} = \frac{\alpha \eta}{(1 - \rho^2)} (y_{b,i} - \rho y_{a,i})(y_{a,i}^2 - 2\rho y_{a,i} y_{b,i} + y_{b,i}^2)^{(\alpha/2)-1} \mathbf{x}_b \quad (10.162)$$

where it is assumed that network b shares the same learning-rate parameter η with network a.

The weight updates for networks a and b are thus respectively expressed as follows:

$$\mathbf{w}_{a,i}^+ = \mathbf{w}_{a,i} + \Delta \mathbf{w}_{a,i} \quad (10.163)$$

$$\mathbf{w}_{b,i}^+ = \mathbf{w}_{b,i} + \Delta \mathbf{w}_{b,i} \quad (10.164)$$

where $i = 1, 2, ..., l$.

The two update rules of Eqs. (10.163) and (10.164)—building on the weight changes $\Delta \mathbf{W}_{a,i}$ and $\Delta \mathbf{W}_{b,i}$ described in Eqs. (10.161) and (10.162) — constitute the *coherent ICA algorithm*.

Interpretations of Eqs. (10.161) and (10.162)

It is instructive to examine the algebraic structures of the learning rules described in Eqs. (10.161) and (10.162). Taking on Eq. (10.161) first, we see that the change $\Delta \mathbf{w}_{a,i}$ applied to the ith column vector of the weight matrix $\mathbf{W}_a$, pertaining to network a in Fig. 10.19, is made up of three basic factors:

1. The scaling factor $\alpha \eta / (1 - \rho^2)$, which may be viewed simply as a modified learning-rate parameter that is common to the computation of $\Delta \mathbf{w}_{a,i}$ as well as $\Delta \mathbf{w}_{b,i}$ for all i. A change in the parameter α merely affects the rate of adaptation of the algorithm.

2. The factor $(y_{a,i} - \rho y_{b,i})\mathbf{x}_a$, which may be expressed as the difference between two quadratic forms, as shown by

$$(y_{a,i} - \rho y_{b,i})\mathbf{x}_a = (\mathbf{x}_a^T \mathbf{w}_{a,i} \mathbf{x}_a) - \rho(\mathbf{x}_b^T \mathbf{w}_{b,i} \mathbf{x}_a)$$

The first quadratic form $(\mathbf{x}_a^T \mathbf{w}_{a,i} \mathbf{x}_a)$ involves network a alone, whereas the second quadratic form $(\mathbf{x}_b^T \mathbf{w}_{b,i} \mathbf{x}_a)$ involves both networks a and b. The important point to note here is the fact the contribution made by the second factor $(y_{a,i} - \rho y_{b,i})\mathbf{x}_a$ is independent of the parameter α; in other words, this factor is completely unaffected by whether or not the distribution of the output vector $\mathbf{y}_i$ deviates from Gaussianity.

3. The third and last factor $(y_{a,i}^2 - 2\rho y_{a,i} y_{b,i} + y_{b,i}^2)$ may also be expressed in terms of quadratic forms, as shown by

$$(y_{a,i}^2 - 2\rho y_{a,i} y_{b,i} + y_{b,i}^2) = (\mathbf{w}_{a,i}^T \mathbf{x}_a \mathbf{x}_a^T \mathbf{w}_{a,i} - 2\rho \mathbf{w}_{a,i}^T \mathbf{x}_a \mathbf{x}_b^T \mathbf{w}_{b,i} + \mathbf{w}_{b,i}^T \mathbf{x}_b \mathbf{x}_b^T \mathbf{w}_{b,i})$$

It is in this factor where the parameter α affects the operation of the algorithm in the most significant manner. In particular, when $\alpha = 2$, the power to which the factor is raised becomes zero, thereby nulling out its impact on the algorithm. It is when $\alpha < 2$, which arises when dealing with super-Gaussian distributions, that the coherent ICA algorithm performs its distinctive signal-processing role.

Similar remarks apply to the learning rule of Eq. (10.162), except for the fact that the subscripts a and b interchange their respective roles.

Practical Considerations

In performing the coherent ICA learning process, it is assumed that the network inputs $\mathbf{x}_a$ and $\mathbf{x}_b$ in Fig. 10.19 are both *prewhitened*, which is normal practice in ICA-related work. Moreover, after each iteration of the learning process, the weights are *normalized*, as shown by

$$\mathbf{w}_{a,i} = \frac{\mathbf{w}_{a,i}^+}{\|\mathbf{w}_{a,i}^+\|} \tag{10.165}$$

and

$$\mathbf{w}_{b,i} = \frac{\mathbf{w}_{b,i}^+}{\|\mathbf{w}_{b,i}^+\|} \tag{10.166}$$

These normalized values are then used in the next iteration of the algorithm.

For applications that involve the modeling of data where we have two streams consisting of spatially shifted data, as exemplified by Fig. 10.19, it is useful to enforce a *weight-sharing constraint* between the two data streams, in which case we set

$$\mathbf{w}_{a,i} = \mathbf{w}_{b,i} \qquad \text{for all } i \tag{10.167}$$

A sensible way of satisfying this constraint is to use the average of $\mathbf{w}_{a,i}$ and $\mathbf{w}_{b,i}$ calculated in Eqs. (10.165) and (10.166). Thus, by starting the weight-adaptation rule for coherent ICA with the same initial weight matrices assigned to networks a and b, the weight-sharing property is maintained in every step of the adaptation rule.

To illustrate an important practical use of the coherent ICA principle, we now discuss how the coherent ICA principle provides a computational tool for learning filters involved in the auditory coding of natural sounds.

Auditory Encoding: Coherent ICA Applied to Natural Sounds

Time manifests itself in many structural and functional specializations of the auditory system. With multiple time scales in acoustic stimuli, we find it informative to distinguish between two specific components in the waveform of an acoustic stimulus (Joris et al., 2004):

1. the *carrier*, represented by the fine structure of the waveform, which waxes and wanes in an "amplitude-modulated" fashion;
2. the *envelope*, which is the contour of the amplitude-modulated waveform.

From amplitude modulation theory, we know that the information-bearing signal (i.e., the modulating signal) is contained in the *envelope* of the modulated signal. From a physiological viewpoint, interest in amplitude modulation is therefore motivated by the desire to know whether envelope processing is actually embedded in the auditory system.

Indeed, across multiple layers of the auditory system, there are neurons that respond differently to an incoming amplitude-modulated speech signal. In particular, the successive layers of the auditory system distinguish themselves by responding to different limited ranges of amplitude-modulation rates: The lower layers are most responsive to fast changes in the energy of incoming acoustic stimuli, with progressively slower changes occurring in the higher layers. In light of this reality, it is not surprising that amplitude modulation is considered to be an important acoustic cue in the perception of sound.

With auditory processing as the issue of interest, the question that we would like to address is the following:

1. *Given an additive mixture of amplitude-modulated speech signals, how can we separate the envelopes of the individual components, ignoring the associated carriers?*

A related question is the following:

2. *In a self-organized manner, can we learn the procedure by which the different processing layers in the auditory system respond to an amplitude-modulated stimulus?*

The answer to this basic question experimentally is to be found in coherent ICA (Haykin and Kan, 2007).

In coherent ICA, the goal is to extract information that is maintained "coherently" across separate sources while, at the same time, information flow across the networks associated with the sources is maximized. Since in amplitude modulation, the envelope varies slowly compared with the carrier, we may view amplitude modulation as a form of *temporal coherence insofar as the envelope is concerned*; that is, across two time-steps Δt seconds apart, with Δt assumed to be just short enough, we may set $x(t + \Delta t) \approx x(t)$.

In Kan (2007) and Haykin and Kan (2007), the coherent ICA algorithm was applied to a set of speech samples of English speakers taken from the TIMIT database.[20] Therein, it was demonstrated experimentally that the two sets of filters learned using coherent ICA on the speech data for two layers of auditory processing are smooth and temporally localized. Most importantly, the results of the experiments exhibit two important features:

1. The passband of the filters in both layers includes only frequencies within the modulation spectrum, ignoring the carrier frequencies.
2. The *baseband* (i.e., modulation-based) filters computed for the first layer of processing have a cutoff frequency that is about 10 times that of the baseband filters computed for the second layer of processing. In other words, the first layer of the

experimental model (based on coherent ICA) is most responsive to fast changes in the input auditory signal, whereas the second layer of the model is responsive to slower changes in the input.

In short, the filters learned by coherent ICA, when applied to natural sounds, are baseband filters that appear to exhibit properties similar to those of biological neurons in the cochlear nucleus and inferior colloculus.

10.19 RATE DISTORTION THEORY AND INFORMATION BOTTLENECK

Up to this point, we have focused on two fundamental concepts of information theory—entropy and mutual information—as pillars in the study of *information-theoretic learning*. In this section, we look to rate distortion theory for another insightful approach to information-theoretic learning. The approach we have in mind, called the *information bottleneck method*, was first described in the literature by Tishby et al. (1999).

Rate distortion theory, which is an integral part of Shannon's information theory (Shannon, 1948), deals with the *compression* of data with possible distortion, the purposeful application of which results in a measurable amount of distortion in the data. The motivation for compressing data is to produce a new stream of data that, on the average, requires a smaller number of bits for its representation or transmission than does the original data stream.

To pave the way for a description of the information bottleneck method, we begin the discussion with rate distortion theory.

Rate Distortion Theory

Given a stream of data produced by a source of information, the goal of rate distortion theory is to find the minimum expected value of distortion that is achievable at a specified rate of information flow, or, equivalently, to find the minimum rate of information flow achievable for a prescribed level of distortion.

To cast the theory in analytic terms, let $\mathbf{X}$ denote a random vector of probability density function $p_\mathbf{X}(\mathbf{x})$, produced by a source of information. Correspondingly, let the random vector $\mathbf{T}$ of probability density function $q_\mathbf{T}(\mathbf{t})$ represent a compressed version of $\mathbf{X}$. (Note that we have used different symbols for the distributions of $\mathbf{X}$ and $\mathbf{T}$.) Following the last line of Eq. (10.28), the mutual information between $\mathbf{X}$ and $\mathbf{T}$ is expressed as

$$I(\mathbf{X}; \mathbf{T}) = \int_{-\infty}^{\infty}\int_{-\infty}^{\infty} \underbrace{p_\mathbf{X}(\mathbf{x})q_{\mathbf{T}|\mathbf{X}}(\mathbf{t}|\mathbf{x})}_{\text{Joint pdf}} \log\left(\frac{q_{\mathbf{T}|\mathbf{X}}(\mathbf{t}|\mathbf{x})}{q_\mathbf{T}(\mathbf{t})}\right)d\mathbf{x}d\mathbf{t}$$

where $q_{\mathbf{T}|\mathbf{X}}(\mathbf{t}|\mathbf{x})$ is the conditional probability density function of $\mathbf{T}$ given $\mathbf{X}$. For the measure of "distance" between the vectors $\mathbf{X}$ and $\mathbf{T}$, we use the symbol $d(\mathbf{x}, \mathbf{t})$, where $\mathbf{x}$ and $\mathbf{t}$ denote sample values of $\mathbf{X}$ and $\mathbf{T}$, respectively. The *expected distortion* is defined by

$$\mathbb{E}[d(\mathbf{x}, \mathbf{t})] = \int_{-\infty}^{\infty}\int_{-\infty}^{\infty} \underbrace{p_\mathbf{X}(\mathbf{x})q_{\mathbf{T}|\mathbf{X}}(\mathbf{t}|\mathbf{x})}_{\text{Joint pdf}}d(\mathbf{x}, \mathbf{t})d\mathbf{x}d\mathbf{t} \qquad (10.168)$$

Rate distortion theory is itself characterized by a function called the *rate distortion function*, denoted by $R(D)$.

With this notational background at hand, we may now formally state *rate distortion theory* as follows (Cover and Thomas, 2006):

Find the rate distortion function

$$R(D) = \min_{q_{\mathbf{T}|\mathbf{X}}(\mathbf{t}|\mathbf{x})} I(\mathbf{X}; \mathbf{T})$$

subject to the distortion constraint

$$\mathbb{E}[d(\mathbf{x}, \mathbf{t})] \leq D$$

From this statement, it is apparent that the computation of the rate distortion function $R(D)$ involves the solution of the following constrained-optimization problem:

Minimize the mutual information between the source and its representation, subject to a prescribed distortion constraint.

This optimization problem can be solved by the Blahut–Arimoto algorithm (Cover & Thomas 2006), which amounts to alternating projections between two convex sets of unknown distributions, as described in Section 10.21.

The main achievement of rate distortion theory is in showing that the rate distortion function is an asymptotically achievable lower bound on the rate (code length) of any description of the data with the given expected distortion.

Information Bottleneck Method

The information bottleneck method builds on rate distortion theory by replacing the distortion term with information on a "relevant variable."[21] In many applications, the "true distortion" measure is unknown or undefined, but there is another variable on which we would like to preserve some given information. A good example is the problem of speech recognition. In this problem, it is notoriously difficult to formulate a distortion function that correctly captures human acoustic perception; it is much easier to give many examples of spoken words together with their phonetic transcription. In such a case, we seek a compression of the high-entropy speech signal that preserves as much information as possible on the lower entropy phonetic sequence. Other important examples of this type of co-occurrence data are those for which distortion functions are not directly available: words and topics, images and objects, gene expression and tissue samples, and stimuli and neural responses. The information bottleneck method has been successfully applied to these types of data (Slonim et al., 2006).

The information bottleneck method is done through the introduction of an *auxiliary (relevant) random vector*, denoted by $\mathbf{Y}$. This new random vector is (stochastically) dependent on the original, usually high-entropy, random vector $\mathbf{X}$; hence, the mutual information $I(\mathbf{X}; \mathbf{Y})$ is nonzero.

With $\mathbf{X}$ being the random vector that is to be *compressed*, $\mathbf{Y}$ is the random vector that we would like to *predict* (or about which we would like to maintain as much information as possible). By introducing the *bottleneck random vector* $\mathbf{T}$ as the compressed representation of the original random vector $\mathbf{X}$, in effect, we have created a *tradeoff* or *bottleneck* between two amounts of information: one is contained in **T** about **X** and the other is contained in **T** about **Y**.

In particular, we would like to resolve the information bottleneck by satisfying two objectives in a combined manner:

1. Partition the sample values of the original (high-entropy) random vector **X** in such a way that as much mutual information as possible is preserved about the *relevant random vector* **Y**.

2. Lose as much information as possible about the original random vector **X** to obtain the simplest form of minimal partitioning.

Thus, among all the characterizations of **X**, the problem is to determine only those which are *most relevant to the prediction of* **Y**.

Basically, the *information bottleneck method* is designed to find optimal relevant data representations. This problem can be formulated as follows :

> *Given the joint probability density function of a random vector* **X** *and a relevant random vector* **Y**, *extract minimal sufficient partitions over the sample values of* **X** *that are informative about* **Y**, *by finding the bottleneck random vector* **T** *through the unknown distribution* $q_{\mathbf{T}|\mathbf{X}}(\mathbf{t}|\mathbf{x})$ *that minimizes the information bottleneck function*
>
> $$J(q_{\mathbf{T}|\mathbf{X}}(\mathbf{t}|\mathbf{x})) = I(\mathbf{X}; \mathbf{T}) - \beta I(\mathbf{T}; \mathbf{Y}) \qquad (10.169)$$
>
> *subject to the requirement that* **T** *is dependent on* **X** *and* **Y** *is dependent on* **T** *and subject to normalization constraints.*

The positive Lagrange multiplier β is the *tradeoff parameter* between compression (minimal representation) and predictability (information preservation). By varying this parameter between zero and infinity, we obtain a concave *information curve*, analogous to the rate distortion function, that provides the optimal achievable tradeoff between compression and prediction.

EXAMPLE 11   Gaussian Information Bottleneck

For an analytic treatment of the information bottleneck method, we may consider a coupled pair of *eigenvector problems* for the logarithmic functional derivatives:

$$\frac{\partial}{\partial \mathbf{t}} \log p_{\mathbf{X}|\mathbf{T}}(\mathbf{x}|\mathbf{t}) \text{ and } \frac{\partial}{\partial \mathbf{t}} \log p_{\mathbf{Y}|\mathbf{T}}(\mathbf{y}|\mathbf{t})$$

To get around the difficulty of solving these problems in general, we turn to the analytically tractable case when the original random vector **X** and its compressed version **Y** are described by joint multivariate Gaussian distributions, as in Chechik et al. (2004). In this Gaussian framework, solving the coupled pair of eigenvector problems lends itself to the *canonical correlation analysis* (CCA), which, as mentioned in Section 10.10, is a special case of the Imax principle. We thus find that the issue to be resolved is that of finding a linear projection onto a subspace, the dimensionality of which is determined by the tradeoff parameter β. In particular, as the parameter β increases, additional dimensions (i.e., eigenvalues) are added to the projection (bottleneck) vector **T**; this addition manifests itself through a series of *critical points*, or *structural phase transitions*, while at the same time the relative Euclidean norm of each basis vector is rescaled. The process of dimension-expansion is continued until all the relevant information about the compressed vector

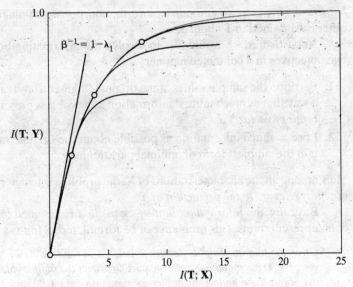

FIGURE 10.21   The information curve for multivariate Gaussian variables. The envelope (red curve) is the optimal compression–prediction tradeoff, captured by varying the Lagrange multiplier β from zero to infinity. The slope of the curve at each point is given by $1/\beta$. There is always a critical lower value of β that determines the slope at the origin, below which there are only trivial solutions. The suboptimal (black) curves are obtained when the dimensionality of $\mathbf{T}$ is restricted to fixed lower values. (This figure is reproduced with the permission of Dr. Naftali Tishby.)

$\mathbf{Y}$ is captured in the bottleneck vector $\mathbf{T}$. The net result of the process is an insightful demonstration of how the information bottleneck method provides a continuous *measure of model complexity* for varying β in information-theoretic terms.

For the Gaussian framework studied in Chechik et al. (2004), Fig. 10.21 plots the mutual information $I(\mathbf{T}; \mathbf{Y})$ versus the mutual information $I(\mathbf{T}; \mathbf{X})$ for varying β. The information curve, shown as the continuous and smooth curve in red in Fig. 10.21, was obtained for four eigenvalues: $\lambda_i = 0.1, 0.5, 0.7, 0.9$. Correspondingly, the critical points are designated by small circles in the figure. The information curve (passing through these critical points) is constructed from several segments, realizing that as the mutual information $I(\mathbf{T}; \mathbf{X})$ increases, additional eigenvectors are used in the projection. For the purpose of comparison, Fig. 10.21 also shows the information curves calculated with small number of eigenvectors for each β.

From the results plotted in Fig. 10.21, we see that the information curve for the Gaussian information bottleneck method is indeed *concave* everywhere. At each value of the mutual information $I(\mathbf{T}; \mathbf{X})$, the information curve is bounded by a tangent with a slope defined by the function $\beta^{-1}(I(\mathbf{T}; \mathbf{X}))$. At the origin, $I(\mathbf{T}; \mathbf{X}) = 0$, the slope $\beta^{-1}(0) = 1-\lambda_1$, where λ_1 is the first eigenvalue of the canonical correlation analysis of the original random vector $\mathbf{X}$ and its compressed version $\mathbf{Y}$. Note also that the asymptotic slope of the information curve is zero, as $\beta \to \infty$. This asymptotic behavior simply reflects the reality of the law of diminishing returns: The addition of more bits of information to the description of the original random vector $\mathbf{X}$ does not provide increased accuracy for the bottleneck vector $\mathbf{T}$.   ∎

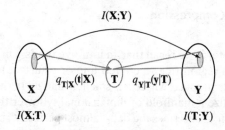

$I(X;Y)$

$q_{T|X}(t|X)$ (T) $q_{Y|T}(y|T)$

$I(X;T)$ $I(T;Y)$

FIGURE 10.22   An illustration of the information bottleneck method. The bottleneck **T** captures the relevant portion of the original random vector **X** with respect to the relevant variable **Y** by minimizing the information $I(\mathbf{X};\mathbf{T})$ while maintaining $I(\mathbf{T};\mathbf{Y})$ as high as possible. The bottleneck **T** is determined by the three distributions $q_{\mathbf{T}|\mathbf{X}}(\mathbf{t}|\mathbf{X})$, $q_{\mathbf{T}}(\mathbf{t})$, and $q_{\mathbf{Y}|\mathbf{T}}(\mathbf{Y}|\mathbf{t})$, which represent the solution of the bottleneck equations (10.170) to (10.172).

Information Bottleneck Equations

The solution of the information bottleneck optimization problem is given through the following bottleneck equations for distributions of the vector **T**:

$$q_{\mathbf{T}|\mathbf{X}}(\mathbf{t}|\mathbf{x}) = \frac{q_{\mathbf{T}}(\mathbf{t})}{Z(\mathbf{x}, \beta)} \exp(-D_{p\|q}) \tag{10.170}$$

$$q_{\mathbf{T}}(\mathbf{t}) = \sum_{\mathbf{X}} q_{\mathbf{T}|\mathbf{X}}(\mathbf{t}|\mathbf{x}) p_{\mathbf{X}}(\mathbf{x}) \tag{10.171}$$

$$q_{\mathbf{Y}|\mathbf{T}}(\mathbf{y}|\mathbf{t}) = \sum_{\mathbf{X}} q_{\mathbf{Y}|\mathbf{T}}(\mathbf{y}|\mathbf{t}) q_{\mathbf{T}|\mathbf{X}}(\mathbf{t}|\mathbf{x}) \left(\frac{p_{\mathbf{X}}(\mathbf{x})}{q_{\mathbf{T}}(\mathbf{t})} \right) \tag{10.172}$$

In Eq. (10.170), $D_{p\|q}$ denotes the Kullback–Leibler divergence between the two conditional probability density functions $p_{\mathbf{Y}|\mathbf{X}}(\mathbf{y}|\mathbf{x})$ and $q_{\mathbf{Y}|\mathbf{T}}(\mathbf{y}|\mathbf{t})$, and $Z(\mathbf{x},\beta)$ is a normalization (partition) function. Figure 10.22 illustrates the idea of information bottleneck in light of these three equations.

The system of Eqs. (10.170) through (10.172) must be solved *self-consistently* for the three unknown distributions $q_{\mathbf{T}|\mathbf{X}}(\mathbf{t}|\mathbf{x})$, $q_{\mathbf{T}}(\mathbf{t})$, and $q_{\mathbf{Y}|\mathbf{T}}(\mathbf{y}|\mathbf{t})$. Tishby et al. (1999) showed that, by iterating these equations from a random starting distribution in a manner similar to the Blahut–Arimoto iterations for rate distortion theory, the equations converge to an optimal solution for any value of the parameter β.

The information bottleneck problem can be solved to obtain relevant continuous manifolds (dimension reduction), as was shown Chechik et al. (2004) for Gaussian variables or as discussed in the next section, in accordance with Chigirev and Bialek (2004).

10.20   OPTIMAL MANIFOLD REPRESENTATION OF DATA

In Chapter 7, we discussed the unsupervised manifold representation of data from the perspective of regularization, using spectral graph theory. In this section, we revisit the same problem, but this time we approach it from an information-theoretic perspective. More specifically, the approach taken here follows that of Chigirev and Bialek (2004), which builds on the following insight:

> *There is analytic benefit to be gained by treating dimensionality reduction as a data compression problem.*

The Chigirev–Bialek approach to data representation is, in fact, a clever application of the information bottleneck method discussed in the previous section.

Dimensionality Reduction Viewed as Data Compression: The Basic Equations

From the discussion presented in Chapter 7, we recall that, in intuitive terms, a *manifold* refers to a k–dimensional continuous region (e.g., a curved line or a surface) that is embedded in an m-dimensional Euclidean space, where k is smaller than m. In the manifold representation of data, we visualize a manifold of dimensionality lower than the data. In particular, we say that the manifold describes the data "almost perfectly," because of the unavoidable presence of additive noise and other forms of data degradation.

Let $\mathcal{M}$ denote a manifold of dimensionality k and $q_{\mathcal{M}}(\mu)$ denote the probability density function of points on the manifold; μ represents one such point. Let $\mathbf{X}$ denote a random data vector of dimensionality m greater than k, which, in effect, implies that the data set $\mathcal{X}$ represented by $\mathbf{X}$ is *sparse*. Indeed, it is the sparseness of the data set that makes its unsupervised representation a challenging task. Let $q_{\mathcal{M}|\mathbf{X}}(\mu|\mathbf{x})$ denote the conditional probability density function of points on the manifold, given the data set $\mathcal{X}$. Thus, the *stochastic map*

$$P_{\mathcal{M}} : \mathbf{x} \rightarrow q_{\mathcal{M}|\mathcal{X}}(\mu|\mathbf{x}) \tag{10.173}$$

describes the mapping of $\mathbf{x}$ into μ.

The manifold is described by the doublet $\{\mathcal{M}, P_{\mathcal{M}}\}$, which embodies a "less than faithful representation" of the data set $\mathcal{X}$, substantiating a similar remark made above. Stated in another way, we may say that the vector μ, denoting a point on the manifold $\mathcal{M}$, is a *distorted* version of the data point $\mathbf{x}$—hence the need for a *distance measure* that we denote by $d(\mathbf{x}, \mu)$. To simplify matters, we adopt a Euclidean distance function for this measure, as shown by

$$d(\mathbf{x}, \mu) = \|\mathbf{x} - \mu\|^2 \tag{10.174}$$

which is commonly used. The *expected distortion* is thus defined by the double multidimensional integral

$$\mathbb{E}[d(\mathbf{x}, \mu)] = \int_{-\infty}^{\infty} \int_{-\infty}^{\infty} p_{\mathcal{X}}(\mathbf{x}) q_{\mathcal{M}|\mathbf{X}}(\mu|\mathbf{x}) \|\mathbf{x} - \mu\|^2 d\mathbf{x} d\mu \tag{10.175}$$

where $p_{\mathcal{X}}(\mathbf{x})$ is the probability density function of the data set $\mathcal{X}$, whose sample value is denoted by the data point $\mathbf{x}$.

Equation (10.175) is one important aspect of the data compression problem. The second important aspect is the mutual information between the manifold $\mathcal{M}$ and the data set $\mathcal{X}$, which is defined by

$$I(\mathcal{X}; \mathcal{M}) = \int_{-\infty}^{\infty} \int_{-\infty}^{\infty} \underbrace{p_{\mathcal{X}}(\mathbf{x}) q_{\mathcal{M}|\mathcal{X}}(\mu|\mathbf{x})}_{\text{Joint pdf}} \log \left(\frac{q_{\mu|\mathcal{X}}(\mu|\mathbf{x})}{q_{\mathcal{M}}(\mu)} \right) d\mathbf{x} d\mu \tag{10.176}$$

When the logarithm is to base 2, this mutual information defines the number of bits required to encode a data point $\mathbf{x}$ into a point μ on the manifold $\mathcal{M}$. Furthermore, by viewing the dimensionality reduction as a data compression problem, $I(\mathcal{X}; \mathcal{M})$ defines the "capacity" of a channel required to transmit the compressed data μ, given the data vector $\mathbf{x}$ treated as input.

When viewed together, Eqs. (10.175) and (10.176) present us with a tradeoff involving two basic issues:

1. For a "faithful" manifold representation of the data, we need to minimize the expected distortion defined in Eq. (10.175).
2. On the other hand, for a "good" compression of the data into points on the manifold, we need to maximize the mutual information defined in Eq. (10.176).

To resolve this tradeoff, we introduce the concept of an *optimal manifold* (Chigirev and Bialek, 2004):

Given a data set $\mathcal{X}$ and a channel capacity $I(\mathcal{X}; \mathcal{M})$, the manifold $\mathcal{M}$ is said to be an optimal representation of the data set $\mathcal{X}$ provided that two conditions are satisfied:

(i) *The expected distortion $\mathbb{E}[d(\mathbf{x}, \boldsymbol{\mu})]$ is minimized.*

(ii) *Only the number of bits defined by the channel capacity $I(\mathcal{X}; \mathcal{M})$ is required to represent the data point $\mathbf{x}$.*

Another way of defining an optimal manifold is to say the following:

The manifold $\mathcal{M}$ is optimal if the channel capacity $I(\mathcal{X}; \mathcal{M})$ is maximized while the expected distortion is fixed at some prescribed value.

Either way, we are faced with a problem in rate distortion theory. Since this problem is a *constrained-optimization problem* in light of the discussion presented in Section 10.19, we introduce a *Lagrange multiplier* λ that accounts for the tradeoff between the expected distortion and the channel capacity, as shown by the Lagrangian

$$F(\mathcal{M}, P_{\mathcal{M}}) = \mathbb{E}[d(\mathbf{x}, \boldsymbol{\mu})] + \lambda I(\mathcal{X}; \mathcal{M}) \tag{10.177}$$

To find the optimal manifold, this functional must be minimized.

To do this minimization in analytic terms, we need to *parameterize* the manifold. Following the information bottleneck method described in Section 10.19, we introduce the *bottleneck vector* $\mathbf{T}$, a sample value of which is denoted by $\mathbf{t} \in \mathbb{R}^l$, where the new dimension l is less than or equal to the dimension m of the data vector $\mathbf{x}$. We also introduce a new vector-valued function

$$\boldsymbol{\gamma}(\mathbf{t}): \mathbf{t} \to \mathcal{M} \tag{10.178}$$

that maps the point $\mathbf{t}$ in the parameter space spanned by the bottleneck vector $\mathbf{T}$ onto the manifold $\mathcal{M}$. The vector-valued function $\boldsymbol{\gamma}(\mathbf{t})$ is therefore a "descriptor" of the manifold $\mathcal{M}$. We also assume that the dimension of $\boldsymbol{\gamma}(\mathbf{t})$ is the same as the dimension of the data point $\mathbf{x}$, so that we may use the squared Euclidean distance $\|\mathbf{x} - \boldsymbol{\mu}(\mathbf{t})\|^2$ as the new measure of the distortion incurred in using the manifold $\mathcal{M}$ as the representation of the data set $\mathcal{X}$.

In light of the manifold parameterization just described, we recast our two basic equations of Eqs. (10.175) and (10.176) in the new respective forms

$$\mathbb{E}[d(\mathbf{x}, \boldsymbol{\gamma}(\mathbf{t}))] = \int_{-\infty}^{\infty} \int_{-\infty}^{\infty} p_{\mathbf{X}}(\mathbf{x}) q_{\mathbf{T}|\mathbf{X}}(\mathbf{t}|\mathbf{x}) \|\mathbf{x} - \boldsymbol{\gamma}(\mathbf{t})\|^2 d\mathbf{x} d\mathbf{t} \tag{10.179}$$

and

$$I(\mathbf{X}; \mathbf{T}) = \int_{-\infty}^{\infty} \int_{-\infty}^{\infty} p_{\mathbf{X}}(\mathbf{x}) q_{\mathbf{T}|\mathbf{X}}(\mathbf{t}|\mathbf{x}) \log\left(\frac{q_{\mathbf{T}|\mathbf{X}}(\mathbf{t}|\mathbf{x})}{q_{\mathbf{T}}(\mathbf{t})}\right) d\mathbf{x}d\mathbf{t} \qquad (10.180)$$

Correspondingly, the functional F of Eq. (10.177) is rewritten in the new form

$$F(\boldsymbol{\gamma}(\mathbf{t}), q_{\mathbf{T}|\mathbf{X}}(\mathbf{t}|\mathbf{x})) = \mathbb{E}[(\mathbf{t}|\mathbf{x}, \boldsymbol{\gamma}(\mathbf{t}))] + \lambda I(\mathbf{X}; \mathbf{T}) \qquad (10.181)$$

The expected distortion and the channel capacity in this latter equation are both *intrinsic properties* of the manifold described by the doublet $\{\mathcal{M}, P_{\mathcal{M}}\}$, and the properties are *invariant* under reparameterization.

With Eqs. (10.179) to (10.181) at hand, the stage is now set to find the optimal manifold. We do so by applying the following two conditions of optimization:

1. $\dfrac{\partial F}{\partial \boldsymbol{\gamma}(\mathbf{t})} = 0$ for $q_{\mathbf{T}|\mathbf{X}}(\mathbf{t}|\mathbf{x})$ fixed $\qquad (10.182)$

2. $\dfrac{\partial F}{q_{\mathbf{T}|\mathbf{X}}(\mathbf{t}|\mathbf{x})} = 0$ for $\boldsymbol{\gamma}(\mathbf{t})$ fixed $\qquad (10.183)$

Thus, applying condition 1, we obtain

$$\int_{-\infty}^{\infty} p_{\mathbf{X}}(\mathbf{x}) q_{\mathbf{T}|\mathbf{X}}(\mathbf{t}|\mathbf{x})(-2\mathbf{x} + 2\boldsymbol{\gamma}(\mathbf{t})) d\mathbf{x} = 0$$

which leads to the following pair of equations that are *consistent* in probabilistic terms:

$$\boldsymbol{\gamma}(\mathbf{t}) = \frac{1}{q_{\mathbf{T}}(\mathbf{t})} \int_{-\infty}^{\infty} \mathbf{x} p_{\mathbf{X}}(\mathbf{x}) q_{\mathbf{T}|\mathbf{X}}(\mathbf{t}|\mathbf{x}) d\mathbf{x} \qquad (10.184)$$

$$q_{\mathbf{T}}(\mathbf{t}) = \int_{-\infty}^{\infty} p_{\mathbf{X}}(\mathbf{x}) q_{\mathbf{T}|\mathbf{X}}(\mathbf{t}|\mathbf{x}) d\mathbf{x} \qquad (10.185)$$

The derivation of this pair of equations hinges only on the expected-distortion component of the functional F, as it is only this component that depends on $\boldsymbol{\gamma}(\mathbf{t})$—hence the absence of the Lagrange multiplier λ.

However, when we go on to apply the second optimizing condition described in Eq. (10.183), we have to recognize that this optimization involves all possible values of the conditional $q_{\mathbf{T}|\mathbf{X}}(\mathbf{t}|\mathbf{x})$ under the constraint

$$\int_{-\infty}^{\infty} q_{\mathbf{T}|\mathbf{X}}(\mathbf{t}|\mathbf{x}) d\mathbf{t} = 1 \qquad \text{for all } \mathbf{x}$$

This constraint is merely the requirement that the area under the curve of $q_{\mathbf{T}|\mathbf{X}}(\mathbf{t}|\mathbf{x})$ be unity, which is a fundamental property of every probability density function. To satisfy this additional constraint, we introduce the new Lagrangian multipliers $\beta(\mathbf{x})$ for all $\mathbf{x}$ and thus expand the definition of the functional F to obtain

$$F(\gamma(t), q_{T|X}(t|x)) = \int_{-\infty}^{\infty} \int_{-\infty}^{\infty} \Big\{ p_X(x) q_{T|X}(t|x) \|x - \gamma(t)\|^2$$

$$+ \lambda p_X(x) q_{T|X}(t|x) \log\left(\frac{q_{T|X}(t|x)}{q_T(t)}\right) + \beta(x) q_{T|X}(t|x) \Big\} dt dx \quad (10.186)$$

where $q_T(t)$ is as previously defined in Eq. (10.185).

Thus, applying the second optimizing condition of Eq. (10.183) to this new formulation of the functional F and simplifying terms through the use of Eq. (10.185), we obtain

$$\frac{1}{\lambda}\|x - \gamma(t)\|^2 + \log\left(\frac{q_{T|X}(t|x)}{q_T(t)}\right) + \frac{\beta(x)}{\lambda p_X(x)} = 0$$

Now, setting

$$\frac{\beta(x)}{\lambda p_X(x)} = \log Z(x, \lambda) \quad (10.187)$$

and solving the resulting equation for the desired conditional $q_{T|X}(t|x)$, we get a second pair of equations that are also *consistent* in probabilistic terms:

$$q_{T|X}(t|x) = \frac{q_T(t)}{Z(x, \lambda)} \exp\left(-\frac{1}{\lambda}\|x - \gamma(t)\|^2\right) \quad (10.188)$$

and

$$Z(x, \lambda) = \int_{-\infty}^{\infty} q_T(t) \exp\left(-\frac{1}{\lambda}\|x - \gamma(t)\|^2\right) dt \quad (10.189)$$

The function $Z(x, \lambda)$ plays the role of a *normalization (partition) function* in that its inclusion in Eq. (10.188) ensures that the constraint imposed on $q_T(t)$ is satisfied, as it should be.

The collectivity of Eqs. (10.184), (10.185), (10.188), and (10.189) describes the *optimal manifold for data representation* in an unsupervised manner. This description naturally requires knowledge of the continuous probability density function $p_X(x)$.

Discretization Process

In practice, however, we only have a training sample $\mathcal{H}$ denoted by $\{x_i\}_{i=1}^N$, where N is the sample size. In light of this practical reality, we introduce the *discrete approximation*

$$p_X(x) \approx \frac{1}{N} \sum_{i=1}^{N} \delta(x - x_i) \quad (10.190)$$

where $\delta(\cdot)$ denotes the *Dirac delta function*. Correspondingly, we model the manifold $\mathcal{M}$ by the discrete set

$$\mathcal{T} = \{t_j\}_{j=1}^{L} \quad (10.191)$$

Then, noting that the sample value $\mathbf{t}$ of the bottleneck vector $\mathbf{T}$ appears only in the arguments of the function $\boldsymbol{\gamma}(\mathbf{t})$, the conditional $q_{\mathbf{T}|\mathbf{X}}(\mathbf{t}|\mathbf{x})$, and the marginal $q_{\mathbf{T}}(\mathbf{t})$, we may replace these three continuous functions by their respective discrete counterparts $\boldsymbol{\gamma}_j$, $q_j(\mathbf{x}_i)$, and q_j, where the indices i and j are included to emphasize the discretization process. To complete the discretization process, we introduce α to denote the coordinate index in the Euclidean space $\mathbb{R}^m$.

Now that we have a discrete model for the manifold, the goal is to develop an algorithm for computing the model in an iterative manner. To this end, we first note that Eqs. (10.188) and (10.189), defining $q_{\mathbf{T}|\mathbf{X}}(\mathbf{t}|\mathbf{x})$ and $Z(\mathbf{x}, \lambda)$, respectively, are both convex functions of their respective variables $\mathbf{t}$ and $\mathbf{x}$; the Lagrange multiplier λ is a prescribed parameter. In a computational context, these two equations are the difficult part of the manifold's discrete model.

To probe further into how we can mitigate this computational difficulty, consider the two convex sets $\mathcal{A}$ and $\mathcal{B}$ depicted in Fig. 10.23. We would like to minimize the Euclidean "distance" between them; the distance is denoted by $d(\mathbf{x}, \mathbf{y})$, where $\mathbf{x}$ and $\mathbf{y}$ are any two points in the sets $\mathcal{A}$ and $\mathcal{B}$, respectively. An intuitively obvious way of minimizing the Euclidean distance $d(\mathbf{x}, \mathbf{y})$ is to do the following (Csiszát and Tusnády, 1984):

> *Fix the point $\mathbf{x}$ in set $\mathcal{A}$, and find the point $\mathbf{y}$ in set $\mathcal{B}$ that is closest to it. Then fix the newly found point $\mathbf{y}$, and find the point $\mathbf{x}$ in the set $\mathcal{A}$ that is closest to it.*

If we continue this process by going back and forth between the sets $\mathcal{A}$ and $\mathcal{B}$, as illustrated in Fig. 10.23, it would seem plausible that the distance $d(\mathbf{x}, \mathbf{y})$ would become smaller after each iteration of this alternating process. This is exactly what is done in the *Blahut–Arimoto algorithm* for minimizing the rate distortion function (Blahut, 1972; Arimoto, 1972). Equations (10.188) and (10.189) have the same mathematical form as those found in the characterization of the rate distortion function (Cover and Thomas, 2006). Moreover, in Csiszár and Tusnády (1984), it is shown that the alternating process between the two convex sets $\mathcal{A}$ and $\mathcal{B}$ will converge, provided that they are both sets of probability distributions and that the distance measure is the Kullback–Leibler divergence between the two distributions.

Iterative Algorithm for Computing the Optimal Manifold Representation of Data

In light of these reassuring findings, we may go on to formulate an iterative algorithm for computing the discrete model of the manifold $\mathcal{M}$. Let n denote the time-step in the iterative algorithm. Then, using the discrete versions of Eqs. (10.184), (10.185), (10.188)

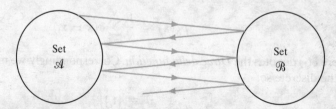

FIGURE 10.23 Illustrating the alternating process of computing the distance between two convex sets $\mathcal{A}$ and $\mathcal{B}$.

and (10.189) and adopting an L-point discrete set $\{\mathbf{t}_1, \mathbf{t}_2, ..., \mathbf{t}_L\}$ to model the manifold represented by the continuous variable t, we may now formulate the desired algorithm based on the following set of four equations, where the time-step $n = 0, 1, 2, ...,$ and the index $j = 1, 2, ..., L$. (Chigirev and Bialek, 2004):

$$p_j(n) = \frac{1}{N} \sum_{i=1}^{N} p_j(\mathbf{x}_i, n) \qquad (10.192)$$

$$\gamma_{j,\alpha}(n) = \frac{1}{p_j(n)} \cdot \frac{1}{N} \sum_{i=1}^{N} x_{i,\alpha} p_j(\mathbf{x}_i, n), \quad \alpha = 1, 2, ..., m \qquad (10.193)$$

$$Z(\mathbf{x}_i, \lambda, n) = \sum_{j=1}^{L} p_j(n) \exp\left(-\frac{1}{\lambda}\|\mathbf{x}_i - \boldsymbol{\gamma}_j(n)\|^2\right) \qquad (10.194)$$

$$p_j(\mathbf{x}_i, n+1) = \frac{p_j(n)}{Z(\mathbf{x}_i, \lambda, n)} \exp\left(-\frac{1}{\lambda}\|\mathbf{x}_i - \boldsymbol{\gamma}_j(n)\|^2\right) \qquad (10.195)$$

where $x_{i,\alpha}$ refers to the αth element of the data vector $\mathbf{x}_i$.

To *initialize* the algorithm, we randomly pick L points from the data set $\mathcal{X}$ and let

$$\left.\begin{array}{c} \boldsymbol{\gamma}_j = x_{i,j} \\[2mm] p_j(0) = \dfrac{1}{L} \end{array}\right\} \quad j = 1, 2, ..., L \qquad (10.195)$$

To *terminate* the computation, let ε denote the precision with which the manifold points are to be located. The algorithm is terminated at time step n once the condition

$$\max_j |\gamma_j(n) - \gamma_j(n-1)| < \varepsilon$$

is reached.

The one remaining parameter that needs to be set is the Lagrange multiplier λ, which determines the tradeoff between the expected distortion and the channel capacity involved in the functional F. This parameter is under the designer's control, depending on how this tradeoff is to be realized.

Practical Considerations

The algorithm for computing the optimal manifold representation of data, described in Eqs. (10.192) to (10.195), is designed to constrain the mutual information between points on the manifold and those in the original data space. This constraint is invariant with respect to all invertible coordinate transformations in either of these two spaces—a condition that may enforce *smoothness* of the manifold in an implicit sense (Chigirev and Bialek, 2004). In a theoretical framework, it may be argued that the justification for a smooth manifold using an information-theoretic approach is not as rigorous as that for an approach rooted in regularization theory. Nevertheless, the optimal manifold representation of data appears to work satisfactorily in practice.

Most importantly, unlike that for other dimensionality-reduction procedures (eg., the Belkin–Niyogi procedure based on regularization and spectral graph theory, as described in Chapter 7), the convergence time of the information-theoretic algorithm described in this section is *linear* in the sample size N. This highly desirable feature of the algorithm, attributed to the inherently *convex* nature of the equations describing the manifold, makes its application rather attractive, particularly when we are challenged to tackle the difficult task of dimensionality reduction for large datasets in practice.

Other highly desirable features of the algorithm include the following include the following two:

- Knowledge of the dimensionality of the manifold under consideration is *not* required.
- The algorithm is well suited for handling the *dimensionality reduction of sparse data*, which is important because, in high-dimensional spaces, all datasets are typically sparse.

10.21   COMPUTER EXPERIMENT: Pattern Classification

This computer experiment addresses the combined use of two algorithms: first, the optimal manifold representation of the input data for unsupervised clustering and second, the least-mean-square (LMS) algorithm for supervised classification that was discribed in Chapter 3. Though different in application, these two algorithms share two useful properties: effective performance and computational efficiency.

To study the performance of the combined "optimal manifold–LMS" algorithm, we again use data drawn randomly from the double-moon configuration of Fig. 1.8, with the vertical separation between the two moons fixed at $d = -6$. Figure 10.24 presents the results of

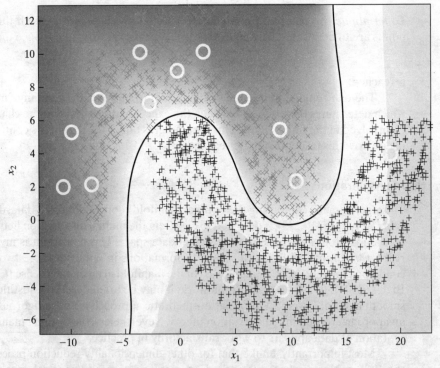

FIGURE 10.24   Pattern classification of the double-moon configuration of Fig. 1.8, using the optimal manifold + LMS algorithm with distance d = −6 and 20 centers.

the experiment, computed with 20 centers shared almost equally between the two moons. The decision boundary, constructed by the algorithm under supervised training with 300 data points, separates data drawn from the two moons in an "almost flawless" manner. More precisely, there were 6 classification errors out of 2,000 test data points, representing a misclassification error rate of 0.3 percent. This performance is close to the error-free performance of the support vector machine (SVM) for the same setting of the double-moon configuration, which was reported in Section 6.7. The important point to take away from this comparison is that the close performance of the "optimal manifold–LMS" algorithm was achieved at a fraction of the computational complexity experienced with the SVM.

10.22   SUMMARY AND DISCUSSION

In this rather long chapter, we established Shannon's information theory as a basic statistical tool for the study of many important aspects of self-organized or unsupervised learning—a truly remarkable achievement.

Mutual Information as the Objective Function of Self-organization

Shannon's mutual information between input and output stochastic processes has some unique properties that commend its adoption as the objective function to be optimized for self-organized learning. Indeed, some important principles of self-organization have emerged from the study presented in this chapter:

1. *The Infomax principle*, which involves maximization of the mutual information between the multidimensional input and output vectors of a neural network. This principle lays down the framework for the development of self-organized models and feature maps.

2. *The principle of minimum redundancy*, which is basically another way of saying that maximization of the mutual information between the input and output of a network leads to the minimization of redundancy.

3. *The Imax principle*, which consists of maximizing the mutual information between the single outputs of a pair of neural networks driven by two spatially shifted multidimensional input vectors. This second principle is well suited for image processing in which the objective is the discovery of properties of a noisy sensory input that exhibits coherence across both space and time.

4. *The Imin principle*, which consists of minimizing the mutual information between the single outputs of a pair of neural networks driven by two spatially shifted multidimensional input vectors. This principle finds application in image processing in which the objective is to minimize the spatiotemporal coherence between two correlatal images of an environment that are obtained through the use of a pair of sensors through orthogonal properties.

Two Fundamental Routes for Independent-Components Analysis

Another important topic discussed in the chapter was that of *independent-components analysis* (ICA), which provides a mathematical basis on which the components of a random vector are made as statistically independent as possible in a strong sense. This principle finds application in solving the blind source separation (BSS) problem, the necessary conditions for which are as follows:

- statistically independent sources of signals;
- non-Gaussian source signals, except for one which is permitted to be Gaussian distributed;
- square mixing matrix, which means that the source signals and the observables are equal in number;
- noise-free mixing model.

Basically, there are two routes for deriving ICA algorithms:

1. *The principle of independent-components analysis* (Comon, 1994). Building on the Kullback–Leibler divergence; this principle leads to the formulation of an expected cost function that depends on two distributions:
   - parameterized probability density function of a demixer's output;
   - corresponding factorial distribution.

   Application of the principle of independent-components analysis manifests itself in two well-known algorithms:

   (i) *The natural-gradient algorithm for ICA*, which is due to Amari et al. (1996).
   (ii) *The Infomax principle for the ICA algorithm*, which is due to Bell and Sejnowski (1995).

   The main virtue of these two algorithms is their ability to adapt to statistical variations of the environment. They are also capable of delivering a robust performance, provided that the right type of activation function is used, depending on whether the original sources are super-Gaussian or sub-Gaussian distribted.

2. *The principle of maximum negentropy* (Comon, 1994). The notion of negentropy provides a measure of the non-Gaussianity of a random variable. The statistical independence of a set of components is realized through the minimization of negentropy. Application of this second principle leads to the formulation by the *FastICA algorithm* due to Hyvärinen and Oja (1997). Attractive features of the FastICA algorithm include the following:
   - fast rate of convergence;
   - absence of learning-rate parameter;
   - robstness, regardless of whether the sources are super-Gaussian or sub-Gaussian distributed;
   - simplicity of implementation.

   However, due to the lack of a learning-rate parameter, the FastICA algorithm does not have the ability to track time-varying mixtures.

A question that begs itself in the context of the three different ICA algorithms highlighted here is the following:

What are the connections among mutual information, entropy and non-Gaussianity in a large ICA framework, without one's resorting to a somewhat arbitrary decorrelation constraint?

In addressing this fundamental question in ICA theory, Cardoso (2003) provides a great deal of mathematical insight insofar as the issues of statistical dependence, correlation, and Gaussianity are concerned. The following is a key result reported in Cardoso's paper:

> When the prewhitening requirement is relaxed, the Kullback–Leibler divergence can be decomposed, under linear transforms, as the sum of two terms: One term expresses the decorrelation of the components, and the other expresses their non-Gaussianity.

By restricting attention to linear transforms, ICA, in effect, permits the non-Gaussian component to express itself only in the marginal distributions.

Some more comments on ICA and BSS are in order. The two concepts are closely related to each other, so much so that frequently one of them is used when the other is really meant. Most importantly, ICA and BSS constitute an ever-expanding field, both in theoretical terms and practical applications. This statement is substantiated by an impressive list of topics, each of which has a practical distinctive direction of its own. (See Note 22 in the List of Notes and References.)

Coherent ICA

One other ICA-related principle discussed in this chapter was that of *coherent ICA* (Kan, 2007; Haykin and Kan, 2007). This new principle combines properties of the Infomax and Imax principles to maximize the spatiotemporal coherence across the outputs of a pair of multiple-input, multiple output (MIMO) networks of similar dimensionalities when the networks are driven by spatially shifted data streams. Using real-life data, two important results in the context of auditory encoding of natural sounds have been demonstrated:

(i) Coherent ICA is capable of exhibiting amplitude-modulation tuning, thereby supporting the notion that envelope processing is embedded in the auditory system.

(ii) Coherent ICA is capable of learning the varying rates at which two successive processing layers of filters respond to acoustic stimuli in a manner that mimics what goes on in the hierarchical auditory system.

Information Bottleneck

In one form or another, all the information-theoretic principles of self-organization summarized thus far build on the concepts of entropy and mutual information that are basic to Shannon's classic information theory. In the latter part of the chapter, we used *rate distortion theory*—another concept basic to Shannon's information theory—to formulate our last principle of the chapter: the *information bottleneck method* (Tishby et al., 1999; Slonim et al., 2006). Following are two important aspects of the method that should be emphasized:

1. The information bottleneck method is not a statistical modeling algorithm; rather, it is a method for finding relevant representations of complex data that can explain the underlying structure and the statistical correlation of interest between a given set of variables.

2. Although the method assumes knowledge of the joint distribution $p_{\mathbf{X},\mathbf{Y}}(\mathbf{x},\mathbf{y})$ between the input vector $\mathbf{X}$ and output vector $\mathbf{Y}$, it is applied in practice to empirical distributions based on finite samples. This plug-in approach is fully justified in Shamir et al. (2008), where theorems on learning, generalization, and consistency are presented.

Equipped with the information bottleneck method, we used it to derive the *optimal manifold representation of data* (Chigirev and Bialek, 2004). The algorithm for implementing this representation has some useful properties:

- The computational complexity of the algorithm is linear in the size of the training sample.
- The algorithm does not require knowledge of the manifold's dimensionality.
- The algorithm is well suited for dealing with high-dimensional data, which are typically sparse.

A concluding comment is in order: The breadth and depth of the material summarized in this section is testimony to the remarkable impact that Shannon's information theory, originally developed for communication systems, has had on unsupervised learning models and their applications.

NOTES AND REFERENCES

1. **Shannon's Information Theory**

   For detailed treatment of information theory, see the book by Cover and Thomas (2006). For a collection of papers on the development of information theory (including the 1948 classic paper by Shannon), see Slepian (1973). Shannon's paper is also reproduced, with minor revisions, in the books by Shannon and Weaver (1949) and Sloane and Wyner (1993).

   For a brief review of the important principles of information theory with neural processing in mind, see Atick (1992). For a treatment of information theory from a biology perspective, see Yockey (1992).

2. For a review of the literature on the relation between information theory and perception, see Linsker (1990b) and Atick (1992).

3. **Entropy**

   The term "entropy," in an information-theoretic context, derives its name from analogy with entropy in thermodynamics; the latter quantity is defined by

   $$H = -k_B \sum_\alpha p_\alpha \log p_\alpha$$

   where k_B is Boltzmann's constant and p_α is the probability that the system is in state α (see Chapter 11). Except for the factor k_B, the formula for entropy H in thermodynamics has exactly the same mathematical form as the definition of entropy given in Eq. (10.8).

4. **Maximum-Entropy Principle**

   In Shore and Johnson (1980), it is proved that the maximum-entropy principle is correct in the following sense:

   > Given prior knowledge in the form of constraints, there is only one distribution satisfying these constraints that can be chosen by a procedure that satisfies the "consistency axioms"; this unique distribution is defined by maximizing entropy.

The consistency axioms are fourfold:

I.   Uniqueness: The result should be unique.
II. Invariance: The choice of coordinates should not affect the result.
III. System independence: It should not matter whether independent information about independent systems is accounted for separately in terms of different densities or together in terms of a joint density.
IV. Subset independence: It should not matter whether an independent subset of system states is treated in terms of a separate conditional density or in terms of the full system density.

In Shore and Johnson (1980), it is shown that the relative entropy or the Kullback–Leibler divergence also satisfies the consistency axioms.

5. Pythagorean Decomposition

To prove the decomposition of Eq. (10.43), we may proceed as follows. By definition we have

$$
\begin{aligned}
D_{p_{\mathbf{X}}\|p_{\mathbf{U}}} &= \int_{-\infty}^{\infty} p_{\mathbf{X}}(\mathbf{x}) \log\left(\frac{p_{\mathbf{X}}(\mathbf{x})}{p_{\mathbf{U}}(\mathbf{x})}\right) d\mathbf{x} \\
&= \int_{-\infty}^{\infty} p_{\mathbf{X}}(\mathbf{x}) \log\left(\frac{p_{\mathbf{X}}(\mathbf{x})}{\tilde{p}_{\mathbf{X}}(\mathbf{x})}\right) \cdot \left(\frac{\tilde{p}_{\mathbf{X}}(\mathbf{x})}{p_{\mathbf{U}}(\mathbf{x})}\right) d\mathbf{x} \\
&= \int_{-\infty}^{\infty} p_{\mathbf{X}}(\mathbf{x}) \log\left(\frac{p_{\mathbf{X}}(\mathbf{x})}{\tilde{p}_{\mathbf{X}}(\mathbf{x})}\right) d\mathbf{x} + \int_{-\infty}^{\infty} p_{\mathbf{X}}(\mathbf{x}) \log\left(\frac{\tilde{p}_{\mathbf{X}}(\mathbf{x})}{p_{\mathbf{U}}(\mathbf{x})}\right) d\mathbf{x} \\
&= D_{p_{\mathbf{X}}\|\tilde{p}_{\mathbf{X}}} + \int_{-\infty}^{\infty} p_{\mathbf{X}}(\mathbf{x}) \log\left(\frac{\tilde{p}_{\mathbf{X}}(\mathbf{x})}{p_{\mathbf{U}}(\mathbf{x})}\right) d\mathbf{x} \qquad \text{(A)}
\end{aligned}
$$

From the definitions of $\tilde{p}_{\mathbf{X}}(\mathbf{x})$ and $p_{\mathbf{U}}(\mathbf{x})$, we see that

$$
\log\left(\frac{\tilde{p}_{\mathbf{X}}(\mathbf{x})}{p_{\mathbf{U}}(\mathbf{x})}\right) = \log\left(\frac{\prod_{i=1}^{m} \tilde{p}_{X_i}(x_i)}{\prod_{i=1}^{m} p_{U_i}(x_i)}\right)
$$
$$
= \sum_{i=1}^{m} \log\left(\frac{\tilde{p}_{X_i}(x_i)}{p_{U_i}(x_i)}\right)
$$

Let I denote the integral in the last line of Eq. (A). We may then write

$$
\begin{aligned}
I &= \int_{-\infty}^{\infty} p_{\mathbf{X}}(\mathbf{x}) \log\left(\frac{\tilde{p}_{\mathbf{X}}(\mathbf{x})}{p_{\mathbf{U}}(\mathbf{x})}\right) d\mathbf{x} \\
&= \int_{-\infty}^{\infty} p_{\mathbf{X}}(\mathbf{x}) \log\left(\frac{\prod_{i=1}^{m} \tilde{p}_{X_i}(x_i)}{\prod_{i=1}^{m} p_{U_i}(x_i)}\right) d\mathbf{x} \\
&= \sum_{i=1}^{m} \int_{-\infty}^{\infty} \left(\log\left(\frac{\tilde{p}_{X_i}(x_i)}{p_{U_i}(x_i)}\right) \int_{-\infty}^{\infty} p_{\mathbf{X}}(\mathbf{x}) \, d\mathbf{x}^{(i)}\right) dx_i \\
&= \sum_{i=1}^{m} \int_{-\infty}^{\infty} \log\left(\frac{\tilde{p}_{X_i}(x_i)}{p_{U_i}(x_i)}\right) \tilde{p}_{X_i}(x_i) \, dx_i \qquad \text{(B)}
\end{aligned}
$$

where, in the last line, we have made use of the defining equation (10.39). The integral in Eq. (B) is the Kullback–Leibler divergence $D_{\tilde{p}_i \| p_{u_i}}$ for $i = 1, 2, \ldots, m$. To put the expression for Eq. (B) in its final form, we note that the area under $\tilde{f}_X(x_j)$ is unity, and therefore write

$$I = \sum_{i=1}^{m} \int_{-\infty}^{\infty} \prod_{j=1}^{m} \tilde{p}_{X_j}(x_j) \left(\log \left(\frac{\tilde{p}_{X_i}(x_i)}{p_{U_i}(x_i)} \right) dx_i \right) dx^{(i)}$$

$$= \int_{-\infty}^{\infty} \tilde{p}_{\mathbf{X}}(\mathbf{x}) \log \left(\frac{\displaystyle\prod_{i=1}^{m} \tilde{p}_{X_i}(x_i)}{\displaystyle\prod_{i=1}^{m} p_{U_i}(x_i)} \right) dx$$

$$= D_{\tilde{p}_{\mathbf{X}} \| p_U} \tag{C}$$

where in the first line we have used the definition $dx = dx_i dx^{(i)}$ as described in Section 10.5. Thus, substituting Eq. (C) into (A), we obtain the desired decomposition:

$$D_{p_{\mathbf{X}} \| p_U} = D_{p_{\mathbf{X}} \| \tilde{p}_{\mathbf{X}}} + D_{p_{\mathbf{X}} \| \tilde{p}_U}$$

6. **Copulas**

The word *copula* is Latin for "link" or "bond"; it is also used in grammar and logic to refer to the part of a proposition that connects a subject and predicate (Nelsen, 2006). In the mathematical literature, the term was first used by Sklar (1959) in the theorem that bears his name: *Sklar's theorem* describes the formation of multivariate distribution functions by "joining together" one-dimensional distribution functions. Nelsen's book provides an interesting historical perspective on copulas and also describes their basic properties, followed by methods for constructing copulas and the role of copulas in modeling and the study of statistical dependence. A detailed list of references on copulas and related issues is given at the end of Nelsen's book.

7. Nadal and Parga (1994, 1997) discuss the relationship between Infomax and redundancy reduction, reaching a similar conclusion that maximization of the mutual information between the input vector and output vector of a neural system leads to data reduction. Haft and van Hemmen (1998) discuss the implementation of Infomax filters for the retina. It is shown that redundancy is essential to the attainment of noise robustness of an internal representation of the environment as it is produced by a sensory system such as the retina.

8. **Canonical Correlation Analysis**

The theory of canonical correlation analysis was originally developed by Hotelling (1935, 1936). To describe the theory, we follow the treatment presented in Anderson (1984).

Consider a zero-mean random vector $\mathbf{X}$ consisting of m components and characterized by an m-by-m covariance matrix Σ. Let $\mathbf{X}$ be partitioned into two subvectors $\mathbf{X}_a$ and $\mathbf{X}_b$ consisting of components m_a and m_b, respectively. Correspondingly, the covariance matrix Σ is partitioned as

$$\Sigma = \mathbb{E}[\mathbf{X}\mathbf{X}^T]$$

$$= \mathbb{E}\left[\begin{pmatrix} \mathbf{X}_a \\ \mathbf{X}_b \end{pmatrix} (\mathbf{X}_a, \mathbf{X}_b)^T \right]$$

$$= \begin{bmatrix} \mathbb{E}[\mathbf{X}_a \mathbf{X}_a^T] & \mathbb{E}[\mathbf{X}_a \mathbf{X}_b^T] \\ \mathbb{E}[\mathbf{X}_b \mathbf{X}_a^T] & \mathbb{E}[\mathbf{X}_b \mathbf{X}_b^T] \end{bmatrix}$$

$$= \begin{bmatrix} \Sigma_{aa} & \Sigma_{ab} \\ \Sigma_{ba} & \Sigma_{bb} \end{bmatrix}$$

where

$$\Sigma_{ba} = \Sigma_{ab}^T$$

The objective of *canonical correlation analysis* (CCA) is to formulate linear transformations of the subvectors $\mathbf{X}_a$ and $\mathbf{X}_b$ so as to clearly exhibit the intercorrelations between the transformed random variables in a maximal manner. To this end, consider the linear transformations

$$Y_a = \mathbf{w}_a^T \mathbf{X}_a$$

and

$$Y_b = \mathbf{w}_b^T \mathbf{X}_b$$

where Y_a and Y_b are both zero-mean random variables and the m_a-by-1 vector $\mathbf{w}_a$ and m_b-by-1 vector $\mathbf{w}_b$ are the *basis vectors* to be determined. Since the cross-correlation function of a multiple of Y_a and a multiple of Y_b is the same as the cross-correlation function of Y_a and Y_b by themselves, we may require that the weight vectors $\mathbf{w}_a$ and $\mathbf{w}_b$ be chosen in such a way that both Y_a and Y_b have unit variance. This requirement leads to the following two conditions:

$$1 = \mathbb{E}[Y_a^2] = \mathbb{E}[\mathbf{w}_a^T \mathbf{X}_a \mathbf{X}_a^T \mathbf{w}_a] = \mathbf{w}_a^T \Sigma_{aa} \mathbf{w}_a \tag{A}$$

and

$$1 = \mathbb{E}[Y_b^2] = \mathbb{E}[\mathbf{w}_b^T \mathbf{X}_b \mathbf{X}_b^T \mathbf{w}_b] = \mathbf{w}_b^T \Sigma_{bb} \mathbf{w}_b \tag{B}$$

With this introductory material at hand, we may now state the problem at hand:

Find the weight vectors $\mathbf{w}_a$ and $\mathbf{w}_b$ so as to maximize the cross-correlation function

$$\mathbb{E}[Y_a Y_b] = \mathbb{E}[\mathbf{w}_a^T \mathbf{X}_a \mathbf{X}_a^T \mathbf{w}_b] = \mathbf{w}_a^T \Sigma_{ab} \mathbf{w}_b$$

subject to the two conditions expressed under Eqs. (A) and (B)

To solve this constrained-optimization problem, we use the method of Lagrange multipliers, for which we write the Lagrangian

$$J(\mathbf{w}_a, \mathbf{w}_b) = \mathbf{w}_a^T \Sigma_{ab} \mathbf{w}_b - \frac{1}{2}\mu_a(\mathbf{w}_a^T \Sigma_{aa} \mathbf{w}_a - 1) - \frac{1}{2}\mu_b(\mathbf{w}_b^T \Sigma_{bb} \mathbf{w}_b - 1)$$

where μ_a and μ_b are Lagrange multipliers and the factors 1/2 are introduced to simplify the presentation. Differentiating the Lagrangian $J(\mathbf{w}_a, \mathbf{w}_b)$ with respect to $\mathbf{w}_a$ and $\mathbf{w}_b$ and setting the results equal to zero yields the following pair of equations:

$$\Sigma_{ab} \mathbf{w}_b - \mu_a \Sigma_{aa} \mathbf{w}_a = \mathbf{0} \tag{C}$$

and

$$\Sigma_{ba} \mathbf{w}_a - \mu_b \Sigma_{bb} \mathbf{w}_b = \mathbf{0} \tag{D}$$

Multiplying the left-hand sides of Eqs. (C) and (D) by $\mathbf{w}_a^T$ and $\mathbf{w}_b^T$, respectively, we obtain

$$\mathbf{w}_a^T \Sigma_{ab} \mathbf{w}_b - \mu_a \mathbf{w}_a^T \Sigma_{aa} \mathbf{w}_a = 0 \tag{E}$$

and

$$\mathbf{w}_b^T \Sigma_{ba} \mathbf{w}_a - \mu_b \mathbf{w}_b^T \Sigma_{bb} \mathbf{w}_b = 0 \tag{F}$$

Next, invoking the conditions of Eqs. (A) and (B) in Eqs. (E) and (F), respectively, shows that

$$\mu_a = \mu_b = \mathbf{w}_a^T \Sigma_{ab} \mathbf{w}_b \tag{G}$$

where we have made use of the relationship $\Sigma_{ba} = \Sigma_{ab}^T$. Hence, the two Lagrange multipliers in the Lagrangian $J(\mathbf{w}_a, \mathbf{w}_b)$ assume a common value, hereafter denoted by μ.

Moreover, recognizing that the variances of both Y_a and Y_b are normalized to unity, it follows from Eq. (G) that the Lagrange multiplier μ is the *canonical correlation* between these two random variables.

The key question now is: How do we determine the basis vectors $\mathbf{w}_a$ and $\mathbf{w}_b$? Using Eqs. (C) and (D), we may readily show that the basis vectors $\mathbf{w}_a$ and $\mathbf{w}_b$ are respectively defined by the pair of eigenequations

$$\underbrace{\Sigma_{aa}^{-1}\Sigma_{ab}\Sigma_{bb}^{-1}\Sigma_{ba}}_{\mathbf{C}_a} \mathbf{w}_a = \lambda \mathbf{w}_a \tag{H}$$

and

$$\underbrace{\Sigma_{bb}^{-1}\Sigma_{ba}\Sigma_{aa}^{-1}\Sigma_{ab}}_{\mathbf{C}_b} \mathbf{w}_b = \lambda \mathbf{w}_b \tag{I}$$

where

$$\lambda = \mu^2 \tag{J}$$

We may therefore make two statements:

1. The eigenvalue λ of the matrix $\mathbf{C}_a$ is equal to the squared value of the canonical correlation, and the associated eigenvector defines the basis vector $\mathbf{w}_a$.
2. The eigenvalue λ of the second matrix $\mathbf{C}_b$ is also equal to the squared value of the canonical correlation, and the associated eigenvector defines the second basis vector $\mathbf{w}_b$.

Note, however, that the number of meaningful solutions of the eigenequations (G), (H), and (I) is limited by the dimension m_a or m_b, whichever is smaller. The largest eigenvalue, λ_1, yields the strongest canonical correlation; the next eigenvalue, λ_2, yields the second-strongest canonical correlation, and so on.

Canonical correlation analysis (CCA), as described herein, can be used to reveal second-order statistical dependencies between two related, but different, datasets. Even though, CCA does not include higher-order statistics, it often performs well in practice.

From Eqs. (H) and (I), it is also apparent that canonical correlation analysis includes principal components as a special case that occurs when the matrices $\mathbf{C}_a$ and $\mathbf{C}_b$ are assigned a common value—that is , when the subectors $\mathbf{X}_a$ and $\mathbf{X}_b$ are one and the same.

It is also of interest to note that, in Fyfe (2005), two different neural implementations of canonical correlation analysis are presented, supported by simulations using artificial and real-life data.

9. **Uttley's Informon**

In Uttley (1970, a *negative information pathway* is considered by optimizing the negative of the mutual information between the signals at the input and the output of the pathway. It is shown that such a system adapts to become a discriminator of the more frequent pattern occurring in the set of input signals during adaptation. The model is called "informon," which is loosely related to the Imin principle.

10. **Fuzzy Imin Processor**

The system described in Ukrainec and Haykin (1996) includes a postdetection processor that uses *a priori* information about the reflector location along the water-land boundary of the waterway. A *fuzzy processor* combines primary detection performance with the output from a vision-based edge detector to effectively remove false alarms, thereby resulting in a further improvement in system performance.

11. **Historical Notes**

Two seminal papers on blind source separation and independent-components analysis are widely recognized in the literature:

- The paper by Herault et al. (1985) on blind source separation (BSS) using Hebbian learning.
- The paper by Comon (1994) on independent-components analysis (ICA), where this term was coined for the firs time.

For a detailed historical account of BSS and ICA, including several other early contributions, see Jutten and Taleb (2000).

12. **Natural Gradient**

The idea of using $\nabla^* D = (\nabla D)\mathbf{W}^T\mathbf{W}$ instead of the usual gradient ∇D for solving the source separation problem is described in Cardoso and Laheld (1996). Therein, $\nabla^* D$ is referred to as the *relative gradient*. This gradient is exactly the same as the *natural gradient*, the definition of which follows from an information-geometric perspective (Amari, 1998; Amari et al. 1996).

13. **Riemannian Space**

In the Riemannian space of dimension n, for example, the squared norm of a vector $\mathbf{a}$ is defined by

$$\|\mathbf{a}\|^2 = \sum_{i=1}^{n} \sum_{j=1}^{n} a_i g_{ij} a_j$$

where the g_{ij} are functions of the coordinates $x_1, x_2, \ldots, x_n$ of the Riemannian space, $g_{ij} = g_{ji}$, and the right-hand side of this expression is always positive. This expression is a generalization of the Euclidean formula for a squared norm:

$$\|\mathbf{a}\|^2 = \sum_{i=1}^{n} a_i^2$$

For a discussion of the Riemannian structure, see Amari (1987), Murray and Rice (1993), and Rosenberg (1997).

14. **Super-Gaussian and Sub-Gaussian Distributions**

Consider a random variable X whose probability density function is denoted by $p_X(x)$, where x is a sample value of X. Let $p_X(x)$ be expressible in the form $\exp(-g(x))$, where $g(x)$ is an even function of x that is differentiable with respect to x, except possibly at the origin; the derivative of $g(x)$ with respect to x is denoted by $g'(x)$.

If $g'(x)/x$ is *strictly decreasing* for $0 < x < \infty$, then the random variable X is said to be *super-Gaussian*. For example, we may have $g(x) = |x|^\beta$ with $\beta < 2$.

If, on the other hand, the random variable X is *uniformly distributed*, or $g(x)$ and $g'(x)/x$ are *strictly increasing* for $0 < x < \infty$, then the random variable X is said to be *sub-Gaussian* For example, we may have $g(x) = |x|^\beta$ with $\beta > 2$.

Perhaps in an abusive way, sometimes we find that the sign of the *kurtosis* of a random variable is used as an indicator of its super-Gaussianity or sub-Gaussianity property. The *kurtosis* of random variable X is defined by

$$K_4 = \frac{\mathbb{E}[X^4]}{(\mathbb{E}[X^2])^2} - 3$$

On this basis, the random variable X is said to be *super-Gaussian* or *sub-Gaussian* if the kurtosis K_4 is *positive* or *negative*, respectively.

15. Another Historical Note

In a historical context, Cardoso (1997) was the first to justify theoretically that it is sufficient to use the right type of nonlinear activation function in the natural-gradient algorithm for it to achieve convergence to a blind source solution.

16. Maximum–likelihood Estimation

Maximum likelihood estimators have some desirable properties. Under quite general conditions, the following *asymptotic* properties may be proved (Kmenta, 1971):

  (i) *Maximum-likelihood estimators are consistent.* Let $L(\theta)$ denote the log-likelihood function and θ_i denote an element of the parameter vector θ. The partial derivative $\partial L/\partial \theta_i$ is called a *score*. We say that a maximum-likelihood estimator is consistent in the sense that the value of θ_i, for which the score $\partial L/\partial \theta_i$ is identically zero, *converges in probability* to the true value of θ_i as the sample size used in the estimation approaches infinity.

  (ii) *Maximum-likelihood estimators are asymptotically efficient.* That is,

$$\lim_{N \to \infty} \left\{ \frac{\mathrm{var}[\theta_i - \hat{\theta}_i]}{I_{ii}} \right\} = 1 \qquad \text{for all } i$$

where N is the sample size, $\hat{\theta}_i$ is the maximum-likelihood estimate of θ_i, and I_{ii} is the ith diagonal element of the inverse of *Fisher's information matrix*. Fisher's information matrix is defined by

$$\mathbf{J} = - \begin{bmatrix} \mathbb{E}\left[\dfrac{\partial^2 LL}{\partial \theta_1^2} \right] & \mathbb{E}\left[\dfrac{\partial^2 LL}{\partial \theta_1 \partial \theta_2} \right] & \cdots & \mathbb{E}\left[\dfrac{\partial^2 LL}{\partial \theta_1 \partial \theta_m} \right] \\[2ex] \mathbb{E}\left[\dfrac{\partial^2 LL}{\partial \theta_2 \partial \theta_1} \right] & \mathbb{E}\left[\dfrac{\partial^2 LL}{\partial \theta_2^2} \right] & \cdots & \mathbb{E}\left[\dfrac{\partial^2 L}{\partial \theta_2 \partial \theta_m} \right] \\[2ex] \mathbb{E}\left[\dfrac{\partial^2 L}{\partial \theta_m \partial \theta_1} \right] & \mathbb{E}\left[\dfrac{\partial^2 L}{\partial \theta_m \partial \theta_2} \right] & \cdots & \mathbb{E}\left[\dfrac{\partial^2 L}{\partial \theta_m^2} \right] \end{bmatrix}$$

where m is the dimension of parameter vector θ.

  (iii) *Maximum-likelihood estimators are asymptotically Gaussian.* That is, as the sample size approaches infinity, each element of the maximum-likelihood estimate $\hat{\theta}$ assumes a Gaussian distribution.

In practice, we find the large-sample (i.e., asymptotic) properties of maximum-likelihood estimators hold rather well for sample size $N \geq 50$.

17. Original Version of Infomax for ICA

Equation (10.127) describes the original version of the Infomax-for ICA algorithm as derived in Bell and Sejnowski (1995). The original algorithm is very slow to converge, due to the presence of the term $\mathbf{W}^{-T}$ denoting the inverse of the transposed demixing matrix $\mathbf{W}$. It was later discovered that, by using the natural gradient in place of the ordinary (Euclidean) gradient, as described in the first line of Eq. (10.128), convergence of the algorithm would be accelerated considerably.

18. The Gram–Schmidt orthogonalization procedure is described in Golub and Van Loan (1996).

19. **Symmetric FastICA**

In addition to the single-unit deflation version of the fast ICA algorithm described in Section 10.17, there is another version of the algorithm, referred to as the *symmetric FastICA algorithm*. This latter version estimates the components of the blind source separation problem in a parallel manner. Specifically, the algorithm involves the parallel computation of single-unit updates for each component, followed by subsequent symmetric orthogonalization of the estimated demixing matrix after each iteration. In Tichavsky et al. (2006), analytic closed-form expressions characterizing the separability of both versions of the algorithm are derived in a "local" sense.

20. **TIMIT Database**

The TIMIT (Texas Instruments (TI) and Massachusetts Institute of Technology (MIT)) database is a standard in speech-recognition experiments. It consists of 8-kHz- bandwidth read (not conversational) speech recorded in a quiet environment. The database contains 630 speakers (438 males and 192 females) with 10 utterances per speaker, each one of which is 3 seconds long, on average.

21. **Another viewpoint on Information Bottleneck**

Another way of thinking about the information bottleneck method is to view it as a generalization of the classical notion of "minimal sufficient statistics." A *sufficient statistic* for parameter vector $\mathbf{a}$ in the sample probability density function $p_{\mathbf{X}|\mathbf{A}}(\mathbf{x}_1, \mathbf{x}_2, ..., \mathbf{x}_n | \mathbf{a})$ is a vectorial function of a sample, $\mathbf{S}(\mathbf{X})$, which preserves all the mutual information in the sample on the parameter $\mathbf{a}$; that is, $I(\mathbf{X}; \mathbf{a}) = I(\mathbf{S}(\mathbf{X}); \mathbf{a})$. A minimal sufficient statistic is the simplest possible sufficient statistic, or one which is a function of any other sufficient statistic, $\mathbf{T}(\mathbf{X}) = f(\mathbf{S}(\mathbf{X}))$. From a basic property of mutual information called the *data-processing inequality* (Cover & Thomas 2006), it follows that $\mathbf{T}(\mathbf{X})$ is minimal if $I(\mathbf{T}; \mathbf{X}) \le I(\mathbf{S}; \mathbf{X})$ for any sufficient statistic $\mathbf{S}(\mathbf{X})$. Minimal sufficient statistics capture the notion of *the relevant part of the sample* $\mathbf{X}$ *about the parameter vector* $\mathbf{a}$. Unfortunately, exact (fixed-dimensional) sufficient statistics exist only for distributions of exponential form. An attractive generalization of this important concept is achieved by the information bottleneck method, which explicitly finds functions of $\mathbf{X}$ with minimum mutual information about $\mathbf{X}$ and maximal information about a relevant variable $\mathbf{Y}$ (or $\mathbf{a}$ in the parametric statistic case).

22. **Beyond Classical ICA Theory**

Earlier in this chapter, we focused on classical ICA theory. Interest in the study of independent-components analysis and blind source separation has expanded considerably on several fronts, including the following:

- *Separation of convolutive mixtures*, in which attention is directed on the fact that convolution plays a key role in the mixture of signals observed in practice.
- *Nonlinear blind source separation*, in which nonlinearity is an underlying characteristic of the mixing process.
- *Blind separation of nonindependent sources*, in which it is recognized that one or more or the source signals may not be statistically independent.
- *Noisy independent-components analysis*, in which the noise-free requirement imposed on classical ICA theory is relaxed, thereby forcing us to confront the practical reality of source signals being noisy.
- *An underdetermined scenario*, in which the number of source signals is greater than the number of observables at the output of the mixing process, which may occur in practice.

- *Multually independent subspaces,* in which the ICA theory is expanded to encompass a situation wherein the sources produce signals that occupy different subspaces that are statistically independent of each other, yet within each subspace the pertinent source signals are dependent.
- *Blind source separation techniques exploiting nonstationarity,* in which the source signals are no longer assumed to be stationary and the challenge is to build on the notion of nonstationarity.
- *Blind source separation techniques,* whose mathematical basis depends on the *time-frequency representation* of source signals.
- *Sparse-components analysis,* in which the notion of the *sparseness* of source signals (e.g., natural images) plays a key role in their separation.
- *Blind source separation techniques based on temporal dependencies,* in which it is possible to separate even independent Gaussian sources under special conditions.

What we have listed here is an array of topics that not only relate to the practical realities of source signals, but also highlight the theoretical challenges involved in ICA and BSS theory and their applications. For more detailed discussion of those topics, the interested reader is referred to the books by Hyvärinen et al., (2001), Roberts and Everson (2001), and Cichocki and Amari (2002), and the review papers of Cardoso (2001) and Choi et al. (2005).

PROBLEMS

MaxEnt Principle

10.1 The support of a random variable X (i.e., the range of values for which it is nonzero) is defined by $[a, b]$; there is no other constraint imposed on this random variable. What is the maximum entropy distribution for this random variable? Justify your answer.

Mutual Information

10.2 (a) Use the definitions of differential entropy $h(X)$ and conditional differential entropy $h(X|Y)$ to go from the first line of Eq. (10.28) to the integral formula in the second line of the equation, defining the mutual information $I(X; Y)$ between a pair of continuous random variables, X and Y.

   (b) Use the derived integral formula for the mutual information $I(X; Y)$ to prove the properties described in Eqs. (10.30) to (10.32).

   (c) Justify the second line of Eq. (10.35), expressing the Kullback-Leibler divergence $D_{p\|g}$ as an expectational formula.

10.3 Consider a random input vector $\mathbf{X}$ made up of a primary component $\mathbf{X}_1$ and a contextual component $\mathbf{X}_2$. Define

$$Y_i = \mathbf{a}_i^T \mathbf{X}_1$$
$$Z_i = \mathbf{b}_i^T \mathbf{X}_2$$

How is the mutual information between $\mathbf{X}_1$ and $\mathbf{X}_2$ related to the mutual information between Y_i and Z_i? Assume that the probability model of $\mathbf{X}$ is defined by the multivariate Gaussian distribution

$$p_{\mathbf{X}}(\mathbf{x}) = \frac{1}{(2\pi)^{m/2}(\det \Sigma)^{1/2}} \exp((\mathbf{x} - \boldsymbol{\mu})^T \Sigma^{-1}(\mathbf{x} - \boldsymbol{\mu}))$$

where $\boldsymbol{\mu}$ is the mean of $\mathbf{X}$ and Σ is its covariance matrix.

10.4 In this problem, we explore the use of the Kullback–Leibler divergence (KLD) to derive a supervised-learning algorithm for multilayer perceptrons (Hopfield, 1987;

Baum and Wilczek, 1988). To be specific, consider a multilayer perceptron consisting of an input layer, a hidden layer, and an output layer. Given a case or example α presented to the input, the output of neuron k in the output layer is assigned the probabilistic interpretation

$$y_{k|\alpha} = p_{k|\alpha}$$

Correspondingly, let $q_{k|\alpha}$ denote the actual (true) value of the conditional probability that the proposition k is true, given the input case α. The KLD for the multilayer perceptron is defined by

$$D_{p\|q} = \sum_\alpha p_\alpha \sum_k \left(q_{k|\alpha} \log \left(\frac{q_{k|\alpha}}{p_{k|\alpha}} \right) + (1 - q_{k|\alpha}) \log \left(\frac{1 - q_{k|\alpha}}{1 - p_{k|\alpha}} \right) \right)$$

where p_α is the a priori probability of occurrence of case α.

Using $D_{p\|q}$ as the cost function to be optimized, derive a learning rule for training the multilayer perceptron.

Copulas

10.5 Prove that the product copula's density $C_{U,V}(u,v) = uv$ joins U and V together when the corresponding random variables X and Y are statistically independent.

10.6 An interesting application of copulas is the generation of new distributions (Genest and MacKay, 1989). Parts (a) and (b) of this problem illustrate that application.

(a) *Product copula*

Each member of a statistically independent pair of random variables X and Y is uniformly distributed, as shown by the formulas

$$p_X(x) = \begin{cases} \frac{1}{2}, & -1 \le x \le +1 \\ 0, & \text{otherwise} \end{cases}$$

$$p_Y(y) = \begin{cases} \frac{1}{2}, & -1 \le y \le 1 \\ 0, & \text{otherwise} \end{cases}$$

Plot the copula $C_{U,V}(u, v)$

(b) *Gaussian copula*

Consider a pair of correlated Gaussian distributions with zero mean and unit variance. Plot the corresponding copula for the following two values of the correlation coefficient:

(i) $\rho = 0.9$

(ii) $\rho = -0.95$

10.7 Consider a pair of random variables X and Y whose mutual information is denoted by $I(X; Y)$. Contrast the formula for $I(X; Y)$ of Eq. (10.28) and that of Eq. (10.49) based on copulas as measures of statistical dependence.

10.8 To derive Eq. (10.50) on the relationship between mutual information and a copula's entropy, we used a direct approach. Following a procedure similar to that described for deriving Eq. (10.49), rederive Eq. (10.50).

Infomax Principle

10.9 Consider two channels whose outputs are represented by the random variables X and Y. The requirement is to maximize the mutual information between X and Y. Show that this requirement is achieved by satisfying two conditions:

(a) The probability of occurrence of X or that of Y is 0.5.

(b) The joint probability distribution of X and Y is concentrated in a small region of the probability space.

10.10 Consider the noise model of Fig. P10.10, which shows m source nodes in the input layer of a two-neuron network. Both neurons are linear. The inputs are denoted by $X_1, X_2, ..., X_m$, and the resulting outputs are denoted by Y_1 and Y_2. You may make the following assumptions:

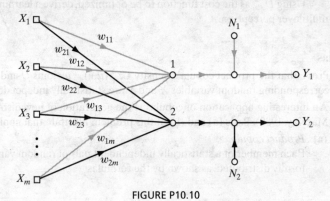

FIGURE P10.10

- The additive noise components N_1 and N_2 at the outputs of the network are Gaussian distributed, with zero mean and common variance σ_N^2. They are also uncorrelated with each other.
- Each noise source is uncorrelated with the input signals.
- The output signals Y_1 and Y_2 are both Gaussian random variables with zero mean.

(a) Determine the mutual information $I(\mathbf{Y}; \mathbf{X})$ between the output vector $\mathbf{Y} = [Y_1, Y_2]^T$ and the input vector $\mathbf{X} = [X_1, X_2, ..., X_m]^T$.

(b) Using the result derived in part (a), investigate the tradeoff between redundancy and diversity under the following conditions:

(i) large noise variance, represented by σ_N^2 being large compared with the variances of Y_1 and Y_2;

(ii) low noise variance, represented by σ_N^2 being small compared with the variances of Y_1 and Y_2.

10.11 In the Imax principle, described in Section 10.10, the objective is to maximize the mutual information $I(Y_a; Y_b)$ between the outputs Y_a and Y_b of a noisy neural system due to the input vectors $\mathbf{X}_a$ and $\mathbf{X}_b$. In another approach, a different objective is used: Maximize the mutual information $I\left(\dfrac{Y_a + Y_b}{2}; S\right)$ between the average of the outputs Y_a and Y_b and the underlying signal component S common to these two outputs.

Using the noisy model described in Example 8, do the following:

(a) Show that

$$I\left(\frac{Y_a + Y_b}{2}; S\right) = \log\left(\frac{\text{var}[Y_a + Y_b]}{\text{var}[N_a + N_b]}\right)$$

where N_a and N_b are the noise components in Y_a and Y_b, respectively.

(b) Demonstrate the interpretation of this mutual information as a ratio of signal-plus-noise to noise.

Independent-Components Analysis

10.12 Justify the statement

Independent-components analysis (ICA) may be viewed as an extension of principal-components analysis (PCA).

10.13 Independent-components analysis may be used as a preprocessing step for approximate data analysis before detection and classification (Comon, 1994). Discuss which property of independent-components analysis can be exploited for this application.

10.14 *Darmois's theorem* states that the sum of independent variables can be Gaussian distributed if, and only if, these variables are themselves Gaussian distributed (Darmois, 1953). Use independent-components analysis to prove this theorem.

10.15 In practice, an algorithmic implementation of independent-components analysis can go only for "as statistically independent as possible." Contrast the solution to the blind source separation problem using such an algorithm with the solution obtained using a decorrelation method. Assume that the covariance matrix of the observation vector is nonsingular.

Natural-Gradient Learning Algorithm for ICA

10.16 Referring to the scheme described in Fig. 10.12, show that minimizing the mutual information between any two components of the demixer output $\mathbf{Y}$ is equivalent to minimizing the Kullback–Leibler divergence between the parameterized probability density function $p_{\mathbf{Y}}(\mathbf{y}, \mathbf{W})$ and the corresponding factorial distribution $\tilde{p}_{\mathbf{Y}}(\mathbf{y}, \mathbf{W})$.

10.17 The adaptive algorithm for blind source separation described in Eq. (10.100) has two important properties: (1) the equivariant property, and (2) the property that the weight matrix $\mathbf{W}$ is maintained as nonsingular. Property (1) is discussed in some detail in the latter part of Section 10.14. In this problem, we consider the second property.

Provided that the initial value $\mathbf{W}(0)$ used in starting the algorithm of Eq. (10.100) satisfies the condition $|\det(\mathbf{W}(0))| \neq 0$, show that

$$|\det(\mathbf{W}(n))| \neq 0 \quad \text{for all } n$$

This is the necessary and sufficient condition for ensuring that $\mathbf{W}(n)$ is nonsingular for all n.

10.18 In this problem, we formulate the batch version of the natural-gradient learning algorithm for ICA described in Eq. (10.100). Specifically, we write

$$\Delta\mathbf{W} = \eta\left(\mathbf{I} - \frac{1}{N}\Phi(\mathbf{Y})\mathbf{Y}^T\right)\mathbf{W}$$

where

$$\mathbf{Y} = \begin{bmatrix} y_1(1) & y_1(2) & \cdots & y_1(N) \\ y_2(1) & y_2(2) & \cdots & y_2(N) \\ \vdots & \vdots & \vdots & \vdots \\ y_m(1) & y_m(2) & \cdots & y_m(N) \end{bmatrix}$$

and

$$\Phi(\mathbf{Y}) = \begin{bmatrix} \varphi(y_1(1)) & \varphi(y_1(2)) & \cdots & \varphi(y_1(N)) \\ \varphi(y_2(1)) & \varphi(y_2(2)) & \cdots & \varphi(y_2(N)) \\ \vdots & \vdots & \vdots & \vdots \\ \varphi(y_m(1)) & \varphi(y_m(2)) & \cdots & \varphi(y_m(N)) \end{bmatrix}$$

where N is the number of available data points. Justify the formulation of the adjustment $\Delta\mathbf{W}$ applied to the weight matrix $\mathbf{W}$ as described.

Infomax for ICA Algorithm

10.19 Consider Fig. 10.16, in which we have (using the symbols for random vectors)

$$\mathbf{Y} = \mathbf{WX}$$

where

$$\mathbf{Y} = [Y_1, Y_2, ..., Y_m]^T$$
$$\mathbf{X} = [X_1, X_2, ..., X_m]^T$$

and $\mathbf{W}$ is an m-by-m weight matrix. Let

$$\mathbf{Z} = [Z_1, Z_2, ..., Z_m]^T$$

where

$$Z_k = \varphi(Y_k), \qquad k = 1, 2, ..., m$$

(a) Show that the joint entropy of $\mathbf{Z}$ is related to the Kullback–Leibler divergence $D_{p\|\tilde{p}}$ according to the relationship

$$h(\mathbf{Z}) = -D_{p\|\tilde{p}} - D_{\tilde{p}\|q}$$

where $D_{\tilde{p}\|q}$ is the Kullback–Leibler divergence between (a) the probability density function of the statistically independent (i.e., factorized) version of the output vector $\mathbf{Y}$ and (b) a "probability density function" defined by $\prod_{i=1}^{m} q(y_i)$.

(b) How is the formula for $h(\mathbf{Z})$ modified for the case when $q(y_i)$ is equal to the probability density function of the original source output S_i, for all i?

10.20 (a) Starting with Eq. (10.124), derive the result given in Eq. (10.125).

(b) For the logistic function described in Eq. (10.126), show that the use of Eq. (10.125) yields the formula given in Eq. (10.127).

(c) Construct a signal-flow graph of the Infomax algorithm for blind source separation that builds on the learning algorithm of Eq. (10.129).

FastICA Algorithm

10.21 Given the functions $\Phi(v)$ defined in Eqs. (10.132) and (10.133)—that is,

1. $\Phi(v) = \log(\cosh(v))$

2. $\Phi(v) = \exp\left(-\dfrac{v^2}{2}\right)$

derive the corresponding expressions for

$$\varphi(v) = \frac{d\Phi(v)}{dv}$$

and

$$\varphi'(v) = \frac{d\varphi(v)}{\partial v}$$

Which of the functions $\Phi(v), \varphi(v)$, and $\varphi'(v)$ for the examples under points 1 and 2 befit the description of a neural activation function? Justify your answer.

10.22 The FastICA algorithm has some desirable features that make it different from the gradient-based ICA algorithms. Which feature(s) of the algorithm make it simpler to design and a useful tool for exploratory data analysis?

Coherent ICA

10.23 State the goal of coherent ICA principle. Given two separate, but dimensionality similar neural networks a and b, with weight matrices W_a and W_b, respectively, determine the objective function $J(W_a, W_b)$ that account for the combined actions of the Infomax and Imax principles on the two networks.

10.24 In computational terms, the coherent ICA algorithm shares two features that are similar to two features of the FastICA algorithm. What are those features? Give details.

10.25 Contrast the distinctive features of coherent ICA with those of ICA.

Information Bottleneck Method

10.26 Consider the information curve obtained by plotting $I(T; Y)$ versus $I(X; T)$ as shown in Fig. 10.21. Show that, for the optimal information bottleneck solution, this curve is an increasing concave curve with slope $1/\beta$ at every point.

10.27 The illustrative depiction of the information bottleneck method presented in Fig. 10.22 and the replicator network (identity map) of Fig. 4.19a bear a strong resemblance to each other. Elaborate on this statement and its relevant implications.

10.28 Equation (10.184) follows from Eq. (10.182).
   (a) Prove Eq. (10.184).
   (b) Justify the formulation of the companion equation (10.185).

10.29 In the course of applying the optimizing condition of Eq. (10.183) to the Lagrangian of Eq.(10.186), we skipped through some critical steps.
   (a) Starting from Eq. (10.183), develop all the steps involved in arriving at the result

$$\frac{1}{\lambda} \|\mathbf{x} - \boldsymbol{\gamma}(\mathbf{t})\|^2 + \log\left(\frac{q_{\mathbf{T|X}}(\mathbf{t|x})}{q_{\mathbf{T}}(\mathbf{t})}\right) + \frac{\beta(\mathbf{x})}{\lambda p_{\mathbf{X}}(\mathbf{x})} = 0$$

   (b) Hence, derive the consistent pair of equations presented in Eqs. (10.188) and (10.189).

Computer Experiments

10.30 Consider the system described in Fig. 10.9 involving the following three independent sources:

$$s_1(n) = 0.1\sin(400n)\cos(30n)$$
$$s_2(n) = 0.01\mathrm{sgn}(\sin(500n + 9\cos(40n)))$$
$$s_3(n) = \text{noise, uniformly distributed in the range } [-1, 1]$$

The mixing matrix **A** is

$$\mathbf{A} = \begin{bmatrix} 0.56 & 0.79 & -0.37 \\ -0.75 & 0.65 & 0.86 \\ 0.17 & 0.32 & -0.48 \end{bmatrix}$$

(a) Plot the waveforms of the three source signals $s_1(n), s_2(n),$ and $s_3(n)$.
(b) Use any of the three ICA algorithms described in Sections 10.14, 10.16, and 10.17 to solve the blind source separation problem, involving the sources $s_1(n), s_2(n), s_3(n)$ and the mixing matrix **A**. Plot the waveforms produced at the output of the demixer, and check them against those plotted in part (a).
(c) Determine the demixing matrix **W**.

10.31 In the computer experiment described in Section 10.21, we used the optimal manifold (for the unsupervised representation of data) and the least-mean-square (LMS) algorithm to perform pattern classification. The data used for the classification was based on a specific setting of the two-moon configuration depicted in Fig. 1.8.

(a) Repeat the computer experiment of Section 10.21, this time using the recursive least-squares (RLS) algorithm in place of the LMS algorithm.
(b) Contrast the results of your experiment against those of Section 10.21 in terms of performance convergence, and computational complexity.

C H A P T E R   1 1

Stochastic Methods Rooted in Statistical Mechanics

ORGANIZATION OF THE CHAPTER

The theme of this chapter is the study of stochastic algorithms for simulation, optimization, and learning by building on ideas rooted in statistical mechanics.

The chapter is organized as follows:

1. Section 11.1 is an introductory section that provides motivation for studying the subject matter just described.
2. Section 11.2 gives an introductory treatment of statistical mechanics, with an emphasis on the concepts of free energy and entropy, as viewed in thermodynamics.
3. Section 11.3 discusses a special kind of stochastic processes known as Markov chains, the use of which is commonly encountered in the study of statistical mechanics.
4. Sections 11.4, 11.5, and 11.6 discuss the following three stochastic simulation/ optimization methods:
   - The Metropolis algorithm
   - Simulated annealing
   - Gibbs sampling

   The Metropolis algorithm and Gibbs sampling provide tools for the simulation of stationary and nonstationary processes, respectively, and simulated annealing is oriented toward optimization.
5. The next three sections, Sections 11.7, 11.8, and 11.9, address the following stochastic machines rooted in statistical mechanics:
   - The Boltzmann machine
   - Logistic belief nets
   - Deep belief nets

   The last machine has some unique properties that overcome practical limitations of the classical Boltzmann machine and logistic belief nets.
6. Section 11.10 describes deterministic annealing, which is an approximation to simulated annealing; despite its name, deterministic annealing is a stochastic algorithm. Section 11.11 introduces the expectation-maximization algorithm and discusses an analogy of deterministic annealing with this algorithm.

The chapter concludes with a summary and discussion in Section 11.12.

11.1   INTRODUCTION

For our last class of unsupervised (self-organized) learning systems, we turn to statistical mechanics as the source of ideas. The subject of *statistical mechanics* encompasses the formal study of macroscopic equilibrium properties of large systems of elements that are subject to the microscopic laws of mechanics. The main aim of statistical mechanics is to derive the thermodynamic properties of macroscopic bodies starting from the motion of microscopic elements such as atoms and electrons (Landau and Lifshitz, 1980; Parisi, 1988). The number of degrees of freedom encountered here is enormous, making the use of probabilistic methods mandatory. As with Shannon's information theory, the concept of entropy plays a vital role in the study of statistical mechanics. In this context, we may say the following:

> *The more ordered the system, or the more concentrated the underlying probability distribution, the smaller the entropy will be.*

By the same token, we can say that the more disordered the system, or the more uniform the underlying probability distribution, the larger the entropy will be. In 1957, Jaynes showed that entropy can be used not only as the starting point of formulating statistical inference as described in the previous chapter, but also for generating the Gibbs distribution that is basic to the study of statistical mechanics.

Interest in the use of statistical mechanics as a basis for the study of neural networks goes back to the early works of Cragg and Tamperley (1954) and Cowan (1968). The *Boltzmann machine* (Hinton and Sejnowski, 1983, 1986; Ackley et al., 1985) is perhaps the first multilayer learning machine inspired by statistical mechanics. The machine is named in recognition of the formal equivalence between Boltzmann's original work on statistical thermodynamics and the network's own dynamic behavior. Basically, the Boltzmann machine is a stochastic system for modeling the underlying probability distribution of a given data set, from which conditional distributions for use in tasks such as pattern completion and pattern classification can be derived. Unfortunately, the learning process in the early version of the Boltzmann machine is painfully slow. This shortcoming has motivated new developments in the Boltzmann machine and inspired the formulation of new stochastic machines. These issues constitute the material presented in this chapter.

11.2   STATISTICAL MECHANICS

Consider a physical system with many degrees of freedom, which can reside in any one of a large number of possible states. Let p_i denote the probability of occurrence of state i of a stochastic system with the following properties:

$$p_i \geq 0 \qquad \text{for all } i \tag{11.1}$$

and

$$\sum_i p_i = 1 \tag{11.2}$$

Let E_i denote the *energy* of the system when it is in state i. A fundamental result from statistical mechanics tells us that when the system is in thermal equilibrium with its surrounding environment, state i occurs with a probability defined by

$$p_i = \frac{1}{Z} \exp\left(-\frac{E_i}{k_B T}\right) \tag{11.3}$$

where T is the *absolute temperature* in kelvins, k_B is *Boltzmann's constant,* and Z is a constant that is independent of all states. One degree kelvin corresponds to $-273°$ on the Celsius scale, and $k_B = 1.38 \times 10^{-23}$ joules/kelvin.

Equation (11.2) defines the condition for the normalization of probabilities. Imposing this condition on Eq. (11.3), we get

$$Z = \sum_i \exp\left(-\frac{E_i}{k_B T}\right) \tag{11.4}$$

The normalizing quantity Z is called the *sum over states,* or the *partition function.* (The symbol Z is commonly used because the German name for this term is *Zustadsumme.*) The probability distribution of Eq. (11.3) is called the *canonical distribution,* or *Gibbs distribution*[1]; the exponential factor $\exp(-E_i/k_B T)$ is called the *Boltzmann factor.*

The following two points are noteworthy from the Gibbs distribution:

1. States of low energy have a higher probability of occurrence than states of high energy.
2. As the temperature T is reduced, the probability is concentrated on a smaller subset of low-energy states.

The parameter T may be viewed as a *pseudotemperature* that controls thermal fluctuations representing the effect of "synaptic noise" in a neuron. Its precise scale is therefore irrelevant. Accordingly, we may choose to measure it by setting the constant k_B equal to unity and thereby redefine the probability p_i and partition function Z as follows, respectively:

$$p_i = \frac{1}{Z} \exp\left(-\frac{E_i}{T}\right) \tag{11.5}$$

and

$$Z = \sum_i \exp\left(-\frac{E_i}{T}\right) \tag{11.6}$$

Henceforth our treatment of statistical mechanics is based on these two definitions, where T is referred to simply as the *temperature of the system.* From Eq. (11.5), we find that $-\log p_i$ may be viewed as a form of "energy" measured at unit temperature.

Free Energy and Entropy

The Helmholtz *free energy* of a physical system, denoted by F, is defined in terms of the partition function Z as

$$F = -T \log Z \tag{11.7}$$

The *average energy* of the system is defined by

$$<E> = \sum_i p_i E_i \tag{11.8}$$

where $<\cdot>$ denotes the ensemble-averaging operation. Thus, using Eqs. (11.5) to (11.8), we see that the difference between the average energy and free energy is given by

$$<E> - F = -T \sum_i p_i \log p_i \qquad (11.9)$$

The quantity on the right-hand side of Eq. (11.9), except for the temperature T, is recognized as the *entropy* of the system, as shown by

$$H = - \sum_i p_i \log p_i \qquad (11.10)$$

(This definition is consistent with that introduced in Chapter 10 on information-theoretic models.)

We may therefore rewrite Eq. (11.9) in the form

$$<E> - F = TH$$

or, equivalently,

$$F = <E> - TH \qquad (11.11)$$

Consider two systems A and A' placed in thermal contact with each other. Suppose that system A is small compared with system A', so that A' acts as a *heat reservoir* at some constant temperature T. The total entropy of the two systems tends to increase in accordance with the relation

$$\Delta H + \Delta H' \geq 0$$

where ΔH and $\Delta H'$ denote the entropy changes of systems A and A', respectively (Reif, 1965). The implication of this relation, in light of Eq. (11.11), is that the free energy of the system, F, tends to decrease and become a minimum in an equilibrium situation. From statistical mechanics, we find that the resulting probability distribution is defined by the Gibbs distribution. We thus have an important principle called the *principle of minimal free energy*, which may be stated as follows (Landau and Lifshitz, 1980; Parisi, 1988):

> The minimum of the free energy of a stochastic system with respect to variables of the system is achieved at thermal equilibrium, at which point the system is governed by the Gibbs distribution.

Nature likes to find a physical system with minimum free energy.

11.3 MARKOV CHAINS

Consider a system whose evolution is described by a stochastic process $\{X_n, n = 1, 2, ...\}$, consisting of a family of random variables. The value x_n, assumed by the random variable X_n at discrete time n, is called the *state* of the system at that time instant. The space of all possible values that the random variables can assume is called the *state space* of the system. If the structure of the stochastic process $\{X_n, n = 1, 2, ...\}$ is such that the dependence of x_{n+1} on the entire past is completely captured by the dependence on the last sample x_n, we say that the process is a *Markov chain* (Feller, 1950; Ash, 1965). More precisely, we have

$$P(X_{n+1} = x_{n+1}|X_n = x_n, ..., X_1 = x_1) = P(X_{n+1} = x_{n+1}|X_n = x_n) \quad (11.12)$$

which is called the *Markov property*. In words, we say the following:

> *A sequence of random variables $X_1, X_2, ..., X_n, X_{n+1}$ forms a Markov chain, if the probability that the system is in state x_{n+1}, given the sequence of past states it has gone through, is exclusively determined by the state of the system at time n.*

We may therefore think of the Markov chain as a *generative model*, consisting of a number of states linked together (on a pairwise basis) by possible transitions. Each time a particular state is visited, the model outputs the symbol associated with that state.

Transition Probabilities

In a Markov chain, the transition from one state to another is *probabilistic*, but the production of an output symbol is deterministic. Let

$$p_{ij} = P(X_{n+1} = j|X_n = i) \quad (11.13)$$

denote the *transition probability* from state i at time n to state j at time $n + 1$. Since the p_{ij} are conditional probabilities, all transition probabilities must satisfy two conditions:

$$p_{ij} \geq 0 \quad \text{for all } i, j \quad (11.14)$$

$$\sum_j p_{ij} = 1 \quad \text{for all } i \quad (11.15)$$

We will assume that the transition probabilities are fixed and do not change with time; that is, Eq. (11.13) is satisfied for all time n. In such a case, the Markov chain is said to be *homogeneous* in time.

In the case of a system with a finite number of possible states K, for example, the transition probabilities constitute the K-by-K matrix

$$\mathbf{P} = \begin{bmatrix} p_{11} & p_{12} & \cdots & p_{1K} \\ p_{21} & p_{22} & \cdots & p_{2K} \\ \vdots & \vdots & & \vdots \\ p_{K1} & p_{K2} & \cdots & p_{KK} \end{bmatrix} \quad (11.16)$$

whose individual elements satisfy the conditions described in Eqs. (11.14) and (11.15); the latter condition says that each row of $\mathbf{P}$ must add to unity. A matrix of this type is called a *stochastic matrix*. Any stochastic matrix can serve as a matrix of transition probabilities.

The definition of one-step transition probability given in Eq. (11.13) may be generalized to cases where the transition from one state to another takes place in some fixed number of steps. Let $p_{ij}^{(m)}$ denote the *m-step transition probability* from state i to state j:

$$p_{ij}^{(m)} = P(X_{n+m} = x_j|X_n = x_i), \quad m = 1, 2, ... \quad (11.17)$$

We may view $p_{ij}^{(m)}$ as the sum over all intermediate states, k, through which the system passes in its transition from state i to state j. Specifically, $p_{ij}^{(m+1)}$ is related to $p_{ij}^{(m)}$ by the recursive relation

$$p_{ij}^{(m+1)} = \sum_k p_{ik}^{(m)} p_{kj}, \qquad m = 1, 2, \dots \tag{11.18}$$

with

$$p_{ik}^{(1)} = p_{ik}$$

Equation (11.18) may be generalized as

$$p_{ij}^{(m+n)} = \sum_k p_{ik}^{(m)} p_{kj}^{(n)}, \qquad m, n = 1, 2, \dots \tag{11.19}$$

which is a special case of the *Chapman–Kolmogorov identity* (Feller, 1950).

Specification of a Markov Chain

With the notions of state and transition probability at hand, we may now summarize how a Markov chain is specified:

(i) *A stochastic model is identified in terms of the following:*
- *a finite set of K possible states denoted by $S = \{1, 2, \dots, K\}$;*
- *a corresponding set of probabilities $\{p_{ij}\}$, where p_{ij} is the transition probability from state i to state j, subject to two conditions:*

$$p_{ij} \geq 0$$

and

$$\sum_j p_{ij} = 1 \qquad \text{for all } i$$

(ii) *Given the stochastic model just described, a Markov chain is specified in terms of a sequence of random variables $X_0, X_1, X_2, \dots$ whose values are taken from the set S in accordance with the Markov property*

$$P(X_{n+1} = j | X_n = i, X_{n-1} = i_{n-1}, \dots, X_0 = i_0) = P(X_{n+1} = j | X_n = i)$$

which holds for all times n, all states $i, j \in S$, and all possible sequences $i_0, \dots, i_{n-1}$ pertaining to earlier states.

Recurrent Properties

Suppose a Markov chain starts in state i. State i is said to be a *recurrent* state if the Markov chain returns to state i with probability 1; that is,

$$p_i = P(\text{ever returning to state } i) = 1$$

If the probability p_i is less than 1, state i is said to be a *transient* state (Leon-Garcia, 1994).

If the Markov chain starts in a recurrent state, that state reoccurs an infinite number of times. If it starts in a transient state, that state reoccurs only a finite number of times, which may be explained as follows: We may view the reoccurrence of state i as a *Bernoulli trial*[2] with a probability of success equal to p_i. The number of returns is thus a geometric random variable with a mean of $(1 - p_i^{-1})$. If $p_i < 1$, it follows that the number of an infinite number of successes is zero. Therefore, a transient state does not reoccur after some finite number of returns.

If a Markov chain has some transient states and some recurrent states, then the process will eventually move only among the recurrent states.

Periodicity

Figure 11.1 shows a Markov chain of the recurrent type. This Markov chain moves through a sequence of substates, ending up in the same substate after three time-steps. The figure illustrates a recurrent Markov chain that is periodic.

In light of Fig. 11.1, a recurrent Markov chain is said to be *periodic* if all of its states can be grouped into d disjoint subsets $S_1, S_2, ..., S_d$, where $d > 1$, and in such a way that all the transitions from one subset lead to the next subset; in the figure, $d = 3$. More precisely, a periodic recurrent Markov chain satisfies the following condition (Bertsekas and Tsitsiklis, 2002):

$$\text{If } i \in S_k \text{ and } p_{ij} > 0, \text{ then } \begin{cases} j \in S_{k+1}, & \text{for } k = 1, ..., d-1 \\ j \in S_1, & \text{for } k = d \end{cases}$$

A recurrent Markov chain is said to be *aperiodic* if it is not periodic.

Irreducible Markov Chains

The state j of a Markov chain is said to be *accessible* from state i if there is a finite sequence of transitions from i to j with positive probability. If the states i and j are accessible to each

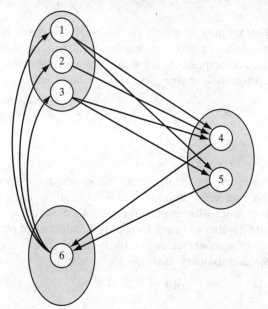

FIGURE 11.1   A periodic recurrent Markov chain with $d = 3$.

other, they are said to *communicate* with each other. This communication is described by writing $i \leftrightarrow j$. Clearly, if state i communicates with state j and state j communicates with state k (that is, $i \leftrightarrow j$ and $j \leftrightarrow k$), then state i communicates with state k (that is, $i \leftrightarrow k$).

If two states of a Markov chain communicate with each other, they are said to belong to the same *class*. In general, the states of a Markov chain consist of one or more disjoint classes. If, however, all the states consist of a single class, the Markov chain is said to be *indecomposible*, or *irreducible*. In other words, by starting at any state of an irreducible Markov chain, we can reach any other state with positive probability. Reducible chains are of little practical interest in most areas of application. Accordingly, we restrict our attention to irreducible chains.

Consider an irreducible Markov chain that starts in a recurrent state i at time $n = 0$. Let $T_i(k)$ denote the time that elapses between the $(k-1)$th and kth returns to state i. The *mean recurrence time* of state i is defined as the expectation of $T_i(k)$ over the returns k. The *steady-state probability* of state i, denoted by π_i, is equal to the reciprocal of the mean recurrence time $\mathbb{E}[T_i(k)]$, as shown by

$$\pi_i = \frac{1}{\mathbb{E}[T_i(k)]}$$

If $\mathbb{E}[T_i(k)] < \infty$—that is, $\pi_i > 0$—the state i is said to be a *positive recurrent (persistent) state*. If $\mathbb{E}[T_i(k)] = \infty$—that is, $\pi_i = 0$—the state i is said to be a *null recurrent (persistent) state*. The implication of $\pi_i = 0$ is that the Markov chain will eventually reach a point where a return to state i is impossible. Positive recurrence and null recurrence are *different* class properties, which means that a Markov chain with positive recurrent and null recurrent states is reducible.

Ergodic Markov Chains

In principle, *ergodicity* means that we may substitute time averages for ensemble averages. In the context of a Markov chain, ergodicity means that the long-term proportion of time spent by the chain in state i corresponds to the steady-state probability π_i, which may be justified as follows: The *proportion of time spent in state i after k returns*, denoted by $v_i(k)$, is defined by

$$v_i(k) = \frac{k}{\displaystyle\sum_{l=1}^{k} T_i(l)}$$

The return times $T_i(l)$ form a sequence of statistically *independent and identically distributed* (iid) random variables, since, by definition, each return time is statistically independent of all previous return times. Moreover, in the case of a recurrent state i, the chain returns to state i an infinite number of times. Hence, as the number of returns, k, approaches infinity, the *law of large numbers* states that the proportion of time spent in state i approaches the steady-state probability, as shown by

$$\lim_{k \to \infty} v_i(k) = \pi_i \qquad \text{for } i = 1, 2, ..., K \qquad (11.20)$$

where K is the total number of states.

A sufficient, but not necessary, condition for a Markov chain to be *ergodic* is for it to be both irreducible and aperiodic.

Convergence to Stationary Distributions

Consider an ergodic Markov chain characterized by a stochastic matrix $\mathbf{P}$. Let the row vector $\boldsymbol{\pi}^{(n-1)}$ denote the *state distribution vector* of the chain at time $n - 1$; the jth element of $\boldsymbol{\pi}^{(n-1)}$ is the probability that the chain is in state x_j at time $n - 1$. The state distribution vector at time n is defined by

$$\boldsymbol{\pi}^{(n)} = \boldsymbol{\pi}^{(n-1)}\mathbf{P} \tag{11.21}$$

By iteration of Eq. (11.21), we obtain

$$\boldsymbol{\pi}^{(n)} = \boldsymbol{\pi}^{(n-1)}\mathbf{P} = \boldsymbol{\pi}^{(n-2)}\mathbf{P}^2 = \boldsymbol{\pi}^{(n-3)}\mathbf{P}^3 = \cdots$$

and finally we may write

$$\boldsymbol{\pi}^{(n)} = \boldsymbol{\pi}^{(0)}\mathbf{P}^n \tag{11.22}$$

where $\boldsymbol{\pi}^{(0)}$ is the *initial value* of the state distribution vector. In words, we say the following:

The state distribution vector of the Markov chain at time n is the product of the initial state distribution vector $\boldsymbol{\pi}^{(0)}$ and the nth power of the stochastic matrix $\mathbf{P}$.

Let $p_{ij}^{(n)}$ denote the ij-th element of $\mathbf{P}^n$. Suppose that as time n approaches infinity, $p_{ij}^{(n)}$ tends to π_j independent of i, where π_j is the steady-state probability of state j. Correspondingly, for large n, the matrix $\mathbf{P}^n$ approaches the limiting form of a square matrix with identical rows as shown by

$$\lim_{n \to \infty} \mathbf{P}^n = \begin{bmatrix} \pi_1 & \pi_2 & \cdots & \pi_K \\ \pi_1 & \pi_2 & \cdots & \pi_K \\ \vdots & \vdots & & \vdots \\ \pi_1 & \pi_2 & \cdots & \pi_K \end{bmatrix} \tag{11.23}$$

$$= \begin{bmatrix} \boldsymbol{\pi} \\ \boldsymbol{\pi} \\ \vdots \\ \boldsymbol{\pi} \end{bmatrix}$$

where $\boldsymbol{\pi}$ is a row vector consisting of $\pi_1, \pi_2, ..., \pi_K$. We then find from Eq. (11.22) that, after rearranging terms,

$$\left[\sum_{j=1}^{K} \pi_j^{(0)} - 1 \right] \boldsymbol{\pi} = \mathbf{0}$$

Since, by definition, $\sum_{j=1}^{K} \pi_j^{(0)} = 1$, this condition is satisfied by the vector $\boldsymbol{\pi}$ independent of the initial distribution.

We may now state the *ergodicity theorem* for Markov chains as follows (Feller, 1950; Ash, 1965):

Let an ergodic Markov chain with states $x_1, x_2, ..., x_K$ and stochastic matrix $\mathbf{P} = \{p_{ij}\}$ be irreducible. The chain then has a unique stationary distribution to which it converges from any *initial state; that is, there is a unique set of numbers $\{\pi_j\}_{j=1}^K$ such that*

1. $\lim\limits_{n\to\infty} p_{ij}^{(n)} = \pi_j$ for all i $\hspace{3cm}$ (11.24)

2. $\pi_j > 0$ for all j $\hspace{4.5cm}$ (11.25)

3. $\sum\limits_{j=1}^K \pi_j = 1$ $\hspace{5.5cm}$ (11.26)

4. $\pi_j = \sum\limits_{i=1}^K \pi_i p_{ij}$ for $j = 1, 2, ..., K$ $\hspace{2.5cm}$ (11.27)

Conversely, suppose that the Markov chain is irreducible and aperiodic and that there exist numbers $\{\pi_j\}_{j=1}^K$ satisfying Eqs. (11.25) through (11.27). Then the chain is ergodic, the π_j are given by Eq. (11.24), and the mean recurrence time of state j is $1/\pi_j$.

The probability distribution $\{\pi_j\}_{j=1}^K$ is called an *invariant*, or *stationary*, *distribution*. It is so called because it persists forever once it is established. In light of the ergodicity theorem, we may thus make the following two-part statement:

1. Starting from an arbitrary initial distribution, the transition probabilities of a Markov chain will converge to a stationary distribution provided that such a distribution exists.

2. The stationary distribution of the Markov chain is completely independent of the initial distribution if the chain is ergodic.

EXAMPLE 1   An Ergodic Markov Chain

Consider a Markov chain whose *state-transition diagram* is depicted in Fig. 11.2. The chain has two states x_1 and x_2. The stochastic matrix of the chain is

$$\mathbf{P} = \begin{bmatrix} \dfrac{1}{4} & \dfrac{3}{4} \\[2mm] \dfrac{1}{2} & \dfrac{1}{2} \end{bmatrix}$$

which satisfies the conditions of Eqs. (11.14) and (11.15).
    Suppose the initial condition is

$$\boldsymbol{\pi}^{(0)} = \begin{bmatrix} \dfrac{1}{6} & \dfrac{5}{6} \end{bmatrix}$$

FIGURE 11.2   State-transition diagram of Markov chain for Example 1: The states x_1 and x_2 may be identified as up-to-date and behind, respectively.

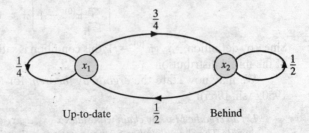

From Eq. (11.21), we find that the state distribution vector at time $n = 1$ is

$$\boldsymbol{\pi}^{(1)} = \boldsymbol{\pi}^{(0)}\mathbf{P}$$

$$= \begin{bmatrix} \dfrac{1}{6} & \dfrac{5}{6} \end{bmatrix} \begin{bmatrix} \dfrac{1}{4} & \dfrac{3}{4} \\ \dfrac{1}{2} & \dfrac{1}{2} \end{bmatrix}$$

$$= \begin{bmatrix} \dfrac{11}{24} & \dfrac{13}{24} \end{bmatrix}$$

Raising the stochastic matrix $\mathbf{P}$ to power $n = 2, 3,$ and 4, we have

$$\mathbf{P}^2 = \begin{bmatrix} 0.4375 & 0.5625 \\ 0.3750 & 0.6250 \end{bmatrix}$$

$$\mathbf{P}^3 = \begin{bmatrix} 0.4001 & 0.5999 \\ 0.3999 & 0.6001 \end{bmatrix}$$

$$\mathbf{P}^4 = \begin{bmatrix} 0.4000 & 0.6000 \\ 0.4000 & 0.6000 \end{bmatrix}$$

Thus, $\pi_1 = 0.4000$ and $\pi_2 = 0.6000$. In this example, convergence to the stationary distribution is accomplished essentially in $n = 4$ iterations. With both π_1 and π_2 being greater than zero, both states are positive recurrent, and the chain is therefore irreducible. Note also that the chain is aperiodic, since the greatest common divisor of all integers $n \geq 1$ such that $(\mathbf{P}^n)_{jj} > 0$ is equal to 1. We therefore conclude that the Markov chain of Fig. 11.2 is ergodic. ∎

EXAMPLE 2   An Ergodic Markov Chain with Stationary Distribution

Consider a Markov chain with a stochastic matrix, some of whose elements are zero, as shown by

$$\mathbf{P} = \begin{bmatrix} 0 & 0 & 1 \\ \dfrac{1}{3} & \dfrac{1}{6} & \dfrac{1}{2} \\ \dfrac{3}{4} & \dfrac{1}{4} & 0 \end{bmatrix}$$

The state transition diagram of the chain is depicted in Fig. 11.3.

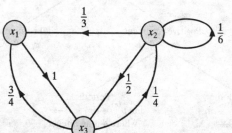

FIGURE 11.3   State-transition diagram of Markov chain for Example 2.

By applying Eq. (11.27), we obtain the following set of simultaneous equations:

$$\pi_1 = \frac{1}{3}\pi_2 + \frac{3}{4}\pi_3$$

$$\pi_2 = \frac{1}{6}\pi_2 + \frac{1}{4}\pi_3$$

$$\pi_3 = \pi_1 + \frac{1}{2}\pi_2$$

By solving these equations for π_1, π_2, and π_3, we get

$$\pi_1 = 0.3953$$

$$\pi_2 = 0.1395$$

$$\pi_3 = 0.4652$$

The given Markov chain is ergodic with its stationary distribution defined by π_1, π_2, and π_3. ∎

Classification of States

On the basis of the material presented in this section, we may develop a summary of the classes to which a state can belong as shown in Fig. 11.4 (Feller, 1950; Leon-Garcia, 1994). This figure also includes the associated long-term behavior of the state.

Principle of Detailed Balance

This principle is commonly used in statistical mechanics. In words, the *principle of detailed balance* asserts the following:

> *At thermal equilibrium, the rate of occurrence of any transition equals the corresponding rate of occurrence of the inverse transition, as shown by*

$$\pi_i p_{ij} = \pi_j p_{ji} \tag{11.28}$$

A Markov chain that satisfies the principle of detailed balance is said to be *reversible*.

FIGURE 11.4   Classification of the states of a Markov chain and their associated long-term *behavior*.

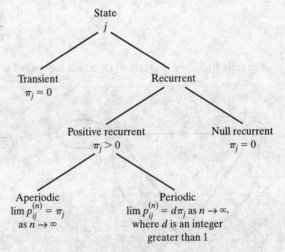

For an illustrative application of this principle, we will use it to derive the relation of Eq. (11.27), which is the definition of a *stationary distribution*. To this end, we may manipulate the summation on the right-hand side of this equation as follows:

$$\sum_{i=1}^{K} \pi_i p_{ij} = \sum_{i=1}^{K} \left(\frac{\pi_i}{\pi_j} p_{ij} \right) \pi_j$$

$$= \sum_{i=1}^{K} (p_{ji}) \pi_j$$

$$= \pi_j$$

In the second line of this expression, we made use of the principle of detailed balance, and in the last line we made use of the fact that the transition probabilities of a Markov chain satisfy the following condition (see Eq. (11.15), with the roles of i and j interchanged):

$$\sum_{i=1}^{K} p_{ji} = 1 \qquad \text{for all } j$$

From this discussion, it follows that the principle of detailed balance implies that the distribution $\{\pi_j\}$ is a stationary distribution. Insofar as a stationary distribution is concerned, the principle of detailed balance is therefore much stronger than Eq. (11.27), in the sense that it is sufficient, but not necessary, for the existence of a stationary distribution.

11.4 METROPOLIS ALGORITHM

Now that we understand the composition of a Markov chain, we will use it to formulate a stochastic algorithm for simulating the evolution of a physical system to thermal equilibrium. The algorithm is called the *Metropolis algorithm* (Metropolis et al., 1953). It is a modified Monte Carlo method, introduced in the early days of scientific computation for the stochastic simulation of a collection of atoms in equilibrium at a given temperature.

Because it is a modified Monte Carlo method, the Metropolis algorithm is commonly referred to as a *Markov chain Monte Carlo (MCMC) method*. In this context, we may formally state the following definition (Robert and Casella, 1999):

> *A Markov Chain Monte Carlo method for the simulation of an unknown probability distribution is any method that produces an ergodic Markov chain whose own stationary distribution is the unknown distribution.*

The Metropolis algorithm fits this definition perfectly, and so does a generalization of it: the Metropolis–Hastings algorithm.[3]

Statistical Analysis of the Metropolis Algorithm

Suppose that the random variable X_n, representing an arbitrary Markov chain, is in state x_i at time n. We randomly generate a new state x_j, representing a realization of another random variable Y_n. It is assumed that the generation of this new state satisfies the symmetry condition

$$P(Y_n = x_j | X_n = x_i) = P(Y_n = x_i | X_n = x_j)$$

Let ΔE denote the energy difference resulting from the transition of the system from state $X_n = x_i$ to state $Y_n = x_j$. Given ΔE, we proceed as follows:

1. If the energy difference ΔE is negative, the transition leads to a state with lower energy, and the transition is accepted. The new state is then accepted as the starting point for the next step of the algorithm; that is, we put $X_{n+1} = Y_n$.

2. If, on the other hand, the energy difference ΔE is positive, the algorithm proceeds in a probabilistic manner at that point. First, we select a random number ξ uniformly distributed in the range $[0, 1]$. If $\xi < \exp(-\Delta E/T)$, where T is the operating temperature, the transition is accepted and we put $X_{n+1} = Y_n$. Otherwise, the transition is rejected and we put $X_{n+1} = X_n$; that is, the old configuration is reused for the next step of the algorithm.

Choice of Transition Probabilities

Let an arbitrary Markov chain have a *proposed set of transition probabilities* denoted by τ_{ij}, which satisfy three conditions:

1. *Nonnegativity:*

$$\tau_{ij} \geq 0 \qquad \text{for all } i, j$$

2. *Normalization:*

$$\sum_j \tau_{ij} = 1 \qquad \text{for all } i$$

3. *Symmetry:*

$$\tau_{ji} = \tau_{ji} \qquad \text{for all } i, j$$

Let π_i denote the steady-state probability that the Markov chain is in state x_i, $i = 1, 2, ..., K$. We may then use the symmetric τ_{ij} and the probability distribution ratio π_j / π_i, to be defined, to formulate the *desired set of transition probabilities* as follows (Beckerman, 1997):

$$p_{ij} = \begin{cases} \tau_{ij}\left(\dfrac{\pi_j}{\pi_i}\right) & \text{for } \dfrac{\pi_j}{\pi_i} < 1 \\[2ex] \tau_{ij} & \text{for } \dfrac{\pi_j}{\pi_i} \geq 1 \end{cases} \qquad (11.29)$$

To ensure that the transition probabilities are normalized to unity, we introduce an additional definition for the probability of no transition, given as

$$p_{ii} = \tau_{ii} + \sum_{j \neq 1} \tau_{ij}\left(1 - \frac{\pi_j}{\pi_i}\right)$$

$$= 1 - \sum_{j \neq i} \alpha_{ij}\tau_{ij} \qquad (11.30)$$

where α_{ij} is the *moving probability* defined by

$$\alpha_{ij} = \min\left(1, \frac{\pi_j}{\pi_i}\right) \tag{11.31}$$

The only outstanding requirement is determining how to choose the ratio π_j/π_i. To cater to this requirement, we choose the probability distribution to which we want the Markov chain to converge to be a Gibbs distribution, as shown by

$$\pi_j = \frac{1}{Z}\exp\left(-\frac{E_j}{T}\right)$$

in which case the probability distribution ratio π_j/π_i takes the simple form

$$\frac{\pi_j}{\pi_i} = \exp\left(-\frac{\Delta E}{T}\right) \tag{11.32}$$

where

$$\Delta E = E_j - E_i \tag{11.33}$$

By using the ratio of probability distributions, we have eliminated dependence on the partition function Z.

By construction, the transition probabilities are all nonnegative and normalized to unity, as required by Eqs. (11.14) and (11.15). Moreover, they satisfy the principle of detailed balance defined by Eq. (11.28). This principle is a sufficient condition for thermal equilibrium. To demonstrate that the principle of detailed balance is indeed satisfied, we offer the following considerations:

Case 1: $\Delta E < 0$. Suppose that in going from state x_i to state x_j, the energy change ΔE is negative. From Eq. (11.32), we find that $(\pi_j/\pi_i) > 1$, so the use of Eq. (11.29) yields

$$\pi_i p_{ij} = \pi_i \tau_{ij} = \pi_i \tau_{ji}$$

and

$$\pi_j p_{ji} = \pi_j\left(\frac{\pi_i}{\pi_j}\tau_{ji}\right) = \pi_i \tau_{ji}$$

Hence, the principle of detailed balance is satisfied for $\Delta E < 0$.

Case 2: $\Delta E > 0$. Suppose next that the energy change ΔE in going from state x_i to state x_j is positive. In this case, we find that $(\pi_j/\pi_i) < 1$, and the use of Eq. (11.29) yields

$$\pi_i p_{ij} = \pi_i\left(\frac{\pi_j}{\pi_i}\tau_{ij}\right) = \pi_j \tau_{ij} = \pi_j \tau_{ji}$$

and

$$\pi_j p_{ji} = \pi_i p_{ij}$$

Here again, we see that the principle of detailed balance is satisfied.

To complete the picture, we need to clarify the use of the proposed set of transition probabilities denoted by τ_{ij}. These transition probabilities are in fact the probabilistic model of the random step in the Metropolis algorithm. From the description of the algorithm presented earlier, we recall that the random step is followed by a random decision. We may therefore conclude that the transition probabilities p_{ij} defined in Eqs. (11.29) and (11.30) in terms of the proposed transition probabilities τ_{ij} and the steady-state probabilities π_j are indeed the correct choice for the Metropolis algorithm.

We therefore conclude that the Metropolis algorithm generates a Markov chain,[4] the transition probabilities of which do indeed converge to a unique and stable Gibbs distribution (Beckerman, 1997).

11.5 SIMULATED ANNEALING

Consider next the problem of finding a low-energy system whose states are ordered in a Markov chain. From Eq. (11.11), we observe that as the temperature T approaches zero, the free energy F of the system approaches the average energy $<E>$. With $F \to <E>$, we observe from the principle of minimal free energy that the Gibbs distribution, which is the stationary distribution of the Markov chain, collapses on the global minima of the average energy $<E>$ as $T \to 0$. In other words, low-energy ordered states are strongly favored at low temperatures. These observations prompt us to raise the question, Why not simply apply the Metropolis algorithm for generating a population of configurations representative of the stochastic system at very low temperatures? We do not advocate the use of such a strategy because the rate of convergence of the Markov chain to thermal equilibrium is extremely slow at very low temperatures. Rather, the preferred method for improved computational efficiency is to operate the stochastic system at a high temperature where convergence to equilibrium is fast, and then maintain the system at equilibrium as the temperature is carefully lowered. That is, we use a combination of two related ingredients:

1. a schedule that determines the rate at which the temperature is lowered;
2. an algorithm—exemplified by the Metropolis algorithm—that iteratively finds the equilibrium distribution at each new temperature in the schedule by using the final state of the system at the previous temperature as the starting point for the new temperature.

The twofold scheme that we have just described is the essence of a widely used stochastic relaxation technique known as *simulated annealing*[5] (Kirkpatrick et al., 1983). The technique derives its name from analogy with an annealing process in physics and chemistry in which we start the process at high temperature and then lower the temperature slowly while maintaining thermal equilibrium.

The primary objective of simulated annealing is to find the global minimum of a cost function that characterizes large and complex systems. As such, this technique provides a powerful tool for solving nonconvex optimization problems, motivated by the following simple idea:

> When optimizing a very large and complex system (i.e., a system with many degrees of freedom), instead of always going downhill, try to go downhill most of the time.

Simulated annealing differs from conventional iterative optimization algorithms in two important respects:

1. The algorithm need not get stuck, since transition out of a local minimum is always possible when the system operates at a nonzero temperature.
2. Simulated annealing is *adaptive* in that gross features of the final state of the system are seen at higher temperatures, while fine details of the state appear at lower temperatures.

Annealing Schedule

As already mentioned, the Metropolis algorithm is the basis for the simulated-annealing process, in the course of which the temperature T is decreased slowly. That is, the temperature T plays the role of a *control parameter*. The simulated-annealing process will converge to a configuration of minimal energy provided that the temperature is decreased no faster than logarithmically. Unfortunately, such an annealing schedule is extremely slow— too slow to be of practical use. In practice, we must resort to a *finite-time approximation* of the asymptotic convergence of the algorithm. The price paid for the approximation is that the algorithm is no longer guaranteed to find a global minimum with a probability of one. Nevertheless, the resulting approximate form of the algorithm is capable of producing near-optimal solutions for many practical applications.

To implement a finite-time approximation of the simulated-annealing algorithm, we must specify a set of parameters governing the convergence of the algorithm. These parameters are combined in a so-called *annealing schedule*, or *cooling schedule*. The annealing schedule specifies a finite sequence of values of the temperature and a finite number of transitions attempted at each value of the temperature. The annealing schedule due to Kirkpatrick et al. (1983) specifies the parameters of interest as follows[6]:

1. *Initial Value of the Temperature.* The initial value T_0 of the temperature is chosen high enough to ensure that virtually all proposed transitions are accepted by the simulated-annealing algorithm
2. *Decrement of the Temperature.* Ordinarily, the cooling is performed *exponentially*, and the changes made in the value of the temperature are small. In particular, the *decrement function* is defined by

$$T_k = \alpha T_{k-1}, \qquad k = 1, 2, \ldots \tag{11.34}$$

where α is a constant smaller than, but close to, unity. Typical values of α lie between 0.8 and 0.99. At each temperature, enough transitions are attempted so that there are 10 *accepted* transitions per experiment, on average.
3. *Final Value of the Temperature.* The system is fixed and annealing stops if the desired number of acceptances is not achieved at three successive temperatures.

The latter criterion may be refined by requiring that the *acceptance ratio*, defined as the number of accepted transitions divided by the number of proposed transitions, is smaller than a prescribed value (Johnson et al., 1989).

TABLE 11.1   Correspondence between Statistical Physics and
            Combinatorial Optimization

Statistical physics	Combinatorial optimization
Sample	Problem instance
State (configuration)	Configuration
Energy	Cost function
Temperature	Control parameter
Ground-state energy	Minimal cost
Ground-state configuration	Optimal configuration

Simulated Annealing for Combinatorial Optimization

Simulated annealing is particularly well suited for solving combinatorial-optimization problems. The objective of *combinatorial optimization* is to minimize the cost function of a finite, discrete system characterized by a large number of possible solutions. Essentially, simulated annealing uses the Metropolis algorithm to generate a sequence of solutions by invoking an analogy between a physical many-particle system and a combinatorial-optimization problem.

In simulated annealing, we interpret the energy E_i in the Gibbs distribution of Eq. (11.5) as a numerical cost and the temperature T as a control parameter. The numerical cost assigns to each configuration in the combinatorial-optimization problem a scalar value that describes how desirable that particular configuration is to the solution. The next issue to be considered in the simulated-annealing procedure is how to identify configurations and generate new configurations from previous ones in a local manner. This is where the Metropolis algorithm performs its role. We may thus summarize the correspondence between the terminology of statistical physics and that of combinatorial optimization as shown in Table 11.1 (Beckerman, 1997).

11.6   GIBBS SAMPLING

Like the Metropolis algorithm, the *Gibbs sampler*[7] generates a Markov chain with the Gibbs distribution as the equilibrium distribution. However, the transition probabilities associated with the Gibbs sampler are nonstationary (Geman and Geman, 1984). In the final analysis, the choice between the Gibbs sampler and the Metropolis algorithm is based on technical details of the problem at hand.

To proceed with a description of this sampling scheme, consider a K-dimensional random vector $\mathbf{X}$ made up of the components $X_1, X_2, ..., X_K$. Suppose that we have knowledge of the conditional distribution of X_k, given values of all the other components of $\mathbf{X}$ for $k = 1, 2, ..., K$. The problem we wish to address is how to obtain a numerical estimate of the marginal density of the random variable X_k for each k. The Gibbs sampler proceeds by generating a value for the conditional distribution for each component of the random vector $\mathbf{X}$, given the values of all other components of $\mathbf{X}$. Specifically, starting from an arbitrary configuration $\{x_1(0), x_2(0), ..., x_K(0)\}$, we make the following drawings on the first iteration of Gibbs sampling:

$x_1(1)$ is drawn from the distribution of X_1, given $x_2(0), x_3(0), ..., x_K(0)$.

$x_2(1)$ is drawn from the distribution of X_2, given $x_1(1), x_3(0), ..., x_K(0)$.

$\vdots$

$x_k(1)$ is drawn from the distribution of X_k, given $x_1(1), ..., x_{k-1}(1), x_{k+1}(0), ..., x_K(0)$.

$\vdots$

$x_K(1)$ is drawn from the distribution of X_K, given $x_1(1), x_2(1), ..., x_{K-1}(1)$.

We proceed in this same manner on the second iteration and every other iteration of the sampling scheme. The following two points should be carefully noted:

1. Each component of the random vector **X** is "visited" in the natural order, with the result that a total of K new variates are generated on each iteration.
2. The new value of component X_{k-1} is used immediately when a new value of X_k is drawn for $k = 2, 3, ..., K$.

From this discussion, we see that the Gibbs sampler is an *iterative adaptive* scheme. After n iterations of its use, we arrive at the K variates $X_1(n), X_2(n), ..., X_K(n)$. Under mild conditions, the following three theorems hold for Gibbs sampling (Geman and Geman, 1984; Gelfand and Smith, 1990):

1. *Convergence theorem. The random variable $X_k(n)$ converges in distribution to the true probability distributions of X_k for $k = 1, 2, ..., K$ as n approaches infinity; that is,*

$$\lim_{n \to \infty} P(X_k^{(n)} \leq x | x_k(0)) = P_{X_k}(x) \qquad \text{for } k = 1, 2, ..., K \qquad (11.35)$$

where $P_{X_k}(x)$ is marginal cumulative distribution function of X_k.

In fact, a stronger result is proven in Geman and Geman (1984). Specifically, rather than requiring that each component of the random vector **X** be visited in repetitions of the natural order, convergence of Gibbs sampling still holds under an arbitrary visiting scheme provided that this scheme does not depend on the values of the variables and that each component of **X** is visited on an "infinitely often" basis.

2. *Rate-of-convergence theorem. The joint cumulative distribution of the random variables $X_1(n), X_2(n), ..., X_K(n)$ converges to the true joint cumulative distribution of $X_1, X_2, ..., X_K$ at a geometric rate in n.*

This theorem assumes that the components of **X** are visited in the natural order. When, however, an arbitrary, but "infinitely often," visiting approach is used, then a minor adjustment to the rate of convergence is required.

3. *Ergodic theorem. For any measurable function g of the random variables $X_1, X_2, ..., X_K$ whose expectation exists, we have*

$$\lim_{n \to \infty} \frac{1}{n} \sum_{i=1}^{n} g(X_1(i), X_2(i), ..., X_K(i)) \to \mathbb{E}[g(X_1, X_2, ..., X_K)] \qquad (11.36)$$

with probability 1 *(i.e., almost surely).*

The ergodic theorem tells us how to use the output of the Gibbs sampler to obtain numerical estimations of the desired marginal densities.

Gibbs sampling is used in the Boltzmann machine to sample from distributions over hidden neurons; this stochastic machine is discussed in the next section. In the context of a stochastic machine using binary units (e.g., the Boltzmann machine), it is noteworthy that the Gibbs sampler is exactly the same as a variant of the Metropolis algorithm. In the standard form of the Metropolis algorithm, we go downhill with a probability of unity. In contrast, in the alternative form of the Metropolis algorithm, we go downhill with a probability equal to unity minus the exponential of the energy gap (i.e., the complement of the uphill rule). In other words, if a change lowers the energy E or leaves it unchanged, that change is accepted; if the change increases the energy, it is accepted with probability $\exp(-\Delta E)$ and is rejected otherwise, with the old state then being repeated (Neal, 1993).

11.7 BOLTZMANN MACHINE

The *Boltzmann machine* is a stochastic binary machine whose composition consists of stochastic neurons. A *stochastic neuron* resides in one of two possible states in a probabilistic manner. These two states may be designated as $+1$ for the "on" state and -1 for the "off" state or as 1 and 0, respectively. We will adopt the former designation. Another distinguishing feature of the Boltzmann machine is the use of *symmetric synaptic connections* between its neurons. The use of this form of synaptic connections is also motivated by statistical physics considerations.

The stochastic neurons of the Boltzmann machine are partitioned into two functional groups, *visible* and *hidden*, as depicted in Fig. 11.5. The visible neurons[8] provide an interface between the network and the environment in which it operates. During the training phase of the network, the visible neurons are all *clamped* onto specific states determined by the environment. The hidden neurons, on the other hand, always operate freely; they are used to explain underlying constraints contained in the environmental input vectors. The hidden neurons accomplish this task by capturing higher-order

FIGURE 11.5 Architectural graph of Botzmann machine; K is the number of visible neurons, and L is the number of hidden neurons. The distinguishing features of the machine are:
1. The connections between the visible and hidden neurons are symmetric.
2. The symmetric connections are extended to the visible and hidden neurons.

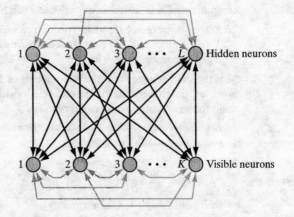

statistical correlations in the clamping vectors. The network described here represents a special case of the Boltzmann machine. It may be viewed as an unsupervised-learning procedure for modeling a probability distribution that is specified by clamping patterns onto the visible neurons with appropriate probabilities. By so doing, the network can perform *pattern completion*. Specifically, when a partial information-bearing vector is clamped onto a subset of the visible neurons, the network performs completion on the remaining visible neurons, provided that it has learned the training distribution properly.

The primary goal of Boltzmann learning is to produce a neural network that correctly models input patterns according to the Boltzmann distribution. In applying this form of learning, two assumptions are made:

1. Each environmental input vector (pattern) persists long enough to permit the network to reach *thermal equilibrium*.

2. There is *no* structure in the sequential order in which the environmental vectors are clamped onto the visible units of the network.

A particular set of synaptic weights is said to constitute a perfect model of the environmental structure if it leads to exactly the same probability distribution of the states of the visible units (when the network is running freely) as when these units are clamped by the environmental input vectors. In general, unless the number of hidden units is exponentially large compared with the number of visible units, it is impossible to achieve such a perfect model. If, however, the environment has a regular structure, and the network uses its hidden units to capture these regularities, it may achieve a good match to the environment with a manageable number of hidden units.

Gibbs Sampling and Simulated Annealing for the Boltzmann Machine

Let $\mathbf{x}$ denote the state vector of the Boltzmann machine, with its component x_i denoting the state of neuron i. The state $\mathbf{x}$ represents a realization of a random vector $\mathbf{X}$. The synaptic connection from neuron i to neuron j is denoted by w_{ji}, with

$$w_{ji} = w_{ij} \qquad \text{for all } i, j \tag{11.37}$$

and

$$w_{ii} = 0 \qquad \text{for all } i \tag{11.38}$$

Equation (11.37) describes symmetry, and Eq. (11.38) emphasizes the absence of self-feedback. The use of a bias is permitted by using the weight w_{j0} from a fictitious node maintained at $+1$ and by connecting it to neuron j for all j.

From an analogy with thermodynamics, the energy of the Boltzmann machine is defined as follows[9]:

$$E(\mathbf{x}) = -\frac{1}{2} \sum_{i} \sum_{\substack{j \\ i \neq j}} w_{ji} x_i x_j \tag{11.39}$$

Invoking the Gibbs distribution of Eq. (11.5), we may define the probability that the network (assumed to be in equilibrium at temperature T) is in state $\mathbf{x}$ as

$$P(\mathbf{X} = \mathbf{x}) = \frac{1}{Z} \exp\left(-\frac{E(\mathbf{x})}{T}\right) \tag{11.40}$$

where Z is the partition function.

To simplify the presentation, define the single event A and joint events B and C as follows:

$A: X_j = x_j$

$B: \{X_i = x_i\}_{i=1}^K$ with $i \neq j$

$C: \{X_i = x_i\}_{i=1}^K$

In effect, the joint event B excludes A, and the joint event C includes both A and B. The probability of B is the marginal probability of C with respect to A. Hence, using Eqs. (11.39) and (11.40), we may write

$$\begin{aligned}P(C) &= P(A, B) \\ &= \frac{1}{Z} \exp\left(\frac{1}{2T} \sum_i \sum_{\substack{j \\ i \neq j}} w_{ji} x_i x_j\right)\end{aligned} \tag{11.41}$$

and

$$\begin{aligned}P(B) &= \sum_A P(A, B) \\ &= \frac{1}{Z} \sum_{x_j} \exp\left(\frac{1}{2T} \sum_i \sum_{\substack{j \\ i \neq j}} w_{ji} x_i x_j\right)\end{aligned} \tag{11.42}$$

The exponent in Eqs. (11.41) and (11.42) may be expressed as the sum of two components, one involving x_j and the other being independent of x_j. The component involving x_j is given by

$$\frac{x_j}{2T} \sum_{\substack{i \\ i \neq j}} w_{ji} x_i$$

Accordingly, by setting $x_j = x_i = \pm 1$, we may express the conditional probability of A given B, as follows:

$$\begin{aligned}P(A|B) &= \frac{P(A, B)}{P(B)} \\ &= \frac{1}{1 + \exp\left(-\dfrac{x_j}{T} \displaystyle\sum_{\substack{i \\ i \neq j}} w_{ji} x_i\right)}\end{aligned}$$

That is, we may write

$$P\left(X_j = x \mid \{X_i = x_i\}_{i=1, i \neq j}^{K}\right) = \varphi\left(\frac{x}{T} \sum_{\substack{i \\ i \neq j}}^{K} w_{ji} x_i\right) \qquad (11.43)$$

where $\varphi(\cdot)$ is the logistic function

$$\varphi(v) = \frac{1}{1 + \exp(-v)} \qquad (11.44)$$

Note that although x varies between -1 and $+1$, the whole argument $v = \frac{x}{T}\sum_{i \neq j} w_{ji} x_i$ for large K may vary between $-\infty$ and $+\infty$, as depicted in Fig. 11.6. Note also that in deriving Eq. (11.43), the need for the partition function Z has been eliminated. This condition is highly desirable, since a direct computation of Z is infeasible for a network of large complexity.

The use of Gibbs sampling exhibits the joint distribution $P(A, B)$. Basically, as explained in Section 11.6, this stochastic simulation starts with the network assigned an arbitrary state, and the neurons are all repeatedly visited in their natural order. On each visit, a new value for the state of each neuron is chosen in accordance with the probability distribution for that neuron, conditional on the values for the states of all other neurons in the network. Provided that the stochastic simulation is performed long enough, the network will reach thermal equilibrium at temperature T.

Unfortunately, the time taken to reach thermal equilibrium can be much too long. To overcome this difficulty, simulated annealing for a finite sequence of temperatures $T_0, T_1, ..., T_{\text{final}}$ is used, as explained in Section 11.5. Specifically, the temperature is initially set to the high value T_0, thereby permitting thermal equilibrium to be reached fast. Thereafter, the temperature T is gradually reduced to the final value T_{final}, at which point the neural states will have (hopefully) reached their desired marginal distributions.

Boltzmann Learning Rule

Since the Boltzmann machine is a stochastic machine, it is natural to look to probability theory for an appropriate index of performance. One such criterion is the *likelihood*

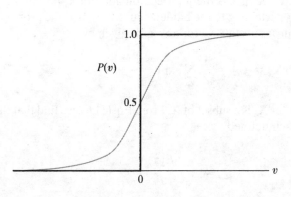

FIGURE 11.6   Sigmoid-shaped function $P(v)$.

function.[10] On this basis, the goal of Boltzmann learning is to maximize the likelihood function—or, equivalently, the log-likelihood function—in accordance with the *maximum-likelihood principle*; this principle was described in Chapter 10.

Let $\mathcal{T}$ denote a training sample drawn from the probability distribution of interest. It is assumed that the examples are all two-valued. Repetition of training examples is permitted in proportion to how common certain cases are known to occur. Let a subset of the state vector $\mathbf{x}$—say, $\mathbf{x}_\alpha$—denote the state of the visible neurons. The remaining part of the state vector $\mathbf{x}$—say, $\mathbf{x}_\beta$—represents the state of the hidden neurons. The state vectors $\mathbf{x}$, $\mathbf{x}_\alpha$, and $\mathbf{x}_\beta$ are realizations of the random vectors $\mathbf{X}$, $\mathbf{X}_\alpha$, and $\mathbf{X}_\beta$, respectively. There are two phases to the operation of the Boltzmann machine:

1. *Positive phase.* In this phase, the network operates in its clamped condition (i.e., under the direct influence of the training sample $\mathcal{T}$).

2. *Negative phase.* In this second phase, the network is allowed to run freely, and therefore with no environmental input.

Given the synaptic-weight vector $\mathbf{w}$ for the whole network, the probability that the visible neurons are in state $\mathbf{x}_\alpha$ is $P(\mathbf{X}_\alpha = \mathbf{x}_\alpha)$. With the many possible values of $\mathbf{x}_\alpha$ contained in the training sample $\mathcal{T}$ assumed to be statistically independent, the overall probability distribution is the factorial distribution $\Pi_{\mathbf{x}_\alpha \in \mathcal{T}} P(\mathbf{X}_\alpha = \mathbf{x}_\alpha)$. To formulate the log-likelihood function $L(\mathbf{w})$, we take the logarithm of this factorial distribution and treat $\mathbf{w}$ as the unknown parameter vector. We may thus write

$$
\begin{aligned}
L(\mathbf{w}) &= \log \prod_{\mathbf{x}_\alpha \in \mathcal{T}} P(\mathbf{X}_\alpha = \mathbf{x}_\alpha) \\
&= \sum_{\mathbf{x}_\alpha \in \mathcal{T}} \log P(\mathbf{X}_\alpha = \mathbf{x}_\alpha)
\end{aligned}
\tag{11.45}
$$

To formulate the expression for the marginal probability $P(\mathbf{X}_\alpha = \mathbf{x}_\alpha)$ in terms of the energy function $E(\mathbf{x})$, we follow two points:

1. The probability $P(\mathbf{X} = \mathbf{x})$ is equal to $\dfrac{1}{Z}\exp(-E(\mathbf{x})/T)$, in accordance with Eq. (11.40).

2. By definition, the state vector $\mathbf{x}$ is the joint combination of $\mathbf{x}_\alpha$ pertaining to the visible neurons and $\mathbf{x}_\beta$ pertaining to the hidden neurons. Hence, the probability of finding the visible neurons in state $\mathbf{x}_\alpha$, for any $\mathbf{x}_\beta$, is given by

$$
P(\mathbf{X}_\alpha = \mathbf{x}_\alpha) = \frac{1}{Z} \sum_{\mathbf{x}_\beta} \exp\left(-\frac{E(\mathbf{x})}{T}\right)
\tag{11.46}
$$

where the random vector $\mathbf{X}_\alpha$ is a subset of $\mathbf{X}$. From Eq. (11.6), we find that the partition function Z is itself defined by

$$
Z = \sum_{\mathbf{x}} \exp\left(-\frac{E(\mathbf{x})}{T}\right)
\tag{11.47}
$$

Thus, substituting Eqs. (11.46) and (11.47) into Eqs. (11.45), we obtain the desired expression for the log-likelihood function:

$$L(\mathbf{w}) = \sum_{\mathbf{x}_\alpha \in \mathcal{T}} \left(\log \sum_{\mathbf{x}_\beta} \exp\left(-\frac{E(\mathbf{x})}{T}\right) - \log \sum_{\mathbf{x}} \exp\left(-\frac{E(\mathbf{x})}{T}\right) \right) \quad (11.48)$$

The dependence on $\mathbf{w}$ is contained in the energy function $E(\mathbf{x})$, as shown in Eq. (11.39).

Differentiating $L(\mathbf{w})$ with respect to w_{ji} and using Eq. (11.39), we obtain the following result after some manipulation of terms (see Problem 11.9):

$$\frac{\partial L(\mathbf{w})}{\partial w_{ji}} = \frac{1}{T} \sum_{\mathbf{x}_\alpha \in \mathcal{T}} \left(\sum_{\mathbf{x}_\beta} P(\mathbf{X}_\beta = \mathbf{x}_\beta | \mathbf{X}_\alpha = \mathbf{x}_\alpha) x_j x_i - \sum_{\mathbf{x}} P(\mathbf{X} = \mathbf{x}) x_j x_i \right) \quad (11.49)$$

To simplify matters, we introduce two definitions:

1. $\rho_{ji}^+ = \langle x_j x_i \rangle^+$
$$= \sum_{\mathbf{x}_\alpha \in \mathcal{T}} \sum_{\mathbf{x}_\beta} P(\mathbf{X}_\beta = \mathbf{x}_\beta | \mathbf{X}_\alpha = \mathbf{x}_\alpha) x_j x_i \quad (11.50)$$

2. $\rho_{ji}^- = \langle x_j x_i \rangle^-$
$$= \sum_{\mathbf{x}_\alpha \in \mathcal{T}} \sum_{\mathbf{x}} P(\mathbf{X} = \mathbf{x}) x_j x_i \quad (11.51)$$

In a loose sense, we may view the first average, ρ_{ji}^+, as the mean firing rate, or *correlation*, between the states of neurons i and j when the network is operating in its clamped, or positive, phase. Similarly, we may view the second average, ρ_{ji}^-, as the *correlation* between the states of neurons i and j when the network is operating in its free-running, or negative, phase. With these definitions, we may simplify Eq. (11.49) to

$$\frac{\partial L(\mathbf{w})}{\partial w_{ji}} = \frac{1}{T}(\rho_{ji}^+ - \rho_{ji}^-) \quad (11.52)$$

The goal of Boltzmann learning is to maximize the log-likelihood function $L(\mathbf{w})$. We may use *gradient ascent* to achieve that goal by writing

$$\Delta w_{ji} = \epsilon \frac{\partial L(\mathbf{w})}{\partial w_{ji}}$$
$$= \eta(\rho_{ji}^+ - \rho_{ji}^-) \quad (11.53)$$

where η is a *learning-rate parameter*; it is defined in terms of ϵ, the constant introduced in the first line of Eq. (11.53), and the operating temperature T as

$$\eta = \frac{\epsilon}{T} \quad (11.54)$$

The gradient ascent rule of Eq. (11.53) is called the *Boltzmann learning rule*. The learning described here is performed in batch; that is, changes to the synaptic weights are made on the presentation of the entire training sample.

Summarizing Remarks

The simplicity of the Boltzmann learning rule described in Eq. (11.53) is attributed to the fact that only *locally available observations* are used under two different operating conditions of neurons, one being clamped and the other free running. Another interesting feature of the rule, which may come as a surprise, is that adjustment of the synaptic weight w_{ji} from neuron i to neuron j is independent of whether the two neurons are both visible, both hidden, whether they are both free running, or whether they are one of each. These desirable features of the Boltzmann machine stem from a key insight by Hinton and Sejnowski (1983, 1986) that ties the machine's abstract mathematical model to neural networks by combining two concepts:

- the Gibbs distribution for describing the stochasticity of neurons, and
- the statistical physics-based energy function of Eq. (11.39) for defining the Gibbs distribution.

However, from a practical perspective, we typically find that the learning process in the Boltzmann machine is very slow, particularly when the number of hidden neurons used in the machine is large. The reason for this undesirable behavior is that the machine takes a long time to reach an equilibrium distribution, which usually happens when the visible units are unclamped.

Nevertheless, over the years, interest has continued in the search for a stochastic machine that would share with the classical Boltzmann machine the capacity to learn probability distributions over binary vectors, but would also be capable of performing the following two functions:

1. Ignore the negative phase of the Boltzmann machine that is responsible for increased computation time, and find some other means for exercising control over the learning process.
2. Operate efficiently in densely connected networks.

In the next two sections, we describe a pair of stochastic machines that have tried to address these two practical issues in their own individual ways.

11.8   LOGISTIC BELIEF NETS

In the first generation of *logistic belief networks*, devised by Neal (1992), the symmetric connections of the Boltzmann machine are replaced with *direct* connections, forming an acyclic *graph*. It is for this reason that Neal's logistic belief net is also referred to as a *directed belief net*; hereafter, both terminologies will be used interchangeably. To be more specific, the network is of a multilayer kind, as illustrated in Fig. 11.7. The acyclic property of the network makes it easy to perform probabilistic calculations. In analogy with the classical Boltzmann machine, the network uses the logistic function of Eq. (11.43) to calculate the conditional probability of a neuron being active in response to its induced local field.

Let the random vector $\mathbf{X}$, consisting of the random variables $X_1, X_2, ..., X_n$, denote the behavior of a logistic belief network comprising N stochastic neurons. The *parents* of element X_j (i.e., the parents of node j in Fig. 11.7) in the vector $\mathbf{X}$ are defined by

$$pa(X_j) \subseteq \{X_1, X_2, ..., X_{j-1}\} \tag{11.55}$$

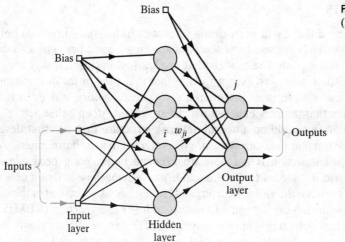

FIGURE 11.7   Directed
(logistic) belief network.

where $\{x_1, x_2, ..., x_j\}$ is the smallest subset of the random vector $\mathbf{X}$ that excites nodes; and for which the conditional probability

$$P(X_j = x_j | X_1 = x_1, ..., X_{j-1} = x_{j-1}) = P(X_j = x_j | pa(X_j)) \qquad (11.56)$$

Referring to Fig. 11.7, for example, node i is a parent of node j as there is a direct link from node i to node j. An important virtue of the logistic belief network is its ability to clearly exhibit the conditional dependencies of the underlying probabilistic model of the input data, with the probability that the jth neuron is active being defined by the logistic function where w_{ji} is the synaptic weight from neuron i to neuron j. This conditional probability depends on $pa(X_j)$ solely through a sum of weighted inputs. Thus, Eq. (11.56) provides the basis for the propagation of beliefs through the network.

Calculations of conditional probabilities are performed under two different *null* conditions:

1. $w_{ji} = 0$ for all X_i not belonging to $pa(X_j)$, which follows from the definition of a parent.
2. $w_{ji} = 0$ for $i \geq j$, which follows from the fact that the network is acyclic.

As with the Boltzmann machine, the learning rule of the logistic belief net is derived by maximizing the log-likelihood function $L(\mathbf{w})$ of Eq. (11.45), computed for the training sample $\mathcal{T}$. It turns out that this maximization is accomplished through the use of gradient ascent in probability space by defining the change in the synaptic weight w_{ji} as

$$\Delta w_{ji} = \eta \frac{\partial}{\partial w_{ji}} L(\mathbf{w})$$

where η is the learning-rate parameter, and the weight vector $\mathbf{w}$ is for the whole net.

However, a serious limitation of the logistic belief learning procedure is that when it is applied to densely connected networks, computation of the posterior distribution over the hidden neurons becomes computationally intractable, except in some simple applications such as linear models with additive Gaussian noise. As with the Boltzmann machine, Gibbs sampling can be used to approximate the posterior distribution, but the use of Gibbs sampling is considerably more complicated in a directed belief net.

11.9   DEEP BELIEF NETS

To overcome the difficulty in performing inference in logistic (directed) belief nets, Hinton et al. (2006) have devised a new way of learning logistic belief nets so that inference is easy to accomplish. The models that are learned in this new way are identical to those in logistic belief nets, except for the fact that they differ in their top layers, which (in the new way) form an undirected *associative memory*. Indeed, it is in virtue of this difference that the new belief networks are called "deep belief nets."

Deep belief nets build on a neural network structure that was first described in Smolensky (1986); at that time, this structure was referred to as a "harmonium." A distinctive feature of the harmonium is that there are no connections among the visible or hidden neurons; otherwise, it is similar to the classical Botzmann machine in that it uses symmetric connections between the visible neurons and hidden ones. On account of the difference cited, the harmonium has been renamed a *restricted Boltzmann machine* (RBM) in Hinton et al. (2006). At first sight, it may appear surprising to find that a symmetrically connected module such as a restricted Boltzmann machine could learn a directed generative model like a logistic belief net.

Since there are no connections between the hidden neurons in the RBM, and since the connections between the visible layer and the hidden layer are undirected, as depicted in Fig. 11.8, it follows that the states of the hidden neurons are *conditionally independent* of each other, given the visible states. Hence, the RBM is capable of extracting an unbiased sample from the posterior distribution, given a data vector clamped onto the visible neurons. This property of the RBM gives it a big advantage over the corresponding directed belief net (Hinton, 2007).

Another point of interest is that learning with an infinitely deep directed belief net, all of whose weight vectors are tied in the manner described in Fig. 11.9, is equivalent to learning with the single restricted Boltzmann machine shown in Fig. 11.8.

Maximum-Likelihood Learning in a Restricted Boltzmann Machine

The probability that a hidden neuron in the RBM is active is defined by the logistic function of Eq. (11.44). Let $\mathbf{x}_\alpha^{(0)}$ denote a data vector clamped onto the visible layer of the RBM at time 0. Then the learning process alternates back and forth between the following two operations:

- Updating the hidden states all in parallel, given the visible states
- Doing the same, but in reverse: updating the visible states all in parallel, given the hidden states

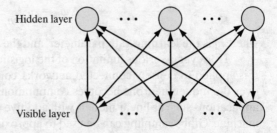

FIGURE 11.8   Neural structure of restricted Boltzmann machine (RBM). Contrasting this with that of Fig. 11.6, we see that unlike the Boltzmann machine, there are no connections among the visible neurons and the hidden neurons in the RBM.

Hidden layer

Visible layer

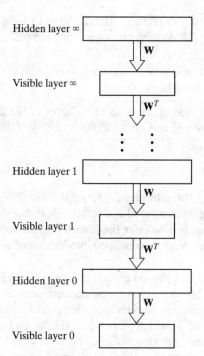

Hidden layer ∞

Visible layer ∞

Hidden layer 1

Visible layer 1

Hidden layer 0

Visible layer 0

FIGURE 11.9   Top-down learning, using logistic belief network of infinite depth.

Let $\mathbf{w}$ denote the weight vector for the whole net. Accordingly, we find that the gradient of the log-likelihood function $L(\mathbf{w})$ with respect to the weight w_{ji}, symmetrically connecting the visible neuron i and the hidden neuron j, is given by

$$\frac{\partial L(\mathbf{w})}{\partial w_{ji}} = \rho_{ji}^{(0)} - \rho_{ji}^{(\infty)} \tag{11.57}$$

where $\rho_{ji}^{(0)}$ and $\rho_{ji}^{(\infty)}$ are the *average correlations* between the states of neurons i and j at zero time and an infinitely long time, respectively (Hinton et al., 2006; Hinton, 2007). Except for insignificant changes in terminology, Eq. (11.57) is of the same mathematical form as that of Eq. (11.52) in classical Boltzmann learning. However, since we do not anneal in an RBM, Eq. (11.57) does not involve the use of temperature as a parameter.

Training of a Deep Belief Net

The training of a deep belief net progresses on a *layer-by-layer* basis, as follows (Hinton, et al., 2006; Hinton, 2007):

1. A restricted Boltzmann machine (RBM) is trained directly on the input data, thereby making it possible for the stochastic neurons in the hidden layer of the RBM to capture the important features that characterize the input data. Hereafter, we refer to this hidden layer as the *first hidden layer* of the deep belief net.

2. The activations of the trained features are then treated as "input data," which, in turn, are used to train a second RBM. In effect, the learning process just described

may be viewed as one of *learning features of features*. The origin of this idea may be traced to an early paper by Selfridge (1958), who proposed a pattern-recognition system called the "pandemonium."

3. The process of learning features of features is continued until a prescribed number of hidden layers in the deep belief net have been trained.

An important point to note here is the fact that every time a new layer of features is added to the deep belief net, a variational lower bound on the log-probability of the original training data is improved (Hinton et al., 2006).

Generative Model

Figure 11.10 pictures a deep belief net after three hidden layers of the net have been trained. The upward arrows indicate the weights computed as a result of learning the features of features. The function of these weights is to *infer* the binary feature values in each hidden layer of the belief net when a data vector is clamped into the neurons of the visible layer.

The *generative model* is identified by the unshaded arrows in Fig. 11.10. Note that the generative model does not include the bottom-up connections represented by the red shaded upward arrows; but most importantly, it does include the up-and-down connections in the top-level RBM (i.e., layers 2 and 3), which plays the dual role of a *bipartite associative memory*. When bottom-up training is performed, the top-level RBM learns from the hidden layer below. When top-down generation is performed, the top-level RBM is the initiator of generative modeling.

With the picture depicted in Fig. 11.10 in mind, data generation proceeds along the following lines:

1. An equilibrium sample is taken from the top-level RBM by the performance of alternating Gibbs sampling for many time-steps in the manner described in Fig. 11.11; this operation is permitted to go on for a sufficiently long time until equilibrium is reached.

2. A single top-down pass starting with the "visible" units of the top-level RBM is then used to stochastically pick the states of all the other hidden layers of the net.

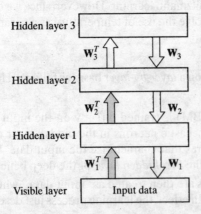

Hidden layer 3

W_3^T W_3

Hidden layer 2

W_2^T W_2

Hidden layer 1

W_1^T W_1

Visible layer   Input data

FIGURE 11.10 A hybrid generative model in which the two top layers form a restricted Boltzmann machine and the lower two layers form a directed model. The weights shown with red shaded arrows are *not* part of the generative model; they are used to infer the feature values given to the data, but they are not used for generating data.

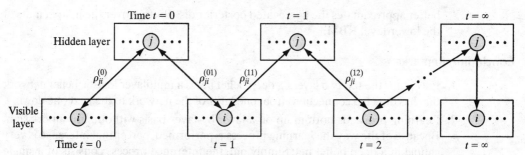

FIGURE 11.11 Illustrating the progression of alternating Gibbs sampling in an RBM. After sufficiently many steps, the visible and hidden vectors are sampled from the stationary distribution defined by the current parameters of the model.

Data generation is slow because, first of all, the top-level RBM must reach its equilibrium distribution. Fortunately, generation is not required for perceptual inference or learning.

Hybrid Learning Process

Each RBM in the deep belief net divides the task of modeling its own "visible" data into two subtasks, as portrayed in Fig. 11.12 (Hinton, 2007):

Subtask 1. The machine learns generative weights $\mathbf{w}$ that convert the aggregated posterior distribution over the hidden neurons into a close approximation to the data distribution over the visible neurons.

Subtask 2. The same set of weights, denoted by the vector $\mathbf{w}$, also define a prior distribution over the hidden state vectors. Sampling for this prior distribution requires extensive alternating Gibbs sampling, as illustrated in Fig. 11.11. However, it is the very existence of this complicated prior that is responsible for making inference so simple in an RBM. When the next RBM is learned under subtask 2, that particular RBM replaces the complicated prior (defined by $\mathbf{w}$) with a new prior that

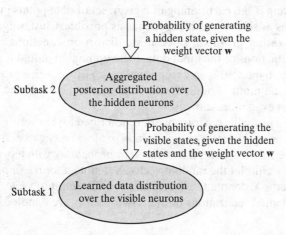

FIGURE 11.12 The task of modeling the sensory data is divided into two subtasks.

better approximates the aggregated posterior distribution over the hidden units of the lower-level RBM.

Concluding Remarks

1. Except for the top two layers, a deep belief net is a multilayer logistic belief network that has directed connections from one layer of the network to the next one down.

2. Learning proceeds bottom up on a layer-by-layer basis without any supervision. Because of the way the learning process is performed, perceptual inference is very simple in a deep belief net: Simply put, the inference process consists of a single bottom-up pass.

3. Deep belief nets provide the designer a great deal of freedom. The challenge for the designer is how to exploit this freedom in a creative way.

11.10   DETERMINISTIC ANNEALING

We now come to the final topic of the chapter, deterministic annealing. In Section 11.5, we discussed simulated annealing, which is a stochastic relaxation technique that provides a powerful method for solving nonconvex optimization problems. However, in the application of simulated annealing, care must be exercised in choosing the annealing schedule. In particular, a global minimum is achieved only if the temperature is decreased at a rate no faster than logarithmically. This requirement makes the use of simulated annealing impractical in many applications. Simulated annealing operates by making random moves on the energy surface (landscape). By contrast, in *deterministic annealing*, some form of randomness is incorporated into the energy or cost function itself, which is then deterministically optimized at a sequence of decreasing temperatures (Rose et al., 1990; Rose, 1998).

In what follows, we describe the idea of deterministic annealing in the context of an unsupervised-learning task: clustering.[11]

Clustering via Deterministic Annealing

The idea of clustering was discussed in Chapter 5. In light of the discussion presented therein, we say that clustering is the partitioning of a given set of data points into subgroups, each one of which is as similar or homogeneous as possible. Clustering is typically a nonconvex-optimization problem, since most distortion functions used in clustering are nonconvex functions of the input data. (The optimal manifold representation of data described in Chapter 10 is an exceptional case.) Moreover, a plot of the distortion function versus the input is riddled with local minima, making the task of finding the global minimum even more difficult.

In Rose (1991, 1998), a probabilistic framework is described for clustering by *randomization of the partition*, or equivalently, *randomization of the encoding rule*. The main principle used here is that each data point is *associated in probability* with a particular cluster (subgroup). To be specific, let the random vector $\mathbf{X}$ denote a *source (input) vector*, and let the random vector $\mathbf{Y}$ denote the best *reconstruction (output) vector* from a codebook of interest. Individual realizations of these two vectors are denoted by vectors $\mathbf{x}$ and $\mathbf{y}$, respectively.

To perform clustering, we need a distortion measure, denoted by $d(\mathbf{x}, \mathbf{y})$. It is assumed that $d(\mathbf{x}, \mathbf{y})$ satisfies two desirable properties:

1. It is a convex function of $\mathbf{y}$ for all $\mathbf{x}$.
2. It is finite whenever its two arguments $\mathbf{x}$ and $\mathbf{y}$ are both finite.

These two mild properties are satisfied, for example, by the squared Euclidean distortion measure:

$$d(\mathbf{x}, \mathbf{y}) = \|\mathbf{x} - \mathbf{y}\|^2 \tag{11.58}$$

which was also used in Chapters 5 and 10. The *expected distortion* for the randomized pattern is defined by

$$D = \sum_{\mathbf{x}} \sum_{\mathbf{y}} P(\mathbf{X} = \mathbf{x}, \mathbf{Y} = \mathbf{y}) d(\mathbf{x}, \mathbf{y}) \tag{11.59}$$

$$= \sum_{\mathbf{x}} P(\mathbf{X} = \mathbf{x}) \sum_{\mathbf{y}} P(\mathbf{Y} = \mathbf{y}|\mathbf{X} = \mathbf{x}) d(\mathbf{x}, \mathbf{y})$$

where $P(\mathbf{X} = \mathbf{x}, \mathbf{Y} = \mathbf{y})$ is the probability of the joint event $\mathbf{X} = \mathbf{x}$ and $\mathbf{Y} = \mathbf{y}$. In the second line of Eq. (11.59), we have used the formula for the probability of a joint event:

$$P(\mathbf{X} = \mathbf{x}, \mathbf{Y} = \mathbf{y}) = P(\mathbf{Y} = \mathbf{y}|\mathbf{X} = \mathbf{x}) P(\mathbf{X} = \mathbf{x}) \tag{11.60}$$

The conditional probability $P(\mathbf{Y} = \mathbf{y}|\mathbf{X} = \mathbf{x})$ is referred to as the *association probability*—that is, the probability of associating the code vector $\mathbf{y}$ with the source vector $\mathbf{x}$.

The expected distortion D is traditionally minimized with respect to the free parameters of the clustering model: the reconstruction vector $\mathbf{y}$ and the association probability $P(\mathbf{Y} = \mathbf{y}|\mathbf{X} = \mathbf{x})$. This form of minimization produces a "hard" clustering solution—hard in the sense that a source vector $\mathbf{x}$ is assigned to the nearest code vector $\mathbf{y}$. In deterministic annealing, on the other hand, the optimization problem is reformulated as that of seeking the probability distribution that minimizes the expected distortion, *subject to a specified level of randomness*. For a principled measure of the level of randomness, we use the joint entropy, defined in the Shannon sense, by the following (see Section 10.2):

$$H(\mathbf{X}, \mathbf{Y}) = -\sum_{\mathbf{x}} \sum_{\mathbf{y}} P(\mathbf{X} = \mathbf{x}, \mathbf{Y} = \mathbf{y}) \log P(\mathbf{X} = \mathbf{x}, \mathbf{Y} = \mathbf{y}) \tag{11.61}$$

The constrained optimization of the expected distortion is then expressed as the minimization of the *Lagrangian*, defined by

$$F = D - TH \tag{11.62}$$

where T is treated as the Lagrange multiplier. From Eq. (11.62), we observe the following points:

- For large values of T, the joint entropy H is maximized.
- For small values of T, the expected distortion D is minimized, resulting in a hard (nonrandom) clustering solution.
- For intermediate values of T, the minimization of F provides a tradeoff between an increase in the entropy H and a reduction in the expected distortion D.

Most importantly, by comparing Eq. (11.62) with Eq. (11.11), we may identify the correspondence between the terms of the constrained-clustering optimization problem and the terms of statistical mechanics, as shown in Table 11.2. In light of this analogy, we henceforth refer to T as the temperature.

To develop further insight into the Lagrangian F, following the formula of Eq. (10.26), we decompose the joint entropy $H(\mathbf{X}, \mathbf{Y})$ into two terms:

$$H(\mathbf{X}, \mathbf{Y}) = H(\mathbf{X}) + H(\mathbf{Y}|\mathbf{X})$$

$H(\mathbf{X})$ is the *source entropy*, and $H(\mathbf{Y}|\mathbf{X})$ is the *conditional entropy* of the reconstruction vector $\mathbf{Y}$ given the source vector $\mathbf{X}$. The source entropy $H(\mathbf{X})$ is independent of clustering. Accordingly, we may drop the source entropy $H(\mathbf{X})$ from the definition of the Lagrangian F and thereby focus on the conditional entropy

$$H(\mathbf{Y}|\mathbf{X}) = -\sum_{\mathbf{x}} P(\mathbf{X} = \mathbf{x}) \sum_{\mathbf{y}} P(\mathbf{Y} = \mathbf{y}|\mathbf{X} = \mathbf{x})\log P(\mathbf{Y} = \mathbf{y}|\mathbf{X} = \mathbf{x}) \quad (11.63)$$

This expression highlights the role of the association probability $P(\mathbf{Y} = \mathbf{y}|\mathbf{X} = \mathbf{x})$. Hence, keeping in mind the correspondence between the constrained-clustering optimization problem and statistical physics, and invoking the principle of minimal free energy described in Section 11.2, we find that minimizing the Lagrangian F with respect to the association probabilities results in the Gibbs distribution

$$P(\mathbf{Y} = \mathbf{y}|\mathbf{X} = \mathbf{x}) = \frac{1}{Z_\mathbf{x}} \exp\left(-\frac{d(\mathbf{x}, \mathbf{y})}{T}\right) \quad (11.64)$$

where $Z_\mathbf{x}$ is the partition function for the problem at hand. It is defined by

$$Z_\mathbf{x} = \sum_{\mathbf{y}} \exp\left(-\frac{d(\mathbf{x}, \mathbf{y})}{T}\right) \quad (11.65)$$

As the temperature T approaches infinity, we find from Eq. (11.64) that the association probability approaches a uniform distribution. The implication of this statement is that at very high temperatures, each input vector is equally associated with all clusters. Such associations may be viewed as "extremely fuzzy." At the other extreme, as the temperature T approaches zero, the association probability approaches a delta function. Accordingly, at very low temperatures, the classification is hard, with each input sample being assigned to the nearest code vector with probability 1.

TABLE 11.2 Correspondence between Constrained-Clustering Optimization and Statistical Physics

Constrained-clustering optimization	Statistical physics
Lagrangian, F	Free energy, F
Expected distortion, D	Average energy, $<E>$
Joint entropy in the Shannon sense, H	Entropy, H
Lagrange multiplier, T	Temperature, T

To find the minimum value of the Lagrangian F, we substitute the Gibbs distribution of Eq. (11.64) into Eqs. (11.59) and (11.63) and then use the resulting expressions in the formula for the Lagrangian F in Eq. (11.62). The result obtained is as follows (see Problem 11.16):

$$
\begin{aligned}
F^* &= \min_{P(Y=y|X=x)} F \\
&= -T \sum_{\mathbf{x}} P(\mathbf{X} = \mathbf{x}) \log Z_{\mathbf{x}}
\end{aligned}
\tag{11.66}
$$

To minimize the Lagrangian with respect to the remaining free parameters—namely, the code vectors $\mathbf{y}$—we set the gradients of F^* with respect to $\mathbf{y}$ to zero. Hence, we obtain the condition

$$
\sum_{\mathbf{x}} P(\mathbf{X} = \mathbf{x}, \mathbf{Y} = \mathbf{y}) \frac{\partial}{\partial \mathbf{y}} d(\mathbf{x}, \mathbf{y}) = 0 \quad \text{for all } \mathbf{y} \in \mathcal{Y}
\tag{11.67}
$$

where $\mathcal{Y}$ is the set of all code vectors. Using the formula of Eq. (11.60) and normalizing with respect to $P(\mathbf{X} = \mathbf{x})$, we may redefine this minimizing condition as

$$
\frac{1}{N} \sum_{\mathbf{x}} P(\mathbf{Y} = \mathbf{y}|\mathbf{X} = \mathbf{x}) \frac{\partial}{\partial \mathbf{y}} d(\mathbf{x}, \mathbf{y}) = 0 \quad \text{for all } \mathbf{y} \in \mathcal{Y}
\tag{11.68}
$$

where the association probability $P(\mathbf{Y} = \mathbf{y}|\mathbf{X} = \mathbf{x})$ is itself defined by the Gibbs distribution of Eq. (11.64). In Eq. (11.68), we have included the scaling factor $1/N$ merely for completeness, where N is the number of available examples.

We may now describe the deterministic-annealing algorithm for clustering (Rose, 1998):

> *The deterministic-annealing algorithm consists of minimizing the Lagrangian F^* with respect to the code vectors at a high value of temperature T and then tracking the minimum while the temperature T is lowered.*

In other words, deterministic annealing operates with a specific annealing schedule whereby the temperature is lowered in an orderly fashion. At each value of the temperature T, a two-step iteration central to the algorithm is performed:

1. The code vectors are fixed, and the Gibbs distribution of Eq. (11.64) for a specific distortion measure $d(\mathbf{x}, \mathbf{y})$ is used to calculate the association probabilities.
2. The associations are fixed, and Eq. (11.68) is used to optimize the distortion measure $d(\mathbf{x}, \mathbf{y})$ with respect to the code vector $\mathbf{y}$.

This two-step iterative procedure is monotonically nonincreasing in F^* and is therefore assured of converging to a minimum. At high values of temperature T, the Lagrangian F^* is fairly smooth and is a convex function of $\mathbf{y}$ under the mild assumptions previously made on the distortion measure $d(\mathbf{x}, \mathbf{y})$. A global minimum of F^* can be found at high temperatures. As the temperature T is lowered, the association probabilities become hard, resulting in a hard-clustering solution.

As the temperature T is lowered in the course of going through the annealing schedule, the system undergoes a sequence of phase transitions, which consists of natural cluster splits through which the clustering model grows in size (i.e., number of

FIGURE 11.13 Clustering at various phases. The lines are equiprobability contours, $p = \frac{1}{2}$ in (b), and $p = \frac{1}{3}$ elsewhere:
(a) 1 cluster ($B = 0$),
(b) 2 clusters ($B = 0.0049$),
(c) 3 clusters ($B = 0.0056$),
(d) 4 clusters ($B = 0.0100$),
(e) 5 clusters ($B = 0.0156$),
(f) 6 clusters ($B = 0.0347$), and
(g) 19 clusters ($B = 0.0605$).

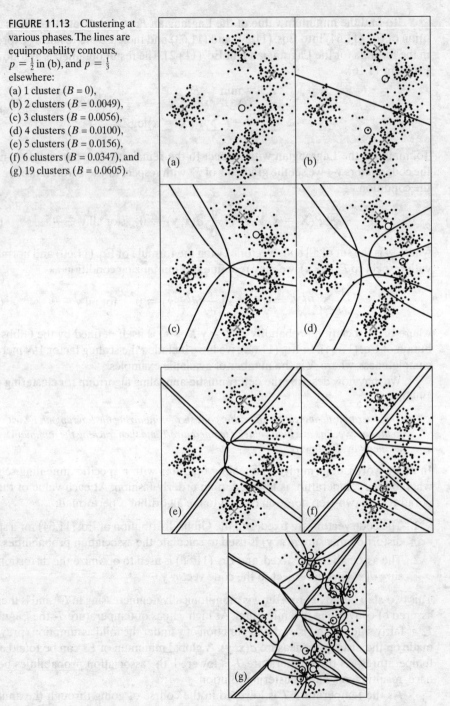

clusters) (Rose et al., 1990; Rose, 1991). This phenomenon is significant for the following reasons:

1. The sequence of phase transitions provides a useful tool for *controlling* the size of the clustering model.

2. As in ordinary physical annealing, the phase transitions are the *critical points* of the deterministic-annealing process during which care has to be exercised with the annealing.

3. The critical points are *computable*, thereby providing information that can be used to accelerate the algorithm in between phase transitions.

4. An *optimum model size* may be identified by coupling a validation procedure with the sequence of solutions produced at various phases, which represent solutions of increasing model size.

Case Study: Mixture of Gaussian Distributions

Figures 11.13 and 11.14 illustrate the evolution of the clustering solution via deterministic annealing at various phases as the temperature T is decreased or the reciprocal of temperature, $B = 1/T$, is increased (Rose, 1991). The data set used to generate these figures is a mixture of six Gaussian distributions whose centers are marked with an "X" in Fig. 11.13. The centers of the computed clusters are marked with an "o." Since the clustering solutions at nonzero temperatures are not hard, this random partition is depicted by contours of equal probability—for example, probability $\frac{1}{3}$ of belonging to a particular cluster. This process starts with one natural cluster containing the training sample (Fig. 11.13a). At the first phase transition, it splits into two clusters (Fig. 11.13b) and then passes

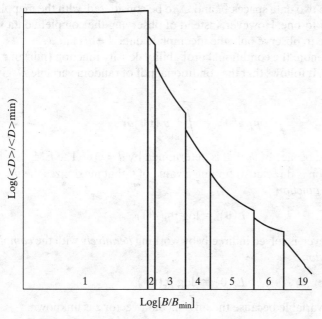

FIGURE 11.14   Phase diagram for the Case Study in deterministic annealing. The number of effective clusters is shown for each phase.

through a sequence of phase transitions until it reaches the "natural" set of six clusters. The next phase transition results in an "explosion" when all clusters split. Figure 11.14 shows the phase diagram, displaying the behavior of the average distortion throughout the annealing process and the number of natural clusters at each phase. In this figure, the average distortion (normalized with respect to its minimum value) is plotted versus the reciprocal of temperature, B, normalized with respect to its minimum value $B_{\min}$. Both axes are labeled in their relative logarithmic forms.

11.11 ANALOGY OF DETERMINISTIC ANNEALING WITH THE EXPECTATION-MAXIMIZATION ALGORITHM

For another important aspect of the deterministic-annealing algorithm, suppose we view the association probability $P(\mathbf{Y} = \mathbf{y} | \mathbf{X} = \mathbf{x})$ as the expected value of a random binary variable $V_{\mathbf{xy}}$ defined as

$$V_{\mathbf{xy}} = \begin{cases} 1 & \text{if the source vector } \mathbf{x} \text{ is assigned to code vector } \mathbf{y} \\ 0 & \text{otherwise} \end{cases} \tag{11.69}$$

Then, from such a perspective, we recognize the two-step iteration of the deterministic-annealing algorithm to be a form of the *expectation-maximization (EM) algorithm*. In order to appreciate the relevance of this point, we will digress briefly to describe the underlying theory of the EM algorithm.

The EM Algorithm[12]

Let the vector $\mathbf{z}$ denote some missing or unobservable data. Let $\mathbf{r}$ denote the complete-data vector, made up of some observable data point d and the missing data vector $\mathbf{z}$. There are therefore two data spaces, $\mathcal{R}$ and $\mathcal{D}$, to be considered, with the mapping from $\mathcal{R}$ to $\mathcal{D}$ being many-to-one. However, instead of observing the complete data vector $\mathbf{r}$, we are actually able to observe only the incomplete data $d = d(\mathbf{r})$ in $\mathcal{D}$.

Let $p_c(\mathbf{r} | \boldsymbol{\theta})$ denote the conditional probability density function (pdf) of $\mathbf{r}$, given a parameter vector $\boldsymbol{\theta}$. It follows that the conditional pdf of random variable D, given $\boldsymbol{\theta}$, is defined by

$$p_D(d | \boldsymbol{\theta}) = \int_{\mathcal{R}(d)} p_c(\mathbf{r} | \boldsymbol{\theta}) d\mathbf{r} \tag{11.70}$$

where $\mathcal{R}(d)$ is the subspace of $\mathcal{R}$ that is determined by $d = d(\mathbf{r})$. The EM algorithm for parameter estimation is directed at finding a value of $\boldsymbol{\theta}$ that maximizes the *incomplete-data log-likelihood function*

$$L(\boldsymbol{\theta}) = \log p_D(d | \boldsymbol{\theta})$$

This problem, however, is solved indirectly by working *iteratively* with the *complete-data log-likelihood function*

$$L_c(\boldsymbol{\theta}) = \log p_c(\mathbf{r} | \boldsymbol{\theta}) \tag{11.71}$$

which is a random variable because the missing data vector $\mathbf{z}$ is unknown.

To be more specific, let $\hat{\boldsymbol{\theta}}(n)$ denote the value of the parameter vector $\boldsymbol{\theta}$ on iteration n of the EM algorithm. In the *E-step* of this iteration, we calculate the expectation

$$Q(\boldsymbol{\theta}, \hat{\boldsymbol{\theta}}(n)) = \mathbb{E}[L_c(\boldsymbol{\theta})] \tag{11.72}$$

where the expectation is performed with respect to $\hat{\boldsymbol{\theta}}(n)$. In the *M-step* of this same iteration, we maximize $Q(\boldsymbol{\theta}, \hat{\boldsymbol{\theta}}(n))$ with respect to $\boldsymbol{\theta}$ over the parameter (weight) space $\mathcal{W}$ and therefore find the updated parameter estimate $\hat{\boldsymbol{\theta}}(n+1)$, as shown by

$$\hat{\boldsymbol{\theta}}(n+1) = \arg \max_{\boldsymbol{\theta}} Q(\boldsymbol{\theta}, \hat{\boldsymbol{\theta}}(n)) \tag{11.73}$$

The algorithm is started with some initial value $\hat{\boldsymbol{\theta}}(0)$ of the parameter vector $\boldsymbol{\theta}$. The E-step and M-step are then alternately repeated in accordance with Eqs. (11.72) and (11.73), respectively, until the difference between $L(\hat{\boldsymbol{\theta}}(n+1))$ and $L(\hat{\boldsymbol{\theta}}(n))$ drops to some arbitrary small value; at that point, the computation is terminated.

Note that after an iteration of the EM algorithm, the incomplete-data log-likelihood function is *not* decreased, as shown by

$$L(\hat{\boldsymbol{\theta}}(n+1) \geq L\hat{\boldsymbol{\theta}}(n)) \quad \text{for } n = 0, 1, 2, ...,$$

where equality usually means that we are at a stationary point of the log-likelihood function.

Discussion of the Analogy (Resumed)

Returning to the analogy between deterministic annealing and the EM algorithm, we now make two highly relevant observations:

  (i) In step 1 of the deterministic-annealing algorithm, which computes the association probabilities, we have the equivalent of the expectation step of the EM algorithm.

  (ii) In step 2 of the deterministic-annealing algorithm, which optimizes the distortion measure $d(\mathbf{x}, \mathbf{y})$ with respect to the code vector $\mathbf{y}$, we have the equivalent of the maximization step of the EM algorithm.

Note, however, that in making this analogy, the task of deterministic annealing is more general than maximum-likelihood estimation. We say so because, unlike maximum-likelihood estimation, deterministic annealing does *not* make any assumption on the underlying probability distribution of the data. The association probabilities are, in fact, derived from the Lagrangian F^* to be minimized.

11.12 SUMMARY AND DISCUSSION

In this chapter, we have discussed the use of ideas rooted in statistical mechanics as the mathematical basis for the formulation of stochastic simulation/optimization methods and learning machines.

Three stochastic methods were discussed:

  1. The Metropolis algorithm, which is a Markov chain Monte Carlo (MCMC) method aimed at the simulation of an unknown probability distribution.

2. Simulated annealing, which is an adaptive procedure in the sense that gross features of the final state of a system under study are seen at higher temperatures, while the fine details of the state appear at lower temperatures. As an optimization algorithm, simulated annealing can avoid getting stuck at a local minimum.

3. Gibbs sampling, which generates a Markov chain with the Gibbs distribution as the equilibrium distribution. Unlike the Metropolis algorithm, the transition probabilities associated with the Gibbs sampler are nonstationary.

Much of the next part of the chapter, dealing with stochastic learning machines, focused on two topics:

1. The classical Boltzmann machine, which uses hidden and visible neurons that are in the form of stochastic binary state units. The machine cleverly exploits the beautiful properties of the Gibbs distribution, thereby offering some appealing properties:

   - Through training, the probability distribution exhibited by the neurons is matched to that of the environment.
   - The machine offers a generalized approach that is applicable to the basic issues of search, representation, and learning.
   - The machine is guaranteed to find the global minimum of the energy surface with respect to the states, provided that the annealing schedule in the learning process is performed slowly enough.

   Unfortunately, the Boltzmann machine takes a long time to reach an equilibrium distribution, thereby limiting its practical usefulness.

2. The deep belief net (DBN), which uses the restricted Boltzmann machine (RBM) as a basic building block. A distinctive feature of the RBM is that there are no connections among the hidden neurons; otherwise, it is similar to the classical Boltzmann machine in that it uses symmetric connections between the visible and hidden neurons. The DBN also builds on the very old idea of learning features of features:

   - The machine starts the learning process by focusing on some features of the raw sensory input data, which should capture interesting irregularities in the input data.
   - It learns another layer of features by treating the previous layer of features as "new" sensory data.
   - Then, it continues the learning process in this manner, one layer after another until the highest level of features learned is so complex that it is very easy to recognize objects of interest in the original raw sensory input data.

   Through a clever use of top-down learning for generative modeling and bottom-up learning for inference, the DBN acquires the capability of learning the density model of unlabeled digit images with an impressive accuracy.

Simulated annealing, discussed early on in the chapter, distinguishes itself by performing random moves on the energy surface, which can make the annealing schedule very slow, with the result that its use is unrealistic for many applications. By contrast, deterministic annealing, discussed in the last part of the chapter, incorporates randomness into the cost function, which is then deterministically optimized at each temperature sequentially, starting at a high temperature and then cooling gradually. Whereas simulated annealing is guaranteed to reach a global minimum, no such guarantee has yet been found for the case of deterministic annealing.

NOTES AND REFERENCES

1. The term "canonical distribution" as a description of Eq. (11.3) was coined by J. Willard Gibbs (1902). On page 33 of *Part One* (*Elementary Principles in Statistical Mechanics*) of his collected works, he wrote,

> "*The distribution represented by...*

$$P = \exp\left(\frac{\psi - \varepsilon}{H}\right)$$

> *where H and ψ are constants, and H positive, seems to represent the most simple case conceivable, since it has the property that when the system consists of parts with separate energies, the laws of the distribution in phase of the separate parts are of the same nature—a property which enormously simplifies the discussion, and is the foundation of extremely important relations to thermodynamics....*
>
> *When an ensemble of systems is distributed in phase in the manner described, i.e., when the index of probability (P) is a linear function of the energy (ε), we shall say that the ensemble is* canonically distributed, *and shall call the divisor of the energy (H) the modulus of distribution.*"

In the physics literature, Eq. (11.3) is commonly referred to as the canonical distribution (Reif, 1965) or Gibbs distribution (Landau and Lifschitz, 1980). In the neural network literature, it has been referred to as the Gibbs distribution, Boltzmann distribution, and Boltzmann–Gibbs distribution.

2. **Bernoulli Trial**

Consider an experiment involving a sequence of independent, but identical, stages—a sequence of *independent trials*. Suppose that there are only two possible outcomes at each stage of the experiment. In such a case, we say that we have a sequence of *Bernoulli trials*. For example, in a coin-tossing experiment, the outcomes are "heads" and "tails."

3. **Metropolis–Hastings Algorithm**

The original Metropolis algorithm was introduced in 1953 for the purpose of optimization in a discrete state space with statistical physics in mind. Later on in 1970, Hastings generalized the Metropolis algorithm for use in statistical simulation under the assumption of a set of nonsymmetric transition probabilities—that is,

$$\tau_{ji} \neq \tau_{ij}$$

Correspondingly, the moving probability is defined by

$$\alpha_{ij} = \min\left(1, \frac{\pi_j \tau_{ji}}{\pi_i \tau_{ij}}\right)$$

The associated Markov chain still satisfies the principle of detailed balance. The Markov chain Monte Carlo method generalized in this manner is referred to as the *Metropolis–Hastings algorithm* (Robert and Casella, 2004). The Metropolis algorithm, for which $\tau_{ji} = \tau_{ij}$, is naturally a special case of the Metropolis–Hastings algorithm.

4. In Tu et al. (2005), an algorithm rooted in Bayesian theory is described for the parsing of an image into its constituent parts. The *image-parsing algorithm* optimizes the posterior distribution, thereby outputting a representation of the scene of interest much like the way in which a sentence is passed in a speech and natural language.

   The computational framework of the algorithm integrates two popular approaches to inference:
   - generative (top-down) approach, which formulates the posterior distribution;
   - discriminative (bottom-up) approach, which computes the discriminative distribution, using a sequence of bottom-up filters (tests).

   In the algorithm design devised by Tu et al., the posterior distribution defined by the generative model provides the target distribution for a Markov chain, and the discriminative distribution is used to construct the posterior distribution that drives the Markov chain. In other words, the Markov chain Monte Carlo method is at the heart of the image-parsing algorithm.

5. The idea of introducing temperature and simulating annealing into combinatorial-optimization problems is due to Kirkpatrick et al. (1983) and independently to Černy (1985).

   In a physical context, annealing is a delicate process by nature. In their 1983 paper, Kirkpatrick et al. discuss the notion of "melting" a solid, which involves raising the temperature to a maximum value at which all particles of the solid arrange themselves "randomly" in the liquid phase. Then the temperature is lowered, permitting all particles to arrange themselves in the low-energy ground state of a corresponding lattice. If the cooling is too rapid—that is, the solid is not allowed enough time to reach thermal equilibrium at each temperature value—the resulting crystal will have many defects, or the substance may form a glass with no crystalline order and only metastable locally optimal structures.

   The notion of "melting" may be right when thinking about glass, and perhaps combinatorial-optimization problems in a corresponding computational context. However, it is misleading when discussing many other application domains (Beckerman, 1997). For example, in image processing, if we raise the "temperature" so that all particles arrange themselves randomly, we lose the image; it becomes uniformly gray. In a corresponding metallurgical sense, when we anneal either iron or copper, we must keep the annealing temperature below the melting point; otherwise, we ruin the sample.

   There are several important parameters that govern metallurgical annealing:
   - *annealing temperature*, which specifies the temperature to which the metal or alloy is heated;
   - *annealing time*, which specifies the duration of time for which the elevated temperature is maintained;
   - *cooling schedule*, which specifies the rate at which the temperature is lowered.

   These parameters have their counterparts in simulated annealing, as described in the subsection on annealing schedule.

6. For more elaborate and theoretically oriented annealing schedules, see the books by Aarts and Korst (1989) and van Laarhoven and Aarts (1988).

7. Gibbs sampling is referred to in statistical physics as a "heat bath" version of the Metropolis algorithm. It is widely used in image processing, neural networks, and statistics, following its formal exposition in the literature by Geman and Geman (1984) and Gelfand and Smith (1990). The latter paper also discusses other variations of sampling-based (or Monte Carlo) approaches to the numerical calculation of estimates of marginal probability distributions.

8. The visible neurons of a Boltzmann machine may also be subdivided into input and output neurons. In this second configuration, the Boltzmann machine performs *association* under the supervision of a teacher. The input neurons receive information from the environment, and the output neurons report the outcome of the computation to an end user.

9. The formula of Eq. (11.39) applies to a Boltzmann machine whose "on" and "off" states are denoted by $+1$ and -1, respectively. In the case of a machine using 1 and 0 to denote its "on" and "off" states, respectively, we have

$$E(\mathbf{x}) = -\sum_i \sum_{\substack{j \\ i \neq j}} w_{ji} x_i x_j$$

10. Traditionally, the Kullback–Leibler divergence has been used as the index of performance for the Boltzmann machine (Ackley et al., 1985; Hinton and Sejnowski, 1986). This criterion was discussed in Chapter 10. In that chapter, we also showed that minimization of the Kullback–Leibler divergence is equivalent to maximum-likelihood estimation.

11. Deterministic annealing has been successfully applied to many learning tasks, including:
    - vector quantization (Rose et al., 1992; Miller and Rose, 1994);
    - statistical classifier design (Miller et al., 1996).

12. The paper by Newcomb (1886), considering the estimation of parameters of a mixture of two univariate Gaussian distributions, appears to be the earliest reference to an EM type of process reported in the literature.

    The name "EM algorithm" was coined by Dempster et al. in their fundamental 1997 paper. In that paper, formulation of the EM algorithm for computing maximum-likelihood estimates from incomplete data at various levels of generality was presented for the first time.

    The first unified account of the theory, methodology, applications, history, and extensions of the EM algorithm was presented in book form by McLachlan and Krishnan (1997).

PROBLEMS

Markov Chains

11.1 Given that the one-step transition probability in a Markov chain from state i to state j is denoted by

$$p_{ij} = P(X_{n+1} = j \mid X_n = i)$$

Give the generalized equation for the m-step transition probability.

11.2 Figure P11.2 shows the state transition diagram for the *random walk* process, where the transition probability p is greater than zero. Is the infinitely long Markov chain depicted here irreducible? Justify your answer.

11.3 Consider the Markov chain depicted in Fig. P11.3, which is reducible. Identify the classes of states contained in this state transition diagram.

11.4 Calculate the steady-state probabilities of the Markov chain shown in Fig. P11.4.

11.5 Consider the example of a Markov chain shown in Fig. P11.5. Using this example, verify the validity of the Chapman–Kolmogorov identity.

Simulation techniques

11.6 State the primary objective of simulated annealing. How is it different from conventional iterative optimization algorithms?

11.7 In this problem, we consider the use of simulated annealing for solving the *traveling-sales-man problem* (TSP). You are given the following:

- N cities;
- the distance between each pair of cities, d;
- a tour represented by a closed path visiting each city once, and only once.

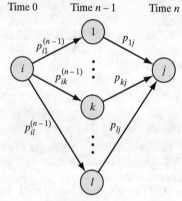

FIGURE P11.1

The objective is to find a tour (i.e., permutation of the order in which the cities are visited) that is of minimal total length L. In this problem, the different possible tours are the configurations, and the total length of a tour is the cost function to be minimized.

(a) Devise an iterative method of generating valid configurations.

(b) The total length of a tour is defined by

$$L_P = \sum_{i=1}^{N} d_{P(i)P(i+1)}$$

where P denotes a permutation with $P(N+1) = P(1)$. Correspondingly, the partition function is

$$Z = \sum_P e^{-L_P/T}$$

where T is a control parameter. Set up a simulated-annealing algorithm for the TSP.

Boltzmann machine

11.8 Consider a stochastic, two-state neuron j operating at temperature T. This neuron *flips* from state x_j to state $-x_j$ with probability

$$P(x_j \to -x_j) = \frac{1}{1 + \exp(-\Delta E_j / T)}$$

where ΔE_j is the energy change resulting from such a flip. The total energy of the Boltzmann machine is defined by

$$E = -\frac{1}{2} \sum_{i} \sum_{\substack{j \\ i \neq j}} w_{ji} x_i x_j$$

where w_{ji} is the synaptic weight from neuron i to neuron j, with $w_{ji} = w_{ij}$ and $w_{ji} = 0$.

(a) Show that

$$\Delta E_j = -2 x_j v_j$$

where v_j is the induced local field of neuron j.

(b) Hence, show that for an initial state $x_j = -1$, the probability that neuron j is flipped into state $+1$ is $1/(1 + \exp(-2v_j/T))$.

(c) Show that the same formula in part (b) holds for neuron j flipping into state -1 when it is initially in state $+1$.

11.9 Derive the formula given in Eq. (11.49) that defines the derivative of the log-likelihood function $L(\mathbf{w})$ with respect to the synaptic weight w_{ji} for the Boltzmann machine.

11.10 The Gibbs distribution may be derived using a self-contained mathematical approach that does *not* rely on concepts from statistical physics. In particular, a *two-step Markov chain model* of a stochastic machine may be used to formalize the assumptions that yield the unique properties of the Boltzmann machine (Mazaika, 1987). This should not come as a surprise, since simulated annealing, basic to the operation of the Boltzmann machine, is known to have a Markov property of its own (van Laarhoven and Aarts, 1988).

Consider, then, a transition model between states of a neuron in a stochastic machine that is composed of two random processes:

- The first process decides which state transition should be attempted.
- The second process decides whether the transition succeeds.

(a) Expressing the transition probability p_{ji} as the product of two factors, that is,

$$p_{ji} = \tau_{ji} q_{ji} \qquad \text{for } j \neq i$$

show that

$$p_{ii} = 1 - \sum_{j \neq i} \tau_{ji} q_{ji}$$

(b) Assume that the attempt-rate matrix is symmetric:

$$\tau_{ji} = \tau_{ij}$$

Also assume that the probability of a successful attempt satisfies the property of complementary conditional transition probability:

$$q_{ji} = 1 - q_{ij}$$

By invoking these two assumptions, show that

$$\sum_j \tau_{ji}(q_{ij}\pi_j + q_{ij}\pi_i - \pi_j) = 0$$

(c) Given that $\tau_{ji} \neq 0$, use the result of part (a) to show that

$$q_{ij} = \frac{1}{1 + (\pi_i/\pi_j)}$$

(d) Finally, make a change of variables to obtain

$$E_i = -T \log \pi_i + T^*$$

where T and T^* are arbitrary constants. Hence, derive the following results, where $\Delta E = E_j - E_i$.

(i) $\pi_i = \dfrac{1}{Z} \exp\left(-\dfrac{E_i}{T}\right)$

(ii) $Z = \sum_j \exp\left(-\dfrac{E_j}{T}\right)$

(iii) $q_{ji} = \dfrac{1}{1 + \exp(-\Delta E/T)}$

(e) What conclusions can you draw from these results?

11.11 In Section 11.7, we used maximum likelihood as the criterion for deriving the Boltzmann learning rule, described in Eq. (11.53). In this problem, we revisit this learning rule with another criterion. From the discussion presented in Chapter 10, the Kullback–Leibler divergence between two probability distributions p_α^+ and p_α^- is defined by

$$D_{p^+\|p^-} = \sum_\alpha p_\alpha^+ \log\left(\frac{p_\alpha^+}{p_\alpha^-}\right)$$

where the summation is over all possible states α. The probability p_α^+ denotes the probability that the visible neurons are in state α when the network is in its clamped (positive) condition, and the probability p_α^- denotes the probability that the same neurons are in a state α when the network is in its free-running (negative) condition. Using $D_{p^+\|p^-}$, rederive the Boltzmann learning rule of Eq (11.53).

11.12 Consider a Boltzmann machine whose visible neurons are divided into input neurons and output neurons. The states of these neurons are denoted by α and γ, respectively. The state of the hidden neurons is denoted by β. The Kullback–Leibler divergence for this machine is defined by

$$D_{p^+\|p^-} = \sum_\alpha p_\alpha^+ \sum_\gamma p_{\gamma|\alpha}^+ \log\left(\frac{p_{\gamma|\alpha}^+}{p_{\gamma|\alpha}^-}\right)$$

where p_α^+ is the probability of state α over the input neurons; $p_{\gamma|\alpha}^+$ is the conditional probability that the output neurons are clamped in state α given an input state α; and $p_{\gamma|\alpha}^-$ is the conditional probability that the output neurons are in thermal equilibrium in state γ given that only the input neurons are clamped in state α. As before, the plus and minus superscripts denote the positive (clamped) and negative (free-running) conditions, respectively.

(a) Derive the formula $D_{p^+\|p^-}$ for a Boltzmann machine that includes input, hidden, and output neurons.

(b) Show that the Boltzmann learning rule for adjusting the synaptic weight w_{ji} in this network configuration may still be expressed in the same form as that described in Eq. (11.53), with new interpretations for the correlations ρ_{ji}^+ and ρ_{ji}^-.

Deep Belief Nets

11.13 Each restricted Boltzmann machine (RBM) in the deep belief net divides the task of modeling its own visible data into two subtasks. Explain these two subtasks.

11.14 An infinitely deep logistic belief net, shown in Fig. 11.9, is equivalent to a single RBM, shown in Fig. 11.8. Justify this statement.

Deterministic Annealing

11.15 In Section 11.10 we developed the idea of deterministic annealing using an information-theoretic approach. The idea of deterministic annealing may also be developed in a principled manner using the maximum-entropy principle discussed in Chapter 10. Justify the rationale of this second approach (Rose, 1998).

11.16 (a) Using Eqs. (11.59), (11.64), and (11.63), derive the result given in Eq. (11.66), which defines the Lagrangian F^* that results from use of the Gibbs distribution for the association probability.

(b) Using the result from part (a) of this problem, derive the condition given in Eq. (11.68) for the minimum of F^* with respect to the code vector $\mathbf{y}$.

(c) Apply the minimizing condition of Eq. (11.68) to the squared distortion measure of Eq. (11.58), and comment on your result.

11.17 Consider a data set that is a mixture of Gaussian distributions. In what way does the use of deterministic annealing offer an advantage over maximum-likelihood estimation in such a situation?

11.18 In this problem, we explore the use of deterministic annealing for pattern classification using a neural network (Miller et al., 1996). The output of neuron j in the output layer is denoted by $F_j(\mathbf{x})$, where $\mathbf{x}$ is the input vector. The classification decision is based on the maximum discriminant $F_j(\mathbf{x})$.

(a) For a probabilistic objective function, consider the expression

$$F = \frac{1}{N} \sum_{(\mathbf{x}, \mathscr{C}) \in \mathscr{T}} \sum_j P(\mathbf{x} \in \mathscr{R}_j) F_j(\mathbf{x})$$

where $\mathscr{T}$ is a training sample of labeled vectors, with $\mathbf{x}$ denoting an input vector and $\mathscr{C}$ its class label, and $P(\mathbf{x} \in \mathscr{R}_j)$ is the probability of association between input vector $\mathbf{x}$

and class region $\mathscr{R}_j$. Using the maximum-entropy principle discussed in Chapter 10, formulate the Gibbs distribution for $P(\mathbf{x} \in \mathscr{R}_j)$.

(b) Let $<P_e>$ denote the average misclassification cost. Formulate the Lagrangian for minimization of $<P_e>$ subject to the constraint that the entropy corresponding to the association probabilities $P(\mathbf{x} \in \mathscr{R}_j)$ is equal to some constant value H.

CHAPTER 1 2

Dynamic Programming

ORGANIZATION OF THE CHAPTER

The purpose this chapter is threefold: (i) to discuss the development of dynamic programming as the mathematical basis of planning a multistage course of action by an agent operating in a stochastic environment, (ii) to give a direct derivation of reinforcement learning as an approximate form of dynamic programming, and (iii) to present indirect methods of approximate dynamic programming to deal with the "curse" of dimensionality.

The chapter is organized as follows:

1. Section 12.1, the introductory section, motivates the study of dynamic programming by discussing Markov decision processes, which is done in Section 12.2.

2. Sections 12.3 through 12.5 discuss Bellman's theory of dynamic programming and the two related methods: policy iteration and value iteration.

3. Section 12.6 describes the rationale behind the direct learning-based approximation of dynamic programming, thereby leading to the developments of temporal-difference learning and Q-learning in Sections 12.7 and 12.8, respectively.

4. Section 12.9 describes the rationale behind the indirect approximation of dynamic programming to deal with the "curse"-of-dimensionality problem, thereby leading to the discussion of least squares policy evaluation and approximate value iteration presented in Sections 12.10 and 12.11, respectively.

The chapter concludes with a summary and discussion in Section 12.12.

12.1 INTRODUCTION

In the introductory chapter, we identified two main paradigms of learning: learning with a teacher and learning without a teacher. The paradigm of learning without a teacher is subdivided into self-organized (unsupervised) learning and reinforcement learning. Different forms of learning with a teacher, or supervised learning, were covered in Chapters 1 through 6, and different forms of unsupervised learning were discussed in Chapters 9 through 11. Semisupervised learning was discussed in Chapter 7. In this chapter, we discuss *reinforcement learning*.

Supervised learning is a "cognitive" learning problem performed under the tutelage of a teacher. It relies on the availability of an adequate set of input–output examples that are representative of the operating environment. In contrast, reinforcement learning is a "behavioral" learning problem. It is performed through *interaction* between an agent and its environment, in which the agent or decision maker seeks to achieve a specific goal despite the presence of uncertainties (Barto et al., 1983; Sutton and Barto, 1998). The fact that this interaction is performed without a teacher makes reinforcement learning particularly attractive for dynamic situations, where it is costly or difficult (if not impossible) to gather a satisfactory set of input–output examples.

There are two approaches to the study of reinforcement learning,[1] summarized as follows:

1. *the classical approach*, in which learning takes place through a process of punishment and reward, with the goal of achieving a *highly skilled behavior*;
2. *the modern approach*, which builds on a mathematical technique known as dynamic programming to decide on a course of action by considering possible future stages without actually experiencing them; the emphasis here is on *planning*.

Our discussion focuses on modern reinforcement learning.

Dynamic programming[2] is a technique that deals with situations where decisions are made in stages, with the outcome of each decision being predictable to some extent before the next decision is made. A key aspect of such situations is that decisions cannot be made in isolation. Rather, the desire for a low cost at the present must be balanced against the undesirability of high cost in the future. This is a *credit assignment problem*, because credit or blame must be assigned to each one of a set of interacting decisions. For optimal planning, it is necessary to have an efficient tradeoff between immediate and future costs. Such a tradeoff is indeed captured by the formalism of dynamic programming. In particular, dynamic programming addresses the following fundamental problem:

> *How can an agent or decision maker improve its long-term performance in a stochastic environment when the attainment of this improvement may require having to sacrifice short-term performance?*

Bellman's dynamic programming provides an optimal solution to this fundamental problem in an elegant and principled manner.

In the art of mathematical model building, the challenge is to strike the right balance between two entities, one practical and the other theoretical. Respectively, the two entities are

- the realistic description of a given problem and
- the power of analytic and computational methods to apply to the problem.

In dynamic programming, an issue of particular concern is that of *decision making* by an agent that operates in a stochastic environment. To address this issue, we build our model around *Markov decision processes*. Given the initial state of a dynamic system, a Markov decision process provides the mathematical basis for choosing a sequence of decisions that will maximize the returns from an N-stage decision-making process. What we have just described is the essence of Bellman's dynamic programming. It is therefore fitting that we begin the study of dynamic programming with a discussion of Markov decision processes.

12.2   MARKOV DECISION PROCESS

Consider an *agent* or *decision maker* that interacts with its environment in the manner illustrated in Fig. 12.1. The agent operates in accordance with a *finite-discrete-time Markovian decision process* that is characterized as follows:

- The environment evolves *probabilistically*, occupying a finite set of discrete states. However, the state does *not* contain past statistics, even though these statistics could be useful to the agent.
- For each environmental stage, there is a *finite set of possible actions* that may be taken by the agent.
- Every time the agent takes an action, a certain *cost* is incurred.
- States are observed, actions are taken, and costs are incurred at *discrete times.*

In the context of our present discussion, we introduce the following definition:

> *The state of the environment is a summary of the entire past experience of an agent gained from its interaction with the environment, such that the information necessary for the agent to predict the future behavior of the environment is contained in that summary.*

The state at time-step n is denoted by the random variable X_n, and the actual state at time-step n is denoted by i_n. The finite set of states is denoted by $\mathscr{X}$. A surprising aspect of dynamic programming is that its applicability depends very little on the nature of the state. We may therefore proceed without any assumption on the structure of the state space. Note also that the *complexity* of the dynamic-programming algorithm is *quadratic* in the dimension of the state space and *linear* in the dimension of the action space.

For state i, for example, the available set of *actions* (i.e., inputs applied to the environment by the agent) is denoted by $\mathscr{A}_i = \{a_{ik}\}$, where the second subscript k in action a_{ik} taken by the agent merely indicates the availability of more than one possible action when the environment is in state i. The transition of the environment from the state i to the new state j, for example, due to action a_{ik} is probabilistic in nature. Most importantly, however, *the transition probability from state i to state j depends entirely on the current state i and the corresponding action a_{ik}.* This is the *Markov property*, which was discussed in Chapter 11. This property is crucial because it means that the current state of the environment provides the necessary information for the agent to decide what action to take.

The random variable denoting the action taken by the agent at time-step n is denoted by A_n. Let $p_{ij}(a)$ denote the transition probability from state i to state j due to

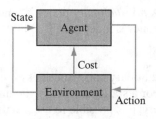

FIGURE 12.1   Block diagram of an agent interacting with its environment.

action taken at time-step n, where $A_n = a$. By virtue of the Markov assumption on the state dynamics, we have

$$p_{ij}(a) = P(X_{n+1} = j | X_n = i, A_n = a) \tag{12.1}$$

The transition probability $p_{ij}(a)$ satisfies two conditions that are imposed on it by probability theory, namely,

1. $p_{ij}(a) \geq 0$ for all i and j $\qquad$ (12.2)

2. $\sum_j p_{ij}(a) = 1$ for all i $\qquad$ (12.3)

where the i and j reside in the state space.

For a given number of states and given transition probabilities, the sequence of environmental states resulting from the actions taken by the agent over time forms a *Markov chain*. Markov chains were discussed in Chapter 11.

At each transition from one state to another, a *cost* is incurred by the agent. Thus, at the nth transition from state i to state j under action a_{ik}, the agent incurs a cost denoted by $\gamma^n g(i, a_{ik}, j)$, where $g(\cdot, \cdot, \cdot)$ is a *prescribed* function and γ is a scalar called the *discount factor*, confined to the range $0 \leq \gamma < 1$. The discount factor reflects intertemporal preferences. By adjusting γ, we are able to control the extent to which the agent is concerned with long-term versus short-term consequences of its own actions. In the limit, when $\gamma = 0$, the agent is *myopic*, in the sense that it is concerned only with the immediate consequences of its actions. In what follows, we will ignore this limiting value; that is, we confine the discussion to $0 < \gamma < 1$. As γ approaches 1, future costs become more important in determining optimal actions.

Our interest is in the formulation of a *policy*, defined as a *mapping of states into actions*. In other words;

> *Policy is a rule used by the agent to decide what to do, given knowledge of the current state of the environment.*
> *The policy is denoted by*

$$\pi = \{\mu_0, \mu_1, \mu_2, ...\} \tag{12.4}$$

where μ_n is a function that maps the state $X_n = i$ into an action $A_n = a$ at time-step $n = 0,$ $1, 2, ...$ This mapping is such that

$$\mu_n(i) \in \mathcal{A}_i \qquad \text{for all states } i \in \mathcal{X}$$

where $\mathcal{A}_i$ denotes the set of all possible actions taken by the agent in state i. Such policies are said to be admissible.

A policy can be nonstationary or stationary. A *nonstationary* policy is time varying, as indicated in Eq. (12.4). When, however, the policy is independent of time,

$$\pi = \{\mu, \mu, \mu, ...\}$$

the policy is said to be *stationary*. In other words, a stationary policy specifies exactly the same action each time a particular state is visited. For a stationary policy, the underlying Markov chain may be stationary or nonstationary; it is possible to use a stationary policy on a nonstationary Markov chain, but this is *not* a wise thing to do. If a stationary policy μ is employed, then the sequence of states $\{X_n, n = 0, 1, 2, ...\}$ forms a Markov chain with transition probabilities $p_{ij}(\mu(i))$, where $\mu(i)$ signifies an action. It is for this reason that the process is referred to as a *Markov decision process*.

The Basic-Problem

A dynamic-programming problem can be of a finite-horizon or infinite-horizon kind. In a *finite-horizon problem*, the cost accumulates over a finite number of stages. In an *infinite-horizon problem*, the cost accumulates over an infinite number of stages. Infinite-horizon problems provide a reasonable approximation to problems involving a finite, but very large, number of stages. They are also of particular interest because discounting ensures that the costs for all states are finite for any policy.

Let $g(X_n, \mu_n(X_n), X_{n+1})$ denote the *observed cost* incurred as a result of the transition from state X_n to state X_{n+1} under the action of policy $\mu_n(X_n)$. The total expected cost in an infinite-horizon problem, starting from an initial state $X_0 = i$ and using a policy $\pi = \{\mu_n\}$, is defined by

$$J^\pi(i) = \mathbb{E}\left[\sum_{n=0}^{\infty} \gamma^n g(X_n, \mu_n(X_n), X_{n+1}) | X_0 = i \right] \tag{12.5}$$

where the expected value is taken with respect to the Markov chain $\{X_1, X_2, ...\}$ and γ is the discount factor. The function $J^\pi(i)$ is called the *cost-to-go function* for policy π, starting from state i. Its *optimal* value, denoted by $J^*(i)$, is defined by

$$J^*(i) = \min_\pi J^\pi(i) \tag{12.6}$$

The policy π is optimal if, and only if, it is *greedy* with respect to $J^*(i)$. The term "greedy" is used to describe the case when an agent seeks to minimize the immediate next cost without paying any attention to the possibility that such an action may do away with access to better alternatives in the future.

When the policy π is stationary—that is, $\pi = \{\mu, \mu, ...\}$—we use the notation $J^\mu(i)$ in place of $J^*(i)$ and say that μ is optimal if

$$J^\mu(i) = J^*(i) \qquad \text{for all initial states } i \tag{12.7}$$

We may now sum up the basic problem in dynamic programming as follows:

Given a stationary Markovian decision process describing the interaction between an agent and its environment, find a stationary policy $\pi = \{\mu, \mu, \mu ...\}$ that minimizes the cost-to-go function $J^\mu(i)$ for all initial states i.

Note that during learning, the behavior of an agent may change with time. However, the optimal policy that the agent seeks will be stationary.

12.3 BELLMAN'S OPTIMALITY CRITERION

The dynamic-programming technique rests on a very simple idea known as the *principle of optimality*, due to Bellman (1957). Simply stated, this principle says the following (Bellman and Dreyfus, 1962):

An optimal policy has the property that whatever the initial state and initial decision are, the remaining decisions must constitute an optimal policy starting from the state resulting from the first decision.

As used here, a "decision" is a choice of control at a particular time, and a "policy" is the entire control sequence or control function.

To formulate the principle of optimality in mathematical terms, consider a finite-horizon problem for which the cost-to-go function is defined by

$$J_0(X_0) = \mathbb{E}\left[g_K(X_K) + \sum_{n=0}^{K-1} g_n(X_n, \mu_n(X_n), X_{n+1}) \right] \tag{12.8}$$

where K is the *planning horizon* (i.e., number of stages) and $g_K(X_K)$ is the *terminal cost*. Given X_0, the expectation in Eq. (12.8) is with respect to the remaining states $X_1, ..., X_{K-1}$. With this terminology, we may now formally state the principle of optimality as follows (Bertsekas, 2005, 2007):

Let $\pi^* = \{\mu_0^*, \mu_1^*, ..., \mu_{K-1}^*\}$ be an optimal policy for the basic finite-horizon problem. Assume that when using the optimal policy π^*, a given state X_n occurs with positive probability. Consider the subproblem where the environment is in state X_n at time n, and suppose we wish to minimize the corresponding cost-to-go function

$$J_n(X_n) = \mathbb{E}\left[g_K(X_K) + \sum_{k=n}^{K-1} g_k(X_k, \mu_k(X_k), X_{k+1}) \right] \tag{12.9}$$

for $n = 0, 1, ..., K - 1$. Then the truncated policy $\{\mu_n^*, \mu_{n+1}^*, ..., \mu_{K-1}^*\}$ is optimal for the subproblem.

We may intuitively justify the principle of optimality by the following argument: If the truncated policy $\{\mu_n^*, \mu_{n+1}^*, ..., \mu_{K-1}^*\}$ was not optimal as stated, then once the state X_n is reached at time n, we could reduce the cost-to-go function $J_n(X_n)$ simply by switching to a policy that is optimal for the subproblem.

The principle of optimality builds on the engineering notion of "divide and conquer." Basically, an optimal policy for a complex multistage planning or control problem is constructed by proceeding as follows:

1. Construct an optimal policy for the "tail subproblem" involving only the last stage of the system.
2. Extend the optimal policy to the "tail subproblem" involving the last two stages of the system.
3. Continue the procedure in this fashion until the entire problem has been dealt with.

Dynamic-Programming Algorithm

On the basis of the procedure just described, we may now formulate the dynamic-programming algorithm, which proceeds backward in time from period $N-1$ to period 0. Let $\pi = \{\mu_0, \mu_1, ..., \mu_{K-1}\}$ denote an admissible policy. For each $n = 0, 1, ..., K-1$, let $\pi^n = \{\mu_n, \mu_{n+1}, ..., \mu_{K-1}\}$, and let $J_n^*(X_n)$ be the optimal cost for the $(K-n)$-stage problem that starts at state X_n and time n and ends at time K; that is, we write

$$J_n^*(X_n) = \min_{\pi^n} \underset{(X_{n+1,...,X_{K-1}})}{\mathbb{E}} \left[g_K(X_K) + \sum_{k=n}^{K-1} g_k(X_k, \mu_k(X_k), X_{k+1}) \right] \quad (12.10)$$

which represents the optimal form of Eq. (12.9). Recognizing that $\pi^n = (\mu_n, \pi^{n+1})$ and partially expanding the summation on the right-hand side of Eq. (12.10), we may write

$$J_n^*(X_n) = \min_{(\mu_n, \pi^{n+1})} \underset{(X_{n+1},...,X_{K-1})}{\mathbb{E}} \bigg[g_n(X_n, \mu_n(X_n), X_{n+1})$$

$$+ g_K(X_K) + \sum_{k=n+1}^{K-1} g_k(X_k, \mu_k(X_k), X_{k+1}) \bigg]$$

$$= \min_{\mu_n} \underset{X_{n+1}}{\mathbb{E}} \bigg\{ g_n(X_n), \mu_n(X_n), X_{n+1}) \quad (12.11)$$

$$+ \min_{\pi^{n+1}} \underset{(X_{n+2},...,X_{K-1})}{\mathbb{E}} \bigg[g_K(X_K) + \sum_{k=n+1}^{K-1} g_k(X_k, \mu_k(X_k), X_{k+1}) \bigg] \bigg\}$$

$$= \min_{\mu_n} \underset{X_{n+1}}{\mathbb{E}} \bigg[g_n(X_n, \mu_n(X_n), X_{n+1}) + J_{n+1}^*(X_{n+1}) \bigg]$$

where, in the last line, we have made use of the defining equation of Eq. (12.10), with $n + 1$ used in place of n. Accordingly, we deduce from Eq. (12.11) that

$$J_n(X_n) = \min_{\mu_n} \underset{X_{n+1}}{\mathbb{E}} \left[g_n(X_n, \mu_n(X_n), X_{n+1}) + J_{n+1}(X_{n+1}) \right] \quad (12.12)$$

We may now formally state the *dynamic-programming algorithm* as follows (Bertsekas, 2005, 2007):

For every initial state X_0, the optimal cost $J^*(X_0)$ of the basic finite-horizon problem is equal to $J_0(X_0)$, where the function J_0 is obtained from the last step of the algorithm

$$J_n(X_n) = \min_{\mu_n} \underset{X_{n+1}}{\mathbb{E}} \left[g_n(X_n, \mu_n(X_n), X_{n+1}) + J_{n+1}(X_{n+1}) \right] \quad (12.13)$$

which runs backward in time, with

$$J_K(X_K) = g_K(X_K) \quad (12.14)$$

Furthermore, if μ_n^* minimizes the right-hand side of Eq. (12.13) for each X_n and n, then the policy $\pi^* = \{\mu_0^*, \mu_1^*, ..., \mu_{K-1}^*\}$ is optimal.

Bellman's Optimality Equation

In its basic form, the dynamic-programming algorithm deals with a finite-horizon problem. We are interested in extending the use of this algorithm to deal with the infinite-horizon discounted problem described by the cost-to-go function of Eq. (12.5) under a stationary policy $\pi = \{\mu, \mu, \mu, ...\}$. With this objective in mind, we do two things:

1. Reverse the time index of the algorithm.
2. Define the cost $g_n(X_n, \mu(X_n), X_{n+1})$ as

$$g_n(X_n, \mu(X_n), X_{n+1}) = \gamma^n g(X_n, \mu(X_n), X_{n+1}) \quad (12.15)$$

We may now reformulate the dynamic-programming algorithm as

$$J_{n+1}(X_0) = \min_{\mu} \mathbb{E}_{X_1} [g(X_0, \mu(X_0), X_1) + \gamma J_n(X_1)] \tag{12.16}$$

which starts from the initial conditions

$$J_0(X) = 0 \qquad \text{for all } X$$

The state X_0 is the initial state, X_1 is the new state that results from the action of policy μ, and γ is the discount factor.

Let $J^*(i)$ denote the optimal infinite-horizon cost for the initial state $X_0 = i$. We may then view $J^*(i)$ as the limit of the corresponding K-stage optimal cost $J_K(i)$ as the horizon K approaches infinity; that is,

$$J^*(i) = \lim_{K \to \infty} J_K(i) \qquad \text{for all } i \tag{12.17}$$

This relation is the connecting link between the finite-horizon and infinite-horizon discounted problems. Substituting $n + 1 = K$ and $X_0 = i$ into Eq. (12.16) and then applying Eq. (12.17), we obtain

$$J^*(i) = \min_{\mu} \mathbb{E}_{X_1} [g(i, \mu(i), X_1) + \gamma J^*(X_1)] \tag{12.18}$$

To rewrite this equation for the optimal infinite-horizon cost $J^*(i)$, we proceed in two stages:

1. Evaluate the expectation of the cost $g(i, \mu(i), X_1)$ with respect to X_1 by writing

$$\mathbb{E}[g(i), \mu(i), X_1] = \sum_{j=1}^{N} p_{ij} g(i, \mu(i), j) \tag{12.19}$$

   where N is the number of states of the environment and p_{ij} is the transition probability from the initial state $X_0 = i$ to the new state $X_1 = j$. The quantity defined in Eq. (12.19) is the *immediate expected cost* incurred at state i by following the action recommended by the policy μ. Denoting this cost by $c(i, \mu(i))$, we write

$$c(i, \mu(i)) = \sum_{j=1}^{N} p_{ij} g(i, \mu(i), j) \tag{12.20}$$

2. Evaluate the expectation of $J^*(X_1)$ with respect to X_1. Here, we note that if we know the cost $J^*(X_1)$ for each state X_1 of a finite-state system, then we may readily determine the expectation of $J^*(X_1)$ in terms of the transition probabilities of the underlying Markov chain by writing

$$\mathbb{E}[J^*(X_1)] = \sum_{j=1}^{N} p_{ij} J^*(j) \tag{12.21}$$

Thus, using Eqs. (12.19) to (12.21) in Eq. (12.18) and p_{ij} expressed as a function of the policy μ for the purpose of generality, we obtain the desired result

$$J^*(i) = \min_{\mu} \left(c(i, \mu(i)) + \gamma \sum_{j=1}^{N} p_{ij}(\mu) J^*(j) \right) \qquad \text{for } i = 1, 2, ..., N \tag{12.22}$$

Equation (12.22) is called *Bellman's optimality equation.* It should *not* be viewed as an algorithm. Rather, it represents a system of N equations with one equation per state. The solution of this system of equations defines the value of the optimal cost-to-go function for the N states of the environment.

There are two basic methods for computing an optimal policy. They are called policy iteration and value iteration. These two methods are described in Sections 12.4 and 12.5, respectively.

12.4 POLICY ITERATION

To set the stage for a description of the policy iteration algorithm, we begin by introducing a concept called the Q-factor, due to Watkins (1989). Consider an existing policy μ for which the cost-to-go function $J^\mu(i)$ is known for all states i. The Q-*factor* for each state $i \in \mathcal{X}$ and action $a \in \mathcal{A}_i$ is defined as *the immediate cost plus the sum of the discounted costs of all successor states under policy* μ, as shown by

$$Q^\mu(i, a) = c(i, a) + \gamma \sum_{j=1}^{n} p_{ij}(a) J^\mu(j) \tag{12.23}$$

where the action $a = \mu(i)$. Note that the Q-factors denoted by $Q^\mu(i, a)$ contain more information than the cost-to-go function $J^\mu(i)$. For example, actions may be ranked on the basis of Q-factors alone, whereas ranking on the basis of the cost-to-go function also requires knowledge of the state-transition probabilities and costs. Note also that $J^*(i)$ in Eq. (12.22) is obtained as $\min_\mu Q^\mu(i, a)$.

We may develop insight into the meaning of the Q-factor by visualizing a new system whose states are made up of the original states $1, 2, ..., N$ and all the possible state–action pairs (i, a), as portrayed in Fig. 12.2. There are two distinct possibilities that can occur:

1. The system is in state (i, a), in which case no action is taken. Transition is made automatically to state j, say, with probability $p_{ij}(a)$, and a cost $g(i, a, j)$ is incurred.
2. The system is in state i, say, in which case action $a \in \mathcal{A}_i$ is taken. The next state is (i, a), deterministically.

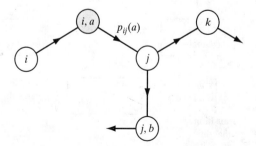

FIGURE 12.2 Illustration of two possible transitions: The transition from state (i, a) to state j is probabilistic, but the transition from state i to (i, a) is deterministic.

In light of what was said previously in Section 12.2, the policy μ is *greedy* with respect to the cost-to-go function $J^\mu(i)$ if, for all states, $\mu(i)$ is an action that satisfies the condition

$$Q^\mu(i, \mu(i)) = \min_{a \in \mathcal{A}_i} Q^\mu(i, a) \quad \text{for all } i \tag{12.24}$$

The following two observations about Eq. (12.24) are noteworthy:

1. It is possible for more than one action to minimize the set of Q-factors for some state, in which case there can be more than one greedy policy with respect to the pertinent cost-to-go function.

2. A policy can be greedy with respect to many different cost-to-go functions.

Moreover, the following fact is basic to all dynamic-programming methods:

$$Q^{\mu^*}(i, \mu^*(i)) = \min_{a \in \mathcal{A}_i} Q^{\mu^*}(i, a) \tag{12.25}$$

In this expression, μ^* is an optimal policy.

With the notions of Q-factor and greedy policy at our disposal, we are ready to describe the *policy iteration algorithm*. Specifically, the algorithm operates by alternating between two steps:

1. *a policy evaluation step*, in which the cost-to-go function for some current policy and the corresponding Q-factor are computed for all states and actions;

2. *a policy improvement step*, in which the current policy is updated in order to be greedy with respect to the cost-to-go function computed in step 1.

These two steps are illustrated in Fig. 12.3. To be specific, we start with some initial policy μ_0 and then generate a sequence of new policies $\mu_1, \mu_2, \ldots$. Given the current policy μ_n, we perform the policy evaluation step by computing the cost-to-go function $J^{\mu_n}(i)$ as the solution of the linear system of equations (see Eq. (12.22))

$$J^{\mu_n}(i) = c(i, \mu_n(i)) + \gamma \sum_{j=1}^{N} p_{ij}(\mu_n(i)) J^{\mu_n}(j), \quad i = 1, 2, \ldots, N \tag{12.26}$$

FIGURE 12.3   Block diagram of the policy iteration algorithm.

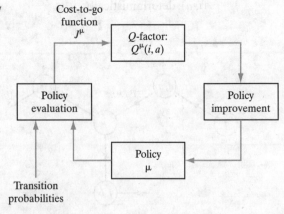

TABLE 12.1   Summary of the Policy Iteration Algorithm

1. Start with an arbitrary initial policy μ_0.
2. For $n = 0, 1, 2, ...$, compute $J^{\mu_n}(i)$ and $Q^{\mu_n}(i, a)$ for all states $i \in \mathcal{X}$ and actions $a \in \mathcal{A}_i$.
3. For each state i, compute

$$\mu_{n+1}(i) = \arg\min_{a \in \mathcal{A}_i} Q^{\mu_n}(i, a)$$

4. Repeat steps 2 and 3 until μ_{n+1} is not an improvement on μ_n, at which point the algorithm terminates with μ_n as the desired policy.

in the unknowns $J^{\mu_n}(1), J^{\mu_n}(2), ..., J^{\mu_n}(N)$. Using these results, we then compute the Q-factor for state–action pair (i, a) as follows (see Eq. (12.23)):

$$Q^{\mu_n}(i, a) = c(i, a) + \gamma \sum_{j=1}^{N} p_{ij}(a)J^{\mu_n}(j), \qquad a \in \mathcal{A}_i \text{ and } i = 1, 2, ..., N \qquad (12.27)$$

Next, we perform the policy improvement step by computing a new policy μ_{n+1} defined by (see Eq. (12.24))

$$\mu_{n+1}(i) = \arg\min_{a \in \mathcal{A}_i} Q^{\mu_n}(i, a), \qquad i = 1, 2, ..., N \qquad (12.28)$$

The two-step process just described is repeated with policy μ_{n+1} used in place of μ_n, until we have

$$J^{\mu_{n+1}}(i) = J^{\mu_n}(i) \qquad \text{for all } i$$

in which case the algorithm is terminated with policy μ_n. With $J^{\mu_{n+1}} \leq J^{\mu_n}$, we may then say that the policy iteration algorithm *will terminate after a finite number of iterations* because the underlying Markov decision process has a finite number of states. Table 12.1 presents a summary of the policy iteration algorithm based on Eqs. (12.26) to (12.28).

In the reinforcement-learning literature, the policy iteration algorithm is referred to as an *actor–critic architecture* (Barto et al., 1983). In this context, the policy improvement assumes the role of *actor*, because it is responsible for the way in which an agent acts. By the same token, the policy evaluation assumes the role of *critic*, because it is responsible for criticizing the action taken by the agent.

12.5   VALUE ITERATION

In the policy iteration algorithm, the cost-to-go function has to be recomputed entirely at each iteration of the algorithm, which is expensive. Even though the cost-to-go function for the new policy may be similar to that for the old policy, unfortunately there is no dramatic shortcut for this computation. There is, however, another method for finding the optimal policy that avoids the burdensome task of repeatedly computing the cost-to-go function. This alternative method, based on successive approximations, is known as the value iteration algorithm.

The *value iteration algorithm* involves solving Bellman's optimality equation, given in Eq. (12.22), for each of a sequence of finite-horizon problems. In the limit, the cost-to-go function of the finite-horizon problem converges uniformly over all states to the corresponding cost-to-go function of the infinite-horizon problem as the number of iterations of the algorithm approaches infinity (Ross, 1983; Bertsekas, 2007).

Let $J_n(i)$ denote the cost-to-go function for state i at iteration n of the value iteration algorithm. The algorithm begins with an arbitrary guess $J_0(i)$ for $i = 1, 2, ..., N$. If some estimate of the optimal cost-to-go function $J^*(i)$ is available, it should be used as the initial value $J_0(i)$. Once $J_0(i)$ has been chosen, we may compute the sequence of cost-to-go functions $J_1(i), J_2(i), ...$, using the value iteration algorithm

$$J_{n+1}(i) = \min_{a \in A_i} \left\{ c(i, a) + \gamma \sum_{j=1}^{N} p_{ij}(a) J_n(j) \right\}, \qquad i = 1, 2, ..., N \qquad (12.29)$$

Application of the update to the cost-to-go function, described in Eq. (12.29) for state i, is referred to as *backing up of i's cost*. This backup is a direct implementation of Bellman's optimality equation, given in Eq. (12.22). Note that the values of the cost-to-go functions in Eq. (12.29) for states $i = 1, 2, ..., N$ are backed up simultaneously on each iteration of the algorithm. This method of implementation represents the traditional *synchronous* form of the value iteration algorithm.[3] Thus, starting from arbitrary initial values $J_0(1), J_0(2), ..., J_0(N)$, the algorithm described by Eq. (12.29) converges to the corresponding optimal values $J^*(1), J^*(2), ..., J^*(N)$ as the number of iterations, n, approaches infinity. In other words, value iteration requires an *infinite number of iterations.*

Unlike the policy iteration algorithm, an optimal policy is not computed directly in the value iteration algorithm. Rather, the optimal values $J^*(1), J^*(2), ..., J^*(N)$ are first computed using Eq. (12.29). Then a greedy policy with respect to that optimal set is obtained as an optimal policy. That is,

$$\mu^*(i) = \arg \min_{a \in \mathcal{A}_i} Q^*(i, a), \qquad i = 1, 2, ..., N \qquad (12.30)$$

where

$$Q^*(i, a) = c(i, a) + \gamma \sum_{j=1}^{N} p_{ij}(a) J^*(j), \qquad i = 1, 2, ..., N \qquad (12.31)$$

A summary of the value iteration algorithm, based on Eqs. (12.29) to (12.31), is presented in Table 12.2. This summary includes a stopping criterion for Eq. (12.29).

EXAMPLE 1 Relationship Between Value Iteration and Policy Iteration

To understand how value iteration works in relation to policy iteration, consider the illustrative example of Fig. 12.4. Part (a) of the figure depicts the backup operations involved in computing the Q-factor $Q^\mu(i, a)$ for policy iteration, and part (b) depicts the corresponding backup operations for computing the Q-factor $Q^*(i, a)$ for value iteration. Each unshaded small circle in the figure represents a state and each red-shaded small circle represents a state-action pair. Suppose we start from state j. The agent may take any one of three possible actions, and the environment

TABLE 12.2   Summary of the Value Iteration Algorithm

1. Start with arbitrary initial value $J_0(i)$ for state $i = 1, 2, ..., N$.
2. For $n = 0, 1, 2, ...,$ compute

$$J_{n+1}(i) = \min_{a \in \mathcal{A}_i} \left\{ c(i, a) + \gamma \sum_{j=1}^{N} p_{ij}(a) J_n(j), \right\}, \qquad \begin{array}{l} a \in \mathcal{A}_i \\ i = 1, 2, ..., N \end{array}$$

Continue this computation until

$$|J_{n+1}(i) - J_n(i)| < \epsilon \qquad \text{for each state } i$$

where ϵ is a prescribed tolerance parameter. It is presumed that ϵ is sufficiently small for $J_n(i)$ to be close enough to the optimal cost-to-go function $J^*(i)$. We may then set

$$J_n(i) = J^*(i) \qquad \text{for all states } i$$

3. Compute the Q-factor

$$Q^*(i, a) = c(i, a) + \gamma \sum_{j=1}^{N} p_{ij}(a) J^*(j) \qquad \begin{array}{l} \text{for } a \in \mathcal{A}_i \text{ and} \\ i = 1, 2, ..., N \end{array}$$

Hence, determine the optimal policy as a greedy policy for $J^*(i)$:

$$\mu^*(i) = \arg \min_{a \in \mathcal{A}_i} Q^*(i, a)$$

could respond with any one of six possible state-action pairs; (i, a) is one such state-action pair, for which the transition cost is denoted by $g(i, j)$.

Examining Fig. 12.4, we see that the backup operations for policy iteration and those for value iteration are identical, except for one basic difference: Value iteration requires that the maximum be taken over all possible state-action pairs as indicated in Fig. 12.4(b).   ∎

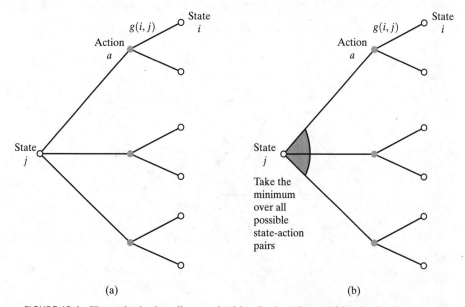

FIGURE 12.4   Illustrative backup diagrams for (a) policy iteration and (b) value iteration.

EXAMPLE 2 The Stagecoach Problem

To illustrate the usefulness of the Q-factor in dynamic programming, we consider the *stagecoach problem*: A fortune seeker in Missouri decided to go west to join the gold rush in California in the mid-nineteenth century (Hiller and Lieberman, 1995). The journey required traveling by stagecoach through unsettled country, which posed a serious danger of attack by marauders along the way. The starting point of the journey (Missouri) and the destination (California) were fixed, but there was considerable choice as to which other eight states to travel through en route, as shown in Fig. 12.5. In this figure, we have the following conditions:

- There is a total of 10 states, with each state represented by a letter.
- The direction of travel is from left to right.
- There are four stages (i.e., stagecoach runs) from the point of embarkation in state A (Missouri) to the destination in state J (California).
- In moving from one state to the next, the action taken by the fortune seeker is to move up, straight, or down.
- There is a total of 18 possible routes from state A to state J.

Figure 12.5 also includes the cost of a life insurance policy for taking any stagecoach run, based on a careful evaluation of the safety of that run. The problem is to find the route from state A to state J with the cheapest insurance policy.

To find the optimum route, we consider a sequence of finite-horizon problems, starting from the destination in state J and working backward. This procedure is in accordance with Bellman's principle of optimality, described in Section 12.3.

Calculating the Q-factors for the last stage before the destination, we readily find in Fig. 12.6a that the terminal Q-values are as follows:

$$Q(H, \text{down}) = 3$$
$$Q(I, \text{up}) = 4$$

These numbers are indicated on states H and I, respectively, in Fig. 12.6a.

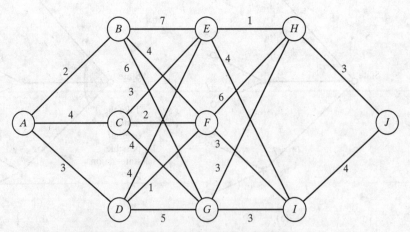

FIGURE 12.5 Flow graph for stagecoach problem.

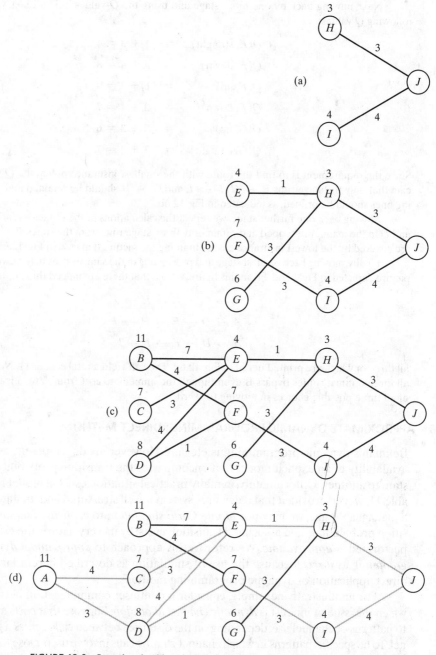

FIGURE 12.6 Steps involved in calculating the Q-factors for the stagecoach problem. The routes (printed in red) from A to J are the optimal ones.

Next, moving back by one more stage and using the Q-values in Fig. 12.6a, we have the following Q values:

$$Q(E, \text{straight}) = 1 + 3 = 4$$
$$Q(E, \text{down}) = 4 + 4 = 8$$
$$Q(F, \text{up}) = 6 + 3 = 9$$
$$Q(F, \text{down}) = 3 + 4 = 7$$
$$Q(G, \text{up}) = 3 + 3 = 6$$
$$Q(G, \text{straight}) = 3 + 4 = 7$$

Since the requirement is to find the route with the smallest insurance policy, the Q-values indicate that only the stage runs $E \rightarrow H, F \rightarrow I$, and $G \rightarrow H$ should be retained and the remaining ones should be pruned, as indicated in Fig. 12.6b.

Moving back one further stage, we repeat the calculations of the Q-factors for states B, C, and D in the manner described and retain only those stage runs from the states B, C, and D that are covered by the lowest insurance costs, obtaining the picture depicted in Fig. 12.6c.

Finally, moving back one last stage and proceeding in the same way as before, we obtain the picture depicted in Fig. 12.6d. From this figure, we see that there are indeed three optimal routes:

$$A \rightarrow C \rightarrow E \rightarrow H \rightarrow J$$
$$A \rightarrow D \rightarrow E \rightarrow H \rightarrow J$$
$$A \rightarrow D \rightarrow F \rightarrow I \rightarrow J$$

all three of which are printed in red in Fig. 12.6d. They all yield a total cost of 11. Note also that all three optimal routes bypass B even though the immediate cost from A to B is the smallest of all three possible choices in moving forward. ∎

12.6 APPROXIMATE DYNAMIC PROGRAMMING: DIRECT METHODS

Bellman's dynamic programming is elegant. However, its development assumes the availability of an explicit model that encompasses the transition probability from one state to another. Unfortunately, in many practical situations, such a model is not available. However, provided that a dynamic system is well structured and its state space has a manageable size, we may use *Monte Carlo simulation* to *explicitly estimate* the transition probabilities and associated transition costs; by its very nature, the estimation so performed is *approximate*. We refer to this approach to *approximate dynamic programming* as *direct*, because the use of simulation as described herein facilitates the direct application of dynamic programming methods.

For an illustrative example, consider a multiuser communication network about which the issue of interest is *dynamic channel allocation*. Suppose that costs are assigned to patterns of channel use, depending on the distances between calls across a given channel. To be specific, patterns in which channel-sharing calls involve users close to each other are favored over patterns in which channel-sharing calls are far apart from each other. In other words, the communication network is equipped with a well-developed cost structure for servicing calls made by users operating in a disciplined manner within the network. Given such a dynamic system, it is possible to use Monte Carlo simulation to permit the direct approximation of dynamic programming to the network (Nie and Haykin, 1998).

Basically, the rationale behind the direct approximation of dynamic programming is to use computer simulation to generate *multiple system trajectories*, which lead to the construction of a *look-up table* with a separate entry for the value of each state; the larger we make the number of system trajectories, the more reliable the simulation results will naturally be. In particular, a separate variable $J(i)$ is kept in memory every time state i is visited by a trajectory of the simulated system. In so doing, we will have simulated a dynamic system with probabilistic transitions from state i to state j and incurring the immediate transition cost $g(i, j)$.

The stage is thus set for direct approximation of the two basic dynamic programming methods: value iteration and policy iteration. In particular,

- in the case of value iteration, we obtain temporal-difference learning;
- in the case of policy iteration, we obtain Q-learning.

These two algorithms, respectively discussed in Sections 12.7 and 12.8, are well known in the reinforcement learning literature. We may therefore view reinforcement learning as the *direct approximation of dynamic programming.*

One final comment is in order: Naturally, the construction of a look-up table is *memory limited*. It follows therefore that the practical use of temporal-difference and Q-learning is limited to situations in which the state-space is of moderate size.

12.7 TEMPORAL-DIFFERENCE LEARNING

The idea of temporal-difference learning was first described in Sutton (1988). We begin the discussion by considering the simplest version of this approximate form of dynamic programming, called the *TD(0) algorithm*; "TD" stands for "temporal difference."

TD(0) Learning Algorithm

Let μ be a policy that leads to the evolution of the states of a Markov decision process. The states are described by the sequence $\{i_n\}_{n=0}^N$; the total number of state transitions is N, and the terminal state $i_N = 0$. Let $g(i_n, i_{n+1})$ be the immediate cost incurred in the transition from state i_n to state i_{n+1}, where the index $n = 0, 1, ..., N-1$. Then according to the Bellman equation, the cost-to-go function is defined by

$$J^\mu(i_n) = \mathbb{E}[g(i_n, i_{n+1}) + J^\mu(i_{n+1})], \qquad n = 0, 1, ..., N - 1 \qquad (12.32)$$

where, for each n, the ensemble averaging is performed over all possible occurrences of the state i_{n+1}. From a practical perspective, what we need is an iterative algorithm that avoids the need for ensemble averaging. To this end, we may invoke the *Robbins–Monro stochastic approximation*, which was discussed in Chapter 3.

To recall the essence of this stochastic approximation, consider the relationship

$$r^+ = (1 - \eta)r + \eta g(r, \bar{v})$$

where r is the old value, η is a small positive *step-size parameter* that could change from one iteration to the next, and the new variable $\bar{v}$ is a random variable generated according to the distribution $p_{V|R}(\bar{v}|r)$; as in previous chapters, the plus sign used as a superscript in r^+ signifies "updating."

Thus, applying the Robbins–Monro stochastic approximation to the Bellman equation given in Eq. (12.32), we obtain

$$J^+(i_n) = (1 - \eta)J(i_n) + \eta[g(i_n, i_{n+1}) + J(i_{n+1})]$$
$$= J(i_n) + \eta[g(i_n, i_{n+1}) + J(i_{n+1}) - J(i_n)] \qquad (12.33)$$

where $J^+(i_n)$ on the left-hand side is an *updated estimate* that is computed every time the state i_n is visited. To simplify matters, we now introduce the *temporal difference*, defined by

$$d_n = g(i_n, i_{n+1}) + J(i_{n+1}) - J(i_n), \qquad n = 0, 1, ..., N - 1 \qquad (12.34)$$

which represents the difference between two quantities:

- the overall cost-to-go function based on the simulated outcome of the current state—namely, $g(i_n, i_{n+1}) + J(i_{n+1})$;
- the current estimate $J(i_n)$.

In effect, the temporal difference d_n provides the signal to determine whether the current estimate $J(i_n)$ should be increased or decreased. Using the definition of Eq. (12.34), we may now rewrite the iterative algorithm of Eq. (12.33) in the simplified form

$$J^+(i_n) = J(i_n) + \eta d_n \qquad (12.35)$$

where $J(i_n)$ is the *current estimate*, $J^+(i_n)$ is the *updated estimate*, and the product term $\eta_n d(n)$ is the *correction* applied to the current estimate in order to produce the updated one.

The one-step update rule of Eq. (12.35) is commonly referred to as the *TD(0) algorithm*; the rationale for this terminology will become apparent later in the section. This update is performed every time the state i_n is visited and the temporal difference d_n becomes available.

Monte Carlo Simulation Algorithm

Equation (12.35) describes one particular iterative algorithm, derived from Bellman's equation. For another point of view and a different algorithm, consider the cost-to-go-function

$$J^\mu(i_n) = \mathbb{E}\left[\sum_{k=0}^{N-n-1} g(i_{n+k}, i_{n+k+1}) \right], \qquad n = 0, 1, ..., N - 1 \qquad (12.36)$$

where, this time, the expectation operator is applied across the individual costs pertaining to the entire sequence of state transition. Here again, applying the Robbins–Monro stochastic approximate to Eq. (12.36), we obtain (after collecting common terms)

$$J^+(i_n) = J(i_n) + \eta_k \left(\sum_{k=0}^{N-n-1} g(i_{n+k}, i_{n+k+1}) - J(i_n) \right) \qquad (12.37)$$

where η_k is a time-varying step-size (learning-rate) parameter. This update formula may be expressed in the equivalent form

$$J^+(i_n) = J(i_n) + \eta_k[g(i_n, i_{n+1}) + J(i_{n+1}) - J(i_n)$$
$$+ g(i_{n+1}, i_{n+2}) + J(i_{n+2}) - J(i_{n+1})$$
$$\vdots$$

$$+ \ g(i_{N-2}, i_{N-1}) + J(i_{N-1}) - J(i_{N-2})$$
$$+ \ g(i_{N-1}, i_N) + J(i_N) - J(i_{N-1})]$$

where, in the last line, we have used the property that the terminal state $i_N = 0$, which, correspondingly, means that the cost $J(i_N) = 0$. Accordingly, invoking the definition of temporal difference introduced in Eq. (12.34), we find that the iterative algorithm of Eq. (12.37) assumes the simplified form

$$J^+(i_n) = J(i_n) + \sum_{k=0}^{N-n-1} d_{n+k} \tag{12.38}$$

which embodies the entire sequence of temporal differences.

In fact, Eq. (12.38) is an iterative implementation of Monte Carlo simulation of the trajectory $\{i_n, i_{n+1}, ..., i_N\}$, where $i_N = 0$—hence the reference to this equation as the *Monte Carlo simulation algorithm*. To justify this statement, we make two assumptions:

1. The different simulated system trajectories are statistically independent.
2. Each trajectory is generated in accordance with a Markov decision process under policy μ.

To proceed with the justification, let $c(i_n)$ denote the total sum of the costs incurred by the sequence $\{i_n, i_{n+1}, ..., i_N\}$ when the state i_n is encountered at time n of the simulation; that is,

$$c(i_n) = \sum_{k=0}^{N-n-1} g(i_{n+k}, i_{n+k+1}), \qquad n = 0, 1, ..., N - 1 \tag{12.39}$$

Then, we may use

$$J(i_n) = \frac{1}{T} \sum_{n=1}^{T} c(i_n) \tag{12.40}$$

which is computed after having visited the state i_n for a total of T simulation trials. Hence, the estimate of the ensemble-averaged cost-to-go function is

$$J^\mu(i_n) = \mathbb{E}[c(i_n)] \qquad \text{for all } n \tag{12.41}$$

It is a straightforward matter to show that the sample mean of Eq. (12.40) may be calculated using the iterative formula

$$J^+(i_n) = J(i_n) + \eta_n(c(i_n) - J(i_n)) \tag{12.42}$$

Starting with the initial condition

$$J(i_n) = 0$$

and setting the step-size parameter

$$\eta_n = \frac{1}{n}, \qquad n = 1, 2, ... \tag{12.43}$$

we find that Eq. (12.42) is simply a rewrite of the iterative algorithm of Eq. (12.38), using the new notations introduced for treating the Monte Carlo simulation viewpoint of temporal differences.

Unified View of Temporal-Difference Learning: TD(λ)

In the discussion just presented on temporal-difference learning, we derived two limiting forms of iterative algorithms:

- The iterative algorithm of Eq. (12.35), derived from the Bellman equation, accounts for the immediate cost of transition from state i_n to state i_{n+1}.
- The iterative algorithm of Eq. (12.38), rooted in Monte Carlo simulation, accounts for the cumulative cost incurred over the entire sequence of state transitions.

Clearly, there must be a middle ground between these two iterative procedures, which deserves consideration of its own. To pursue this middle ground, we introduce two modifications (Bertsekas and Tsitsiklis, 1996):

1. We expand the Bellman equation so as to account for the individual costs incurred in the first $l + 1$ state transitions for some fixed l:

$$J^{\mu}(i_n) = \mathbb{E}\left[\sum_{k=0}^{l} g(i_{n+k}, i_{n+k+1}) + J^{\mu}(i_{n+l+1})\right] \tag{12.44}$$

2. With no prior knowledge that would favor one desirable value of l over another, we form a *weighted average* over all the possible multistep Bellman equations by multiplying the right-hand side of Eq. (12.44) by $(1 - \lambda)\lambda^l$ and then summing over l for some fixed $\lambda < 1$:

$$J^{\mu}(i_n) = (1 - \lambda)\mathbb{E}\left[\sum_{l=0}^{\infty}\lambda^l\left(\sum_{k=0}^{l} g(i_{n+k}, i_{n+k+1}) + J^{\mu}(i_{n+l+1})\right)\right]$$

Since we are dealing with linear equations, we may interchange the order of summations:

$$J^{\mu}(i_n) = \mathbb{E}\left[(1 - \lambda)\sum_{k=0}^{l} g(i_{n+k}, i_{n+k+1})\sum_{l=k}^{\infty}\lambda^l + (1 - \lambda)\sum_{l=0}^{\infty}\lambda^l J^{\mu}(i_{n+l+1})\right] \tag{12.45}$$

We now take note of the following two equalities:

1.
$$(1 - \lambda)\sum_{l=k}^{\infty}\lambda^l = \sum_{l=k}^{\infty}\lambda^l - \sum_{l=k}^{\infty}\lambda^{l+1}$$

$$= \lambda^k$$

2.
$$(1 - \lambda)\sum_{l=0}^{\infty}\lambda^l J^{\mu}(i_{n+l+1}) = \sum_{l=0}^{\infty}\lambda^l J^{\mu}(i_{n+l+1}) - \sum_{l=0}^{\infty}\lambda^{l+1}J^{\mu}(i_{n+l+1})$$

$$= \sum_{l=0}^{\infty}\lambda^l J^{\mu}(i_{n+l+1}) - \sum_{l=0}^{\infty}\lambda^l J^{\mu}(i_{n+l}) + J^{\mu}(i_n)$$

Accordingly, we may recast Eq. (12.45) in the equivalent form

$$J^{\mu}(i_n) = \mathbb{E}\left[\sum_{k=0}^{\infty}\lambda^k(g(i_{n+k}, i_{n+k+1}) + \lambda^k J^{\mu}(i_{n+k+1}) - \lambda^k J^{\mu}(i_{n+k}))\right] + J^{\mu}(i_n) \tag{12.46}$$

where, for the three terms inside the square brackets on the right-hand side, we have simply used k in place of l for compactness of the presentation.

The stage is now set for us to simplify matters by making use of the definition of the temporal difference introduced in Eq. (12.34). To do so, we rewrite Eq. (12.46) one more time in the simplified form

$$J^\mu(i_n) = \mathbb{E}\left[\sum_{k=0}^{\infty} \lambda^k d_{n+k}\right] + J^\mu(i_n)$$

$$= \mathbb{E}\left[\sum_{k=n}^{\infty} \lambda^{k-n} d_k\right] + J^\mu(i_n), \quad \text{for } n = 0, 1, ..., N - 1 \qquad (12.47)$$

Recognizing that for some fixed value of λ, we have $\mathbb{E}[d_k] = 0$ for all k in accordance with Bellman's equation, we hardly find Eq. (12.47) surprising. In a sense, we may sum up the net result of the analysis following the modifications under points 1 and 2 as merely adding the expectation $\mathbb{E}\left[\sum_{k=n}^{\infty} \lambda^{k-n} d_k\right] = 0$ to the right-hand side of the equality $\mathbb{E}[J^\mu(i_n)] = \mathbb{E}[J^\mu(i_n)]$ for all n. Nevertheless, this result does have significant implications when we go on to apply the Robbins–Monro stochastic approximation, as shown next.

Specifically, the application of this approximation to Eq. (12.47) yields the iterative algorithm

$$J^+(i_n) = (1 - \eta)J(i_n) + \eta\left(\sum_{k=n}^{\infty} \lambda^{k-n} d_k + J(i_n)\right)$$

which, after the cancellation of terms, simplifies to

$$J^+(i_n) = J(i_n) + \eta\sum_{k=n}^{\infty} \lambda^{k-n} d_k \qquad (12.48)$$

The iterative algorithm of Eq. (12.48) is commonly referred to as TD(λ); as mentioned previously, TD stands for "temporal difference". This algorithm was originated by Sutton (1988). It is noteworthy that for the derivation of this algorithm, we used ideas from Bellman's dynamic programming, Monte Carlo simulation, and stochastic approximation.

Moreover, TD(λ) includes the iterative algorithms of Eqs. (12.35) and (12.38) as two special cases:

1. If we let $\lambda = 0$ and use the convention that $0^0 = 1$, then Eq. (12.48) reduces to

$$J^+(i_n) = J(i_n) + \eta d_n$$

which is a repeat of Eq. (12.35), derived using the dynamic-programming method. Indeed, it is for this reason that the algorithm of Eq. (12.35) is referred to as TD(0), as pointed out earlier.

2. For the other limiting case, if we let $\lambda = 1$, then Eq. (12.48) reduces to

$$J^+(i_n) = J(i_n) + \eta\sum_{k=0}^{N-n-1} d_{n+k}$$

which, except for the scaling factor η, is a repeat of Eq. (12.38), derived using the Monte Carlo evaluation method. Here it is noted that the temporal difference d_n is zero for n equal to or greater than the planning horizon N.

In summary, we may state:

The TD methods, described in Eq. (12.48), are on-line prediction methods that learn how to compute their estimates, partly, on the basis of other estimates.

In other words, TD methods are of a *bootstraping* kind. Most importantly, they do not require a model of the environment.

Practical Considerations

According to Bertsekas and Tsitsiklis (1996), the estimate $J(i_n)$, for some state i_n, produced by the TD(λ) algorithm is guaranteed to converge to the ensemble-averaged value $J^\mu(\lambda)$ for policy μ, provided that two conditions are satisfied:

1. The state i_n is visited by trajectories infinitely often for all n.
2. The step-size parameter η is allowed to diminish toward zero at an appropriate rate.

The proof of convergence presented in Bertsekas and Tsitsiklis (1996) appears to show that there is no theoretical obstacle to changing the parameter λ in the course of learning performed by the TD(λ) algorithm. The theoretical considerations presented therein suggest that a sensible strategy for choosing a suitable value for λ is to start the operation of the TD(λ) algorithm with a large value of λ close to unity (i.e., initially favoring Monte Carlo estimation of the ensemble-averaged cost-to-go function) and then allow λ to decrease slowly to zero (i.e., moving toward estimates produced in accordance with the Bellman equation). In a loose sense, λ is put through a form of annealing over the course of time.

12.8 Q-LEARNING

The TD(λ) algorithm, derived in the previous section as a stochastic approximation of dynamic programming, is a model-free algorithm. In this section, we describe another stochastic algorithm, known as *Q-learning*, that also does not require explicit knowledge of the environment. Q-learning was first derived in Watkins (1989). The letter Q in Q-learning does not signify anything special; it is merely a notation that was adopted by Watkins in his original derivation of the algorithm.

To motivate the discussion of Q-learning, consider the reinforcement-learning system depicted in Fig. 12.1. The behavioral task of this system is to find an optimal (i.e., minimal-cost) policy after trying out various possible sequences of actions and observing the costs incurred and the state transitions that occur. The policy used to generate behavior is called the *behavior policy*. This policy is separated from the *estimation policy*, the purpose of which is to estimate the value of a policy. With these two policies being separated from each other, Q-learning is said to be an *off-policy method* for control. A side benefit gained from this separation is that the estimation policy can be greedy, while the behavior policy is left to sample all possible actions. An off-policy method is to be distinguished from an *on-policy method*, where the value of a policy is being estimated while it is being used for control at the same time.

The Q-learning Algorithm

To proceed with the derivation of the Q-learning algorithm, let

$$s_n = (i_n, a_n, j_n, g_n) \tag{12.49}$$

denote a *four-tuple sample* consisting of a trial action a_n performed on state i_n that results in a transition to the new state $j_n = i_n + 1$ at a cost defined by

$$g_n = g(i_n, a_n, j_n) \tag{12.50}$$

where n denotes discrete time. Given such a scenario, we may now raise the following fundamental question:

> *Is there any on-line procedure for learning an optimal control policy through experience that is gained solely on the basis of observing samples of the form s_n defined in Eqs. (12.49) and (12.50)?*

The answer to this question is an emphatic yes, and it is to be found in Q-learning.[4]

The *Q-learning algorithm* is an incremental dynamic-programming procedure that determines the optimal policy in a step-by-step manner. It is highly suited for solving Markov decision problems without explicit knowledge of the transition probabilities. However, in a manner similar to TD(λ), successful use of Q-learning hinges on the assumption that the state of the environment is *fully observable*, which, in turn, means that the environment is a fully observable Markov chain.

We recall from Section 12.4 that the Q-factor $Q(i, a)$ for state–action pair (i, a) is defined by Eq. (12.23), and Bellman's optimality equation is defined by Eq. (12.22). By combining these two equations and using the definition of the immediate expected cost $c(i, a)$ given in Eq. (12.20), we obtain

$$Q^*(i, a) = \sum_{j=1}^{N} p_{ij}(a) \left(g(i, a, j) + \gamma \min_{b \in \mathcal{A}_i} Q^*(j, b) \right) \quad \text{for all } (i, a) \tag{12.51}$$

which can be viewed as a two-step version of Bellman's optimality equation. The solutions to the linear system of equations in Eq. (12.51) define the optimal Q-factors $Q^*(i, a)$ uniquely for all state–action pairs (i, a).

We may use the value iteration algorithm formulated in Section 12.4 in terms of the Q-factors to solve this linear system of equations. Thus, for one iteration of the algorithm, we have

$$Q^*(i, a) = \sum_{j=1}^{N} p_{ij}(a) \left(g(i, a, j) + \gamma \min_{b \in \mathcal{A}_i} Q(j, b) \right) \quad \text{for all } (i, a)$$

The small step-size version of this iteration is described by

$$Q^*(i, a) = (1 - \eta)Q(i, a) + \eta \sum_{j=1}^{N} p_{ij}(a) \left(g(i, a, j) + \gamma \min_{b \in \mathcal{A}_i} Q(j, b) \right) \quad \text{for all } (i, a) \tag{12.52}$$

where η is a small *learning-rate parameter* that lies in the range $0 < \eta < 1$.

As it stands, an iteration of the value iteration algorithm described in Eq. (12.52) requires knowledge of the transition probabilities. We may eliminate the need for this prior knowledge by formulating a *stochastic* version of this equation. Specifically, the averaging performed in an iteration of Eq. (12.52) over all possible states is replaced by a single sample, thereby resulting in an update for the Q-factor given as

$$Q_{n+1}(i, a) = (1 - \eta_n(i, a))Q_n(i, a) + \eta_n(i, a)[g(i, a, j) + \gamma J_n(j)] \quad \text{for } (i, a) = (i_n, a_n)$$
(12.53)

where

$$J_n(j) = \min_{b \in \mathcal{A}_i} Q_n(j, b)$$
(12.54)

and j is the successor state to the state i and $\eta_n(i, a)$ is the learning-rate parameter at time-step n for the state–action pair (i, a). The update equation of Eq. (12.53) applies to the current state–action pair (i_n, a_n), for which $j = j_n$ in accordance with Eq. (12.49). For all other admissible state–action pairs, the Q-factors remain unchanged, as shown by

$$Q_{n+1}(i, a) = Q_n(i, a) \quad \text{for all } (i, a) \neq (i_n, a_n)$$
(12.55)

Equations (12.53) to (12.55) constitute one iteration of the *Q-learning algorithm*.

Convergence Theorem[5]

Suppose that the learning-rate parameter $\eta_n(i, a)$ satisfies the conditions

$$\sum_{n=0}^{\infty} \eta_n(i, a) = \infty \quad \text{and} \quad \sum_{n=0}^{\infty} \eta_n^2(i, a) < \infty \quad \text{for all } (i, a)$$
(12.56)

Then, the sequence of Q-factors $\{Q_n(i, a)\}$ generated by the Q-learning algorithm converges with probability 1 to the optimal value $Q^*(i, a)$ for all state–action pairs (i, a) as the number of iterations n approaches infinity, provided that all state–action pairs are visited infinitely often.

An example of a time-varying learning parameter that guarantees convergence of the algorithm is

$$\eta_n = \frac{\alpha}{\beta + n}, \quad n = 1, 2, \dots$$
(12.57)

where α and β are positive numbers.

Summarizing Remarks

The Q-learning algorithm may be viewed in one of two equivalent ways:

> *as a Robins-Monro stochastic approximation algorithm, or*
> *as a combination of value iteration and Monte Carlo simulation.*

The algorithm backs up the Q-factor for a *single* state-action pair at each iteration. Most importantly, in the limit, the algorithm converges to the optimal Q-values without having to form an explicit model of the underlying Markovian decision process. Once the optimal Q-values have been computed, an optimal policy is determined with relatively small computational effort by using the formula of Eq. (12.30).

The convergence of Q-learning to an optimal policy assumes the use of a *look-up table* representation of the Q-factors $Q_n(i, a)$ for the state-action pair (i, a). This method of representation is straightforward and computationally efficient; however, it only works provided that the joint input space consisting of state-action pairs is of a moderate size.

Exploration

In policy iteration, all potentially important parts of the state space should be explored. In Q-learning, we have an additional requirement: All potentially profitable actions should be tried as well. In particular, all admissible state–action pairs should be explored often enough to satisfy the convergence theorem. For a greedy policy denoted by μ, only the state–action pairs $(i, \mu(i))$ are explored. Unfortunately, there is no guarantee that all profitable actions would be tried, even if the entire state space is explored.

What we need is a strategy that expands on Q-learning by providing a compromise between two conflicting objectives (Thrun, 1992):

- *exploration*, which ensures that all admissible state–action pairs are explored often enough to satisfy the Q-learning convergence theorem;
- *exploitation*, which seeks to minimize the cost-to-go function by following a greedy policy.

One way to achieve this compromise is to follow a *mixed nonstationary policy* that switches between an auxiliary Markov process and the original Markov process controlled by a stationary greedy policy determined by Q-learning (Cybenko, 1995). The auxiliary process has the following interpretation: The transition probabilities between possible states are determined by the transition probabilities of the original controlled process, with the added ingredient that the corresponding actions are uniformly randomized. The mixture policy starts in any state of the auxiliary process and chooses actions by following it; then it switches to the original controlled process, back and forth between the two processes in the manner illustrated in Fig. 12.7. The time spent operating on the auxiliary process occupies a fixed number of steps, L, defined as twice the longest expected time to visit all states of the auxiliary process. The time spent operating on the original controlled process increases progressively with every switch. Let n_k denote the times at which we switch from the auxiliary process to the original controlled process, and m_k denote the times at which we switch back to the auxiliary process, with n_k and m_k defined as follows, respectively:

$$n_k = m_{k-1} + L, \qquad k = 1, 2, ..., \text{ and } m_0 = 1 \qquad (12.58)$$

and

$$m_k = n_k + kL, \qquad k = 1, 2, ...$$

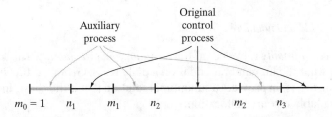

Auxiliary process

Original control process

$m_0 = 1 \quad n_1 \qquad m_1 \qquad n_2 \qquad\qquad m_2 \qquad n_3$

FIGURE 12.7   The time slots pertaining to the auxiliary and original control processes.

The auxiliary process is constructed in such a way that as $k \to \infty$, there is an infinite number of visits to all states with probability 1, thereby guaranteeing convergence to the optimal Q-factors. Moreover, as $k \to \infty$, the time spent by the mixed policy operating in the auxiliary process becomes an asymptotically small fraction of the time spent operating in the original controlled process, which in turn means that the mixed policy asymptotically converges to a greedy policy. Hence, given the convergence of the Q-factors to their optimal values, the greedy policy must indeed be optimal, provided that the policy becomes greedy slowly enough.

12.9 APPROXIMATE DYNAMIC PROGRAMMING: INDIRECT METHODS

Typically, large-scale dynamic systems have a state space of high dimensionality. Consequently, when we deal with such a system, we experience the *"curse"-of-dimensionality problem*, which refers to the exponential growth in computational complexity with the dimension of the state space. Unfortunately, the curse of dimensionality renders not only Bellman's dynamic programming, but, naturally, its two direct approximate forms— temporal difference learning and Q-learning—intractable. To illustrate this important practical problem, consider a dynamic-programming problem involving a total of N possible states and M admissible actions for each state; in such a system, each iteration of the value-iteration algorithm, for example, requires N^2M operations for a stationary policy. This computational level of operations makes it impossible to complete even one iteration of the algorithm when N is very large.

In order to deal with difficult real-world problems involving a large number of states, we may look to some appropriate form of approximate dynamic programming, which is different from the direct approach discussed in Section 12.6. In particular, rather than explicitly estimate the transition probabilities and associated transition costs as we did in Section 12.6, we now do the following:

> *Use Monte Carlo simulation to generate one or more system trajectories, so as to approximate the cost-to-go function of a given policy, or even the optimal cost-to-go function, and then optimize the approximation in some statistical sense.*

We refer to this approach to approximate dynamic programming as *indirect*,[6] to distinguish it from the direct approach discussed in Section 12.6. In any event, it is presumed that the state space of the simulated dynamic system has a dimensionality lower than that of the original dynamic system.

Thus, having abandoned the notion of optimality, we may capture the goal of the indirect approach to approximate dynamic programming in the following simple statement (Werbos, 2003):

> *Do as well as possible, and not more.*

In effect, *performance optimality* is traded off for *computational tractability*. This kind of strategy is precisely what the human brain does on a daily basis: Given a difficult decision-making problem, the brain provides a suboptimal solution that is the "best" in terms of reliability and available resource allocation.

With Bellman's theory of dynamic programming as the *frame of reference*, the goal of approximate dynamic programming may now be stated as follows:

Find a function $\tilde{J}(i, \mathbf{w})$ that approximates the optimal cost-to-go function $J^*(i)$ for state i, such that the cost difference $J^*(i) - \tilde{J}(i, \mathbf{w})$ is minimized according to some statistical criterion.

With this goal in mind, we may now raise two basic questions:

Question 1: How do we choose the approximation function $\tilde{J}(i, \mathbf{w})$ in the first place?

Question 2: Having chosen an appropriate approximation function $\tilde{J}(i, \mathbf{w})$, how do we adapt the weight vector $\mathbf{w}$ so as to provide the "best fit" to Bellman's equation of optimality?

To answer question 1, we have the option of a linear or nonlinear approximating function, which in turn will determine the answer to question 2. In what follows, we will consider the linear approach first, followed by the nonlinear approach.

Linear Approach to Approximate Dynamic Programming

In this approach, the common way to proceed is to express the approximating function $\tilde{J}(i, \mathbf{w})$ as a linear function in the parameter vector $\mathbf{w}$; that is,

$$\tilde{J}(i, \mathbf{w}) = \sum_j \varphi_{ij} w_j$$
$$= \boldsymbol{\phi}_i^T \mathbf{w} \quad \text{for all } i \qquad (12.59)$$

where the $\boldsymbol{\phi}_i$ are preprogrammed *basis functions*, or *features*, chosen by the designer of the approximating scheme. The approximation of Eq. (12.59) is illustrated in Fig. 12.8.

The linear approach to approximate dynamic programming has a number of appealing virtues:

(i) A linear function approximator is easy to formulate and analyze in mathematical terms; consequently, the approximator's underlying behavior is equally easy to understand.

(ii) Ordinarily, mathematical formalism of a linear approximator provides insight into what could go wrong in its actual operation, thereby making it feasible to fix whatever may have gone wrong.

(iii) Nonlinearities in the true cost-to-go function may be captured approximately in specially chosen basis functions that can be constructed in light of intuition about the dynamic programming problem at hand.

(iv) Above all, a linear approximator is relatively easy to implement.

With respect to point (iii), it should be noted that the choice of good basis functions may pose serious difficulty in practice.

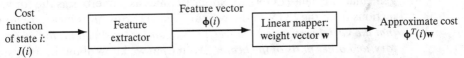

FIGURE 12.8 Architectural layout of the linear approach to approximate dynamic programming.

The choice of Eq. (12.59) provides the answer to question 1 for the linear approach. As for the answer to question 2, the method most commonly used for providing the *best fit* to the Bellman equation of optimality is the *method of least squares*, which was discussed in Chapter 2. In Section 12.10, we will describe one way in which this issue is formulated.[7]

Nonlinear Approach to Approximate Dynamic Programming

Despite its appeal, the linear approach to approximate dynamic programming is considered to be a useful stepping-stone toward a still higher goal, expressed by considering the *general* case:

> *Recognizing that many of the dynamic environments encountered in practice are inherently nonlinear, the approximate dynamic programming should not only be nonlinear itself, but also be required to approximate "any" nonlinear dynamic environment to "any desired degree of accuracy."*

In other words, what we are advocating here as the answer to question 1 for the nonlinear approach is an approximating function that is a *universal approximator*.

From previous discussions presented on multilayer perceptrons and radial-basis functions (RBFs), we know that both of these networks are universal approximators. Moreover, recurrent multilayer perceptrons, to be discussed later in Chapter 15, are also universal approximators. Given such a wide choice of networks, we assert that recurrent multilayer perceptrons provide the practical basis for the optimal design of non-linear, approximate dynamic programming systems. Insofar as the issue of universal approximation is concerned, we say so for two important reasons:

1. Unlike *shallow architectures* (exemplified by RBF networks), which have a single nonlinear hidden layer and a linear output layer, recurrent multilayer perceptrons can be designed to have two or more hidden layers. With one layer feeding the other, recurrent multilayer perceptrons have the property of "learning features of features," whereby lower level features are progressively combined into more abstract and higher level representations. In Bengio and LeCun (2007), it is argued that *deep architectures* have the potential to generalize in nonlocal ways (i.e., beyond intermediate neighbors) and that such a property is crucial to making progress in the design of machine learning algorithms applicable to highly complex tasks.

2. Recurrent multilayer perceptrons have built-in *global feedback* that could be of a multiple kind (i.e., encompassing two or more network layers). Here, we need to remind ourselves that brain systems have an abundance of global feedback built into them. In particular, there are almost always feedback connections between different areas in the brain that are at least as rich in number as the feedforward connections (Churchland and Sejnowski, 1992). For example, the recurrent projections from the primary visual cortex back to the lateral geniculate nucleus (LGN) are about 10 times as numerous as the forward projections from the LGN to the primary visual cortex.[8] *It is therefore no wonder that the visual system is as powerful as it, and so it is with motor control, auditory, and other parts of the brain.* Given what we know about brain systems, we are emboldened to say that *global feedback is a facilitator of computational intelligence*—hence the practical importance of recurrent neural networks as

the candidate neural network in the simulation of approximate dynamic programming systems.

Comparing recurrent multilayer perceptrons with ordinary multilayer perceptrons, we see that they both share point 1 insofar as architectural depth is concerned. However, it is property 2 on global feedback that gives recurrent multilayer perceptrons the advantage over ordinary multilayer perceptrons. Given that we opt for the use of a recurrent multilayer perceptron, the challenge is how to configure the feedforward and feedback connections of the network in the most effective and efficient manner.

Now that we have answered question 1 for the nonlinear approach to approximate dynamic programming, we move on to address question 2 on how to adapt the weight vector $\mathbf{w}$ in the approximating function $\tilde{J}(i, \mathbf{w})$ so as to provide the best fit to Bellman's equation of optimality. For the present, it suffices to say the following:

> *The supervised training of a recurrent multilayer perceptron can be accomplished most effectively with the use of a nonlinear sequential-state estimation algorithm that is* derivative free.

By adopting such an approach to supervised learning, we need no longer be concerned with how nonlinear the decision-making system happens to be. It is in situations of this kind where derivative-free, nonlinear sequential state-estimation algorithms, to be discussed in Chapter 14, become particularly important. The use of sequential state-estimation algorithms for the supervised training of recurrent multilayer perceptrons (or ordinary multilayer perceptrons for that matter) is discussed in Chapter 15.

12.10   LEAST-SQUARES POLICY EVALUATION

For our first indirect method of approximate dynamic programming, we discuss an algorithm called the *least-squares policy evaluation algorithm*, or the *LSPE(λ) algorithm* for short. The λ plays a role in LSPE(λ) similar to that in the TD(λ) algorithm.

The basic idea behind the LSPE(λ) algorithm may be summed up as follows:

> *Perform value iteration within a lower dimensional subspace spanned by a set of basis functions.*

To be specific, let s denote the dimension of feature vector $\boldsymbol{\phi}_i$ representing state i. We may than define the N-by-s matrix

$$\boldsymbol{\Phi} = \begin{bmatrix} \boldsymbol{\phi}_1^T \\ \boldsymbol{\phi}_2^T \\ \vdots \\ \boldsymbol{\phi}_N^T \end{bmatrix} \tag{12.60}$$

Let $\mathcal{T}$ denote a *mapping* that has the cost J as a unique fixed point for policy μ, and let Π denote a projection (of suitable norm) onto the subspace of vectors defined by the matrix product $\boldsymbol{\Phi}\mathbf{w}$, where $\mathbf{w}$ is a parameter vector of dimension s. With simulation as the basis for the LSPE(λ) algorithm, we may analytically describe it as follows (Bertsekas, 2007):

$$\boldsymbol{\Phi}\mathbf{w}_{n+1} = \Pi\mathcal{T}(\boldsymbol{\Phi}\mathbf{w}_n) + \text{(simulation noise)} \tag{12.61}$$

The algorithm is formulated in such a way that the additive simulation noise converges to zero as the number of iterations, n, approaches infinity.

Background and Assumptions

Consider a finite-state Markov chain whose states, denoted by $i = 1, 2, ..., N$, are controlled by a stationary policy μ. We may recast Eq. (12.5) in the form

$$J(i) = \mathbb{E}\left[\sum_{n=0}^{\infty} \gamma^n g(i_n, i_{n+1}) | i_0 = i\right]$$

where i_n is the ith state at time n, γ is the discount factor, and $g(i_n, i_{n+1})$ is the transition cost from state i_n to i_{n+1}. With a linear architecture in mind, the cost $J(i)$ is approximated as

$$J(i) \approx \tilde{J}(i, \mathbf{w})$$
$$= \boldsymbol{\phi}^T(i)\mathbf{w} \tag{12.62}$$

With the feature vector $\boldsymbol{\phi}(i)$ assumed to be dimension s, it follows that the weight vector $\mathbf{w}$ must also have the same dimension. The issue of interest is to approximate the *parameterized cost* $\tilde{J}(i, \mathbf{w})$ within the subspace

$$\mathcal{S} = \{\boldsymbol{\Phi}\mathbf{w} | \mathbf{w} \in \mathbb{R}^s\} \tag{12.63}$$

that is spanned by the columns of the matrix $\boldsymbol{\Phi}$. Note that dimensionality of the matrix product $\boldsymbol{\Phi}\mathbf{w}$ is equal to the number of possible states, N.

Forthwith, we make two assumptions:

1. *The Markov chain has positive steady-state probabilities*; that is,

$$\lim_{n\to\infty} \frac{1}{n} \sum_{k=1}^{n} P(i_k = j | i_0 = i) = \pi_j > 0 \qquad \text{for all } i \tag{12.64}$$

The implication of this assumption is that the Markov chain has a single recurrent class with no transient states.

2. *The rank of matrix $\boldsymbol{\Phi}$ is s.*

The implication of this second assumption is that the columns of the feature matrix $\boldsymbol{\Phi}$, and therefore the basis functions represented by $\boldsymbol{\Phi}\mathbf{w}$, are linearly independent.

Projected Value Iteration for Policy Evaluation

With value iteration in mind, we may use Eqs. (12.20) and (12.29) to write

$$\mathcal{T}J(i) = \sum_{j=1}^{N} p_{ij}(g(i, j) + \gamma J(i)), \qquad i = 1, 2, ..., N \tag{12.65}$$

where $\mathcal{T}$ denotes a mapping. Now, let

$$\mathbf{g} = \begin{bmatrix} \sum_j p_{1j}g(1, j) \\ \sum_j p_{2j}g(2, j) \\ \vdots \\ \sum_j p_{Nj}g(N, j) \end{bmatrix} \tag{12.66}$$

$$\mathbf{P} = \begin{bmatrix} p_{11} & p_{12} & \cdots & p_{1N} \\ p_{21} & p_{22} & \cdots & p_{2N} \\ \vdots & \vdots & & \vdots \\ p_{N1} & p_{N2} & \cdots & p_{NN} \end{bmatrix} \qquad (12.67)$$

and

$$\mathbf{J} = \begin{bmatrix} J(1) \\ J(2) \\ \vdots \\ J(N) \end{bmatrix}$$

$$\approx \mathbf{\Phi w} \qquad (12.68)$$

where we used the approximate formula of Eq. (12.62). We may then rewrite Eq. (12.65) in terms of the vectors $\mathbf{g}, \mathbf{J}$, and the stochastic matrix $\mathbf{P}$ in the compact matrix form

$$\mathcal{T}\mathbf{J} = \mathbf{g} + \gamma \mathbf{P} \mathbf{J} \qquad (12.69)$$

We are interested in an approximate form of the value iteration

$$\mathbf{J}_{n+1} = \mathcal{T}\mathbf{J}_n$$

which is confined within the subspace $\mathcal{S}$ and which involves the projection of the value iterate onto $\mathcal{S}$. Specifically, in light of Eq. (12.68), we may write

$$\mathbf{\Phi w}_{n+1} = \Pi \mathcal{T}(\mathbf{\Phi w}_n), \quad n = 0, 1, 2, \dots \qquad (12.70)$$

where, as pointed our earlier, Π denotes projection onto the subspace $\mathcal{S}$. Equation (12.70) is referred to as the *projected value iteration (PVI) method*, the essence of which may be stated as follows:

> At iteration n, the current iterate $\mathbf{\Phi w}_n$ is operated on by the mapping $\mathcal{T}$ and the new vector $\mathcal{T}(\mathbf{\Phi w}_n)$ is projected onto the subspace $\mathcal{S}$, thereby yielding the updated iterate $\mathbf{\Phi w}_{n+1}$.

The PVI method is illustrated in Fig. 12.9.

The PVI method may be viewed as a *projected* or *approximate* form of the value iteration method for solving the Bellman equation. In Bertsekas (2007) the following findings are demonstrated:

1. The mappings $\mathcal{T}$ and $\Pi\mathcal{T}$ are *contractions* of modulus with respect to the weighted Euclidean norm $\|\cdot\|_\pi$, where, $\pi_1, \pi_2, \dots, \pi_N$ (representing the steady-state

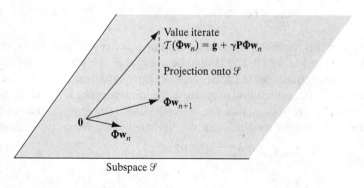

Value iterate
$\mathcal{T}(\mathbf{\Phi w}_n) = \mathbf{g} + \gamma \mathbf{P\Phi w}_n$

Projection onto $\mathcal{S}$

$\mathbf{\Phi w}_{n+1}$

0

$\mathbf{\Phi w}_n$

Subspace $\mathcal{S}$

FIGURE 12.9 Illustration of the projected value iteration (PVI) method.

probabilities of the Markov chain) play the role of scaling factors in defining the Euclidean norm.

2. The matrix product $\mathbf{\Phi}\mathbf{w}^*$ is the unique fixed point of the mapping ΠT for the weight vector $\mathbf{w}^*$. (In the context of the present discussion, when we speak of a *fixed point*, we mean a solution, that is, a vector $\mathbf{w}^*$ that satisfies the condition $\Pi T \mathbf{w}^* = \mathbf{w}^*$.)

We may therefore say that the PVI method is an analytic method for approximating the Bellman equation.

Despite its good points, however, the PVI method has two serious drawbacks:

1. With $\mathbf{\Phi}\mathbf{w}$ having the dimensionality N, it follows that the transformed vector $T(\mathbf{\Phi}\mathbf{w}_n)$ is an N-dimensional vector, so, for large-scale applications for which N is large, the computational complexity of the method becomes unmanageable.

2. The projection of the vector $T(\mathbf{\Phi}\mathbf{w}_n)$ onto the subspace $\mathcal{S}$ requires knowledge of the steady-state probabilities $\pi_1, \pi_2, ..., \pi_N$. In general, these probabilities are not known.

Fortunately, both of these drawbacks can be alleviated through the use of Monte Carlo Simulation.

From Projected Value Iteration to Least-Squares Policy Evaluation

Using least-squares minimization for the projection Π, we may express Eq. (12.70) in the form

$$\mathbf{w}_{n+1} = \arg\min_{\mathbf{w}} \|\mathbf{\Phi}\mathbf{w} - T(\mathbf{\Phi}\mathbf{w}_n)\|_{\pi}^2 \tag{12.71}$$

Equivalently, we may express the least-squares version of the PVI algorithm in the form

$$\mathbf{w}_{n+1} = \arg\min_{\mathbf{w}} \sum_{i=1}^{N} \pi_i \left(\mathbf{\phi}^T(i)\mathbf{w} - \left(\sum_{j=1}^{N} p_{ij}g(i,j) + \gamma\mathbf{\phi}^T(j)\mathbf{w}_n \right) \right) \tag{12.72}$$

To perform the optimization in Eq. (12.72) in practical terms, we propose to approximate it through the use of Monte Carlo simulation by generating an infinitely long trajectory $(i_0, i_1, i_2, ...)$ for state i and updating the weight vector $\mathbf{w}_n$ after each iteration (i_n, i_{n+1}) in accordance with the formula

$$\mathbf{w}_{n+1} = \arg\min_{\mathbf{w}} \sum_{k=1}^{n} (\mathbf{\phi}^T(i_k)\mathbf{w} - g(i_k, i_{k+1}) - \gamma\mathbf{\phi}^T(i_{k+1})\mathbf{w}_n)^2 \tag{12.73}$$

For obvious reasons, this recursion is called *least-squares policy evaluation*, or LSPE for short. As illustrated in Fig. 12.10, LSPE may be viewed as the PVI with an *additive simulation noise* that accounts for the least-squares approximation.

Moreover, due to the contraction property of the joint mapping ΠT and the asymptotically diminishing nature of the simulation noise, the LSPE converges to the same limit as the PVI, namely, the unique weight vector $\mathbf{w}^*$ that satisfies the fixed-point equation

$$\mathbf{\Phi}\mathbf{w}^* = \Pi T(\mathbf{\Phi}\mathbf{w}^*) \tag{12.74}$$

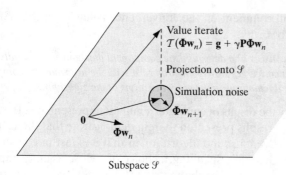

Value iterate
$T(\Phi\mathbf{w}_n) = \mathbf{g} + \gamma\mathbf{P}\Phi\mathbf{w}_n$

Projection onto $\mathscr{S}$

Simulation noise

$\Phi\mathbf{w}_{n+1}$

0

$\Phi\mathbf{w}_n$

Subspace $\mathscr{S}$

FIGURE 12.10
Illustration of the least-squares policy evaluation (LSPE) as a stochastic version of the projected value iteration (PVI).

The LSPE (λ)

In a manner similar to the way we introduced TD(λ) in Section 12.7, let us introduce the temporal difference (see Eq. (12.34))

$$d_n(i_k, i_{k+1}) = g(i_k, i_{k+1}) + \gamma\boldsymbol{\phi}^T(i_{k+1})\mathbf{w}_n - \boldsymbol{\phi}^T(i_k)\mathbf{w}_n \qquad (12.75)$$

Accordingly, we may express the simulation-based LSPE(λ) algorithm as follows:

$$\mathbf{w}_{n+1} = \arg\min_{\mathbf{w}} \sum_{k=0}^{n}\left(\boldsymbol{\phi}^T(i_k)\mathbf{w} - \boldsymbol{\phi}^T(i_k)\mathbf{w}_n - \sum_{m=k}^{n}(\gamma\lambda)^{m-k}d_n(i_m, i_{m+1})\right)^2 \qquad (12.76)$$

where $(i_0, i_1, i_2, ...)$ is an infinitely long trajectory generated by Monte Carlo simulation. In words,

> *At iteration $n + 1$ of the LSPE(λ) algorithm, the updated weight vector $\mathbf{w}_{n+1}$ is computed as the particular value of the weight vector $\mathbf{w}$ that minimizes the least-squares difference between the following two quantities:*
>
> - *the inner product $\boldsymbol{\phi}^T(i_k)\mathbf{w}$ approximating the cost function $J(i_k)$;*
> - *its temporal difference counterpart*
>
> $$\boldsymbol{\phi}^T(i_k)\mathbf{w}_n + \sum_{m=k}^{n}(\gamma\lambda)^{m-k}d_n(i_m, i_{m+1})$$
>
> *which is extracted from a single simulated trajectory for $k = 0, 1, ..., n$.*

Note that the current value of the weight vector $\mathbf{w}_n$ is maintained constant in performing each iteration of the least-squares minimization in Eq. (12.76).

The approximate nature of the LSPE(λ) algorithm is attributed to two factors:

1. The use of simulation-based empirical frequencies for estimating the steady-state probabilities π_i and transition probabilities p_{ij}.
2. The use of the finite discounted sum of temporal differences in Eq. (12.76) for approximating the PVI method.

Nevertheless, as the number of iterations, n, approaches infinity, the empirical frequencies converge to the true probabilities and the finite discounted sum converges to an infinitely discounted sum. Consequently, the LSPE(λ) algorithm converges to its PVI counterpart in an asymptotic sense.

The following insightful comment on the convergence behavior of the LSPE(λ) algorithm is particularly noteworthy:

The LSPE(λ) algorithm consists of a deterministic component that converges rapidly and a stochastic component that converges slowly towards zero, with the deterministic component dominating the stochastic fluctuations in the early iterations of the algorithm.

This statement is borne out by the results of computer simulations presented in Bertsekas et al. (2004). In particular, the results presented therein demonstrate that the LSPE(λ) algorithm for $0 \leq \lambda \leq 1$ is indeed a sound algorithm, in that it is fast in convergence and reliable in performance. Generally speaking, a choice of λ close to unity improves the computational accuracy (i.e., it makes the matrix product $\phi^T(i)\mathbf{w}^*$ closer to $J(i)$), but increases the effect of simulation noise, so more samples and longer trajectories are required to achieve convergence.

12.11 APPROXIMATE POLICY ITERATION

The LSPE algorithm provides a powerful linear approach for approximate dynamic programming. In this section, we describe the use of neural networks as a tool for the non-linear approach to approximate dynamic programming. To this end, suppose then we have a dynamic-programming problem for which the numbers of possible states and admissible actions are very large, making the use of a traditional approach impractical. It is assumed that we do have a model of the system; that is, the transition probabilities $p_{ij}(a)$ and the observed costs $g(i, a, j)$ are all known. To deal with this situation, we propose to use an approximation to policy iteration, based on Monte Carlo simulation and the method of least squares, as described next.

Figure 12.11 shows a simplified block diagram of the *approximate policy-iteration algorithm*, where the policy evaluation step in Fig. 12.3 has been replaced with an *approximate one*. Thus, the approximate policy-iteration algorithm proceeds by alternating between an approximate policy evaluation step and a policy improvement step as follows:

1. *Approximate policy evaluation step.* Given the current policy μ, we compute a cost-to-go function $\tilde{J}^\mu(i, \mathbf{w})$ approximating the actual cost-to-go function $J^\mu(i)$ for all

FIGURE 12.11 Block diagram of the approximate policy iteration algorithm.

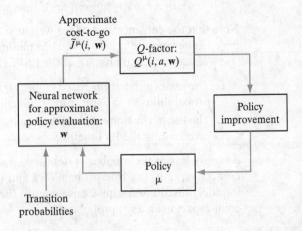

states i. The vector $\mathbf{w}$ is the weight vector of the neural network used to perform the approximation.

2. *Policy improvement step.* Using the approximate cost-to-go function $\tilde{J}^{\mu}(i, \mathbf{w})$, we generate an improved policy μ. This new policy is designed to be greedy with respect to $\tilde{J}^{\mu}(i, \mathbf{w})$ for all i.

For the approximate policy-iteration algorithm to yield satisfactory results, it is important to carefully choose the policy used to initialize the algorithm. This can be done through the use of heuristics. Alternatively, we may start with some weight vector $\mathbf{w}$ and use it to derive a greedy policy, which is, in turn, used as the initial policy.

Suppose, then, in addition to the known transition probabilities and observed costs, we have the following items:

- a stationary policy μ as the initial policy;
- a set of states $\mathcal{X}$ representative of the operating environment;
- a set of $M(i)$ samples of the cost-to-go function $J^{\mu}(i)$ for each state $i \in \mathcal{X}$; one such sample is denoted by $k(i, m)$, where $m = 1, 2, ..., M(i)$.

The weight vector $\mathbf{w}$ of the neural network is determined by using the *method of least squares*—that is, by minimizing the cost function

$$\mathcal{E}(\mathbf{w}) = \sum_{i \in \mathcal{X}} \sum_{m=1}^{M(i)} (k(i, m) - \tilde{J}^{\mu}(i, \mathbf{w}))^2 \tag{12.75}$$

Having determined the optimal value of weight vector $\mathbf{w}$, and therefore the approximate cost-to-go function $\tilde{J}^{\mu}(i, \mathbf{w})$, we next determine the approximate Q-factors. To this end, we use Eqs. (12.20) and (12.23) to approximate the Q-factor as

$$Q(i, a, \mathbf{w}) = \sum_{j \in \mathcal{X}} p_{ij}(a)(g(i, a, j) + \gamma \tilde{J}^{\mu}(j, \mathbf{w})) \tag{12.76}$$

where the $p_{ij}(a)$ is the transition probability from state i to state j under action a (known), $g(i, a, j)$ is the observed cost (also known), and γ is a prescribed discount factor. The iteration is completed by using the approximate Q-factor to determine an improved policy based on the following formula (see Eq. (12.28)):

$$\mu(i) = \arg \min_{a \in \mathcal{A}_i} Q(i, a, \mathbf{w}) \tag{12.77}$$

It is important to note that Eqs. (12.76) and (12.77) are used by the simulator to generate actions only at the states that are *actually visited* by the simulation, rather than for all states. As such, these two equations need not suffer from the curse of dimensionality.

The block diagram of Fig. 12.12 presents a more detailed picture of the approximate policy-iteration algorithm. This diagram consists of four interconnected functional modules (Bertsekas and Tsitsiklis, 1996):

1. *Simulator*, which uses the given state-transition probabilities and observed one-step costs to construct a surrogate model of the environment. The simulator generates two things: (a) states that mimic the environment's response to actions, and (b) samples of the cost-to-go function for a given policy μ.

FIGURE 12.12   Block diagram of the approximate policy-iteration algorithm.

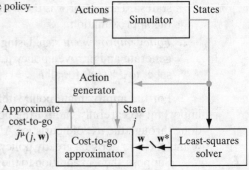

2. *Action generator*, which generates an improved policy (i.e., sequence of actions) in accordance with Eq. (12.77).

3. *Cost-to-go approximator*, which generates the approximate cost-to-go function $\tilde{J}^{\mu}(i, \mathbf{w})$ for state i and parameter vector $\mathbf{w}$, for use in Eqs. (12.76) and (12.77).

4. *Least-squares solver*, which takes samples of the cost-to-go function $J^{\mu}(i)$ supplied by the simulator for policy μ and state i, and then computes the optimum parameter vector $\mathbf{w}$ that minimizes the cost function of Eq. (12.75). The link from the least-squares solver to the cost-to-go approximator is switched on only after a policy has been fully evaluated and an optimal weight vector $\mathbf{w}^{*}$ has been determined. At that point, the cost-to-go approximation $\tilde{J}^{\mu}(i, \mathbf{w})$ is replaced by $\tilde{J}^{\mu}(i, \mathbf{w}^{*}.)$

Table 12.3 presents a summary of the approximate policy-iteration algorithm.

TABLE 12.3   Summary of the Approximate Policy-Iteration Algorithm

---

Known parameters: transition probabilities $p_{ij}(a)$ and costs $g(i, a, j)$.

Computation:
1. Choose a stationary policy μ as the initial policy.
2. Using a set of samples $\{k(i, m)\}_{m=1}^{M(i)}$ of the cost-to-go function $J^{\mu}(i)$ generated by the simulator, determine the parameter vector $\mathbf{w}$ of the neural network employed as the least-squares solver:

$$\mathbf{w}^{*} = \min_{\mathbf{w}} \mathscr{E}(\mathbf{w})$$
$$= \min_{\mathbf{w}} \sum_{i \in \mathscr{X}} \sum_{m=1}^{M(i)} (k(i, m) - \tilde{J}^{\mu}(i, \mathbf{w}))^{2}$$

3. For the optimized vector $\mathbf{w}^{*}$ determined in step 2, compute the approximate cost-to-go function $\tilde{J}^{\mu}(i, \mathbf{w}^{*})$ for the states visited. Determine the approximate Q-factors:

$$Q(i, a, \mathbf{w}^{*}) = \sum_{j \in \mathscr{X}} p_{ij}(a)(g(i, a, j) + \gamma \tilde{J}^{\mu}(j, \mathbf{w}^{*}))$$

4. Determine the improved policy

$$\mu(i) = \arg \min_{a \in \mathscr{A}_{i}} Q(i, a, \mathbf{w}^{*})$$

5. Repeat steps 2 through 4.

Note: Steps 3 and 4 apply only to actions at the states that are actually visited, rather than all states.

Naturally, the operation of this algorithm is subject to errors due to unavoidable imperfections in the design of the simulator and least-squares solver. The neural network used to perform the least-squares approximation of the desired cost-to-go function may lack adequate computing power—hence the first source of error. Optimization of the neural network approximator, and therefore tuning of the weight vector $\mathbf{w}$, is based on a desired response provided by the simulator—hence the second source of error. Assuming that all policy evaluations and all policy improvements are performed within certain error tolerances of ϵ and δ, respectively, it is shown in Bertsekas and Tsitsiklis (1996) that the approximate policy-iteration algorithm will produce policies whose performances differ from the optimal policies by a factor that decreases to zero as ϵ and δ are reduced. In other words, the approximate policy-iteration algorithm is sound with minimal performance guarantees. According to Bertsekas and Tsitsiklis (1996), the approximate policy-iteration algorithm tends initially to make rapid and fairly monotonic progress, but a sustained policy oscillation of a random nature may result as a limiting condition. This oscillatory behavior occurs after the approximating cost-to-go function $\tilde{J}$ gets within a zone of $O(\delta + 2\gamma\epsilon)/(1 - \gamma)^2)$ of the optimal value J^*, where γ is the discount factor. Apparently, there is a fundamental structure common to all variants of approximate policy iteration that causes an oscillatory behavior.

12.12 SUMMARY AND DISCUSSION

The early part of this chapter presented a detailed discussion of Bellman's theory of dynamic programming for multistage decision making. Building on Markov decision processes for stationary policies, the theory rests its case on the availability of an explicit model of the environment that embodies transition probabilities and associated costs. We also discussed the two methods of policy iteration and value iteration for solving the Bellman equation of optimality.

Approximate Dynamic Programming: Direct Methods

Dynamic programming lies at the *core* of reinforcement learning. This statement was confirmed in this chapter by using dynamic programming to derive two model-free, on-line learning algorithms widely known in the reinforcement learning literature:

- Temporal difference (TD) learning, due to Sutton (1988).
- Q-learning, due to Watkins (1989).

Being model free, both algorithms bypass the need for transition probabilities. However, memory limitations restrict their practical use to decision-making problems in which the state space is of a moderate size.

Approximate Dynamic Programming: Indirect Methods

In the latter part of the chapter, we addressed an issue of practical importance: the so-called *curse of dimensionality*. This issue, encountered in solving large-scale decision-making problems, renders Bellman's dynamic programming intractable. To overcome the difficulty, we may resort to *indirect approximate dynamic programming*, which builds on

Bellman's theory. The implementation of indirect approximate dynamic programming may proceed in one of two ways:

1. *The linear structural approach*, which involves two steps:
   - feature extraction of the state i;
   - least-squares minimization of the cost $\tilde{J}(i, \mathbf{w})$, where $\mathbf{w}$ is the weight vector associated with state i.

   We illustrated the applicability of this approach by deriving the least-squares policy evaluation (LSPE) algorithm.
2. *The nonlinear structural approach*, the development of which relies on the use of a *universal approximator* that can approximate any nonlinear function to any desired degree of accuracy. Neural networks have established themselves as universal approximators.

Despite the significant progress we have made in approximate dynamic programming,[9] much remains to be done in terms of building systems that are capable of making high-level decisions for large-scale applications, reliably and in a computationally tractable manner. In this context, the issue of partial observability stands out as perhaps the most challenging of all practical problems that afflict dynamic programming.

Partial Observability

Bellman's dynamic programming theory assumes a *fully observable system*. To be more precise, in order to solve the dynamic programming problem for an optimal policy, it is assumed that the states of the environment obey the Markov property: The state at time $n + 1$ depends only on the state and policy at time n and is therefore independent of everything that may have occurred prior to time n. This stringent assumption is frequently violated in practice due to the unavoidable presence of unobservable states. Accordingly, instead of a model based on Markov decision processes (MDPs) that is the cornerstone of Bellman's dynamic programming theory, we have to deal with *partially observable Markov decision processes* (POMDPs) if we are to bring the theory of approximate dynamic programming closer to practical reality. In a sense, partial observability may be viewed as the second "curse" of dynamic programming, namely, the *curse of modeling*, in that the observables contain incomplete information about the underlying dynamics of the environment. We may therefore describe dynamic programming as a *global optimization methodology that suffers from the twin curses of modeling and dimensionality*.

The POMDP problem has been recognized as a serious problem in the literature for many years, posing a major obstacle to progress in applications that involve *planning under uncertainty* (e.g., robotics). The problem is difficult because of the need to learn strategies of action selection that would be contingent under all possible types of uncertainty. The list of references presented in Note 10 under the Notes and References is intended to provide a sense of research directions on how the POMDP problem is being addressed in the literature.

Relationship between Dynamic Programming and Viterbi Algorithm

Dynamic programming has featured prominently throughout this chapter. As such, a study of dynamic programming would be incomplete without discussion of its relationship to the

Viterbi algorithm, so named after its originator Viterbi (1968). In actual fact, Bellman's dynamic programming (Bellman, 1957; Bellman and Dreyfus, 1962) preceded Viterbi's paper by many years. The equivalence between these two algorithms was found by Omura (1969).

In the context of optimization, dynamic programming seeks to find the shortest path across a weighted graph (e.g., the graph depicted in Fig. 12.5 for the stagecoach problem) by starting from the destination and working backward to the starting point in a methodical stage-by-stage manner. In the context of convolutional decoding, on the other hand, the Viterbi algorithm works on a weighted graph of its own, called the *trellis diagram*. This diagram represents a graphical description of the convolutional encoder, viewed as a finite state machine (Lin and Costello, 2004). Optimality of the Viterbi algorithm for convolutional decoding in the maximum likelihood sense was recognized by Forney (1973).

NOTES AND REFERENCES

1. The classical approach to reinforcement learning is rooted in psychology, going back to the early work of Thorndike (1911) on animal learning and that of Pavlov (1927) on conditioning. Contributions to classical reinforcement learning also include the work of Widrow et al. (1973); in that paper, the notion of a *critic* was introduced. Classical reinforcement learning is discussed in book form in Hampson (1990).

   Major contributions to reinforcement learning include the works of Samuel (1959) on his celebrated checkers playing program, Barto et al. (1983) on adaptive critic systems, Sutton (1988) on temporal difference methods, and Watkins (1989) on Q-learning. Reinforcement learning is treated in great detail in the book by Sutton and Barto (1998).

   In a neurobiological context, reward signals are processed by midbrain neurons known as dopamine neurons. To elaborate, in a series of experiments reported in Schultz (1998), instrumental conditioning was used to train a monkey to respond to stimuli (e.g., light and sound). To get a reward, in the form of food or drink, the monkey had to release a resting key followed by pressing another key. The resulting activities of dopamine neurons were averaged over a total of 20 trials of each experiment. The results obtained by Schultz revealed that the dopamine neurons did fire after the stimulus presentation and reward delivery. Given Schultz's remarkable findings, how do we model them? Well, viewing the dopamine neurons as "a retina of the rewards system," we may consider the responses produced by dopamine neurons as teaching signals for Pavlovian conditioning and TD-learning (Schultz, 2007; Iszhikevich, 2007b); it should however be noted that the relevant form of TD-learning is TD(λ) and not TD(0), both of which are discussed in Section 12.7.

   One last comment is in order: When considering TD-learning in the reinforcement-learning literature, rewards are maximized. In contrast, when the same algorithm is considered in dynamic programming, cost-to-go functions are minimized.

2. In this book, we have discussed dynamic programming in the general context of stochastic environments. It may therefore be tempting to retitle the chapter as "Stochastic Dynamic Programming." However, we have resisted this temptation, because "Dynamic Programming" describes the field adequately for researchers working in it.

3. Policy iteration and value iteration are two principal methods of dynamic programming. There are two other dynamic programming methods that deserve to be mentioned: the *Gauss–Seidel method* and *asynchronous dynamic programming* (Barto et al., 1995; Bertsekas, 1995). In the Gauss-Seidel method, the cost-to-go function is updated at one state at a time in a sequential sweep of all the states, with the competition for each state based on the most recent costs of the other states. Asynchronous dynamic programming

differs from the Gauss–Seidel method in that it is not organized in terms of systematic successive sweeps of the set of states.

4. On page 96 of his Ph.D. thesis, Watkins (1989) makes the following remarks on Q-learning:

   "Appendix 1 presents a proof that this learning method does work for finite Markov decision processes. The proof also shows that the learning method will converge rapidly to the optimal action-value function. Although this is a very simple idea, it has not, as far as I know, been suggested previously. However, it must be said that finite Markov decision processes and stochastic dynamic programming have been extensively studied for use in several different fields for over thirty years, and it is unlikely that nobody has considered the Monte-Carlo method before."

   In a footnote commentary on these remarks, Barto et al. (1995) point out that although the idea of assigning values to state–action pairs formed the basis of the approach to dynamic programming taken in Denardo (1967), they have not seen algorithms like Q-learning for estimating these values that predate Watkins's 1989 thesis.

5. The outline of a proof of the convergence theorem for Q-learning was presented in Watkins (1989); it was refined later in Watkins and Dayan (1992). More general results on the convergence of Q-learning were presented in Tsitsiklis (1994); see also Bertsekas and Tsitsiklis (1996).

6. The early development of approximate dynamic programming may be traced to Werbos's 1977 paper, in which the idea of *heuristic dynamic programming* to bypass the curse of dimensionality was described for the first time. The idea of heuristic dynamic programming was proposed therein as a simple way of approximating the iterative procedure due to Howard (1960) through the supervised training of a network with adjustable weights.

   Nowadays, "approximate dynamic programming" is commonly used to refer to methods that use approximation to overcome limitations of Bellman's dynamic programming. Volume 2 of the book by Bertsekas (2007) has a chapter on approximate dynamic programming that identifies direct and indirect methods of approximation.

7. **Least-Squares Temporal-Difference (LSTD) Algorithm**
   The LSTD algorithm, due to Bradtke and Barto (1996), provides another method for a linear architectural approach to the indirect approximation of dynamic programming. Development of the LSTD algorithm proceeds as follows:

   - With a basis function used for the representation of each state, the Bellman equation is first approximated in such a way that the input and output observations appear as noisy variables.
   - Then, clever use is made of the *method of instrumental variables* discussed in Chapter 2, so as to avoid the asymptotic bias introduced by the "errors-in-variables" problem; the stage is thereby set for the application of the method of least squares.
   - With a procedure similar to that used for the recursive least-squares (RLS) algorithm in Chapter 5, a similar recursive implementation of the LSTD algorithm is derived.

   The original version of the LSTD algorithm was derived for $\lambda = 0$. Building on the work of Bradtke and Barto, Boyan (2002) extended the LSTD algorithm to $\lambda > 0$. The LSTD algorithm has also been discussed by Lagoudakis and Parr (2003) in the context of approximate policy iteration.

   The relationship between LSTD and LSPE algorithms is discussed in Bertsekas (2007).

8. **Feedback in the Visual Cortex**

The primary Visual Cortex—visual area 1, commonly abbreviated as V1—has distinct anatomical layers, each having characteristic functions of its own. V1 is adjacent to and interconnects with higher order visual areas that are concerned with more detailed analyses of sensation (Kandel et al., 1991).

The lateral geniculate nucleus (LGN) is the part of the brain where visual information is processed (Kandel et al., 1991).

9. **Books on Approximate Dynamic Programming**

The classic book *Neuro-dynamic Programming* by Bertsekas and Tsitsiklis (1996) was the first book devoted to approximate dynamic programming. The edited volume by Si et al. (2004) presents a broad coverage of topics under the umbrella of learning and approximate dynamic programming (ADP), technical advances in ADP, and their applications.

10. **Partial Observability**

The problem of having to plan in a partially observable environment is notoriously difficult. The following short list of references is intended to provide some sense of interesting directions of research in this highly challenging field:

(i) *Hierarchical Approach*   Planning in a partially observable environment may be simplified by decomposing a difficult task into a hierarchy of simple planning problems, a technique that may be viewed as an application of the well-known engineering "divide and conquer" paradigm. Charlin et al. (2007) investigate the problem of automatically discovering the hierarchy by framing the optimization of a hierarchical policy as a nonconvex optimization problem that can be tackled with general nonlinear solvers.

In Guestrin and Gordon (2002), another approach to the hierarchical decomposition of POMDPs is described for collaborative multiagent dynamic systems. During both the planning and execution phases, the computation is distributed among the agents, with each agent needing to model and plan only a small part of the system. The subsystems are connected together through a hierarchy that takes care of coordination and communication among the agents via a message-passing algorithm; a globally consistent plan is thereby achieved. Another message-passing algorithm allows for execution of the resulting policy.

(ii) *POMDP value iteration*   An optimal policy for a POMDP can be represented via its cost-to-go function, denoted by $J(b)$. This function maps a *belief state b* (representing a posterior distribution over the possibly true, but unobserved, configurations of the world) to an estimate of the total return that an optimal policy can achieve, given that b is the correct belief state. Although it is not possible to compute the cost-to-go function exactly (Sondik, 1971), many authors have proposed algorithms to approximate it. In particular, the so-called *point-based* algorithms have shown substantial promise (Smith, 2007). These algorithms estimate both the value and the gradient of $J(b)$ at a discrete sample of beliefs and generalize to arbitrary beliefs by using the convexity of $J(b)$. The belief samples are collected either by simulating the POMDP to get a tree of reachable beliefs or by filling up the simplex of possible beliefs with the use of samples chosen randomly or placed in a grid.

(iii) *Belief Compression*   In real POMDP problems, most "belief" states are unlikely. Most importantly, there is a structured low-dimensional manifold of plausible beliefs embedded in a high-dimensional belief space. Roy and Gordon (2003) introduce a new method, termed "belief compression," for solving large-scale POMDP problems by taking advantage of the sparsity of the belief space. In particular, the dimensionality of the belief space is reduced by using exponential family principal-components analysis (Collins et al., 2002). (Differentiable manifolds were discussed in Chapter 10.)

(iv) *Natural Policy Gradient* In direct policy-gradient methods for approximate planning in large-scale MDPs, the motivation is to find a good policy μ among a restricted class of policies by following the gradient of future returns. Kakade (2002) describes a natural gradient method that represents the direction of steepest descent, based on the underlying structure of the parameter space. A connection to policy iteration is established by showing that the natural gradient moves toward choosing a greedy policy action. (Amari's natural gradient was discussed in Chapter 10.)

PROBLEMS

Bellman's optimality criterion

12.1 Eq. (12.22) is called Bellman's optimality equation. The equation should not be viewed as an algorithm. Justify the rationale of this statement.

12.2 In this problem, we present another proof of Bellman's optimality equation of Eq. (12.22), due to Ross (1983).

   (a) Let π be any arbitrary policy, and suppose that π chooses action a at time-step 0 with probability p_a and $a \in \mathcal{A}_i$. Then, we have

$$J^\pi(i) = \sum_{a \in \mathcal{A}_i} p_a \left(c(i, a) + \sum_{j=1}^{N} p_{ij}(a) W^\pi(j) \right)$$

   where $W^\pi(j)$ represents the expected cost-to-go function from time-step 1 onward, given that policy π is being used and that j is the state at time-step 1. Hence, show that

$$J^\pi(i) \geq \min_{a \in \mathcal{A}_i} \left(c(i, a) + \gamma \sum_{j=1}^{N} p_{ij}(a) J(j) \right)$$

   where

$$W^\pi(j) \geq \gamma J(j)$$

   (b) Let π be the policy that chooses action a_0 at time-step 0. If the next state is j, it views the process as originating in state j, following a policy π_j such that

$$J^{\pi_j}(j) \leq J(j) + \epsilon$$

   where ϵ is a small positive number. Hence, show that

$$J(i) \geq \min_{a \in \mathcal{A}_i} \left(c(i, a) + \gamma \sum_{j=1}^{N} p_{ij}(a) J(j) \right) + \gamma\epsilon$$

   (c) Using the results derived in parts (a) and (b), prove Eq. (12.22).

12.3 Equation (12.22) represents a linear system of N equations, with one equation per state. Let

$$\mathbf{J}^\mu = [J^\mu(1), J^\mu(2), ..., J^\mu(N)]^T$$

$$\mathbf{c}(\mu) = [c(1, \mu), c(2, \mu), ..., c(N, \mu)]^T$$

$$\mathbf{P}(\mu) = \begin{bmatrix} p_{11}(\mu) & p_{12}(\mu) & \cdots & p_{1N}(\mu) \\ p_{21}(\mu) & p_{22}(\mu) & \cdots & p_{2N}(\mu) \\ \vdots & \vdots & \vdots & \vdots \\ p_{N1}(\mu) & p_{N2}(\mu) & \cdots & p_{NN}(\mu) \end{bmatrix}$$

Show that Eq. (12.22) may be reformulated in the equivalent matrix form

$$(\mathbf{I} - \gamma \mathbf{P}(\mu))\mathbf{J}^{\mu} = \mathbf{c}(\mu)$$

where $\mathbf{I}$ is the identity matrix. Comment on the uniqueness of the vector $\mathbf{J}^{\mu}$, representing the cost-to-go functions for the N states.

12.4 In Section 12.3, we derived the dynamic-programming algorithm for a finite-horizon problem. In this problem, we rederive this algorithm for a discounted problem for which the cost-to-go function is defined by

$$J^{\mu}(X_0) = \lim_{K \to \infty} \left[\sum_{n=0}^{K-1} \gamma^n g(X_n, \mu(X_n), X_{n+1}) \right]$$

In particular, show that

$$J_K(X_0) = \min_{\mu} \underset{X_1}{E} \left[g(X_0, \mu(X_0), X_1) + \gamma J_{K-1}(X_1) \right]$$

Policy iteration

12.5 In Section 12.4, we said that the cost-to-go function satisfies the statement

$$J^{\mu_{n+1}}(i) \leq J^{\mu_n}(i) \quad \text{for all } i$$

Justify this assertion.

12.6 The policy iteration algorithm operates by alternating between two steps. Explain these steps with the help of a block diagram.

12.7 Using a *controller-critic system*, illustrate the interaction between the policy update and policy evaluation in the policy-iteration algorithm.

Value iteration

12.8 A dynamic-programming problem involves a total of N possible states and M admissible actions. Assuming the use of a stationary policy, show that a single iteration of the value iteration algorithm requires on the order of N^2M operations.

12.9 Table 12.2 presents a summary of the value iteration algorithm formulated in terms of the cost-to-go function $J^{\mu}(i)$ for states $i \in \mathcal{X}$. Reformulate this algorithm in terms of the Q-factors $Q(i, a)$.

12.10 Policy iteration always terminates after a finite number of steps, whereas value iteration may require an infinite number of iterations. Discuss other differences between these two methods of dynamic programming.

Temporal-difference learning

12.11 **(a)** Construct a signal-flow graph representation of the TD(0) algorithm described in Eqs. (12.34) and (12.35).

(b) The TD(0) algorithm has a mathematical composition similar to that of the LMS algorithm described in Chapter 3. Discuss the similarities and differences between these two algorithms.

12.12 The one-step update rule of Eq. (12.35) is commonly referred to as the TD(0) algorithm. Justify the rationale of this terminology.

12.13 **(a)** Prove the equalities 1 and 2 that were used to go from Eq. (12.45) to Eq. (12.46).

(b) Construct a signal-flow graph representation of Eq. (12.48), describing the TD(λ) algorithm.

Q-learning

12.14 Show that

$$J^*(i) = \min_{a \in \mathcal{A}_i} Q(i, a)$$

12.15 Why the *Q*-learning system is said to be an off-policy method for control? How an off-policy method is different from an on-policy method?

12.16 Construct a signal-flow graph for the approximate *Q*-learning algorithm summarized in Table P12.16.

12.17 The approximate *Q*-learning algorithm summarized in Table P12.16 assumes lack of knowledge of the state-transition probabilities. Reformulate this algorithm assuming the availability of these probabilities.

Approximate Dynamic Programming: Indirect Methods

12.18 Equation (12.70) is the least-squares version of the projected value iteration (PVI) algorithm. To implement this algorithm in practical terms, we proposed to apply Monte Carlo simulation to approximate it with the use of the least-squares policy evaluation (LSPE) algorithm described in Eq. (12.71).

(a) By setting the gradient of the cost function in Eq. (12.70) to zero, derive a closed formula for $\mathbf{w}_{n+1}$.

(b) Do likewise for Eq. (12.71). Find empirical frequencies of state *i* and transition (*i*, *j*) (i.e., estimates of the steady-state probability π_i and transition probability p_{ij}) to demonstrate that the PVI and LSPE algorithms coincide asymptotically.

TABLE P12.16 Summary of the Approximate Q-Learning Algorithm

1. Start with an initial weight vector $\mathbf{w}_0$, resulting in the Q-factor $Q(i_0, a_0, \mathbf{w}_0)$; the weight vector $\mathbf{w}_0$ refers to a neural network used to perform the approximation.

2. For iteration $n = 1, 2, ...$, do the following:

   (a) For the setting $\mathbf{w}$ of the neural network, determine the optimal action

   $$a_n = \min_{a \in \mathcal{A}_{i_n}} Q_n(i_n, a, \mathbf{w})$$

   (b) Determine the target Q-factor

   $$Q_n^{\text{target}}(i_n, a_n, \mathbf{w}) = g(i_n, a_n, j_n) + \gamma \min_{b \in \mathcal{A}_{i_n}} Q_n(j_n, b, \mathbf{w}), j_n = i_{n+1}$$

   (c) Update the Q-factor

   $$Q_{n+1}(i_n, a_n, \mathbf{w}) = Q_n(i_n, a_n, \mathbf{w}) + \Delta Q_n(i_n, a_n, \mathbf{w})$$

   where

   $$\Delta Q_n(i, a, \mathbf{w}) = \begin{cases} \eta_n(i_n, a_n)(Q_n^{\text{target}}(i_n, a_n, \mathbf{w}) - Q_n(i_n, a_n, \mathbf{w})), & (i, a) = (i_n, a_n) \\ 0, & \text{otherwise} \end{cases}$$

   (d) Apply (i_n, a_n) as input to the neural network producing the output $\hat{Q}_n(i_n, a_n, \mathbf{w})$ as an approximation to the target Q-factor $Q_n^{\text{target}}(i_n, a_n, \mathbf{w})$. Change the weight vector $\mathbf{w}$ slightly in a way that brings $\hat{Q}_n(i_n, a_n, \mathbf{w})$ closer to the target value $Q_n^{\text{target}}(i_n, a_n, \mathbf{w})$.

   (e) Go back to step (a) and repeat the computation.

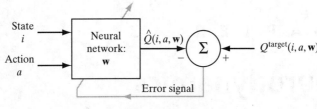

FIGURE P12.20

12.19 The LSPE(λ) algorithm has a faster rate of convergence than the TD(λ) algorithm. Justify this statement.

12.20 Figure P12.20 depicts a neural-network-based scheme for approximating the target Q-factor, denoted by $Q^{\text{target}}(i, a, \mathbf{w})$, where i denotes the state of the network, a denotes the action to be taken, and $\mathbf{w}$ denotes the weight vector of the neural network used in the approximation. Correspondingly, Table P12.16 presents a summary of the *approximate Q-learning algorithm*. Explain the operation of the approximate dynamic programming scheme of Fig. P12.20 to justify the summary presented in Table P12.16.

CHAPTER 13

Neurodynamics

ORGANIZATION OF THE CHAPTER

This chapter studies recurrent neural networks, with particular emphasis on the direct method of Laypunov for solving the stability problem.

The material in the chapter is organized as follows:

1. The introductory Section 13.1 motivates the study of stability in deterministic neurodynamic systems, pointing out some historical aspects of the problem.
2. Sections 13.2 through 13.6 provide background material. In particular, Section 13.2 introduces some fundamental concepts in dynamic systems, followed by a discussion of the stability of equilibrium points in Section 13.3. In Section 13.4, we describe various types of attractors that arise in the study of dynamic systems. In Section 13.5, we revisit the additive model of a neuron. Section 13.6 discusses the manipulations of attractors as a neural network paradigm.
3. The next part of the chapter, consisting of Sections 13.7 through 13.9, deals with associative memories. Section 13.7 is devoted to the Hopfield model and use of its discrete form as a content-addressable memory. Section 13.8 presents the Cohen–Grossberg theorem for nonlinear dynamic systems, including the Hopfield network and other associative memories as special cases. In Section 13.9, we describe another neurodynamic model known as the brain-state-in-a-box model, which is well suited for clustering.
4. The last part of the chapter, consisting of Sections 13.10 and 13.11, deals with the topic of chaos. Section 13.10 discusses the invariant characteristics of a chaotic process, followed by a discussion of the closely related topic of dynamic reconstruction of a chaotic process in Section 13.11.

The chapter concludes with some final remarks in Section 13.12.

13.1 INTRODUCTION

In one form or another, *time plays a critical role in learning*, a concept that is exemplified by much of the material presented in preceding chapters of this book. Basically, there are two ways in which time manifests itself in the learning process:

1. A static neural network (e.g., multilayer perceptron, studied in Chapter 4) is made into a dynamic mapper by stimulating it via a *memory structure*, short term or long term.

2. Time is built into the operation of a neural network through the use of *feedback*.

In the context of a neural network, there are two basic ways of applying feedback:

1. *local feedback*, which is applied to a single neuron inside the network;

2. *global feedback*, which encompasses one or more layers of hidden neurons—or better still, the whole network.

Local feedback is a relatively simple matter to deal with, but global feedback has much more profound implications. In the neural network literature, neural networks with one or more global feedback loops are referred to as recurrent networks.

Basically, there are two functional uses of recurrent networks:

1. *associative memories*;

2. *input–output mapping networks*.

The use of recurrent networks as associative memories is considered in this chapter, and their use as mappers is deferred to Chapter 15. Whichever one of these two is the application of interest, an issue of particular concern is that of *stability*, which is considered in this chapter.

Feedback is like a double-edged sword in that when it is applied improperly, it can produce harmful effects. In particular, the application of feedback can cause a system that is originally stable to become unstable. Our primary interest in this chapter is in the stability of recurrent networks.

The subject of neural networks viewed as nonlinear dynamic systems, with particular emphasis on the *stability* problem, is referred to as *neurodynamics*. An important feature of the stability (or instability) of a nonlinear dynamic system is that it is a property of the whole system. As a corollary we may make the following statement:

> *The presence of stability always implies some form of coordination between the individual parts of the system.*

It appears that the study of neurodynamics began in 1938 with the work of Nicholas Rashevsky, in whose visionary mind the application of dynamics to biology came into view for the first time.

The stability of a nonlinear dynamic system is a difficult mathematical issue to deal with. When we speak of the stability problem, those with an engineering background usually think in terms of the *bounded-input–bounded-output (BIBO) stability criterion*. According to this criterion, stability means that the output of a system must *not* grow without bound as a result of a bounded input, initial condition, or unwanted disturbance. The BIBO stability criterion is well suited for a linear dynamic system. However, it is useless to apply it to recurrent neural networks; all such nonlinear dynamic systems are BIBO stable because of the saturating nonlinearity built into the constitution of a neuron.

When we speak of stability in the context of a nonlinear dynamic system, we usually mean *stability in the sense of Lyapunov*. In a celebrated mémoire dated 1892, Lyapunov, a Russian mathematician and engineer, presented the fundamental concepts of stability theory known as the *direct method of Lyapunov*. This method is widely used for the stability analysis of linear and nonlinear systems, both time invariant and time varying. As such, it is directly applicable to the stability analysis of neural networks. Indeed, much of the material presented in this chapter is concerned with the direct method of Lyapunov. However, its application is no easy task.

The study of neurodynamics may follow one of two routes, depending on the application of interest:

- *Deterministic neurodynamics*, in which the neural network model has a deterministic behavior. In mathematical terms, it is described by a set of *nonlinear differential equations* that define the exact evolution of the model as a function of time (Grossberg, 1967; Cohen and Grossberg, 1983; Hopfield, 1984).
- *Statistical neurodynamics*, in which the neural network model is perturbed by the presence of noise. In this case, we have to deal with *stochastic nonlinear differential equations*, thereby expressing the solution in probabilistic terms (Amari et al., 1972; Peretto, 1984; Amari, 1990). The combination of stochasticity and nonlinearity makes the subject more difficult to handle.

In this chapter, we restrict ourselves to deterministic neurodynamics.

13.2 DYNAMIC SYSTEMS

In order to proceed with the study of neurodynamics, we need a *mathematical model* for describing the dynamics of a nonlinear system. A model most naturally suited for this purpose is the *state-space model*. According to this model, we think in terms of a set of *state variables* whose values (at any particular instant of time) are supposed to contain sufficient information to predict the future evolution of the system. Let $x_1(t)$, $x_2(t)$, ..., $x_N(t)$ denote the state variables of a nonlinear dynamic system, where continuous time t is the *independent variable* and N is the *order* of the system. For convenience of notation, these state variables are collected into an N-by-1 vector $\mathbf{x}(t)$ called the *state vector*, or simply *state*, of the system. The dynamics of a large class of nonlinear dynamic systems may then be cast in the form of a system of first-order differential equations written as

$$\frac{d}{dt} x_j(t) = F_j(x_j(t)), \qquad j = 1, 2, ..., N \tag{13.1}$$

where the function $F_j(\cdot)$ is, in general, a nonlinear function of its argument. We may express this system of equations in a compact form by using vector notation, as shown by

$$\frac{d}{dt}\mathbf{x}(t) = \mathbf{F}(\mathbf{x}(t)) \tag{13.2}$$

where the nonlinear function $\mathbf{F}$ is vector valued, each element of which operates on a corresponding element of the state vector:

$$\mathbf{x}(t) = [x_1(t), x_2(t), ..., x_N(t)]^T \tag{13.3}$$

A nonlinear dynamic system for which the vector function $\mathbf{F}(\mathbf{x}(t))$ does not depend *explicitly* on time t, as in Eq. (13.2), is said to be *autonomous*; otherwise, it is *nonautonomous*.[1] We will concern ourselves with autonomous systems only.

Regardless of the exact form of the nonlinear function $\mathbf{F}(\cdot)$, the state $\mathbf{x}(t)$ must vary with time t; otherwise, $\mathbf{x}(t)$ is constant, and the system is no longer dynamic. We may therefore formally define a dynamic system as follows:

> *A dynamic system is a system whose state varies with time.*

Moreover, we may think of $d\mathbf{x}/dt$ as a "velocity" vector—not in a physical sense, but rather in an abstract one. Then, according to Eq. (13.2), we may refer to the vector function $\mathbf{F}(\mathbf{x})$ as a velocity vector field, or simply a *vector field*.

State Space

It is informative to view the state-space equation of Eq. (13.2) as describing the *motion* of a point in an N-dimensional *state space*. The state space can be a *Euclidean space* or a subset thereof. It can also be a non-Euclidean space such as a circle, a sphere, a torus, or some other *differentiable manifold*. Our interest in this chapter is confined to Euclidean spaces. (Differential manifolds were discussed in Chapter 7.)

The state space is important because it provides us with a visual and conceptual tool for analyzing the dynamics of a nonlinear system described by Eq. (13.2). It does so by focusing attention on the *global characteristics* of the motion rather than the detailed aspects of analytic or numeric solutions of the equation.

At a particular instant of time t, the observed state of the system (i.e., the state vector $\mathbf{x}(t)$) is represented by a single point in the N-dimensional state space. Changes in the state of the system with time t are represented as a curve in the state space, with each point on the curve carrying (explicitly or implicitly) a label that records the time of observation. This curve is called a *trajectory* or *orbit* of the system. Figure 13.1

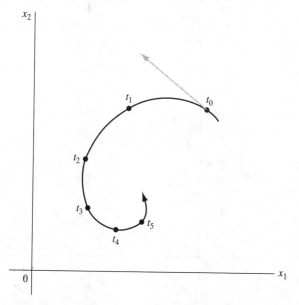

FIGURE 13.1 A two-dimensional trajectory (orbit) of a dynamic system.

illustrates the trajectory of a two-dimensional system. The instantaneous velocity of the trajectory (i.e., the velocity vector $d\mathbf{x}(t)/dt$) is represented by the *tangent vector*, shown as a red line in Fig. 13.1 for time $t = t_0$. We may thus derive a velocity vector for each point of the trajectory.

The family of trajectories for different initial conditions is referred to as the *state portrait* of the system. The state portrait includes *all* those points in the state space where the vector field $\mathbf{F}(\mathbf{x})$ is defined. Note that for an autonomous system, there will be only one trajectory passing through an initial state. A useful idea that emerges from the state portrait is the *flow* of a dynamic system, defined as the motion of the space of states within itself. In other words, we may imagine the space of states to flow, just like a fluid, around in itself, with each point (state) following a particular trajectory. The idea of flow as described here is vividly illustrated in the state portrait in Fig. 13.2.

Given a state portrait of a dynamic system, we may construct a field of velocity (tangent) vectors, one for every point of the state space. The picture so obtained in turn provides a portrayal of the vector field of the system. Figure 13.3 shows a number of velocity vectors to help us develop a feeling for what a full field looks like. The usefulness of a vector field thus lies in the fact that it gives us a visual description of the inherent tendency of a dynamic system to move with a habitual velocity at each specific point of a state space.

Lipschitz Condition

For the state-space equation of Eq. (13.2) to have a solution and for that solution to be unique, we must impose certain restrictions on the vector function $\mathbf{F}(\mathbf{x})$. For convenience of presentation, we have dropped dependence of the state $\mathbf{x}$ on time t, a practice that we follow from time to time. For a solution to exist, it is sufficient that $\mathbf{F}(\mathbf{x})$ be

FIGURE 13.2 A two-dimensional state (phase) portrait of a dynamic system.

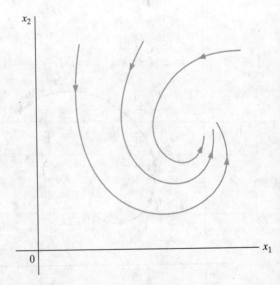

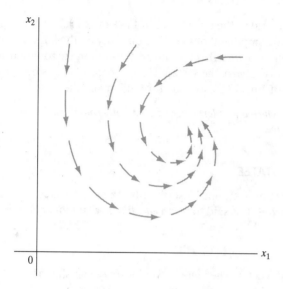

FIGURE 13.3 A two-dimensional vector field of a dynamic system.

continuous in all of its arguments. However, this restriction by itself does not guarantee uniqueness of the solution. To do so, we must impose a further restriction known as the *Lipschitz condition*. Let $\|\mathbf{x}\|$ denote the *norm*, or *Euclidean length*, of the vector $\mathbf{x}$. Let $\mathbf{x}$ and $\mathbf{u}$ be a pair of vectors in an open set $\mathcal{M}$ in a normal vector (state) space. Then, according to the Lipschitz condition, there exists a constant K such that

$$\|\mathbf{F}(\mathbf{x}) - \mathbf{F}(\mathbf{u})\| \leq K\|\mathbf{x} - \mathbf{u}\| \tag{13.4}$$

for all $\mathbf{x}$ and $\mathbf{u}$ in $\mathcal{M}$ (Hirsch and Smale, 1974; Jackson, 1989). A vector function $\mathbf{F}(\mathbf{x})$ that satisfies Eq. (13.4) is said to be *Lipschitz*, and K is called the *Lipschitz constant* for $\mathbf{F}(\mathbf{x})$. Equation (13.4) also implies the continuity of the function $\mathbf{F}(\mathbf{x})$ with respect to $\mathbf{x}$. It follows, therefore, that in the case of autonomous systems, the Lipschitz condition guarantees both the existence and uniqueness of solutions for the state-space equation of Eq. (13.2). In particular, if all partial derivatives $\partial F_i / \partial x_j$ are finite everywhere, then the function $\mathbf{F}(\mathbf{x})$ satisfies the Lipschitz condition.

Divergence Theorem

Consider a region of volume V and surface S in the state space of an autonomous system, and assume a "flow" of points from this region. From our earlier discussion, we recognize that the velocity vector $d\mathbf{x}/dt$ is equal to the vector field $\mathbf{F}(\mathbf{x})$. Provided that the vector field $\mathbf{F}(\mathbf{x})$ within the volume V is "well behaved," we may apply the *divergence theorem* from vector calculus (Jackson, 1975). Let $\mathbf{n}$ denote a unit vector normal to the elemental surface dS pointing outward from the enclosed volume. Then, according to the divergence theorem, the relation

$$\int_S (\mathbf{F}(\mathbf{x}) \cdot \mathbf{n})dS = \int_V (\nabla \cdot \mathbf{F}(\mathbf{x}))dV \tag{13.5}$$

holds between the volume integral of the divergence of $\mathbf{F}(\mathbf{x})$ and the surface integral of the outwardly directed normal component of $\mathbf{F}(\mathbf{x})$. The quantity on the left-hand side of Eq. (13.5) is recognized as the net *flux* flowing out of the region surrounded by the closed surface S. If this quantity is zero, the system is *conservative*; if it is negative, the system is *dissipative*. In light of Eq. (13.5), we may formally make the statement:

> *If the divergence* $\nabla \cdot \mathbf{F}(\mathbf{x})$ *(which is a scalar) is zero, the system is conservative, and if it is negative, the system is dissipative.*

13.3   STABILITY OF EQUILIBRIUM STATES

Consider an autonomous dynamic system described by the state-space equation of Eq. (13.2). A constant vector $\bar{\mathbf{x}} \in \mathcal{M}$ is said to be an *equilibrium* (*stationary*) *state* of the system if the condition

$$\mathbf{F}(\bar{\mathbf{x}}) = \mathbf{0} \qquad (13.6)$$

is satisfied, where $\mathbf{0}$ is the null vector. The velocity vector $d\mathbf{x}/dt$ vanishes at the equilibrium state $\bar{\mathbf{x}}$, and therefore the constant function $\mathbf{x}(t) = \bar{\mathbf{x}}$ is a solution of Eq. (13.2). Furthermore, because of the uniqueness property of solutions, no other solution curve can pass through the equilibrium state $\bar{\mathbf{x}}$. The equilibrium state is also referred to as a *singular point*, signifying the fact that in the case of an equilibrium point, the trajectory will degenerate into the point itself.

In order to develop a deeper understanding of the equilibrium condition, suppose that the nonlinear function $\mathbf{F}(\mathbf{x})$ is smooth enough for the state-space equation of Eq. (13.2) to be linearized in the neighborhood of the equilibrium state $\bar{\mathbf{x}}$. Specifically, let

$$\mathbf{x}(t) = \bar{\mathbf{x}} + \Delta\mathbf{x}(t) \qquad (13.7)$$

where $\Delta\mathbf{x}(t)$ is a small deviation from $\bar{\mathbf{x}}$. Then, retaining the first two terms in the Taylor series expansion of $\mathbf{F}(\mathbf{x})$, we may approximate it as follows:

$$\mathbf{F}(\mathbf{x}) \approx \bar{\mathbf{x}} + \mathbf{A}\,\Delta\mathbf{x}(t) \qquad (13.8)$$

The matrix $\mathbf{A}$ is the *Jacobian* of the nonlinear function $\mathbf{F}(\mathbf{x})$, evaluated at the point $\mathbf{x} = \bar{\mathbf{x}}$, as shown by

$$\mathbf{A} = \frac{\partial}{\partial \mathbf{x}} \mathbf{F}(\mathbf{x})\big|_{\mathbf{x}=\bar{\mathbf{x}}} \qquad (13.9)$$

Using Eqs. (13.7) and (13.8) in Eq. (13.2), followed by the definition of an equilibrium state, we get

$$\frac{d}{dt} \Delta\mathbf{x}(t) \approx \mathbf{A}\,\Delta\mathbf{x}(t) \qquad (13.10)$$

Provided that the Jacobian $\mathbf{A}$ is nonsingular—that is, the inverse matrix $\mathbf{A}^{-1}$ exists— the approximation described in Eq. (13.10) is sufficient to determine the *local* behavior of the trajectories of the system in the neighborhood of the equilibrium state $\bar{\mathbf{x}}$. If $\mathbf{A}$ is nonsingular, the nature of the equilibrium state is essentially determined by its

TABLE 13.1   Classification of the Equilibrium State of a Second-Order System

Type of Equilibrium State $\bar{x}$	Eigenvalues of the Jacobian **A**
Stable node	Real and negative
Stable focus	Complex conjugate with negative real parts
Unstable node	Real and positive
Unstable focus	Complex conjugate with positive real parts
Saddle point	Real with opposite signs
Center	Conjugate purely imaginary

eigenvalues and may therefore be classified in a corresponding fashion. In particular, when the Jacobian matrix **A** has m eigenvalues with positive real parts, we say that the equilibrium state $\bar{x}$ is of *type m*.

For the special case of a *second-order system*, we may classify the equilibrium state as summarized in Table 13.1 and illustrated in Fig. 13.4 (Cook, 1986; Arrowsmith and Place, 1990). Without loss of generality, the equilibrium state is assumed to be at the origin of the state space—that is, $x = 0$. Note also that in the case of a *saddle point*, shown in Fig. 13.4e, the trajectories going to the saddle point are stable, whereas the trajectories coming out from the saddle point are unstable.

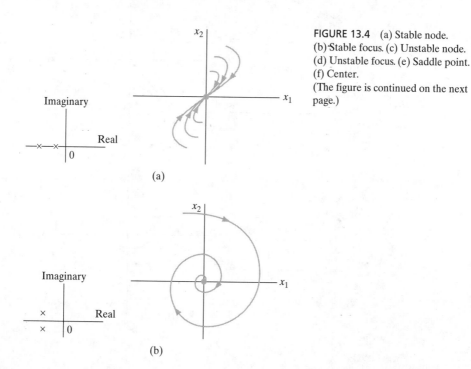

(a)

(b)

FIGURE 13.4   (a) Stable node. (b) Stable focus. (c) Unstable node. (d) Unstable focus. (e) Saddle point. (f) Center. (The figure is continued on the next page.)

FIGURE 13.4 (*continued*)

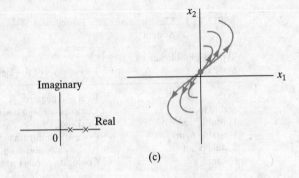

(c)

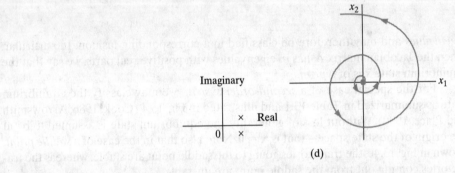

(d)

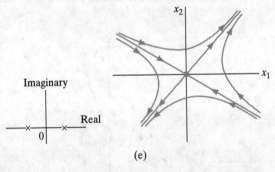

(e)

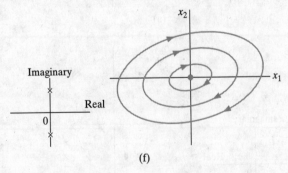

(f)

Definitions of Stability

Linearization of the state-space equation, as outlined previously, provides useful information about the *local stability* properties of an equilibrium state. However, for us to be able to investigate the stability of a nonlinear dynamic system in a more detailed fashion, we need precise definitions of the stability and convergence of an equilibrium state.

In the context of an autonomous nonlinear dynamic system with equilibrium state $\bar{\mathbf{x}}$, the definitions of stability and convergence are as follows (Khalil, 1992):

Definition 1. The equilibrium state $\bar{\mathbf{x}}$ is said to be *uniformly stable* if, for any positive constant ϵ, there exists another positive constant $\delta = \delta(\epsilon)$ such that the condition

$$\|\mathbf{x}(0) - \bar{\mathbf{x}}\| < \delta$$

implies that

$$\|\mathbf{x}(t) - \bar{\mathbf{x}}\| < \epsilon$$

for all $t > 0$.

In effect, this definition states that a trajectory of the system can be made to stay within a small neighborhood of the equilibrium state $\bar{\mathbf{x}}$ if the initial state $\mathbf{x}(0)$ is close to $\bar{\mathbf{x}}$. Otherwise, the system is unstable.

Definition 2. The equilibrium state $\bar{\mathbf{x}}$ is said to be *convergent* if there exists a positive constant δ such that the condition

$$\|\mathbf{x}(0) - \bar{\mathbf{x}}\| < \delta$$

implies that

$$\mathbf{x}(t) \rightarrow \bar{\mathbf{x}} \quad \text{as } t \rightarrow \infty$$

The meaning of this second definition is that if the initial state $\mathbf{x}(0)$ of a trajectory is close enough to the equilibrium state $\bar{\mathbf{x}}$, then the trajectory described by the state vector $\mathbf{x}(t)$ will approach $\bar{\mathbf{x}}$ as time t approaches infinity.

Definition 3. The equilibrium state $\bar{\mathbf{x}}$ is said to be *asymptotically stable* if it is both stable and convergent.

Here, we note that stability and convergence are independent properties. It is only when both properties are satisfied that we have asymptotic stability.

Definition 4. The equilibrium state $\bar{\mathbf{x}}$ is said to be *globally asymptotically* stable if it is stable and all trajectories of the system converge to $\bar{\mathbf{x}}$ as time t approaches infinity.

This last definition implies that the system cannot have other equilibrium states, and it requires that every trajectory of the system remain bounded for all time $t > 0$. In other words, global asymptotic stability implies that the system will ultimately settle down to a steady state for any choice of initial conditions.

EXAMPLE 1 Uniform Stability

Let a solution $\mathbf{u}(t)$ of the nonlinear dynamic system described by Eq. (13.2) vary with time t as indicated in Fig. 13.5. For the solution $\mathbf{u}(t)$ to be uniformly stable, we require that $\mathbf{u}(t)$ and any other solution $\mathbf{v}(t)$ remain close to each other for the same values of t (i.e., time "ticks"), as illustrated in Fig. 13.5. This kind of behavior is referred to as an *isochronous correspondence* of the two solutions $\mathbf{v}(t)$ and $\mathbf{u}(t)$. The solution $\mathbf{u}(t)$ is convergent provided that, for every other solution $\mathbf{v}(t)$ for which $\|\mathbf{v}(0) - \mathbf{u}(0)\| \le \delta(\epsilon)$ at time $t = 0$, the solutions $\mathbf{v}(t)$ and $\mathbf{u}(t)$ converge to an equilibrium state as t approaches infinity. ∎

Lyapunov's Theorems

Now that we have defined stability and asymptotic stability for an equilibrium state of a dynamic system, the next issue to be considered is that of determining stability. Obviously, we may do so by actually finding all possible solutions to the state-space equation of the system; however, such an approach is often difficult, if not impossible. A more elegant approach is to be found in *modern stability theory*, founded by Lyapunov (1892). Specifically, we may investigate the stability problem by applying the *direct method of Lyapunov*, which makes use of a continuous scalar function of the state, called a Lyapunov function, to be defined.

Lyapunov's theorems on the stability and asymptotic stability of the state-space equation of Eq. (13.2), describing an autonomous nonlinear dynamic system with state vector $\mathbf{x}(t)$ and equilibrium state $\bar{\mathbf{x}}$, may be stated as follows (Khalil, 1992):

Theorem 1. *The equilibrium state $\bar{\mathbf{x}}$ is stable if, in a small neighborhood of $\bar{\mathbf{x}}$, there exists a positive-definite function $V(\mathbf{x})$ such that its derivative with respect to time is negative semidefinite in that region.*

Theorem 2. *The equilibrium state $\bar{\mathbf{x}}$ is asymptotically stable if, in a small neighborhood of $\bar{\mathbf{x}}$, there exists a positive-definite function $V(\mathbf{x})$ such that its derivative with respect to time is negative definite in that region.*

A scalar function $V(\mathbf{x})$ that satisfies the requirements of these two theorems is called a *Lyapunov function* for the equilibrium state $\bar{\mathbf{x}}$.

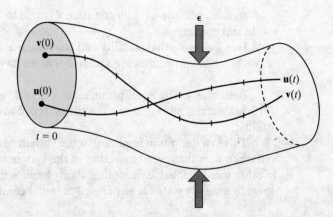

FIGURE 13.5 Illustration of the notion of uniform stability of a state vector.

Theorems 1 and 2 require the Lyapunov function $V(\mathbf{x})$ to be a positive-definite function. Such a function is defined as follows:

1. *The function $V(\mathbf{x})$ has continuous partial derivatives with respect to the elements of the state* $\mathbf{x}$.
2. $V(\bar{\mathbf{x}}) = 0$.
3. $V(\mathbf{x}) > 0$ if $\mathbf{x} \in \mathcal{U} - \bar{\mathbf{x}}$.

  where $\mathcal{U}$ is a small neighborhood around $\bar{\mathbf{x}}$.

Given that $V(\mathbf{x})$ is a Lyapunov function, then according to Theorem 1, the equilibrium state $\bar{\mathbf{x}}$ is stable if the following condition holds[2]:

$$\frac{d}{dt} V(\mathbf{x}) \leq 0 \qquad \text{for } \mathbf{x} \in \mathcal{U} - \bar{\mathbf{x}} \tag{13.11}$$

Furthermore, according to Theorem 2, the equilibrium state $\bar{\mathbf{x}}$ is asymptotically stable if

$$\frac{d}{dt} V(\mathbf{x}) < 0 \qquad \text{for } \mathbf{x} \in \mathcal{U} - \bar{\mathbf{x}} \tag{13.12}$$

The important point of this discussion is that Lyapunov's theorems can be applied without having to solve the state-space equation of the system. Unfortunately, the theorems give no indication of how to find a Lyapunov function; it is a matter of ingenuity and trial and error in each case. In many problems of interest, the energy function can serve as a Lyapunov function. The inability to find a suitable Lyapunov function does not, however, prove instability of the system. The existence of a Lyapunov function is a sufficient, but not necessary, condition for stability.

The Lyapunov function $V(\mathbf{x})$ provides the mathematical basis for stability analysis of the nonlinear dynamic system described by Eq. (13.2). On the other hand, the use of Eq. (13.10), based on the Jacobian $\mathbf{A}$, provides the basis for *local* stability analysis of the system. Simply put, the Lyapunov stability analysis is much more powerful in its conclusions than the local stability analysis.

Lyapunov Surface

For an intuitive understanding of the two Lyapunov theorems, we introduce the notion of a *Lyapunov surface*, which is formally defined by

$$V(\mathbf{x}) = c \qquad \text{for some constant } c > 0$$

Under Theorem 1, the condition

$$\frac{d}{dt} V(\mathbf{x}) \leq 0$$

implies that once a trajectory crosses a Lyapunov surface for some positive constant c, the trajectory moves inside a set of points defined by

$$\mathbf{x} \in \mathbb{R}^N \quad \text{given } V(\mathbf{x}) \leq 0$$

and can never come out of the Lyapunov surface. It is in this sense that we speak of the stability of the system under Theorem 1.

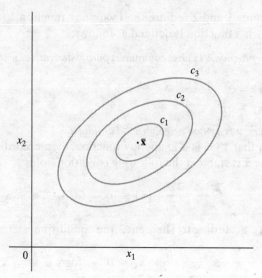

FIGURE 13.6 Lyapunov surfaces for decreasing value of constant c, with $c_1 < c_2 < c_3$. The equilibrium state is denoted by the point $\bar{\mathbf{x}}$.

On the other hand, under Theorem 2, the condition

$$\frac{d}{dt}V(\mathbf{x}) < 0$$

implies that the trajectory will move from one Lyapunov surface to an inner Lyapunov surface with a smaller constant c, as illustrated in Fig. 13.6. In particular, as the constant c decreases in value, the Lyapunov surface moves closer to the equilibrium state $\bar{\mathbf{x}}$ in a corresponding fashion, the implication being that as time t progresses the trajectory approaches the equilibrium state $\bar{\mathbf{x}}$. However, we cannot be sure that the trajectory will actually converge onto $\bar{\mathbf{x}}$ as $t \to \infty$. Nevertheless, we can conclude that the equilibrium state $\bar{\mathbf{x}}$ is stable in the restricted sense that the trajectory is contained inside any ball $\mathcal{B}_\varepsilon$ of some small radius ε, requiring that the initial condition $\mathbf{x}(0)$ lies inside a Lyapunov surface contained in that ball (Khalil, 1992). As a matter of interest, this is the condition that we referred to in Section 8.5 on the asymptotical stability of the maximum eigenfilter.

13.4 ATTRACTORS

Dissipative systems are generally characterized by the presence of attracting sets or manifolds of dimensionality lower than that of the state space. The notion of a manifold was discussed at some length in Chapter 7. In short, by a "manifold," we mean a k-dimensional surface embedded in the N-dimensional state space, which is defined by the set of equations

$$M_j(x_1, x_2, ..., x_N) = 0, \qquad \begin{cases} j = 1, 2, ..., k \\ k < N \end{cases} \tag{13.13}$$

where $x_1, x_2, ..., x_N$ are elements of the N-dimensional state of the system and M_j is some function of these elements. These manifolds are called *attractors*[3] in that they are bounded subsets to which regions of initial conditions of a nonzero state-space volume converge as time t increases.

The manifold may consist of a single point in the state space, in which case we speak of a *point attractor*. Alternatively, it may be in the form of a periodic orbit, in which case we speak of a stable *limit cycle*—stable in the sense that nearby trajectories approach it asymptotically. Figure 13.7 illustrates these two types of attractors. Attractors represent only the *equilibrium states* of a dynamic system that may be *observed experimentally*. Note, however, that in the context of attractors, an equilibrium state does *not* imply a static equilibrium, nor does it imply a steady state. For example, a limit cycle represents a stable state of an attractor, but it varies continuously with time.

In Fig. 13.7, we note that each attractor is encompassed by a distinct region of its own. Such a region is called a *basin (domain) of attraction*. Note also that every initial state of the system is in the basin of some attractor. The boundary separating one basin of attraction from another is called a *separatrix*. In the case of Fig. 13.7, the basin boundary is represented by the union of the trajectory T_1, the saddle point Q, and the trajectory T_2.

A limit cycle constitutes the typical form of an oscillatory behavior that arises when an equilibrium point of a nonlinear system becomes unstable. As such, it can arise in nonlinear systems of any order. Nevertheless, limit cycles are particularly characteristic of second-order systems.

Hyperbolic-Attractors

Consider a point attractor whose nonlinear dynamic equations are linearized around the equilibrium state $\bar{x}$ in the manner described in Section 13.2. Let $\mathbf{A}$ denote the Jacobian of the system evaluated at $\mathbf{x} = \bar{\mathbf{x}}$. The attractor is said to be a *hyperbolic attractor* if the eigenvalues of the Jacobian $\mathbf{A}$ all have an absolute value less than 1 (Ott, 1993). For example, the flow of a second-order hyperbolic attractor may have the form shown in Fig. 13.4a or that of Fig. 13.4b; in both cases, the eigenvalues of the Jacobian $\mathbf{A}$ have negative real parts. Hyperbolic attractors are of particular interest in the study of the "vanishing-gradients problem," which arises in dynamically driven recurrent networks; this problem will be discussed in Chapter 15.

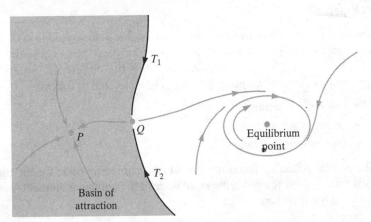

FIGURE 13.7   Illustration of the notion of a basin of attraction and the idea of a separatrix.

13.5   NEURODYNAMIC MODELS

Having familiarized ourselves with the behavior of nonlinear dynamic systems, we are now ready to discuss some of the important issues involved in neurodynamics, which we do in this section and the ones to follow. We emphasize that there is no universally agreed-upon definition of what we mean by neurodynamics. Rather than try to present such a definition, we will instead define the most general properties of the neurodynamic systems considered in this chapter. In particular, the discussion is limited to neurodynamic systems whose state variables are continuous valued and whose equations of motion are described by differential equations or difference equations. The systems of interest possess four general characteristics (Peretto and Niez, 1986; Pineda, 1988a):

1. *A large number of degrees of freedom.* The human cortex is a *highly parallel, distributed system* that is estimated to possess about 10 billion neurons, with each neuron modeled by one or more state variables. It is generally believed that both the computational power and the fault-tolerant capability of such a neurodynamic system are the result of the *collective dynamics* of the system. The system is characterized by a very large number of coupling constants represented by the strengths (efficacies) of the individual synaptic junctions.

2. *Nonlinearity.* A neurodynamic system is inherently nonlinear. In fact, nonlinearity is essential for creating a universal computing machine.

3. *Dissipation.* A neurodynamic system is dissipative. It is therefore characterized by the convergence of the state-space volume onto a manifold of lower dimensionality as time goes on.

4. *Noise.* Finally, noise is an intrinsic characteristic of neurodynamic systems. In real-life neurons, membrane noise is generated at synaptic junctions (Katz, 1966).

The presence of noise necessitates the use of a probabilistic treatment of neural activity, adding another level of complexity to the analysis of neurodynamic systems. A detailed treatment of stochastic neurodynamics is beyond the scope of this book, as previously noted. The effect of noise is therefore ignored in the material that follows.

Additive Model

Consider the noiseless, dynamic model of a neuron shown in Fig. 13.8. In physical terms, the synaptic weights $w_{j1}, w_{j2}, ..., w_{jN}$ represent *conductances*, and the respective inputs $x_1(t), x_2(t), ..., x_N(t)$ represent *potentials*; N is the number of inputs. These inputs are applied to a *current-summing junction*, characterized as follows:

- low input resistance;
- current gain of unity;
- high output resistance.

The current-summing junction thus acts as a summing node for the input currents. The total current flowing *toward* the input node of the nonlinear element (activation function) in Fig. 13.8 is therefore

$$\sum_{i=1}^{N} w_{ji}x_i(t) + I_j$$

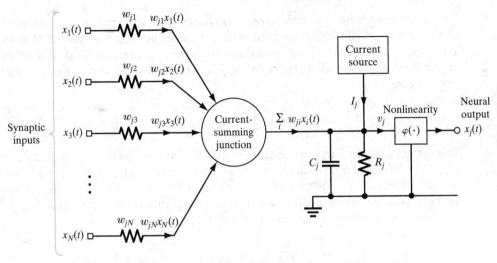

FIGURE 13.8 Additive model of a neuron, labeled j.

where the first (summation) term is due to the stimuli $x_1(t), x_2(t), ..., x_N(t)$ acting on the synaptic weights (conductances) $w_{j1}, w_{j2}, ..., w_{jN}$, respectively, and the second term is due to the current source I_j representing an externally applied bias. Let $v_j(t)$ denote the induced local field at the input of the nonlinear activation function $\varphi(\cdot)$. We may then express the total current flowing *away* from the input node of the nonlinear element as the sum of two terms:

$$\frac{v_j(t)}{R_j} + C_j\frac{dv_j(t)}{dt}$$

where the first term is due to leakage resistance R_j and the second term is due to leakage capacitance C_j. From *Kirchoff's current law*, we know that the total current flowing toward any node of an electrical circuit is zero. By applying Kirchoff's current law to the input node of the nonlinearity in Fig. 13.8, we get

$$C_j\frac{dv_j(t)}{dt} + \frac{v_j(t)}{R_j} = \sum_{i=1}^{N} w_{ji}x_i(t) + I_j \qquad (13.14)$$

The capacitive term $C_j dv_j(t)/dt$ on the left-hand side of Eq. (13.14) is the simplest way to add dynamics (memory) to the model of a neuron. Given the induced local field $v_j(t)$, we may determine the output of neuron j by using the nonlinear relation

$$x_j(t) = \varphi(v_j(t)) \qquad (13.15)$$

The RC model described by Eq. (13.14) is commonly referred to as the *additive model*; this terminology is used to distinguish the model from multiplicative (or shunting) models, in which w_{ji} is dependent on x_i.

A characteristic feature of the additive model described by Eq. (13.14) is that the signal $x_i(t)$ applied to neuron j by adjoining neuron i is a slowly varying function of time t. The model thus described constitutes the basis of *classical neurodynamics*.[4]

To proceed further, consider a *recurrent network* consisting of an interconnection of N neurons, each of which is assumed to have the same mathematical model described in Eqs. (13.14) and (13.15). Then, ignoring interneuron propagation time delays, we may define the dynamics of the network by the following *system of coupled first-order differential equations*:

$$C_j \frac{dv_j(t)}{dt} = -\frac{v_j(t)}{R_j} + \sum_{i=1}^{N} w_{ji}x_i(t) + I_j, \qquad j = 1, 2, ..., N \qquad (13.16)$$

This system of equations has the same mathematical form as the state equations of Eq. (13.1); it follows from a simple rearrangement of terms in Eq. (13.14). It is assumed that the activation function $\varphi(\cdot)$ relating the output $x_j(t)$ of neuron j to its induced local field $v_j(t)$ is a continuous function and therefore differentiable with respect to time t. A commonly used activation function is the logistic function

$$\varphi(v_j) = \frac{1}{1 + \exp(-v_j)}, \qquad j = 1, 2, ..., N \qquad (13.17)$$

A necessary condition for the learning algorithms described in Sections 13.6 through 13.11 to exist is that a recurrent network described by Eqs. (13.15) and (13.16) possesses fixed points (i.e., point attractors).

Related Model

To simplify the exposition, we assume that the time constant $\tau_j = R_j C_j$ of neuron j in Eq. (13.16) is the same for all j. Then, by normalizing time t with respect to the common value of this time constant, and normalizing w_{ji} and I_j with respect to R_j, we may recast the model of Eq. (13.16) in the simplified form

$$\frac{dv_j(t)}{dt} = -v_j(t) + \sum_{i} w_{ji}\varphi(v_i(t)) + I_j, \qquad j = 1, 2, ..., N \qquad (13.18)$$

where we have also incorporated Eq. (13.15). The attractor structure of the system of coupled first-order nonlinear differential equations given in Eq. (13.18) is basically the same as that of a closely related model described in Pineda (1987):

$$\frac{dx_j(t)}{dt} = -x_j(t) + \varphi\left(\sum_{i} w_{ji}x_i(t)\right) + K_j, \qquad j = 1, 2, ..., N \qquad (13.19)$$

In the additive model described by Eq. (13.18), the induced local fields $v_1(t), v_2(t), ..., v_N(t)$ of the individual neurons constitute the state vector. On the other hand, in the related model of Eq. (13.19), the outputs of the neurons $x_1(t), x_2(t), ..., x_N(t)$ constitute the state vector.

These two neurodynamic models are in fact related to each other by a linear, invertible transformation. Specifically, by multiplying both sides of Eq. (13.19) by w_{kj}, summing with respect to j, and then substituting the transformation

$$v_k(t) = \sum_{j} w_{kj}x_j(t)$$

we obtain a model of the type described by Eq. (13.18) and thereby find that the bias terms of the two models are related by

$$I_k = \sum_j w_{kj} K_j$$

The important point to note here is that results concerning the stability of the additive model of Eq. (13.18) are applicable to the related model of Eq. (13.19).

For block-diagram descriptions of the neurodynamic models of Eqs. (13.18) and (13.19), the reader is referred to Problem 13.2.

13.6   MANIPULATION OF ATTRACTORS AS A RECURRENT NETWORK PARADIGM

When the number of neurons, N, is very large, the neurodynamic noiseless model described by Eq. (13.16) possesses the general properties outlined in Section 13.5: very many degrees of freedom, nonlinearity, and dissipation. Accordingly, such a neurodynamic model can have complicated attractor structures and may therefore exhibit useful computational capabilities.

The identification of attractors with computational objects (e.g., associative memories and input–output mappers) is one of the foundations of neural network paradigms. In order to implement this idea, we must exercise *control* over the locations of the attractors in the state space of the system. A learning algorithm then takes the form of a nonlinear dynamic equation that manipulates the locations of the attractors for the purpose of encoding information in a desired form or learning temporal structures of interest. In this way, it is possible to establish an intimate relationship between the physics of the machine and the algorithms of the computation.

One way in which the collective properties of a neural network may be used to implement a computational task is by way of the concept of *energy minimization*. The Hopfield network and the brain-state-in-a-box model, to be considered in Sections 13.7 and 13.9, respectively, are well-known examples of such an approach. Both of these models are energy-minimizing networks; they differ from each other in their areas of application. The Hopfield network could be used as a content-addressable memory or an analog computer for solving combinatorial-type optimization problems. The brain-state-in-a-box model, on the other hand, is useful for clustering types of applications. More will be said about these applications in subsequent sections of the chapter.

The Hopfield network and brain-state-in-a-box model are examples of an *associative memory* with no hidden neurons; an associative memory is an important resource for intelligent behavior. Another neurodynamic model is that of an input–output mapper, the operation of which relies on the availability of hidden neurons. In this latter case, the method of steepest descent is often used to minimize a cost function defined in terms of the network parameters, and thereby to change the attractor locations. This latter application of a neurodynamic model is exemplified by the dynamically driven recurrent networks discussed in Chapter 15.

13.7 HOPFIELD MODEL

The *Hopfield network (model)* consists of a set of neurons and a corresponding set of unit-time delays, forming a *multiple-loop feedback system*, as illustrated in Fig. 13.9. The number of feedback loops is equal to the number of neurons. Basically, the output of each neuron is fed back, via a unit-time delay element, to each of the other neurons in the network. In other words, there is *no* self-feedback in the model; the reason for avoiding the use of self-feedback is explained later.

To study the dynamics of the Hopfield network, we use the neurodynamic model described in Eq. (13.16), which is based on the additive model of a neuron.

Recognizing that $x_i(t) = \varphi_i(v_i(t))$, we may rewrite Eq. (13.16) in the form

$$C_j \frac{d}{dt} v_j(t) = -\frac{v_j(t)}{R_j} + \sum_{i=1}^{N} w_{ji}\varphi_i(v_i(t)) + I_j, \quad j = 1, ..., N \quad (13.20)$$

To study the stability of this system of differential equations, we make three assumptions:

1. The matrix of synaptic weights is *symmetric*—that is,

$$w_{ji} = w_{ij} \quad \text{for all } i \text{ and } j \quad (13.21)$$

2. Each neuron has a *nonlinear* activation of its own—hence the use of $\varphi_i(\cdot)$ in Eq. (13.20).

FIGURE 13.9 Architectural graph of a Hopfield network consisting of $N = 4$ neurons.

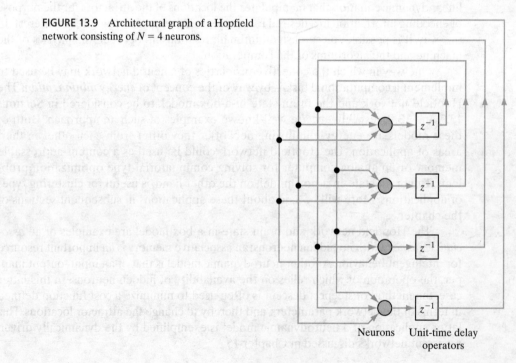

Neurons   Unit-time delay operators

3. The *inverse* of the nonlinear activation function exists, so we may write

$$v = \varphi_i^{-1}(x) \tag{13.22}$$

Let the sigmoid function $\varphi_i(v)$ be itself defined by the hyperbolic tangent function

$$x = \varphi_i(v) = \tanh\left(\frac{a_i v}{2}\right) = \frac{1 - \exp(-a_i v)}{1 + \exp(-a_i v)} \tag{13.23}$$

which has a slope of $a_i/2$ at the origin, as shown by

$$\frac{a_i}{2} = \left.\frac{d\varphi_i}{dv}\right|_{v=0} \tag{13.24}$$

Henceforth, we refer to a_i as the *gain* of neuron i.

Based on the sigmoid function of Eq. (13.23), the inverse output–input relation of Eq. (13.22) may be expressed as

$$v = \varphi_i^{-1}(x) = -\frac{1}{a_i}\log\left(\frac{1 - x}{1 + x}\right) \tag{13.25}$$

The *standard* form of the inverse output–input relation for a neuron of unity gain is defined by

$$\varphi^{-1}(x) = -\log\left(\frac{1 - x}{1 + x}\right) \tag{13.26}$$

We may rewrite Eq. (13.25) in terms of this standard relation as

$$\varphi_i^{-1}(x) = \frac{1}{a_i}\varphi^{-1}(x) \tag{13.27}$$

Figure 13.10a shows a plot of the standard sigmoidal nonlinearity $\varphi(v)$, and Fig. 13.10b shows the corresponding plot of the inverse nonlinearity $\varphi^{-1}(x)$.

The energy (Lyapunov) function of the Hopfield network in Fig. 13.9 is defined as follows:

$$E = -\frac{1}{2}\sum_{i=1}^{N}\sum_{j=1}^{N}w_{ji}x_i x_j + \sum_{j=1}^{N}\frac{1}{R_j}\int_0^{x_j}\varphi_j^{-1}(x)dx - \sum_{j=1}^{N}I_j x_j \tag{13.28}$$

The energy function E defined by Eq. (13.28) may have a complicated *landscape* with many minima. The dynamics of the network are described by a mechanism that seeks out those minima.

With minima in mind, differentiating E with respect to time t, we get

$$\frac{dE}{dt} = -\sum_{j=1}^{N}\left(\sum_{i=1}^{N}w_{ji}x_i - \frac{v_j}{R_j} + I_j\right)\frac{dx_j}{dt} \tag{13.29}$$

FIGURE 13.10 Plots of (a) the standard sigmoidal nonlinearity, and (b) its inverse.

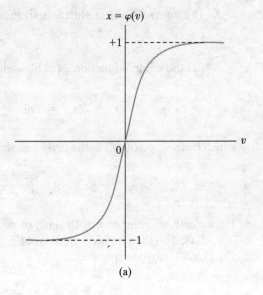

(a)

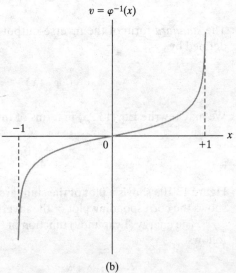

(b)

The quantity inside the parentheses on the right-hand side of Eq. (13.29) is recognized as $C_j \, dv_j/dt$ by virtue of Eq. (13.20). We may thus simplify Eq. (13.29) to

$$\frac{dE}{dt} = -\sum_{j=1}^{N} C_j \left(\frac{dv_j}{dt} \right) \frac{dx_j}{dt} \tag{13.30}$$

We now recognize the inverse relation that defines v_j in terms of x_j. The use of Eq. (13.22) in Eq. (13.30) yields

$$\frac{dE}{dt} = -\sum_{j=1}^{N} C_j \left[\frac{d}{dt} \varphi_j^{-1}(x_j) \right] \frac{dx_j}{dt} \tag{13.31}$$

$$= -\sum_{j=1}^{N} C_j \left(\frac{dx_j}{dt} \right)^2 \left[\frac{d}{dx_j} \varphi_j^{-1}(x_j) \right]$$

From Fig. 13.10b, we see that the inverse output–input relation $\varphi_j^{-1}(x_j)$ is a monotonically increasing function of the output x_j. It therefore follows that

$$\frac{d}{dx_j} \varphi_j^{-1}(x_j) \geq 0 \quad \text{for all } x_j \tag{13.32}$$

We also note that

$$\left(\frac{dx_j}{dt} \right)^2 \geq 0 \quad \text{for all } x_j \tag{13.33}$$

Hence, all the factors that make up the sum on the right-hand side of Eq. (13.31) are nonnegative. In other words, for the energy function E defined in Eq. (13.28), we have

$$\frac{dE}{dt} \leq 0 \quad \text{for all } t$$

From the definition of Eq. (13.28), we note that the function E is bounded. Accordingly, we may now make two statements:

1. *The energy function E is a Lyapunov function of the continuous Hopfield model.*
2. *The model is stable in accordance with Lyapunov's theorem 1.*

In other words, the time evolution of the continuous Hopfield model described by the system of nonlinear first-order differential equations given in Eq. (13.20) represents a trajectory in state space that seeks out the minima of the energy (Lyapunov) function E and comes to a stop at such fixed points. From Eq. (13.31), we also note that the derivative dE/dt vanishes only if

$$\frac{d}{dt} x_j(t) = 0 \quad \text{for all } j$$

We may thus go one step further and write

$$\frac{dE}{dt} < 0 \quad \text{except at a fixed point} \tag{13.34}$$

Equation (13.34) provides the basis for the following statement:

> *The (Lyapunov) energy function E of a Hopfield network is a monotonically decreasing function of time.*

Accordingly, the Hopfield network is asymptotically stable in the Lyapunov sense; the attractor fixed points are the minima of the energy function, and vice versa.

Relation between the Stable States of the Discrete and Continuous Versions of the Hopfield Model

The Hopfield network may be operated in a continuous mode or a discrete mode, depending on the model adopted for describing the neurons. The continuous mode of operation is based on an additive model, as previously described. On the other hand, the discrete mode of operation is based on the McCulloch–Pitts model. We may readily establish the relationship between the stable states of the continuous Hopfield model and those of the corresponding discrete Hopfield model by redefining the input–output relation for a neuron such that we may satisfy two simplifying characteristics:

1. The output of neuron j has the asymptotic values

$$x_j = \begin{cases} +1 & \text{for } v_j = \infty \\ -1 & \text{for } v_j = -\infty \end{cases} \tag{13.35}$$

2. The midpoint of the activation function of the neuron lies at the origin, as shown by

$$\varphi_j(0) = 0 \tag{13.36}$$

Correspondingly, we may set the bias I_j equal to zero for all j.

In formulating the energy function E for a continuous Hopfield model, the neurons are permitted to have self-loops. A discrete Hopfield model, on the other hand, need not have self-loops. We may therefore simplify our discussion by setting $w_{jj} = 0$ for all j in both models.

In light of these observations, we may redefine the energy function of a continuous Hopfield model given in Eq. (13.28) as

$$E = -\frac{1}{2} \sum_{\substack{i=1 \\ i \neq j}}^{N} \sum_{j=1}^{N} w_{ji} x_i x_j + \sum_{j=1}^{N} \frac{1}{R_j} \int_0^{x_j} \varphi_j^{-1}(x) dx \tag{13.37}$$

The inverse function $\varphi_j^{-1}(x)$ is defined by Eq. (13.27). We may thus rewrite the energy function of Eq. (13.37) in the form

$$E = -\frac{1}{2} \sum_{\substack{i=1 \\ i \neq j}}^{N} \sum_{j=1}^{N} w_{ji} x_i x_j + \sum_{j=1}^{N} \frac{1}{a_j R_j} \int_0^{x_j} \varphi^{-1}(x) dx \tag{13.38}$$

The integral

$$\int_0^{x_j} \varphi^{-1}(x) dx$$

has the standard form plotted in Fig. 13.11. Its value is zero for $x_j = 0$, and positive otherwise. It assumes a very large value as x_j approaches ± 1. If, however, the gain a_j of neuron j becomes infinitely large (i.e., the sigmoidal nonlinearity approaches the idealized hard-limiting form), the second term of Eq. (13.38) becomes negligibly small. In the limiting case when $a_j = \infty$ for all j, the maxima and minima of the continuous Hopfield model

FIGURE 13.11   Plot of the
integral $\int_0^{x_j} \varphi^{-1}(x)dx$.

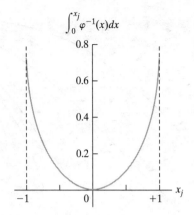

$$\int_0^{x_j} \varphi^{-1}(x)dx$$

become identical to those of the corresponding discrete Hopfield model. In the latter case, the energy (Lyapunov) function is defined simply by

$$E = -\frac{1}{2} \sum_{\substack{i=1 \\ i\neq j}}^{N} \sum_{j=1}^{N} w_{ji}x_ix_j \tag{13.39}$$

where the jth neuron's state $x_j = \pm 1$. We conclude, therefore, that the only stable points of the very high-gain, continuous, deterministic Hopfield model correspond to the stable points of the discrete stochastic Hopfield model.

When, however, each neuron j has a large, but finite, gain a_j, we find that the second term on the right-hand side of Eq. (13.38) makes a noticeable contribution to the energy function of the continuous model. In particular, this contribution is large and positive near all surfaces, edges, and corners of the unit hypercube that defines the state space of the model. On the other hand, the contribution is negligibly small at points that are far removed from the surface. Accordingly, the energy function of such a model has its maxima at corners, but the minima are displaced slightly toward the interior of the hypercube.

Figure 13.12 depicts the *energy contour map*, or *energy landscape*, for a continuous Hopfield model using two neurons. The outputs of the two neurons define the two axes of the map. The lower left- and upper right-hand corners of Fig. 13.12 represent stable minima for the limiting case of infinite gain; the minima for the case of finite gain are displaced inward. The flow to the fixed points (i.e., stable minima) may be interpreted as the solution to the minimization of the energy function E defined in Eq. (13.28).

The Discrete Hopfield Model as a Content-Addressable Memory

In the application of the Hopfield network as a *content-addressable memory*, we know a priori the fixed points of the network in that they correspond to the patterns to be stored. However, the synaptic weights of the network that produce the desired fixed points are unknown, and the problem is how to determine them. The primary function of a content-addressable memory is to retrieve a pattern (item) stored in memory in response to the presentation of an incomplete or noisy version of that pattern. To illustrate

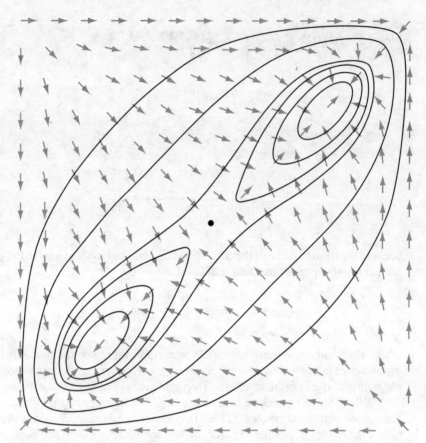

FIGURE 13.12 An energy contour map for a two-neuron, two-stable-state system. The ordinate and abscissa are the outputs of the two neurons. Stable states are located near the lower left and upper right corners, and unstable extrema are located at the other two corners. The arrows show the motion of the state. This motion is not generally perpendicular to the energy contours. *(From J.J. Hopfield, 1984, with permission of the National Academy of Sciences of the U.S.A.)*

the meaning of this statement in a succinct way, we can do no better than to quote from Hopfield's 1982 paper:

> *Suppose that an item stored in memory is "H.A. Kramers & G.H. Wannier Physi Rev. 60, 252 (1941)." A general content-addressable memory would be capable of retrieving this entire memory item on the basis of sufficient partial information. The input "& Wannier (1941)" might suffice. An ideal memory could deal with errors and retrieve this reference even from the input "Wannier, (1941)."*

An important property of a content-addressable memory is therefore the ability to retrieve a stored pattern, given a reasonable subset of the information content of that pattern. Moreover, a content-addressable memory is *error correcting* in the sense that it can override inconsistent information in the cues presented to it.

The essence of a content-addressable memory (CAM) is to map a fundamental memory $\boldsymbol{\xi}_\mu$ onto a fixed (stable) point $\mathbf{x}_\mu$ of a dynamic system, as illustrated in Fig. 13.13. Mathematically, we may express this mapping as

$$\boldsymbol{\xi}_\mu \rightleftharpoons \mathbf{x}_\mu$$

The arrow from left to right describes the *encoding* operation, whereas the arrow from right to left describes the *decoding* operation. The attractor's fixed points of the state space of the network are the *fundamental memories*, or *prototype states*, of the network. Suppose now that the network is presented a pattern containing partial, but sufficient, information about one of the fundamental memories. We may then represent that particular pattern as a starting point in the state space. In principle, provided that the starting point is close to the fixed point representing the memory being retrieved (i.e., it lies inside the basin of attraction belonging to the fixed point), the system should evolve with time and finally converge onto the memory state itself. At that point, the entire memory is generated by the network. Consequently, the Hopfield network has an *emergent property*, which helps it retrieve information and cope with errors.

With the Hopfield model's use of the formal neuron of McCulloch and Pitts (1943) as its basic processing unit, each such neuron has two states determined by the level of the induced local field acting on it. The "on," or "firing," state of neuron i is denoted by the output $x_i = +1$, and the "off," or "quiescent," state is represented by $x_i = -1$. For a network made up of N such neurons, the *state* of the network is thus defined by the vector

$$\mathbf{x} = [x_1, x_2, ..., x_N]^T$$

With $x_i = \pm1$, the state of neuron i represents one *bit* of information, and the N-by-1 state vector $\mathbf{x}$ represents a binary word of N bits of information.

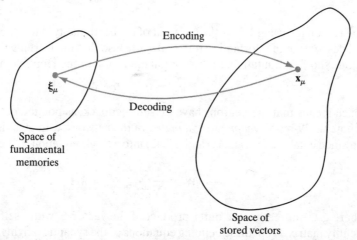

Encoding

Decoding

$\boldsymbol{\xi}_\mu$

$\mathbf{x}_\mu$

Space of
fundamental
memories

Space of
stored vectors

FIGURE 13.13   Illustration of the encoding–decoding performed by a recurrent network.

The induced local field v_j of neuron j is defined by

$$v_j = \sum_{i=1}^{N} w_{ji}x_i + b_j \qquad (13.40)$$

where b_j is a fixed *bias* applied externally to neuron j. Hence, neuron j modifies its state x_j according to the *deterministic rule*

$$x_j = \begin{cases} +1 & \text{if } v_j > 0 \\ -1 & \text{if } v_j < 0 \end{cases}$$

This relation may be rewritten in the compact form

$$x_j = \text{sgn}(v_j)$$

where sgn is the *signum function*. What if v_j is exactly zero? The action taken here can be quite arbitrary. For example, we may set $x_j = \pm 1$ if $v_j = 0$. However, we will use the following convention: If v_j is zero, neuron j remains in its previous state, regardless of whether it is on or off. The significance of this assumption is that the resulting flow diagram is symmetrical, as will be illustrated later.

There are two phases to the operation of the discrete Hopfield network as a content-addressable memory, namely, the storage phase and the retrieval phase, as described here:

1. *Storage Phase.* Suppose that we wish to store a set of N-dimensional vectors (binary words) denoted by $\{\boldsymbol{\xi}_\mu | \mu = 1, 2, ..., M\}$. We call these M vectors *fundamental memories*, representing the patterns to be memorized by the network. Let $\xi_{\mu,i}$ denote the ith element of the fundamental memory $\boldsymbol{\xi}_\mu$, where the class $\mu = 1, 2, ..., M$. According to the *outer-product rule* of storage—that is, the generalization of *Hebb's postulate of learning*—the synaptic weight from neuron i to neuron j is defined by

$$w_{ji} = \frac{1}{N}\sum_{\mu=1}^{M} \xi_{\mu,j}\xi_{\mu,i} \qquad (13.41)$$

The reason for using $1/N$ as the constant of proportionality is to simplify the mathematical description of information retrieval. Note also that the learning rule of Eq. (13.41) is a "one shot" computation. In the normal operation of the Hopfield network, we set

$$w_{ii} = 0 \qquad \text{for all } i \qquad (13.42)$$

which means that the neurons have *no* self-feedback, as pointed out previously. Let **W** denote the N-by-N *synaptic-weight matrix* of the network, with w_{ji} as its ji-th element. We may then combine Eqs. (13.41) and (13.42) into a single equation written in matrix form as

$$\mathbf{W} = \frac{1}{N}\sum_{\mu=1}^{M} \boldsymbol{\xi}_\mu \boldsymbol{\xi}_\mu^T - M\mathbf{I} \qquad (13.43)$$

where $\boldsymbol{\xi}_\mu \boldsymbol{\xi}_\mu^T$ represents the outer product of the vector $\boldsymbol{\xi}_\mu$ with itself and **I** denotes the identity matrix. From these defining equations of the synaptic weights and weight matrix, we may reconfirm the following:

- The output of each neuron in the network is fed back to all other neurons.
- There is no self-feedback in the network (i.e., $w_{ii} = 0$).
- The weight matrix of the network is symmetric, as shown by the following relation (see Eq. (13.21)):

$$\mathbf{W}^T = \mathbf{W} \tag{13.44}$$

2. *Retrieval Phase.* During the retrieval phase, an N-dimensional vector $\boldsymbol{\xi}_{\text{probe}}$, called a *probe*, is imposed on the Hopfield network as its state. The probe vector has elements equal to ± 1. Typically, it represents an incomplete or noisy version of a fundamental memory of the network. Information retrieval then proceeds in accordance with a *dynamic rule*, in which each neuron j of the network *randomly*, but at some fixed rate, examines the induced local field v_j (including any nonzero bias b_j) applied to it. If, at that instant of time, v_j is greater than zero, neuron j will switch its state to $+1$ or remain in that state if it is already there. Similarly, if v_j is less than zero, neuron j will switch its state to -1 or remain in that state if it is already there. If v_j is exactly zero, neuron j is left in its previous state, regardless of whether it is on or off. The state's update from one iteration to the next is therefore deterministic, but the selection of a neuron to perform the updating is done randomly. The *asynchronous* (serial) updating procedure described here is continued until there are no further changes to report. That is, starting with the vector $\boldsymbol{\xi}_{\text{probe}}$, the network finally produces a time-invariant state vector $\mathbf{y}$ whose individual elements satisfy the following *condition for stability*:

$$y_j = \text{sgn}\left(\sum_{i=1}^{N} w_{ji} y_i + b_j \right), \qquad j = 1, 2, ..., N \tag{13.45}$$

In matrix form, Eq. (13.45) is expressed as

$$\mathbf{y} = \text{sgn}(\mathbf{W}\mathbf{y} + \mathbf{b}) \tag{13.46}$$

where $\mathbf{W}$ is the synaptic-weight matrix of the network and $\mathbf{b}$ is the externally applied *bias vector*. The stability condition described here is also referred to as the *alignment condition*. The state vector $\mathbf{y}$ that satisfies the alignment condition is called a *stable state* or *fixed point* of the state space of the system. We may therefore say that the Hopfield network will always converge to a stable state when the retrieval operation is performed *asynchronously*.[5]

Table 13.2 presents a summary of the steps involved in the storage phase and retrieval phase of operating a Hopfield network.

EXAMPLE 2   Emergent Behavior of a Hopfield Model with Three Neurons

To illustrate the emergent behavior of the Hopfield model, consider the network of Fig. 13.14a, which consists of three neurons. The weight matrix of the network is

$$\mathbf{W} = \frac{1}{3} \begin{bmatrix} 0 & -2 & +2 \\ -2 & 0 & -2 \\ +2 & -2 & 0 \end{bmatrix}$$

The weight matrix $\mathbf{W}$ is legitimate because it satisfies the necessary conditions of Eqs. (13.42) and (13.44). The bias applied to each neuron is assumed to be zero. With three neurons in the network,

TABLE 13.2 Summary of the Hopfield Model

1. *Learning.* Let $\xi_1, \xi_2, ..., \xi_\mu$ denote a known set of N-dimensional fundamental memories. Use the outer-product rule (i.e., Hebb's postulate of learning) to compute the synaptic weights of the network as

$$w_{ji} = \begin{cases} \dfrac{1}{N}\displaystyle\sum_{\mu=1}^{M}\xi_{\mu,j}\,\xi_{\mu,i}, & j \neq i \\[4mm] 0, & j = i \end{cases}$$

where w_{ji} is the synaptic weight from neuron i to neuron j. The elements of the vector ξ_μ equal ± 1. Once they are computed, the synaptic weights are kept fixed.

2. *Initialization.* Let ξ_{probe} denote an unknown N-dimensional input vector (probe) presented to the network. The algorithm is initialized by setting

$$x_j(0) = \xi_{j,\,probe}, \qquad j = 1, ..., N$$

where $x_j(0)$ is the state of neuron j at time $n = 0$ and $\xi_{j,\,probe}$ is the jth element of the probe ξ_{probe}.

3. *Iteration Until Convergence.* Update the elements of state vector $\mathbf{x}(n)$ asynchronously (i.e., randomly and one at a time) according to the rule

$$x_j(n+1) = \text{sgn}\left(\sum_{i=1}^{N} w_{ji}x_i(n)\right), \qquad j = 1, 2, ..., N$$

Repeat the iteration until the state vector $\mathbf{x}$ remains unchanged.

4. *Outputting.* Let $\mathbf{x}_{fixed}$ denote the fixed point (stable state) computed at the end of step 3. The resulting output vector $\mathbf{y}$ of the network is

$$\mathbf{y} = \mathbf{x}_{fixed}$$

Step 1 is the storage phase, and steps 2 through 4 constitute the retrieval phase.

---

there are $2^3 = 8$ possible states to consider. Of these eight states, only the two states $(1, -1, 1)$ and $(-1, 1, -1)$ are stable; the remaining six states are all unstable. We say that these two particular states are stable because they both satisfy the alignment condition of Eq. (13.46). For the state vector $(1, -1, 1)$, we have

$$\mathbf{Wy} = \frac{1}{3}\begin{bmatrix} 0 & -2 & +2 \\ -2 & 0 & -2 \\ +2 & -2 & 0 \end{bmatrix}\begin{bmatrix} +1 \\ -1 \\ +1 \end{bmatrix} = \frac{1}{3}\begin{bmatrix} +4 \\ -4 \\ +4 \end{bmatrix}$$

for which the use of hard-limiting yields the result

$$\text{sgn}(\mathbf{Wy}) = \begin{bmatrix} +1 \\ -1 \\ +1 \end{bmatrix} = \mathbf{y}$$

Similarly, for the state vector $(-1, 1, -1)$, we have

$$\mathbf{Wy} = \frac{1}{3}\begin{bmatrix} 0 & -2 & +2 \\ -2 & 0 & -2 \\ +2 & -2 & 0 \end{bmatrix}\begin{bmatrix} -1 \\ +1 \\ -1 \end{bmatrix} = \frac{1}{3}\begin{bmatrix} -4 \\ +4 \\ -4 \end{bmatrix}$$

FIGURE 13.14
(a) Architectural graph of
Hopfield network for $N = 3$
neurons. (b) Diagram
depicting the two stable
states and flow of the
network.

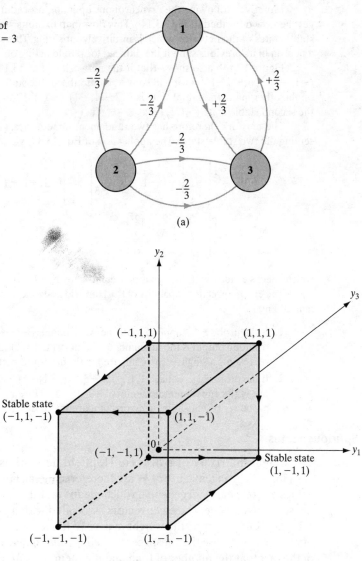

(a)

(b)

which, after hard limiting, yields

$$\text{sgn}(\mathbf{Wy}) = \begin{bmatrix} -1 \\ +1 \\ -1 \end{bmatrix} = \mathbf{y}$$

Hence, both of these state vectors satisfy the alignment condition. Note that the two stable states
of the model are the negative of each other.

Moreover, following the asynchronous updating procedure summarized in Table 13.2, we get the flow described in Fig. 13.14b. This flow map exhibits symmetry with respect to the two stable states of the network, which is intuitively satisfying. This symmetry is the result of leaving a neuron in its previous state if the induced local field acting on it is exactly zero.

Figure 13.14b also shows that if the network of Fig. 13.14a is in the initial state $(1, 1, 1)$, $(-1, -1, 1)$, or $(1, -1, -1)$, it will converge onto the stable state $(1, -1, 1)$ after one iteration. If, on the other hand, the initial state is $(-1, -1, -1)$, $(-1, 1, 1)$, or $(1, 1, -1)$, it will converge onto the second stable state $(-1, 1, -1)$.

The network therefore has two fundamental memories, $(1, -1, 1)$ and $(-1, 1, -1)$, representing the two stable states. The application of Eq. (13.43) yields the synaptic-weight matrix

$$\mathbf{W} = \frac{1}{3} \begin{bmatrix} +1 \\ -1 \\ +1 \end{bmatrix} [+1, -1, +1] + \frac{1}{3} \begin{bmatrix} -1 \\ +1 \\ -1 \end{bmatrix} [-1, +1, -1] - \frac{2}{3} \begin{bmatrix} 1 & 0 & 0 \\ 0 & 1 & 0 \\ 0 & 0 & 1 \end{bmatrix}$$

$$= \frac{1}{3} \begin{bmatrix} 0 & -2 & +2 \\ -2 & 0 & -2 \\ +2 & -2 & 0 \end{bmatrix}$$

which checks exactly with the synaptic weights shown in Fig. 13.14a.

The error-correcting capability of the Hopfield network is readily seen by examining the flow map of Fig. 13.14b:

1. If the probe $\boldsymbol{\xi}_{\text{probe}}$ applied to the network equals $(-1, -1, 1)$, $(1, 1, 1)$, or $(1, -1, -1)$, the resulting output is the fundamental memory $(1, -1, 1)$. Each of these values of the probe represents a single error, compared with the stored pattern.

2. If the probe $\boldsymbol{\xi}_{\text{probe}}$ equals $(1, 1, -1)$, $(-1, -1, -1)$, or $(-1, 1, 1)$, the resulting network output is the fundamental memory $(-1, 1, -1)$. Here again, each of these values of the probe represents a single error, compared with the stored pattern. ∎

Spurious States

The weight matrix $\mathbf{W}$ of a discrete Hopfield network is symmetric, as indicated in Eq. (13.44). The eigenvalues of $\mathbf{W}$ are therefore all real. However, for large M, the eigenvalues are ordinarily *degenerate*, which means that there are several eigenvectors with the same eigenvalue. The eigenvectors associated with a degenerate eigenvalue form a subspace. Furthermore, the weight matrix $\mathbf{W}$ has a degenerate eigenvalue with a value of zero, in which case the subspace is called the *null space*. The null space exists by virtue of the fact that the number of fundamental memories, M, is smaller than the number of neurons, N, in the network. The presence of a null subspace is an intrinsic characteristic of the Hopfield network.

An eigenanalysis of the weight matrix $\mathbf{W}$ leads us to take the following viewpoint of the discrete Hopfield network used as a content-addressable memory (Aiyer et al., 1990):

1. The discrete Hopfield network acts as a *vector projector* in the sense that it projects a probe onto a subspace $\mathcal{M}$ spanned by the fundamental memory vectors.

2. The underlying dynamics of the network drive the resulting projected vector to one of the corners of a unit hypercube where the energy function is minimized.

The unit hypercube is N-dimensional. The M fundamental memory vectors, spanning the subspace $\mathcal{M}$, constitute a set of fixed points (stable states) represented by certain corners of the unit hypercube. The other corners of the unit hypercube that lie in or near subspace $\mathcal{M}$ are potential locations for *spurious states*, also referred to as *spurious attractors*. Unfortunately, spurious states represent stable states of the Hopfield network that are different from the fundamental memories of the network

In the design of a Hopfield network as a content-addressable memory, we are therefore faced with a tradeoff between two conflicting requirements:

- the need to preserve the fundamental memory vectors as fixed points in the state space;
- the desire to have few spurious states.

However, the fundamental memories of a Hopfield network are not always stable. Moreover, spurious states representing other stable states that are different from the fundamental memories can arise. These two phenomena tend to decrease the efficiency of the Hopfield network as a content-addressable memory.

13.8   THE COHEN–GROSSBERG THEOREM

In Cohen and Grossberg (1983), a general principle for assessing the stability of a certain class of neural networks is described by a system of coupled nonlinear differential equations, given as

$$\frac{d}{dt} u_j = a_j(u_j)\left[b_j(u_j) - \sum_{i=1}^{N} c_{ji}\varphi_i(u_i) \right], \quad j = 1, ..., N \tag{13.47}$$

which admits a Lyapunov function defined as

$$E = \frac{1}{2}\sum_{i=1}^{N}\sum_{j=1}^{N} c_{ji}\varphi_i(u_i)\varphi_j(u_j) - \sum_{j=1}^{N}\int_{0}^{u_j} b_j(\lambda)\varphi_j'(\lambda)d\lambda \tag{13.48}$$

where $\varphi_j'(\lambda)$ is the derivative of $\varphi_j(\lambda)$ with respect to λ. For the definition of Eq. (13.48) to be valid, however, we require three conditions to hold:

1. The synaptic weights of the network are *symmetric*—that is,

$$c_{ij} = c_{ji} \tag{13.49}$$

2. The function $a_j(u_j)$ satisfies the *nonnegativity* condition—that is,

$$a_j(u_j) \geq 0 \tag{13.50}$$

3. The nonlinear input–output function $\varphi_j(u_j)$ satisfies the *monotonicity* condition— that is,

$$\varphi_j'(u_j) = \frac{d}{du_j}\varphi_j(u_j) \geq 0 \tag{13.51}$$

With this background, we may now formally state the *Cohen–Grossberg theorem*:

> *Provided that the system of nonlinear differential equations (13.47) satisfies the conditions of symmetry, nonegativity, and monotonicity, the Lyapunov function E of the system defined by Eq. (13.48) satisfies the condition*

$$\frac{dE}{dt} \leq 0$$

> *Once this basic property of the Lyapunov function E is in place, stability of the system follows from Lyapunov's theorem 1.*

The Hopfield Model as a Special Case of the Cohen–Grossberg Theorem

By comparing the general system of Eq. (13.47) with the system of Eq. (13.20) for a continuous Hopfield model, we may make the correspondences between the Hopfield model and the Cohen–Grossberg theorem that are summarized in Table 13.3. The use of this table in Eq. (13.48) yields a Lyapunov function for the continuous Hopfield model given as

$$E = -\frac{1}{2} \sum_{i=1}^{N} \sum_{j=1}^{N} w_{ji} \varphi_i(v_i) \varphi_j(v_j) + \sum_{j=1}^{N} \int_0^{v_j} \left(\frac{v_j}{R_j} - I_j \right) \varphi_j'(v) dv \qquad (13.52)$$

where the nonlinear activation function $\varphi_j(\cdot)$ is defined by Eq. (13.23).

We next make the following observations:

1. $\varphi_i(v_i) = x_i$
2. $\int_0^{v_j} \varphi_j'(v) dv = \int_0^{x_j} dx = x_j$
3. $\int_0^{v_j} v \varphi_j'(v) dv = \int_0^{x_j} v dx = \int_0^{x_i} \varphi_j^{-1}(x) dx$

Basically, relations 2 and 3 result from the use of $x = \varphi_i(v)$. Thus, the use of these observations in the Lyapunov function of Eq. (13.52) yields a result identical to the one we defined earlier; see Eq. (13.28). Note, however, that although $\varphi_i(v)$ must be a nondecreasing function of the input v, it does not need to have an inverse in order for the generalized Lyapunov function of Eq. (13.52) to hold.

The Cohen–Grossberg theorem is a general principle of neurodynamics with a wide range of applications (Grossberg, 1990). In the next section, we consider another application of this important theorem.

TABLE 13.3 Correspondences between the Cohen–Grossberg Theorem and the Hopfield Model

Cohen–Grossberg Theorem	Hopfield Model
u_j	$C_j v_j$
$a_j(u_j)$	1
$b_j(u_j)$	$-(v_j/R_j) + I_j$
c_{ji}	$-w_{ji}$
$\varphi_i(u_i)$	$\varphi_i(v_i)$

13.9 BRAIN-STATE-IN-A-BOX MODEL

In this section, we continue the neurodynamic analysis of an associative memory by studying the *brain-state-in-a-box (BSB) model*, which was first described by Anderson et al. (1977). The BSB model is basically a *positive feedback system with amplitude limitation*. It consists of a highly interconnected set of neurons that feed back upon themselves. This model operates by using the built-in positive feedback to *amplify* an input pattern until all the neurons in the model are driven into saturation. The BSB model may thus be viewed as a categorization device in that an analog input pattern is given a digital representation, defined by a stable state of the model.

Let $\mathbf{W}$ denote a *symmetric-weight matrix* whose largest eigenvalues have positive real components. Let $\mathbf{x}(0)$ denote the *initial state vector* of the model, representing an input activation pattern. Assuming that there are N neurons in the model, the state vector of the model has dimension N, and the weight matrix $\mathbf{W}$ is an N-by-N matrix. The BSB model is then completely defined by the pair of equations

$$\mathbf{y}(n) = \mathbf{x}(n) + \beta\mathbf{W}\mathbf{x}(n) \tag{13.53}$$

and

$$\mathbf{x}(n + 1) = \varphi(\mathbf{y}(n)) \tag{13.54}$$

where β is a small positive constant called the *feedback factor* and $\mathbf{x}(n)$ is the state vector of the model at discrete time n. Figure 13.15a shows a block diagram of the combination of Eqs. (13.53) and (13.54); the block labeled $\mathbf{W}$ represents a single-layer

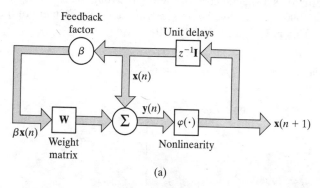

(a)

FIGURE 13.15   (a) Block diagram of the brain-state-in-a-box (BSB) model. (b) Signal-flow graph of the linear associator represented by the weight matrix $\mathbf{W}$.

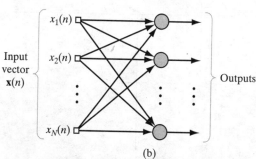

(b)

linear neural network, as depicted in Fig. 13.15b. The activation function φ is a *piecewise-linear function* that operates on $y_j(n)$, the jth component of the vector $\mathbf{y}(n)$, as follows (see Fig. 13.16):

$$x_j(n+1) = \varphi(y_j(n))$$
$$= \begin{cases} +1 & \text{if } y_j(n) > +1 \\ y_j(n) & \text{if } -1 \le y_j(n) \le +1 \\ -1 & \text{if } y_j(n) < -1 \end{cases} \tag{13.55}$$

Equation (13.55) constrains the state vector of the BSB model to lie within an N-dimensional unit cube centered on the origin.

The model thus proceeds as follows: An activation pattern $\mathbf{x}(0)$ is input into the BSB model as the initial state vector, and Eq. (13.53) is used to compute the vector $\mathbf{y}(0)$. Equation (13.54) is then used to truncate $\mathbf{y}(0)$, obtaining the updated state vector $\mathbf{x}(1)$. Next, $\mathbf{x}(1)$ is cycled through Eqs. (13.53) and (13.54), thereby obtaining $\mathbf{x}(2)$. This procedure is repeated until the BSB model reaches a *stable state* represented by a particular corner of the unit hypercube. Intuitively, positive feedback in the BSB model causes the initial state vector $\mathbf{x}(0)$ to increase in Euclidean length (norm) with an increasing number of iterations until it hits a wall of the box (unit hypercube) and then slides along the wall, eventually ending up in a stable corner of the box, where it keeps on "pushing," but cannot get out of the box (Kawamoto and Anderson, 1985)—hence the name of the model.

Lyapunov Function of the BSB Model

The BSB may be redefined as a special case of the neurodynamic model described in Eq. (13.16) (Grossberg, 1990). To see this, we first rewrite the jth component of the BSB algorithm described by Eqs. (13.53) and (13.54) in the form

FIGURE 13.16 Piecewise-linear activation function used in the BSB model.

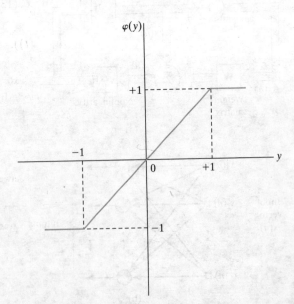

$$x_j(n + 1) = \varphi\left(\sum_{i=1}^{N} c_{ji} x_i(n) \right), \qquad j = 1, 2, ..., N \tag{13.56}$$

The coefficients c_{ji} are defined by

$$c_{ji} = \delta_{ji} + \beta w_{ji} \tag{13.57}$$

where δ_{ji} is the Kronecker delta equal to 1 if $j = i$ and 0 otherwise, and w_{ji} is the ji-th element of the weight matrix $\mathbf{W}$. Equation (13.56) is written in discrete-time form. To proceed further, we need to reformulate it in a continuous-time form, as shown by

$$\frac{d}{dt} x_j(t) = -x_j(t) + \varphi\left(\sum_{i=1}^{N} c_{ji} x_i(t) \right), \qquad j = 1, 2, ..., N \tag{13.58}$$

where the bias I_j is zero for all j. However, for us to apply the Cohen–Grossberg theorem, we have to go one step further and transform Eq. (13.58) into the same form as the additive model. We may do so by introducing a new set of variables,

$$v_j(t) = \sum_{i=1}^{N} c_{ji} x_i(t) \tag{13.59}$$

Then, by virtue of the definition of c_{ji} given in Eq. (13.57), we find that

$$x_j(t) = \sum_{i=1}^{N} c_{ji} v_i(t) \tag{13.60}$$

Correspondingly, we may recast the model of Eq. (13.58) in the equivalent form

$$\frac{d}{dt} v_j(t) = -v_j(t) + \sum_{i=1}^{N} c_{ji} \varphi(v_i(t)), \qquad j = 1, 2, ..., N \tag{13.61}$$

We are now ready to apply the Cohen–Grossberg theorem to the BSB model. By comparing Eq. (13.61) with Eq. (13.47), we may deduce the correspondences listed in Table 13.4 between the BSB model and the Cohen–Grossberg theorem. Therefore, using

TABLE 13.4   Correspondences between the Cohen–Grossberg Theorem and the BSB Model

Cohen–Grossberg Theorem	BSB Model
u_j	v_j
$a_j(u_j)$	1
$b_j(u_j)$	$-v_j$
c_{ji}	$-c_{ji}$
$\varphi_j(u_j)$	$\varphi_j(v_j)$

the results of Table 13.4 in Eq. (13.48), we find that the Lyapunov function of the BSB model is given by

$$E = -\frac{1}{2}\sum_{j=1}^{N}\sum_{i=1}^{N}c_{ji}\varphi(v_j)\varphi(v_i) + \sum_{j=1}^{N}\int_0^{v_j}v\varphi'(v)dv \qquad (13.62)$$

where $\varphi'(v)$ is the derivative of the piecewise linear function $\varphi(v)$ with respect to its argument. Finally, substituting the definitions of Eqs. (13.55), (13.57) and (13.59) into Eq. (13.62), we can define the Lyapunov (energy) function of the BSB model in terms of the original state variables as follows (Grossberg, 1990):

$$E = -\frac{\beta}{2}\sum_{i=1}^{N}\sum_{j=1}^{N}w_{ji}x_jx_i$$

$$= -\frac{\beta}{2}\mathbf{x}^T\mathbf{W}\mathbf{x} \qquad (13.63)$$

The evaluation of the Lyapunov function of the Hopfield network presented in Section 13.7 assumes the existence of the derivative of the inverse of the model's sigmoidal nonlinearity, which is satisfied by the use of a hyperbolic tangent function. In contrast, this condition is not satisfied in the BSB model when the state variable of the jth neuron in the model is either $+1$ or -1. Despite this difficulty, the Lyapunov function of the BSB model can be evaluated via the Cohen–Grossberg theorem, which clearly illustrates the general applicability of this important theorem.

Dynamics of the BSB Model

In a direct analysis carried out by Golden (1986), it is demonstrated that the BSB model is in fact a gradient descent algorithm that minimizes the energy function E, defined by Eq. (13.63). This property of the BSB model, however, presumes that the weight matrix $\mathbf{W}$ satisfies two conditions:

1. The weight matrix $\mathbf{W}$ is *symmetric:*

$$\mathbf{W} = \mathbf{W}^T$$

2. The weight matrix $\mathbf{W}$ is *positive semidefinite;* that is, in terms of the eigenvalues of $\mathbf{W}$, we have

$$\lambda_{min} \geq 0$$

where λ_{min} is the smallest eigenvalue of $\mathbf{W}$.

Accordingly, the energy function E of the BSB model decreases with increasing n (number of iterations) whenever the state vector $\mathbf{x}(n+1)$ at time $n+1$ is different from the state vector $\mathbf{x}(n)$ at time n. Moreover, the minimum points of the energy function E define the *equilibrium states* of the BSB model that are characterized by

$$\mathbf{x}(n+1) = \mathbf{x}(n)$$

In other words, like the Hopfield model, the BSB model is an *energy-minimizing network*.

The equilibrium states of the BSB model are defined by certain corners of the unit hypercube and its origin. In the latter case, any fluctuation in the state vector, no matter how small, is amplified by positive feedback in the model and therefore causes the state of the model to shift away from the origin in the direction of a stable configuration; in other words, the origin is a saddle point. For every corner of the hypercube to serve as a possible equilibrium state of the BSB model, the weight matrix **W** has to satisfy a third condition (Greenberg, 1988):

- The weight matrix **W** is *diagonal dominant*, which means that

$$w_{jj} \geq \sum_{i \neq j} |w_{ij}| \quad \text{for } j = 1, 2, ..., N \tag{13.64}$$

where w_{ij} is the ij-th element of **W**.

For an equilibrium state **x** to be *stable*—that is, for a certain corner of the unit hypercube to be a fixed point *attractor*—there has to be a basin of attraction $\mathcal{N}(\mathbf{x})$ in the unit hypercube such that for all initial-state vectors $\mathbf{x}(0)$ in $\mathcal{N}(\mathbf{x})$, the BSB model converges onto **x**. For every corner of the unit hypercube to be a possible point attractor, the weight matrix **W** has to satisfy a fourth condition (Greenberg, 1988):

- The weight matrix **W** is *strongly diagonal dominant*, as shown by

$$w_{jj} \geq \sum_{i \neq j} |w_{ij}| + \alpha \quad \text{for } j = 1, 2, ..., N \tag{13.65}$$

where α is a positive constant.

The important point to take from this discussion is that in the case of a BSB model for which the weight matrix **W** is symmetric and positive semidefinite, as is often the case, only some (but not all) of the corners of the unit hypercube act as point attractors. For all the corners of the unit hypercube to act as potential point attractors, the weight matrix **W** has to satisfy Eq. (13.65) as well, which, of course, subsumes the condition of Eq. (13.64).

Clustering

A natural application for the BSB model is *clustering* (Anderson, 1995). This follows from the fact that the stable corners of the unit hypercube act as point attractors with well-behaved basins of attraction, which therefore divide the state space into a corresponding set of well-defined regions. Consequently, the BSB model may be used as an *unsupervised* clustering algorithm, with each stable corner of the unit hypercube representing a "cluster" of related data. The self-amplification provided by positive feedback (in conformity with Principle 1 of self-organization described in Chapter 8) is an important ingredient of this clustering property.

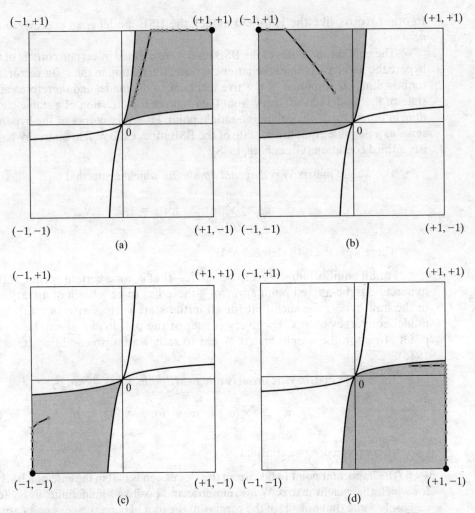

FIGURE 13.17   Illustrative example of a two-neuron BSB model, operating under four different initial conditions:
- the four shaded areas of the figure represent the model's basins of attraction;
- the corresponding trajectories of the model are plotted in red;
- the four corners, where the trajectories terminate, are printed as black dots.

EXAMPLE 3   Autoassociation

Consider a BSB model containing two neurons. The two-by-two matrix of the model is defined by

$$\mathbf{W} = \begin{bmatrix} 0.035 & -0.005 \\ -0.005 & 0.035 \end{bmatrix}$$

which is symmetric and positive definite and therefore satisfies Eq. (13.65).

The four parts of Fig. 13.17 correspond to different settings of the initial state of the model:

(a) $\mathbf{x}(0) = [0.1, 0.2]^T$
(b) $\mathbf{x}(0) = [-0.2, 0.3]^T$

(c) $\mathbf{x}(0) = [-0.8, -0.4]^T$
(d) $\mathbf{x}(0) = [0.6, 0.1]^T$

The areas shown shaded in the figure are the four basins of attraction characterizing the model. The figure clearly illustrates that when the initial state of the model lies in a particular basin of attraction, the underlying dynamics of the model continually drive the weight matrix $\mathbf{W}(n)$ with increasing number of iterations n, until the state $\mathbf{x}(n)$ of the model terminates on a fixed point attractor, exemplified by the corresponding corner of the two-by-two square. A case of particular interest is shown in part (d) of the figure. In this case, the initial condition $\mathbf{x}(0)$ lies in the first quadrant, yet the trajectory terminates on the corner $(+1, -1)$ in the fourth quadrant, which is where the pertinent fixed point attractor resides.

In this example, the square state space of the two-neuron BSB model is partitioned completely into four distinct basins of attraction; each basin embraces a corner of the square, representing a stable state with minimum energy. Thus, the BSB model may be viewed as an example of an *autoassociative network*, in the sense that *all* the points lying in any one of the basins of attraction are associated with a minimum-energy stable-state point of its own. ∎

13.10 STRANGE ATTRACTORS AND CHAOS

Up to this point in our discussion of neurodynamics, we have focused attention on the kind of behavior exhibited by nonlinear dynamic systems characterized as fixed-point attractors. In this section, we consider another class of attractors called *strange attractors*, which characterize certain nonlinear dynamic systems of order greater than two.

A strange attractor exhibits a chaotic behavior that is highly complex. What makes the study of strange attractors and chaos particularly interesting is the fact that the system in question is *deterministic* in the sense that its operation is governed by *fixed* rules, yet, with only a few degrees of freedom, can exhibit a behavior so complicated that it looks random. Indeed, the randomness is fundamental in the sense that the second-order statistics of a chaotic time series seem to indicate that it is random. However, unlike a true random phenomenon, the randomness exhibited by a chaotic system does not go away by gathering more information! In principle, the future behavior of a chaotic system is completely determined by the past, but, in practice, any uncertainty in the choice of initial conditions, no matter how small, grows exponentially with time. Consequently, even though the dynamic behavior of a chaotic system is predictable in the short term, it is impossible to predict the long-term behavior of the system. A chaotic time series is therefore paradoxical in the sense that its generation is governed by a deterministic dynamic system, yet its evolution as a function of time has a randomlike appearance. It is this attribute of a chaotic phenomenon that was originally emphasized by Lorenz with the discovery of an attractor that bears his name (Lorenz, 1963).

In a nonlinear dynamic system, when the orbits in an attractor with neighboring initial conditions tend to move apart with increasing time, the system is said to possess a *strange attractor*, and the system itself is said to be *chaotic*. In other words, a fundamental property that makes an attractor "strange" is the *sensitive dependence on initial conditions*. Sensitivity in this context means that if two identical nonlinear systems are started at slightly different initial conditions—namely, $\mathbf{x}$ and $\mathbf{x} + \boldsymbol{\epsilon}$, where $\boldsymbol{\epsilon}$ is a very small vector—their dynamic states will diverge from each other in state space, and their separation will increase exponentially on the average.

Invariant Characteristics of Chaotic Dynamics

Two major features—namely, fractal dimensions and Lyapunov exponents—have emerged as the classifiers of a chaotic process. Fractal dimensions characterize the geometric structure of a strange attractor. The term "fractal" was coined by Mandelbrot (1982). Unlike integer dimensions (as in a two-dimensional surface or a three-dimensional object), fractal dimensions are *not* integers. As for Lyapunov exponents, they describe how orbits on the attractor move under the evolution of the system dynamics. These two invariant characteristics of chaotic dynamics are discussed in what follows. The term "invariant" signifies the fact that both fractal dimensions and Lyapunov exponents of a chaotic process remain unchanged under smooth nonlinear changes of the coordinate system of the process.

Fractal Dimensions

Consider a strange attractor whose dynamics in d-dimensional state space are described by

$$\mathbf{x}(n+1) = \mathbf{F}(\mathbf{x}(n)), \qquad n = 0, 1, 2, \ldots \qquad (13.66)$$

which is the discrete-time version of Eq. (13.2). This correspondence is readily seen by setting $t = n\Delta t$, where Δt is the sampling period. Assuming that Δt is sufficiently small, we may correspondingly set

$$\frac{d}{dt}\mathbf{x}(t) = \frac{1}{\Delta t}[\mathbf{x}(n\Delta t + \Delta t) - \mathbf{x}(n\Delta t)]$$

We may thus formulate the discrete-time version of Eq. (13.2) as

$$\frac{1}{\Delta t}[\mathbf{x}(n\Delta t + \Delta t) - \mathbf{x}(n\Delta t)] = \mathbf{F}(\mathbf{x}(n\Delta t)) \quad \text{for small } \Delta t$$

Setting $\Delta t = 1$ for convenience of presentation and rearranging terms, we get

$$\mathbf{x}(n+1) = \mathbf{x}(n) + \mathbf{F}(\mathbf{x}(n))$$

which may be cast into the form shown in Eq. (13.66) simply by absorbing $\mathbf{x}(n)$ in a redefined version of the vector-valued function $\mathbf{F}(\cdot)$.

Returning to Eq. (13.66), suppose we construct a small sphere of radius r around some location $\mathbf{y}$ on or near an orbit of the attractor. We may then define a *natural distribution* of points for the attractor as

$$\rho(\mathbf{y}) = \lim_{N \to \infty} \frac{1}{N} \sum_{n=1}^{N} \delta(\mathbf{y} - \mathbf{x}(n)) \qquad (13.67)$$

where $\delta(\cdot)$ is a d-dimensional delta function and N is the number of data points. Note the change of notation concerning the use of N. The natural distribution $\rho(\mathbf{y})$ plays a role for a strange attractor that is analogous to that of the probability density function of a random variable. Accordingly, we may define an invariant $\bar{f}$ with respect to a function $f(\mathbf{y})$ under the evolution of the dynamics described as the multifold integral

$$\bar{f} = \int_{-\infty}^{\infty} f(\mathbf{y})\rho(\mathbf{y})d\mathbf{y} \tag{13.68}$$

A function $f(\mathbf{y})$ of interest is one that gives us a measure of how the number of points within the small sphere scales as the radius r of the sphere is reduced to zero. Recognizing that the volume occupied by the d-dimensional sphere is proportional to r^d, we may get a sense of attractor dimension by seeing how the density of points on the attractor behaves at small distances in state space.

The Euclidean distance between the center $\mathbf{y}$ of the sphere and the point $\mathbf{x}(n)$ at time-step n is $\|\mathbf{y} - \mathbf{x}(n)\|$. Hence, the point $\mathbf{x}(n)$ lies inside the sphere of radius r, provided that

$$\|\mathbf{y} - \mathbf{x}(n)\| < r$$

or, equivalently,

$$r - \|\mathbf{y} - \mathbf{x}(n)\| > 0$$

Thus, the function $f(\mathbf{x})$ for the situation described here may be written in the general form

$$f(\mathbf{x}) = \left(\frac{1}{N-1} \sum_{\substack{k=1 \\ k \neq n}}^{N} \theta(r - \|\mathbf{y} - \mathbf{x}(k)\|) \right)^{q-1} \tag{13.69}$$

where q is an integer, and $\theta(\cdot)$ is the *Heaviside function*, defined by

$$\theta(z) = \begin{cases} 1 & \text{for } z > 0 \\ 0 & \text{for } z < 0 \end{cases}$$

On substituting Eqs. (13.67) and (13.69) into Eq. (13.68), we get a new function $C(q,r)$ that depends on q and r, as shown by

$$C(q,r) = \int_{-\infty}^{\infty} \left(\frac{1}{N-1} \sum_{\substack{k=1 \\ k \neq n}}^{N} \theta(r - \|\mathbf{y} - \mathbf{x}(k)\|) \right)^{q-1} \left(\frac{1}{N} \sum_{n=1}^{N} \delta(\mathbf{y} - \mathbf{x}(n)) \right) d\mathbf{y} \tag{13.70}$$

Hence, using the sifting property of the delta function, namely,

$$\int_{-\infty}^{\infty} g(\mathbf{y})\delta(\mathbf{y} - \mathbf{x}(n))d\mathbf{y} = g(\mathbf{x}(n))$$

for some function $g(\cdot)$ and interchanging the order of summation, we may redefine the function $C(q,r)$ in Eq. (13.70) as

$$C(q,r) = \frac{1}{N} \sum_{n=1}^{N} \left(\frac{1}{N-1} \sum_{\substack{k=1 \\ k \neq n}}^{N} \theta(r - \|\mathbf{x}(n) - \mathbf{x}(k)\|) \right)^{q-1} \tag{13.71}$$

The function $C(q, r)$ is called the *correlation function*.[6] In words, it is defined as follows:

> *The correlation function of an attractor, denoted by $C(q, r)$, is a measure of the probability that any two points on the attractor, $\mathbf{x}(n)$ and $\mathbf{x}(k)$, are separated by a distance r for some integer q.*

It is assumed that the number of data points, N, in the defining equation of Eq. (13.71) is large.

The correlation function $C(q, r)$ is an invariant of the attractor in its own right. Nevertheless, the customary practice is to focus on the behavior of $C(q, r)$ for small r. This limiting behavior is described by

$$C(q, r) \approx r^{(q-1)D_q} \tag{13.72}$$

where D_q, called a *fractal dimension* of the attractor, is assumed to exist. Taking the logarithm of both sides of Eq. (13.72), we may formally define D_q as

$$D_q = \lim_{r \to 0} \frac{\log C(q, r)}{(q - 1)\log r} \tag{13.73}$$

However, since we usually have a finite number of data points, the radius r must be just small enough to permit a sufficient number of points to fall inside the sphere. For a prescribed q, we may then determine the fractal dimension D_q as the slope of the part of the function $C(q, r)$ that is *linear* in $\log r$.

For $q = 2$, the definition of the fractal dimension D_q assumes a simple form that lends it to reliable computation. The resulting dimension D_2 is called the *correlation dimension* of the attractor (Grassberger and Procaccia, 1983). The correlation dimension reflects the complexity of the underlying dynamic system and bounds the degrees of freedom required to describe the system.

Lyapunov Exponents

The Lyapunov exponents are statistical quantities that describe the uncertainty about the future state of an attractor. More specifically, they quantify the exponential rate at which nearby trajectories separate from each other while moving on the attractor. Let $\mathbf{x}(0)$ be an initial condition and $\{\mathbf{x}(n), n = 0, 1, 2, ...\}$ be the corresponding orbit of the attractor. Consider an infinitesimal displacement from the initial condition $\mathbf{x}(0)$ in the direction of a vector $\mathbf{y}(0)$ tangential to the orbit. Then, the evolution of the tangent vector determines the evolution of the infinitesimal displacement of the perturbed orbit $\{\mathbf{y}(n), n = 0, 1, 2, ...\}$ from the unperturbed orbit $\{\mathbf{x}(n), n = 0, 1, 2, ...\}$. In particular, the ratio $\mathbf{y}(n)/\|\mathbf{y}(n)\|$ defines the infinitesimal displacement of the orbit from $\mathbf{x}(n)$, and the ratio $\|\mathbf{y}(n)\|/\|\mathbf{y}(0)\|$ is the factor by which the infinitesimal displacement *grows* if $\|\mathbf{y}(n)\| > \|\mathbf{y}(0)\|$ or *shrinks* if $\|\mathbf{y}(n)\| < \|\mathbf{y}(0)\|$. For an initial condition $\mathbf{x}(0)$ and initial displacement $\boldsymbol{\alpha}_0 = \mathbf{y}(0)/\|\mathbf{y}(0)\|$, the *Lyapunov exponent* is defined by

$$\lambda(\mathbf{x}(0), \boldsymbol{\alpha}) = \lim_{n \to \infty} \frac{1}{n} \log\left(\frac{\|\mathbf{y}(n)\|}{\|\mathbf{y}(0)\|}\right) \tag{13.74}$$

A d-dimensional chaotic process has a total of d Lyapunov exponents that can be positive, negative, or zero. Positive Lyapunov exponents account for the instability of an orbit throughout the state space. This condition may be stated in another way as follows:

- *Positive Lyapunov exponents are responsible for the* sensitivity of a chaotic process to initial conditions.
- *Negative Lyapunov exponents, on the other hand, govern the decay of transients in the orbit.*
- *A zero Lyapunov exponent signifies the fact that the underlying dynamics responsible for the generation of chaos are describable by a coupled system of nonlinear differential equations: that is, the chaotic process is a flow.*

A volume in d-dimensional state space behaves as $\exp(L(\lambda_1 + \lambda_2 + \cdots + \lambda_d))$, where L is the number of time-steps into the future. It follows, therefore, that for a *dissipative* process, the sum of all Lyapunov exponents must be negative. This is a necessary condition for a volume in state space to shrink as time progresses, which is a requirement for physical realizability.

Lyapunov Dimension

Given the Lyapunov spectrum defined by the set of exponents $\lambda_1, \lambda_2, ..., \lambda_d$, Kaplan and Yorke (1979) proposed a *Lyapunov dimension* for a strange attractor, given as

$$D_L = K + \frac{\sum_{i=1}^{K} \lambda_i}{|\lambda_{K+1}|} \tag{13.75}$$

where K is an integer that satisfies the two conditions

$$\sum_{i=1}^{K} \lambda_i > 0 \quad \text{and} \quad \sum_{i=1}^{K+1} \lambda_i < 0$$

Ordinarily, the Lyapunov dimension D_L is about the same size as the correlation dimension D_2. This is an important property of a chaotic process. That is, although the Lyapunov and correlation dimensions are defined in entirely different ways, their values for a strange attractor are usually quite close to each other.

Definition of a Chaotic Process

Throughout this section, we have spoken of a chaotic process without providing a formal definition of it. In light of what we now know about Lyapunov exponents, we can offer the following definition:

> *A chaotic process is generated by a nonlinear deterministic system with at least one positive Lyapunov exponent.*

The positivity of at least one Lyapunov exponent of the attractor is a necessary condition for sensitivity to initial conditions, which is the hallmark of a strange attractor.

The largest Lyapunov exponent also defines the *horizon of predictability* of a chaotic process. Specifically, the short-term predictability of a chaotic process is approximately equal to the reciprocal of the largest Lyapunov exponent (Abarbanel, 1996).

13.11 DYNAMIC RECONSTRUCTION OF A CHAOTIC PROCESS

Dynamic reconstruction may be defined as the identification of a mapping that provides a model for an unknown dynamic system of dimensionality m. Our interest here is in the dynamic modeling of a time series produced by a physical system that is known to be chaotic. In other words, given a time series $\{y(n)\}_{n=1}^{N}$, we wish to build a model that captures the underlying dynamics responsible for generation of the observable $y(n)$. As we pointed out earlier in the previous section, N denotes the sample size. The primary motivation for dynamic reconstruction is to make physical sense from such a time series, hopefully bypassing the need for a detailed mathematical knowledge of the underlying dynamics. The system of interest is typically much too complex to characterize in mathematical terms. The only information available to us is contained in a time series obtained from measurements on one of the observables of the system.

A fundamental result in dynamic-reconstruction theory[7] is a geometric theorem called the delay-embedding theorem, due to Takens (1981). Takens considered a noise-free situation, focusing on *delay coordinate maps* or *predictive models* that are constructed from a time series, representing an observable from a dynamic system. In particular, Takens showed that under certain conditions, the delay coordinate map from a d-dimensional smooth compact manifold to $\mathbb{R}^{2d+1}$ is a *diffeomorphism* on that manifold, where d is the dimension of the state space of the dynamic system. (Diffeomorphism was discussed in Chapter 7.)

For an interpretation of Takens's theorem in signal-processing terms, first consider an unknown dynamic system whose evolution in discrete time is described by the non-linear difference equation

$$\mathbf{x}(n + 1) = \mathbf{F}(\mathbf{x}(n)) \tag{13.76}$$

where $\mathbf{x}(n)$ is the d-dimensional state of the system at time n and $\mathbf{F}(\cdot)$ is a vector-valued function. It is assumed here that the sampling period is normalized to unity. Let the time series $\{y(n)\}$ observable at the output of the system be defined in terms of the state vector $\mathbf{x}(n)$ as

$$y(n) = g(\mathbf{x}(n)) + v(n) \tag{13.77}$$

where $g(\cdot)$ is a scalar-valued function and $v(n)$ denotes additive noise. The noise $v(n)$ accounts for the combined effects of imperfections and imprecisions in the observable $y(n)$. Equation (13.76) and (13.77) describe the state-space behavior of the dynamic system. According to Takens's theorem, the geometric structure of the multivariable dynamics of the system can be unfolded from the observable $y(n)$ with $v(n) = 0$ in a D-dimensional space constructed from the new vector

$$\mathbf{y}_R(n) = [y(n), y(n - \tau), ..., y(n - (D - 1)\tau)]^{T} \tag{13.78}$$

where τ is a positive integer called the *normalized embedding delay*. That is, given the observable $y(n)$ for varying discrete time n, which pertains to a single observable (component) of an unknown dynamic system, dynamic reconstruction is possible using the D-dimensional vector $\mathbf{y}_R(n)$ provided that $D \geq 2d + 1$, where d is the dimension of the state space of the system. Hereafter, we refer to this statement as the *delay-embedding theorem*. The condition $D \geq 2d + 1$ is a *sufficient*, but not necessary, condition for dynamic reconstruction. The procedure for finding a suitable D is called *embedding*, and the minimum integer D that achieves dynamic reconstruction is called the *embedding dimension*; it is denoted by D_E.

The delay-embedding theorem has a powerful implication: Evolution of the points $\mathbf{y}_R(n) \rightarrow \mathbf{y}_R(n + 1)$ in the reconstruction space follows that of the unknown dynamics $\mathbf{x}(n) \rightarrow \mathbf{x}(n + 1)$ in the original state space. That is, many important properties of the unobservable state vector $\mathbf{x}(n)$ are reproduced without ambiguity in the reconstruction space defined by $\mathbf{y}_R(n)$. However, for this important result to be attainable, we need *reliable estimates* of the embedding dimension D_E and the normalized embedding delay τ, as summarized here:

1. The sufficient condition $D \geq 2d + 1$ makes it possible to undo the intersections of an orbit of the attractor with itself, which arise from projection of that orbit to lower dimensions. The embedding dimension D_E can be less than $2d + 1$. The recommended procedure is to estimate D_E directly from the observable data. A reliable method for estimating D_E is the *method of false nearest neighbors*, described in Abarbanel (1996). In this method, we systematically survey the data points and their neighbors in dimension $d = 1$, then $d = 2$, and so on. We thereby establish the condition when apparent neighbors stop being "unprojected" by the addition of more elements to the reconstruction vector $\mathbf{y}_R(n)$, and thus obtain an estimate for the embedding dimension D_E.

2. Unfortunately, the delay-embedding theorem has nothing to say on the choice of the normalized embedding delay τ. In fact, it permits the use of any τ so long as the available time series is infinitely long. In practice, however, we always have to work with observable data of finite length N. The proper prescription for choosing τ is to recognize that the normalized embedding delay τ should be large enough for $y(n)$ and $y(n - \tau)$ to be essentially independent of each other so as to serve as coordinates of the reconstruction space, but not so independent as to have no correlation with each other. This requirement is best satisfied by using the particular τ for which the *mutual information* between $y(n)$ and $y(n - \tau)$ attains its first minimum (Fraser, 1989). (Mutual information was discussed in Chapter 10.)

Recursive Prediction

From the discussion presented, the dynamic-reconstruction problem may be interpreted as one of representing the signal dynamics properly (the embedding step), as well as of constructing a predictive mapping (the identification step). Thus, in practical terms, we have the following network topology for dynamic modeling:

- a *short-term memory* (e.g., delay-line memory) structure to perform the embedding, whereby the reconstruction vector $\mathbf{y}_R(n)$ is defined in terms of the observable $y(n)$ and its delayed versions (see Eq. (13.78));

- a multiple-input, single-output (MISO) adaptive nonlinear dynamic system trained as a *one-step predictor* (e.g., neural network) to identify the unknown mapping $f{:}\mathbb{R}^{D} \to \mathbb{R}^{1}$, which is defined by

$$\hat{y}(n+1) = f(\mathbf{y}_R(n)) \tag{13.79}$$

The predictive mapping described in Eq. (13.79) is the centerpiece of dynamic modeling: Once it is determined, the evolution $\mathbf{y}_R(n) \to \mathbf{y}_R(n+1)$ becomes known, which, in turn, determines the unknown evolution $\mathbf{x}(n) \to \mathbf{x}(n+1)$.

Presently, we do not have a rigorous theory to help us decide if the nonlinear predictor has successfully identified the unknown mapping f. In linear prediction, minimizing the mean-square value of the prediction error may lead to an accurate model. However, a chaotic time series is different. Two trajectories in the same attractor are vastly different on a sample-by-sample basis, so minimizing the mean-square value of the prediction error is a necessary, but not sufficient, condition of a successful mapping.

The dynamic invariants—namely, correlation dimension and Lyapunov exponents—measure global properties of the attractor, so they should gauge the success of dynamic modeling. Hence, *a pragmatic approach for testing the dynamic model is to seed it with a point on the strange attractor and to feed the output back to its input, forming an autonomous system*, as illustrated in Fig. 13.18. Such an operation is called *iterated prediction* or *recursive prediction*. Once the initialization is completed, the output of the autonomous system is a realization of the dynamic-reconstruction process. This method, of course, presumes that the predictor has been designed properly in the first place.

For a reliable dynamic reconstruction, we may define the reconstruction vector $\mathbf{y}_R(n)$ as a full m-dimensional vector

$$\mathbf{y}_R(n) = [y(n), y(n-1), ..., y(n-m+1)]^T \tag{13.80}$$

where m is an integer defined by

$$m \geq D_E\tau \tag{13.81}$$

This formulation of the reconstruction vector $\mathbf{y}_R(n)$ supplies more information to the predictive model than that provided by Eq. (13.78) and may therefore yield a more accurate dynamic reconstruction. However, both formulations share a common feature: Their compositions are uniquely defined by knowledge of the embedding dimension D_E. In any event, it is wise to use the minimum permissible value of D—namely, D_E—to minimize the effect of additive noise $v(n)$ on the quality of dynamic reconstruction.

FIGURE 13.18 Feedback system used as an iterated predictor for the dynamic reconstruction of a chaotic process.

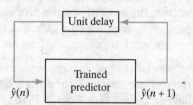

Dynamic Reconstruction Is an Ill-Posed Filtering Problem

In reality, the dynamic-reconstruction problem is an *ill-posed inverse problem*. We say so because it is highly likely that one or more of Hadamard's three conditions for the well-posedness of an inverse problem—which were formulated in Chapter 7—may be violated:

1. For some unknown reason, the existence condition may be violated.
2. There may not be sufficient information in the observable time series to reconstruct the nonlinear dynamics uniquely; hence, the uniqueness criterion is violated.
3. The unavoidable presence of additive noise or some form of imprecision in the observable time series adds uncertainty to the dynamic reconstruction.

In particular, if the noise level is too high, it is possible for the continuity criterion to be violated.

How, then, do we make the dynamic-reconstruction problem well posed? The answer lies in the inclusion of some form of *prior knowledge* about the input–output mapping as an essential requirement. In other words, some form of constraints (e.g., smoothness of input–output mapping) would have to be imposed on the predictive model designed for solving the dynamic-reconstruction problem. One effective way in which this requirement can be satisfied is to invoke Tikhonov's *regularization theory*, which was also discussed in Chapter 7. Simply put, without regularization, the iterated predictor may well *not* work.

Another issue that needs to be considered is the ability of the predictive model to solve the inverse problem with sufficient accuracy. In this context, the use of a neural network to build the predictive model is appropriate. In particular, the universal approximation property of a multilayer perceptron or that of a radial-basis function network means that we can take care of the issue of reconstruction accuracy by using one or the other of these networks with an appropriate number of hidden neurons. In addition, however, we need the solution to be regularized for the reasons already explained. In theory, both multilayer perceptrons and radial-basis function networks lend themselves to the use of regularization, but as explained in Chapter 7, it is in radial-basis function networks that we find regularization theory included in a mathematically tractable manner as an integral part of their design.

Case Study: Dynamic Reconstruction of Lorenz Attractor

To illustrate the idea of dynamic reconstruction, consider the system of three coupled ordinary differential equations, abstracted by Lorenz (1963) from the Galerkin approximation to the partial differential equations of thermal convection in the lower atmosphere; the *Lorenz attractor* provides a workhorse set of equations for testing ideas in nonlinear dynamics. The equations for the Lorenz attractor are

$$\frac{dx(t)}{dt} = -\sigma x(t) + \sigma y(t)$$

$$\frac{dy(t)}{dt} = -x(t)z(t) + rx(t) - y(t)$$

$$\frac{dz(t)}{dt} = x(t)y(t) - bz(t) \tag{13.82}$$

where σ, r, and b are dimensionless parameters. Typical values for these parameters are $\sigma = 10$, $b = 8/3$, and $r = 28$.

Figure 13.19 shows the results of iterated prediction performed on a regularized RBF network with 400 centers using a "noisy" time series based on the component $x(t)$ of the Lorenz attractor. The signal-to-noise ratio was $+25$ dB. For the design of the regularized RBF network, we used the following parameters:

size of the input layer, $m = 20$

regularization parameter $\lambda = 10^{-2}$

The size of the input layer was determined using Eq. (13.81); the regularization parameter λ was determined using the generalized cross-validation procedure described in Chapter 7.

The solution to the dynamic-reconstruction problem, presented in Fig. 13.19 using a regularized form of the RBF network, has *learned* the dynamics, in the sense that the output of the network under iterated prediction closely approximates the actual trajectory of the Lorenz attractor in the short term. This outcome is borne out by the results presented in Table 13.5, where we have a summary of Lorenz data for two cases:

(a) Noisy Lorenz system with signal-to-noise ratio SNR $= 25$ dB.

(b) Reconstructed data, using the noisy version of Lorenz time series as described in Table 13.5.

The invariants of the reconstructed time series using noisy data are close to the corresponding ones pertaining to the noise-free Lorenz data. The deviations in absolute values are due to the residual effect of noise embedded in the reconstructed attractor and to inaccuracies in the estimation procedure. Figure 13.19 clearly shows that there is more to dynamic modeling than just prediction. This figure, and many others not included

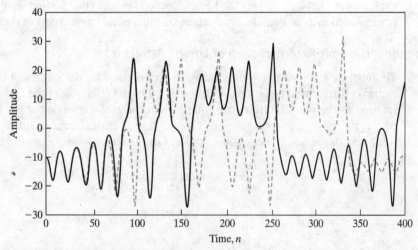

FIGURE 13.19 Regularized iterated prediction ($N = 400$, $m = 20$) on Lorenz data at SNR $= +25$ dB; the solid curve is the actual chaotic signal, and the red curve is the reconstructed signal.

TABLE 13.5   Summary of Parameters for Experiment on
Dynamic Reconstruction Using the Lorenz System

(a)   *Noisy Lorenz system: 25 dB SNR*
Number of samples (data points) used: 35,000

1. Normalized embedding delay $\tau = 4$
2. Embedding dimension $D_E = 5$
3. Lyapunov exponents:
$$\lambda_1 = 13.2689$$
$$\lambda_2 = -5.8562$$
$$\lambda_3 = -3.1447$$
$$\lambda_4 = -18.0082$$
$$\lambda_5 = -47.0572$$
4. Horizon of predictability ≈ 100 samples

(b)   *Reconstructed system using the noisy Lorenz data of Fig. 13.19*
Number of samples generated (recursively): 35,000

1. Normalized embedding delay $\tau = 4$
2. Embedding dimension $D_E = 3$
3. Lyapunov exponents:
$$\lambda_1 = 2.5655$$
$$\lambda_2 = -0.6275$$
$$\lambda_3 = -15.0342$$
4. Horizon of predictability ≈ 61 samples

Notes: All of the Lyapunov exponents are expressed in nats per second; a *nat* is a natural unit for measuring information as discussed in Chapter 10. Note also that in case (b), dynamic reconstruction restores the Lyapunov spectrum to its correct size of three (equal to the number of equations) with only one positive Lyapunov exponent.

here, demonstrates the "robustness" of the regularized RBF solution with respect to the point on the attractor that is used to initialize the iterated prediction process.

The following two observations from Fig. 13.19, pertaining to the use of regularization, are particularly noteworthy:

1. The short-term predictability of the reconstructed time series in Fig. 13.19 is about 60 samples. The theoretical horizon of predictability computed from the Lyapunov spectrum of the noiseless Lorenz attractor is approximately 100 samples. The experimental deviation from the horizon of predictability of the noise-free Lorenz attractor is merely a manifestation of the presence of noise in the actual data used to perform the dynamic reconstruction. The theoretical horizon of predictability computed from the reconstructed data was 61 (see Table 13.5), which is quite close to the experimentally observed value of short-term predictability.

2. Once the period of short-term predictability is over, the reconstructed time series in Fig. 13.19 begins to deviate from the noiseless realization of the actual Lorenz attractor. This result is basically a manifestation of chaotic dynamics—namely, sensitivity to initial conditions. As mentioned previously, sensitivity to initial conditions is a hallmark of chaos.

13.12   SUMMARY AND DISCUSSION

The Stability Problem in Recurrent Networks

In this chapter, we presented an introductory treatment of the mathematical foundations of deterministic neurodynamic systems, described by Eq. (13.2), reproduced here for convenience of presentation:

$$\frac{d}{dt}\mathbf{x}(t) = \mathbf{F}(\mathbf{x}(t))$$

where t denotes continuous-time, $\mathbf{x}(t)$ is the state of the system; and $\mathbf{F}(\cdot)$ is a vector-valued function, each element of which operates on a corresponding element of the state $\mathbf{x}(t)$.

Much of the discussion in the early part of the chapter focused on the issue of stability of the system. In particular, we described the *direct method of Lyapunov*, which provides a powerful mathematical tool for investigating the stability problem in teims of a continuous scalar function of the state $\mathbf{x}(t)$, which is called a *Lyapunov function*. The method embodies two theorems that enable us to establish whether a given autonomous nonlinear dynamic system is stable or asymptotically stable. A cautionary word is in order here: The method does not show us how to find a Lyapunov function; rather, the task is left to the investigator's ingenuity to do the finding. In many problems of practical interest, however, the energy function can serve as a Lyapunov function.

Models of Associative Memory

In the next part of the chapter, we discussed two models of an associative memory: the Hopfield model and the brain-state-in-a-box (BSB) model. These two models share some common points:

- they both employ positive feedback in accordance with Hebb's postulate of learning;
- they both have an energy (Lyapunov) function, and their underlying dynamics tend to minimize it in an iterative fashion;
- they are both capable of performing computation using attractor dynamics.

Naturally, they differ in their areas of application. The BSB model has an inherent capability to perform clustering of data. On the other hand, the Hopfield model has a capability of its own to operate as a content-addressable memory; however, its error-correcting capability is not as good as that of the well-established error-correcting codes in the digital communications literature.[8] The analog version of the Hopfield network has also been considered as a model for solving the traveling-salesman problem.[9]

The Hopfield Model Discussed Further

Hopfield's 1982 paper has had a significant impact on the neural network literature. Indeed, it was one of the catalysts responsible for reviving sustained interest in the study of neural networks in the 1980s.

Most importantly, by doing the following in that classic paper:

- considering a recurrent neural network, artificially configured to have its synaptic weights satisfy the symmetry condition of Eq. (13.21);

- formulating an energy function E, as defined in Eq. (13.28);
- proving that the energy function E is a Lyapunov function;
- then minimizing the energy function in an iterative fashion to demonstrate that the network is capable of exhibiting emergent behavior with a set of stable points;

and doing all of this in a relatively short paper, it made Hopfield's paper (1982) all the more elegant and impressive. Indeed, it was responsible for generating a great deal of excitement among physicists and mathematicians for over a decade.

In short, Hopfield showed us that it is indeed possible for a *simple, structured behavior to emerge from the evolution of a complex, nonlinear dynamic system over time.* The possibility of this kind of dynamic behavior had been studied previously by other investigators, but it was in Hopfield's paper that the underpinnings of the emergent behavior of recurrent neural networks were brought together for the first time in a visible and convincing manner.

A word of caution is in order: It would be somewhat naive to think of the Hopfield model and other models of associative memories described in the literature on neural networks, as useful as they are, to be applicable to human memory (Anderson, 1995).

Large-Scale Computer Model as a Facilitator of Understanding Mammalian Brains

With modeling of some function of the brain or, to be even more ambitious, modeling the whole brain itself, as a challenging task, it is very inspiring to refer to the pioneering work done by Izhikevich and Edelman on the structural and dynamic complexity of mammalian brains. In their 2008 paper, a *large-scale computer model of mammalian thalamo-cortical systems* is described. It is known that the thalamo-cortical system is essential for onsciousness in the sense that losing a thalamus or cortex abolishes consciousness; on the other hand, for example, losing the hippocampus or cerebellum impairs the function of the brain, but spares consciousness. The focus on the thalamo-cortical system makes the *Izhikevich-Edelman model* all the more interesting.

Major characteristics of the model include the following:

1. *The simulation of one million multicompartmental spiking neurons.* For the simulation, the neurons were calibrated to reproduce known responses *in vitro* in rats; previous work done by Izhikevich (2007a) on the spiking dynamics of neurons featured prominently in the simulation.

2. *Almost half a billion synapses.* This large-scale synaptic model exhibits autonomouly three highly relevant neural activities:

    (i) *Neurodynamics.* The simulated spiking dynamics of each neuron and each dendritic compartment are described by the following pair of differential equations:

$$C\frac{dv}{dt} = k(v - v_r)(v - v_{thr}) - u + I \tag{13.83}$$

$$\frac{du}{dt} = a[b(v - v_r) - u] \tag{13.84}$$

where C = membrane capacitance,

v = membrane potential,

v_r = resting potential,

v_{thr} = instantaneous threshold potential,

u = recovery variable that defines the difference between all inward and outward voltage-gated currents,

I = dendritic and synaptic current,

and a and b are constants. When the membrane potential assumes a value greater than the peak of the spike, the neural model fires a spike (i.e., action potential), and all variables of the model are reset.

(ii) *Short-term synaptic plasticity.* In the model, the conductance (i.e., strength) of each synapse can be scaled down or up, respectively representing depression or facilitation, on a short time-scale.

(iii) *Long-term spike-timing-dependent plasticity.* For this second plastic feature of the model, each synapse is potentiated or depressed, depending on the order of firing the presynaptic neuron and the corresponding dendritic compartment of the postsynaptic neuron.

3. *Generalization performance.* This performance was demonstrated by having the model exhibit behavioral regimes of normal brain activity that were not built into the model.

A large-scale computer model, endowed with these neurobiologically motivated performances, demonstrates that we are gradually but surely moving closer to the building of large-scale computer models of mammalian brains that will be capable of real-time operations.

NOTES AND REFERENCES

1. A *nonautonomous* dynamic system is defined by the state equation

$$\frac{d}{dt}\mathbf{x}(t) = \mathbf{F}(\mathbf{x}(t), t)$$

with the initial condition $\mathbf{x}(t_0) = \mathbf{x}_0$. For a nonautonomous system, the vector field $\mathbf{F}(\mathbf{x}(t), t)$ depends on time t. Therefore, unlike the case of an autonomous system, we generally cannot set the initial time equal to zero (Parker and Chua, 1989).

2. In addition to Eq. (13.11), global stability of a nonlinear dynamic system generally requires that the condition of radial unboundedness

$$V(\mathbf{x}) \to \infty \qquad \text{as } \|\mathbf{x}\| \to \infty$$

holds (Slotine and Li, 1991). This condition is usually satisfied by Lyapunov functions constructed for neural networks with sigmoid activation functions.

3. For a rigorous definition of an attractor, we offer the following (Lanford, 1981; Lichtenberg and Lieberman, 1992):

A subset (manifold) $\mathcal{M}$ of the state space is called an attractor if

- *$\mathcal{M}$ is invariant under the flow;*
- *there is an (open) neighborhood around $\mathcal{M}$ that shrinks down to $\mathcal{M}$ under the flow;*
- *no part of $\mathcal{M}$ is transient;*
- *$\mathcal{M}$ cannot be decomposed into two nonoverlapping invariant pieces.*

4. **Integrate-and-Fire Neuron**

The additive model of Eq. (13.14) does not fully capture the essence of what a biological neuron does. In particular, it ignores the timing information encoded into action potentials; action potentials are described briefly in qualitative terms in the introductory chapter. Hopfield (1994) describes a dynamic model that accounts for action potentials by considering an integrate-and-fire neuron. The operation of such a neuron is described by the first-order differential equation

$$C\frac{d}{dt}u(t) = -\frac{1}{R}(u(t) - u_0) + i(t) \tag{A}$$

where

$$
\begin{aligned}
u(t) &= \text{interior potential of the neuron,}\\
C &= \text{capacitance of the membrane surrounding the neuron,}\\
R &= \text{leakage resistance of the membrane,}\\
i(t) &= \text{electrical current injected into the neuron by another neuron,}\\
u_0 &= \text{potential to which the neuron is reduced when } i(t) \text{ vanishes.}
\end{aligned}
$$

An action potential is generated each time the interior potential $u(t)$ reaches a threshold value. The action potentials are treated as Dirac delta (impulse) functions as shown by

$$g_k(t) = \sum_n \delta(t - t_{k,n}) \tag{B}$$

where $t_{k,n}$, n, $= 1, 2, 3, \ldots$, denotes the times at which neuron k *fires* action potentials. These times are defined by Eq. (A).

The behavior of total current $i_k(t)$ flowing into neuron k is modeled as

$$\frac{d}{dt}i_k(t) = -\frac{1}{\tau}i_k(t) + \sum_j w_{kj}g_j(t) \tag{C}$$

where w_{kj} is the synaptic weight from neuron j to neuron k, τ is a characteristic time constant of neuron k, and the function $g_j(t)$ is defined in accordance with Eq. (B).

The additive model of Eq. (13.14) may be viewed as a special case of Eq. (C). Specifically, the spiky nature of $g_j(t)$ is ignored by replacing it with the convolution of $g_j(t)$ with a smoothing function. Such a move is justified if, during a reasonable time interval, there are many contributions to the sum on the right-hand side of Eq. (C) due to high connectivity, and all that we are really interested in is the short-term behavior of the firing rate of neuron k.

5. The *Little model* (Little, 1974; Little and Shaw, 1978) uses the same synaptic weights as the Hopfield model. However, they differ from each other in that the Hopfield model uses *asynchronous (serial) dynamics*, whereas the Little model uses *synchronous (parallel)*

dynamics. Accordingly, they exhibit different convergence properties (Bruck, 1990; Goles and Martinez, 1990): The Hopfield network will always converge to a stable state, whereas the Little model will always converge to a stable state or a limit cycle of length two, at most. By such a "limit cycle," we mean that the cycles in the state space of the network are of a length less than or equal to two.

6. The idea of a correlation function $C(q, r)$ as defined in Eq. (13.71) was known in statistics from the work of Rényi (1970). However, the use of it to characterize a strange attractor is due to Grassberger and Procaccia (1983). They originally discussed the use of $C(q, r)$ in the context of correlation dimension for $q = 2$.

7. The construction of dynamics using independent coordinates from a time series was first advocated by Packard et al. (1980). However, this paper does not give proof, and it uses "derivative" embeddings rather than time-delay embeddings. The idea of time-delay, or delay-coordinate, embeddings is attributed to Takens. Specifically, in 1981, Takens published a mathematically profound paper on time-delay embeddings, which applies to attractors that are surfaces, or like a torus; see also the paper by Mañé (1981) on the same subject published in the same issue. Takens's paper is difficult to read for non-mathematicians, and Mañé's paper is even more difficult to read. The idea of delay-coordinate mapping was refined in 1991 by Sauer et al. The approach taken in this latter paper integrates and expands on previous results due to Whitney (1936) and Takens (1981).

8. Spurious states disturb the retrieval phase of the Hopfield model as they tend to resemble mixtures of stored patterns. Accordingly, the error-correcting capability of the Hopfield model is degraded by the generation of superious states. The net result is that as an error-correcting system, the Hopfield model is not that good. This is particularly so when the Hopfield model is compared with well-established error-correcting codes in the digital communications literature (Lin and Costello, 2004). These latter codes are impressive in that—through the insertion of parity-check bits in accordance with cleverly formulated encodinag schemes—they are capable of approaching the so-called Shannon limit, a challenge that has occupied the attention of coding theorists ever since Shannon's 1948 classic paper on information theory.

9. *Combinatorial-optimization problems* rank among the most difficult known to mathematicians. This class of optimization problems includes the *traveling-salesman problem* (TSP), considered to be a classic. Given the positions of a specified number of cities, assumed to lie in a plane, the problem is to find the shortest tour that starts and finishes at the same city. The TSP is simple to state, but hard to solve exactly in that there is no known method of finding the optimum tour, short of computing the length of every possible tour and then selecting the shortest one. It is said to be *NP complete* (Hopcroft and Ullman, 1979).

  In a 1985 paper, Hopfield and Tank proposed the use of an analog network, based on the system of N coupled first-order differential equations in Eq. (13.20), for representing a solution of the TSP. Specifically, the synaptic weights of the network were determined by distances between the cities visited on the tour, and the optimum solution to the problem was treated as a fixed point of the equations in Eq. (13.20). Herein lie the difficulties encountered with "mapping" combinatorial-optimization problems onto the continuous (analog) Hopfield model. The model acts to minimize a single energy (Lyapunov) function, performing the role of an objective function subject to some hard constraints. If any of these constraints are violated, the solution is considered to be invalid. In Gee et al. (1993), it was shown that the success of the Hopfield model is highly sensitive to the way in which the Lyapunov function for the system of coupled equations is constructed.

PROBLEMS

Dynamic Systems

13.1 Given that $V(x)$ is a Lyapunov function, then state the condition in which the equilibrium state $\bar{x}$ is stable and the condition in which it is asymptotically stable.

13.2 Parts (a) and (b) of Fig. P13.2 are the block-diagram representations of the neurodynamic equations described in Eqs. (13.18) and (13.19), respectively. Using this pair of equations, verify the validity of the two block-diagrams in Fig. P13.2.

13.3 Consider a general neurodynamic system with an unspecified dependence on internal dynamic parameters, external dynamic stimuli, and state variables. The system is defined by the state equations

$$\frac{dx_j}{dt} = \varphi_j(\mathbf{W}, \mathbf{u}, \mathbf{x}), \qquad j = 1, 2, ..., N$$

where the matrix $\mathbf{W}$ represents the internal dynamic parameters of the system, the vector $\mathbf{u}$ represents the external dynamic stimuli, and $\mathbf{x}$ is the state vector whose jth element is denoted by x_j. Assume that trajectories of the system converge onto point attractors for values of $\mathbf{W}$, $\mathbf{u}$, and initial states $\mathbf{x}(0)$ in some operating region of the state space (Pineda, 1988b). Discuss how the system described here may be used for the following applications:

(a) a continuous mapper, with $\mathbf{u}$ as input and $\mathbf{x}(\infty)$ as output;
(b) an autoassociative memory, with $\mathbf{x}(0)$ as input and $\mathbf{x}(\infty)$ as output.

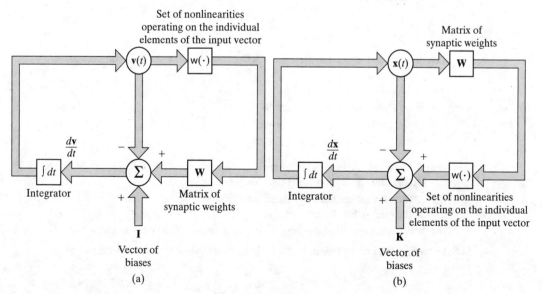

FIGURE P13.2

Hopfield Models

13.4 Consider a Hopfield network made up of five neurons, which is required to store the following three fundamental memories:

$$\boldsymbol{\xi}_1 = [+1, +1, +1, +1, +1]^T$$
$$\boldsymbol{\xi}_2 = [+1, -1, -1, +1, -1]^T$$
$$\boldsymbol{\xi}_3 = [-1, +1, -1, +1, +1]^T$$

(a) Evaluate the 5-by-5 synaptic-weight matrix of the network.

(b) Use asynchronous updating to demonstrate that all three fundamental memories $\boldsymbol{\xi}_1, \boldsymbol{\xi}_2$, and $\boldsymbol{\xi}_3$ satisfy the alignment condition.

(c) Investigate the retrieval performance of the network when it is presented with a noisy version of $\boldsymbol{\xi}_1$ in which the second element is reversed in polarity.

13.5 Investigate the use of synchronous updating for the retrieval performance of the Hopfield network described in Problem 13.4.

13.6 (a) Show that

$$\boldsymbol{\xi}_1 = [-1, -1, -1, -1, -1]^T$$
$$\boldsymbol{\xi}_2 = [-1, +1, +1, -1, +1]^T$$
$$\boldsymbol{\xi}_3 = [+1, -1, +1, -1, -1]^T$$

are also fundamental memories of the Hopfield network described in Problem 13.4. How are these fundamental memories related to those of Problem 13.4?

(b) Suppose that the first element of the fundamental memory $\boldsymbol{\xi}_3$ in Problem 13.4 is masked (i.e., reduced to zero). Determine the resulting pattern produced by the Hopfield network. Compare this result with the original form of $\boldsymbol{\xi}_3$.

13.7 Consider a simple Hopfield network made up of two neurons. The synaptic-weight matrix of the network is

$$\mathbf{W} = \begin{bmatrix} 0 & -1 \\ -1 & 0 \end{bmatrix}$$

The bias applied to each neuron is zero. The four possible states of the network are

$$\mathbf{x}_1 = [+1, +1]^T$$
$$\mathbf{x}_2 = [-1, +1]^T$$
$$\mathbf{x}_3 = [-1, -1]^T$$
$$\mathbf{x}_4 = [+1, -1]^T$$

(a) Demonstrate that states $\mathbf{x}_2$ and $\mathbf{x}_4$ are stable, whereas states $\mathbf{x}_1$ and $\mathbf{x}_3$ exhibit a limit cycle. Do this demonstration using the following tools:

1. the alignment (stability) condition;
2. the energy function.

(b) What is the length of the limit cycle characterizing the states $\mathbf{x}_1$ and $\mathbf{x}_3$?

13.8 Show that the energy function of a Hopfield network may be expressed as

$$E = -\frac{N}{2} \sum_{v=1}^{M} m_v^2$$

where m_v denotes overlaps defined by

$$m_v = \frac{1}{N}\sum_{j=1}^{N} x_j \xi_{v,j}, \qquad v = 1, 2, ..., M$$

where x_j is the jth element of the state vector $\mathbf{x}$, $\xi_{v,j}$ is the jth element of the fundamental memory ξ_v, and M is the number of fundamental memories.

13.9 Depending on the model adopted for describing the neurons, the Hopfield network may be operated in a continuous mode or a discrete mode. State the condition when the maxima and minima of the continuous Hopfield model become identical to those of the corresponding discrete Hopfield model.

13.10 The Boltzmann machine, studied in Chapter 11, may be viewed as an extension of the Hopfield network. Make up a list of the similarities and differences between these two unsupervised learning systems.

Cohen–Grossberg Theorem

13.11 Consider the Lyapunov function E defined in Eq. (13.48). Show that

$$\frac{dE}{dt} \leq 0$$

provided that the conditions in Eqs. (13.49) to (13.51) are satisfied.

13.12 In Section 13.9, we derived the Lyapunov function of the BSB model by applying the Cohen–Grossberg theorem. In carrying out the derivation, we omitted some of the details leading to Eq. (13.63). Fill in the details.

13.13 Figure P13.13 shows a plot of the nonmonotonic activation function due to Morita (1993) discussed in Note 6 under the Notes and References. This activation function is used in place of the hyperbolic tangent function in the construction of a Hopfield network. Is the Cohen–Grossberg theorem applicable to the associative memory so constructed? Justify your answer.

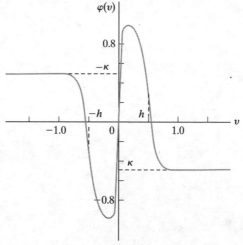

FIGURE P13.13

Data Representation

13.14 In Chapter 10, we described an algorithm for data representation using the idea of an optimal manifold, due to Chigirev and Bialek (2005). Given a set of unlabeled data as input applied to the algorithm, two results are produced by the algorithm as follows:

- a set of manifold points, around which the input data are clustered;
- a stochastic map, which projects the input data onto the manifold.

Using the idea of the Grassberger-Procacia correlation dimension described in Section 13.10, outline an experiment for validating the Chigirev-Bialek algorithm as a possible estimator of manifold-dimensional complexity.

C H A P T E R   1 4

Bayesian Filtering for State Estimation of Dynamic Systems

ORGANIZATION OF THE CHAPTER

This chapter focuses on an issue of fundamental importance: the estimation of the hidden state of a dynamic system, given a set of observations.

The chapter is organized as follows:

1. The introductory section, Section 14.1, motivates interest in the study of sequential state estimation.
2. Section 14.2 discusses the notion of a state space and the different ways of modeling it.
3. The celebrated Kalman filter is derived in Section 14.3, which is followed by treatment of square-root implementation of the filter for assured numerical stability in Section 14.4. Section 14.5 derives the extended Kalman filter for dealing with situations where the nonlinearity is of a "mild" sort.
4. Section 14.6 discusses Bayesian filtering, which provides a unifying framework for the state estimation of dynamic systems, at least conceptually; this filtering model includes the Kalman filter as a special case.
5. Section 14.7 presents a description of the cubature rule for direct numerical approximation of the Bayesian filter, paving the way for the description of a new filter, the cubature Kalman filter, which builds on ideas from Kalman filter theory.
6. Section 14.8 addresses another approach for approximating the Bayesian filter; this one is rooted in Monte Carlo simulation. In particular, a detailed treatment of particle filters is presented. A computer experiment comparing the performance of the extended Kalman filter and a particular form of the particle filter is presented in Section 14.9.
7. Section 14.10 discusses the role of Kalman filtering in modeling different parts of the human brain.

The chapter concludes with a summary and discussion in Section 14.11.

14.1   INTRODUCTION

In the neurodynamic systems studied in Chapter 13, the main issue of concern was stability. In this chapter, we consider another important issue: estimation of the state of a dynamic system, given a sequence of observations dependent on the state in some fashion.

The observations take place in discrete time, not for mathematical convenience, but because that is how they arise naturally. Moreover, the state is not only unknown, but also *hidden* from the observer. We may therefore view the state-estimation problem as an inverse problem.

As an illustrative example, consider a dynamically driven multiplayer perceptron with feedback loops from one layer of the network to a preceding one (e.g., from a hidden layer to the input layer). The state of the network could be viewed as a vector made up of all the synaptic weights of the network, arranged in some orderly fashion. What we would like to do is to use sequential state-estimation theory to adjust the weight vector of the network in a supervised manner, given a training sample. This application is discussed in detail in the next chapter. For this application, however, we need a sequential procedure for state estimation, the rationale for which is deferred to that chapter.

The first rigorous treatment of sequential state-estimation theory appeared in Kalman's classic paper, published in 1960. Kalman's exposition was based on two simplifying assumptions for mathematical tractability:

1. The dynamic system is entirely *linear*.
2. The noise processes perturbing the state of the dynamic system and the observables are *additive and Gaussian*.

In making these assumptions, Kalman derived an *optimal estimate* of the unknown state of the system, the computation of which was performed *recursively*. Within its domain of applicability, the Kalman filter has undoubtedly withstood the test of time.

Sequential state-estimation theory remains an active area of research. Much of this research has focused on how to deal with the practical issues of nonlinearity and non-Gaussianity. Under one or both of these conditions, optimal estimation of the state is no longer an option. Rather, we have to settle on the realization of an *approximate estimator*. The challenge is how to derive such an estimator that is both principled and computationally efficient.

14.2 STATE-SPACE MODELS

All dynamic systems share a basic feature: the *state* of the system. We formally define this feature as follows:

> *The state of a stochastic dynamic system is defined as the minimal amount of information about the effects of past inputs applied to the system that is sufficient to completely describe the future behavior of the system.*

Typically, the state is *not* measurable directly. Rather, in an indirect manner, the state makes its effect on the outside world measurable through a set of *observables*. As such, the characterization of an unknown dynamic system is described by a *state-space model*, which embodies a pair of equations:

1. *The system (state) model*, which, formulated as a *first-order Markov chain*, describes the evolution of the state as a function of time, as shown by

$$\mathbf{x}_{n+1} = \mathbf{a}_n(\mathbf{x}_n, \boldsymbol{\omega}_n) \tag{14.1}$$

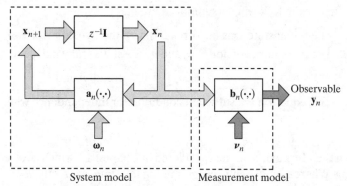

FIGURE 14.1   Generic state-space model of a time-varying, nonlinear dynamic system, where $z^{-1}\mathbf{I}$ denotes a block of unit-time delays.

where n denotes discrete time, the vector $\mathbf{x}_n$ denotes the current value of the state, and $\mathbf{x}_{n+1}$ denotes the subsequent value of the state; the vector $\boldsymbol{\omega}_n$ denotes *dynamic noise*, or *process noise*, and $\mathbf{a}_n(\cdot,\cdot)$ is a vectorial function of its two arguments.

2. *The measurement (observation) model*, which is formulated as

$$\mathbf{y}_n = \mathbf{b}_n(\mathbf{x}_n, \boldsymbol{\nu}_n) \qquad (14.2)$$

where the vector $\mathbf{y}_n$ denotes a set of observables, the vector $\boldsymbol{\nu}_n$ denotes *measurement noise*, and $\mathbf{b}_n(\cdot,\cdot)$ denotes another vectorial function.

The subscript n in both $\mathbf{a}_n$ and $\mathbf{b}_n$ is included to cover situations where these two functions are *time varying*. For the state-space model to be of practical value, it must closely describe the underlying physics of the system under study.

Figure 14.1 depicts a signal-flow graph representation of the state-space model defined by Eqs. (14.1) and (14.2), and Fig. 14.2 depicts the state's evolution across time as a *Markov chain*. The time-domain representation of the model depicted in these two figures offers certain attributes:

- mathematical and notational convenience;
- a close relationship of the model to physical reality;
- a meaningful basis of accounting for the statistical behavior of the system.

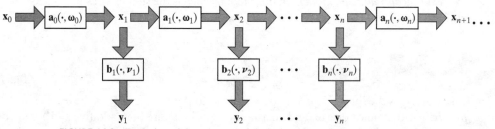

FIGURE 14.2   Evolution of the state across time, viewed as a first-order Markov chain.

Justifiably, the following assumptions are made:

1. The initial state $\mathbf{x}_0$ is uncorrelated with the dynamic noise $\boldsymbol{\omega}_n$ for all n.
2. The two sources of noise, $\boldsymbol{\omega}_n$ and $\boldsymbol{v}_n$, are statistically independent, which means that

$$\mathbb{E}[\boldsymbol{\omega}_n \boldsymbol{v}_k^T] = \mathbf{0} \quad \text{for all } n \text{ and } k \tag{14.3}$$

This equation is a sufficient condition for independence when $\boldsymbol{\omega}_n$ on $\boldsymbol{v}_n$ are *jointly Gaussian*.

It is noteworthy that the Markovian model of Fig. 14.2 is fundamentally *different* from the Morkovian model considered in Chapter 12, which covered dynamic programming. Whereas in dynamic programming the state is directly *accessible* to the observer, in sequential state estimation the state is *hidden* from the observer.

Statement of the Sequential State-Estimation Problem

Given an entire record of observations consisting of $\mathbf{y}_1, \mathbf{y}_2, ..., \mathbf{y}_n$, compute an estimate of the hidden state $\mathbf{x}_k$ that is optimal in some statistical sense, with the estimation being performed in a sequential manner.

In a way, this statement embodies two systems:

- the unknown dynamic system, whose observable $\mathbf{y}_n$ is a function of the hidden state;
- the sequential state estimator or filter, which exploits the information about the state that is contained in the observables.

In a loose sense, we may view this problem as an "encoding–decoding" problem, with the observables representing an encoded version of the state and the state estimate produced by the filter representing a decoded version of the observables.

In any event, the state-estimation problem is called *prediction* if $k > n$, *filtering* if $k = n$, and *smoothing* if $k < n$. Typically, a smoother is statistically more accurate than both the predictor and filter, as it uses more observables. On the other hand, both prediction and filtering can be performed in real time, whereas smoothing cannot.

Hierarchy of State-Space Models

The mathematical difficulty of solving the state-estimation problem is highly dependent on how the state-space model is actually described, leading to the following hierarchy of models:

1. *Linear, Gaussian model.* In this model, which is the simplest of state-space models, Eqs. (14.1) and (14.2) respectively reduce to

$$\mathbf{x}_{n+1} = \mathbf{A}_{n+1,n}\mathbf{x}_n + \boldsymbol{\omega}_n \tag{14.4}$$

and

$$\mathbf{y}_n = \mathbf{B}_n\mathbf{x}_n + \boldsymbol{v}_n \tag{14.5}$$

where $\mathbf{A}_{n+1,n}$ is the *transition matrix* from state $\mathbf{x}_n$ to state $\mathbf{x}_{n+1}$ and $\mathbf{B}_n$ is the *measurement matrix*. The dynamic noise $\boldsymbol{\omega}_n$ and measurement noise $\boldsymbol{v}_n$ are both additive and assumed to be *statistically independent zero-mean Gaussian processes*[1] whose covariance matrices are respectively denoted by $\mathbf{Q}_{\omega,n}$ and $\mathbf{Q}_{v,n}$. The state-space model defined by Eqs. (14.4) and (14.5) is indeed the model that was used by Kalman to derive his recursive filter, which is mathematically elegant and devoid of any approximation. Kalman filters are discussed in Section 14.3.

   2. *Linear, non-Gaussian model.* In this second model, we still use Eqs. (14.4) and (14.5), but the dynamic noise $\boldsymbol{\omega}_n$ and measurement noise $\boldsymbol{v}_n$ are now assumed to be additive, statistically independent, *non-Gaussian* processes. The non-Gaussianity of these two processes is therefore the only source of mathematical difficulty. In situations of this kind, we may extend the application of the Kalman filter by using the *Gaussian-sum approximation*, summarized as follows:

> *Any probability density function p(x) describing a multidimensional non-Gaussian vector, represented by the sample value* **x**, *can be approximated as closely as desired by the Gaussian-sum formula*
>
> $$p(\mathbf{x}) = \sum_{i=1}^{N} c_i \mathcal{N}(\bar{\mathbf{x}}_i, \boldsymbol{\Sigma}_i) \tag{14.6}$$
>
> *for some integer N and positive scalers c_i, with $\sum_{i=1}^{N} c_i = 1$. The term $\mathcal{N}(\bar{\mathbf{x}}_i, \boldsymbol{\Sigma}_i)$ stands for a Gaussian (normal) density function with mean $\bar{\mathbf{x}}_i$ and covariance matrix $\boldsymbol{\Sigma}_i$ for $i = 1, 2, ..., N$.*

The Gaussian sum on the right-hand side of Eq. (14.6) converges uniformly to the given probability density function $p_{\mathbf{X}}(\mathbf{x})$ as the number of terms, N, increases and the covariance matrices $\boldsymbol{\Sigma}_i$ approach zero for all i (Anderson and Moore, 1971). To compute the Gaussian-sum approximation of Eq. (14.6) for a prescribed probability density function $p(\mathbf{x})$, we may, for example, use a procedure based on the *expectation-maximization* (EM) algorithm; this algorithm was described in Chapter 11. Then, having computed this approximation, we may use a bank of Kalman filters to solve the sequential state-estimation problem described by a linear, non-Gaussian model (Alspach and Sorenson, 1972). Note, however, that the terms in a Gaussian-sum model tend to grow exponentially over the course of time, which may therefore require the use of a pruning algorithm.

   3. *Nonlinear, Gaussian model.* The third model in the hierarchy of state-space models of increasing complexity is formulated as

$$\mathbf{x}_{n+1} = \mathbf{a}_n(\mathbf{x}_n) + \boldsymbol{\omega}_n \tag{14.7}$$

and

$$\mathbf{y}_n = \mathbf{b}_n(\mathbf{x}_n) + \boldsymbol{v}_n \tag{14.8}$$

where the dynamic noise $\boldsymbol{\omega}_n$ and measurement noise $\boldsymbol{v}_n$ are both assumed to be additive and Gaussian. This is where we start to experience mathematical difficulty in solving a sequential state-estimation problem. There are basically two radically different approaches for computing an approximate solution to the problem:

   (i) *Local approximation.*   In this first approach to nonlinear filtering, the *nonlinear function* $\mathbf{a}_n(\cdot)$ in the system model of Eq. (14.7) and the nonlinear function $\mathbf{b}_n(\cdot)$ in the measurement model of Eq. (14.8) are approximated around localized estimates of the state, whereby both equations are *linearized*. The stage is then set for applying the Kalman filter to compute the approximate solution. The extended Kalman filter discussed in Section 14.5 is an example of the local-approximation approach to nonlinear filtering.

(ii) *Global approximation.*   In this second approach to nonlinear filtering, the solution is formulated in a *Bayesian estimation framework* in such a way that difficult interpretations inherent to the problem are made mathematically tractable. Particle filters, discussed in Section 14.7, belong to this second approach to nonlinear filtering.

4. *Nonlinear, non-Gaussian model.* This last class of state-space models is described by Eqs. (14.1) and (14.2), where both the system model and the measurement model are nonlinear, and the dynamic noise $\boldsymbol{\omega}_n$ and measurement noise $\boldsymbol{v}_n$ are not only non-Gaussian, but may also be nonadditive. In this kind of scenario, particle filters are currently the method of choice, but not necessarily the only method, for solving the sequential state-estimation problem.

14.3   KALMAN FILTERS

The state-space model for the Kalman filter is defined by Eqs. (14.4) and (14.5). This linear Gaussian model is parameterized as follows:

- the transition matrix $\mathbf{A}_{n+1,n}$, which is invertible;
- the measurement matrix $\mathbf{B}_n$, which, in general, is a rectangular matrix;
- the Gaussian dynamic noise $\boldsymbol{\omega}_n$, which is assumed to have zero mean and covariance matrix $\mathbf{Q}_{\omega,n}$;
- the Gaussian measurement noise $\boldsymbol{v}_n$, which is assumed to have zero mean and covariance matrix $\mathbf{Q}_{v,n}$.

All these parameters are assumed to be known. We are also given the sequence of observables $\{\mathbf{y}_k\}_{k=1}^n$. The requirement is to derive an estimate of the state $\mathbf{x}_k$ that is optimized in *the minimum mean-square-error sense*. We will confine the discussion to filtering for which $k = n$, and one-step prediction for which $k = n + 1$.

The Innovations Process

An insightful way of deriving this optimum estimate is to use the so-called *innovations process* associated with the observable $\mathbf{y}_n$, which is defined by

$$\boldsymbol{\alpha}_n = \mathbf{y}_n - \hat{\mathbf{y}}_{n|n-1} \tag{14.9}$$

where $\hat{\mathbf{y}}_{n|n-1}$ is the minimum mean-square-error estimate of $\mathbf{y}_n$, given all the observables up to and including time $n - 1$. In effect, we can say the following:

The innovations process $\boldsymbol{\alpha}_n$ is that part of the observable $\mathbf{y}_n$ that is new, since the predictable part of $\mathbf{y}_n$—namely, $\hat{\mathbf{y}}_{n|n-1}$—is completely determined by the sequence $\{\mathbf{y}_k\}_{k=1}^{n-1}$.

The innovations process has some important properties:

Property 1. The innovations process $\boldsymbol{\alpha}_n$ associated with the observable $\mathbf{y}_n$ is orthogonal to all past observables $\mathbf{y}_1, \mathbf{y}_2, ..., \mathbf{y}_{n-1}$, as shown by

$$\mathbb{E}[\boldsymbol{\alpha}_n \mathbf{y}_k^T] = \mathbf{0}, \qquad 1 \le k \le n - 1 \tag{14.10}$$

Property 2. The innovations process consists of a sequence of random vectors that are orthogonal to each other, as shown by

$$\mathbb{E}[\boldsymbol{\alpha}_n \boldsymbol{\alpha}_k^T] = \mathbf{0}, \qquad 1 \le k \le n - 1 \tag{14.11}$$

Property 3. There is a one-to-one correspondence between the sequence of random vectors $\{\mathbf{y}_1, \mathbf{y}_2, ..., \mathbf{y}_n\}$, representing the observed data, and the sequence $\{\boldsymbol{\alpha}_1, \boldsymbol{\alpha}_2, ..., \boldsymbol{\alpha}_n\}$, representing the innovations process, in that the one sequence may be obtained from the other by means of linear stable operators *without any loss of information*. Thus, we may write

$$\{\mathbf{y}_1, \mathbf{y}_2, ..., \mathbf{y}_n\} \rightleftharpoons \{\boldsymbol{\alpha}_1, \boldsymbol{\alpha}_2, ..., \boldsymbol{\alpha}_n\} \tag{14.12}$$

In light of these properties, we now see why it is easier to work with the innovations process rather than the observables themselves: In general, the observables are *correlated*, whereas the corresponding elements of the innovations processes are *not*.

Covariance Matrix of the Innovations Process

Starting with the initial condition $\mathbf{x}_0$, we may use the system model of Eq. (14.4) to express the state at time k as

$$\mathbf{x}_k = \mathbf{A}_{k,0}\mathbf{x}_0 + \sum_{i=1}^{k-1} \mathbf{A}_{k,i}\boldsymbol{\omega}_i \tag{14.13}$$

Equation (14.13) indicates that the state $\mathbf{x}_k$ is a linear combination of $\mathbf{x}_0$ and $\boldsymbol{\omega}_1, \boldsymbol{\omega}_2, ..., \boldsymbol{\omega}_{k-1}$.

By hypothesis, the measurement noise $\boldsymbol{v}_n$ is uncorrelated with both the initial state $\mathbf{x}_0$ and the dynamic noise $\boldsymbol{\omega}_i$. Accordingly, postmultiplying both sides of Eq. (14.13) by $\boldsymbol{v}_n^T$ and taking expectations, we obtain

$$\mathbb{E}[\mathbf{x}_k \boldsymbol{v}_n^T] = \mathbf{0}, \qquad k, n \ge 0 \tag{14.14}$$

Correspondingly, we find from the measurement equation of Eq. (14.5) that

$$\mathbb{E}[\mathbf{y}_k \boldsymbol{v}_k^T] = \mathbf{0}, \qquad 0 \le k \le n - 1 \tag{14.15}$$

and

$$\mathbb{E}[\mathbf{y}_k \boldsymbol{\omega}_n^T] = \mathbf{0}, \qquad 0 \le k \le n \tag{14.16}$$

Given the past observations $\mathbf{y}_1, ..., \mathbf{y}_{n-1}$, we also find from the measurement equation of Eq. (14.5) that the minimum mean-square estimate of the current observation $\mathbf{y}_n$ is

$$\hat{\mathbf{y}}_{n|n-1} = \mathbf{B}_n\hat{\mathbf{x}}_{n|n-1} + \hat{\mathbf{v}}_{n|n-1} \tag{14.17}$$

where $\hat{\mathbf{v}}_{n|n-1}$ is the corresponding estimate of the measurement noise, given the past observations $\mathbf{y}_1, ..., \mathbf{y}_{n-1}$. The estimate $\hat{\mathbf{v}}_{n|n-1}$ is zero, since $\mathbf{v}_n$ is orthogonal to the past observations in light of Eq. (14.15). We may therefore reduce Eq. (14.17) to

$$\hat{\mathbf{y}}_{n|n-1} = \mathbf{B}_n\hat{\mathbf{x}}_{n|n-1} \tag{14.18}$$

Substituting Eqs. (14.5) and (14.18) into Eq. (14.9) and then collecting terms, we obtain

$$\boldsymbol{\alpha}_n = \mathbf{B}_n\boldsymbol{\varepsilon}_{n|n-1} + \mathbf{v}_n \tag{14.19}$$

where the new term $\boldsymbol{\varepsilon}_{n|n-1}$ is the *state prediction-error vector*, defined by

$$\boldsymbol{\varepsilon}_{n,n-1} = \mathbf{x}_n - \hat{\mathbf{x}}_{n|n-1} \tag{14.20}$$

In Problem 14.1, it is shown that $\boldsymbol{\varepsilon}_{n|n-1}$ is orthogonal to both the dynamic noise $\boldsymbol{\omega}_n$ and the measurement noise $\mathbf{v}_n$. Then, defining the *covariance matrix of the zero-mean innovations process* $\boldsymbol{\alpha}_n$ as

$$\mathbf{R}_n = \mathbb{E}[\boldsymbol{\alpha}_n\boldsymbol{\alpha}_n^T] \tag{14.21}$$

and using Eq. (14.19), we may readily show that

$$\mathbf{R}_n = \mathbf{B}_n\mathbf{P}_{n|n-1}\mathbf{B}_n^T + \mathbf{Q}_{v,n} \tag{14.22}$$

where $\mathbf{Q}_{v,n}$ is the covariance matrix of the measurement noise $\mathbf{v}_n$ and the new term

$$\mathbf{P}_{n|n-1} = \mathbb{E}[\boldsymbol{\varepsilon}_{n|n-1}\boldsymbol{\varepsilon}_{n|n-1}^T] \tag{14.23}$$

is the *prediction-error covariance matrix*. Equation (14.22) is our first entry into the Kalman filtering algorithm.

Estimation of the Filtered State Using the Innovations Process: The predictor-corrector formula

Our next task is to derive the minimum mean-square-error estimate of the state $\mathbf{x}_i$ at some time i, based on the innovations process. To this end, given the innovations sequence $\boldsymbol{\alpha}_1, \boldsymbol{\alpha}_2, ..., \boldsymbol{\alpha}_m$, we first express the corresponding estimate of $\mathbf{x}_i$ as the linear expansion

$$\hat{\mathbf{x}}_{i|n} = \sum_{k=1}^{n} \mathbf{C}_{i,k}\boldsymbol{\alpha}_k \tag{14.24}$$

where $\{\mathbf{C}_{i,k}\}_{k=1}^{n}$ is a set of matrices assuming the role of coefficients of the expansion for time i. The state-prediction error and the innovations process satisfy the following orthogonality condition (see Problem 14.3):

$$\mathbb{E}[\boldsymbol{\varepsilon}_{i|n}\boldsymbol{\alpha}_k^T] = \mathbf{0} \qquad \text{for } k = 1, 2, ..., n \\ \text{and } i \geq n \tag{14.25}$$

Hence, substituting Eq. (14.24) into Eq. (14.25) and using the orthogonality property of the innovations process described in Eq. (14.11), we obtain

$$\mathbb{E}[\mathbf{x}_i\boldsymbol{\alpha}_k^T] = \mathbf{C}_{i,k}\mathbf{R}_k$$

where, as defined previously, $\mathbf{R}_k$ is the convariance matrix of the innovations process. Solving this equation for the coefficient matrix $\mathbf{C}_{i,k}$, we thus have

$$\mathbf{C}_{i,k} = \mathbb{E}[\mathbf{x}_i \boldsymbol{\alpha}_k^T] \mathbf{R}_k^{-1}$$

The use of this expression in Eq. (14.24) yields

$$\hat{\mathbf{x}}_{i|n} = \sum_{k=1}^{n} \mathbb{E}[\mathbf{x}_i \boldsymbol{\alpha}_k^T] \mathbf{R}_k^{-1} \boldsymbol{\alpha}_k \qquad (14.26)$$

For $i = n$, corresponding to the process of *filtering*, we may use Eq. (14.26) to express the filtered estimate of the state as

$$\hat{\mathbf{x}}_{n|n} = \sum_{k=1}^{n} \mathbb{E}[\mathbf{x}_n \boldsymbol{\alpha}_k^T] \mathbf{R}_k^{-1} \boldsymbol{\alpha}_k$$

$$= \sum_{k=1}^{n-1} \mathbb{E}[\mathbf{x}_n \boldsymbol{\alpha}_k^T] \mathbf{R}_k^{-1} \boldsymbol{\alpha}_k + \mathbb{E}[\mathbf{x}_n \boldsymbol{\alpha}_n^T] \mathbf{R}_n^{-1} \boldsymbol{\alpha}_n \qquad (14.27)$$

where, in the second line, the term corresponding to $k = n$ has been isolated from the summation. In order to put Eq. (14.27) into an interpretable form, we first use Eq. (14.26) to write

$$\hat{\mathbf{x}}_{n|n-1} = \sum_{k=1}^{n-1} \mathbb{E}[\mathbf{x}_n \boldsymbol{\alpha}_k^T] \mathbf{R}_k^{-1} \boldsymbol{\alpha}_k \qquad (14.28)$$

To simplify the second term in Eq. (14.27), we introduce the following definition:

$$\mathbf{G}_n = \mathbb{E}[\mathbf{x}_n \boldsymbol{\alpha}_n^T] \mathbf{R}_n^{-1} \qquad (14.29)$$

Accordingly, we may now express the filtered estimate of the state as the recursion:

$$\hat{\mathbf{x}}_{n|n} = \hat{\mathbf{x}}_{n|n-1} + \mathbf{G}_n \boldsymbol{\alpha}_n \qquad (14.30)$$

The two terms comprising the right-hand side of Eq. (14.30) may now be interpreted as follows:

1. The term $\hat{\mathbf{x}}_{n|n-1}$ represents *one-step prediction*: It represents a predicted estimate of the state $\mathbf{x}_n$, given all the observations up to and including time $n - 1$.
2. The product term $\mathbf{G}_n \boldsymbol{\alpha}_n$ represents a *correction term*: The innovations process $\boldsymbol{\alpha}_n$, representing new information brought to the filtering process by the observation $\mathbf{y}_n$, is multiplied by a "gain factor" $\mathbf{G}_n$. For this reason, $\mathbf{G}_n$ is commonly referred to as the *Kalman gain*, in recognition of the pioneering work done by Kalman in his classic 1960 paper.

In light of these two insightful points, Eq. (14.30) is known as the *predictor-corrector formula* in Kalman filter theory.

Computation of the Kalman Gain

In Eq. (14.30), we now have our second equation for the recursive computation of the Kalman filter. However, for this equation to be of practical value, we need a formula for computing the Kalman gain that befits a recursive procedure for estimating the state.

With this objective in mind, we use Eq. (14.19) to write

$$\mathbb{E}[\mathbf{x}_n\boldsymbol{\alpha}_n^T] = \mathbb{E}[\mathbf{x}_n(\mathbf{B}_n\boldsymbol{\varepsilon}_{n|n-1} + \boldsymbol{v}_n)^T]$$
$$= \mathbb{E}[\mathbf{x}_n\boldsymbol{\varepsilon}_{n|n-1}^T]\mathbf{B}_n^T$$

where, in the second line, we used the fact that the state $\mathbf{x}_n$ and measurement noise $\boldsymbol{v}_n$ are uncorrelated. Next, we note that the state-prediction error vector $\boldsymbol{\varepsilon}_{n|n-1}$ is orthogonal to the state estimate $\hat{\mathbf{x}}_{n|n-1}$ in accordance with the *principle of orthogonality*. Therefore, the expectation of the outer product of $\hat{\mathbf{x}}_{n|n-1}$ and $\boldsymbol{\varepsilon}_{n|n-1}$ is zero, so the expectation $\mathbb{E}[\mathbf{x}_n\boldsymbol{\alpha}_n^T]$ is unaffected if we replace $\mathbf{x}_n$ with $\boldsymbol{\varepsilon}_{n|n-1}$. We may thus write

$$\mathbb{E}[\mathbf{x}_n\boldsymbol{\alpha}_n^T] = \mathbb{E}[\boldsymbol{\varepsilon}_{n|n-1}\boldsymbol{\varepsilon}_{n|n-1}^T]\mathbf{B}_n^T$$
$$= \mathbf{P}_{n|n-1}\mathbf{B}_n^T$$

Therefore, using this formula for the expectation $\mathbb{E}[\mathbf{x}_n\boldsymbol{\alpha}_n^T]$ in Eq. (14.29), we may express the Kalman gain $\mathbf{G}_n$ in terms of the prediction-error covariance matrix $\mathbf{P}_{n|n-1}$ as

$$\mathbf{G}_n = \mathbf{P}_{n|n-1}\mathbf{B}_n^T\mathbf{R}_n^{-1} \tag{14.31}$$

which is the third equation for the recursive computation of the Kalman filter.

Riccati Difference Equation for Updating the Prediction-Error Covariance Matrix

To complete the recursive procedure for computing the Kalman filter, we need a recursive formula to update the prediction-error covariance matrix from one iteration to the next.

To tackle this last step of the state-estimation procedure, we first replace n with $n + 1$ in Eq. (14.20):

$$\boldsymbol{\varepsilon}_{n+1|n} = \mathbf{x}_{n+1} - \hat{\mathbf{x}}_{n+1|n}$$

Next, we find it instructive to express the predicted estimate of the state in terms of its filtered estimate. To this end, replacing n with $n + 1$ in Eq. (14.28) and using Eq. (14.4), we write

$$\hat{\mathbf{x}}_{n+1|n} = \sum_{k=1}^{n} \mathbb{E}[\mathbf{x}_{n+1}\boldsymbol{\alpha}_k^T]\mathbf{R}_k^{-1}\boldsymbol{\alpha}_k$$

$$= \sum_{k=1}^{n} \mathbb{E}[(\mathbf{A}_{n+1,n}\mathbf{x}_n + \boldsymbol{\omega}_n)\boldsymbol{\alpha}_k^T]\mathbf{R}_k^{-1}\boldsymbol{\alpha}_k$$

$$= \mathbf{A}_{n+1,n}\sum_{k=1}^{n} \mathbb{E}[\mathbf{x}_n\boldsymbol{\alpha}_n^T]\mathbf{R}_k^{-1}\boldsymbol{\alpha}_k$$

$$= \mathbf{A}_{n+1,n}\hat{\mathbf{x}}_{n|n} \tag{14.32}$$

In the third line of Eq. (14.32), we used the fact that the dynamic noise $\boldsymbol{\omega}_n$ is independent of the observations, and therefore the expectation $\mathbb{E}[\boldsymbol{\omega}_n\boldsymbol{\alpha}_k^T]$ is zero; and finally, we used the first line of the defining formula of Eq. (14.27) for the filtered estimate $\hat{\mathbf{x}}_{n|n}$. With the relationship of Eq. (14.32) between the predicted and filtered estimates of the state $\mathbf{x}_n$ at hand, we now use the formula for $\boldsymbol{\varepsilon}_{n+1|n}$ to write

$$\boldsymbol{\varepsilon}_{n+1|n} = \underbrace{(\mathbf{A}_{n+1,n}\mathbf{x}_n + \boldsymbol{\omega}_n)}_{\text{State } \mathbf{x}_{n+1}} - \underbrace{\mathbf{A}_{n+1,n}\hat{\mathbf{x}}_{n|n}}_{\substack{\text{Predicted estimate} \\ \hat{\mathbf{x}}_{n+1|n}}}$$

$$= \mathbf{A}_{n+1,n}(\mathbf{x}_n - \hat{\mathbf{x}}_{n|n}) + \boldsymbol{\omega}_n$$

$$= \mathbf{A}_{n+1,n}\boldsymbol{\varepsilon}_{n|n} + \boldsymbol{\omega}_n \tag{14.33}$$

where the *state-filtering-error vector* is defined by

$$\boldsymbol{\varepsilon}_{n|n} = \mathbf{x}_n - \hat{\mathbf{x}}_{n|n} \tag{14.34}$$

Hence, recognizing that the state-filtering-error vector $\boldsymbol{\varepsilon}_{n|n}$ and the dynamic noise $\boldsymbol{\omega}_n$ are uncorrelated, we may express the prediction-error covariance matrix as

$$\mathbf{P}_{n+1|n} = \mathbb{E}[\boldsymbol{\varepsilon}_{n+1|n}\boldsymbol{\varepsilon}_{n+1|n}^T]$$

$$= \mathbf{A}_{n+1,n}\mathbf{P}_{n|n}\mathbf{A}_{n+1,n}^T + \mathbf{Q}_{\omega,n} \tag{14.35}$$

where $\mathbf{Q}_{\omega,n}$ is the covariance matrix of the dynamic noise $\boldsymbol{\omega}_n$. In Eq. (14.35), we have introduced our last parameter, namely, the *filtering-error covariance matrix*, which is defined by

$$\mathbf{P}_{n|n} = \mathbb{E}[\boldsymbol{\varepsilon}_{n|n}\boldsymbol{\varepsilon}_{n|n}^T] \tag{14.36}$$

To complete the recursion cycle in the Kalman filtering algorithm, we need a formula for computing the filtering-error covariance matrix $\mathbf{P}_{n|n}$. To this end, we first use Eq. (14.30) in Eq. (14.34), obtaining

$$\boldsymbol{\varepsilon}_{n|n} = \mathbf{x}_n - \hat{\mathbf{x}}_{n|n-1} - \mathbf{G}_n\boldsymbol{\alpha}_n$$

$$= \boldsymbol{\varepsilon}_{n|n-1} - \mathbf{G}_n\boldsymbol{\alpha}_n$$

Hence, using the definition of Eq. (14.36), we obtain

$$\mathbf{P}_{n|n} = \mathbb{E}[(\boldsymbol{\varepsilon}_{n|n-1} - \mathbf{G}_n\boldsymbol{\alpha}_n)(\boldsymbol{\varepsilon}_{n|n-1} - \mathbf{G}_n\boldsymbol{\alpha}_n)^T]$$

$$= \mathbb{E}[\boldsymbol{\varepsilon}_{n|n-1}\boldsymbol{\varepsilon}_{n|n-1}^T] - \mathbf{G}_n\mathbb{E}[\boldsymbol{\alpha}_n\boldsymbol{\varepsilon}_{n|n-1}^T] - \mathbb{E}[\boldsymbol{\varepsilon}_{n|n-1}\boldsymbol{\alpha}_n^T]\mathbf{G}_n^T + \mathbf{G}_n\mathbb{E}[\boldsymbol{\alpha}_n\boldsymbol{\alpha}_n^T]\mathbf{G}_n^T$$

$$= \mathbf{P}_{n|n-1} - \mathbf{G}_n\mathbb{E}[\boldsymbol{\alpha}_n\boldsymbol{\varepsilon}_{n|n-1}^T] - \mathbb{E}[\boldsymbol{\varepsilon}_{n|n-1}\boldsymbol{\alpha}_n^T]\mathbf{G}_n^T + \mathbf{G}_n\mathbf{R}_n\mathbf{G}_n^T \tag{14.37}$$

Next, we note that since the estimate $\hat{\mathbf{x}}_{n|n-1}$ is orthogonal to the innovations process $\boldsymbol{\alpha}_n$, we have

$$\mathbb{E}[\boldsymbol{\varepsilon}_{n|n-1}\boldsymbol{\alpha}_n^T] = \mathbb{E}[(\mathbf{x}_n - \hat{\mathbf{x}}_{n|n-1})\boldsymbol{\alpha}_n^T]$$

$$= \mathbb{E}[\mathbf{x}_n\boldsymbol{\alpha}_n^T]$$

Similarly,

$$\mathbb{E}[\boldsymbol{\alpha}_n\boldsymbol{\varepsilon}_{n|n-1}^T] = \mathbb{E}[\boldsymbol{\alpha}_n\mathbf{x}_n^T]$$

By using this pair of relationships and the defining formula of Eq. (14.29) for the Kalman gain, it is a straightforward matter to show that

$$\mathbf{G}_n\mathbb{E}[\boldsymbol{\alpha}_n\boldsymbol{\varepsilon}_{n|n-1}^T] = \mathbb{E}[\boldsymbol{\varepsilon}_{n|n-1}\boldsymbol{\alpha}_n^T]\mathbf{G}_n^T = \mathbf{G}_n\mathbf{R}_n\mathbf{G}_n^T$$

Accordingly, Eq. (14.37) is reduced to

$$\mathbf{P}_{n|n} = \mathbf{P}_{n|n-1} - \mathbf{G}_n \mathbf{R}_n \mathbf{G}_n^T$$

Finally, using the formula of Eq. (14.31) for the Kalman gain and invoking the symmetric properties of the covariance matrices $\mathbf{R}_n$ and $\mathbf{P}_{n|n-1}$, we write

$$\mathbf{P}_{n|n} = \mathbf{P}_{n|n-1} - \mathbf{G}_n \mathbf{B}_n \mathbf{P}_{n|n-1} \qquad (14.38)$$

Thus, the pair of equations in Eqs. (14.38) and (14.35) provides the means of updating the prediction-error covariance matrix. In particular, Eq. (14.38) is commonly referred to as the discrete form of the *Riccati equation*, which is well known in control theory.

Together with Eq. (14.32), this pair of equations completes the formulation of the Kalman filtering algorithum.

Summary of the Kalman Filter

Table 14.1 presents a summary of the variables and parameters used to formulate the solution of the Kalman filtering problem. The input of the filter is the sequence of observables $\mathbf{y}_1, \mathbf{y}_2, ..., \mathbf{y}_n$, and the output of the filter is the filtered estimate $\hat{\mathbf{x}}_{n|n}$. The computational procedure is recursive, as summarized in Table 14.2. The summary also includes the *initial conditions* needed to start the recursive computation. Note that the formula for the innovation $\boldsymbol{\alpha}_n$ in Table 14.2 follows from Eqs. (14.9) and (14.18).

The version of the Kalman filter summarized in Table 14.2 is commonly referred to as the *covariance (Kalman) filtering algorithm*.[2] This terminology follows from the fact that the *algorithm propagates the covariance matrix* $\mathbf{P}_{n|n-1}$ across one complete cycle of the recursive computation, where $\mathbf{P}_{n|n-1}$ refers to the prediction.

TABLE 14.1   Summary of the Kalman Variables and Parameters

Variable	Definition	Dimension
$\mathbf{x}_n$	State at time n	M by 1
$\mathbf{y}_n$	Observation at time n	L by 1
$\mathbf{A}_{n+1,n}$	Invertible transition matrix from state at time n to state at time $n+1$	M by M
$\mathbf{B}_n$	Measurement matrix at time n	L by M
$\mathbf{Q}_{\omega,n}$	Covariance matrix of dynamic noise $\boldsymbol{\omega}_n$	M by M
$\mathbf{Q}_{v,n}$	Covariance matrix of measurement noise $\boldsymbol{v}_n$	L by L
$\hat{\mathbf{x}}_{n|n-1}$	Predicted estimate of the state at time n, given the observations $\mathbf{y}_1, \mathbf{y}_2, ..., \mathbf{y}_{n-1}$	M by 1
$\hat{\mathbf{x}}_{n|n}$	Filtered estimate of the state at time n, given the observations $\mathbf{y}_1, \mathbf{y}_2, ..., \mathbf{y}_n$	M by 1
$\mathbf{G}_n$	Kalman gain at time n	M by L
$\boldsymbol{\alpha}_n$	Innovations process at time n	L by 1
$\mathbf{R}_n$	Covariance matrix of the innovations process $\boldsymbol{\alpha}_n$	L by L
$\mathbf{P}_{n|n-1}$	Prediction-error covariance matrix	M by M
$\mathbf{P}_{n|n}$	Filtering-error covariance matrix	M by M

TABLE 14.2   Summary of the Kalman Filter Based on Filtered Estimate of the State

Observations $= \{\mathbf{y}_1, \mathbf{y}_2, ..., \mathbf{y}_n\}$

Known parameters

   Transition matrix $= \mathbf{A}_{n+1,n}$
   Measurement matrix $= \mathbf{B}_n$
   Covariance matrix of dynamic noise $= \mathbf{Q}_{\omega,n}$
   Covariance matrix of measurement noise $= \mathbf{Q}_{v,n}$

Computation: n = 1, 2, 3, ...

$$\mathbf{G}_n = \mathbf{P}_{n|n-1}\mathbf{B}_n^T[\mathbf{B}_n\mathbf{P}_{n|n-1}\mathbf{B}_n^T + \mathbf{Q}_{v,n}]^{-1}$$
$$\boldsymbol{\alpha}_n = \mathbf{y}_n - \mathbf{B}_n\hat{\mathbf{x}}_{n|n-1}$$
$$\hat{\mathbf{x}}_{n|n} = \hat{\mathbf{x}}_{n|n-1} + \mathbf{G}_n\boldsymbol{\alpha}_n$$
$$\hat{\mathbf{x}}_{n+1|n} = \mathbf{A}_{n+1,n}\hat{\mathbf{x}}_{n|n}$$
$$\mathbf{P}_{n|n} = \mathbf{P}_{n|n-1} - \mathbf{G}_n\mathbf{B}_n\mathbf{P}_{n|n-1}$$
$$\mathbf{P}_{n+1|n} = \mathbf{A}_{n+1,n}\mathbf{P}_{n|n}\mathbf{A}_{n+1,n}^T + \mathbf{Q}_{\omega,n}$$

Initial conditions

$$\hat{\mathbf{x}}_{1|0} = \mathbb{E}[\mathbf{x}_1]$$
$$\mathbf{P}_{1,0} = \mathbb{E}[(\mathbf{x}_1 - \mathbb{E}[\mathbf{x}_1])(\mathbf{x}_1 - \mathbb{E}[\mathbf{x}_1])^T] = \mathbf{\Pi}_0$$

The matrix $\mathbf{\Pi}_0$ is a diagonal matrix with diagonal elements all set equal to δ^{-1}, where δ is a small number.

Figure 14.3 depicts a signal-flow graph of the Kalman filter, where $z^{-1}\mathbf{I}$ represents a bank of unit-time delays. This figure clearly shows that the Kalman filter is a *double-loop feedback system*. One feedback loop, embodying the transition matrix $\mathbf{A}_{n,n-1}$ of the system (state) model, acts as the *predictor*. The second feedback loop, embodying the matrix $\mathbf{B}_n$ of the measurement model, acts as the *corrector*. These two feedback loops work together to generate the filtered estimate of the state $\mathbf{x}_n$—namely, $\hat{\mathbf{x}}_{n|n}$—in response to the observation $\mathbf{y}_n$. It follows, therefore, that the Kalman filter, as depicted in Figure 14.3, is indeed a causal system in that it is capable of operating in real time. In fact, we also have an *overall* feedback loop that encompasses these two feedback loops.

The Kalman gain $\mathbf{G}_n$, central to the operation of the Kalman filter, varies with time n. Thus, we say that the Kalman filter is a *time-varying filter*. This property holds even if the state-space model of the original dynamic system is time invariant.

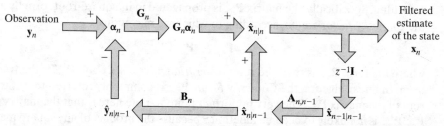

FIGURE 14.3   Signal-flow graph of the Kalman filter, depicting it as a double-loop feedback system.

14.4   THE DIVERGENCE PHENOMENON AND SQUARE-ROOT FILTERING

The covariance filtering algorithm summarized in Table 14.2 is prone to serious numerical difficulties that are well documented in the literature (Kaminski et al., 1971; Bierman and Thornton, 1977).

In practice, numerical difficulties can arise in two basic ways. One way is through *numerical imprecision*. To be specific, the matrix $\mathbf{P}_{n|n}$ is computed as the difference between two nonnegative-definite matrices, as shown in Eq. (14.38). Hence, unless the numerical accuracy employed at every iteration of the algorithm is high enough, there is a possibility that the matrix resulting from this computation will violate the properties of symmetry and nonnegative definiteness. But, according to Eq. (14.36), $\mathbf{P}_{n|n}$ is a covariance matrix and must therefore be nonnegative definite. We thus have a conflicting situation between theory and practice, with the result that the presence of numerical inaccuracies in the computation leads to "unstable" behavior of the Kalman filter. This undesirable behavior of the Kalman filter is commonly referred to as the *divergence phenomenon*.

The divergence phenomenon may also arise in practice in another way. The derivation of the Kalman filter is based on the linear, Gaussian state-space model, described in Eqs. (14.4) and (14.5). Serious deviations of this model from the underlying physics of the dynamic system under study may also contribute to unstable behavior of the algorithm. After all, the algorithm is driven by a real-life sequence of observables, whereas mathematical derivation of the algorithm is based on a hypothesized state-space model. Here, again, we have another conflicting situation between theory and practice, which, in its own way, could lead to divergence of the algorithm.

Given these practical relations, we may now pose the following question:

> *How do we overcome the divergence phenormenon so as to assure stable operation of the Kalman filter in practice?*

A practical answer to this important question is discussed next.

Square-Root Filtering

A mathematically elegant and computationally plausible method of resolving the divergence problem is to use *square-root filtering*. Basically, in this modification of the Kalman filter, we use numerically stable orthogonal transformations at every iteration of the algorithm. Specifically, the matrix $\mathbf{P}_{n|n}$ is propagated in its square-root form by applying the *Cholesky factorization*, according to which we may write

$$\mathbf{P}_{n|n} = \mathbf{P}_{n|n}^{1/2}\mathbf{P}_{n|n}^{T/2} \tag{14.39}$$

where the term $\mathbf{P}_{n|n}^{1/2}$ is reserved for a *lower triangular matrix* and $\mathbf{P}_{n|n}^{T/2}$ is the transposed term. In linear algebra, the *Cholesky factor* $\mathbf{P}_{n|n}^{1/2}$ is commonly referred to as the square root of the matrix $\mathbf{P}_{n,n}$. The very important point to note here is that the matrix product $\mathbf{P}_{n|n}^{1/2}\mathbf{P}_{n|n}^{T/2}$ is *not* likely to become indefinite, because the product of any square matrix and its transpose is always nonnegative definite. Indeed, even in the presence of numerical errors, the matrix conditioning of the Cholesky factor $\mathbf{P}_{n|n}^{1/2}$ is generally better than that of $\mathbf{P}_{n|n}$ itself.

Square-Root Implementation of the Kalman Filter

A lemma in matrix algebra, called the matrix factorization lemma, is pivotal to the derivation of square-root filtering algorithms. Consider any two L-by-M matrices $\mathbf{X}$ and $\mathbf{Y}$ with the dimension $L \leq M$. The *matrix factorization lemma* states the following (Stewart, 1973; Golub and Van Loan, 1996):

> The matrix equality $\mathbf{XX}^T = \mathbf{YY}^T$ holds if, and only if, there exists an orthogonal matrix $\boldsymbol{\Theta}$ such that

$$\mathbf{Y} = \mathbf{X}\boldsymbol{\Theta} \qquad (14.40)$$

To prove this lemma, we express the matrix product $\mathbf{YY}^T$ as

$$\begin{aligned} \mathbf{YY}^T &= \mathbf{X}\boldsymbol{\Theta}(\mathbf{X}\boldsymbol{\Theta})^T \\ &= \mathbf{X}\boldsymbol{\Theta}\boldsymbol{\Theta}^T\mathbf{X}^T \\ &= \mathbf{XX}^T \end{aligned}$$

In the last line of this equation, we invoked the defining property of the orthogonal matrix $\boldsymbol{\Theta}$:

> The product of an orthogonal matrix with its transpose is equal to the identity matrix.

As a corollary to this property, we may equivalently write

$$\boldsymbol{\Theta}^{-1} = \boldsymbol{\Theta}^T \qquad (14.41)$$

That is, the inverse of an orthogonal matrix is equal to its own transpose.

With the matrix factorization lemma at our disposal, we may now proceed with the derivation of the square-root covariance implementation of the Kalman filter. To begin, we first use Eq. (14.31), defining the gain matrix $\mathbf{G}(n)$, in Eq. (14.38), obtaining

$$\mathbf{P}_{n|n} = \mathbf{P}_{n|n-1} - \mathbf{P}_{n|n-1}\mathbf{B}_n^T\mathbf{R}_n^{-1}\mathbf{B}_n\mathbf{P}_{n|n-1} \qquad (14.42)$$

where the matrix $\mathbf{R}_n$ is itself defined by Eq. (14.22), reproduced here for convenience of presentation:

$$\mathbf{R}_n = \mathbf{B}_n\mathbf{P}_{n|n-1}\mathbf{B}_n^T + \mathbf{Q}_{v,n}$$

Examining the reformulated Riccati equation of Eq. (14.42), we find that the expression on its right-hand side consists of three distinct matrix terms:

M-by-M matrix: covariance matrix of the predicted state $\mathbf{P}_{n|n-1}$;

L-by-M matrix: measurement matrix $\mathbf{B}_n$ multiplied by $\mathbf{P}_{n|n-1}$;

L-by-L matrix: covariance matrix $\mathbf{R}_n$ of the innovations process.

Keeping in mind the different dimensionalities of these three matrix terms, we may order all three of them in a compatible way in the N-by-N block matrix

$$\begin{aligned} \mathbf{H}_n &= \left[\begin{array}{c|c} \mathbf{R}_n & \mathbf{B}_n\mathbf{P}_{n|n-1} \\ \hline \mathbf{P}_{n|n-1}\mathbf{B}_n^T & \mathbf{P}_{n|n-1} \end{array}\right] \\[2mm] &= \left[\begin{array}{c|c} \mathbf{Q}_{v,n} + \mathbf{B}_n\mathbf{P}_{n|n-1}\mathbf{B}_n^T & \mathbf{B}_n\mathbf{P}_{n|n-1} \\ \hline \mathbf{P}_{n|n-1}\mathbf{B}_n^T & \mathbf{P}_{n|n-1} \end{array}\right] \end{aligned} \qquad (14.43)$$

where, in the second line, we inserted the formula for $\mathbf{R}_n$. The size of the matrix in Eq. (14.43), denoted by N, equals $L + M$. The new block matrix $\mathbf{H}_n$ is nonnegative-definite by definition. We may therefore apply the Cholesky factorization to it, obtaining

$$\mathbf{H}_n = \begin{bmatrix} \mathbf{Q}_{v,n}^{1/2} & \mathbf{B}_n\mathbf{P}_{n|n-1}^{1/2} \\ \hline \mathbf{O} & \mathbf{P}_{n|n-1}^{1/2} \end{bmatrix} \begin{bmatrix} \mathbf{Q}_{v,n}^{1/2} & \mathbf{O}^T \\ \hline \mathbf{P}_{n|n-1}^{1/2}\mathbf{B}_n^T & \mathbf{P}_{n|n-1}^{1/2} \end{bmatrix} \tag{14.44}$$

where $\mathbf{P}_{n|n-1}^{1/2}$ is the square root of the covariance matrix $\mathbf{P}_{n|n-1}$ and $\mathbf{O}$ is a null matrix.

The matrix product on the right-hand side of Eq. (14.44) may be interpreted as the product of matrix $\mathbf{X}_n$, introduced earlier, and its transpose $\mathbf{X}_n^T$. The stage is therefore set for invoking the matrix factorization lemma, according to which the use of Eq. (14.40) yields

$$\underbrace{\begin{bmatrix} \mathbf{Q}_{v,n}^{1/2} & \mathbf{B}_n\mathbf{P}_{n|n-1}^{1/2} \\ \hline \mathbf{O} & \mathbf{P}_{n|n-1}^{1/2} \end{bmatrix}}_{\mathbf{X}_n} \mathbf{\Theta}_n = \underbrace{\begin{bmatrix} \mathbf{Y}_{11,n} & \mathbf{O}^T \\ \hline \mathbf{Y}_{21,n} & \mathbf{Y}_{22,n} \end{bmatrix}}_{\mathbf{Y}_n} \tag{14.45}$$

where the matrix $\mathbf{\Theta}_n$ is an orthogonal matrix. To be more specific, $\mathbf{\Theta}_n$ is an orthogonal matrix that operates on $\mathbf{X}_n$ in such a way that the resulting matrix $\mathbf{Y}_n$ is a *lower triangular matrix*; that is, all the elements of $\mathbf{Y}_n$ above its main diagonal are zero. It is because of this action that the matrix $\mathbf{\Theta}_n$ is also referred to as an *orthogonal rotation*. Invoking the orthogonality property of $\mathbf{\Theta}_n$, we may expand on Eq. (14.45) by writing

$$\underbrace{\begin{bmatrix} \mathbf{Q}_{v,n}^{1/2} & \mathbf{B}_n\mathbf{P}_{n|n-1}^{1/2} \\ \hline \mathbf{O} & \mathbf{P}_{n|n-1}^{1/2} \end{bmatrix}}_{\mathbf{X}_n} \underbrace{\begin{bmatrix} \mathbf{Q}_{v,n}^{1/2} & \mathbf{O}^T \\ \hline \mathbf{P}_{n|n-1}^{1/2}\mathbf{B}_n^T & \mathbf{P}_{n|n-1}^{T/2} \end{bmatrix}}_{\mathbf{X}_n^T} = \underbrace{\begin{bmatrix} \mathbf{Y}_{11,n} & \mathbf{O}^T \\ \hline \mathbf{Y}_{21,n} & \mathbf{Y}_{22,n} \end{bmatrix}}_{\mathbf{Y}_n} \underbrace{\begin{bmatrix} \mathbf{Y}_{11,n}^T & \mathbf{Y}_{21,n}^T \\ \hline \mathbf{O}^T & \mathbf{Y}_{22,n}^T \end{bmatrix}}_{\mathbf{Y}_n^T} \tag{14.46}$$

Expanding the matrix products $\mathbf{X}_n\mathbf{X}_n^T$ and $\mathbf{Y}_n\mathbf{Y}_n^T$ and then equating corresponding terms in the two sides of Eq. (14.46), we get three identifies:

$$\mathbf{Q}_{v,n} + \mathbf{B}_n\mathbf{P}_{n|n-1}\mathbf{B}_n^T = \mathbf{Y}_{11,n}\mathbf{Y}_{11,n}^T \tag{14.47}$$

$$\mathbf{B}_n\mathbf{P}_{n|n-1} = \mathbf{Y}_{11,n}\mathbf{Y}_{21,n}^T \tag{14.48}$$

$$\mathbf{P}_{n|n-1} = \mathbf{Y}_{21,n}\mathbf{Y}_{21,n}^T + \mathbf{Y}_{22,n}\mathbf{Y}_{22,n}^T \tag{14.49}$$

The left-hand side of Eq. (14.47) is recognized as the covariance matrix $\mathbf{R}_n$, which is factorizable into $\mathbf{R}_n^{1/2}\mathbf{R}_n^{T/2}$. The identity in Eq. (14.47) is therefore satisfied by setting the first unknown as follows:

$$\mathbf{Y}_{11,n} = \mathbf{R}_n^{1/2} \tag{14.50}$$

Next, substituting this value of $\mathbf{Y}_{11,n}$ into the identify in Eq. (14.48) and solving for $\mathbf{Y}_{21,n}$, we find the second unknown:

$$\mathbf{Y}_{21,n} = \mathbf{P}_{n|n-1}\mathbf{B}_n^T\mathbf{R}_n^{-T/2} \tag{14.51}$$

In light of the definition of the Kalman gain $\mathbf{G}_n$, developed previously in Eq. (14.31), we may also express $\mathbf{Y}_{21,n}$ as

$$\mathbf{Y}_{21,n} = \mathbf{G}_n\mathbf{R}_n^{1/2} \tag{14.52}$$

Moreover, substituting the value of $\mathbf{Y}_{21,n}$ given in Eq. (14.51) into Eq. (14.49), solving for the matrix product $\mathbf{Y}_{22,n}\mathbf{Y}_{22,n}^T$, and then using Eq. (14.42), we get

$$\mathbf{Y}_{22,n}\mathbf{Y}_{22,n}^T = \mathbf{P}_{n|n-1} - \mathbf{P}_{n|n-1}\mathbf{B}_n^T\mathbf{R}_n^{-1}\mathbf{B}_n\mathbf{P}_{n|n-1}$$
$$= \mathbf{P}_{n|n}$$

Factorizing the covariance matrix $\mathbf{P}_{n,n}$ into $\mathbf{P}_{n|n}^{1/2}\mathbf{P}_{n|n}^{T/2}$, we find the third unknown:

$$\mathbf{Y}_{22,n} = \mathbf{P}_{n|n}^{1/2} \tag{14.53}$$

With all three nonzero submatrices of $\mathbf{Y}_n$ determined, we may now fill in the unknowns in Eq. (14.45), obtaining

$$\begin{bmatrix} \mathbf{Q}_{v,n}^{1/2} & \mathbf{B}_n\mathbf{P}_{n,n-1}^{1/2} \\ \hline \mathbf{0} & \mathbf{P}_{n|n-1}^{1/2} \end{bmatrix}\mathbf{\Theta}_n = \begin{bmatrix} \mathbf{R}_n^{1/2} & \mathbf{0}^T \\ \hline \mathbf{G}_n\mathbf{R}_n^{1/2} & \mathbf{P}_{n|n}^{1/2} \end{bmatrix} \tag{14.54}$$

In the final solution derived in Eq. (14.54), we may now distinguish between two well-defined arrays of numbers that deserve close scrutiny:

1. *Prearray.* This array of numbers, on the left-hand side of Eq. (14.54), is operated on by the orthogonal rotation $\mathbf{\Theta}_n$, which is designed to *annihilate* the submatrix $\mathbf{B}_n\mathbf{P}_{n|n-1}^{1/2}$, element by element. The measurement matrix $\mathbf{B}_n$ and the covariance matrix of the measurement noise, $\mathbf{Q}_{v,n}$, are both given parameters. The square root $\mathbf{P}_{n|n-1}^{1/2}$, being an *old value that is being updated*, is also known. Therefore, the submatrices constituting the prearray are all known at time n.

2. *Postarray.* This second array of numbers, on the right-hand side of Eq. (14.54), is a lower triangular matrix that results from the annihilation performed by the orthogonal rotation on the prearray. In particular, the inclusion of the square root $\mathbf{Q}_{v,n}^{1/2}$ in the prearray induces the generation of two useful matrices:
   - the matrix $\mathbf{R}_n^{1/2}$, representing the square root of the covariance matrix of the innovations process $\mathbf{\alpha}_n$;
   - the matrix product $\mathbf{G}_n\mathbf{R}_n^{1/2}$, which makes it possible to compute the Kalman gain.

   One other important matrix resulting from computing the postarray is the square root of the filtering-error covariance matrix, $\mathbf{P}_{n|n}^{1/2}$.

With all of this information extracted from the postarray, we are ready to summarize the computations involved in the square-root covariance filtering algorithm, as listed in Table 14.3. A complete *recursion cycle* of the algorithm consists of the transformation of the prearray into the postarray and the computation of updated parameters, which are respectively listed under items 3 and 4 of the table. From this table, it is apparent that the algorithm does indeed propagate the square root of the prediction-error covariance matrix—namely, $\mathbf{P}_{n|n-1}^{1/2}$.

Givens Rotations

Thus far in formulating the square-root covariance filtering algorithm, we have not paid attention to the way in which the orthogonal matrix $\mathbf{\Theta}$ is to be specified, other than to require

TABLE 14.3 Summary of Computations in the Square-Root Filtering Algorithm

1. *Given parameters:*
   Transition matrix: $\mathbf{A}_{n+1,n}$
   Measurement matrix: $\mathbf{B}_n$
   Covariance matrix of measurement noise: $\mathbf{Q}_{v,n}$
   Covariance matrix of dynamic noise: $\mathbf{Q}_{\omega,n}$

2. *Old values of parameters to be updated:*
   Predicted estimate of the state: $\hat{\mathbf{x}}_{n|n-1}$
   Square root of the prediction-error covariance matrix: $\mathbf{P}_{n|n-1}^{1/2}$

3. *Orthogonal rotation of the prearray into the postarray:*
$$\begin{bmatrix} \mathbf{Q}_{v,n}^{1/2} & \mathbf{B}_n\mathbf{P}_{n,n-1}^{1/2} \\ \hline \mathbf{0} & \mathbf{P}_{n|n-1}^{1/2} \end{bmatrix}\boldsymbol{\Theta}_n = \begin{bmatrix} \mathbf{R}_n^{1/2} & \mathbf{O}^T \\ \hline \mathbf{G}_n\mathbf{R}_n^{1/2} & \mathbf{P}_{n|n}^{1/2} \end{bmatrix}$$

4. *Updated parameters:*
$$\mathbf{G}_n = [\mathbf{G}_n\mathbf{R}_n^{1/2}][\mathbf{R}_n^{1/2}]^{-1}$$
$$\boldsymbol{\alpha}_n = \mathbf{y}_n - \mathbf{B}_n\hat{\mathbf{x}}_{n|n-1}$$
$$\hat{\mathbf{x}}_{n|n} = \hat{\mathbf{x}}_{n|n-1} + \mathbf{G}_n\boldsymbol{\alpha}_n$$
$$\hat{\mathbf{x}}_{n+1|n} = \mathbf{A}_{n+1|n}\hat{\mathbf{x}}_{n|n}$$
$$\mathbf{P}_{n|n} = \mathbf{P}_{n|n}^{1/2}[\mathbf{P}_{n|n}^{1/2}]^T$$
$$\mathbf{P}_{n+1|n} = [\mathbf{A}_{n+1|n}\mathbf{P}_{n|n}^{1/2} \mid \mathbf{Q}_{\omega,n}^{1/2}]\begin{bmatrix} \mathbf{P}_{n|n}^{T/2}\mathbf{A}_{n\pm1|n}^T \\ \mathbf{Q}_{\omega,n}^{T/2} \end{bmatrix}$$

Notes:
1. Under point 4, all the matrices inside the brackets are extracted from the postarray and known parameters.
2. In writing the updated parameters, we have made use of the corresponding computational formulas of Table 14.2.

that the prearray should be transformed into a lower triangular postarray through a process of annihilations. An elegant way of performing this process is to use *Givens rotations*, the application of which proceeds in a step-by-step manner (Golub and Van Loan, 1996).

Under this procedure, the orthogonal matrix $\boldsymbol{\Theta}$ is expressed as a product of N orthogonal rotation components, as shown by

$$\boldsymbol{\Theta} = \prod_{k=1}^{N}\boldsymbol{\Theta}_k$$

where we have ignored reference to discrete time n to simplify the presentation. The characteristics of each rotation component are as follows:

1. Except for four *strategic elements*, the diagonal elements of $\boldsymbol{\Theta}_k$ are all unity, and the off-diagonal elements are all zero.
2. The subscript k in $\boldsymbol{\Theta}_k$ refers to a *pivotal point*, around which the four strategic elements of $\boldsymbol{\Theta}_k$ are located. As a rule, the pivotal point is always located on the main diagonal of the prearray.
3. Two of the strategic elements of $\boldsymbol{\Theta}_k$ are *cosine parameters*, and the remaining two are *sine parameters*. To add mathematical significance to these cosine and sine

parameters, suppose that the requirement is to annihilate the kl-th element of the pre-array, where k refers to row and l refers to column. Then, the corresponding cosine (diagonal) parameters θ_{kk} and θ_{ll} are assigned the same value, but one of the sine (off-diagonal) parameters is assigned a negative value, as shown by the two-by-two matrix

$$\begin{bmatrix} \theta_{kk} & \theta_{kl} \\ \theta_{lk} & \theta_{ll} \end{bmatrix} = \begin{bmatrix} c_k & -s_k \\ s_k & c_k \end{bmatrix} \tag{14.55}$$

All four parameters are real numbers, which is a requirement for satisfying the constraint

$$c_k^2 + s_k^2 = 1 \qquad \text{for all } k \tag{14.56}$$

The following example illustrates the steps involved in the transformation of a prearray into a lower triangular postarray.

EXAMPLE 1.   Givens rotations for 3-by-3 prearray

Consider the 3-by-3 prearray $\mathbf{X}$, which is to be transformed into a lower triangular 3-by-3 postarray $\mathbf{Y}$. The transformation will proceed in three steps.

Step 1: For this first step, we write

$$\begin{bmatrix} x_{11} & x_{12} & x_{13} \\ 0 & x_{22} & x_{23} \\ 0 & x_{32} & x_{33} \end{bmatrix} \begin{bmatrix} c_1 & -s_1 & 0 \\ s_1 & c_1 & 0 \\ 0 & 0 & 1 \end{bmatrix} = \begin{bmatrix} u_{11} & u_{12} & u_{13} \\ u_{21} & u_{22} & u_{23} \\ u_{31} & u_{32} & u_{33} \end{bmatrix} \tag{14.57}$$

Prearray of step 1   1st Givens   Postarray of step 1
rotation

where the two zeros in the prearray follow from Eq. (14.54), and

$$u_{12} = -x_{11}s_1 + x_{12}c_1$$

The requirement is to set $u_{12} = 0$, for which the following condition must hold:

$$s_1 = \frac{x_{12}}{x_{11}} c_1$$

Hence, by setting $c_1^2 + s_1^2 = 1$ and solving for c_1 and s_1, we define the first orthogonal rotation used in Eq. (14.57) as

$$\begin{aligned} c_1 &= \frac{x_{11}}{\sqrt{x_{11}^2 + x_{12}^2}} \\ s_1 &= \frac{x_{12}}{\sqrt{x_{11}^2 + x_{12}^2}} \end{aligned} \tag{14.58}$$

Step 2: For this second step, we write

$$\begin{bmatrix} u_{11} & 0 & u_{13} \\ u_{21} & u_{22} & u_{23} \\ u_{31} & u_{32} & u_{33} \end{bmatrix} \begin{bmatrix} c_2 & 0 & -s_2 \\ 0 & 1 & 0 \\ s_2 & 0 & c_2 \end{bmatrix} = \begin{bmatrix} v_{11} & 0 & v_{13} \\ v_{21} & v_{22} & v_{23} \\ v_{31} & v_{32} & v_{33} \end{bmatrix} \tag{14.59}$$

Prearray of step 2   2nd Givens   Postarray of step 2
rotation

where

$$v_{13} = -u_{11}s_2 + u_{13}c_2$$

The requirement is to set $v_{13} = 0$, for which the following condition must hold:

$$s_2 = \frac{u_{13}}{u_{11}}c_2$$

Hence, by setting $s_2^2 + c_2^2 = 1$ and solving for s_2 and c_2, we define the second orthogonal rotation used in Eq. (14.59) as

$$c_2 = \frac{u_{11}}{\sqrt{u_{11}^2 + u_{13}^2}}$$

$$s_2 = \frac{u_{13}}{\sqrt{u_{11}^2 + u_{13}^2}} \tag{14.60}$$

Step 3:   For this third and final, step, we write

$$
\underbrace{\begin{bmatrix} v_{11} & 0 & 0 \\ v_{21} & v_{22} & v_{23} \\ v_{31} & v_{32} & v_{33} \end{bmatrix}}_{\text{Prearray of step 3}}
\underbrace{\begin{bmatrix} 1 & 0 & 0 \\ 0 & c_3 & -s_3 \\ 0 & s_3 & c_3 \end{bmatrix}}_{\text{3rd Givens rotation}}
=
\underbrace{\begin{bmatrix} y_{11} & 0 & 0 \\ y_{21} & y_{22} & y_{23} \\ y_{31} & y_{32} & y_{33} \end{bmatrix}}_{\text{Postarray of step 3}}
\tag{14.61}
$$

where

$$y_{23} = -v_{22}s_3 + v_{23}c_3$$

The requirement is to set $y_{23} = 0$, for which the following condition must hold:

$$s_3 = \frac{v_{23}}{v_{22}}c_3$$

Hence, by setting $s_3^2 + c_3^2 = 1$ and solving for s_3 and c_3, we define the third orthogonal rotation used in Eq. (14.61) as

$$c_3 = \frac{v_{22}}{\sqrt{v_{22}^2 + v_{23}^2}}$$

$$s_3 = \frac{v_{23}}{\sqrt{v_{22}^2 + v_{23}^2}} \tag{14.62}$$

The final product of the three-step transformation is the lower triangular postarray

$$\mathbf{Y} = \begin{bmatrix} y_{11} & 0 & 0 \\ y_{21} & y_{22} & 0 \\ y_{31} & y_{32} & y_{33} \end{bmatrix}$$

which is the desired result.   ∎

14.5   THE EXTENDED KALMAN FILTER

The Kalman filtering problem, studied in Section 14.3, addressed the state estimation of a dynamic system described by the linear state-space model of Eqs. (14.4) and (14.5). If, however, the dynamic system is intrinsically nonlinear, but Gaussian, as described in Eqs. (14.7) and (14.8), we may extend the use of the Kalman filter through *linearization* of the nonlinear state-space model of the system. The resulting state estimator is correspondingly referred to as the *extended Kalman filter*. Such an extension is feasible by virtue of the fact that the Kalman filter is described in terms of difference equations in the case of discrete-time systems.

To set the stage for derivation of the extended Kalman filter, we will first reformulate the equations defining the Kalman filter into a slightly different form that is more convenient for our present discussion.

Reformulation of the Kalman Filter

We begin the reformulation by using Eqs. (14.9) and (14.18) to redefine the innovation process as

$$\alpha_n = \mathbf{y}_n - \mathbf{b}_n(\hat{\mathbf{x}}_{n|n-1}) \tag{14.63}$$

Next, we make the following observation: Suppose that instead of the state equations of Eqs. (14.4) and (14.5) used to derive the Kalman filter, we are given the following alternative form of the state-space model:

$$\mathbf{x}_{n+1} = \mathbf{A}_{n+1,n}\mathbf{x}_n + \boldsymbol{\omega}_n + \boldsymbol{\xi}_n \tag{14.64}$$

and

$$\mathbf{y}_n = \mathbf{B}_n\mathbf{x}_n + \boldsymbol{\nu}_n \tag{14.65}$$

The measurement model of Eq. (14.65) is exactly the same as that of Eq. (14.5). However, the system model of Eq. (14.64) differs from that of Eq. (14.4) by virtue of the new term $\boldsymbol{\xi}_n$, which is assumed to be a *known (i.e., non-random) vector*. In this case, we readily find that the Kalman filter equations apply, except for a modification of Eq. (14.32), which now takes the form

$$\hat{\mathbf{x}}_{n+1|n} = \mathbf{A}_{n+1,n}\hat{\mathbf{x}}_{n|n} + \boldsymbol{\xi}_n \tag{14.66}$$

The need for this modification arises in the derivation of the extended Kalman filter, to be discussed next.

Preliminary Steps Leading to Derivation of the Extended Kalman Filter

As mentioned previously, the extended Kalman filter (EKF) is an *approximate* solution that allows us to extend the Kalman filtering idea to *nonlinear state-space models* (Jazwinski, 1970; Maybeck, 1982). The nonlinear state-space model considered here has the form described in Eqs. (14.7) and (14.8), reproduced here merely for convenience of presentation:

$$\mathbf{x}_{n+1} = \mathbf{a}_n(\mathbf{x}_n) + \boldsymbol{\omega}_n \tag{14.67}$$

and

$$\mathbf{y}_n = \mathbf{b}_n(\mathbf{x}_n) + \boldsymbol{\nu}_n \tag{14.68}$$

As before, the dynamic noise $\boldsymbol{\omega}_n$ and measurement noise $\boldsymbol{\nu}_n$ are uncorrelated zero-mean Gaussian-noise processes with covariance matrices $\mathbf{Q}_{\omega,n}$ and $\mathbf{Q}_{\nu,n}$, respectively. Moreover, the nonlinear model may vary with time, as signified by the subscript n in the vectorial functions $\mathbf{a}_n(\cdot)$ and $\mathbf{b}_n(\cdot)$

The basic idea of the EKF is to linearize the state-space model of Eqs. (14.67) and (14.68) at each time instant around *the most recent state estimate*. This particular estimate is taken to be either a filtered-estimate or a predicted estimate, depending on which functional is being considered in the course of linearization. Once a linearized model is obtained, we are ready to apply the Kalman filter equations.

The approximation proceeds in two stages:

Stage I. Construction of new matrices

Through partial differentiations, the following two matrices are constructed:

$$\mathbf{A}_{n+1,n} = \left. \frac{\partial \mathbf{a}_n(\mathbf{x})}{\partial \mathbf{x}} \right|_{\mathbf{x}=\hat{\mathbf{x}}_{n|n}} \tag{14.69}$$

and

$$\mathbf{B}_n = \left. \frac{\partial \mathbf{b}_n(\mathbf{x})}{\partial \mathbf{x}} \right|_{\mathbf{x}=\hat{\mathbf{x}}_{n|n-1}} \tag{14.70}$$

In more specific terms, the *ij*-th entry of the transition matrix $\mathbf{A}_{n+1,n}$ is equal to the partial derivative of the *i*th component of the vector-valued functional $\mathbf{a}_n(\mathbf{x})$ with respect to the *j*th component of $\mathbf{x}$. Likewise, the *ij*-th entry of the measurement matrix $\mathbf{B}_n$ is equal to the partial derivative of the *i*th component of the vector-valued function $\mathbf{b}_n(\mathbf{x})$ with respect to the *j*th component of $\mathbf{x}$. In the former case, the derivatives are evaluated at the filtered state $\hat{\mathbf{x}}_{n|n}$, whereas in the latter case, the derivatives are evaluated at the predicted estimate $\hat{\mathbf{x}}_{n|n-1}$. The entries of both matrices $\mathbf{A}_{n+1,n}$ and $\mathbf{B}_n$ are computable, given the availability of $\hat{\mathbf{x}}_{n|n}$ and $\hat{\mathbf{x}}_{n|n-1}$.

EXAMPLE 2   Two-dimensional nonlinear model

Consider a dynamic system described by the following two-dimensional nonlinear state-space model:

$$\begin{bmatrix} x_{1,n+1} \\ x_{2,n+1} \end{bmatrix} = \begin{bmatrix} x_{1,n} + x_{2,n}^2 \\ nx_{1,n} - x_{1,n} x_{2,n} \end{bmatrix} + \begin{bmatrix} \omega_{1,n} \\ \omega_{2,n} \end{bmatrix}$$

$$y_n = x_{1,n} x_{2,n}^2 + v_n$$

In this example, we have

$$\mathbf{a}_n(\mathbf{x}_n) = \begin{bmatrix} x_{1,n} + x_{2,n}^2 \\ nx_{1,n} - x_{1,n} x_{2,n} \end{bmatrix}$$

and

$$\mathbf{b}_n(\mathbf{x}_n) = x_{1,n} x_{2,n}^2$$

Applying the definitions of Eqs. (14.69) and (14.70), we readily obtain

$$\mathbf{A}_{n+1,n} = \begin{bmatrix} 1 & 2\hat{x}_{2,n|n} \\ n - \hat{x}_{2,n|n} & -\hat{x}_{1,n|n} \end{bmatrix}$$

and

$$\mathbf{B}_n = \begin{bmatrix} \hat{x}_{2,n|n-1}^2 & 2\hat{x}_{1,n|n-1}\hat{x}_{2,n|n-1} \end{bmatrix}$$ ∎

Stage II. Linearization of the state-space model

Once the transition matrix $\mathbf{A}_{n+1,n}$ and the measurement matrix $\mathbf{B}_n$ have been constructed, they are used in a *first-order Taylor approximation* of the nonlinear functionals $\mathbf{a}_n(\mathbf{x}_n)$ and $\mathbf{b}_n(\mathbf{x}_n)$ around the state estimates $\hat{\mathbf{x}}_{n+1,n}$ and $\hat{\mathbf{x}}_{n|n}$, respectively. Specifically, we write

$$\mathbf{a}_n(\mathbf{x}_n) \approx \mathbf{a}_n(\hat{\mathbf{x}}_{n|n}) + \mathbf{A}_{n+1,n}[\mathbf{x}_n - \hat{\mathbf{x}}_{n|n}] \tag{14.71}$$

and

$$\mathbf{b}_n(\mathbf{x}_n) \approx \mathbf{b}_n(\hat{\mathbf{x}}_{n|n-1}) + \mathbf{B}_n[\mathbf{x}_n - \hat{\mathbf{x}}_{n|n-1}] \tag{14.72}$$

With the foregoing approximate expressions at hand, we may now proceed to approximate the nonlinear state equations of Eqs. (14.64) and (14.65). The respective results of the approximations are

$$\mathbf{x}_{n+1} \approx \mathbf{A}_{n+1,n}\mathbf{x}_n + \boldsymbol{\omega}_n + \boldsymbol{\xi}_n \tag{14.73}$$

and

$$\bar{\mathbf{y}}_n \approx \mathbf{B}_n\mathbf{x}_n + \boldsymbol{\nu}_n \tag{14.74}$$

where we have introduced two new quantities: $\boldsymbol{\xi}_n$ in the system model, and $\bar{\mathbf{y}}_n$ in the measurement model. These two new quantities are themselves defined as

$$\boldsymbol{\xi}_n = \mathbf{a}_n(\hat{\mathbf{x}}_{n|n}) - \mathbf{A}_{n+1,n}\hat{\mathbf{x}}_{n|n} \tag{14.75}$$

and

$$\bar{\mathbf{y}}_n = \mathbf{y}_n - [\mathbf{b}_n(\hat{\mathbf{x}}_{n|n-1}) - \mathbf{B}_n\hat{\mathbf{x}}_{n|n-1}] \tag{14.76}$$

where $\mathbf{a}_n(\hat{\mathbf{x}}_{n|n})$ and $\mathbf{b}_n(\hat{\mathbf{x}}_{n|n-1})$ are the values of the given nonlinear functions $\mathbf{a}_n(\mathbf{x}_n)$ and $\mathbf{b}_n(\mathbf{x}_n)$ evaluated at $\mathbf{x}_n = \hat{\mathbf{x}}_{n|n}$ and $\mathbf{x}_n = \hat{\mathbf{x}}_{n|n-1}$, respectively. If we recall that we also know $\mathbf{A}_{n+1,n}$ from Eq. (14.69), it therefore follows that the entries in the new additive term $\boldsymbol{\xi}_n$ are all *known* at time n, which confirms the validity of our previous observation. Likewise, since $\mathbf{B}_n$ is known from Eq. (14.70), all the entries in the second new term $\bar{\mathbf{y}}_n$ are also known at time n; we may therefore regard $\bar{\mathbf{y}}_n$ as the effective *observation vector of the linearized model* at time n.

Derivation of the Extended Kalman Filter

The *approximate state-space model* of Eqs. (14.73) and (14.74) is a linear model of the same mathematical form as that described in Eqs. (14.64) and (14.65), with only one minor difference: The observation $\mathbf{y}(n)$ in Eq. (14.65) is replaced with the new observation $\bar{\mathbf{y}}_n$ for the linearized model. Indeed, it is with this objective in mind that we had previously formulated the state-space model of Eqs. (14.64) and (14.65) in the first place.

Hence, the defining equations for the EKF follow simply by modifying the second and fourth equations of Table 14.2 on the Kalman filter in the manner described in Table 14.4.

TABLE 14.4 Summary of the Extended Kalman Filter

Input process:
 Observations = $\{\mathbf{y}_1, \mathbf{y}_2, ..., \mathbf{y}_n\}$

Known parameters:
 Nonlinear state vectorial function = $\mathbf{a}_n(\mathbf{x}_n)$
 Nonlinear measurement vectorial function = $\mathbf{b}_n(\mathbf{x}_n)$
 Covariance matrix of process noise vector = $\mathbf{Q}_{\omega,n}$
 Covariance matrix of measurement noise vector = $\mathbf{Q}_{v,n}$

Computation: $n = 1, 2, 3, ...$

$$\mathbf{G}_n = \mathbf{P}_{n,n-1}\mathbf{B}_n^T[\mathbf{B}_n\mathbf{P}_{n,n-1}\mathbf{B}_n^T + \mathbf{Q}_{v,n}]^{-1}$$
$$\boldsymbol{\alpha}_n = \mathbf{y}_n - \mathbf{b}_n(\hat{\mathbf{x}}_{n|n-1})$$
$$\hat{\mathbf{x}}_{n|n} = \hat{\mathbf{x}}_{n|n-1} + \mathbf{G}_n\boldsymbol{\alpha}_n$$
$$\hat{\mathbf{x}}_{n+1|n} = \mathbf{a}_n(\hat{\mathbf{x}}_{n|n})$$
$$\mathbf{P}_{n|n} = \mathbf{P}_{n|n-1} - \mathbf{G}_n\mathbf{B}_n\mathbf{P}_{n|n-1}$$
$$\mathbf{P}_{n+1|n} = \mathbf{A}_{n+1,n}\mathbf{P}_{n|n}\mathbf{A}_{n+1,n}^T + \mathbf{Q}_{\omega,n}$$

Notes:
1. The linearized matrices $\mathbf{A}_{n+1,n}$ and $\mathbf{B}_n$ are computed from their nonlinear counterparts $\mathbf{a}_n(\mathbf{x}_n)$ and $\mathbf{b}_n(\mathbf{x}_n)$ by using Eqs. (14.69) and (14.70), respectively.
2. The values $\mathbf{a}_n(\hat{\mathbf{x}}_{n|n})$ and $\mathbf{b}_n(\hat{\mathbf{x}}_{n|n-1})$ are obtained by substituting the filtered state estimate $\hat{\mathbf{x}}_{n|n}$ and the predicted state estimate $\hat{\mathbf{x}}_{n|n-1}$ for the state $\mathbf{x}_n$ in the nonlinear vectorial functions $\mathbf{a}_n(\mathbf{x}_n)$ and $\mathbf{b}_n(\mathbf{x}_n)$, respectively.
3. Examining the order of iterations in Table 14.4, we now see the reason for evaluating $\mathbf{A}_{n+1,n}$ and $\mathbf{B}_n$ in the manner described in Eqs. (14.69) and (14.70).

Initial conditions:
$$\hat{\mathbf{x}}_{1|0} = \mathbb{E}[\mathbf{x}_1]$$
$$\mathbf{P}_{1,0} = \mathbb{E}[(\mathbf{x}_1 - \mathbb{E}[\mathbf{x}_1])(\mathbf{x}_1 - \mathbb{E}[\mathbf{x}_1])^T] = \mathbf{\Pi}_0$$

where $\mathbf{\Pi}_0 = \delta^{-1}\mathbf{I}$, and δ is a small positive constant and $\mathbf{I}$ is the identity matrix.

Summarizing Remarks on the Extended Kalman Filter

The extended Kalman filter is attractive for nonlinear state estimation for two reasons:

1. It builds on the framework of Kalman filter theory in a principled way.
2. It is relatively simple to understand and therefore straightforward to put into practical use, for which it has established a long track record.

However, it has two fundamental drawbacks that tend to limit its usefulness:

1. For the extended Kalman filter to function satisfactorily, the nonlinearity of the state-space model has to be of a *mild* sort, so as to justify the use of the first-order Taylor series expansion, upon which its theory is built.
2. Its derivation requires knowledge of first-order partial derivatives (i.e., the Jacobians) of the state-space model of the nonlinear dynamic system under study; however, for many practical applications, the computation of Jacobians is undesirable or simply not feasible.

To address the limitations of the extended Kalman filter, we find it instructive to describe the Bayesian approach to state estimation in the next section.

14.6   THE BAYESIAN FILTER

The adoption of a Bayesian filter to solve the state estimation of a dynamic system, be it linear or nonlinear, is motivated by the fact that it provides a *general unifying framework for sequential state estimation*, at least in a conceptual sense, hence the title of the chapter.

Naturally, probability theory is central to the Bayesian approach to state estimation. To simplify the presentation, henceforth, we use the term "distribution" to refer to a probability density function. Moreover, referring back to the system (state) model of Eq. (14.1) and the measurement model of Eq. (14.2), we use the following notation[3]:

$\mathbf{Y}_n$ = *sequence of observations*, denoting $\{\mathbf{y}_i\}_{i=1}^n$.

$p(\mathbf{x}_n|\mathbf{Y}_{n-1})$ = *predictive distribution* of the state $\mathbf{x}_n$ at the current time n, given the entire sequence of observations up to and including $\mathbf{y}_{n-1}$.

$p(\mathbf{x}_n|\mathbf{Y}_n)$ = *posterior distribution* of the current state $\mathbf{x}_n$, given the entire sequence of observations up to and including the current time n; this distribution is commonly referred to simply as the "posterior."

$p(\mathbf{x}_n|\mathbf{x}_{n-1})$ = *transition-state distribution* of the current state $\mathbf{x}_n$, given the immediate past state $\mathbf{x}_{n-1}$; this distribution is commonly referred to as the "transition prior" or simply "prior."

$l(\mathbf{y}_n|\mathbf{x}_n)$ = *likelihood function* of the current observation $\mathbf{y}_n$, given the current state $\mathbf{x}_n$.

For the derivation of the Bayesian filter, the only assumption that we will make is that the evolution of the state is *Markovian*; this assumption is also implicitly embodied in the formulation of the Kalman filter and its variants discussed in preceding sections of the chapter. Basically, the assumption embodies the combination of two conditions:

1. Given the sequence of states $\mathbf{x}_0, \mathbf{x}_1, ..., \mathbf{x}_{n-1}, \mathbf{x}_n$, the current state $\mathbf{x}_n$ depends only on the immediate past state $\mathbf{x}_{n-1}$ through the state-transition distribution $p(\mathbf{x}_n|\mathbf{x}_{n-1})$. The *initial state* $\mathbf{x}_0$ is distributed according to

$$p(\mathbf{x}_0|\mathbf{y}_0) = p(\mathbf{x}_0)$$

2. The observations $\mathbf{y}_1, \mathbf{y}_2, ..., \mathbf{y}_n$ are conditionally dependent only on the corresponding states $\mathbf{x}_1, \mathbf{x}_2, ..., \mathbf{x}_n$; this assumption implies that the conditional joint likelihood function of the observations (i.e., the joint distribution of all the observations conditional upon all the states up to and including time n) factors as

$$l(\mathbf{y}_1, \mathbf{y}_2, ..., \mathbf{y}_n|\mathbf{x}_1, \mathbf{x}_2, ..., \mathbf{x}_n) = \prod_{i=1}^n l(\mathbf{y}_i|\mathbf{x}_i) \tag{14.77}$$

The posterior distribution $p(\mathbf{x}_n|\mathbf{Y}_n)$ plays a key role in Bayesian analysis in that it embodies the entire knowledge that we have about the state $\mathbf{x}_n$ at time n *after* having received the *entire* observation sequence $\mathbf{Y}_n$. Accordingly, $p(\mathbf{x}_n|\mathbf{Y}_n)$ contains all the information necessary for state estimation. Suppose, for example, we wish to determine the *filtered estimate* of the state $\mathbf{x}_n$, optimized in the minimum mean-square error (MMSE) sense; according to the *Bayes estimator*, [4] the desired solution is

$$\hat{\mathbf{x}}_{n|n} = \mathbb{E}_p[\mathbf{x}_n|\mathbf{Y}_n]$$

$$= \int \mathbf{x}_n p(\mathbf{x}_n|\mathbf{Y}_n)d\mathbf{x}_n \tag{14.78}$$

Correspondingly, for an assessment of accuracy of the filtered estimate $\hat{\mathbf{x}}_{n|n}$, we compute the *covariance matrix*

$$\mathbf{P}_{n|n} = \mathbb{E}_p[(\mathbf{x}_n - \hat{\mathbf{x}}_{n|n})(\mathbf{x}_n - \hat{\mathbf{x}}_{n|n})^T]$$

$$= \int (\mathbf{x}_n - \hat{\mathbf{x}}_{n|n})(\mathbf{x}_n - \hat{\mathbf{x}}_{n|n})^T p(\mathbf{x}_n|\mathbf{Y}_n)d\mathbf{x}_n \tag{14.79}$$

With *computational efficiency* being a compelling practical factor, there is a strong desire to compute the filtered estimate $\hat{\mathbf{x}}_{n|n}$ and related parameters in a *recursive* manner. Suppose that we have the posterior distribution of the state $\mathbf{x}_{n-1}$ at time $n-1$ as $p(\mathbf{x}_{n-1}|\mathbf{Y}_{n-1})$. Then the updated value of the posterior distribution of the state at time n is governed by two basis time-steps:

1. *Time update*, which involves computing the *predictive distribution* of $\mathbf{x}_n$, given the observations sequence $\mathbf{Y}_{n-1}$, as shown by

$$\underbrace{p(\mathbf{x}_n|\mathbf{Y}_{n-1})}_{\text{Predictive distribution}} = \int \underbrace{p(\mathbf{x}_n|\mathbf{x}_{n-1})}_{\text{Prior}}\underbrace{p(\mathbf{x}_{n-1}|\mathbf{Y}_{n-1})}_{\text{Old posterior}}d\mathbf{x}_{n-1} \tag{14.80}$$

This formula is justified as follows by the basic laws of probability theory: Multiplication of the old posterior distribution $p(\mathbf{x}_{n-1}|\mathbf{Y}_{n-1})$ by the prior $p(\mathbf{x}_n|\mathbf{x}_{n-1})$ results in a joint distribution of the old state $\mathbf{x}_{n-1}$ and the current state $\mathbf{x}_n$ conditional upon $\mathbf{Y}_{n-1}$. Integrating this joint distribution with respect to $\mathbf{x}_{n-1}$ yields the predictive distribution $p(\mathbf{x}_n|\mathbf{Y}_{n-1})$.

2. *Measurement update*, which computes the updated posterior distribution $p(\mathbf{x}_n|\mathbf{Y}_n)$ by exploiting information about the current state $\mathbf{x}_n$ that is contained in the new observation $\mathbf{y}_n$. In particular, applying the well-known *Bayes theorem* to the predictive distribution $p(\mathbf{x}_n|\mathbf{Y}_{n-1})$ yields

$$\underbrace{p(\mathbf{x}_n|\mathbf{Y}_n)}_{\text{Updated posterior}} = \frac{1}{Z_n}\underbrace{p(\mathbf{x}_n|\mathbf{Y}_{n-1})}_{\text{Predictive distribution}}\underbrace{l(\mathbf{y}_n|\mathbf{x}_n)}_{\text{Likelihood function}} \tag{14.81}$$

where

$$Z_n = p(\mathbf{y}_n|\mathbf{Y}_{n-1})$$

$$= \int l(\mathbf{y}_n|\mathbf{x}_n)p(\mathbf{x}_n|\mathbf{Y}_{n-1})d\mathbf{x}_n \tag{14.82}$$

is a *normalizing constant* (also referred to as the *partition function*); it ensures that the total volume under the multidimensional curve of the posterior distribution $p(\mathbf{x}_n|\mathbf{Y}_n)$ is unity, as it should be. The sequence of normalization constants $\{Z_i\}_{i=1}^n$

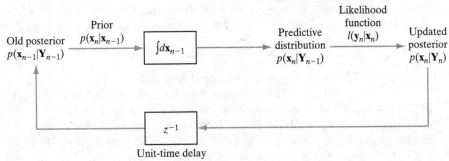

FIGURE 14.4 Block diagram of the Bayesian filter, with its updated posterior $p(\mathbf{x}_n|\mathbf{Y}_n)$ as the output of interest.

produces the joint *log likelihood* of the corresponding sequence of observations $\{\mathbf{Y}_i\}_{i=1}^{N}$, as shown by

$$\log(p(\mathbf{y}_1, \mathbf{y}_2, ..., \mathbf{y}_n)) = \sum_{i=1}^{n} \log(Z_i) \qquad (14.83)$$

The formulas of Eqs. (14.80) through (14.83) are all consequences of the Markovian assumption described previously.

The time update and measurement update are both carried out at every time-step throughout the computation of the Bayesian model. In effect, they constitute a *recursion*, or *cycle*, of the computation, as depicted in Fig. 14.4; the factor Z_n has been left out for convenience of presentation.

Approximate Bayesian Filtering

The Bayesian filter of Fig. 14.4 is *optimal* in a conceptual sense, with two interesting properties:

1. The model operates in a *recursive* manner by propagating the posterior distribution $p(\mathbf{x}_n|\mathbf{Y}_n)$.
2. Knowledge of the model about the state $\mathbf{x}_n$, extracted from the entire observations process $\mathbf{Y}_n$, is completely contained in the posterior distribution $p(\mathbf{x}_n|\mathbf{Y}_n)$.

With this distribution as the focus of attention, we now lay down the groundwork for our filtering objective. To be specific, consider an arbitrary function of the state $\mathbf{x}_n$, denoted by $h(\mathbf{x}_n)$. In practical filtering applications, we are interested in the *on-line estimation of signal characteristics* of the function $h(\mathbf{x}_n)$. These characteristics are embodied in the *Bayes estimator*, defined by the ensemble average of the function $h(\mathbf{x}_n)$, namely,

$$\bar{h}_n = \mathbb{E}_p[h(\mathbf{x}_n)]$$

$$= \int \underbrace{h(\mathbf{x}_n)}_{\text{Arbitrary}} \underbrace{p(\mathbf{x}_n|\mathbf{Y}_n)}_{\text{Posterior}} d\mathbf{x}_n \qquad (14.84)$$

$$\text{Arbitrary} \qquad \text{Posterior}$$
$$\text{function}$$

where $\mathbb{E}_p$ is the expectation operator with respect to the posterior distribution $p(\mathbf{x}_n|\mathbf{Y}_n)$ that pertains to a dynamic system, be it linear or nonlinear. The formula of Eq. (14.84) includes Eq. (14.78) for the filtered estimate of the state and Eq. (14.79) for the covariance matrix of the estimate as two special cases, illustrating the general unifying framework of the Bayesian model. For Eq. (14.78) we have $h(\mathbf{x}_n) = \mathbf{x}_n$, and for Eq. (14.79) we have

$$h(\mathbf{x}_n) = (\mathbf{x}_n - \hat{\mathbf{x}}_{n|n})(\mathbf{x}_n - \hat{\mathbf{x}}_{n|n})^T$$

where h now assumes the form of a vectorial function.

For the special case of a dynamic system described by the linear, Gaussian model of Eqs. (14.4) and (14.5), the recursive solution of Eq. (14.84) is realized *exactly* through the Kalman filter; see Problem 14.10. However, when the dynamic system is nonlinear or non-Gaussian, or both, then the product distribution constituting the integrand of Eq. (14.84) is no longer Gaussian, which makes computation of the optimal Bayes estimator $\bar{h}_n$ a difficult proposition. In situations of this latter kind, we have no option but to abandon the notion of optimality in the Bayesian sense and seek an *approximate* estimator that is computationally feasible.

In light of this practical reality, we are now ready to formally state our *nonlinear-filtering objective*:

> Given the entire observations sequence $\mathbf{Y}_n$ at time n pertaining to the nonlinear state-space model of Eqs. (14.7) and (14.8), derive an approximate realization of the Bayes estimator $h(\mathbf{x}_n)$, defined in Eq. (14.84), that is subject to two practical requirements:
> 1. *computational plausibility*;
> 2. *recursive implementability*.

Suboptimal solutions of the nonlinear-filtering problem, obtained by approximating the Bayesian filter, may be derived via one of two routes, depending on the way in which the approximation is made:

1. *Direct Numerical Approximation of the Posterior.* The rationale behind this direct approach to nonlinear filtering is summed up as follows:

   > In general, it is easier to approximate the posterior distribution $p(\mathbf{x}_n|\mathbf{Y}_n)$ directly and in a local sense than it is to approximate the nonlinear function characterizing the system (state) model of the filter.

   To be specific, the posterior distribution $p(\mathbf{x}_n|\mathbf{Y}_n)$ is approximated *locally* around the point $\mathbf{x}_n = \hat{\mathbf{x}}_{n|n}$, where $\hat{\mathbf{x}}_{n|n}$ is the *filtered estimate* of the state $\mathbf{x}_n$, given all the observables up to and including time n; the emphasis on locality makes the design of the filter computationally simple and fast to execute. The objective of the approximation is to facilitate the subsequent application of Kalman filter theory. In fact, the widely used extended Kalman filter is an example of approximate Bayesian filtering via the direct use of numerical methods. Most importantly, in Section 14.7, we describe a new approximate Bayesian filter called the cubature Kalman filter, which is much more powerful than the extended Kalman filter.

2. *Indirect Numerical Approximation of the Posterior.* The rationale behind this second approach to nonlinear filtering is summed up as follows:

   > The posterior distribution $p(\mathbf{x}_n|\mathbf{Y}_n)$ is approximated indirectly and in a global sense through the use of Monte Carlo simulation, so as to make the Bayesian framework for nonlinear filtering computationally tractable.

Particle filters, to be discussed in Section 14.8, are a popular example of this second approach to nonlinear filtering. To be more specific, particle filters rely on a technique called the *sequential Monte Carlo (SMC) method*, which uses a set of randomly chosen samples with associated weights to approximate the posterior distribution $p(\mathbf{x}_n|\mathbf{Y}_n)$. As the number of samples used in the simulation becomes larger, the Monte Carlo computation of the posterior distribution becomes more accurate, which is a desirable objective. However, the increased number of samples makes the use of the SMC method computationally more expensive. In other words, computational cost is traded for improved filtering accuracy.

From this brief discussion, it is apparent that the locally direct approach to approximate Bayesian filtering builds on Kalman filter theory, whereas the globally indirect approach charts a path of its own by departing from that theory. Generally speaking, the globally indirect approach to nonlinear filtering is more demanding in computational terms than the locally direct approach.

14.7   CUBATURE KALMAN FILTER: BUILDING ON THE KALMAN FILTER

By now, we know that the Bayesian filter is rendered computationally tractable when all conditional distributions are assumed to be Gaussian. In this special case, approximation of the Bayesian filter reduces to computing multidimensional integrals of a special form described as

$$(nonlinear\ function) \times (Gaussian\ function)$$

Specifically, given an arbitrary nonlinear function $\mathbf{f}(\mathbf{x})$ of the vector $\mathbf{x} \in \mathbb{R}^M$ and using a Gaussian function, we consider an integral of the form

$$h(\mathbf{f}) = \int_{\mathbb{R}^M} \underbrace{\mathbf{f}(\mathbf{x})}_{\substack{\text{Arbitrary} \\ \text{function}}} \underbrace{\exp(-\mathbf{x}^T\mathbf{x})}_{\substack{\text{Gaussian} \\ \text{function}}} d\mathbf{x} \tag{14.85}$$

which is defined in the Cartesian coordinate system. For the numerical approximation of the nonlinear function $h(\mathbf{f})$, we propose the use of a *third-degree spherical–radial cubature rule* (Stroud, 1971; Cools, 1997). The cubature rule is constructed by forcing cubature points to obey some form of *symmetry*. In so doing, the complexity in solving a set of nonlinear equations for a set of desired weights and cubature points is reduced markedly. Before going into detail about the cubature rule, we introduce a number of notations and definitions:

- Using $\mathscr{D}$ to denote the region of integration, we say that the weighting function $w(\mathbf{x})$ defined on $\mathscr{D}$ is *fully symmetric* if the following two conditions hold:
  1. $\mathbf{x} \in \mathscr{D}$ implies $\mathbf{y} \in \mathscr{D}$, where $\mathbf{y}$ is any point obtainable from $\mathbf{x}$ by permutations and changes of sign of the coordinates of $\mathbf{x}$.
  2. $w(\mathbf{x}) = w(\mathbf{y})$ on $\mathscr{D}$.
- In a fully symmetric region, we call a point $\mathbf{u}$ a generator if $\mathbf{u} = (u_1, u_2, ..., u_r, 0, ..., 0) \in \mathbb{R}^M$, where $u_i \geq u_{i+i} > 0$ for $i = 1, 2, ..., (r - 1)$.

- We use the notation $[u_1, u_2, ..., u_r]$ to represent the complete set of points that can be obtained by permuting and changing the signs of the generator $\mathbf{u}$ in all possible ways. For the sake of brevity, we suppress the $(n - r)$ zero nodes in the notation. For example $[1] = \mathbb{R}^2$ represents the following set of points:

$$\left\{ \begin{pmatrix} 1 \\ 0 \end{pmatrix}, \begin{pmatrix} 0 \\ 1 \end{pmatrix}, \begin{pmatrix} -1 \\ 0 \end{pmatrix}, \begin{pmatrix} 0 \\ -1 \end{pmatrix} \right\}$$

- We use the notation $[u_1, u_2, ..., u_r]_i$ to denote the ith point from the generator $\mathbf{u}$.

Converting to Spherical–Radial Integration

The key step in this conversion is a change of variables from the Cartesian vector $\mathbf{x} \in \mathbb{R}^M$ to a spherical–radial vector defined by a radius r and direction vector $\mathbf{z}$, as outlined here:

Let $\mathbf{x} = r\mathbf{z}$ with $\mathbf{z}^T\mathbf{z} = 1$, so that $\mathbf{x}^T\mathbf{x} = r^2$ for $r \in [0, \infty)$.

Then the integral of Eq. (14.85) can be rewritten in a "spherical–radial" coordinate system as shown by the double integral

$$h(\mathbf{f}) = \int_0^\infty \int_{\mathcal{U}_M} \mathbf{f}(r\mathbf{z})r^{M-1}\exp(-r^2)d\sigma(\mathbf{z})dr \qquad (14.86)$$

where $\mathcal{U}_M$ is the region defined by $\mathcal{U}_M = \{\mathbf{z}; \mathbf{z}^T\mathbf{z} = 1\}$, and $\sigma(\cdot)$ is the *spherical surface measure* on $\mathcal{U}_M$ in the integral

$$S(r) = \int_{\mathcal{U}_M} \mathbf{f}(r\mathbf{z})d\sigma(\mathbf{z}) \qquad (14.87)$$

The integral of Eq. (14.87) is computed numerically by the spherical rule. Then, having computed $S(r)$, we find that the radial integral

$$h = \int_0^\infty S(r)r^{M-1}\exp(-r^2)dr \qquad (14.88)$$

is computed numerically by using the Gaussian quadrature. With the calculation of h, the computation of Eq. (14.85) is accomplished. Both of these rules are described next, in that order.

Spherical Rule

We first derive a third-degree spherical rule that takes the form

$$\int_{\mathcal{U}_M} \mathbf{f}(\mathbf{z})d\sigma(\mathbf{z}) \approx w \sum_{i=1}^{2M} \mathbf{f}[u]_i \qquad (14.89)$$

The rule in Eq. (14.89) entails a total of $2M$ cubature points from the generator $[u]$; the cubature points are located at the intersections of an M-dimensional sphere and its axes. To find the unknown parameters u and w, it suffices to consider *monomials* $\mathbf{f}(\mathbf{z}) = 1$ and $\mathbf{f}(\mathbf{z}) = z_1^2$ due to the fully symmetric generators, given as

$$\mathbf{f}(\mathbf{z}) = 1: \qquad 2Mw = \int_{\mathcal{U}_M} d\sigma(\mathbf{z}) = A_M \qquad (14.90)$$

$$\mathbf{f}(\mathbf{z}) = z_1^2: \qquad 2wu^2 = \int_{\mathcal{U}_M} z_1^2 d\sigma(\mathbf{z}) = \frac{A_M}{M} \qquad (14.91)$$

where M is the dimension of the vector $\mathbf{x}$, and the surface area of the unit hypersphere is defined by

$$A_M = \frac{2\sqrt{\pi^M}}{\Gamma(M/2)}$$

where

$$\Gamma(M) = \int_0^\infty x^{M-1} \exp(-x) dx$$

is the *gamma function*. Given A_M as just defined, solving Eqs. (14.90) and (14.91) for w and u yields

$$w = \frac{A_M}{2M} \text{ and } u^2 = 1$$

Radial Rule

For the radial rule, we propose the use of a Gaussian quadrature, which is known to be the most efficient numerical method for computing an integral in a single dimension. An m-point *Gaussian quadrature* is exact up to polynomials of degree $(2M - 1)$ and constructed as

$$\int_{\mathcal{D}} f(x)w(x)dx \approx \sum_{i=1}^{m} w_i f(x_i) \qquad (14.92)$$

where $w(x)$ denotes a weighting function (Press et al., 1988). Respectively, the x_i and the w_i are *quadrature points* and associated *weights* to be determined. Comparison of the integrals in Eqs (14.88) and (14.92) yields the weighting function and the region of integration to be $w(x) = x^{M-1} \exp(-x^2)$ and $[0, \infty)$, respectively. Thus, using $t = x^2$ as a final change of variables, we obtain the desired radial integral

$$\int_0^\infty f(x)x^{M-1} \exp(-x^2)dx = \frac{1}{2}\int_0^\infty \tilde{f}(t)t^{(M/2)-1} \exp(-t)dt \qquad (14.93)$$

where $\tilde{f}(t) = f(\sqrt{t})$. The integral on the right-hand side of Eq. (14.93) is now in the form of the well-known *generalized Gauss–Laguerre formula* (Stroud, 1966; Press and Teukolsky, 1990).

A first-degree Gauss–Laguerre rule is exact for $\tilde{f}(t) = 1, t$. Correspondingly, the rule is exact for $f(x) = 1, x^2$; it is not exact for odd-degree polynomials, such as that in $f(x) = x, x^3$. Fortunately, when the radial rule is combined with the spherical rule to compute the integral Eq. (14.85), the resulting spherical–radial rule vanishes for all odd-degree polynomials. The reason for this nice result is that the spherical rule vanishes by virtue of the symmetry for any odd-degree polynomial; see Eq. (14.86). Hence, the spherical–radial rule for computing Eq. (14.85) is exact for all odd-degree polynomials.

Following this argument, for a spherical–radial rule to be exact for all third-degree polynomials in $\mathbf{x} \in R^M$, it suffices to consider the first-degree generalized Gauss–Laguerre rule, which entails the use of a single point and a single weight. We may thus write

$$\int_0^\infty f(x)x^{M-1}\exp(-x^2)dx \approx w_1 f(x_1)$$

where

$$w_1 = \frac{1}{2}\Gamma\left(\frac{M}{2}\right) \text{ and } x_1 = \sqrt{M/2}$$

Spherical–Radial Rule

In this final subsection, we describe two useful results that are used to (i) combine the spherical and radial rules, and (ii) extend the spherical–radial rule for a Gaussian-weighted integral. The respective results are presented as two theorems (Arasaratnam and Haykin, 2009):

Theorem 1: *Let the radial integral be computed numerically by an m_r-point Gaussian quadrature rule:*

$$\int_0^\infty f(r)r^{M-1}\exp(-r^2)dr = \sum_{i=1}^{m_r} a_i f(r_i)$$

Let the spherical integral be computed numerically by an m_s-point spherical rule:

$$\int_{\mathcal{U}_M} \mathbf{f}(r\mathbf{s})d\sigma(\mathbf{s}) = \sum_{j=1}^{m_s} b_j \mathbf{f}(r\mathbf{s}_j)$$

Then, an $(m_s \times m_r)$-point spherical–radial cubature rule is approximately given by the double summation

$$\int_{\mathbb{R}^M} \mathbf{f}(\mathbf{x})\exp(-\mathbf{x}^T\mathbf{x})d\mathbf{x} \approx \sum_{j=1}^{m_s}\sum_{i=1}^{m_r} a_i b_j \mathbf{f}(r_i\mathbf{s}_j)$$

Theorem 2: *Let two weighting functions be denoted by $w_1(\mathbf{x}) = \exp(-\mathbf{x}^T\mathbf{x})$ and $w_2(\mathbf{x}) = \mathcal{N}(\mathbf{x}; \boldsymbol{\mu}, \boldsymbol{\Sigma})$, where, for a given vector $\mathbf{x}$, the term $\mathcal{N}(\mathbf{x}; \boldsymbol{\mu}, \boldsymbol{\Sigma})$ denotes a Gaussian distribution with mean $\boldsymbol{\mu}$ and covariance matrix $\boldsymbol{\Sigma}$. Then, for every square-root matrix $\boldsymbol{\Sigma}^{1/2}$ such that $\boldsymbol{\Sigma}^{1/2}\boldsymbol{\Sigma}^{T/2} = \boldsymbol{\Sigma}$, we have*

$$\int_{\mathbb{R}^M} \mathbf{f}(\mathbf{x})w_2(\mathbf{x})d\mathbf{x} = \frac{1}{\sqrt{\pi^M}}\int_{\mathbb{R}^M} f(\sqrt{2\boldsymbol{\Sigma}}\mathbf{x} + \boldsymbol{\mu})w_1(\mathbf{x})d\mathbf{x}$$

For the third-degree spherical–radial rule, $m_r = 1$ and $m_s = 2M$. Accordingly, we require a total of only $2M$ cubature points. Moreover, the rule is exact for integrands that can be written as a linear combination of polynomials of degree up to three and all other odd-degree polynomials. Invoking Theorems 1 and 2, we may now extend this third-degree spherical–radial rule to numerically compute the *standard Gaussian-weighted integral*

$$h_N(\mathbf{f}) = \int_{\mathbb{R}^M} \mathbf{f}(\mathbf{x})\mathcal{N}(\mathbf{x}; \mathbf{0}, \mathbf{I})d\mathbf{x} \approx \sum_{i=1}^m w_i \mathbf{f}(\xi_i) \qquad (14.94)$$

where

$$\xi_i = \sqrt{\frac{m}{2}}\,[1]_i \ \text{ and } \ w_i = \frac{1}{m}, \qquad i = 1, 2, ..., m = 2M$$

In effect, the ξ_i are the cubature-point representations of the M-dimensional vector $\mathbf{x}$.

Derivation of the Cubature Kalman Filter

The formula of Eq. (14.94) is the *cubature rule* we have been seeking for the *numerical approximation* of the moment integral of Eq. (14.85). Indeed, the cubature rule is central to the computation of all the integrals contained in the Bayesian framework for nonlinear filtering. As with the extended Kalman filter, we assume that the dynamic noise $\boldsymbol{\omega}_n$ and measurement noise $\boldsymbol{\nu}_n$ are jointly Gaussian. This assumption may be justified on the following grounds:

1. From a mathematical perspective, Gaussian processes are simple and mathematically easy to handle.

2. Noise processes encountered in many real-world problems may be modeled as Gaussian processes, due to the central limit theorem of probability theory.

Under the assumption of Gaussianity, we may now approximate the Bayesian filter by using the cubature rule as follows:

1. *Time update.* Suppose that the prior distribution $p(\mathbf{x}_{n-1}|\mathbf{Y}_{n-1})$ is approximated by a Gaussian distribution whose mean is $\hat{\mathbf{x}}_{n-1|n-1}$ and whose covariance matrix is equal to the filtering-error covariance matrix $\mathbf{P}_{n-1|n-1}$. Then, using the formula for the Bayes estimator, we may express the predicted estimate of the state as

$$\hat{\mathbf{x}}_{n|n-1} = \mathbb{E}[\mathbf{x}_n|\mathbf{Y}_{n-1}]$$

$$= \int_{\mathbb{R}^M} \underbrace{\mathbf{a}(\mathbf{x}_{n-1})}_{\substack{\text{Nonlinear} \\ \text{state-} \\ \text{transition} \\ \text{function}}} \underbrace{\mathcal{N}(\mathbf{x}_{n-1}; \hat{\mathbf{x}}_{n-1|n-1}, \mathbf{P}_{n-1|n-1})}_{\text{Gaussian distribution}} d\mathbf{x}_{n-1} \qquad (14.95)$$

where we have used knowledge of the system model of Eq. (14.7) and the fact that the dynamic noise $\boldsymbol{\omega}_{n-1}$ is uncorrelated with the sequence of observations $\mathbf{Y}_{n-1}$. Similarly, we obtain the prediction-error covariance matrix

$$\mathbf{P}_{n|n-1} = \int_{\mathbb{R}^M} \mathbf{a}(\mathbf{x}_{n-1})\, \mathbf{a}^T(\mathbf{x}_{n-1}) \mathcal{N}(\mathbf{x}_{n-1}; \hat{\mathbf{x}}_{n-1|n-1}, \mathbf{P}_{n-1, n-1}) d\mathbf{x}_{n-1} \qquad (14.96)$$
$$- \hat{\mathbf{x}}_{n|n-1}\hat{\mathbf{x}}_{n|n-1}^T + \mathbf{Q}_{w,n}$$

2. *Measurement update.* Equation (14.95) is an approximate formula for the time update. Next, to find a formula for the measurement update, suppose that the joint distribution of the state $\mathbf{x}_n$ and the observation $\mathbf{y}_n$, conditional on the sequence $\mathbf{Y}_{n-1}$, is also Gaussian, as shown by

$$\mathcal{N} = \left(\underbrace{\begin{bmatrix} \mathbf{x}_n \\ \mathbf{y}_n \end{bmatrix}}_{\substack{\text{Joint} \\ \text{variables}}}; \underbrace{\begin{bmatrix} \hat{\mathbf{x}}_{n|n-1} \\ \hat{\mathbf{y}}_{n|n-1} \end{bmatrix}}_{\substack{\text{Joint} \\ \text{mean}}}, \underbrace{\begin{bmatrix} \mathbf{P}_{n|n-1} & \mathbf{P}_{xy,\,n|n-1} \\ \mathbf{P}_{yx,\,n|n-1} & \mathbf{P}_{yy,\,n|n-1} \end{bmatrix}}_{\text{Joint covariance matrix}} \right) \qquad (14.97)$$

where $\hat{\mathbf{x}}_{n|n-1}$ is defined in Eq. (14.95) and $\hat{\mathbf{y}}_{n|n-1}$ is the predicted estimate of the observation $\mathbf{y}_n$ given the sequence $\mathbf{Y}_{n-1}$, as shown by

$$\hat{\mathbf{y}}_{n|n-1} = \int_{\mathbb{R}^M} \underbrace{\mathbf{b}(\mathbf{x}_n)}_{\substack{\text{Nonlinear} \\ \text{measurement} \\ \text{function}}} \underbrace{\mathcal{N}(\mathbf{x}_n; \hat{\mathbf{x}}_{n|n-1}, \mathbf{P}_{n|n-1}) d\mathbf{x}_n}_{\text{Gaussian distribution}} \tag{14.98}$$

The innovations covariance matrix is defined by

$$\mathbf{P}_{yy,\,n|n-1} = \int_{\mathbb{R}^M} \underbrace{\mathbf{b}(\mathbf{x}_n)\mathbf{b}^T(\mathbf{x}_n)}_{\substack{\text{Outer product} \\ \text{of the} \\ \text{nonlinear} \\ \text{measurement} \\ \text{function with} \\ \text{itself}}} \underbrace{\mathcal{N}(\mathbf{x}_n; \hat{\mathbf{x}}_{n|n-1}, \mathbf{P}_{n|n-1}) d\mathbf{x}_n}_{\text{Gaussian distribution}} - \underbrace{\hat{\mathbf{y}}_{n|n-1}\hat{\mathbf{y}}_{n|n-1}^T}_{\substack{\text{Outer product} \\ \text{of the} \\ \text{estimate } \hat{\mathbf{y}}_{n|n-1} \\ \text{with itself}}} + \underbrace{\mathbf{Q}_{v,\,n}}_{\substack{\text{Covariance} \\ \text{matrix of} \\ \text{measurement} \\ \text{noise}}} \tag{14.99}$$

Lastly, the cross-covariance matrix of the state $\mathbf{x}_n$ and the observation $\mathbf{y}_n$ is given by

$$\mathbf{P}_{xy,\,n|n-1} = \mathbf{P}_{yx,\,n|n-1}^T$$

$$= \int_{\mathbb{R}^M} \underbrace{\mathbf{x}_n \mathbf{b}^T(\mathbf{x}_n)}_{\substack{\text{Outer} \\ \text{product} \\ \text{of } \mathbf{x}_n \text{ with} \\ \mathbf{b}(\mathbf{x}_n)}} \underbrace{\mathcal{N}(\mathbf{x}_n; \hat{\mathbf{x}}_{n|n-1}, \mathbf{P}_{n|n-1}) d\mathbf{x}_n}_{\text{Gaussian distribution}} - \underbrace{\hat{\mathbf{x}}_{n|n-1}\hat{\mathbf{y}}_{n|n-1}^T}_{\substack{\text{Outer product} \\ \text{of the estimates} \\ \hat{\mathbf{x}}_{n|n-1} \text{ and } \hat{\mathbf{y}}_{n|n-1}}} \tag{14.100}$$

The five integral formulas of Eqs. (14.95), (14.96) and (14.98) through (14.100) address different aspects of approximating the Bayesian filter. However, as different as these formulas are, their integrands have a common form: the product of a nonlinear function and a corresponding Gaussian function of known mean and covariance matrix. Therefore, all five integrals lend themselves to approximation by means of the cubature rule.

Most importantly, recursive computation of the filtered estimate of the state builds on linear Kalman filter theory by proceeding as follows:

- The Kalman gain is computed as

$$\mathbf{G}_n = \mathbf{P}_{xy,\,n|n-1}\mathbf{P}_{yy,\,n|n-1}^{-1} \tag{14.101}$$

where $\mathbf{P}_{yy,\,n|n-1}^{-1}$ is the inverse of the covariance matrix $\mathbf{P}_{yy,\,n|n-1}$.
- Upon receipt of the new observation $\mathbf{y}_n$, the filtered estimate of the state $\mathbf{x}_n$ is computed in accordance with the predictor-corrector formula:

$$\underbrace{\hat{\mathbf{x}}_{n|n}}_{\substack{\text{Updated} \\ \text{estimate}}} = \underbrace{\hat{\mathbf{x}}_{n|n-1}}_{\substack{\text{Old} \\ \text{estimate}}} + \underbrace{\mathbf{G}_n}_{\substack{\text{Kalman} \\ \text{gain}}} \underbrace{(\mathbf{y}_n - \hat{\mathbf{y}}_{n|n-1})}_{\substack{\text{Innovations} \\ \text{process}}} \tag{14.102}$$

- Correspondingly, the covariance matrix of the filtered state-estimation error is computed as follows:

$$\mathbf{P}_{n|n} = \mathbf{P}_{n|n-1} - \mathbf{G}_n \mathbf{P}_{yy,\,n|n-1}\mathbf{G}_n^T \tag{14.103}$$

Note the correspondences between Eqs. (14.101), (14.102), and (14.103) for the new nonlinear filter and Eqs. (14.31), (14.30), and the unnumbered equation preceding (14.38) for the Kalman filter, respectively. In any event, the posterior distribution may finally be computed as a Gaussian distribution defined by

$$p(\mathbf{x}_n|\mathbf{Y}_n) = \mathcal{N}(\mathbf{x}_n; \hat{\mathbf{x}}_{n|n}, \mathbf{P}_{n|n}) \tag{14.104}$$

where the mean $\hat{\mathbf{x}}_{n|n}$ is defined by Eq. (14.102) and the covariance matrix $\mathbf{P}_{n|n}$ is defined by Eq. (14.103).

Thus, having started the computation with the prior distribution $p(\mathbf{x}_{n-1}|\mathbf{Y}_{n-1})$ under the time update, the recursion cycle has moved forward systematically through the measurement update, culminating in the computation of the posterior distribution $p(\mathbf{x}_n|\mathbf{Y}_n)$; the cycle may then be repeated as required.

For obvious reasons, this new nonlinear filter is called the *cubature Kalman filter* (Arasaratnam and Haykin, 2009). Important properties of this new nonlinear filter are summarized as follows:

1. The cubature Kalman filter (CKF) is a *derivative-free on-line sequential-state estimator.*

2. The approximations of the moment integrals resulting from the use of the cubature rule are all *linear* in the number of function evaluations. Moreover, the points and associated weights in the cubature rule are independent of the nonlinear function $\mathbf{f}(\mathbf{x})$ in Eq. (14.84); hence, they can be computed off-line and stored to speed up the filtering execution.

3. As with the EKF, the computational complexity of the CKF, measured in terms of *flops*, grows as M^3, where M is the dimension of the state space.

4. In a principled way, the CKF builds on the Kalman filter theory, including the use of square-root filtering for the attainment of improved numerical accuracy; the resulting filter is called the *square-root cubature Kalman filter (SCKF)*, which propagates the square roots of the predictive and posterior error covariance matrices (Arasaratnam and Haykin, 2009).

5. Most importantly, the second-order moments in the prior distribution are completely preserved in the posterior distribution. Since the information we have about the state is actually contained in the observations, we may go on to say that the CKF completely preserves second-order information about the state that is contained in the sequence of observations, thereby outperforming the EKF in terms of accuracy and reliability.

6. The CKF is the closest known direct approximation to the Bayesian filter, in that *it eases the curse-of-dimensionality problem the most* but, by itself, does not overcome it.

It is the combination of these properties that makes the cubature Kalman filter an attractive choice for the supervised training of recurrent multilayer perceptrons, as discussed in Chapter 15. In that chapter, we also present a computer experiment that clearly demonstrates the practicality of this new powerful tool.

14.8 PARTICLE FILTERS

In this section, we continue the discussion on nonlinear filtering by describing the indirect global approximation of the Bayesian filter. Much, if not all, of the underlying theory involved in this second approach to nonlinear filtering resides in the literature on *Monte Carlo statistical methods* (Robert and Casella, 2004). This new class of nonlinear filter is best exemplified by particle filters. Most importantly, particle filters have become an important tool for solving nonlinear filtering problems because of their general applicability in a variety of fields such as signal processing, tracking of targets in radar and acoustic media, computer vision, and neural computation, just to name a few.

Before going into a detailed description of particle filters, we introduce some new notations and definitions. Let $\mathbf{X}_n$ denote the sequence of all target states $\{\mathbf{x}_i\}_{i=1}^n$. As before, $\mathbf{Y}_n$ denotes the sequence of all observations $\{\mathbf{y}_i\}_{i=1}^n$. Correspondingly, we may express the *joint posterior distribution* of all the states, $\mathbf{X}_n$, given the sequence of observations $\mathbf{Y}_n$ as $p(\mathbf{X}_n|\mathbf{Y}_n)$. Since the sequence of states represented by $\mathbf{X}_n$ is hidden from the observer, it is not usually feasible to obtain random samples directly from the posterior distribution $p(\mathbf{X}_n|\mathbf{Y}_n)$ for computing the integral of Eq. (14.84). To get around this practical difficulty, we sample from another distribution called the *instrumental*, or *importance*, *distribution*. Henceforth, this new distribution is denoted by $q(\mathbf{X}_n|\mathbf{Y}_n)$. Naturally, for the importance distribution to be an effective replacement for the posterior distribution, $q(\mathbf{X}_n|\mathbf{Y}_n)$ must have a support broad enough to completely include the support of $p(\mathbf{X}_n|\mathbf{Y}_n)$.

Monte Carlo Integration

Following the so-called *method of importance sampling*, we randomly draw a set of N *statistically independent and identically distributed* (iid) samples from the importance distribution $q(\mathbf{X}_n|\mathbf{Y}_n)$. Let the randomly drawn samples at time n be denoted by $\mathbf{x}_n^{(i)}$, $i = 1, 2, ..., N$. Starting from time 0 and moving forward to time n, step by step, the N samples trace individual "trajectories" of their own in the state space in accordance with the importance distribution $q(\mathbf{X}_n|\mathbf{Y}_n)$. These trajectories, denoted by $\mathbf{X}_n^{(i)}$, where $i = 1, 2, ..., N$, are called *particles*—hence the name "particle filtering."

Next, we define the *importance function*

$$r(\mathbf{X}_n|\mathbf{Y}_n) = \frac{p(\mathbf{X}_n|\mathbf{Y}_n)}{q(\mathbf{X}_n|\mathbf{Y}_n)} \tag{14.105}$$

Then, using this definition in Eq. (14.84), we may reformulate the Bayes estimator as

$$\overline{h}_n = \int h(\mathbf{X}_n)\left(\frac{p(\mathbf{X}_n|\mathbf{Y}_n)}{q(\mathbf{X}_n|\mathbf{Y}_n)}\right)q(\mathbf{X}_n|\mathbf{Y}_n)d\mathbf{x}_n$$

$$= \int h(\mathbf{X}_n)r(\mathbf{X}_n|\mathbf{Y}_n)q(\mathbf{X}_n|\mathbf{Y}_n)d\mathbf{x}_n \tag{14.106}$$

where we have used $h(\mathbf{X}_n)$ as the arbitrary function in order to be consistent with the particle-filtering terminology.

Applying the *method of importance sampling* to the Bayes estimator of Eq. (14.106), we obtain the corresponding *Monte Carlo estimator*

$$\hat{h}_n(N) \approx \frac{1}{N}\sum_{i=1}^N \tilde{w}_n^{(i)}h(\mathbf{X}_n^{(i)}) \tag{14.107}$$

where the $\tilde{w}_n^{(i)}$ are *importance weights*, defined by

$$\tilde{w}_n^{(i)} = r(\mathbf{X}_n^{(i)}|\mathbf{Y}_n)$$

$$= \frac{p(\mathbf{X}_n^{(i)}|\mathbf{Y}_n)}{q(\mathbf{X}_n^{(i)}|\mathbf{Y}_n)}, \qquad i = 1, 2, ..., N \tag{14.108}$$

To ensure that the Monte Carlo estimator $\hat{h}_n(N)$ does *not* need to know the normalizing constant of the distribution $p(\mathbf{X}_n^{(i)}|\mathbf{Y}_n)$, which might be troublesome or perhaps impossible to compute, it is customary to *normalize* the importance weights so that they sum to unity. To this end, we reformulate the estimator of Eq. (14.107) as

$$\hat{h}_n(N) \approx \sum_{i=1}^{N} w_n^{(i)} h(\mathbf{X}_n^{(i)}) \tag{14.109}$$

where

$$w_n^{(i)} = \frac{\tilde{w}_n^{(i)}}{\sum_{j=1}^{N} \tilde{w}_n^{(j)}}, \qquad i = 1, 2, ..., N \tag{14.110}$$

are *normalized importance weights*.

For a finite number of particles, N, the estimator $\hat{h}_n(N)$ is "biased." But, in an asymptotic sense, we find that the following is the case (Doucet et al., 2001):

$$\lim_{N \to \infty} \hat{h}_n(N) \to \bar{h}_n \tag{14.111}$$

To improve on the method of importance sampling, we may follow it up with a second stage of resampling, as in the *sampling–importance-resampling (SIR) method*, due to Rubin (1988). In the first stage of the SIR method, a set of iid samples $\{\mathbf{X}_n^{(i)}\}_{i=1}^{N}$ is randomly drawn from the importance distribution $q(\mathbf{X}_n|\mathbf{Y}_n)$ at iteration n in the usual way, and the corresponding set of normalized importance weights $\{w_n^{(i)}\}_{i=1}^{N}$ is then computed in accordance with Eq. (14.110). In the second stage of the SIR method, a second set of samples, denoted by $\{\tilde{\mathbf{X}}_n^{(i)}\}_{i=1}^{M}$, is drawn from the intermediate set $\{\mathbf{X}_n^{(i)}\}_{i=1}^{N}$, taking into account the relative strengths of the normalized importance weights $w_n^{(i)}$; in effect, each of these weights is viewed as a probability of occurrence of the pertinent sample. The rationale behind the second stage of sampling is as follows:

> *A sample $\tilde{\mathbf{X}}_n^{(i)}$ picked in the second stage of resampling, for which the normalized importance weight $w_n^{(i)}$ is large, is most likely to be under the joint posterior distribution $p(\mathbf{X}_n|\mathbf{Y}_n)$; such a sample should therefore be selected with higher probability than a sample for which the normalized importance weight is small.*

There are several ways of implementing SIR. In one particular method described in Cappé et al. (2005), at each iteration we proceed as follows:

1. *Sampling.* Randomly draw an iid set of N samples $\{\mathbf{X}^{(i)}\}_{i=1}^{N}$ from the importance distribution $q(\mathbf{X}|\mathbf{Y})$.

2. *Weighting.* Using Eq. (14.110), compute the corresponding set of normalized weights $\{w^{(i)}\}_{i=1}^{N}$.

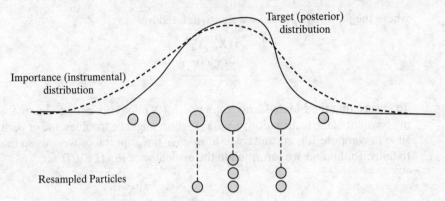

FIGURE 14.5 Illustration of the resampling process for the example of the number of samples and resamples being equal to six.

3. *Resampling.*
   (i) Given the intermediate samples $\mathbf{X}^{(1)}, \mathbf{X}^{(2)}, ..., \mathbf{X}^{(N)}$, conditionally and independently draw a set of L discrete random variables $\{I^{(1)}, I^{(2)}, ..., I^{(L)}\}$ that take values in the set $\{1, 2, ..., N\}$ with probabilities $(w^{(1)}, w^{(2)}, ..., w^{(N)})$ as shown by, for example,

$$P(I^{(1)} = j) = w^{(j)} \qquad \text{for } j = 1, 2, ..., N$$

   and so on for $I^{(2)}, ..., I^{(L)}$; typically, we have $L \leq N$.
   (ii) Set $\tilde{\mathbf{X}}^{(i)} = \mathbf{X}^{(I_i)}$ for $i = 1, 2, ..., L$

The set $\{I^{(1)}, I^{(2)}, ..., I^{(L)}\}$ is recognized as a *multinomial trial process*. Accordingly, the SIR method just described is said to be of a multinomial kind, which is illustrated in Fig. 14.5 for the example case of $L = N = 6$.

Later on in this section, we will discuss the role of resampling in overcoming the effects of a problem known as "degeneracy" of the importance weights. However, the use of resampling introduces some practical limitations of its own:

1. Resampling *limits the scope of parallel implementation* of particle filters, due to the very nature of the process.
2. Particles associated with large importance weights are selected several times in the course of resampling, which results in a loss of diversity among the particles; this phenomenon is referred to as *sample improvishment* or *weight degeneracy*. When, for example, the dynamic noise in the state-space model is relatively small, all the particles may end up collapsing to a single one in a matter of few iterations, which is obviously undesirable.
3. Invariably, resampling *increases the variance* of the Monte Carlo estimator.

Sequential Importance Sampling

The Monte Carlo estimator $\hat{h}_n(N)$ of Eq. (14.109), produced by the method of importance sampling, provides a computationally viable solution for approximating the

Bayesian estimator $\hat{h}_n$ of the arbitrary function $h(\mathbf{X}_n)$, thereby fulfilling the first practical requirement of our nonlinear filtering objective, stated previously on page 758. However, we still have to fulfill the second requirement: recursive implementation of the Monte Carlo estimator.

Unfortunately, the method of importance sampling in its simple form does *not* cater to recursive computation. This is because we require the entire observation sequence denoted by $\mathbf{Y}_n$ before we are in a position to estimate the posterior distribution $p(\mathbf{X}_n|\mathbf{Y}_n)$. In particular, as each new observation $\mathbf{y}_n$ becomes available, we need to compute the importance weights $\{\tilde{w}_n^{(i)}\}_{i=1}^N$ over the entire state sequence $\mathbf{X}_n$. To satisfy this need, the computational complexity of the importance-sampling process would have to continue increasing with time n, which is impractical for obvious reasons. To overcome this computational difficulty, we resort to a sequential implementation of importance sampling, commonly referred to as *sequential-importance-sampling (SIS)*.

To describe the underlying theory of the SIS procedure, we first use the time update of Eq. (14.80) and the measurement update of Eq. (14.81) to eliminate the predictive distribution, where we now write $p(\mathbf{X}_n|\mathbf{Y}_{n-1})$ and $p(\mathbf{X}_{n-1}|\mathbf{Y}_{n-1})$ in place of $p(\mathbf{x}_n|\mathbf{Y}_{n-1})$ and $p(\mathbf{x}_{n-1}|\mathbf{Y}_{n-1})$, respectively, so as to fit into the particle-filtering terminology. We thus obtain

$$\underbrace{p(\mathbf{X}_n|\mathbf{Y}_n)}_{\substack{\text{updated} \\ \text{posterior}}} = \int \frac{1}{Z_n} p(\mathbf{x}_n|\mathbf{x}_{n-1})l(\mathbf{y}_n|\mathbf{x}_n)p(\mathbf{X}_{n-1}|\mathbf{Y}_{n-1})d\mathbf{x}_{n-1}$$

$$= \int \frac{1}{Z_n}\underbrace{p(\mathbf{x}_n|\mathbf{x}_{n-1})}_{\text{Prior}}\underbrace{l(\mathbf{y}_n|\mathbf{x}_n)}_{\substack{\text{Likelihood}\\\text{function}}}\frac{p(\mathbf{X}_{n-1}|\mathbf{Y}_{n-1})}{q(\mathbf{X}_n|\mathbf{Y}_n)}\underbrace{q(\mathbf{X}_n|\mathbf{Y}_n)}_{\substack{\text{Importance}\\\text{distribution}}}d\mathbf{x}_{n-1} \quad (14.112)$$

In the first line of this equation, we moved the likelihood function $l(\mathbf{y}_n|\mathbf{x}_n)$ inside the integral, since, under the Markovian assumption, it is independent of the previous value of the state—namely, $\mathbf{x}_{n-1}$; in the second line of the equation, we introduced the importance distribution $q(\mathbf{X}_n|\mathbf{Y}_n)$. In the importance-sampling framework, the multiple-product term

$$\frac{1}{Z_n} p(\mathbf{x}_n|\mathbf{x}_{n-1})l(\mathbf{y}_n|\mathbf{x}_n)\frac{p(\mathbf{X}_{n-1}|\mathbf{Y}_{n-1})}{q(\mathbf{X}_n|\mathbf{Y}_n)}$$

accounts for the importance weights associated with the importance distribution $q(\mathbf{X}_n|\mathbf{Y}_n)$ at time n. Specifically, with Z_n being a constant, we may write

$$w_n^{(i)} \propto \frac{p(\mathbf{x}_n^{(i)}|\mathbf{X}_{n-1}^{(i)})l(\mathbf{y}_n|\mathbf{x}_n^{(i)})p(\mathbf{X}_{n-1}^{(i)}|\mathbf{Y}_{n-1})}{q(\mathbf{X}_n^{(i)}|\mathbf{Y}_n)} \quad (14.113)$$

where $\propto$ denotes proportionality.

Suppose now the importance distribution is chosen in such a way that in the denominator of Eq. (14.113), the *factorization*

$$q(\mathbf{X}_n^{(i)}|\mathbf{Y}_n) = q(\mathbf{X}_{n-1}^{(i)}|\mathbf{Y}_{n-1})q(\mathbf{x}_n^{(i)}|\mathbf{X}_{n-1}^{(i)}, \mathbf{y}_n) \quad (14.114)$$

holds for all i. Then, the updated sequence of samples from the importance distribution $q(\mathbf{X}_n^{(i)}|\mathbf{Y}_n)$ is obtained simply by augmenting the old sequence of samples drawn from the importance distribution $q(\mathbf{X}_{n-1}^{(i)}|\mathbf{Y}_{n-1})$ with a sequence of samples drawn from the new importance distribution $q(\mathbf{x}_n^{(i)}|\mathbf{X}_{n-1}^{(i)}, \mathbf{y}_n)$, receipt upon the new observation $\mathbf{y}_n$. Thus, Eq. (14.114) may be viewed as the "trick" behind sequential importance sampling. In any event, using the decomposition of Eq. (14.114) in the formula of Eq. (14.113), we obtain

$$\tilde{w}_n^{(i)} \propto \frac{p(\mathbf{X}_{n-1}^{(i)}|\mathbf{Y}_{n-1})}{q(\mathbf{X}_{n-1}^{(i)}|\mathbf{Y}_{n-1})} \times \frac{p(\mathbf{x}_n^{(i)}|\mathbf{X}_{n-1}^{(i)})l(\mathbf{y}_n|\mathbf{x}_n^{(i)})}{q(\mathbf{x}_n^{(i)}|\mathbf{X}_{n-1}^{(i)}, \mathbf{y}_n)} \tag{14.115}$$

A case of practical interest is when only a *filtered* estimate of the posterior distribution $p(\mathbf{X}_n|\mathbf{Y}_n)$ is required at each time-step n. In such a case, we may set

$$q(\mathbf{x}_n^{(i)}|\mathbf{X}_{n-1}^{(i)}, \mathbf{y}_n) = q(\mathbf{x}_n^{(i)}|\mathbf{x}_{n-1}^{(i)}, \mathbf{y}_n) \qquad \text{for all } i$$

and similarly for $p(\mathbf{x}_n^{(i)}|\mathbf{X}_{n-1}^{(i)})$. In a scenario of this kind, we require only that the current state $\mathbf{x}_n^{(i)}$ be stored, and therefore we discard the old trajectory $\mathbf{X}_{n-1}^{(i)}$ and the corresponding history of observations $\mathbf{Y}_{n-1}$. Accordingly, the formula of Eq. (14.115) for updating the importance weights simplifies to

$$\underbrace{w_n^{(i)}}_{\substack{\text{Updated} \\ \text{importance} \\ \text{weight}}} \propto \underbrace{w_{n-1}^{(i)}}_{\substack{\text{Old} \\ \text{importance} \\ \text{weight}}} \times \underbrace{\frac{p(\mathbf{x}_n^{(i)}|\mathbf{x}_{n-1}^{(i)})l(\mathbf{y}_n|\mathbf{x}_n^{(i)})}{q(\mathbf{x}_n^{(i)}|\mathbf{x}_{n-1}^{(i)}, \mathbf{y}_n)}}_{\text{Incremental correction factor}} \qquad \text{for all } i \tag{14.116}$$

where $\propto$ is the symbol for proportionality. Equation (14.116) is the desired formula for evaluating the normalized importance weights recursively in time; it satisfies the second requirement of the nonlinear filtering objective on recursive implementability of particle filters. In particular, the SIS procedure *propagates the importance weights* at each time-step as a new observation is received. The multiplicative factor on the right-hand side of Eq. (14.116), permitting the "old" importance weight $\tilde{w}_{n-1}^{(i)}$ to be updated when the new observation $\mathbf{y}_n$ is received at time-step n, is called the *incremental correction factor*.

Clearly, sequential importance sampling applies equally well to the Monte Carlo estimation of the posterior distribution $p(\mathbf{x}_n|\mathbf{Y}_n)$; in light of Eqs. (14.112) and (14.116), we may write

$$p(\mathbf{x}_n|\mathbf{Y}_n) \approx \sum_{i=1}^{N} w_n^{(i)} \delta(\mathbf{x}_n - \mathbf{x}_n^{(i)}) \tag{14.117}$$

where $\delta(\mathbf{x}_n - \mathbf{x}_n^{(i)})$ is the *Dirac delta function* positioned at $\mathbf{x}_n = \mathbf{x}_n^{(i)}$ for $i = 1, 2, ..., N$ and the weights are updated in accordance with Eq. (14.116) for the filtering scenario. As the number of particles, N, approaches infinity, the estimator of Eq. (14.117) approaches the true posterior distribution $p(\mathbf{x}_n|\mathbf{Y}_n)$.

The Weight-Degeneracy Problem

The importance distribution $q(\mathbf{X}_n|\mathbf{Y}_n)$ plays a pivotal role in the design of particle filters. With it being invariably different from the posterior distribution $p(\mathbf{X}_n|\mathbf{Y}_n)$, we find that *the variance of the importance weights, defined in Eq. (14.108), can only increase over the course of time.* This phenomenon, experienced in the use of sequential importance sampling, leads to the *weight-degeneracy problem* mentioned previously.

For an intuitive explanation of the weight-degeneracy problem, consider a particle $\mathbf{X}_n^{(i)}$ with a small normalized importance weight $w_n^{(i)}$ at time-step n. By definition, a small weight implies that the particle $w_n^{(i)}$ has been drawn from the importance distribution $q(\mathbf{X}_n|\mathbf{Y}_n)$ a good distance away from the main body of the posterior distribution $p(\mathbf{X}_n|\mathbf{Y}_n)$, which therefore means that the contribution of this particular particle to the Monte Carlo estimator $\hat{h}_n(N)$ of Eq. (14.109) is rather ineffective. When the degeneracy problem is severe, there is a large number of ineffective particles, with the result that the Monte Carlo estimator $\hat{h}_n(N)$ is inefficient in statistical as well as computational terms. In such a situation, a small number of particles carries the computational burden. Most seriously, however, as the time-step n increases, we find that diversity among the ensemble of particles is reduced and the variance of the estimator $\hat{h}_n(N)$ is increased, constituting a bad situation to be in.

To guard against the weight-degeneracy problem in sequential importance sampling, we clearly need a degeneracy measure. With such a measure in mind, Liu (1996) defined an effective *sample size* as

$$N_{\text{eff}} = \left[\sum_{i=1}^{N} (w_n^{(i)})^2 \right]^{-1} \tag{14.118}$$

where $w_n^{(i)}$ is the normalized importance weight of Eq. (14.110). There are two extreme cases to be considered in applying this simple formula:

1. The N weights are all uniformly distributed with $w_n^{(i)} = 1/N$ for all i, in which case $N_{\text{eff}} = N$.
2. All the N weights are zero, except for one weight whose value is unity; in this case, $N_{\text{eff}} = 1$.

It follows, therefore, that N_{eff} lies inside the range $[1, N]$. In particular, a small N_{eff} implies a severe case of weight degeneracy, and vice versa.

The key question is therefore as follows:

Recognizing that the weight-degeneracy problem in sequential importance sampling is the rule rather than the exception, how do we overcome it?

The answer to this fundamental question lies in the use of *resampling* described earlier on in this section. For example, the algorithmic formulation of a particle filter could include a prescribed *threshold*, denoted by N_{thr}. When the effective sample size N_{eff} drops below the threshold N_{thr}, the SIS procedure is momentarily stopped and a resampling step is applied, after which the SIS procedure is resumed; this process is repeated until the filtering is terminated.

The Sampling–Importance-Resampling Particle Filter

The first practical implementation of a particle filter was demonstrated by Gordon, Salmond, and Smith (1993) under the name "bootstrap filter." Prior to the publication of the Gordon–Salmond–Smith paper, the serious problem of weight degeneracy in sequential importance sampling was neither clearly identified nor satisfactorily cured. In this 1993 paper, the weight-degeneracy problem was solved through a rejuvenation process whereby particles associated with small weights are pruned away, and particles with large weights are not only retained, but also replicated, much in the same way as in the traditional nonsequential sampling procedure. Indeed, it is for this reason that nowadays the bootstrap filter is commonly referred to as the *sampling–importance-resampling (SIR) filter*. The important point to take from this brief historical account is that the SIR filter was the first successful demonstration of nonlinear filtering using Monte Carlo simulation.

The SIR filter is simple to implement—hence its popular use for solving nonlinear filtering problems. The distinctive features of the filter are twofold:

1. *The prior as the importance distribution.* Examining the recursive formula of Eq. (14.116) for updating the weights, we see that the importance distribution is defined by how we choose the denominator $q(\mathbf{x}_n^{(i)}|\mathbf{x}_{n-1}^{(i)}, \mathbf{y}_n)$ on the right-hand side of the equation. In the SIR filter, this choice is made by setting

$$q(\mathbf{x}_n|\mathbf{x}_{n-1}, \mathbf{y}_n) = p(\mathbf{x}_n|\mathbf{x}_{n-1}) \tag{14.119}$$

where, on the right-hand side of the equation, $p(\mathbf{x}_n|\mathbf{x}_{n-1})$ is the prior, or state-transition distribution. In effect, the SIR filter *blindly* samples from the prior $p(\mathbf{x}_n|\mathbf{x}_{n-1})$, completely ignoring the information about the state $\mathbf{x}_n$ contained in the observation $\mathbf{y}_n$. Equation (14.119) follows from the Markovian assumption.

2. *Sampling importance resampling.* In the SIR filter, resampling is applied at every time-step of the nonlinear filtering process; consequently, in Eq. (14.116) we have

$$w_{n-1}^{(i)} = 1/N \qquad \text{for } i = 1, 2, ..., N \tag{14.120}$$

Because $1/N$ is a constant, it may be ignored. Thus, the need for an accumulation over time of the incremental correction factor in Eq. (14.116) is no longer needed.

Accordingly, the use of Eqs. (14.119) and (14.120) in Eq. (14.116) yields the much simplified formula

$$\tilde{w}_n^{(i)} \propto l(\mathbf{y}_n|\mathbf{x}_n^{(i)}) \qquad \text{for } i = 1, 2, ..., N \tag{14.121}$$

where $l(\mathbf{y}_n|\mathbf{x}_n^{(i)})$ is the likelihood function of the observation $\mathbf{y}_n$, given the state $\mathbf{x}_n^{(i)}$ for particle i. Naturally, normalization of the importance weights calculated using the proportionality equation of Eq. (14.121) is carried out after each resampling step of the SIR filtering algorithm.

Table 14.5 presents a summary of the SIR filter.

From the discussion just presented, it is apparent that the assumptions made in formulating the SIR filter are of a mild sort, as summarized here:

1. The nonlinear function $\mathbf{a}_n(\cdot, \cdot)$ in the process model of Eq. (14.1) and the nonlinear function $\mathbf{b}_n(\cdot, \cdot)$ in the measurement model of Eq. (14.2) must be both known.

TABLE 14.5   Summary of the SIR Algorithm for Particle Filtering

Notation
The particles are denoted by $i = 1, 2, ..., N$, where N is the total number of particles.

Initialization
Given the state distribution $p(\mathbf{x})$ and $\mathbf{x}_0$ as the initial value of $\mathbf{x}$, randomly sample

$$\mathbf{x}_0^{(i)} \sim p(\mathbf{x}_0)$$

where the notation "$x \sim p$" is short for "x is an observation from the distribution p," and set the initial weight

$$w_0^{(i)} = \frac{1}{N}$$

where $i = 1, 2, ..., N$.

Recursions
For each time-step $n = 1, 2, 3, ...$, followed by the index $i = 1, 2, ..., N$, do the following:

1. With the importance distribution defined by

   $$q(\mathbf{x}_n | \mathbf{x}_{n-1}^{(i)}, \mathbf{y}_n) = p(\mathbf{x}_n | \mathbf{x}_{n-1}^{(i)})$$

   where the prior $p(\mathbf{x}_n | \mathbf{x}_{n-1}^{(i)})$ is assumed to be known, draw samples

   $$\mathbf{x}_n^{(i)} \sim p(\mathbf{x}_n | \mathbf{x}_{n-1}^{(i)})$$

2. Compute the importance weights

   $$\tilde{w}_n^{(i)} = l(\mathbf{y}_n | \mathbf{x}_n^{(i)})$$

   where the likelihood $l(\mathbf{y}_n | \mathbf{x}_n^{(i)})$ is also assumed to be known. Hence, compute the normalized weights

   $$w_n^{(i)} = \frac{\tilde{w}_n^{(i)}}{\sum_{j=1}^{N} \tilde{w}_n^{(j)}}$$

3. To resample, draw a set of N discrete random variables $\{I^{(1)}, I^{(2)}, ..., I^{(N)}\}$ that take values in the corresponding set $\{1, 2, ..., N\}$ with probabilities

   $$P(I^{(s)} = i) = w_n^{(i)}$$

   Hence, set

   $$\tilde{\mathbf{x}}_n^{(i)} = \mathbf{x}_n^{(i)}$$

   and

   $$w_n^{(i)} = \frac{1}{N}$$

4. Continue the computation until the filtering is completed.

2. Determining the prior $p(\mathbf{x}_n | \mathbf{x}_{n-1})$ requires knowledge of the statistics of the dynamic noise $\boldsymbol{\omega}_n$ in Eq. (14.1); drawing samples (particles) from the underlying distribution of the dynamic noise $\boldsymbol{\omega}_n$ must therefore be permissible.

3. The likelihood function $l(\mathbf{y}_n | \mathbf{x}_n)$, involved in formulating Eq. (14.121), must be known, which, in turn, means that the statistics of the measurement noise $\boldsymbol{v}_n$ in Eq. (14.2) are available.

One other issue that needs to be addressed in designing the SIR filter (and, for that matter, any particle filter) is the selection of a suitable value for the number of particles, N. On one hand, N should be large enough to satisfy the asymptotic result of Eq. (14.111). On the other hand, N should be small enough to keep the total computational burden at a manageable level, since the particles are acting in parallel at each time-step of the filtering. (Here, we are assuming that the number of particles is maintained at the same value N after the importance sampling and resampling operations.) The value selected for N must therefore be a "compromise" between these two conflicting situations, which can be resolved only on a problem-by-problem basis.

The Optimal Choice of Importance Distribution

The prior distribution $p(\mathbf{x}_n|\mathbf{x}_{n-1})$ provides an appealing way of choosing the importance distribution, as is the case in the SIR filter. However, such a choice in the design of particle filters could lead to a poor performance under unfavorable conditions. For example, if the input data are corrupted by outliers, we have "noninformative" observations, and if the variance of measurement noise is small then we have "highly informative" observations. In such situations, there is the potential for a *mismatch* between the predictive prior distribution and the posterior distribution of the state given the observations. In order to mitigate this mismatch in an "optimal" fashion, the particles should be chosen to move in the state space under an *importance distribution*, defined by (Doucet et al., 2000; Cappé et al., 2007) as

$$q(\mathbf{x}_n|\mathbf{x}_{n-1}, \mathbf{y}_n)_{\text{opt}} = \frac{p(\mathbf{x}_n|\mathbf{x}_{n-1})\, l(\mathbf{y}_n|\mathbf{x}_n)}{\int p(\mathbf{x}_n|\mathbf{x}_{n-1})\, l(\mathbf{y}_n|\mathbf{x}_n)\, d\mathbf{x}_n} \tag{14.122}$$

This particular choice of the importance distribution is optimal in the sense that the conditional variance of the weights is zero, given the prior history of the particles.

Substituting Eq. (14.122) into the SIS formula of Eq. (14.116) yields the weight update formula

$$\underbrace{w_n^{(i)}}_{\text{Updated weight}} \propto \underbrace{w_{n-1}^{(i)}}_{\text{Old weight}} \int \underbrace{p(\mathbf{x}_n|\mathbf{x}_{n-1}^{(i)})}_{\text{Prior}}\, \underbrace{l(\mathbf{y}_n|\mathbf{x}_n)}_{\text{Likelihood}} d\mathbf{x}_n \tag{14.123}$$

where we now see that the incremental correction factor (i.e., the integral term) depends only on the "past" position of the proposed particle $\mathbf{x}_{n-1}^{(i)}$ and the current observation $\mathbf{y}_n$.

An important difference between the optimal formula of Eq. (14.123) and the SIR formula of Eq. (14.121) should be noted: In the SIR filter, the particles are allowed to move blindly in the state space, whereas under the optimal importance distribution of Eq. (14.122), the particles are allowed to cluster in locations where the posterior distribution has a mass of high probability, which is clearly a desirable situation.

However, computation of the optimal importance distribution defined in Eq. (14.122) may *not* be a straightforward matter, except in some special cases. For example, in a class of state-space models for which the conditional distribution $p(\mathbf{x}_n|\mathbf{x}^{(i)}_{n-1}, \mathbf{y}_n)$ is Gaussian, choosing the optimal importance distribution to design a particle filter is indeed possible (Doucet et al., 2000).

14.9   COMPUTER EXPERIMENT: COMPARATIVE EVALUATION OF EXTENDED KALMAN AND PARTICLE FILTERS

The experimental setup for this comparative evaluation is based on the state-space model of a nonlinear, Gaussian dynamic system described by the following pair of equations:

System (state) model:

$$x_n = 0.5x_{n-1} + \frac{25x_{n-1}}{1 + x_{n-1}^2} + 8\cos(1.2(n - 1)) + \omega_n$$

Measurement (observation) model:

$$y_n = \frac{1}{20} x_n^2 + v_n$$

In this system, the dynamic noise ω_n is Gaussian $\mathcal{N}(0, 1)$, and the measurement noise v_n is also Gaussian $\mathcal{N}(0, 10)$. The true initial value of the state is $x_0 = 0.1$.

The SIR version of the particle filter was used in the experiment. The following experimental conditions were applied to both the EKF and SIR filters:

Simulated state trajectory: 50 time-steps long

Number of independent Monte Carlo runs: 100

Intial value of the filtered estimate: $\hat{x}_{0|0} = \mathcal{N}(x_0, 2)$

The specifications of the SIR particle filter were as follows:

- The number of particles, N, was 100.
- At each time-step of the filtering process, resampling was applied, followed by normalization of the importance weights.
- The prior (i.e., state transition) distribution was used as the importance distribution.

The results of the experiment are plotted in Figs. 14.6 and 14.7 for the EKF and SIR particle filter, respectively. In each figure, the solid curve is the true state, and the points shown as asterisks (printed in red) are the averaged results of 50 such runs. The upper and lower dotted curves in Figs. 14.6 and 14.7 define the confidence intervals of the state estimates produced by the EKF and the PF, respectively.

Examination of these two figures reveals the following observations:

- For the EKF, the averaged trajectory of the filtered estimate of the state deviates markedly from the true trajectory.

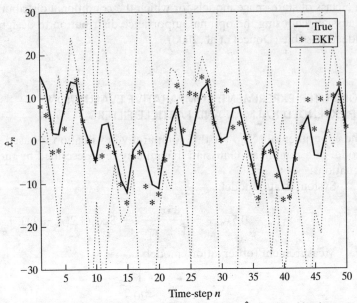

FIGURE 14.6 Plots of the ensemble-averaged state estimate $\hat{x}_n$ produced by the extended Kalman filter (EKF), shown as a sequence of points *. The upper and lower dotted curves (around the estimates) define the confidence interval of the state estimate produced by the extended Kalman filter. The continuous line is the actual evolution of the state across time n.

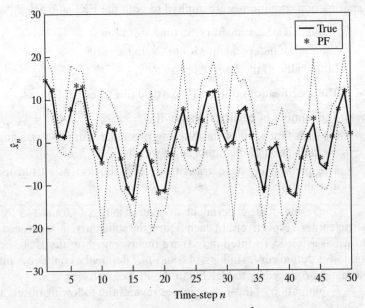

FIGURE 14.7 Plots of the ensemble-averaged state estimate $\hat{x}_n$ produced by the SIR particle filter, shown as a sequence of points *. The upper and lower dotted curves (around the estimates) define the confidence interval of the state estimate produced by the particle filter (PF). The continuous line is the actual evolution of the state across time n.

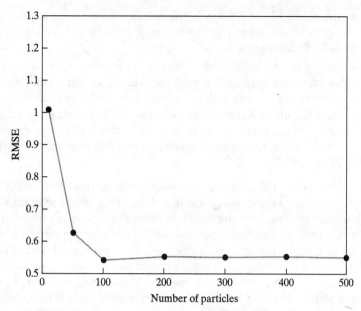

FIGURE 14.8   Plot of the root mean-square error (RMSE) versus the number of particles produced by the SIR particle filter; the points ● are experimentally computed.

- On the other hand, the corresponding averaged trajectory computed by the SIR particle filter follows the true trajectory quite closely.

One other experimental result, pertaining to the particle filter, is shown in Fig 14.8, where the root-mean-square error (RMSE) of the filtered estimate of the state is plotted against the number of particles used in the SIR particle filter. We see that the RMSE is initially high, progressively decreasing as the number of particles is increased. Beyond $N = 100$ particles, there is no significant change in the RMSE; the choice of $N = 100$ particles for the SIR filter in the experiment is therefore justified.

14.10   KALMAN FILTERING IN MODELING OF BRAIN FUNCTIONS

The discussion presented thus far in the chapter has focused on Kalman filter theory, followed by the Bayesian filter and its approximate forms. In so doing, we have emphasized the practical virtues of these filters as sequential state estimators, each in its own way. In this section, we present an overview of "Kalman-like filtering" for modeling different brain functions (Chen et al., 2007).

Dynamic Model of Visual Recognition

The visual cortex contains a hierarchically layered structure (from V1 to V5) and massive interconnections within the cortex and between the cortex and the visual thalamus (i.e., lateral geniculate nucleus, or LGN); for a brief description of these parts of the visual system, see Note 8 under the Notes and References of Chapter 12. Specifically, the visual cortex is endowed with two key anatomical properties (Chen et al., 2007):

- *Abundant Use of Feedback.* The connections between any two areas of the visual cortex are bilateral, thereby accommodating the transmission of forward as well as feedback signals.

- *Hierarchical Multiscale Structure.* The receptive fields of lower area cells in the visual cortex span only a small fraction of the visual field, whereas the receptive fields of higher area cells increase in size until they span almost the entire visual field. It is this constrained network structure that makes it possible for the fully connected visual cortex to perform prediction in a high-dimensional data space with a reduced number of free parameters, and therefore in a computationally efficient manner.

In a series of studies over a period extending from 1997 to 2003, Rao and collaborators exploited these two properties of the visual cortex to build a dynamic model of visual recognition, with the understanding that vision is fundamentally a nonlinear dynamic process. The *Rao–Ballard model* of visual recognition is a hierarchically organized neural network, with each intermediate level of the hierarchy receiving two kinds of information: bottom-up information from the preceding level and top-down information from the higher level. For its implementation, the model uses a multiscale estimation algorithm that may be viewed as a hierarchical from of the extended Kalman filter. In particular, the EKF is used to simultaneously learn the feedforward, feedback, and prediction parameters of the model, using visual experiences in a dynamic environment. The resulting adaptive processes operate on two different time scales:

- The *fast* dynamic state-estimation process allows the dynamic model to anticipate incoming stimuli.

- The *slow* Hebbian learning process provides for synaptic-weight adjustments in the model.

Specifically, the Rao–Ballard model can be viewed as a neural network implementation of the EKF that employs top-down feedback between layers and is able to learn the visual receptive fields for both static images and time-varying image sequences. The model is very appealing in that it is simple and flexible, yet powerful. Above all, it allows a Bayesian interpretation of visual perception (Knill and Richards, 1995; Lee and Mumford, 2003).

Dynamic Model of Sound-Stream Segregation

It is well known in the computational neuroscience literature that auditory perception shares many common features with visual perception (Shamma, 2001). Specifically, Elhilali (2004) addressed the problem of sound-stream segregation within the framework of computational auditory scene analysis (CASA). In the computational model described therein, the hidden vector contains an internal (abstract) representation of sound streams; the observation is represented by a set of feature vectors or acoustic cues (e.g., pitch and onset) derived from the sound mixture. Since temporal continuity in sound streams is an important characteristic, it can be used to construct the system (state) model. The measurement model describes the cortical filtering process with the cortical model's parameters. The basic component of dynamic sound-stream segregation is twofold: First, infer the distribution of sound patterns into a set of streams at each time instant; second, estimate the state of each cluster, given the new observations. The second estimation problem is solved by a Kalman filtering operation, and the first clustering problem is solved by a Hebbian-like competitive-learning operation.

The dynamic nature of the Kalman filter is important not only for sound-stream segregation, but also for sound localization and tracking, all of which are regarded as the key ingredients for *active audition* (Haykin and Chen, 2006).

Dynamic Models of Cerebellum and Motor Learning

The cerebellum has an important role to play in the control and coordination of movements, which are ordinarily carried out in a very smooth and almost effortless manner. In the literature, it has been suggested that the cerebellum plays the role of a controller or the neural analog of a dynamic state estimator. The key point in support of the dynamic state-estimation hypothesis is embodied in the following statement, the validity of which has been confirmed by decades of work on the design of automatic tracking and guidance systems:

> *Any system, be it a biological or artificial system, required to predict or control the trajectory of a stochastic multivariate dynamic system can do so only by using or invoking the essence of Kalman filtering in one way or another.*

Building on this key point, Paulin (1997) presents several lines of evidence which favor the hypothesis that the cerebellum is a neural analog of a dynamic state estimator. A particular line of evidence presented by Paulin relates to the vestibular–ocular reflex (VOR), which is part of the oculomotor system. The function of the VOR is to maintain visual (i.e., retinal) image stability by making eye rotations that are opposite to head rotations, as discussed in the introductory chapter. This function is mediated by a neural network that includes the cerebellar cortex and vestibular nuclei. From the discussion presented in Section 14.3, we know that a Kalman filter is an optimum linear system with minimum variance for predicting the state trajectory of a dynamic system using noisy measurements; it does so by estimating the particular state trajectory that is most likely, given an assumed model for the underlying dynamics of the system. A consequence of this strategy is that, when the dynamic system deviates from the assumed model, the Kalman filter produces estimation errors of a predictable kind, which may be attributed to the filter "believing in" the assumed model rather than the actual sensory data. According to Paulin (1997), estimation errors of this kind are observed in the behavior of the VOR.

Summarizing Comments

To summarize, the predictor–corrector property of the Kalman filter lends itself as a potentially useful candidate for *predictive coding* in computational neural modeling, which is a fundamental property of the autonomous brain functions in a dynamic environment. It is also important to note that in the aforementioned examples, the hypothesis that the neural system (e.g., cerebellum or neocortex) is a neural analog of a Kalman filter is not to be taken to imply that, in physical terms, the neural system resembles a

Kalman filter. Rather, in general, biological systems do perform some form of state estimation, and the pertinent neural algorithms may have the general "flavor" of a Kalman filter. Moreover, it is plausible that some form of state estimation is broadly distributed throughout other parts of the central nervous system.[5]

14.11 SUMMARY AND DISCUSSION

The theme throughout the material presented in this chapter has been that of estimating the unknown (hidden) state of a dynamic system, given a sequence of observations that are dependent on the state. Basic to the solution of this problem is a state-space model that consists of a pair of equations: One equation models the evolution of the state across time with a dynamic noise driving that evolution, and the other models the noisy version of observations on the state. It is assumed that the state-space model is Markovian.

Kalman Filter Theory

When the dynamic system is linear and Gaussian, the optimal estimator of the state is the celebrated Kalman filter. When the dynamic system is nonlinear and Gaussian, we may use the extended Kalman filter by using first-order Taylor-series approximations of the state-space model. This approximate approach to nonlinear filtering yields acceptable results, provided that the nonlinearity is of a mild sort.

Bayesian Filter

In theory, the Bayesian filter is the most generic nonlinear filter and includes the Kalman filter as a special case. However, to implement the Bayesian filter in practice, it has to be approximated. The approximation may follow one of two routes:

1. *Direct numerical approximation of the posterior.* The idea behind this first approach is summed up as follows:

   > *Use numerical methods to facilitate the approximate estimation of the state of a nonlinear dynamic system through linear Kalman filter theory.*

   Examples of this approach to nonlinear filtering include the extended Kalman filter, the unscented Kalman filter (Julier et al., 2000), the quadrature Kalman filter (Ito and Xing, 2000; Arasaratnam et al., 2007), and the cubature Kalman filter (Arasaratnam and Haykin, 2009). Among these nonlinear filters, the extended Kalman filter is the simplest, and the cubature Kalman filter is the most powerful. Simply put, increased computational complexity is progressively traded for increased reliability.

2. *Indirect numerical approximation of the posterior.* The most prominent and widely used example of this second approach to nonlinear filtering is the particle filter. With the posterior distribution of the Bayesian filter being inaccessible, we resort to drawing samples randomly from an importance, or instrumental, distribution whose support must include that of the posterior distribution. Moreover, recursive

implementation of the particle filter is realized through the sequential importance-sampling (SIS) procedure. To circumvent the likelihood of the filter running into the undesirable situation of weight degeneracy, the common practice is to follow the importance sampling with resampling, whereby relatively weak normalized weights are pruned away and the remaining normalized weights are replicated in accordance with their probability of occurrence.

Although the Kalman filter and its variants and approximate extensions on one hand, and particle filters on the other hand, are radically different in their analytic derivations and practical implementations, they do share an important property: *The predictor–corrector property.*

Computational Considerations

(i) *Kalman Filters.* Whenever we develop a filtering algorithm, it is customary to examine the convergence behavior of the algorithm. In particular, a user of the algorithm would like to know the conditions under which the algorithm is likely to diverge, and how to fix the divergence problem. For example, it is well known that the Kalman filter suffers from the divergence phenomenon, which can arise because of the following two factors:

- model mismatch between the state-space model (on which the derivation of the Kalman filter is based) and the underlying physics of the actual dynamic environment responsible for generation of the observations;
- inadequate arithmetic precision used in actual implementation of the Kalman filter.

The root of the divergence phenomenon may be traced to the matrix $\mathbf{P}_{n|n}$ violating the nonnegative-definite property of a covariance matrix. Square-root filtering provides a method for mitigating the divergence phenomenon.

(ii) *Particle Filters.* Turning next to the computational aspects of particle filters, we find that coverage of this topic in the literature has been somewhat controversial. This observation may not be surprising, given the Monte Carlo-based roots of particle filtering. In any event, here we summarize some important results reported in the literature:

1. For a prescribed number of particles, N, the error incurred in the Monte Carlo estimate of the integral in Eq. (14.84) is on the order of $O(N^{-1/2})$, which is independent of the dimension of the state vector (Ristic et al., 2004). This result is based on two assumptions:

   - The posterior distribution $p(\mathbf{x}_n|\mathbf{Y}_n)$ in the integrand of Eq. (14.84) is known exactly.
   - The particles (i.e., samples) are statistically independent.

   However, both of these assumptions are violated in particle filtering: Exact knowledge of $p(\mathbf{x}_n|\mathbf{Y}_n)$ is not available, and in a particle filter using resampling, the particle trajectories become actually dependent.

2. In Crisan and Doucet (2002), an upper bound on the variance of the estimation error produced by a particle filter is shown to be $O(N^{-1/2})$ multiplied by a constant scaling factor c.

Unfortunately, this result has led to the erroneous conclusion that the estimation error produced by a particle filter is independent of the dimension of the state vector and therefore immune from the curse of dimensionality. In Daum and Huang (2003), it is argued that the multiplying factor is not a constant; rather, it increases exponentially with time n—hence the notation c_n. Moreover, it depends strongly on the dimension of the state vector, which means that particle filters do suffer from the curse of dimensionality.

3. In an independent study reported in Bengtsson et al. (2008), it is demonstrated that "brute-force-only" implementations of a particle filter to describe high-dimensional posterior distributions will *fail*, due to the curse of dimensionality. The recommended remedy to this phenomenon is to achieve some form of *dimensionality reduction* prior to particle filtering; as pointed out in Chapter 10, high-dimensional data are usually sparse and therefore open to dimensionality reduction.

NOTES AND REFERENCES

1. *Correlated Dynamic and Measurement Noise.* In a linear Gaussian state-space model, correlation between the dynamic noise ω_n and measurement noise v_n is sometimes permitted. This condition is used in econometrics. Specifically, we now have

$$\mathbb{E}[\omega_n v_k^T] = \begin{cases} \mathbf{C}_n & \text{for } k = n \\ \mathbf{0} & \text{for } k \neq n \end{cases}$$

where $\mathbf{C}_n$ is a known matrix. According to this equation, the two noise processes ω_n and v_n are contemporaneously correlated, but they remain uncorrelated at nonzero lags. In such a situation, formulation of the Kalman filter has to be modified. It appears that this issue was first discussed in Jazwinski (1970); see also Harvey (1989).

2. *Information Filtering Algorithm.* The covariance-filtering algorithm is one way of implementing the Kalman filter. In another form called the information-filtering algorithm, the Kalman filter is implemented by propagating the inverse of the covariance matrix $\mathbf{P}_{n|n}$; this inverse is related to *Fisher's information matrix*, which permits an interpretation of the filter in information-theoretic terms. For more detail on the information-filtering algorithm, see Chapter 10 of Haykin (2002).

3. *Notation.* To be rigorously correct in Eq. (14.6) and consistent with the notation used earlier in the book, we should write $p_{\mathbf{X}}(\mathbf{x})$ in place of $p(\mathbf{x})$, where the subscript $\mathbf{X}$ in $p_{\mathbf{X}}(\mathbf{x})$ stands for the random vector $\mathbf{X}$ whose sample value is denoted by $\mathbf{x}$. We have used the notation $p(\mathbf{x})$ in Eq. (14.6) and other similar situations in the chapter for two reasons:

   - to simplify the presentation, as this chapter is rather rich in the probabilistic characterization of stochastic processes, and
   - most importantly, to avoid confusion in the latter part of the chapter, where the symbol $\mathbf{X}$ is used to represent a sequence of states.

4. *Bayes Estimation.* A classic problem in estimation theory is that of the *Bayes estimation of a random parameter*. There are different answers to this problem, depending on how the *cost function* in the Bayes estimation is formulated. A particular type of the Bayes estimator of interest to us is the so-called *conditional mean estimator*. In this note, we do two things:

(1) derive the formula for the conditional mean estimator from first principles, and (2) show that such an estimator is the same as a minimum mean-square-error estimator.

Toward those ends, consider a *random parameter x*. We are given an *observation y* that depends on *x*, and the requirement is to estimate *x*. Let $\hat{x}(y)$ denote an *estimate* of the parameter *x*; the symbol $\hat{x}(y)$ emphasizes the fact that the estimate is a function of the observation *y*. Let *R* denote a cost function that depends on both *x* and its estimate. Then, according to Bayes's estimation theory, we may define the *Bayes risk* as

$$R = \mathbb{E}[C(x, \hat{x}(y))]$$
$$= \int_{-\infty}^{\infty} \int_{-\infty}^{\infty} C(x, \hat{x}(y))p(x, y)dx\,dy \tag{A}$$

where $p(x,y)$ is the joint probability density function of *x* and *y*. For a specifie cost function $C(x, \hat{x}(y))$, the *Bayes estimate* is defined as the estimate $\hat{x}(y)$ that *minimizes* the risk *R*.

A cost function of particular interest (and that is very much in the spirit of the material covered in this book) is the *mean-square error*, specified as the square of the *estimation error*, which is itself defined as the difference between the actual parameter value *x* and the estimate $\hat{x}(y)$; that is,

$$\varepsilon = x - \hat{x}(y)$$

Correspondingly, we write

$$C(x, \hat{x}(y)) = C(x - \hat{x}(y))$$

or, more simply,

$$C(\varepsilon) = \varepsilon^2$$

We may therefore rewrite Eq. (A) as

$$R_{ms} = \int_{-\infty}^{\infty} \int_{-\infty}^{\infty} (x - \hat{x}(y))^2\, p(x, y)dx\,dy \tag{B}$$

where the subscripts in the risk R_{ms} indicate the use of the mean-square error as its basis. From probability theory, we have

$$p(x, y) = p(x|y)p(y) \tag{C}$$

where $p(x|y)$ is the conditional probability density function of *x* given *y*, and $p(y)$ is the (marginal) probability density function of *y*. Hence, using Eq. (C) in Eq. (B), we get

$$R_{ms} = \int_{-\infty}^{\infty} \left[\int_{-\infty}^{\infty} (x - \hat{x}(y))^2\, p(x|y)dx \right] p(y)dy \tag{D}$$

We now recognize that the inner integral (inside the square brackets) and $p(y)$ in Eq. (D) are both nonnegative. We may therefore minimize the risk R_{ms} simply by minimizing the inner integral. Let the estimate so obtained be denoted by $\hat{x}_{ms}(y)$. We find $\hat{x}_{ms}(y)$ by differentiating the inner integral with respect to $\hat{x}(y)$ and then setting the result equal to zero.

To simplify the presentation, let *I* denote the inner integral in Eq. (D). Then differentiating *I* with respect to $\hat{x}(y)$ yields

$$\frac{dI}{d\hat{x}} = -2\int_{-\infty}^{\infty} xp(x|y)dx + 2\hat{x}(y)\int_{-\infty}^{\infty} p(x|y)dx \tag{E}$$

The second integral on the right-hand side of Eq. (E) represents the total area under a probability density function and therefore equals unity. Hence, setting the derivative $dI/d\hat{x}$ equal to zero, we obtain

$$\hat{x}_{ms}(y) = \int_{-\infty}^{\infty} x p(x|y) dx \tag{F}$$

The solution defined by Eq. (F) is a unique minimum.

The estimator $\hat{x}_{ms}(y)$ defined in Eq. (F) is naturally a *minimum mean-square-error estimator*. For another interpretation of this estimator, we recognize that the integral on the right-hand side of the equation is just the *conditional mean* of the parameter x, given the observation y.

We therefore conclude that the *minimum mean-square-error estimator and the conditional mean estimator are indeed one and the same*. In other words, we have

$$\hat{x}_{ms}(y) = \mathbb{E}[x|y] \tag{G}$$

Substituting Eq. (G) for the estimate $\hat{x}(y)$ into Eq. (D), we find that the inner integral is just the *conditional variance* of the parameter x, given y. Accordingly, the minimum value of the risk R_{ms} is just the average of this conditional variance over all observations y.

5. *Bayesian Filtering Based on Spike Trains.* In the discussion presented in Section (14.10) on the dynamic modeling of brain functions, we followed a traditional signal-processing framework, with emphasis on the role of Kalman filter theory.

In fact, however, cortical neural networks observe an uncertain dynamic environment through spike trains received from sensory afferents, and not directly from the environment. *Spike trains* provide the principal communication channels among neurons in the brain; they are represented in terms of the arrival times of the spikes (Koch, 1999; Rieke et al., 1997). Bobrowski et al. (2007) considered the problem of optimally estimating the probability distribution of the hidden state of a dynamic environment, given noisy observations in the form of spike trains. Most importantly, they described a linear recurrent network model that is capable of exactly implementing Bayesian filtering in real time. The input may be multimodal, consisting of two different subsets—one visual and the other auditory, for example. Moreover, synthetic examples were presented to demonstrate the operation of the system.

It is noteworthy that nonlinear filtering in continuous time, based on point-process observations, was first described by Snyder (1972); see also Snyder's 1975 book on random point processes.

PROBLEMS

Kalman Filters

14.1 The predicted state-error vector is defined by

$$\boldsymbol{\varepsilon}_{n|n-1} = \mathbf{x}_n - \hat{\mathbf{x}}_{n|n-1}$$

where $\hat{\mathbf{x}}_{n|n-1}$ is the minimum mean-square estimate of the state $\mathbf{x}_n$, given the observed data sequence $\mathbf{y}_1, ..., \mathbf{y}_{n-1}$. Let $\boldsymbol{\omega}_n$ and $\boldsymbol{v}_n$ denote the dynamic-noise and measurement-noise vectors, respectively. Show that $\boldsymbol{\varepsilon}_{n|n-1}$ is orthogonal to both $\boldsymbol{\omega}_n$ and $\boldsymbol{v}_n$; that is, show that

$$\mathbb{E}[\boldsymbol{\varepsilon}_{n|n-1}\boldsymbol{\omega}_n^T] = \mathbf{0}$$

and

$$\mathbb{E}[\boldsymbol{\varepsilon}_{n|n-1}\boldsymbol{v}_n^T] = \mathbf{0}$$

14.2 Consider a set of scalar observations y_n of zero mean that is transformed into the corresponding set of innovation process α_n of zero mean and variance $\sigma_{\alpha,n}^2$. Let the estimate of the state vector x_i, given this set of data, be expressed as

$$\hat{x}_{i|n} = \sum_{k=1}^{n} b_{i,k}\alpha_k,$$

where $b_{i,k}, k = 1, 2, ..., n$, is a set of vectors to be determined. The requirement is to choose the $b_{i,k}$ so as to minimize the expected value of the squared norm of the estimated state-error vector

$$\varepsilon_{i,n} = x_i - \hat{x}_{i|n}.$$

Show that this minimization yields the result

$$\hat{x}_{i|n} = \sum_{k=1}^{n} \mathbb{E}[x_i\varphi_k]\varphi_k,$$

where

$$\varphi_k = \frac{\alpha_k}{\sigma_{\alpha,k}}$$

is the normalized innovation. This result may be viewed as a special case of Eqs. (14.24) and (14.26).

14.3 Given a sequence of observables $\{y_k\}_{k=1}^{n}$. How can you define the innovations process associated with the observable y_n, Discuss why it is easier to work with the innovations process rather than the observables themselves.

14.4 The following equation represents the filtered estimated of the state.

$$\hat{x}_{n|n} = \hat{x}_{n|n-1} + G_n\alpha_n$$

Why this equation is known as the predictor-corrector formula in Kalman filter theory?

14.5 The Kalman gain G_n, defined in Eq. (14.31), involves the inverse matrix R_n^{-1}. The matrix R_n is itself defined in Eq. (14.22). The matrix R_n is nonnegative definite, but not necessarily nonsingular.

(a) Why is R_n nonnegative definite?

(b) What prior condition would you impose on the matrix $Q_{v,n}$ to ensure that the inverse matrix R_n^{-1} exists?

14.6 In many cases, the prediction-error covariance matrix $P_{n+1|n}$ converges to the steady-state value P as the number of iterations, n, approaches infinity. Show that the limiting value P satisfies the *algebraic Riccati equation*

$$PB^T(BPB^T + Q_v)^{-1}(BP - Q_\omega) = 0$$

where it is assumed that the state-transition matrix equals the identity matrix and the matrices B, Q_ω, and Q_v are the limiting values of $B_n, Q_{\omega,n}$, and $Q_{v,n}$, respectively.

14.7 The Kalman filter is a double-loop feedback system. Discuss the role of the two feedback loops.

14.8 Examination of the predictor–corrector framework in the Kalman filter reveals the following two properties:

(a) Computation of the predicted state $\hat{x}_{n+1|n}$ and the prediction-error covariance matrix $P_{n+1|n}$ relies only on information extracted from the system (state) model.

(b) Computation of the filtered stated $\hat{x}_{n|n}$ and the filtering-error covariance matrix $P_{n|n}$ relies only on information extracted from the measurement model.

Justify these two properties of the Kalman filter.

14.9 The prediction-error covariance matrix $\mathbf{P}_{n+1|n}$ and the filtering-error covariance matrix $\mathbf{P}_{n|n}$ can never assume a common value. Why?

14.10 The derivation of the Kalman filter presented in Section 14.3 is based on the notion of minimum mean-square-error estimation. In this problem, we explore another derivation of the Kalman filter, based on the *maximum a posteriori (MAP) probability criterion*. For this derivation, it is assumed that the dynamic noise $\boldsymbol{\omega}_n$ and measurement noise $\boldsymbol{\nu}_n$ are both zero-mean Gaussian processes with covariance matrices $\mathbf{Q}_{\omega,n}$ and $\mathbf{Q}_{\nu,n}$ respectively. Let $p(\mathbf{x}|\mathbf{Y}_n)$ denote the conditional probability distribution of $\mathbf{x}_n$, given that $\mathbf{Y}_n$ denotes the set of observations $\mathbf{y}_1, ..., \mathbf{y}_n$. The MAP estimate of $\mathbf{x}_n$, denoted by $\hat{\mathbf{x}}_{\text{MAP},n}$, is defined as that particular value of $\mathbf{x}_n$ which maximizes $p(\mathbf{x}_n|\mathbf{Y}_n)$, or, equivalently, the logarithm of $p(\mathbf{x}_n|\mathbf{Y}_n)$. This evaluation requires that we solve for the condition

$$\frac{\partial \log p(\mathbf{x}_n|\mathbf{Y}_n)}{\partial \mathbf{x}_n}\bigg|_{\mathbf{x}_n=\hat{\mathbf{x}}_{\text{MAP},n}} = \mathbf{0} \tag{A}$$

Show that

$$\frac{\partial^2 \log p(\mathbf{x}_n|\mathbf{Y}_n)}{\partial^2 \mathbf{x}_n}\bigg|_{\mathbf{x}_n=\hat{\mathbf{x}}_{\text{MAP},n}} < \mathbf{0} \tag{B}$$

(a) We may express the distribution $p(\mathbf{x}_n|\mathbf{Y}_n)$ as

$$p(\mathbf{x}_n|\mathbf{Y}_n) = \frac{p(\mathbf{y}_n/\mathbf{Y}_{n-1})}{p(\mathbf{Y}_n)}$$

which, in light of the definition of a joint distribution, may also be expressed as

$$p(\mathbf{x}_n|\mathbf{Y}_n) = \frac{p(\mathbf{x}_n, \mathbf{y}_n, \mathbf{Y}_{n-1})}{p(\mathbf{y}_n, \mathbf{Y}_{n-1})}$$

Hence, show that

$$p(\mathbf{x}_n|\mathbf{Y}_n) = \frac{p(\mathbf{y}_n|\mathbf{x}_n)p(\mathbf{x}_n|\mathbf{Y}_{n-1})}{p(\mathbf{y}_n, \mathbf{Y}_{n-1})}$$

(b) Using the Gaussian characterizations of the dynamic noise $\boldsymbol{\omega}_n$ and measurement noise $\boldsymbol{\nu}_n$, derive expressions for $p(\mathbf{y}_n|\mathbf{x}_n)$ and $p(\mathbf{x}_n|\mathbf{Y}_{n-1})$. Next recognizing that $p(\mathbf{y}_n|\mathbf{Y}_{n-1})$ may be treated as a constant, since it does not depend on the state $\mathbf{x}_n$, formulate the expression for $p(\mathbf{x}_n|\mathbf{Y}_n)$.

(c) Using the results of part (b) in Eq. (A), followed by the matrix inversion lemma (discussed in Chapter 5), derive the formula for $\hat{\mathbf{x}}_{\text{MAP},n}$ and show that it is exactly the same as the Kalman filter derived in Section 14.3.

(d) Finally, show that the MAP estimate $\hat{\mathbf{x}}_{\text{MAP},n}$ derived in part (c) does indeed satisfy Eq. (B).

14.11 Consider a linear dynamic system described by the noiseless state-space model

$$\mathbf{x}_{n+1} = \mathbf{A}\mathbf{x}_n$$

and

$$\mathbf{y}_n = \mathbf{B}\mathbf{x}_n$$

where $\mathbf{x}_n$ is the state, $\mathbf{y}_n$ is the observation, $\mathbf{A}$ is the transition matrix, and $\mathbf{B}$ is the measurement matrix.

(a) Show that

$$\hat{\mathbf{x}}_{n|n} = (\mathbf{I} - \mathbf{G}_n\mathbf{B})\hat{\mathbf{x}}_{n|n-1} + \mathbf{G}_n\mathbf{y}_n$$
$$\boldsymbol{\alpha}_n = \mathbf{y}_n - \mathbf{B}\hat{\mathbf{x}}_{n|n-1}$$

where $\mathbf{G}_n$ is the Kalman gain and $\boldsymbol{\alpha}_n$ denotes the innovations process. How is $\mathbf{G}_n$ defined?

(b) Using the results of part (a), justify the statement that the Kalman filter is a *whitening filter* in that it produces a "white" estimation error in response to $\mathbf{y}_n$.

14.12 Table 14.2 presents a summary of the Kalman filter based on filtered estimation of the state. Develop another summary of the Kalman filter, this time using the predicted estimate of the state as its basis, and depict the corresponding signal-flow graph of the Kalman filter.

Square-Root Kalman Filter

14.13 The identities of Eqs. (14.47) through (14.49) follow from equating corresponding terms in the two sides of Eq. (14.46). There is actually a fourth identity to be considered. Find this identity and show that it is the transpose of one of the identities already known.

Extended Kalman Filter

14.14 Starting with the modified system (state) model of Eq. (14.64), show that $\boldsymbol{\xi}_n$, a known (i.e., nonrandom) vector, is defined by Eq. (14.75).

14.15 Let $\mathbf{P}_{xy,n}$ denote the cross-covariance matrix between the state-error vector $\mathbf{x}_n - \hat{\mathbf{x}}_{n|n-1}$ and the measurement-error vector $\mathbf{y}_n - \hat{\mathbf{y}}_{n|n-1}$. Let $\mathbf{P}_{yy,n}$ denote the covariance matrix of the measurement-error vector $\mathbf{y}_n - \hat{\mathbf{y}}_{n|n-1}$. Show that the modified Kalman gain in

$$\mathbf{G}_{f,n} = \mathbf{A}_{n+1,n}^{-1}\mathbf{G}_n$$

may be expressed in terms of these two covariance matrices as

$$\mathbf{G}_{f,n} = \mathbf{P}_{xy,n}\mathbf{P}_{yy,n}^{-1}$$

Bayesian Filter

14.16 (a) Prove Eq. (14.77)
(b) Prove Eq. (14.83).

Particle Filters

14.17 The extended Kalman filter and particle filter represent two different examples of nonlinear filters in the following sense:

- Derivation of the extended Kalman filter is based on a *local approach* under statistical distribution constraints.
- On the other hand, derivation of particle filters is based on a *global approach* with no statistical constraints.

Elaborate on these two statements.

14.18 To improve on the method of importance sampling, another stage of resampling is performed in which a second set of samples is drawn from the intermediate set, taking into account the relative strengths of the normalized importance weights. However, the use of resampling introduces some practical limitations of its own. Discuss these limitations.

14.19 Consider a nonlinear dynamic system whose state-space model is defined by

$$\mathbf{x}_{n+1} = \mathbf{a}_n(\mathbf{x}_n) + \boldsymbol{\omega}_n$$

and

$$\mathbf{y}_n = \mathbf{b}_n(\mathbf{x}_n) + \boldsymbol{\nu}_n$$

where the dynamic noise $\boldsymbol{\omega}_n$ and the measurement noise $\boldsymbol{v}_n$ are both zero-mean, white-noise Gaussian processes with covariance matrices $\mathbf{Q}_{\omega,n}$ and $\mathbf{Q}_{v,n}$, respectively. Determine the following distributions:

(a) The prior predictive distribution $p(\mathbf{x}_n|\mathbf{Y}_{n-1})$.

(b) The likelihood $p(\mathbf{y}_n|\mathbf{x}_n)$.

(c) The posterior $p(\mathbf{x}_n|\mathbf{Y}_n)$, where $\mathbf{Y}_n$ denotes the observation sequence $\mathbf{y}_1, \mathbf{y}_2, ..., \mathbf{y}_n$.

14.20 Continuing from Problem 14.19, show that the optimal importance density $p(\mathbf{x}_n|\mathbf{x}_{n-1}, \mathbf{y}_n)$ is Gaussian.

Computer experiment

14.21 In this problem, we use a particle filter to solve a nonlinear-tracking problem in computer vision. An object that is made up of 5×5 pixels moves along a trajectory defined by the following pair of equations:

$$x_n = 200\left|\sin\left(\frac{2\pi n}{N}\right)\right| + 50$$

$$y_n = 100\sin\left(\frac{3.5\pi n}{N}\right) + 150$$

where x_n and y_n are the image coordinates for step n and N is the total number of frames. The scene of size 300×300 pixels is visualized in Fig. P14.21. The white background area is divided by four equally spaced bars of height $h = 10$ pixels in black, which indicate the foreground areas. The object can be distinguished by its red color.

(a) Simulate the trajectory shown in light red as an image sequence using $N = 150$ frames. Make sure to show the object if it moves over background areas and to hide it if it is occluded by foreground areas.

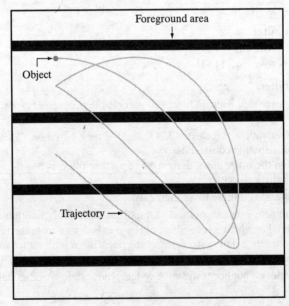

FIGURE P14.21   Scene and trajectory for Problem 14.21.

(b) Using the simulated data as input, implement a particle filter to track the object. In areas where the object is visible, you can use the color information to get a position measurement, but where it is occluded, you have to rely on the filter estimates. What assumptions do you need to make when setting up the state-space model? Visualize the true and estimated trajectory in the scene.

(c) Now continually increase the height h of the foreground areas for different trials. Explain the trade-off necessary to keep track of the object throughout the image sequence. What influence do the frame rate and the number of particles have?

(d) The information gathered during this tracking process can be used to estimate foreground and background parts of the scene—that is, to get the depth of the object relative to the parts it interacts with. Discuss possible approaches to this task.

CHAPTER 15

Dynamically Driven Recurrent Networks

ORGANIZATION OF THE CHAPTER

This chapter studies the many facets of a dynamically driven recurrent network as an input–output mapper.

The subject matter of the chapter is organized as follows:

1. By linking up with Chapters 13 and 14, the introductory section, Section 15.1, motivates the study of dynamically driven recurrent networks.
2. Section 15.2 deals with different recurrent network architectures.
3. Sections 15.3 and 15.4 discuss theoretical aspects of recurrent networks, with an emphasis on the universal approximation theorem and on controllability and observability.
4. Section 15.5 addresses the computational power of recurrent networks.
5. Sections 15.6 to 15.8 are devoted to learning algorithms, with introductory remarks in Section 15.6, followed by a treatment of two gradient-based algorithms: the back-propagation-through-time algorithm in Section 15.7 and the real-time recurrent learning algorithm in Section 15.8.
6. Section 15.9 discusses the vanishing-gradient problem, which limits the practical applicability of gradient-based recurrent learning algorithms; also discussed is how to mitigate the problem through the use of second-order methods.
7. Section 15.10 describes the framework for solving the supervised training of a recurrent neural network (i.e., estimating its synaptic weights) through the use of a sequential state estimator. A computer experiment follows in Section 15.11.
8. Section 15.12 addresses a limited form of adaptive behavior that is observed only in recurrent neural networks after fixing the weights on the completion of supervised training. To enhance this adaptive behavior, the structure of the network is correspondingly expanded by including an adaptive critic.
9. Section 15.13 highlights a case study involving the use of a model-reference neurocontroller.

The chapter concludes with a summary and discussion in Section 15.14.

15.1 INTRODUCTION

We begin the last chapter of the book with the following statement:

Global feedback is a facilitator of computational intelligence.

This statement is well illustrated by the study of recurrent networks as *associative memories*, which was presented in Chapter 13. Therein, we demonstrated how the use of global feedback in a recurrent network makes it possible to achieve some useful tasks:

- *content-addressable memory*, exemplified by the Hopfield network;
- *autoassociation*, exemplified by Anderson's brain-state-in-a-box model;
- *dynamic reconstruction of a chaotic process*, using feedback built around a regularized one-step predictor.

In this chapter, we study the other important application of recurrent networks: *input–output mapping*, the study of which naturally benefits from Chapter 14 on sequential state estimation. Consider, for example, a multilayer perceptron with a single hidden layer as the basic building block of a recurrent network. The application of global feedback around the multilayer perceptron can take a variety of forms. We may apply feedback from the outputs of the hidden layer of the multilayer perceptron to the input layer. Alternatively, we may apply the feedback from the output layer to the input of the hidden layer. We may even go one step further and combine all these possible feedback loops in a single recurrent network structure. We may also, of course, consider other neural network configurations as the building blocks for the construction of recurrent networks. The important point is that recurrent networks have a very rich repertoire of architectural layouts, which makes them all the more powerful in computational terms.

By definition, the input space of a mapping network is mapped onto an output space. For this kind of application, a recurrent network responds *temporally* to an externally applied input signal. We may therefore speak of the recurrent networks considered in this chapter as *dynamically driven recurrent networks*—hence the title of the chapter. Moreover, the application of feedback enables recurrent networks to acquire *state* representations, which makes them desirable tools for such diverse applications as nonlinear prediction and modeling, adaptive equalization of communication channels, speech processing, and plant control, to name just a few.

15.2   RECURRENT NETWORK ARCHITECTURES

As mentioned in the introduction, the architectural layout of a recurrent network takes many different forms. In this section, we describe four specific network architectures, each of which highlights a specific form of global feedback.[1] They share the following common features:

- They all incorporate a *static* multilayer perceptron or parts thereof.
- They all exploit the nonlinear mapping capability of the multilayer perceptron.

Input–Output Recurrent Model

Figure 15.1 shows the architecture of a generic recurrent network that follows naturally from a multilayer perceptron. The model has a single input that is applied to a tapped-delay-line memory of q units. It has a single output that is fed back to the input via another tapped-delay-line memory, also of q units. The contents of these two tapped-delay-line memories are used to feed the input layer of the multilayer perceptron. The present value

FIGURE 15.1 Nonlinear autoregressive with exogenous inputs (NARX) model; the feedback part of the network is shown in red.

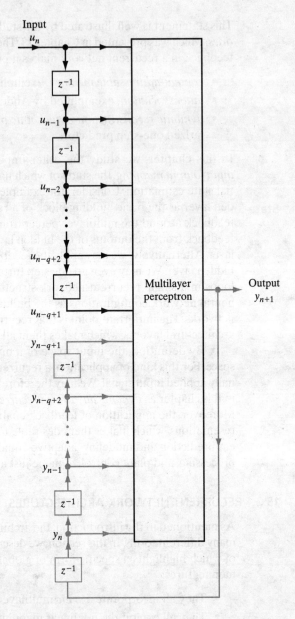

of the model input is denoted by u_n, and the corresponding value of the model output is denoted by y_{n+1}; that is, the output is ahead of the input by one time unit. Thus, the signal vector applied to the input layer of the multilayer perceptron consists of a data window made up of the following components:

- present and past values of the input, namely, $u_n, u_{n-1}, ..., u_{n-q+1}$, which represent *exogenous* inputs originating from outside the network;

- delayed values of the output, namely, $y_n, y_{n-1}, ..., y_{n-q+1}$, on which the model output y_{n+1} is *regressed*.

The recurrent network of Fig. 15.1 is referred to as a *nonlinear autoregressive with exogenous inputs (NARX) model*.[2] The dynamic behavior of the NARX model is described by

$$y_{n+1} = F(y_n, ..., y_{n-q+1}; u_n, ..., u_{n-q+1}) \tag{15.1}$$

where F is a nonlinear function of its arguments. Note that in Fig. 15.1 we have assumed that the two delay-line memories in the model are both of size q; they are generally different, however.

State-Space Model

Figure 15.2 shows the block diagram of another generic recurrent network, called a *state-space model*, the basic idea of which was discussed in Chapter 14. The hidden neurons define the *state* of the network. The output of the hidden layer is fed back to the input layer via a bank of unit-time delays. The input layer consists of a concatenation of feedback nodes and source nodes. The network is connected to the external environment via the source nodes. The number of unit-time delays used to feed the output of the hidden layer back to the input layer determines the *order* of the model. Let the m-by-1 vector $\mathbf{u}_n$ denote the input vector and the q-by-1 vector $\mathbf{x}_n$ denote the output of the hidden layer at time n. We may then describe the dynamic behavior of the model in Fig. 15.2 by the following pair of equations:

$$\mathbf{x}_{n+1} = \mathbf{a}(\mathbf{x}_n, \mathbf{u}_n) \tag{15.2}$$

$$\mathbf{y}_n = \mathbf{B}\mathbf{x}_n \tag{15.3}$$

where $\mathbf{a}(\cdot, \cdot)$ is a nonlinear function characterizing the hidden layer and $\mathbf{B}$ is the matrix of synaptic weights characterizing the output layer. The hidden layer is nonlinear, but the output layer is linear.

The recurrent network of Fig. 15.2 includes several recurrent architectures as special cases. For example, the *simple recurrent network* (SRN) described in Elman (1990, 1996), and depicted in Fig. 15.3, has an architecture similar to that of Fig. 15.2, except for

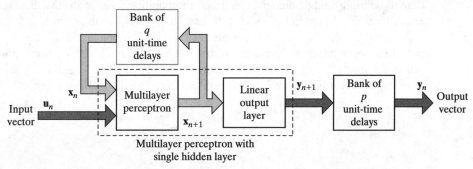

FIGURE 15.2   State-space model; the feedback part of the model is shown in red.

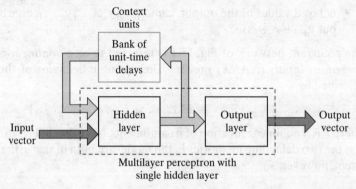

FIGURE 15.3 Simple recurrent network (SRN); the feedback part of the network is shown in red.

the fact that the output layer may be nonlinear and the bank of unit-time delays at the output is omitted. It is commonly referred to in the literature as a simple recurrent network in the sense that the error derivatives computed by the recurrent network are "simply" delayed by one time-step back into the past; however, this simplification does not prevent the network from storing information from the distant past.

Elman's network contains recurrent connections from the hidden neurons to a layer of *context units* consisting of unit-time delays. These context units store the outputs of the hidden neurons for one time-step and then feed them back to the input layer. The hidden neurons thus have some record of their prior activations, which enables the network to perform learning tasks that extend over time. The hidden neurons also feed the output neurons that report the response of the network to the externally applied stimulus. Due to the nature of the feedback around the hidden neurons, these neurons may continue to recycle information through the network over multiple time-steps and thereby discover abstract representations of time, hence the power of feedback.

Recurrent Multilayer Perceptrons

The third recurrent architecture considered here is known as a *recurrent multilayer perceptron* (RMLP) (Puskorius et al., 1996). It has one or more hidden layers, basically for the same reasons that static multilayer perceptrons are often more effective and parsimonious than those using a single hidden layer. Each computation layer of an RMLP has feedback around it, as illustrated in Fig. 15.4 for the case of an RMLP with two hidden layers.[3]

Let the vector $\mathbf{x}_{I,n}$ denote the output of the first hidden layer, $\mathbf{x}_{II,n}$ denote the output of the second hidden layer, and so on. Let the vector $\mathbf{x}_{o,n}$ denote the ultimate output of the output layer. Then the general dynamic behavior of the RMLP in response to an input vector $\mathbf{u}_n$ is described by a system of coupled equations given as

$$\mathbf{x}_{I,n+1} = \boldsymbol{\phi}_I(\mathbf{x}_{I,n}, \mathbf{u}_n)$$
$$\mathbf{x}_{II,n+1} = \boldsymbol{\phi}_{II}(\mathbf{x}_{II,n}, \mathbf{x}_{I,n+1})$$
$$\vdots \tag{15.4}$$
$$\mathbf{x}_{o,n+1} = \boldsymbol{\phi}_o(\mathbf{x}_{o,n}, \mathbf{x}_{K,n+1})$$

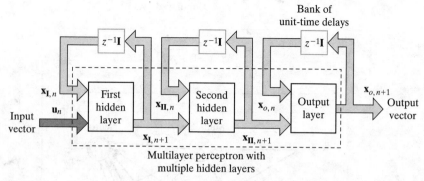

FIGURE 15.4   Recurrent multilayer perceptron; feedback paths in the network are printed in red.

where $\phi_I(\cdot\,,\cdot)$, $\phi_{II}(\cdot\,,\cdot)$, ..., $\phi_o(\cdot\,,\cdot)$ denote the activation functions characterizing the first hidden layer, second hidden layer, ..., and output layer of the RMLP, respectively, and K denotes the number of hidden layers in the network; in Fig. 15.4, $K = 2$.

The RMLP described herein subsumes the Elman network of Fig. 15.3 and the state-space model of Fig. 15.2, since neither the output layer of the RMLP nor any of its hidden layers is constrained to have a particular form of activation function.

Second-Order Network

In describing the state-space model of Fig. 15.2, we used the term "order" to refer to the number of hidden neurons whose outputs are fed back to the input layer via a bank of time-unit delays.

In yet another context, the term "order" is sometimes used to refer to the way in which the induced local field of a neuron is defined. Consider, for example, a multilayer perceptron where the induced local field v_k of neuron k is defined by

$$v_k = \sum_j w_{a,kj} x_j + \sum_i w_{b,ki} u_i \qquad (15.5)$$

where x_j is the feedback signal derived from hidden neuron j and u_i is the source signal applied to node i in the input layer; the w's represent the pertinent synaptic weights in the network. We refer to a neuron described in Eq. (15.5) as a *first-order neuron*. When, however, the induced local field v_k is combined using multiplications, as shown by

$$v_k = \sum_i \sum_j w_{kij} x_i u_j \qquad (15.6)$$

we refer to the neuron as a *second-order neuron*. The second-order neuron k uses a single weight w_{kji} that connects it to the input nodes i and j.

Second-order neurons constitute the basis of *second-order recurrent networks* (Giles et al., 1990), an example of which is shown in Fig. 15.5. The network accepts a time-ordered sequence of inputs and evolves with dynamics defined by the pair of equations:

$$v_{k,n} = b_k + \sum_i \sum_j w_{kij} x_{i,n} u_{j,n} \qquad (15.7)$$

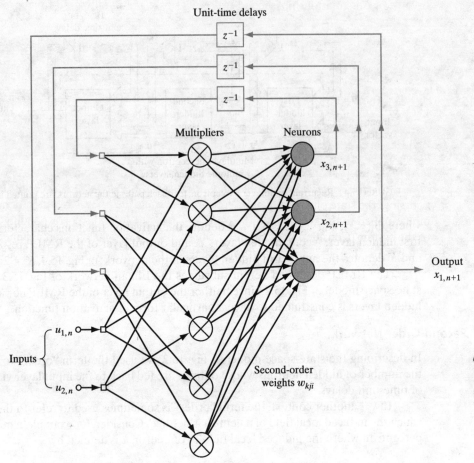

FIGURE 15.5 Second-order recurrent network; bias connections to the neurons are omitted to simplify the presentation. The network has 2 inputs and 3 state neurons, hence the need for $3 \times 2 = 6$ multipliers. The feedback links in the figure are printed in red to emphasize their global role.

$$x_{k,n+1} = \varphi(v_{k,n})$$

$$= \frac{1}{1 + \exp(-v_{k,n})} \tag{15.8}$$

where $v_{k,n}$ is the induced local field of hidden neuron k, b_k is the associated bias, $x_{k,n}$ is the state (output) of neuron k, $u_{j,n}$ is the input applied to source node j, and w_{kij} is a weight of second-order neuron k.

Unique features of the second-order recurrent network in Fig. 15.5 are that the product $x_{j,n}u_{j,n}$ represents the pair {state, input} and that a positive weight w_{kij} represents the presence of the state transition, {state, input} → {next state}, while a negative weight represents the absence of the transition. The state transition is described by

$$\delta(x_i, u_j) = x_k \tag{15.9}$$

In light of this relationship, second-order networks are readily used for representing and learning *deterministic finite-state automated* (DFA)[4]; a DFA is an information-processing system with a finite number of states. More information on the relationship between neural networks and automata is given in Section 15.5.

15.3   UNIVERSAL APPROXIMATION THEOREM

The notion of *state* plays a vital role in the mathematical formulation of a dynamic system, as explained in detail in Chapter 14. To recap, the state of a dynamic system is defined as a *set of quantities that summarizes all the information about the past behavior of the system that is needed to uniquely describe its future behavior, except for the purely external effects arising from the applied input (excitation)*. Let the q-by-1 vector $\mathbf{x}_n$ denote the state of a nonlinear discrete-time system, the m-by-1 vector $\mathbf{u}_n$ denote the input applied to the system, and the p-by-1 vector $\mathbf{y}_n$ denote the corresponding output of the system. Consider a recurrent network whose dynamic behavior, assumed to be *noise free*, is described by the pair of nonlinear equations

$$\mathbf{x}_{n+1} = \boldsymbol{\phi}(\mathbf{W}_a\mathbf{x}_n + \mathbf{W}_b\mathbf{u}_n) \tag{15.10}$$

$$\mathbf{y}_n = \mathbf{W}_c\mathbf{x}_n \tag{15.11}$$

where $\mathbf{W}_a$ is a q-by-q matrix, $\mathbf{W}_b$ is a q-by-m matrix, $\mathbf{W}_c$ is a p-by-q matrix, and $\boldsymbol{\phi}: \mathbb{R}^q \to \mathbb{R}^q$ is a diagonal map described by

$$\boldsymbol{\phi}: \begin{bmatrix} x_1 \\ x_2 \\ \vdots \\ x_q \end{bmatrix} \to \begin{bmatrix} \varphi(x_1) \\ \varphi(x_2) \\ \vdots \\ \varphi(x_q) \end{bmatrix} \tag{15.12}$$

for some memoryless, componentwise nonlinearity $\varphi: \mathbb{R} \to \mathbb{R}$. The spaces $\mathbb{R}^m$, $\mathbb{R}^q$, and $\mathbb{R}^p$ are called the *input space, state space*, and *output space*, espectively. The dimensionality of the state space—namely, q—is the *order* of the system. Thus, the state-space model of Fig. 15.2 is an *m-input, p-output recurrent model of order q*. Equation (15.10) is the *system (state) equation* of the model, and Eq. (15.11) is the *measurement equation*. The system (state) equation of Eq. (15.10) is a special form of Eq. (15.2).

The recurrent network of Fig. 15.2, based on the use of a static multilayer perceptron and two delay-line memories, provides a method for implementing the nonlinear feedback system described by Eqs. (15.10) to (15.12). Note that in Fig. 15.2, *only those neurons in the multilayer perceptron that feed back their outputs to the input layer via delays are responsible for defining the state of the recurrent network*. This statement therefore excludes the neurons in the output layer from the definition of the state.

For the interpretation of matrices $\mathbf{W}_a, \mathbf{W}_b$, and $\mathbf{W}_c$ and nonlinear vectorial function $\boldsymbol{\phi}(\cdot)$, we may say the following:

- The matrix $\mathbf{W}_a$ represents the synaptic weights of the q neurons in the hidden layer that are connected to the feedback nodes in the input layer. The matrix $\mathbf{W}_b$ represents the synaptic weights of these hidden neurons that are connected to the source nodes in the input layer. To simplify the composition of Eq. (15.10), the use of bias has been excluded from the state model.

- The matrix $\mathbf{W}_c$ represents the synaptic weights of the p linear neurons in the output layer that are connected to the hidden neurons. Here again, the use of bias in the output layer has been ignored to simplify the presentation.
- The nonlinear function $\varphi(\cdot)$ represents the sigmoidal activation function of a hidden neuron. This activation function typically takes the form of a hyperbolic tangent function,

$$\varphi(x) = \tanh(x) = \frac{1 - e^{-2x}}{1 + e^{-2x}} \tag{15.13}$$

or a logistic function,

$$\varphi(x) = \frac{1}{1 + e^{-x}} \tag{15.14}$$

An important property of a recurrent neural network described by the state-space model of Eqs. (15.10) and (15.11) is that it is a *universal approximator* of all nonlinear dynamic systems. Specifically, we may make the following statement (Lo, 1993):

> *Any nonlinear dynamic system may be approximated by a recurrent neural network to any desired degree of accuracy and with no restrictions imposed on the compactness of the state space, provided that the network is equipped with an adequate number of hidden neurons.*

Indeed, this profound statement on universal approximation is testimony to the computing power of recurrent neural networks for signal-processing and control applications.

EXAMPLE 1   Fully Connected Recurrent Network

To illustrate the compositions of matrices $\mathbf{W}_a, \mathbf{W}_b$ and $\mathbf{W}_c$, consider the *fully connected recurrent network* shown in Fig. 15.6, where the feedback paths originate from the hidden neurons In this example, we have $m = 2, q = 3$, and $p = 1$. The matrices $\mathbf{W}_a$ and $\mathbf{W}_b$ are defined as

$$\mathbf{W}_a = \begin{bmatrix} w_{11} & w_{12} & w_{13} \\ w_{21} & w_{22} & w_{23} \\ w_{31} & w_{32} & w_{33} \end{bmatrix}$$

and

$$\mathbf{W}_b = \begin{bmatrix} b_1 & w_{14} & w_{15} \\ b_2 & w_{24} & w_{25} \\ b_3 & w_{34} & w_{35} \end{bmatrix}$$

where the first column of $\mathbf{W}_b$, consisting of b_1, b_2, and b_3, represents the bias terms applied to neurons 1, 2, and 3, respectively. The matrix $\mathbf{W}_c$ is a row vector defined by

$$\mathbf{W}_c = [1, \quad 0, \quad 0] \qquad \blacksquare$$

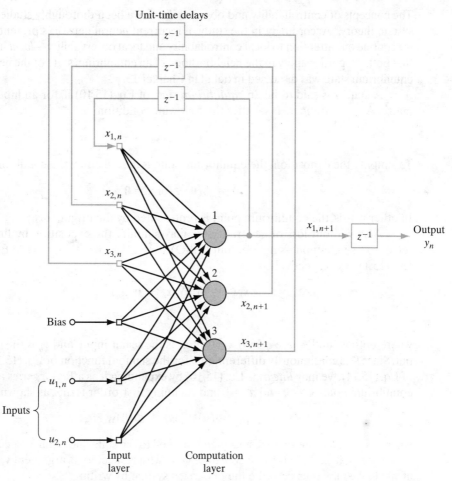

Unit-time delays

FIGURE 15.6   Fully connected recurrent network with two inputs, two hidden neurons, and one output neuron. The feedback connections are shown in red to emphasize their global role.

15.4   CONTROLLABILITY AND OBSERVABILITY

As mentioned earlier, many recurrent networks can be represented by the state-space model shown in Fig. 15.2, where the state is defined by the output of the hidden layer fed back to the input layer via a set of unit-time delays. In this context, it is insightful to know whether the recurrent network is controllable and observable or not. Controllability is concerned with whether we can control the dynamic behavior of the recurrent network. Observability is concerned with whether we can observe the result of the control applied to the recurrent network.

Formally, a dynamic system is said to be *controllable* if any initial state of the system is steerable to any desired state within a finite number of time-steps; the output of the system is irrelevant to this definition. Correspondingly, the system is said to be *observable* if the state of the system can be determined from a finite set of input–output measurements.

The concepts of controllability and observability have been thoroughly studied in linear system theory.[5] Accordingly, in the study of recurrent neural networks presented herein, we confine our attention to local controllability and local observability—*local* in the sense that both properties apply in the neighborhood of an equilibrium state of the network; the equilibrium state was discussed in detail in Chapter 13.

A state $\bar{\mathbf{x}}$ is said to be an *equilibrium state* of Eq. (15.10) if, for an input $\mathbf{u}$, and a matrix $\mathbf{A}_1$ to be defined, it satisfies the following condition:

$$\bar{\mathbf{x}} = \mathbf{A}_1\bar{\mathbf{x}} \tag{15.15}$$

To simplify the exposition, the equilibrium state is described by the condition

$$\mathbf{0} = \boldsymbol{\phi}(\mathbf{0}) \quad \text{for } \mathbf{x} = \mathbf{0},$$

In other words, the equilibrium point is represented by the origin, $(\mathbf{0}, \mathbf{0})$.

Also without loss of generality, we may simplify the exposition by limiting our selves to a single-input–single-output (SISO) system. We may then rewrite Eqs. (15.10) and (15.11) as, respectively,

$$\mathbf{x}_{n+1} = \boldsymbol{\phi}(\mathbf{W}_a\mathbf{x}_n + \mathbf{w}_b u_n) \tag{15.16}$$

and

$$y_n = \mathbf{w}_c^T\mathbf{x}_n \tag{15.17}$$

where both $\mathbf{w}_b$ and $\mathbf{w}_c$ are q-by-1 vectors, u_n is the scalar input, and y_n is the scalar output. Since φ is continuously differentiable for the sigmoid function of Eq. (15.13) or that of Eq. (15.14), we may *linearize* Eq. (15.16) by expanding it as a Taylor series around the equilibrium point $\bar{\mathbf{x}} = \mathbf{0}$ and $\bar{u} = 0$ and retaining first-order terms, as shown by

$$\delta\mathbf{x}_{n+1} = \boldsymbol{\Phi}(\mathbf{0})\mathbf{W}_a\delta\mathbf{x}_n + \boldsymbol{\Phi}(\mathbf{0})\mathbf{w}_b\delta u_n \tag{15.18}$$

where $\delta\mathbf{x}_n$ and δu_n are small displcements applied to the state and input, respectively, and the q-by-q matrix $\boldsymbol{\Phi}(\mathbf{0})$ is the Jacobian of $\boldsymbol{\phi}(\mathbf{v})$ with respect to its argument $\mathbf{v}$, evaluated at $\mathbf{v} = \mathbf{0}$. We may thus describe the linearized system by writing

$$\delta\mathbf{x}_{n+1} = \mathbf{A}_1\delta\mathbf{x}_n + \mathbf{a}_2\delta u_n \tag{15.19}$$

and

$$\delta y_n = \mathbf{w}_c^T\delta\mathbf{x}_n \tag{15.20}$$

where the q-by-q matrix $\mathbf{A}_1$, and the q-by-1 vector $\mathbf{a}_2$ are respectively defined by

$$\mathbf{A}_1 = \boldsymbol{\Phi}(\mathbf{0})\mathbf{W}_a \tag{15.21}$$

and

$$\mathbf{a}_2 = \boldsymbol{\Phi}(\mathbf{0})\mathbf{w}_b \tag{15.22}$$

The state equations of Eqs. (15.19) and (15.20) are in the standard linear form. We may therefore make use of well-known results on the controllability and observability of linear dynamic systems that are a standard part of mathematical control theory.

Local Controllability

We readily find that repeated use of the linearized equation of Eq. (15.19) yields the following equations

$$\delta\mathbf{x}_{n+1} = \mathbf{A}_1\delta\mathbf{x}_n + \mathbf{a}_2\delta u_n$$

$$\delta\mathbf{x}_{n+2} = \mathbf{A}_1^2\delta\mathbf{x}_n + \mathbf{A}_1\mathbf{a}_2\delta u_n + \mathbf{a}_2\delta u_{n+1}$$

$$\vdots$$

$$\delta\mathbf{x}_{n+q} = \mathbf{A}_1^q\delta\mathbf{x}_n + \mathbf{A}_1^{q-1}\mathbf{a}_2\delta u_n + \cdots + \mathbf{A}_1\mathbf{a}_2\delta u_{n+q-2} + \mathbf{a}_2\delta u_{n+q-1}$$

where q is the dimensionality of the state space. Accordingly, we may make the following statement (Levin and Narendra, 1993):

The linearized system represented by Eq. (15.19) is controllable if the matrix

$$\mathbf{M}_c = [\mathbf{A}_1^{q-1}\mathbf{a}_2, ..., \mathbf{A}_1\mathbf{a}_2, \mathbf{a}_2] \tag{15.23}$$

is of rank q—that is, full rank—because then the linearized system of Eqs. (15.23) has a unique representation of $\delta\mathbf{x}_{n+q}$ in terms of $u_n, u_{n+1}, ..., u_{n+q-1}$, given $\mathbf{A}_1, \mathbf{a}_2,$ and $\delta\mathbf{x}_n$.

The matrix $\mathbf{M}_c$ is called the *controllability matrix* of the linearized system.

Let the recurrent network described by Eqs. (15.16) and (15.17) be driven by a sequence of inputs $\mathbf{u}_{q,n}$ defined by

$$\mathbf{u}_{q,n} = [u_n, u_{n+1}, ..., u_{n+q-1}]^T \tag{15.24}$$

Hence, we may consider the mapping

$$\mathbf{G}(\mathbf{x}_n, \mathbf{u}_{q,n}) = (\mathbf{x}_n, \mathbf{x}_{n+q}) \tag{15.25}$$

where $\mathbf{G}: \mathbb{R}^{2q} \to \mathbb{R}^{2q}$. In Problem 15.4, it is shown that:

- the state $\mathbf{x}_{n+q}$ is a nested nonlinear function of its past value $\mathbf{x}_n$ and the inputs $u_n, u_{n+1}, ..., u_{n+q-1}$, and
- the Jacobian of $\mathbf{x}_{n+q}$ with respect to $\mathbf{u}_{q,n}$, evaluated at the origin, is equal to the controllability matrix $\mathbf{M}_c$ of Eq. (15.23).

We may express the Jacobian of the mapping $\mathbf{G}$, defined in Eq. (15.25), with respect to $\mathbf{x}_n$ and $\mathbf{u}_{q,n}$, evaluated at the origin $(\mathbf{0}, \mathbf{0})$, as

$$\mathbf{J}_{(0,0)}^{(c)} = \begin{bmatrix} \left(\dfrac{\delta\mathbf{x}_n}{\delta\mathbf{x}_n}\right)_{(0,0)} & \left(\dfrac{\delta\mathbf{x}_{n+q}}{\delta\mathbf{x}_n}\right)_{(0,0)} \\ \left(\dfrac{\delta\mathbf{x}_n}{\delta\mathbf{u}_{q,n}}\right)_{(0,0)} & \left(\dfrac{\delta\mathbf{x}_{n+q}}{\delta\mathbf{u}_{q,n}}\right)_{(0,0)} \end{bmatrix} \tag{15.26}$$

$$= \begin{bmatrix} \mathbf{I} & \mathbf{X} \\ \mathbf{0} & \mathbf{M}_c \end{bmatrix}$$

where $\mathbf{I}$ is the identity matrix, $\mathbf{0}$ is the null matrix, and the entry $\mathbf{X}$ is of no interest. Because of its special form, the determinant of the Jacobian $\mathbf{J}_{(0,0)}^{(c)}$ is equal to the product of the determinant of the identity matrix $\mathbf{I}$ (which equals 1) and the determinant of the controllability matrix $\mathbf{M}_c$. If $\mathbf{M}_c$ is of full rank, then so is $\mathbf{J}_{(0,0)}^{(c)}$.

To proceed further, we need to invoke the *inverse function theorem*, which may be stated as follows (Vidyasagar, 1993):

> *Consider the mapping* $\mathbf{f}: \mathbb{R}^q \to \mathbb{R}^q$. *Suppose that each component of the mapping* $\mathbf{f}$ *is differentiable with respect to its argument at the equilibrium point* $\mathbf{x}_0 \in \mathbb{R}^q$, *and let* $\mathbf{y}_0 = \mathbf{f}(\mathbf{x}_0)$. *Then there exist open sets* $\mathcal{U} \subseteq \mathbb{R}^q$ *containing* $\mathbf{x}_0$ *and* $\mathcal{V} \subseteq \mathbb{R}^q$ *containing* $\mathbf{y}_0$ *such that* $\mathbf{f}$ *is a diffeomorphism of* $\mathcal{U}$ *onto* $\mathcal{V}$. *If, in addition,* $\mathbf{f}$ *is smooth, then the inverse mapping* $\mathbf{f}^{-1}: \mathbb{R}^q \to \mathbb{R}^q$ *is also smooth—that is,* $\mathbf{f}$ *is a smooth diffeomorphism.*

The mapping $\mathbf{f}: \mathcal{U} \to \mathcal{V}$ is said to be a *diffeomorphism* of $\mathcal{U}$ onto $\mathcal{V}$ if it satisfies the following three conditions (see Chapter 7):

1. $\mathbf{f}(\mathcal{U}) = \mathcal{V}$.
2. The mapping $\mathbf{f}: \mathcal{U} \to \mathcal{V}$ is one to one (i.e., invertible).
3. Each component of the inverse mapping $\mathbf{f}^{-1}: \mathcal{V} \to \mathcal{U}$ is continuously differentiable with respect to its argument.

Returning to the issue of controllability, we may identify $\mathbf{f}(\mathcal{U}) = \mathcal{V}$ in the inverse function theorem with the mapping defined in Eq. (15.25). By using the inverse function theorem, we may say that if the controllability matrix $\mathbf{M}_c$ is of rank q, then locally there exists an inverse mapping defined by

$$(\mathbf{x}_n, \mathbf{x}_{n+q}) = \mathbf{G}^{-1}(\mathbf{x}_n, \mathbf{u}_{q,n}) \tag{15.27}$$

Equation (15.27), in effect, states that there exists an input sequence $(\mathbf{u}_{q,n})$ that can locally drive the network from state $\mathbf{x}_n$ to state $\mathbf{x}_{n+q}$ in q time-steps. Accordingly, we may formally state the *local controllability theorem* as follows (Levin and Narendra, 1993):

> *Let a recurrent network be defined by Eqs. (15.16) and (15.17), and let its linearized version around the origin (i.e., equilibrium point) be defined by Eqs. (15.19) and (15.20). If the linearized system is controllable, then the recurrent network is locally controllable around the origin.*

Local Observability

Using the linearized equations of Eqs. (15.19) and (15.20) repeatedly, we may write

$$\delta y_n = \mathbf{w}_c^T \delta \mathbf{x}_n$$
$$\delta y_{n+1} = \mathbf{w}_c^T \delta \mathbf{x}_{n+1}$$
$$= \mathbf{w}_c^T \mathbf{A}_1 \delta \mathbf{x}_n + \mathbf{w}_c^T \mathbf{a}_2 \delta u_n$$
$$\vdots$$
$$\delta y_{n+q-1} = \mathbf{w}_c^T \mathbf{A}_1^{q-1} \delta \mathbf{x}_n + \mathbf{w}_c^T \mathbf{A}_1^{q-2} \mathbf{a}_2 \delta u_n + \cdots + \mathbf{w}_c^T \mathbf{A}_1 \mathbf{a}_2 \delta u_{n+q-3}$$
$$+ \mathbf{w}_c^T \mathbf{a}_2 \delta u_{n+q-2}$$

where q is the dimensionality of the state space. Accordingly, we may make the following statement (Levin and Narendra, 1993):

> *The linearized system described by Eqs. (15.19) and (15.20) is observable if the matrix*

$$\mathbf{M}_o = [\mathbf{w}_c, \mathbf{w}_c \mathbf{A}_1^T, ..., \mathbf{w}_c(\mathbf{A}_1^T)^{q-1}] \tag{15.28}$$

is of rank q—*that is, full rank.*

The matrix $\mathbf{M}_o$ is called the *observability matrix* of the linearized system.

Let the recurrent network described by Eqs. (15.16) and (15.17) be driven by a sequence of inputs defined by

$$\mathbf{u}_{q-1,n} = [u_n, u_{n+1}, ..., u_{n+q-2}]^T \tag{15.29}$$

Correspondingly, let

$$\mathbf{y}_{q,n} = [y_n, y_{n+1}, ..., y_{n+q-1}]^T \tag{15.30}$$

denote the vector of outputs produced by the initial state $\mathbf{x}_n$ and the sequence of inputs $\mathbf{u}_{q-1,n}$. We may then consider the mapping

$$\mathbf{H}(\mathbf{u}_{q-1,n}, \mathbf{x}_n) = (\mathbf{u}_{q-1,n}, \mathbf{y}_{q,n}) \tag{15.31}$$

where $\mathbf{H}\colon \mathbb{R}^{2q-1} \to \mathbb{R}^{2q-1}$. In Problem 15.5, it is shown that the Jacobian of $\mathbf{y}_{q,n}$ with respect to $\mathbf{x}_n$, evaluated at the origin, is equal to the observability matrix $\mathbf{M}_o$ of Eq. (15.28). We may thus express the Jacobian of $\mathbf{H}$ with respect to $\mathbf{u}_{q-1,n}$ and $\mathbf{x}_n$, evaluated at the origin, $(\mathbf{0}, \mathbf{0})$, as

$$\mathbf{J}_{(0,0)}^{(o)} = \begin{bmatrix} \left(\dfrac{\partial \mathbf{u}_{q-1,n}}{\partial \mathbf{u}_{q-1,n}}\right)_{(0,0)} & \left(\dfrac{\partial \mathbf{y}_{q,n}}{\partial \mathbf{u}_{q-1,n}}\right)_{(0,0)} \\ \left(\dfrac{\partial \mathbf{u}_{q-1,n}}{\delta \mathbf{x}_n}\right)_{(0,0)} & \left(\dfrac{\partial \mathbf{y}_{q,n}}{\delta \mathbf{x}_n}\right)_{(0,0)} \end{bmatrix} \tag{15.32}$$

$$= \begin{bmatrix} \mathbf{I} & \mathbf{X} \\ \mathbf{0} & \mathbf{M}_o \end{bmatrix}$$

where again the entry $\mathbf{X}$ is of no interest. The determinant of the Jacobian $\mathbf{J}_{(0,0)}^{(o)}$ is equal to the product of the determinant of the identity matrix $\mathbf{I}$ (which equals 1) and the determinant of $\mathbf{M}_o$. If $\mathbf{M}_o$ is of full rank, then so is $\mathbf{J}_{(0,0)}^{(o)}$. Invoking the inverse function theorem one more time, we may therefore say that if the observability matrix $\mathbf{M}_o$ of the linearized system is of full rank, then locally there exists an inverse mapping defined by

$$(\mathbf{u}_{q-1,n}, \mathbf{x}_n) = \mathbf{H}^{-1}(\mathbf{u}_{q-1,n}, \mathbf{y}_{q,n}) \tag{15.33}$$

In effect, this equation states that in the local neighborhood of the origin, $\mathbf{x}_n$ is some nonlinear function of both $\mathbf{u}_{q-1,n}$ and $\mathbf{y}_{q,n}$, and that nonlinear function is an observer of the recurrent network. We may therefore formally state the *local observability theorem* as follows (Levin and Narendra, 1993):

> *Let a recurrent network be defined by Eqs. (15.16) and (15.17), and let its linearized version around the origin (i.e., equilibrium point) be defined by Eqs. (15.19) and (15.20). If the linearized system is observable, then the recurrent network is locally observable around the origin.*

EXAMPLE 2   Controllability and Observability of a Simple State-Space Model

Consider a state-space model with matrix $\mathbf{A}_1 = a\mathbf{I}$, where a is a scalar and $\mathbf{I}$ is the identity matrix. Then the controllability matrix $\mathbf{M}_c$ of Eq. (15.23) reduces to

$$\mathbf{M}_c = a[\mathbf{a}_2, ..., \mathbf{a}_2, \mathbf{a}_2]$$

The rank of this matrix is 1. Hence, the linearized system with this value of matrix $\mathbf{A}_1$ is not controllable.

Putting $\mathbf{A}_1 = a\mathbf{I}$ in Eq. (15.28), we obtain the observability matrix

$$\mathbf{M}_o = a[\mathbf{w}_c, \mathbf{w}_c, ..., \mathbf{w}_c]$$

whose rank is also 1. The linearized system is also not observable.   ∎

15.5   COMPUTATIONAL POWER OF RECURRENT NETWORKS

Recurrent networks, exemplified by the state-space model of Fig. 15.2 and the NARX model of Fig. 15.1, have an inherent ability to simulate finite-state automata. *Automata* represent abstractions of information-processing systems such as computers. Indeed, automata and neural networks share a long history.[6] On p. 55 of his 1967 book, entitled *Computation: Finite and Infinite Machines*, Minsky makes the following consequential statement:

> "*Every finite-state machine is equivalent to, and can be 'simulated' by, some neural net. That is, given any finite-state machine $\mathcal{M}$, we can build a certain neural net $\mathcal{N}^{\mathcal{M}}$ which, regarded as a black-box machine, will behave precisely like $\mathcal{M}$!*"

The early work on recurrent networks used hard threshold logic for the activation function of a neuron rather than soft sigmoid functions.

Perhaps the first experimental demonstration of whether a recurrent network could learn the contingencies implied by a small finite-state grammar was reported in Cleeremans et al. (1989). Specifically, the simple recurrent network (see Fig. 15.3) was presented with strings derived from the grammar and required to predict the next letter at every step. The predictions were context-dependent, since each letter appeared twice in the grammar and was followed in each case by different successors. It was shown that the network is able to develop internal representations in its hidden neurons that correspond to the states of the automaton (finite-state machine). In Kremer (1995), it is formally proved that the simple recurrent network has a computational power as great as that of any finite-state machine.

In a generic sense, the computational power of a recurrent network is embodied in two main theorems:

Theorem I   (Siegelmann and Sontag, 1991)

> *All Turing machines may be simulated by fully connected recurrent networks built on neurons with sigmoidal activation functions.*

The *Turing machine* is an abstract computing device invented by Turing in 1936; its mathematical model is more general than that of finite-state automata. Hence, simulation of the Turing machine by a recurrent network is a more challenging proposition. The machine consists of three functional blocks, as depicted in Fig. 15.7 (Fischler and Firschein, 1987):

1. *a control unit, which can assume any one of a finite number of possible states;*
2. *linear tape, assumed to be infinitely long in both directions, which is marked off into discrete squares, where each square is available to store a single symbol taken from a finite set of symbols;*
3. *a read–write head, which moves along the tape and transmits information to and from the control unit.*

A function $f(x)$ is said to be *computable* if there exists a Turing machine that, given a tape representing the argument x, eventually comes to a stop when the tape represents the

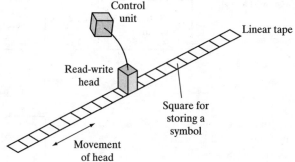

FIGURE 15.7   Turing machine.

value $f(x)$. However, this idea is rather problematic, because the idea of computation lacks a formal definition. Nevertheless, the *Church–Turing thesis*, which states that the Turing machine is capable of computing any computable function, is generally accepted as a sufficient condition (Russell and Norvig, 1995).

Theorem II   (Siegelmann et al., 1997)

NARX networks with one layer of hidden neurons with bounded, one-sided saturated activation functions and a linear output neuron can simulate fully connected recurrent networks with bounded, one-sided saturated activation functions, except for a linear slowdown.

A "linear slowdown" means that if the fully connected recurrent network with N neurons computes a task of interest in time T, then the total time taken by the equivalent NARX network is $(N + 1)T$. A function $\varphi(\cdot)$ is said to be a *bounded, one-sided saturated (BOSS) function* if it satisfies the following three conditions:

1. *The function $\varphi(\cdot)$ has a bounded range; that is, $a \le \varphi(x) \le b, a \ne b$, for all $x \in \mathbb{R}$.*
2. *The function $\varphi(\cdot)$ is saturated on the left side; that is, there exist values s and S such that $\varphi(x) = S$ for all $x \le s$.*
3. *The function $\varphi(\cdot)$ is nonconstant; that is, $\varphi(x_1) \ne \varphi(x_2)$ for some x_1 and x_2.*

The threshold (Heaviside) and piecewise-linear functions satisfy the BOSS conditions. However, in a strict sense, a sigmoid function is not a BOSS function because it does not satisfy condition 2. Nevertheless, with a minor modification, it can be made into a BOSS function by writing (in the case of a logistic function)

$$\varphi(x) = \begin{cases} \dfrac{1}{1 + \exp(-x)} & \text{for } x > s \\ 0 & \text{for } x \le s \end{cases}$$

where $x \in \mathbb{R}$. In effect, the logistic function is truncated for $x \le s$.

As a corollary to Theorems I and II, we may state the following (Giles, 1996):

NARX networks with one hidden layer of neurons with BOSS activations functions and a linear output neuron are Turing equivalent.

Figure 15.8 presents a portrayal of Theorems I and II and this corollary. It should, however, be noted that when the network architecture is constrained, the computational

FIGURE 15.8   Illustration of Theorems I and II,
and corollary to them.

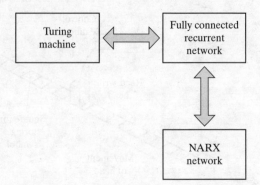

power of a recurrent network may no longer hold, as described in Sperduti (1997). References to examples of constrained network architectures are presented in Note 7 under Notes and References.

15.6   LEARNING ALGORITHMS

We now turn to the issue of training recurrent networks. From Chapter 4, we recall that there are two modes of training an ordinary (static) multilayer perceptron: batch mode and stochastic (sequential) mode. In the batch mode, the sensitivity of the network is computed for the entire training sample before adjusting the free parameters of the network. In the stochastic mode, on the other hand, parameter adjustments are made after the presentation of each pattern in the training sample. Likewise, we have two modes of training a recurrent network, described as follows (Williams and Zipser, 1995):

1. *Epochwise training.* For a given epoch, the recurrent network uses a temporal sequence of input–target response pairs and starts running from some initial state until it reaches a new state, at which point the training is stopped and the network is reset to an initial state for the next epoch. The initial state doesn't have to be the same for each epoch of training. Rather, what is important is for the initial state for the new epoch to be different from the state reached by the network at the end of the previous epoch. Consider, for example, the use of a recurrent network to emulate the operation of a finite-state machine. In such a situation, it is reasonable to use epochwise training, since there is a good possibility that a number of distinct initial states and a set of distinct final states in the machine will be emulated by the recurrent network. In epochwise training for recurrent networks, the term "epoch" is used in a sense different from that for an ordinary multilayer perceptron. Although an epoch in the training of a multilayer perceptron involves the entire training sample of input–target response pairs, an epoch in the training of a recurrent neural network involves a single string of temporally consecutive input–target response pairs.

2. *Continuous training.* This second method of training is suitable for situations where there are no reset states available or on-line learning is required. The distinguishing feature of continuous training is that the *network learns while performing signal processing.* Simply put, the learning process never stops. Consider, for example, the use of a recurrent network to model a nonstationary process such as a speech signal. In this kind of situation, continuous operation of the network offers no convenient times at which to stop the training and begin anew with different values for the free parameters of the network.

Keeping these two modes of training in mind, in the next two sections we will describe two different learning algorithms for recurrent networks, summarized as follows:

- The back-propagation-through-time (BPTT) algorithm, discussed in Section 15.7, operates on the premise that the temporal operation of a recurrent network may be unfolded into a multilayer perceptron. This condition would then pave the way for application of the standard back-propagation algorithm. The back-propagation-through-time algorithm can be implemented in the epochwise mode, continuous (real-time) mode, or a combination thereof.

- The real-time recurrent learning (RTRL) algorithm, discussed in Section 15.8, is derived from the state-space model described by Eqs. (15.10) and (15.11).

Basically, BPTT and RTRL involve the propagation of derivatives, one in the backward direction and the other in the forward direction. They can be used in any training process that requires the use of derivatives. BPTT requires less computation than RTRL does, but the memory space required by BPTT increases fast as the length of a sequence of consecutive input–target response pairs increases. Generally speaking, we therefore find that BPTT is better for off-line training, and RTRL is more suitable for on-line continuous training.

In any event, these two algorithms share many common features. First, they are both based on the method of gradient descent, whereby the instantaneous value of a cost function (based on a squared-error criterion) is minimized with respect to the synaptic weights of the network. Second, they are both relatively simple to implement, but can be slow to converge. Third, they are related in that the signal-flow graph representation of the back-propagation-through-time algorithm can be obtained from *transposition* of the signal-flow graph representation of a certain form of the real-time recurrent learning algorithm (Lefebvre, 1991; Beaufays and Wan, 1994).

Some Heuristics

Before proceeding to describe these two learning algorithms, we list some heuristics for the improved training of recurrent networks that involve the use of gradient-descent methods (Giles, 1996):

- Lexigraphic order of training samples should be followed, with the shortest strings of symbols being presented to the network first.

- The training should begin with a small training sample. The size of the training sample should be incrementally increased as the training proceeds.

- The synaptic weights of the network should be updated only if the absolute error on the training sample currently being processed by the network is greater than some prescribed criterion.

- The use of weight decay during training is recommended; weight decay, a crude form of complexity regularization, was discussed in Chapter 4.

The first heuristic is of particular interest. If implementable, it may provide a procedure for alleviating the vanishing-gradients problem that arises in recurrent networks trained by means of gradient-descent methods. Detailed discussion of this problem is deferred to Section 15.9.

15.7 BACK PROPAGATION THROUGH TIME

The *back-propagation-through-time (BPTT) algorithm* for training a recurrent network is an extension of the standard back-propagation algorithm.[8] It may be derived by *unfolding* the temporal operation of the network into a layered feedforward network, the topology of which grows by one layer at every time-step.

To be specific, let $\mathcal{N}$ denote a recurrent network required to learn a temporal task, starting from time n_0 all the way up to time n. Let $\mathcal{N}^*$ denote the feedforward network that results from unfolding the temporal operation of the recurrent network $\mathcal{N}$. The unfolded network $\mathcal{N}^*$ is related to the original network $\mathcal{N}$ as follows:

1. For each time-step in the interval $(n_0, n]$, the network $\mathcal{N}^*$ has a layer containing K neurons, where K is the number of neurons contained in the network $\mathcal{N}$.
2. In every layer of the network $\mathcal{N}^*$, there is a copy of each neuron in the network $\mathcal{N}$.
3. For each time-step $l \in [n_0, n]$, the synaptic connection from neuron i in layer l to neuron j in layer $l + 1$ of the network $\mathcal{N}^*$ is a copy of the synaptic connection from neuron i to neuron j in the network $\mathcal{N}$.

These points are illustrated in the following example.

EXAMPLE 3 Unfolding of two-neuron recurrent network

Consider the two-neuron recurrent network $\mathcal{N}$ shown in Fig. 15.9a. To simplify the presentation, we have omitted the unit-time delay operators z^{-1} that should be inserted in each of the synaptic connections (including the self-loops) in Fig. 15.9a. By unfolding the temporal operation of this network in a step-by-step manner, we get the signal-flow graph shown in Fig. 15.9b, where the starting time $n_0 = 0$. The graph in Fig. 15.9b represents the layered feedforward network $\mathcal{N}^*$, where a new layer is added at each step of the temporal operation. ∎

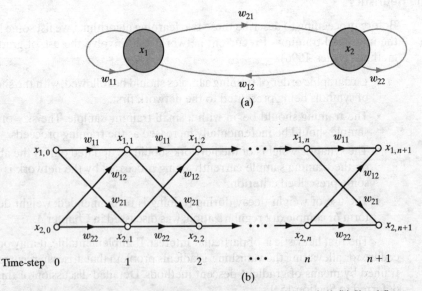

FIGURE 15.9 (a) Architectural graph of a two-neuron recurrent network $\mathcal{N}$. (b) Signal-flow graph of the network $\mathcal{N}$ unfolded in time.

Application of the unfolding procedure leads to two basically different implementations of back propagation through time, depending on whether epochwise training or continuous (real-time) training is used. These two methods of recurrent learning are now described in that order.

Epochwise Back Propagation Through Time

Let the data set used to train a recurrent network be partitioned into independent epochs, with each epoch representing a temporal pattern of interest. Let n_0 denote the start time of an epoch and n_1 denote its end time. Given this epoch, we may define the cost function

$$\mathcal{E}_{\text{total}} = \frac{1}{2} \sum_{n=n_0}^{n_1} \sum_{j \in \mathcal{A}} e_{j,n}^2 \tag{15.34}$$

where $\mathcal{A}$ is the set of indices j pertaining to those neurons in the network for which desired responses are specified, and $e_{j,n}$ is the error signal at the output of such a neuron measured with respect to some desired (target) response. We wish to compute sensitivity of the network—that is, the partial derivatives of the cost function $\mathcal{E}_{\text{total}}(n_0, n_1)$ with respect to synaptic weights of the network. To do so, we may use the *epochwise back-propagation-through-time (BPTT) algorithm*, which builds on the batch mode of standard back-propagation learning that was described in Chapter 4. The epochwise BPTT algorithm proceeds as follows (Williams and Peng, 1990):

- First, a single forward pass of the data through the network for the interval (n_0, n_1) is performed. The complete record of input data, network state (i.e., synaptic weights of the network), and desired responses over this interval is *saved*.

- A single backward pass over this past record is performed to compute the values of the local gradients

$$\delta_{j,n} = -\frac{\partial \mathcal{E}_{\text{total}}}{\partial v_{j,n}} \tag{15.35}$$

for all $j \in \mathcal{A}$ and $n_0 < n \le n_1$. This computation is performed by using the formula

$$\delta_{j,n} = \begin{cases} \varphi'(v_{j,n}) \, e_{j,n} & \text{for } n = n_1 \\ \varphi'(v_{j,n}) \left[e_{j,n} + \sum_{k \in \mathcal{A}} w_{jk} \delta_{k,n+1} \right] & \text{for } n_0 < n < n_1 \end{cases} \tag{15.36}$$

where $\varphi'(\cdot)$ is the derivative of an activation function with respect to its argument and $v_{j,n}$ is the induced local field of neuron j. It is assumed that all neurons in the network have the same activation function $\varphi(\cdot)$. The use of Eq. (15.36) is repeated, starting from time n_1 and working back, step by step, to time n_0; the number of steps involved here is equal to the number of time-steps contained in the epoch.

- Once the computation of back propagation has been performed back to time $n_0 + 1$, an adjustment is applied to the synaptic weight w_{ji} of neuron j, given by

$$\Delta w_{ji} = -\eta \frac{\partial \mathcal{E}_{\text{total}}}{\partial w_{ji}} \tag{15.37}$$

$$= \eta \sum_{n=n_0+1}^{n_1} \delta_{j,n} x_{i,n-1}$$

where η is the learning-rate parameter and $x_{i,n-1}$ is the input applied to the ith synapse of neuron j at time $n-1$.

Comparing the procedure just described for epochwise BPTT with the batch mode of standard back-propagation learning, we see that the basic difference between them is that in the former case, the desired responses are specified for neurons in many layers of the network because the actual output layer is replicated many times when the temporal behavior of the network is unfolded.

Truncated Back Propagation Through Time

To use back propagation through time in a real-time fashion, we use the instantaneous value of the sum of squared errors, namely,

$$\mathcal{E}_n = \frac{1}{2} \sum_{j \in \mathcal{A}} e_{j,n}^2$$

as the cost function to be minimized. As with the stochastic mode of standard back-propagation learning, we use the negative gradient of the cost function $\mathcal{E}_n$ to compute the appropriate adjustments to the synaptic weights of the network at each time instant n. The adjustments are made on a continuous basis while the network is running. However, in order to do this in a computationally feasible manner, we save the relevant history of input data and network state only for a fixed number of time-steps, called the *truncation depth*. Henceforth, the truncation depth is denoted by h. Any information older than h time-steps into the past is considered irrelevant and may therefore be ignored. If we were not to truncate the computation, thereby permitting it to go back to the starting time, the computation time and storage requirement would grow linearly with time as the network runs, eventually reaching a point where the whole learning process becomes impractical.

This second form of the algorithm is called the *truncated back-propagation-through-time (BPTT(h)) algorithm* (Williams and Peng, 1990). The *local gradient* for neuron j is now defined by

$$\delta_{j,l} = -\frac{\partial \mathcal{E}_l}{\partial v_{j,l}} \quad \begin{array}{l} \text{for all } j \in \mathcal{A} \\ \text{and } n - h < l \leq n \end{array} \tag{15.38}$$

which, in turn, leads to the formula

$$\delta_{j,l} = \begin{cases} \varphi'(v_{j,l}) e_{j,l} & \text{for } l = n \\ \varphi'(v_{j,l}) \sum_{k \in \mathcal{A}} w_{jk,l} \delta_{k,l+1} & \text{for } n - h < l < n \end{cases} \tag{15.39}$$

Once the computation of back propagation has been performed back to time $n - h + 1$, the following adjustment is applied to the synaptic weight w_{ji} of neuron j, where η and $x_{i,l-1}$ are as defined previously:

$$\Delta w_{ji,n} = \eta \sum_{j=n-h+1}^{n} \delta_{j,l} x_{i,l-1} \qquad (15.40)$$

Note that the use of $w_{jk,l}$ in Eq. (15.39) requires that a history of weight values be maintained. The use of $w_{jk,l}$ in this equation may be justified only if the learning-rate parameter η is small enough to ensure that the weight values do not change significantly from one time-step to the next.

In comparing Eq. (15.39) with (15.36), we see that, unlike the epochwise BPTT algorithm, the error signal is injected into the computation only at the current time n. This explains the reason for not keeping a record of past values of the desired responses. In effect, the truncated back-propagation-through-time algorithm treats the computation for all earlier time-steps similar to the way in which the stochastic back-propagation algorithm (discussed in Chapter 4) treats the computations for hidden neurons in a multilayer perceptron.

Some Practical Considerations

In real-life applications of BPTT(h), the use of truncation is not as artificial as it may sound. Unless the recurrent network is unstable, there should be a convergence of the derivatives $\partial \mathcal{E}_l / \partial v_{j,l}$ because computations farther back in time correspond to higher powers of feedback strengths (roughly equal to sigmoid slopes multiplied by weights). In any event, the truncation depth h must be large enough to produce derivatives that closely approximate the actual values. This requirement places a lower bound on the value of h. For example, in the application of dynamically driven recurrent networks to engine idle-speed control, the value $h = 30$ is considered to be a reasonably conservative choice for that learning task to be accomplished (Puskorius et al., 1996).

The Ordered Derivative Approach

One other practical matter needs to be discussed. The unfolding procedure described in this section for back propagation through time provides a useful tool for picturing the algorithm in terms of a cascade of similar layers progressing forward in time, thereby helping us to develop an understanding of how the procedure functions. This strong point is, unfortunately, also the cause of its weakness. The procedure works perfectly fine for relatively simple recurrent networks consisting of a few neurons. However, the underlying formulas, particularly Eq. (15.39), become unwieldy when the unfolding procedure is applied to more general architectures that are typical of those encountered in practice. In situations of this kind, the preferred procedure is to use the more general approach described in Werbos (1990), in which each expression in the forward propagation of a layer gives rise to a corresponding set of back-propagation expressions. An advantage of this approach is its homogeneous treatment of forward and recurrent (feedback) connections.

To describe the mechanics of this latter form of BPTT(h), let $\mathbf{F}_{-x}^{l}$ denote an *ordered derivative* of the network output at node l with respect to x. To derive the back-propagation equations, the forward-propagation equations are considered in reverse order. From each equation, we derive one or more back-propagation expressions according to the following principle:

$$\text{If } a = \varphi(b, c), \text{ then } \mathbf{F}^l_{-b} = \frac{\partial \varphi}{\partial b} \mathbf{F}^l_{-a} \quad \text{and} \quad \mathbf{F}^l_{-c} = \frac{\partial \varphi}{\partial c} \mathbf{F}^l_{-a} \qquad (15.41)$$

Example 4 Illustration of Eq. (15.41)

To clarify the notion of ordered derivatives, consider a nonlinear system described by the following pair of equations:

$$x_1 = \log u + x_2^3$$
$$y = x_1^2 + 3x_2$$

The variable x_2 influences the output y in two ways: directly via the second equation, and indirectly via the first equation. The ordered derivative of y with respect to x_2 is defined by the total causal impact that includes the direct and indirect effects of x_2 on y, as shown by

$$\mathbf{F}_{-x_2} = \frac{\partial y}{\partial x_2} + \frac{\partial y}{\partial x_1} \times \frac{\partial x_1}{\partial x_2}$$
$$= 3 + (2x_1)(3x_2^2)$$
$$= 3 + 6x_1 x_2^2 \qquad \blacksquare$$

Other Desirable Features of the Ordered Derivative Approach

In programming the ordered derivatives for BPTT(h), the quantity on the right-hand side of each ordered derivative in Eq. (15.41) is added to the previous value of the left-hand side. In this way, the appropriate derivatives are distributed from a given node in the network to all the nodes and synaptic weights that feed it in the forward direction, with due allowance being made for any delays that may be present in each connection.

The simplicity of the ordered-derivative formulation described in Eq. (15.41) also reduces the need for visualizations such as unfolding in time or signal-flow graphs. In Feldkamp and Puskorius (1998) and Puskorius et al. (1996), this procedure is used to develop a pseudocode for implementing the BPTT(h) algorithm.

15.8 REAL-TIME RECURRENT LEARNING

In this section, we describe the second learning algorithm, *real-time recurrent learning (RTRL)*,[9] which was briefly described in Section 15.6. The algorithm derives its name from the fact that adjustments are made to the synaptic weights of a fully connected recurrent network in real time—that is, while the network continues to perform its signal-processing function (Williams and Zipser, 1989). Figure 15.10 shows the layout of such a recurrent network. It consists of q neurons with m external inputs. The network has two distinct layers: a *concatenated input-feedback layer* and a *processing layer of computation nodes*. Correspondingly, the synaptic connections of the network are made up of feedforward and feedback connections; the feedback connections are shown in red in Fig. 15.10.

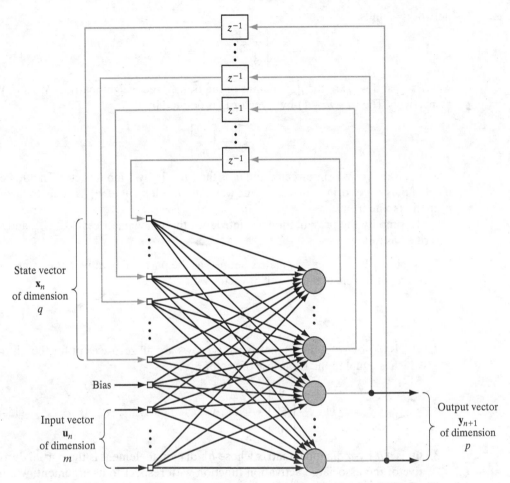

FIGURE 15.10   Fully connected recurrent network for formulation of the RTRL algorithm; the feedback connections are all shown in red.

The state-space description of the network is defined by Eqs. (15.10) and (15.11). The system (state) equation of Eq. (15.10) is reproduced here in the expanded form

$$\mathbf{x}_{n+1} = \begin{bmatrix} \varphi(\mathbf{w}_1^T \boldsymbol{\xi}_n) \\ \vdots \\ \varphi(\mathbf{w}_j^T \boldsymbol{\xi}_n) \\ \vdots \\ \varphi(\mathbf{w}_q^T \boldsymbol{\xi}_n) \end{bmatrix} \tag{15.42}$$

where it is assumed that all the neurons have a common activation function $\varphi(\cdot)$. The $(q + m + 1)$-by-1 vector $\mathbf{w}_j$ is the synaptic-weight vector of neuron j in the recurrent network—that is,

$$\mathbf{w}_j = \begin{bmatrix} \mathbf{w}_{a,j} \\ \mathbf{w}_{b,j} \end{bmatrix}, \qquad j = 1, 2, ..., q \tag{15.43}$$

where $\mathbf{w}_{a,j}$ and $\mathbf{w}_{b,j}$ are the jth columns of the transposed weight matrices $\mathbf{W}_a^T$ and $\mathbf{W}_b^T$, respectively. The $(q + m + 1)$-by-1 vector $\boldsymbol{\xi}_n$ is defined by

$$\boldsymbol{\xi}_n = \begin{bmatrix} \mathbf{x}_n \\ \mathbf{u}_n \end{bmatrix} \tag{15.44}$$

where $\mathbf{x}_n$ is the q-by-1 state vector and $\mathbf{u}_n$ is the $(m + 1)$-by-1 input vector. The first element of $\mathbf{u}_n$ is $+ 1$, and, in a corresponding way, the first element of $\mathbf{w}_{b,j}$ is equal to the bias b_j applied to neuron j.

To simplify the presentation, we introduce three new matrices $\boldsymbol{\Lambda}_{j,n}$, $\mathbf{U}_{j,n}$, and $\boldsymbol{\Phi}_n$, described as follows:

1. $\boldsymbol{\Lambda}_{i,n}$ is a q-by-$(q + m + 1)$ matrix defined as the partial derivative of the state vector $\mathbf{x}_n$ with respect to the weight vector $\mathbf{w}_j$:

$$\boldsymbol{\Lambda}_{j,n} = \frac{\partial \mathbf{x}_n}{\partial \mathbf{w}_j}, \qquad j = 1, 2, ..., q \tag{15.45}$$

2. $\mathbf{U}_{j,n}$ is a q-by-$(q + m + 1)$ matrix whose rows are all zero, except for the jth row, which is equal to the transpose of vector $\boldsymbol{\xi}_n$:

$$\mathbf{U}_{j,n} = \begin{bmatrix} \mathbf{0} \\ \boldsymbol{\xi}_n^T \\ \mathbf{0} \end{bmatrix} \leftarrow j\text{th row}, \qquad j = 1, 2, ..., q \tag{15.46}$$

3. $\boldsymbol{\Phi}_n$ is a q-by-q diagonal matrix whose jth diagonal element is the partial derivative of the associated activation function with respect to its argument; we thus write:

$$\boldsymbol{\Phi}_n = \text{diag}(\varphi'(\mathbf{w}_1^T \boldsymbol{\xi}_n), ..., \varphi'(\mathbf{w}_j^T \boldsymbol{\xi}_n), ..., \varphi'(\mathbf{w}_q^T \boldsymbol{\xi}_n)) \tag{15.47}$$

With these definitions, we may now differentiate Eq. (15.42) with respect to $\mathbf{w}_j$. Then, using the chain rule of calculus, we obtain the following recursive equation:

$$\boldsymbol{\Lambda}_{j,n+1} = \boldsymbol{\Phi}_n(\mathbf{W}_{a,n} \boldsymbol{\Lambda}_{j,n} + \mathbf{U}_{j,n}), \qquad j = 1, 2, ..., q \tag{15.48}$$

This recursive equation describes the *nonlinear state dynamics* (i.e., evolution of the state) of the real-time recurrent learning process.

To complete the description of this learning process, we need to relate the matrix $\boldsymbol{\Lambda}_{j,n}$ to the gradient of the error surface with respect to $\mathbf{w}_j$. To do this, we first use the measurement equation of Eq. (15.11) to define the p-by-1 error vector:

$$\begin{aligned} \mathbf{e}_n &= \mathbf{d}_n - \mathbf{y}_n \\ &= \mathbf{d}_n - \mathbf{W}_c \mathbf{x}_n \end{aligned} \tag{15.49}$$

where p is the dimension of the output vector $\mathbf{y}_n$. The instantaneous sum of squared errors at time-step n is defined in terms of $\mathbf{e}_n$ by

$$\mathscr{E}_n = \frac{1}{2}\,\mathbf{e}_n^T\mathbf{e}_n \qquad (15.50)$$

The objective of the learning process is to minimize a cost function obtained by summing $\mathscr{E}_n$ over all time-steps n; that is,

$$\mathscr{E}_{\text{total}} = \sum_n \mathscr{E}_n$$

To accomplish this objective, we may use the method of steepest descent, which requires knowledge of the *gradient matrix*, written as

$$\begin{aligned}
\nabla_{\mathbf{W}}\mathscr{E}_{\text{total}} &= \frac{\partial\mathscr{E}_{\text{total}}}{\partial\mathbf{W}} \\
&= \sum_n \frac{\partial\mathscr{E}_n}{\partial\mathbf{W}} \\
&= \sum_n \nabla_{\mathbf{W}}\mathscr{E}_n
\end{aligned}$$

where $\nabla_{\mathbf{W}}\mathscr{E}_n$ is the gradient of $\mathscr{E}_n$ with respect to the weight matrix $\mathbf{W} = \{\mathbf{w}_k\}$. We may, if desired, continue with this process and derive update equations for the synaptic weights of the recurrent network without invoking approximations. However, in order to develop a learning algorithm that can be used to train the recurrent network in *real time*, we must use an instantaneous *estimate* of the gradient—namely, $\nabla_{\mathbf{W}}$—which results in an *approximation* to the method of steepest descent. In a sense, we follow an approach similar to that we used for the least-mean-square (LMS) algorithm in Chapter 3.

Returning to Eq. (15.50) as the cost function to be minimized, we differentiate it with respect to the weight vector $\mathbf{w}_j$, obtaining

$$\begin{aligned}
\frac{\partial\mathscr{E}_n}{\partial\mathbf{w}_j} &= \left(\frac{\partial\mathbf{e}_n}{\partial\mathbf{w}_j}\right)\mathbf{e}_n \\
&= -\mathbf{W}_c\left(\frac{\partial\mathbf{x}_n}{\partial\mathbf{w}_j}\right)\mathbf{e}_n \qquad (15.51) \\
&= -\mathbf{W}_c\Lambda_{j,n}\mathbf{e}_n, \qquad j = 1, 2, ..., q
\end{aligned}$$

The adjustment applied to the synaptic-weight vector $\mathbf{w}_{j,n}$ of neuron j is therefore determined by

$$\begin{aligned}
\Delta\mathbf{w}_{j,n} &= -\eta\frac{\partial\mathscr{E}_n}{\partial\mathbf{w}_j} \qquad (15.52) \\
&= \eta\mathbf{W}_c\Lambda_{j,n}\mathbf{e}_n, \qquad j = 1, 2, ..., q
\end{aligned}$$

where η is the learning-rate parameter and $\Lambda_{j,n}$ is the matrix governed by Eq. (15.48).

The only remaining task is that of specifying the *initial conditions* to start the learning process. For this purpose, we set

$$\Lambda_{j,0} = \mathbf{0} \qquad \text{for all } j \qquad (15.53)$$

the implication of which is that the recurrent network initially resides in a constant state.

TABLE 15.1 Summary of the Real-Time Recurrent Learning Algorithm

---

Parameters:
m = dimensionality of the input space
q = dimensionality of the state space
p = dimensionality of the output space
$\mathbf{w}_j$ = synaptic-weight vector of neuron $j, j = 1, 2, ..., q$

Initialization:
  1. Set the synaptic weights of the algorithm to small values selected from a uniform distribution.
  2. Set the initial value of the state vector $\mathbf{x}(0) = \mathbf{0}$.
  3. Set $\Lambda_{j,0} = \mathbf{0}$ for $j = 1, 2, ..., q$.

Computations: Compute the following for $n = 0, 1, 2, ...$;

$$\mathbf{e}_n = \mathbf{d}_n - \mathbf{W}_c \mathbf{x}_n$$

$$\Delta \mathbf{w}_{j,n} = \eta \mathbf{W}_c \Lambda_{j,n} \mathbf{e}_n$$

$$\Lambda_{j,n+1} = \Phi_n(\mathbf{W}_{a,n} \Lambda_{j,n} + \mathbf{U}_{j,n}), \quad j = 1, 2, ..., q$$

The definitions of $\mathbf{x}_n$, Λ_n, $\mathbf{U}_{j,n}$ and Φ_n are given in Eqs. (15.42). (15.45), (15.46), and (15.47), respectively.

Table 15.1 presents a summary of the *real-time recurrent learning algorithm*. The formulation of the algorithm as described here applies to an arbitrary activation function $\varphi(\cdot)$ that is differentiable with respect to its argument. For the special case of a sigmoidal nonlinearity in the form of a hyperbolic tangent function, for example, we have

$$x_{j,n+1} = \varphi(v_{j,n})$$
$$= \tanh(v_{j,n})$$

and

$$\varphi'(v_{j,n}) = \frac{\partial \varphi(v_{j,n})}{\partial v_{j,n}}$$
$$= \text{sech}^2(v_{j,n}) \qquad (15.54)$$
$$= 1 - x_{j,n+1}^2$$

where $v_{j,n}$ is the induced local field of neuron j and $x_{j,n+1}$ is its state at $n + 1$.

Deviation From the True Gradient Behavior

The use of the instantaneous gradient $\nabla_\mathbf{W} \mathscr{E}_n$ means that the real-time recurrent-learning (RTRL) algorithm deviates from a non-real-time one based on the true gradient $\nabla_\mathbf{W} \mathscr{E}_\text{total}$. However, this deviation is exactly analogous to that encountered in the standard back-propagation algorithm used in Chapter 4 to train an ordinary multilayer perceptron, where weight changes are made after each pattern presentation. While the real-time recurrent-learning algorithm is not guaranteed to follow the precise negative gradient of the total errror function $\mathscr{E}_\text{total}(\mathbf{W})$ with respect to the weight matrix $\mathbf{W}$, the practical differences between the real-time and non-real-time versions are often slight; these two versions become nearly identical as the learning-rate parameter η is reduced. The most severe potential consequence of this deviation from the true gradient-following behavior is that the observed trajectory (obtained by plotting $\mathcal{E}_n$ versus the elements of the weight matrix $\mathbf{W}$) may itself depend on the weight changes produced by the algorithm, which may be viewed as another source of feedback and therefore become a cause of instability in the system. We can avoid this effect by using a learning-rate parameter η that is small enough to make the time scale of the weight changes much smaller than the time scale of the network operation. Basically, this is the same recipe for algorithmic stability that was proposed for the LMS algorithm in Chapter 3.

Example 5   Illustration of the RTRL Algoithm

In this example, we formulate the RTRL algorithm for the fully recurrent network shown in Fig. 15.6 with two inputs and a single output. The network has three neurons, with the composition of matrices $\mathbf{W}_a$, $\mathbf{W}_b$, and $\mathbf{W}_c$ as described in Example 1.

With $m = 2$, $q = 3$, and $p = 1$, we find from Eq. (15.44) that

$$\boldsymbol{\xi}_n = \begin{bmatrix} x_{1,n} \\ x_{2,n} \\ x_{3,n} \\ 1 \\ u_{1,n} \\ u_{2,n} \end{bmatrix}$$

Let $\lambda_{j,kl,n}$ denote the kl-th element of matrix $\boldsymbol{\Lambda}_{j,n}$ at time-step n. The use of Eqs. (15.48) and (15.52) then yields, respectively,

$$\Delta w_{kl,n} = \eta(d_{1,n} - x_{1,n})\lambda_{1,kl,n}$$

$$\lambda_{j,kl,n+1} = \varphi'(v_{j,n})\left(\sum_{i=1}^{3} w_{a,ji}\lambda_{i,kl,n} + \delta_{kj}\xi_{l,n} \right)$$

where δ_{kj} is the Kronecker delta, which is equal to 1 for $k = j$ and zero otherwise; $j, k = 1, 2, 3$, and $l = 1, 2, ..., 6$. Figure 15.11 presents a *sensitivity graph* determining the evolution of the weight adjustment $\Delta w_{kl,n}$. Note that $\mathbf{W}_a = \{w_{ji}\}$ for $(j, i) = 1, 2, 3$, and $\mathbf{W}_b = \{w_{jl}\}$ for $j = 1, 2, 3$ and $l = 4, 5, 6$. Also, the Kronecker delta is not to be confused with the local gradient in Section 15.7 on the BPTT. ∎

Teacher Forcing

A strategy that is frequently used in the training of recurrent networks is *teacher forcing* (Williams and Zipser, 1989, 1995); in adaptive filtering, teacher forcing is known as the *equation-error method* (Mendel, 1995). Basically, teacher forcing involves replacing the actual output of a neuron, during training of the network, with the corresponding desired response (i.e., target signal) in subsequent computation of the dynamic behavior of the network, whenever that desired response is available. Although we are describing teacher forcing in a section on the RTRL algorithm, its use applies to any other learning algorithm. For it to be applicable, however, the neuron in question must feed its output back to the network input.

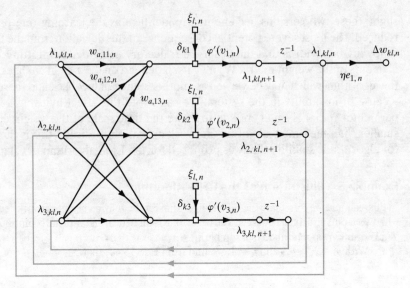

FIGURE 15.11 Sensitivity graph of the fully recurrent network of Fig. 15.6. *Note:* The three nodes, labeled $\xi_{l,n}$ are all to be viewed as a single input.

Beneficial effects of teacher forcing include the following (Williams and Zipser, 1995):

- *Teacher forcing may lead to faster training.* The reason for this improvement is that the use of teacher forcing amounts to the assumption that the network has correctly learned all the earlier parts of the task that pertain to the neurons where teacher forcing has been applied.

- *Teacher forcing may serve as a corrective mechanism during training.* For example, the synaptic weights of the network may have the correct values, but somehow the network is currently operating in the wrong region of the state space. Clearly, adjusting the synaptic weights is the wrong strategy in such a situation.

A gradient-based learning algorithm that uses teacher forcing is, in fact, optimizing a cost function different from its unforced counterpart. The teacher-forced and -unforced versions of the algorithm may therefore yield different solutions, unless the pertinent error signals are zero, in which case learning is unnecessary.

15.9 VANISHING GRADIENTS IN RECURRENT NETWORKS

A problem that requires attention in practical applications of a recurrent network is the *vanishing-gradients problem*, which arises in the training of the network to produce a desired response at the current time that depends on input data in the distant past. Because of the combined nonlinearities, an infinitesimal change of a temporally distant input may have almost no effect on network training. The problem may arise even if a large change in the temporally distant input has an effect, but the effect is not measurable by the gradient. This vanishing-gradients problem makes the learning of long-term dependencies in gradient-based training algorithms difficult, if not virtually impossible, in certain cases.

In Bengio et al. (1994), it is argued that for many practical applications, it is necessary that a recurrent network be able to store state information for an arbitrary duration and to do so in the presence of noise. The long-term storage of definite bits of information in the state variables of the recurrent network is referred to as *information latching*. The information latching must be *robust* so that the stored state information cannot be easily deleted by events that are unrelated to the learning task at hand. In specific terms, we may state the following (Bengio et al., 1994):

> *Robust information latching in a recurrent network is accomplished if the states of the network are contained in the reduced attracting set of a hyperbolic attractor.*

The notion of a hyperbolic attractor was discussed in Chapter 13. The *reduced attracting set* of a hyperbolic attractor is the set of points in the basin of attraction for which all the eigenvalues of the associated Jacobian have an absolute value less than 1. The implication here is that if a state $\mathbf{x}_n$ of the recurrent network is in the basin of attraction of a hyperbolic attractor, but not in the reduced attracting set, then the size of a ball of uncertainty around $\mathbf{x}_n$ will grow exponentially with increasing time n, as illustrated in Fig. 15.12a. Therefore, small perturbations (noise) in the input applied to the recurrent

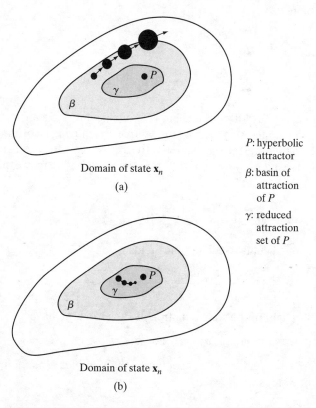

Domain of state $\mathbf{x}_n$

(a)

FIGURE 15.12   Illustration of the vanishing-gradient problem: (a) State $\mathbf{x}_n$ resides in the basin of attraction, β, but outside the reduced attration set γ. (b) State $\mathbf{x}_n$ resides inside the reduced attraction set γ.

P: hyperbolic attractor

β: basin of attraction of P

γ: reduced attraction set of P

Domain of state $\mathbf{x}_n$

(b)

network could push the trajectory toward another (possibly wrong) basin of attraction. If, however, the state $\mathbf{x}_n$ remains in the reduced attracting set of the hyperbolic attractor, a bound on the input can be found that guarantees $\mathbf{x}_n$ to remain within a certain distance of the attractor, as illustrated in Fig. 15.12b.

Long-Term Dependencies

To appreciate the impact of robust information latching on gradient-based learning, we note that the adjustment applied to the weight vector $\mathbf{w}$ of a recurrent network at time-step n is defined by

$$\Delta \mathbf{w}_n = -\eta \frac{\partial \mathcal{E}_{\text{total}}}{\partial \mathbf{w}}$$

where η is the learning-rate parameter and $\partial \mathcal{E}_{\text{total}}/\partial \mathbf{w}$ is the gradient of the cost function $\mathcal{E}_{\text{total}}$ with respect to $\mathbf{w}$. The cost function $\mathcal{E}_{\text{total}}$ is typically defined by

$$\mathcal{E}_{\text{total}} = \frac{1}{2} \sum_i \|\mathbf{d}_{i,n} - \mathbf{y}_{i,n}\|^2$$

where the vector $\mathbf{d}_{i,n}$ is the desired response and the corresponding vector $\mathbf{y}_{i,n}$ is the actual response of the network at time-step n for the ith pattern. Hence, using these two equations, we may go on to write

$$\begin{aligned} \Delta \mathbf{w}_n &= \eta \sum_i \left(\frac{\partial \mathbf{y}_{i,n}}{\partial \mathbf{w}} \right) (\mathbf{d}_{i,n} - \mathbf{y}_{i,n}) \\ &= \eta \sum_i \left(\frac{\partial \mathbf{y}_{i,n}}{\partial \mathbf{x}_{i,n}} \times \frac{\partial \mathbf{x}_{i,n}}{\partial \mathbf{w}} \right) (\mathbf{d}_{i,n} - \mathbf{y}_{i,n}) \end{aligned} \tag{15.55}$$

where, in the second line, we have used the chain rule of calculus; the state vector $\mathbf{x}_{i,n}$ pertains to the ith pattern (example) in the training sample. In applying algorithms such as back propagation through time, the partial derivatives of the cost function are computed with respect to independent weights at different time indices. We may expand on the result in Eq. (15.55) by writing

$$\Delta \mathbf{w}_n = \eta \sum_i \left(\frac{\partial \mathbf{y}_{i,n}}{\partial \mathbf{x}_{i,n}} \sum_{k=1}^{n} \frac{\partial \mathbf{x}_{i,n}}{\partial \mathbf{w}_k} \right) (\mathbf{d}_{i,n} - \mathbf{y}_{i,n})$$

Applying the chain rule of calculus a second time yields

$$\Delta \mathbf{w}_n = \eta \sum_i \left(\frac{\partial \mathbf{y}_{i,n}}{\partial \mathbf{x}_{i,n}} \sum_{k=1}^{n} \left(\frac{\partial \mathbf{x}_{i,n}}{\partial \mathbf{x}_{i,k}} \times \frac{\partial \mathbf{x}_{i,k}}{\partial \mathbf{w}_k} \right) \right) (\mathbf{d}_{i,n} - \mathbf{y}_{i,n}) \tag{15.56}$$

We now recognize that in light of the state equation of Eq. (15.2), we have

$$\mathbf{x}_{i,n} = \boldsymbol{\phi}(\mathbf{x}_{i,k}, \mathbf{u}_n), \qquad 1 \le k < n$$

Hence, we may interpret $\partial \mathbf{x}_{i,n}/\partial \mathbf{x}_{i,k}$ as the Jacobian of the nonlinear function $\boldsymbol{\phi}(\cdot, \cdot)$ expanded over $n - k$ time-steps, as shown by

$$\frac{\partial \mathbf{x}_{i,n}}{\partial \mathbf{x}_{i,k}} = \frac{\partial \boldsymbol{\phi}(\mathbf{x}_{i,k}, \mathbf{u}_n)}{\partial \mathbf{x}_{i,k}}$$

$$= \mathbf{J}_{\mathbf{x},n,k} \qquad\qquad (15.57)$$

In Bengio et al. (1994), it is shown that if the input $\mathbf{u}_n$ is such that the recurrent network remains robustly latched to a hyperbolic attractor after time $n = 0$, then the Jacobian $\mathbf{J}_{\mathbf{x},n,k}$ is an exponentially decreasing function of k so that

$$\det(\mathbf{J}_{\mathbf{x},n,k}) \to 0 \quad \text{as} \quad k \to \infty \qquad \text{for all } n \qquad (15.58)$$

The implication of Eq. (15.58) is that a *small* change in the weight vector $\mathbf{w}$ of the network is experienced mostly in the near past (i.e., values of k close to the current time-step n). There may exist an adjustment $\Delta\mathbf{w}$ to the weight vector $\mathbf{w}$ at time n that would permit the current state $\mathbf{x}_n$ to move to another, possibly better, basin of attraction, but the gradient of the cost function $\mathscr{E}_{\text{total}}$ with respect to $\mathbf{w}$ does not carry that information.

To conclude, assuming that hyperbolic attractors are used to store state information in a recurrent network by means of gradient-based learning, we find that either

- *the network is* not *robust to the presence of noise in the input signal, or else*
- *the network is unable to discover* long-term dependencies *(i.e., relationships between target outputs and inputs that occur in the distant past).*

Second-Order Methods for Mitigating the Vanishing-Gradients Problem

Gradient-based learning algorithms rely entirely on first-order information—namely, the Jacobian—for their operation. They are therefore inefficient in using the information content of the training data. To improve the utilization of information contained in the training data and thereby provide a remedy for the vanishing-gradients problem, we need to look to *second-order methods*. In this context, we have two options:

1. We can use *second-order optimization techniques*, such as the quasi-Newton, Levenberg–Marquardt, and conjugate gradient algorithms, which were discussed in Chapters 2 and 4. Although these nonlinear optimization techniques have shown promise, they are frequently plagued by convergence to poor local minima.[10]

2. We can use *nonlinear sequential state-estimation* procedures, which were discussed in Chapter 14. During the training of a neural network, two functions are performed:
   - The evolution of the weights in the neural network is tracked in a *sequential* manner.
   - *Second-order information about the training data* is provided in the form of a prediction-error covariance matrix, which is also maintained and evolved sequentially.

The extensive works reported in Puskorius and Feldkamp (2001), Feldkamp et al. (2001), and Prokhorov (2006, 2007) have demonstrated that nonlinear sequential state-estimation procedures form the basis of a second-order neural network training method that is practical and effective as an alternative method to the batch-oriented nonlinear optimization techniques mentioned previously. Accordingly, hereafter we will focus our attention on the use of nonlinear sequential state-estimate procedures for the training of recurrent multilayer perceptrons.

15.10 SUPERVISED TRAINING FRAMEWORK FOR RECURRENT NETWORKS USING NONLINEAR SEQUENTIAL STATE ESTIMATORS

To describe how a nonlinear sequential state estimator can be used to train a recurrent network in a supervised manner, consider such a recurrent network built around a multilayer perceptron with s synaptic weights and p output nodes. With n denoting a time-step in the supervised training of the network, let the vector $\mathbf{w}_n$ denote the entire set of synaptic weights in the network computed at time-step n. For example, we may construct the vector $\mathbf{w}_n$ by stacking the weights associated with neuron 1 in the first hidden layer on top of each other, followed by those of neuron 2, carrying on in this manner until we have accounted for all the neurons in the first hidden layer; then we do the same for the second and any other hidden layer in the network, until all the weights in the network have been accounted for in the vector $\mathbf{w}_n$ in the orderly fashion just described.

With sequential state estimation in mind, the *state-space model* of the network under training is defined by the following pair of models (see Fig. 15.13):

1. *System (state) model*, which is described by the *random-walk* equation

$$\mathbf{w}_{n+1} = \mathbf{w}_n + \boldsymbol{\omega}_n \qquad (15.59)$$

The *dynamic noise* $\boldsymbol{\omega}_n$ is a white Gaussian noise of zero mean and covariance matrix $\mathbf{Q}_\omega$, which is purposely included in the system model to *anneal* the supervised training of the network over time. In the early stages of the training, the covariance matrix $\mathbf{Q}_\omega$ is large in order to encourage the supervised-learning algorithm to escape local minima, and then it is gradually reduced to some finite, but small, value.

2. *Measurement model*, which is described by the equation

$$\mathbf{d}_n = \mathbf{b}(\mathbf{w}_n, \mathbf{v}_n, \mathbf{u}_n) + \boldsymbol{\nu}_n \qquad (15.60)$$

where the new entities are defined as follows:

- $\mathbf{d}_n$ is the *observable*.
- $\mathbf{v}_n$ is the vector representing the *recurrent node activities* inside the network, with its elements listed in an order consistent with those of the weight vector $\mathbf{w}_n$; hereafter, $\mathbf{v}_n$ is referred to as the *internal state*.

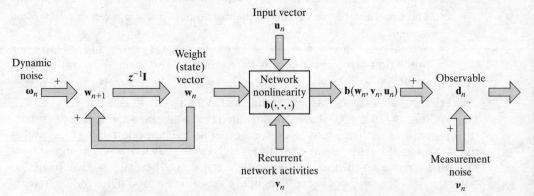

FIGURE 15.13 Nonlinear state-space model depicting the underlying dynamics of a recurrent network undergoing supervised training.

- $\mathbf{u}_n$ is the vector denoting the input signal applied to the network; that is, $\mathbf{u}_n$ is a *driving force* applied to the network.
- $\boldsymbol{\nu}_n$ is the vector denoting *measurement noise* corrupting the vector $\mathbf{d}_n$; it is assumed to be a *multivariate white-noise process of zero mean and diagonal covariance matrix* $\mathbf{R}_n$. The source of this noise is attributed to the way in which $\mathbf{d}_n$ is actually obtained.

The *vector-valued measurement function* $\mathbf{b}(\cdot, \cdot, \cdot)$ in Eq. (15.60) accounts for the overall *nonlinearity* of the multilayer perceptron from the input to the output layer; it is the only source of nonlinearity in the state-space model of the recurrent network.

Insofar as the notion of *state* is concerned, there are two different contexts in which this notion naturally features in the supervised training of the network:

1. An *externally adjustable state*, which manifests itself in adjustments applied to the network's weights through supervised training—hence the inclusion of the weight vector $\mathbf{w}_n$ in the state-space model described by both Eq. (15.59) and Eq. (15.60).
2. An *internally adjustable state*, which is represented by the vector of recurrent node activities, $\mathbf{v}_n$; these activities are outside the scope of the presently configured supervised-training process, and it is for this reason that the vector $\mathbf{v}_n$ is included only in the measurement model of Eq. (15.60). The externally applied driving force (input vector) $\mathbf{u}_n$, the dynamic noise $\boldsymbol{\omega}_n$, and the global feedback around the multilayer perceptron account for the evolution of $\mathbf{v}_n$ over time n.

Description of the Supervised-Training Framework using the Extended Kalman Filter

Given the training sample $\{\mathbf{u}_n, \mathbf{d}_n\}_{n=1}^N$, the issue of interest is how to undertake the supervised training of the recurrent multilayer perceptron (RMLP) by means of a sequential state estimator. Since the RMLP is nonlinear by virtue of the nonlinear measurement model of Eq. (15.60), the sequential state estimator would have to be correspondingly nonlinear. With this requirement in mind, we begin the discussion by considering how the *extended Kalman filter (EKF)*, studied in Chapter 14, can be used to fulfill this role.[11]

For the purpose of our present discussion, the relevant equations in the EKF algorithm summarized in Table 15.2 are the following two, using the terminology of the state-space model of Eqs. (15.59) and (15.60):

1. the *innovations process*, defined by

$$\boldsymbol{\alpha}_n = \mathbf{d}_n - \mathbf{b}(\hat{\mathbf{w}}_{n|n-1}, \mathbf{v}_n, \mathbf{u}_n) \tag{15.61}$$

where the desired (target) response $\mathbf{d}_n$ plays the role of the "observable" for the EKF;

2. the *weight (state) update*, defined by

$$\hat{\mathbf{w}}_{n|n} = \hat{\mathbf{w}}_{n|n-1} + \mathbf{G}_n \boldsymbol{\alpha}_n \tag{15.62}$$

where $\hat{\mathbf{w}}_{n|n-1}$ is the *predicted (old) estimate* of the RMLP's weight vector $\mathbf{w}$ at time n, given the desired response up to and including time $n-1$, and $\hat{\mathbf{w}}_{n|n}$ is the *filtered (updated) estimate* of $\mathbf{w}$ on receipt of the observable $\mathbf{d}_n$. The matrix $\mathbf{G}_n$ is the *Kalman gain*, which is an integral part of the EKF algorithm.

TABLE 15.2   Summary of the EKF algorithm for Supervised Training of the RMLP

Training sample:

$$\mathcal{T} = \{\mathbf{u}_n, \mathbf{d}_n\}_{n=1}^{N}$$

where $\mathbf{u}_n$ is the input vector applied to the RMLP and $\mathbf{d}_n$ is the corresponding desired response.

RMLP and Kalman filter: parameters and variables

$\mathbf{b}(\cdot, \cdot, \cdot)$	:	vector-valued measurement function
$\mathbf{B}$	:	linearized measurement matrix
$\mathbf{w}_n$	:	weight vector at time-step n
$\hat{\mathbf{w}}_{n\vert n-1}$	:	predicted estimate of the weight vector
$\hat{\mathbf{w}}_{n\vert n}$	:	filtered estimate of the weight vector
$\mathbf{v}_n$	:	vector of recurrent node activities in the RMLP
$\mathbf{y}_n$	:	output vector of the RMLP produced in response to the input vector $\mathbf{u}_n$
$\mathbf{Q}_\omega$	:	covariance matrix of the dynamic noise $\boldsymbol{\omega}_n$
$\mathbf{Q}_v$	:	covariance matrix of the measurement noise $\boldsymbol{v}_n$
$\mathbf{G}_n$	:	Kalman gain
$\mathbf{P}_{n\vert n-1}$	:	prediction-error covariance matrix
$\mathbf{P}_{n\vert n}$	:	filtering-error covariance matrix

Computation:

For $n = 1, 2, \ldots$, compute the following:

$$\mathbf{G}_n = \mathbf{P}_{n\vert n-1}\mathbf{B}_n^T[\mathbf{B}_n\mathbf{P}_{n\vert n-1}\mathbf{B}_n^T + \mathbf{Q}_{v,n}]^{-1}$$

$$\boldsymbol{\alpha}_n = \mathbf{d}_n - \mathbf{b}_n(\hat{\mathbf{w}}_{n\vert n-1}, \mathbf{v}_n, \mathbf{u}_n)$$

$$\hat{\mathbf{w}}_{n\vert n} = \hat{\mathbf{w}}_{n\vert n-1} + \mathbf{G}_n\boldsymbol{\alpha}_n$$

$$\hat{\mathbf{w}}_{n+1\vert n} = \hat{\mathbf{w}}_{n\vert n}$$

$$\mathbf{P}_{n\vert n} = \mathbf{P}_{n\vert n-1} - \mathbf{G}_n\mathbf{B}_n\mathbf{P}_{n\vert n-1}$$

$$\mathbf{P}_{n+1\vert n} = \mathbf{P}_{n\vert n} + \mathbf{Q}_{\omega,n}$$

Initilization:

$$\hat{\mathbf{w}}_{1\vert 0} = \mathbb{E}[\mathbf{w}_1]$$

$\mathbf{P}_{1\vert 0} = \delta^{-1}\mathbf{I}$, where δ is a small positive constant and $\mathbf{I}$ is the identity matrix

---

Examining the underlying operation of the RMLP, we find that the term $\mathbf{b}(\hat{\mathbf{w}}_{n\vert n-1}, \mathbf{v}_n, \mathbf{u}_n)$ is the *actual output vector* $\mathbf{y}_n$ produced by the RMLP with its "old" weight vector $\hat{\mathbf{w}}_{n\vert n-1}$ and internal state $\mathbf{v}_n$ in response to the input vector $\mathbf{u}_n$. We may therefore rewrite the combination of Eqs. (15.61) and (15.62) as a single equation:

$$\hat{\mathbf{w}}_{n\vert n} = \hat{\mathbf{w}}_{n\vert n-1} + \mathbf{G}_n(\mathbf{d}_n - \mathbf{y}_n) \qquad (15.63)$$

On the basis of this insightful equation, we may now depict the supervised training of the RMLP as the combination of two *mutually coupled components forming a closed-loop feedback system*, such as that shown in Fig. 15.14:

1. The top part of the figure depicts the supervised-learning process as viewed partly from the *network's perspective*. With the weight vector set at its old (predicted) value $\hat{\mathbf{w}}_{n\vert n-1}$, the RMLP computes the actual output vector $\mathbf{y}_n$ in response to the input vector $\mathbf{u}_n$. Thus, the RMLP supplies the EKF with $\mathbf{y}_n$ as the predicted estimate of the observable—namely, $\hat{\mathbf{d}}_{n\vert n-1}$.

2. The bottom part of the figure depicts the EKF in its role as the *facilitator* of the training process. Supplied with $\hat{\mathbf{d}}_{n\vert n-1} = \mathbf{y}_n$, the EKF updates the old estimate of the

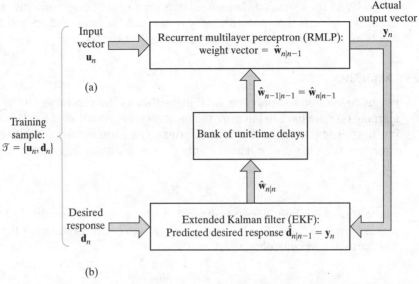

FIGURE 15.14   Closed-loop feedback system embodying the RMLP and the EKF: (a) The RMLP, with weight vector $\hat{\mathbf{w}}_{n|n-1}$, operates on the input vector $\mathbf{u}_n$ to produce the output vector $\mathbf{y}_n$. (b) The EKF, supplied with the prediction $\hat{\mathbf{d}}_{n|n-1} = \mathbf{y}_n$, operates on the desired response $\mathbf{d}_n$ to produce the filtered weight vector $\hat{\mathbf{w}}_{n|n} = \hat{\mathbf{w}}_{n+1|n}$, thereby preparing the closed-loop feedback system for the next iteration.

weight vector by operating on the current desired response $\mathbf{d}_n$. The filtered estimate of the weight vector—namely, $\hat{\mathbf{w}}_{n|n}$—is thus computed in accordance with Eq. (15.63). The $\hat{\mathbf{w}}_{n|n}$ so computed is supplied by the EKF to the RMLP via a *bank of unit-time delays*.

With the transition matrix being equal to the identity matrix, as evidenced by Eq. (15.59), we may set $\hat{\mathbf{w}}_{n+1|n}$ equal to $\hat{\mathbf{w}}_{n|n}$ for the next iteration. This equality permits the supervised-training cycle to be repeated until the training is terminated.

Note that in the supervised-training framework of Fig. 15.14, the training sample $\mathcal{T} = \{\mathbf{u}_n, \mathbf{d}_n\}$ is split between the RMLP and EKF: The input vector $\mathbf{u}_n$ is applied to the RMLP as the excitation, and the desired response $\mathbf{d}_n$ is applied to the EKF as the observable, which is dependent on the hidden weight (state) vector $\mathbf{w}_n$.

In Chapter 14, we emphasized the *predictor–corrector property* as an intrinsic property of the Kalman filter, its variants, and extensions. In light of this property, examination of the block diagram of Fig. 15.14 leads us to make the following insightful statement:

> *The recurrent neural network, undergoing training, performs the role of the predictor; and the extended Kalman filter, providing the supervision, performs the role of the corrector.*

Thus, whereas in traditional applications of the Kalman filter for sequential state estimation, the roles of predictor and corrector are embodied in the Kalman filter itself, in supervised-training applications these two roles are split between the recurrent neural network and the extended Kalman filter. Such a split of responsibilities in supervised learning is in perfect accord with the way in which the input and desired response elements of the training sample $\mathcal{T}$ are split in Fig. 15.14.

The EKF Algorithm

For us to be able to apply the EKF algorithm as the facilitator of the supervised-learning task, we have to linearize the measurement equation of Eq. (15.60) by retaining first-order terms in the Taylor-series expansion of the nonlinear part of the equation. With $\mathbf{b}(\mathbf{w}_n, \mathbf{v}_n, \mathbf{u}_n)$ as the only source of nonlinearity, we may *approximate* Eq. (15.60) as

$$\mathbf{d}_n = \mathbf{B}_n \mathbf{w}_n + \boldsymbol{v}_n \tag{15.64}$$

where $\mathbf{B}_n$ is the *p-by-s measurement matrix of the linearized model*. The linearization process involves computing the partial derivatives of the p outputs of the RMLP with respect to its s weights, obtaining the matrix

$$\mathbf{B} = \begin{bmatrix} \dfrac{\partial b_1}{\partial w_1} & \dfrac{\partial b_1}{\partial w_2} & \cdots & \dfrac{\partial b_1}{\partial w_s} \\[2ex] \dfrac{\partial b_2}{\partial w_1} & \dfrac{\partial b_2}{\partial w_2} & \cdots & \dfrac{\partial b_2}{\partial w_s} \\[2ex] \vdots & \vdots & \vdots & \vdots \\[2ex] \dfrac{\partial b_p}{\partial w_1} & \dfrac{\partial b_p}{\partial w_2} & \cdots & \dfrac{\partial b_p}{\partial w_s} \end{bmatrix} \tag{15.65}$$

the dimensions of which are p-by-s. Recognizing that dimensionality of the weight vector $\mathbf{w}$ is s, it follows that the matrix product $\mathbf{Bw}$ is a p-by-1 vector, which is in perfect agreement with the dimensionality of the observable $\mathbf{d}$.

The vector $\mathbf{v}_n$ in $\mathbf{b}(\mathbf{w}, \mathbf{v}_n, \mathbf{u}_n)$ is maintained constant at some value; reference to the time-step n has been omitted in Eq. (15.65) to simplify the presentation. The $b_i, i = 1, 2, \ldots, p$, in this equation denotes the ith element of the vectorial function $\mathbf{b}(\mathbf{w}_n, \mathbf{v}_n, \mathbf{u}_n)$. In accordance with Eq. (14.70) of Chapter 14, partial derivatives on the right-hand side of the equation are evaluated at $\mathbf{w}_n = \hat{\mathbf{w}}_{n|n-1}$, where $\hat{\mathbf{w}}_{n|n-1}$ is the prediction of the weight vector $\mathbf{w}_n$ at time n, given the desired response up to and including time $n-1$.

In practice, the partial derivatives in Eq. (15.65) are computed by using the back-propagation-through-time (BPTT) or the real-time recurrent learning (RTRL) algorithm. In effect, the EKF builds on one or the other of these two algorithms, which are described in Sections 15.7 and 15.8, respectively. The implication here is that $\mathbf{b}$ must be a function of the recurrent node activities, which it is, as shown in the measurement model of Eq. (15.60).

The state-evolution equation of Eq. (15.59) is linear to begin with; it is therefore unaffected by the linearization of the measurement equation. Thus, the *linearized state-space model* of the recurrent network, permitting the application of the EKF, is defined by Eqs. (15.59) and (15.64).

Decoupled Extended Kalman Filter

The computational requirements of the extended Kalman filter (EKF), summarized in Table 15.2, are dominated by the need to *store* and *update* the filtering-error covariance matrix $\mathbf{P}_{n|n}$ at each time-step n. For a recurrent neural network containing p output nodes and s weights, the computational complexity of the EKF is $O(ps^2)$ and its storage requirement is $O(s^2)$. For large s, these requirements may be highly demanding. In such situations, we may look to the *decoupled extended Kalman filter (DEKF)* as a practical remedy for the proper management of computational resources (Puskorius and Feldkamp, 2001).

The basic idea behind the DEKF is to *ignore* the interactions between the estimates of certain weights in the recurrent neural network. In so doing, a controllable number of zeros is introduced into the covariance matrix $\mathbf{P}_{n|n}$. More specifically, if the weights in the network are decoupled in such a way that we create *mutually exclusive weight groups*, then the covariance matrix $\mathbf{P}_{n|n}$ is structured into a *block-diagonal form*, as illustrated in Fig. 15.15.

Let g denote the designated number of disjoint weight groups created in the manner just described. Also, for $i = 1, 2, ..., g$, let

$$\hat{\mathbf{w}}_{n|n}^{(i)} = \text{filtered weight vector for group } i,$$
$$\mathbf{P}_{n|n}^{(i)} = \text{subset of the filtering-error covariance matrix for group } i,$$
$$\mathbf{G}_n^{(i)} = \text{Kalman gain matrix for group } i,$$

and so on for the other entries in the DEKF. The concatenation of the filtered weight vectors $\hat{\mathbf{w}}_{n|n}^{(i)}$ forms the overall filtered weight vector $\hat{\mathbf{w}}_{n|n}$; similar remarks apply to $\mathbf{P}_{n|n}^{(i)}$, $\mathbf{G}_n^{(i)}$, and the other entries in the DEKF algorithm. In light of these new notations, we may now rewrite the DEKF algorithm for the ith weight group as follows:

$$\mathbf{G}_n^{(i)} = \mathbf{P}_{n|n-1}^{(i)}(\mathbf{B}_n^{(i)})^T \left[\sum_{j=1}^{g} \mathbf{B}_n^{(j)}\mathbf{P}_{n|n-1}^{(j)}(\mathbf{B}_n^{(j)})^T + \mathbf{Q}_{v,n}^{(i)} \right]^{-1}$$

$$\boldsymbol{\alpha}_n^{(i)} = \mathbf{d}_n^{(i)} - \mathbf{b}_n^{(i)}(\hat{\mathbf{w}}_{n|n-1}^{(i)}, \mathbf{v}_n^{(i)}, \mathbf{u}_n^{(i)})$$

$$\hat{\mathbf{w}}_{n|n}^{(i)} = \hat{\mathbf{w}}_{n|n-1}^{(i)} + \mathbf{G}_n^{(i)}\boldsymbol{\alpha}_n^{(i)}$$

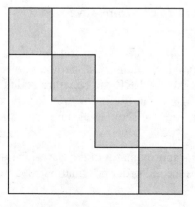

FIGURE 15.15   Block-diagonal representation of the filtering-error covariance matrix $\mathbf{P}_{n|n}^{(i)}$ pertaining to the decoupled Kalman filter (DEKF). The shaded parts of the square represent nonzero values of $\mathbf{P}_{n|n}^{(i)}$, where $i = 1, 2, 3, 4$ for the example illustrated in the figure. As we make the number of disjoint weight groups, g, larger, more zeros are created in the covariance matrix $\mathbf{P}_{n|n}$; in other words, the matrix $\mathbf{P}_{n|n}$ becomes more sparse. The computational burden is therefore reduced, but the numerical accuracy of the state estimation becomes degraded.

$$\hat{\mathbf{w}}_{n+1|n}^{(i)} = \hat{\mathbf{w}}_{n|n}^{(i)}$$

$$\mathbf{P}_{n|n}^{(i)} = \mathbf{P}_{n|n-1}^{(i)} - \mathbf{G}_n^{(i)} \mathbf{B}_n^{(i)} \mathbf{P}_{n|n-1}^{(i)}$$

$$\mathbf{P}_{n+1|n}^{(i)} = \mathbf{P}_{n|n}^{(i)} + \mathbf{Q}_{\omega,n}^{(i)}$$

Initialization of the DEKF algorithm proceeds in the manner described previously in Table 15.2 for the EKF algorithm.

The computational requirements of the DEKF assume the following orders:

$$\text{Computational complexity: } O\left(p^2 s + p \sum_{i=1}^{g} s_i^2 \right)$$

$$\text{Storage requirement: } O\left(\sum_{i=1}^{g} s_i^2 \right)$$

where s_i is the size of the state in group i and s in the total state size; p is the number of output nodes. Depending on the number of disjoint groups, g, the computational requirements of the DEKF can be made significantly smaller than those of the EKF.

Summarizing Remarks on the EKF

An attractive feature of using the EKF as the sequential state estimator for the supervised training of a recurrent neural network is that its basic algorithmic structure (and therefore its implementation) is relatively simple, as evidenced by the summary presented in Table 15.2. However, it suffers from two practical limitations:

1. The EKF requires linearization of the recurrent neural network's vectorial measurement function $\mathbf{b}(\mathbf{w}_n, \mathbf{v}_n, \mathbf{u}_n)$.

2. Depending on the size of the weight vector $\mathbf{w}$ (i.e., the dimensionality of the state space), we may have to resort to the use of the DEKF to reduce computational complexity and storage requirements. The practical issue, however, is that we thereby sacrifice computational accuracy.

We may bypass the first limitation by using a derivative-free nonlinear sequential state estimator, as discussed next.

Supervised Training of Neural Networks with the Use of a Derivative-free Sequential State Estimator

In Chapter 14, we discussed the *cubature Kalman filter* (Arasaratnam and Haykin, 2009), the formulation of which rests on applying a numerical method known as the *cubature rule* (Stroud, 1971; Cools, 1997). Like the EKF, the cubature Kalman filter (CKF) is an approximate realization of the Bayesian filter; however, in a theoretical context the CKF is the optimum nonlinear filter for sequential state estimation. The CKF has some unique properties:

1. The CKF is a more numerically *accurate* approximator of the Bayesian filter than the EKF, in that it completely preserves second-order information about the state that is contained in the observations.

2. The CKF is *derivative free*; hence, there is no need for linearizing the measurement matrix of the recurrent neural network.

3. Last, but by no means least, the cubature rule is used to approximate the time-update integral that embodies the posterior distribution and all the other integral formulas involved in the formulation of the Bayesian filter operating in a Gaussian environment; as a rule, integration is preferred over differentiation because of its "smoothing" property.

In light of these properties, it can be argued that the CKF is a highly attractive choice for the supervised training of a recurrent neural network. The experiment to be described in Section 15.11, involving the dynamic reconstruction of a chaotic attractor, demonstrates the superior performance of the CKF over the EKF and of another derivative-free sequential state estimator known as the *central-difference Kalman filter* (CDKF).[12] The CDKF, due to Nörgaard et al. (2000), is derived by replacing a Taylor series expansion of the nonlinear measurement equation in the vicinity of the current estimate of the weight vector with a corresponding expansion based on *Stirling's formula* for interpolating an analytic function over a specified interval. In a one-dimensional setting, Stirling's formula may be obtained from the Taylor expansion by respectively replacing first- and second-order partial derivatives with first- and second-order *central differences*, commonly used in numerical analysis.[13] Then, once the approximate linearization of the measurement equation has been derived in the multidimensional setting of interest, the formulation of the CDKF algorithm follows Kalman filter theory. The original CDKF algorithm described in Nörgaard et al. (2000) employs square-root filtering for improved numerical accuracy; such a procedure was described in Chapter 14 in the context of Kalman filtering.

15.11   COMPUTER EXPERIMENT: DYNAMIC RECONSTRUCTION OF MACKEY–GLASS ATTRACTOR

The *Mackey–Glass attractor* was originally formulated by Mackey and Glass (1977) for modeling the dynamic formation of blood cells in the body. It is described by a single continuous-time differential equation, namely,

$$\frac{d}{dt}x_t = -bx_t + \frac{ax_{t-\Delta t}}{1 + x_{t-\Delta t}^{10}} \tag{15.66}$$

where t denotes continuous time, the coefficients $a = 0.2$ and $b = 0.1$, and the time delay $\Delta t = 30$. In a formal sense, the Mackey–Glass attractor has an infinite number of degrees of freedom, because we require knowledge of the initial value of the function $x(t)$ across a continuous-time interval. Yet, it behaves like a strange attractor with a finite dimension.

To solve Eq. (15.66) numerically, we used the fourth-order Runge-Kutta method (Press et al., 1988) with a sampling period of 6s and an initial condition $x_n = 0.9$ for $0 \le n \le \Delta t$, where, as usual, n denotes discrete time. We thus obtained a time series of length 1000, of which the first half was used for training and the rest for testing. Given a chaotic attractor, we recall from Chapter 13 that the next data sample $x_{n+\tau}$ can be predicted from a properly chosen time series $\{x_n, x_{n-\tau}, ..., x_{n-[d_E-2]\tau}, x_{n-[d_E-1]\tau}\}$, where d_E and τ are called the *embedding dimension* and *embedding delay*, respectively. For the chaotic Mackey–Glass system, d_E and τ were chosen to be 7 and 1, respectively.

Recurrent multilayer perceptrons (RMLPs) have proven to be numerically robust in learning time-correlated signals. For this experiment, we implemented an RMLP having seven inputs, representing an embedding of the observed time series, one output, and one self-recurrent hidden layer with five neurons. Hence, the RMLP has a total of 71 synaptic weights (with bias parameters included). The output neuron uses a linear activation function, whereas all the hidden neurons use the hyperbolic tangent function

$$\varphi(v) = \tanh(v)$$

The square-root versions of three algorithms were used to train the RMLP: The extended Kalman filter, the central-difference Kalman filter, and the cubature Kalman filter. To *unfold* the recurrent loop of the neural network, we used a truncation depth $h = 1$, which was found to be adequate for the experiment. Moreover, for the EKF algorithm, we used the back-propagation algorithm to compute the partial derivatives of the nonlinear measurement function $\mathbf{b}_n$, in accordance with the procedure described in Section 15.7.

For all three algorithms, 10 epochs per run were used to train the RMLP. Each epoch was obtained from a long subsequence involving 107 time-steps, starting from a randomly selected point. To be more precise, each epoch was made up of 100 examples gleaned by a sliding window of length 8 over the subsequence. The weights of the RMLP were initialized to zero-mean Gaussian with a diagonal covariance matrix of $10^{-2} \times \mathbf{I}_s$ where $\mathbf{I}_s$ is an *s*-by-*s* identity matrix.

To compare the performance of CKF-trained RMLPs against the CDKF and against EKF-trained RMLPs in a fair-minded way, we made 50 independent training runs. To measure the performance in predicting 100 time-steps ahead starting from a time index of 500, we used the ensemble-averaged cumulative absolute error, defined by

$$\mathscr{E}_n = \frac{1}{50} \sum_{r=1}^{50} \sum_{i=1}^{n} |d_i^{(r)} - \hat{d}_i^{(r)}|; \qquad n = 1, 2, ..., 100$$

where $d_i^{(r)}$ is the desired response at time i for the rth run and $\hat{d}_i^{(r)}$ is the estimate computed at the output of the RMLP. The long-term accumulative prediction error is an increasing function of time n.

As has already been pointed out, three different approximations of the Bayesian filter were used in the experiment:

- Extended Kalman filter (EKF)
- Central-difference Kalman filter (CDKF)
- Cubature Kalman filter (CKF)

Results of the experiment are presented in Fig. 15.16, where the ensemble-averaged cumulative absolute error in dynamic reconstruction is plotted against the number of

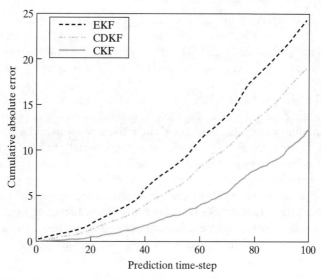

FIGURE 15.16   Ensemble-averaged cumulative absolute error curves during the autonomous prediction phase of dynamic reconstruction of the Mackey-Glass attractor.

predictive time-steps that were used in the dynamic reconstruction. As expected, the results of the experiment provide clear evidence for the superior performance, and therefore improved computational accuracy, of the CKF over the CDKF and the EKF in that order.

15.12   ADAPTIVITY CONSIDERATIONS

An interesting property of a recurrent neural network (e.g., RMLP), observed after the network has been trained in a supervised manner, is the *emergence of an adaptive behavior*.[14] This phenomenon occurs despite the fact that the synaptic weights in the network have been fixed. The root of this adaptive behavior may be traced to a fundamental theorem, which is stated as follows (Lo and Yu, 1995b):

> *Consider a recurrent neural network embedded in a stochastic environment with relatively small variability in its statistical behavior. Provided that that the underlying probability distribution of the environment is fully represented in the supervised-training sample supplied to the network, it is possible for the network to adapt to the relatively* small *statistical variations in the environment without any further on-line adjustments being made to the synaptic weights of the network.*

This fundamental theorem is valid *only* for recurrent networks. We say so because the dynamic state of a recurrent network actually acts as a "short-term memory" that carries an estimate or statistic of the uncertain environment for adaptation, in which the network is embodied.

This adaptive behavior has been referred to differently in the literature. In Lo (2001), it is referred to as *accommodative learning*. In another paper published in the same year (Younger et al., 2001), it is referred to as *meta-learning*, meaning "learning how to learn." Hereafter, we will refer to this adaptive behavior as meta-learning as well.

Regardless of how this adaptive behavior is termed, it is not expected that it will work as effectively as a truly adaptive neural network, where provision is made for automatic on-line weight adjustments if the environment exhibits large statistical variability. This observation has been confirmed experimentally in Lo (2001), where comparative performance evaluations were made between a recurrent neural network with meta-learning and an adaptive neural network with long-term as well as short-term memories; the comparative evaluations were performed in the context of system identification.

Nevertheless, the meta-learning capability of recurrent neural networks should be viewed as a desirable property in control and signal-processing applications, particularly where on-line adjustments of synaptic weights are not practically feasible or they are too costly to perform.

Adaptive Critic

If a desired response is not available for the supervised training of a recurrent neural network and existing unsupervised training methodology does not converge fast enough for the application of interest, then reinforcement learning (i.e., approximate dynamic programming) may be the only viable option. From Chapter 12, we recall that in approximate dynamic programming, an agent (i.e., learning system) requires, from the environment in which it is embedded, merely a response to the action taken by the agent. Basically, the interaction between the agent and its environment in real time is all that we need for the construction of a short-term memory that could permit the internal states of the recurrent neural network to adapt to statistical variations of the environment.

With the synaptic weights of the recurrent neural network fixed, the only way in which its internal states can be adapted is through adjustments applied to the network's internal recurrent node activities, denoted by the vector $\mathbf{v}_n$ in the measurement equation of Eq. (15.60). Thus, unlike the supervised adjustment applied to the hidden weight vector $\mathbf{w}_n$, the adjustments to the vector $\mathbf{v}_n$ are applied *directly* to the measurement equation of Eq. (15.60).

The block diagram of Fig. 15.17 depicts a scheme built around a recurrent neural network with fixed weights whereby the recurrent node activities can be adapted in real time. Specifically, we have an *adaptive critic* that receives two inputs, one from the network and the other from the environment in response to some relevant action taken by the network (acting as the agent). In response to these two inputs, the adaptive critic computes the appropriate adjustments to the network's internal recurrent node activities.

To summarize, we may say that through the use of an adaptive critic, a recurrent neural network becomes equipped with two forms of memory:

1. long-term memory, which is acquired by the network itself through supervised training that results in a set of fixed weights;

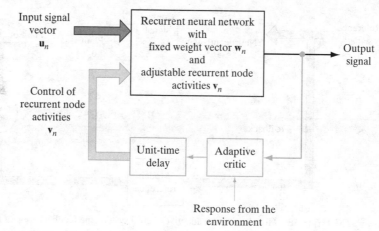

FIGURE 15.17   Block diagram illustrating the use of an adaptive critic for the control of recurrent node activities $\mathbf{v}_n$ in a recurrent neural network (assumed to have a single output); the part of the figure involving the critic is shown in red.

2. short-term memory, which enables the network to adapt its internal state (i.e., recurrent node activities) to statistical variations in the environment without disturbing the fixed weights.

It is also noteworthy that through continuing interactions with the environment, the short-term memory can be developed in a *model-free setting*, as described in Prokhorov (2007).

15.13 CASE STUDY: MODEL REFERENCE APPLIED TO NEUROCONTROL

In this last topic covered in this chapter, we discuss a case study that not only fits quite nicely into the chapter, but also brings together several topics discussed in previous chapters of the book.

To be specific, we discuss an important application of recurrent neural networks in the design of *feedback control systems*, where the states of a plant are coupled non-linearly with imposed controls. The design of the system is further complicated by other factors such as the presence of unmeasured and random disturbances, the possibility of a nonunique plant inverse, and the presence of plant states that are unobservable.

A control strategy well suited for the use of recurrent neural networks is the *model-reference control* (Narendra and Annaswamy, 1989; Puskorius and Feldkamp, 2001; Prokhorov, 2006). As depicted in Fig. 15.18, the model-reference control system consists of five functional components:

1. The *plant*, which is to be controlled so as to compensate for changes in the plant dynamics. The plant's output evolves over time n as a function of a control signal and its own parameter vector $\boldsymbol{\theta}_k$, where the time index k in $\boldsymbol{\theta}_k$ changes far less frequently than the time index n. For example, $\boldsymbol{\theta}_k$ could be *piecewise constant*, where it switches from one constant level to another with varying k.

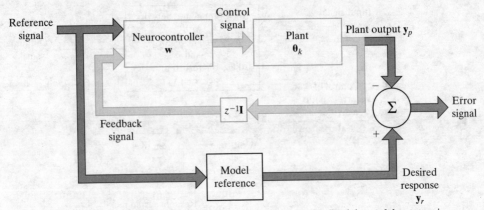

FIGURE 15.18   Model-reference adaptive control system; the feedback loop of the system is printed in red.

2. The *neurocontroller*, which consists of a recurrent network exemplified by a recurrent multilayer perceptron. It supplies the *control signal*, applied to the plant input. This signal varies as a function of the *reference signal*, *feedback signal*, and the controller's weight vector denoted by **w**.

3. The *model reference*, which is assumed to be stable. The model reference supplies a *desired signal* in response to the reference signal as input.

4. The *comparator*, represented by the summing unit, which compares the plant output against the desired response from the model reference to produce an error signal.

5. The *bank of unit-time delays*, represented by $z^{-1}\mathbf{I}$, which closes the feedback loop around the plant by aligning the elements of the plant output vector with those of the reference signal; in effect, an *external recurrent network* is realized by the feedback loop.

From this description, it is apparent that the plant output is an indirect function of the neurocontroller's weight vector **w** through the control signal and a direct function of the plant's own parameter vector $\boldsymbol{\theta}_k$. We may therefore express the plant output as $\mathbf{y}_{i,p}(n, \mathbf{w}, \boldsymbol{\theta}_k)$, where the subscript i refers to a particular instance of the plant's operation. The explicit dependence of the plant output on time n is included to emphasize the *nonstationary* behavior of the plant. Correspondingly, let $\mathbf{y}_{i,r}(n)$ denote the output of the model reference for the same instance i. The reference signal is common to both forward paths of the *model-reference adaptive-control system*; we have simplified matters by not including the dependence on the reference signal in the plant output or in the model-reference output.

The error signal is defined by the difference between the model-reference output and the plant output for each instance i. We may therefore formulate the *mean-square error*

$$J(\mathbf{w}, \boldsymbol{\theta}_k) = \frac{1}{T} \sum_{n=1}^{T} \sum_{i} \|\mathbf{y}_{i,r}(n) - \mathbf{y}_{i,p}(n, \mathbf{w}, \boldsymbol{\theta}_k)\|^2 \qquad (15.66)$$

where the inner summation is taken over the entire set of instances used in training the neurocontroller, and the outer summation is taken over the entire duration of training

$1 \leq n \leq T$. To provide for a design of the neurocontroller that is *robust* with respect to parameter changes and external disturbances (the latter are not shown in Fig. 15.18), adjustments to the neurocontroller's weight vector $\mathbf{w}$ are made in such a way that the root mean-square error $J(\mathbf{w}, \boldsymbol{\theta}_k)$ and its maximum value are both reduced over all possible values of the plant's parameter vector $\boldsymbol{\theta}_k$ (Prokhorov, 2006). This optimization makes the plant output *track* the model-reference output.

The block labeled "Plant" in the model-reference control system of Fig. 15.18 has a double meaning, depending on how it is seen from the perspective of the neurocontroller:

- One meaning refers to the *actual system being controlled* as the plant.
- The other meaning refers to a *model* of that actual system.

Accordingly, we may compensate for uncertainties in the plant dynamics by using *direct control* in which the actual plant is used in the control system, or *indirect control* in which the plant model is used in the control system (Adetona et al., 2000).

In many cases, we find that a *physics-based model* of the plant (i.e., the actual system being controlled) is already in place; the availability of such a model is common in industry, resulting from the investment of a great amount of both time and effort. Alternatively, we may use the *principle of system identification*, discussed in the introductory chapter to build a neural-network-based model of the plant. Typically, however, we find the following situation (Prokhorov, 2006):

1. The physics-based model is more accurate than the neural-network-based model.
2. The physics-based model does *not* include exclusively differentiable elements.

The method used to train the neurocontroller in the study reported by Prokhorov (2006) is a modified version of a square-root state-estimation algorithm originally derived by Nørgaard et al. (2000). As pointed out previously, this algorithm is appropriately referred to as the central-difference Kalman filter (CDKF).

In Prokhorov (2006), experimental results are presented that not only validate the training of a neurocontroller via the nonlinear sequential state-estimation framework, but also demonstrate the superior accuracy obtained with the derivative-free CDKF algorithm versus the derivative-dependent EKF algorithm.

15.14   SUMMARY AND DISCUSSION

Recurrent Network Models

In this chapter, we discussed recurrent neural networks that involve the use of *global feedback* applied to a static (memoryless) multilayer perceptron. The application of feedback enables neural networks to acquire state representations, making them suitable systems for diverse applications in signal processing and control. We identified four main network models belonging to the class of recurrent networks with global feedback:

- nonlinear autoregressive networks with exogenous inputs (NARX networks), which use feedback from the output layer to the input layer;
- fully connected recurrent networks, which use feedback from the hidden layer to the input layer;

- recurrent multilayer perceptrons with more than one hidden layer, which use feedback from the output of each computation layer to its own input, and possibly all the way from the output to the input;
- second-order recurrent networks, which use second-order neurons.

In all of these recurrent networks, the feedback is applied via tapped-delay-line memories.

The first three recurrent networks permit the use of a *state-space framework* for studying their dynamic behavior. This approach, rooted in modern control theory, provides a powerful method for studying the nonlinear dynamics of recurrent neural networks.

Properties of Recurrent Neural Networks

The following are some important properties of recurrent neural networks:

1. They are universal approximators of nonlinear dynamic systems, provided that they are equipped with an adequate number of hidden neurons.
2. They are locally controllable and locally observable, provided that their linearized versions satisfy certain conditions around the equilibrium point.
3. Given any finite-state machine, we can build a recurrent neural network which, regarded as a black-box machine, will behave like that finite-state machine.
4. Recurrent neural networks exhibit a meta-learning (i.e., learning to learn) capability.

Indeed, it is precisely these properties that befit recurrent neural networks for applications in computing, control, and signal-processing.

Gradient-based Learning Algorithms

In this chapter, we also discussed two basic supervised-learning algorithms for the training of recurrent neural networks: back propagation through time (BPTT) and real-time recurrent learning (RTRL). Both of these algorithms are gradient based, which makes them computationally simple to implement. The BPTT is most suitable for off-line learning, whereas, by definition, the RTRL is designed for on-line learning. However, a practical limitation of both algorithms is the vanishing-gradients problem, which arises due to their inability to use second-order information contained in the training data.

Supervised-learning Algorithms Based on Nonlinear Sequential State Estimation

An effective method for overcoming the vanishing-gradients problem is to use a nonlinear sequential state estimator to provide for the supervised training of a recurrent multilayer perceptron. Here we have two choices available to us:

1. We can use the extended Kalman filter (EKF) on account of its computational simplicity. However, we then have to provide for linearization of the measurement model pertaining to the recurrent neural network by using the BPTT or RTRL algorithm.
2. We can use a derivative-free nonlinear sequential state estimator, exemplified by the cubature Kalman filter (CKF) described in Chapter 14 or the central-difference Kalman filter (CDKF) described briefly in this chapter. In so doing, we not only broaden the applicability of this novel approach to supervised learning, but also improve numerical accuracy. However, the price to be paid for these benefits is increased computational requirements.

Among these three nonlinear filters, the CKF stands out not only as the closest approximation to the Bayesian filter (that is optimal, at least, in a conceptual sense) but also the most powerful of them all. Assuming Gaussianity, formulation of the CKF is influenced by Kalman filter theory (e.g., the innovations process), as discussed in Chapter 14.

In any event, this new approach to supervised learning is elegant, as evidenced by the block diagram of Fig. 15.14 for EKF. Most importantly, the procedure is applicable to recurrent neural networks as well as other neural networks (e.g., multilayer perceptrons). Indeed, it is because of this universal applicability that we may look to the class of nonlinear sequential state-estimation algorithms (embodying the EKF, CDKF, and CKF) for supervised learning as an *enabling technology*, which makes them capable of solving difficult signal-processing and control problems, particularly large-scale learning problems where the use of second-order information may very well be a "must."

In theory, a recurrent network with global feedback (e.g., a recurrent multilayer perceptron trained with the EKF algorithm) can learn the underlying dynamics of a *nonstationary* environment by storing the knowledge gained from the training sample in a *fixed* set of weights. Most importantly, the network can *track* the statistical variations of the environment, provided that two conditions are satisfied:

- The recurrent network does not suffer from underfitting or overfitting.
- The training sample is representative of an environment that exhibits small statistical variations.

Multistream Training

The approach to supervised training of recurrent networks described in Fig. 15.14 may benefit from a procedure known as *multistream training*. This procedure applies to situations, in which a *coordinated weight update* could be advantageous by virtue of using multiple training patterns (Puskorius and Feldkamp, 2001).

In the supervised training of a neural network, two scenarios may arise, depending on the nature of the training sequence of input–target response pairs:

1. *Homogeneous sequences*, where one or more passes through the training data may well produce satisfactory results.
2. *Heterogenous sequences*, where, for example, there may be regions of rapid changes in the input–target response pairs followed by regions of slow changes.

In the latter scenario, there is a tendency in standard training processes for the network weights to be adapted unduly in favor of the currently presented training data, so we speak of the *recency effect*. For feedforward networks, the effective solution is to *shuffle* the order in which the training data are presented to the network or to use the *batch* form of training; both of these procedures were discussed in Chapter 4. For recurrent neural networks, the direct analog of shuffling the order of data presentation is to present the network with randomly selected subsequences; this has the effect of making a weight update only for the last input–target response pair of the subsequence. In the case of a training procedure using the EKF algorithm, for example, a full batch update involves running the recurrent network through the entire training sample, computing the necessary partial derivatives for each input–target response pair, and then making an update of the network weights on the basis of the entire set of estimation errors.

The multistream training procedure overcomes the recency effect through the combined use of shuffling (i.e., presentation of randomly selected subsequences) and batch updating. In particular, multistream training is based on the principle that each weight update should account for the information contents of multiple input–target response pairs in a simultaneous manner.

One last comment is in order: Multistream training is applicable not only to the use of the EKF algorithm, but also to the use of derivative-free nonlinear sequential state algorithms (e.g., the CDKF and CKF).

The Final Concluding Remarks: Large-scale Learning Problems

With this subsection being the very last one of this chapter, and the chapter itself being the very last chapter of the whole book, it is *a propos* that we devote the subsection to the issue of large-scale learning problems. In particular, this issue was discussed at some length in three previous chapters:

- in Chapter 4 on multilayer perceptrons, where the study of large-scale learning problems was contrasted with small-scale learning problems;
- in Chapter 7 on regularization theory, where we used differentiable manifolds to formulate a semi-supervised learning strategy capable of exploiting information contained in the training data of labeled as well as unlabeled kinds;
- then, again, in Chapter 12 on dynamic programming, where the curse-of-dimensionality problem was raised as an issue of serious concern in dealing with large-scale dynamic environments.

In the context of supervised learning problems on pattern classification and nonlinear regression that are of a small-scale kind, the procedures for solving these problems are well-understood, as evidenced by the material presented in this book. On the other hand, it can be justifiably asserted that the study of large-scale learning problems is in its early stages of development.

Indeed, we may view problems on large-scale learning as a window on the *future of learning*. This window leads us directly into the real world. Accordingly, we may identify four specific stages involved in tackling large-scale learning problems:

1. *Development of an inventory of resources for use as training data.* This first stage is highly critical because, after all, the training data provide the linkage between the real world pertaining to the problem at hand and the design of the learning machine that is being researched for solving the problem. The inventory of the available resources may include
   - high-quality labeled data;
   - labeled data of not as high a quality;
   - an abundance of unlabeled data.

   Given such a mixture of training data, the challenge is how to formulate different scenarios for training strategies that deserve to be pursued, realizing that computational resources are limited.

2. *Modeling of the environment responsible for generation of the training data.* In this second stage, the challenge is to formulate a *network model*, which has a large enough number of degrees of freedom that are also of the right kind. In this formulation, the goal is to capture the underlying statistical physics (nature) of the environment responsible for the data generation. The fact of the matter is that unless this issue is tackled properly, there will inevitably be a mismatch between the physical reality of the data generation and the theoretical basis being proposed for the network model. If this model mismatch is serious, then no matter what is done thereafter will not cure the shortcomings of the model.

3. *Selection of the algorithm for estimating the adjustable parameters of the network model.* This third stage is also challenging in its own right in that we have to select an algorithm that is well-suited for estimating the unknown parameters of the model in a computationally effective manner. More precisely, a network model should have sufficient depth, extending from the input to the output, in order to tackle the problem effectively.

4. *Optimal estimation of the adjustable parameters.* The final challenge is to select an optimization algorithm that has the built-in capability to reliably extract the information content of the training data. Typically, second-order information is considered to be adequate. Most importantly, the optimization algorithm should be computationally efficient. In this context, the two potential candidates are:

- nonlinear sequential estimation algorithms, exemplified by the cubature Kalman filter;
- second-order optimization algorithms, exemplified by refined on-line versions of the Gauss-Newton and Levenberg-Marquardt algorithms, where ways are found to dispense with exact calculation of the Hessian while estimation accuracy is being reasonably well maintained.

We conclude the book by saying that in solving real-world, large-scale learning problems, it is only when careful attention has been given to all the four stages described herein that we can be assured of realizing successful solutions, which will make a difference.

NOTES AND REFERENCES

1. For other recurrent network architectures, see Jordan (1986), Back and Tsoi (1991), and Frasconi et al. (1992).

2. The NARX model encompasses an important class of discrete-time nonlinear systems (Leontaritis and Billings, 1985). In the context of neural networks, it is discussed in Chen et al. (1990), Narendra and Parthasarathy (1990), Lin et al. (1996), and Siegelmann et al., (1997).

It has been demonstrated that the NARX model is well suited for modeling nonlinear systems such as heat exchangers (Chen et al., 1990), wastewater treatment plants (Su and McAvoy, 1991; Su et al., 1992), catalytic reforming systems in a petroleum refinery (Su et al., 1992), nonlinear oscillations associated with multilegged locomotion in biological systems (Venkataraman, 1994), and grammatical inference (Giles and Horne, 1994).

The NARX model is also referred to as the nonlinear autoregressive-moving average (NARMA) model, with "moving average" referring to the inputs.

3. Recurrent multilayer perceptrons are a special case of time-lagged recurrent neural networks (TLRNN). This generic class of recurrent networks admits the use of an *arbitrary* *pattern of connectivity* between the nodes of a neural network; on the other hand, recurrent multilayer perceptrons have a layered pattern of connectivity. TLRNNs offer the following important characteristics (Lo, 1993):

(i) They include conventional structures such as finite-duration impulse response (FIR).

(ii) They have the built-in ability to account for strongly hidden states of nonlinear dynamic systems.

(iii) They are universal approximations of nonlinear dynamic systems.

4. Omlin and Giles (1996) show that any known finite-state automata can be mapped into second-order recurrent networks, and the correct classification of temporal sequences of finite length is guaranteed.

5. For a rigorous treatment of controllability and observability, see Zadeh and Desoer (1963), Kailath (1980), and Sontag (1990).

6. The first work on neural networks and automata (actually, sequential machines and automata implementations), also referenced as the first paper on finite-state automata, artificial intelligence, and recurrent neural networks was the classic paper by McCulloch and Pitts (1943). The recurrent network (with instantaneous feedback) in the second part of this paper was interpreted as a finite-state automaton in Kleene (1956). Kleene's paper appeared in the book *Automata Studies*, edited by Shannon and McCarthy, (1956); authors in this amazing book include Moore, Minsky, von Neumann, Uttley, McCarthy, and Shannon, among others. Sometimes Kleene's paper is cited as the first article on finite-state machines (Perrin, 1990). Minsky (1967) discussed automata and neural networks in his book entitled *Computation: Finite and Infinite Machines*.

All of the early work on automata and neural networks was concerned with synthesis—that is, how automata are built or designed into neural networks. Because most automata (when implemented as sequential machines) require feedback, the neural networks were necessarily recurrent ones. Note that the early work (with the exception of Minsky) did not make a clear distinction between automata (directed, labeled, and acyclic graphs) and sequential machines (logic and feedback delays) and was concerned mostly with finite-state automata. There was little interest (with the exception of Minsky) in moving up the automata hierarchy to push down automata and Turing machines.

After the "Dark Ages" of neural networks, research on automata and neural networks started again in the 1980s. This work could be broadly classified into three areas: (1) learning automata; (2) automata synthesis, extraction, and refinement of knowledge; and (3) representation. The first mention of automata and neural networks was in Jordan (1986).

7. A single-layer recurrent network using McCulloch–Pitts neurons cannot simulate any finite-state machines (Goudreau et al., 1994), but Elman's simple recurrent network can (Kremer, 1995). Recurrent networks with only local feedback cannot represent all finite-state machines (Frasconi and Gori, 1996; Giles et al., 1995; Kremer, 1996). In other words, the use of global feedback is a necessary requirement for the simulation of finite-state machines by neural networks.

8. The idea behind back propagation through time is that for every recurrent network, it is possible to construct a feedforward network with identical behavior over a particular time interval (Minsky and Papert, 1969). Back propagation through time was first described in the Ph.D. dissertation of Werbos (1974); see also Werbos (1990). The algorithm was rediscovered independently by Rumelhart et al. (1986b). A variant of the back-propagation-through-time algorithm is described in Williams and Peng (1990). For a review of the algorithm and related issues, see Williams and Zipser (1995).

9. The real-time recurrent learning algorithm was described in the neural network literature for the first time by Williams and Zipser (1989). Its origin may be traced to an earlier

paper by McBride and Narendra (1965) on system identification for tuning the parameters of an arbitrary dynamic system.

The derivation given in Williams and Zipser is for a single layer of fully recurrent neurons. It has since been extended to more general architectures; see, for example, Kechriotis et al. (1994) and Puskorius and Feldkamp (1994).

10. Schraudolph (2002) describes an algorithm called the *stochastic meta-descent (SMD) algorithm*, in which the notion of calculating the exact Hessian is abandoned in favor of an iterative approximation. In particular, a special curvature matrix–vector product is introduced to iteratively approximate second-order gradient methods such as the Gauss–Newton and Levenberg–Marquardt methods, resulting in improved stability and performance.

11. Singhal and Wu (1989) were perhaps the first to demonstrate the improved mapping performance of a supervised neural network using the extended Kalman filter. Unfortunately, the training algorithm described therein is limited by its computational complexity. To overcome this limitation, Kollias and Anastassiou (1989) and Shah and Palmieri (1990) tried to simplify the application of extended Kalman filtering by partitioning the global problem into a number of subproblems, each of which addresses a single neuron. However, the treatment of each neuron as an identification problem does not rigorously adhere to Kalman filter theory. Moreover, such an approach may lead to unstable behavior during training and may result in solutions that are inferior to those obtained by other methods (Puskorius and Feldkamp, 1991).

12. In Prokhorov (2006, 2007) and related papers, the sequential state-estimation algorithm due to Nørgaard, Poulsen, and Ravn (2000) is referred to as the *nprKF algorithm*, where "npr" is taken from the first letters in the names of the algorithm's three co-authors. In this chapter, we have expressed preference for naming the algorithm as the *central-difference Kalman filter (CDKF)*, which is more descriptive of what the algorithm is based on.

13. Consider a function of the variable x, denoted by $f(x)$. Let f_k denote the value of this function for $x = x_k$. The *central difference* is defined by

$$\delta f_{k+\frac{1}{2}} = f_{k+1} - f_k \qquad \text{for every } k$$

where the subscript on the left is the *average* of the two subscripts on the right. The following table illustrates how higher-order central differences can be formulated:

x	f			
x_0	f_0			
		$\delta f_{1/2}$		
x_1	f_1		$\delta^2 f_1$	
		$\delta f_{3/2}$		$\delta^2 f_{3/2}$
x_2	f_2		$\delta^2 f_2$		$\delta^4 f_2$
		$\delta f_{5/2}$		$\delta^2 f_{5/2}$
x_3	f_3		$\delta^2 f_3$	
		$\delta f_{7/2}$		
x_4	f_4			

Note that elements of the table with the same subscript always lie on lines extending horizontally, or *centrally*, into the table (Wylie and Barrett, 1982).

14. The emergence of adaptive behavior in recurrent neural networks, exemplified by recurrent multilayer perceptrons, was first discussed in Lo and Yu (1995). For additional references on this phenomenon, see the overview paper by Prokhorov et al. (2002).

PROBLEMS

State-space Model

15.1 Formulate the state-space equations for Elman's simple recurrent network shown in Fig. 15.3.

15.2 Show that the recurrent multilayer perceptron of Fig. 15.4 can be represented by the state-space model:

$$\mathbf{x}_{n+1} = \mathbf{f}(\mathbf{x}_n, \mathbf{u}_n)$$
$$\mathbf{y}_n = \mathbf{g}(\mathbf{x}_n, \mathbf{u}_n)$$

where $\mathbf{u}_n$ denotes the input, $\mathbf{y}_n$ denotes the output, $\mathbf{x}_n$ denotes the state, and $\mathbf{f}(\cdot,\cdot)$ and $\mathbf{g}(\cdot,\cdot)$ denote vector-valued nonlinear functions.

15.3 When a dynamic system is said to be controllable and observable? Why is it important to know about the controllability and observability of recurrent networks?

15.4 Referring to the problem of local controllability discussed in Section 15.4, show that

  a. the state $\mathbf{x}_{n+q}$ is a nested nonlinear function of its past value $\mathbf{x}_n$ and the input vector $\mathbf{u}_{q,n}$ of Eq. (15.24), and

  b. the Jacobian of $\mathbf{x}_{n+q}$ with respect to $\mathbf{u}_{q,n}$, evaluated at the origin, is equal to the controllability matrix $\mathbf{M}_c$ of Eq. (15.23).

15.5 Referring to the problem of local observability discussed in Section 15.4, show that the Jacobian of the observation vector $\mathbf{y}_{q,n}$ defined in Eq. (15.30) with respect to the state $\mathbf{x}_n$, evaluated at the origin, is equal to the observability matrix $\mathbf{M}_o$ of Eq. (15.28).

15.6 The system equation of a nonlinear dynamic system is described by

$$\mathbf{x}_{n+1} = \mathbf{f}(\mathbf{x}_n, \mathbf{u}_n)$$

where $\mathbf{u}_n$ is the input vector at time n and $\mathbf{x}_n$ is the corresponding state of the system. The input $\mathbf{u}_n$ appears in the system equation in a nonadditive manner. In this problem, we wish to reformulate the process equation so that the input $\mathbf{u}_n$ appears additively. This is done by writing

$$\mathbf{x}'_{n+1} = \mathbf{f}_{\text{new}}(\mathbf{x}'_n) + \mathbf{u}'_n$$

Formulate definitions for the vectors $\mathbf{x}'_n$ and $\mathbf{u}'_n$ and the function $\mathbf{f}_{\text{new}}(\cdot)$.

15.7 Figure P15.7 presents two examples of recurrent network architectures using local feedback at the neural level. The architectures shown in parts (a) and (b) of the figure are called *local activation feedback* and *local output feedback*, respectively (Tsoi and Back, 1994). Formulate state-space models for these two recurrent network architectures, and comment on their controllability and observability.

Nonlinear Antoregressive with Exogenous Inputs (NARX) Model

15.8 Considering the NARX network of Fig. P15.8, do the following:

  a. Construct the state-space model equivalent of this single-input, single-output recurrent network.

  b. Repeat part (a) of the problem for the case when the network of Fig. P15.8 is expanded to embody two inputs and single output.

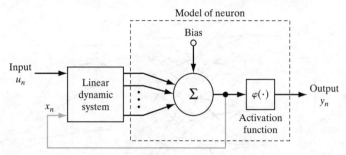

(a) Local activation feedback architecture

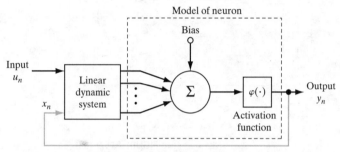

(b) Local output feedback architecture

FIGURE P15.7

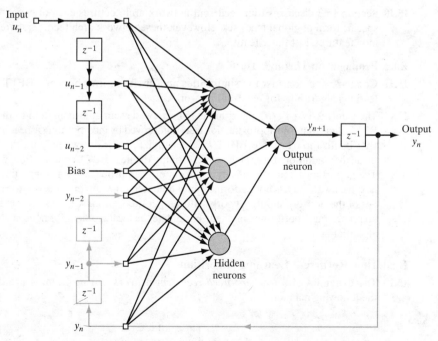

FIGURE P15.8   NARX network with $q = 3$ hidden neurons.

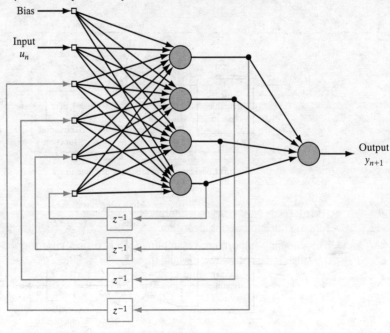

FIGURE P15.9

15.9 Construct the NARX equivalent for the fully recurrent network shown in Fig. P15.9.

15.10 Section 15.2 discusses four recurrent network architectures each of which highlights a specific form of global feedback. However, these network architectures share some common features. List those features.

Back Propagation Through Time

15.11 Compare and contrast the similarities and dissimilarities between BPTT and RTRL learning algorithms for recurrent networks.

15.12 The truncated BPTT(h) algorithm may be viewed as an approximation to the epochwise BPTT algorithm. The approximation can be improved by incorporating aspects of epochwise BPTT into the truncated BPTT(h) algorithm. Specifically, we may let the network go through h' additional steps before performing the next BPTT computation, where $h' < h$. The important feature of this hybrid form of back propagation through time is that the next backward pass is not performed until time step $n + h'$. In the intervening time, past values of the network input, network state, and desired responses are stored in a buffer, but no processing is performed on them. Formulate the local gradient for neuron j in this hybrid algorithm.

Real-Time Recurrent Learning Algorithm

15.13 The dynamics of a *teacher-forced recurrent network* during training are described in the following manner:

$$\xi_{i,n} = \begin{cases} u_{i,n} & \text{if } i \in \mathcal{A} \\ d_{i,n} & \text{if } i \in \mathcal{C} \\ y_{i,n} & \text{if } i \in \mathcal{B} - \mathcal{C} \end{cases}$$

where $\mathcal{A}$ denotes the set of indices i for which ξ_i is an external input, $\mathcal{B}$ denotes the set of indices i for which ξ_i is the output of a neuron, and $\mathcal{C}$ denotes the set of output neurons that are visible.

a. Show that for this scheme, the partial derivative $\partial y_{j,n+1}/\partial w_{kl,n}$ is given by

$$\frac{\partial y_{j,n+1}}{\partial w_{kl,n}} = \varphi'(v_{j,n})\left(\sum_{i \in \mathcal{B}-\mathcal{C}} w_{ji,n}\left(\frac{\partial y_{i,n}}{\partial w_{kl,n}}\right) + \delta_{kj}\xi_{l,n} \right)$$

b. Derive the training algorithm for a teacher-forced recurrent network.

Nonlinear Sequential State Estimators

15.14 Describe how the DEKF algorithm can be used to train the simple recurrent network shown in Fig. 15.3 You may also invoke the BPTT algorithm for this training.

15.15 Table 15.2 presents a summary of the EKF algorithm for the supervised training of an RMLP. Using the square-root filtering theory described in Chapter 14, formulate the square-root modification of this algorithm.

15.16 The sampling–importance-resampling (SIR) particle filter was described in Chapter 14. This filter is derivative free; it would therefore be tempting to suggest its use as an alternative to the EKF algorithm for supervised training of a recurrent multilayer perceptron. Discuss the possible difficulty of such an approach.

Computer Experiment

15.17 In this problem, we continue with the computer experiment described in Problem 6.25 on support vector machines, page 312. Specifically, we address a difficult pattern-classification experiment involving the tightly fisted multicircular structure of Fig. P6.25 reproduced here as Fig. P15.18 for convenience of presentation. This time however, we study the supervised

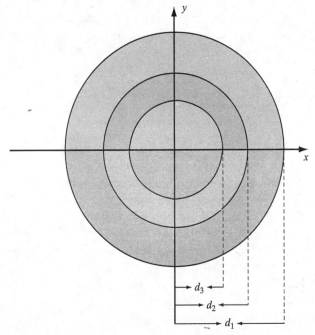

FIGURE P15.17   Diameters of the three circles: $d_1 = 3, d_2 = 6, d_3 = 9$.

training of a multilayer perceptron, based on the extended Kalman filtering algorithm, along the lines described in Section 15.10.

For the multilayer perceptron, use the following structure:

- Two hidden layers, with four neurons in the first hidden layer and three in the second hidden layer; the activation function $\varphi(v) = \tanh(v)$ is to be used for all the hidden neurons.
- Linear output layer.

To perform the pattern classification, generate 100 epochs with each one consisting of 200 randomly distributed training examples and an equal size of test data for the two regions of Fig. P15.17. Hence, do the following:

1. For a varying number of epochs, construct the decision boundary computed by the EKF algorithm so as to determine the "best" classification performance.
2. For the classification performance considered to be the "best," determine the misclassification error.

Finally, compare the results of your findings for the EKF algorithm against the corresponding results obtained for the support vector machine in Problem 6.25.

Bibliography

Aarts, E., and J. Korst, 1989. *Simulated Annealing and Boltzmann Machines: A Stochastic Approach to Combinatorial Optimization and Neural Computing*, New York: Wiley.

Abarbanel, H.D.I., 1996. *Analysis of Observed Chaotic Data*, New York: Springer-Verlag.

Abraham, R., J.E. Marsden, and T. Ratiu, 1988. *Manifolds, Tensor Analysis, and Applications*, 2d ed., New York: Springer-Verlag.

Abraham, R.H., and C.D. Shaw, 1992. *Dynamics of the Geometry of Behavior*, Reading, MA: Addison-Wesley.

Abramowitz, M., and I.A. Stegun, 1965. *Handbook of Mathematical Functions with Formulas, Graphs and Mathematical Tables*, New York: Dover Publications.

Abu-Mostafa, Y.S., 1995. "Hints," *Neural computation*, vol. 7, pp. 639–671.

Ackley, D.H., G.E. Hinton, and T.J. Sejnowski, 1985. "A Learning Algorithm for Boltzmann Machines," *Cognitive Science*, vol. 9, pp. 147–169.

Adetona, O., E. Garcia, and L.H. Keel, 2000. "A new method for control of discrete nonlinear dynamic systems using neural networks," *IEEE Trans. Neural Networks*, vol. 11, pp. 102–112.

Aiyer, S.V.B., N. Niranjan, and F. Fallside, 1990. "A theoretical investigation into the performance of the Hopfield model," *IEEE Transactions on Neural Networks*, vol. 15, pp. 204–215.

Aizerman, M.A., E.M. Braverman, and L.I. Rozonoer, 1964a. "Theoretical foundations of the potential function method in pattern recognition learning," *Automation and Remote Control*, vol. 25, pp. 821–837.

Aizerman, M. A., E.M. Braverman, and L.I. Rozonoer, 1964b. "The probability problem of pattern recognition learning and the method of potential functions," *Automation and Remote Control*, vol. 25, pp. 1175–1193.

Alspach, D.L. and H.W. Sorenson, 1972. "Nonlinear Bayesian estimation using Gaussian sum approximations," *IEEE Trans. Automatic Control*, vol. 17, pp. 439–448.

Aleksander, I., and H. Morton, 1990, *An Introduction to Neural Computing*, London: Chapman and Hall.

Amari, S., 1998. "Natural gradient works efficiently in learning." *Neural Computation*, vol. 10, pp. 251–276.

Amari, S., 1993. "A universal theorem on learning curves," *Neural Networks*, vol. 6, pp. 161–166.

Amari, S., 1990. "Mathematical foundations of neurocomputing," *Proceedings of the IEEE*, vol. 78, pp. 1443–1463.

Amari, S., 1987. "Differential geometry of a parametric family of invertible systems—Riemanian metric, dual affine connections and divergence," *Mathematical Systems Theory,* vol. 20, pp. 53–82.

Amari, S., 1985. *Differential-Geometrical Methods in Statistics,* New York: Springer-Verlag.

Amari, S., 1983. "Field theory of self-organizing neural nets," *IEEE Transactions on Systems, Man, and Cybernetics* vol. SMC-13, pp. 741–748.

Amari, S., 1980. "Topographic organization of nerve fields," *Bulletin of Mathematical Biology,* vol. 42, pp. 339–364.

Amari, S., 1977a. "Neural theory of association and concept-formation," *Biological Cybernetics,* vol. 26, pp. 175–185.

Amari, S., 1977b. "Dynamics of pattern formation in lateral-inhibition type neural fields," *Biological Cybernetics,* vol. 27, pp. 77–87.

Amari, S., 1972. "Characteristics of random nets of analog neuron-like elements," *IEEE Transactions on Systems, Man, and Cybernetics,* vol. SMC-2, pp. 643–657.

Amari, S., 1967. "A theory of adaptive pattern classifiers," *IEEE Trans. Electronic Computers,* vol. EC-16, pp. 299–307.

Amari, S., and M.A. Arbib, 1977. "Competition and cooperation in neural nets," in J. Metzler, ed., *Systems Neuroscience,* pp. 119–165, New York: Academic Press.

Amari, S., and J.-F. Cardoso, 1997. "Blind source separation—Semiparametric statistical approach," *IEEE Transactions on Signal Processing,* vol. 45, pp. 2692–2700.

Amari, S., T.-P. Chen, and A. Cichoki, 1997. "Stability analysis of learning algorithms for blind source separation," *Neural Networks,* vol. 10, pp. 1345–1351.

Amari, S., A. Cichoki, and H.H. Yang, 1996. "A new learning algorithm for blind signal separation." *Advances in Neural Information Processing Systems,* vol. 8, pp. 757–763, Cambridge, MA: MIT Press.

Amari, S., and K. Maginu, 1988. "Statistical neurodynamics of associative memory," *Neural Networks,* vol. 1, pp. 63–73.

Amari, S., K. Yoshida, and K.-I. Kanatani, 1977. "A mathematical foundation for statistical neurodynamics," *SIAM Journal of Applied Mathematics,* vol. 33, pp. 95–126.

Ambros-Ingerson, J., R. Granger, and G. Lynch, 1990. "Simulation of paleo-cortex performs hierarchical clustering," *Science,* vol. 247, pp. 1344–1348.

Amit, D.J., 1989. *Modeling Brain Function: The World of Attractor Neural Networks,* New York: Cambridge University Press.

Anastasio T.J., 2003. "Vestibulo-ocular reflex," In M.A. Arbib, ed., *The Handbook of Brain Theory and Neural Networks,* 2d ed., pp. 1192–1196, Cambridge, MA: MIT Press.

Anastasio, T.J., 1993. "Modeling vestibulo-ocular reflex dynamics: From classical analysis to neural networks," in F. Eeckman, ed., *Neural Systems: Analysis and Modeling,* pp. 407–430, Norwell, MA: Kluwer.

Anderson, B.D.O., and J.B. Moore, 1971. *Linear Optimal Control,* Englewood Cliffs, NJ: Prentice-Hall.

Anderson, J.A., 1995. *Introduction to Neural Networks,* Cambridge, MA: MIT Press.

Anderson, J.A., 1993. "The BSB model: A simple nonlinear autoassociative neural network," in *Associative Neural Memories* (M. Hassoun, ed.) pp. 77–103, Oxford: Oxford University Press.

Anderson, J.A., and E. Rosenfeld, eds., 1988. *Neurocomputing: Foundations of Research,* Cambridge, MA: MIT Press.

Anderson, J.A., A. Pellionisz, and E. Rosenfeld, eds., 1990a. *Neurocomputing 2: Directions for Research,* Cambridge, MA: MIT Press.

Anderson, J.A., J.W. Silverstein, S.A. Ritz, and R.S. Jones, 1977. "Distinctive features, categorical perception, and probability learning: Some applications of a neural model," *Psychological Review,* vol. 84, pp. 413–451.

Anderson, J.A., and J.P. Sutton, 1995. "A network of networks: Computation and neurobiology," *World Congress on Neural Networks,* vol. I, pp. 561–568.

Anderson, T.W., 1984. *An Introduction to Multivariate Statistical Analysis,* 2d ed., New York: Wiley.

Ansari, N., and E. Hou, 1997. *Computational Intelligence for Optimization,* Norwell, MA: Kluwer.

Arasaratnam, I., and S. Haykin, 2009. "Cubature Kalman filters," *IEEE Trans. Automatic Control,* vol. 54, June.

Arasaratnam, I., S. Haykin, and R.J. Elliott, 2007. "Discrete-time nonlinear-filtering algorithms using Gauss–Hermite quadrature," *Proc. IEEE,* vol. 95, pp. 953–977.

Arbib, M.A., 1989. *The Metaphorical Brain,* 2d ed., New York: Wiley.

Arbib, M.A., 1987. *Brains, Machines, and Mathematics,* 2d ed., New York: Springer-Verlag.

Arbib, M.A., 2003. *The Handbook of Brain Theory and Neural Networks,* 2d ed., Cambridge, MA: MIT Press.

Arimoto, S., 1972. "An algorithm for calculating the capacity of an arbitrary memoryless channel," *IEEE Trans. Information Theory,* vol. IT-18, pp. 14–20.

Aronszajn, N., 1950. "Theory of reproducing kernels," *Trans. American Mathematical Society,* vol. 68, pp. 337–404.

Arrowsmith, D.K., and C.M. Place, 1990. *An Introduction to Dynamical Systems,* Cambridge, U.K.: Cambridge University Press.

Ash, R.E., 1965. *Information Theory,* New York: Wiley.

Ashby, W.R., 1960. *Design for a Brain,* 2d ed., New York: Wiley.

Ashby, W.R., 1952. *Design for a Brain,* New York: Wiley.

Aspray, W., and A. Burks, 1986. *Papers of John von Neumann on Computing and Computer Theory,* Charles Babbage Institute Reprint Series for the History of Computing, vol. 12. Cambridge, MA: MIT Press.

Atick, J.J., 1992. "Could information theory provide an ecological theory of sensory processing?" *Network: Computation in Neural Systems,* vol. 3, pp. 213–251.

Atick, J.J., and A.N. Redlich, 1990. "Towards a theory of early visual processing," *Neural Computation,* vol. 2, pp. 308–320.

Atiya, A.F., 1987, "Learning on a general network," In *Neural Information Processing Systems,* D.Z. Anderson, ed., pp. 22–30, New York: American Institute of Physics.

Attneave, F., 1954. "Some informational aspects of visual perception," *Psychological Review,* vol. 61, pp. 183–193.

Back, A.D., and A.C. Tsoi, 1991. "FIR and IIR synapses, a new neural network architecture for time series modeling," *Neural Computation,* vol. 3, pp. 375–385.

Bakir, G.H., T. Hofmann, B. Schölkopf, A.J. Smola, B. Taskar, and S.V.N. Vishwanathan, eds., 2007. *Predicting Structured Data,* Cambridge, MA: MIT Press.

Barlow, H.B., 1989. "Unsupervised learning," *Neural Computation,* vol. 1, pp. 295–311.

Barlow, H.B., 1959. "Sensory mechanisms, the reduction of redundancy, and intelligence," in *The Mechanisation of Thought Processes, National Physical Laboratory Symposium No. 10,* Her Majesty's Stationary Office, London.

Barlow, H., and P. Földiák, 1989. "Adaptation and decorrelation in the cortex," in *The Computing Neuron,* R. Durbin, C. Miall, and G. Mitchison, eds., pp. 54–72. Reading, MA: Addison-Wesley.

Barnard, E., and D. Casasent, 1991. "Invariance and neural nets," *IEEE Transactions on Neural Networks,* vol. 2, pp. 498–508.

Barron, A.R., 1993. "Universal approximation bounds for superpositions of a sigmoidal function," *IEEE Transactions on Information Theory,* vol. 39, pp. 930–945.

Barron, A.R., 1992. "Neural net approximation," in *Proceedings of the Seventh Yale Workshop on Adaptive and Learning Systems,* pp. 69–72, New Haven, CT: Yale University.

Barto, A.G., S.J. Bradtke, and S. Singh, 1995. "Learning to act using real-time dynamic programming," *Artificial Intelligence,* vol. 72, pp. 81–138.

Barto, A.G., R.S. Sutton, and C.W. Anderson, 1983. "Neuronlike adaptive elements that can solve difficult learning control problems," *IEEE Transactions on Systems, Man, and Cybernetics,* vol. SMC-13, pp. 834–846.

Battiti, R., 1992. "First- and second-order methods for learning: Between steepest descent and Newton's method," *Neural Computation,* vol. 4, pp. 141–166.

Bauer, H.-U., and K.R. Pawelzik, 1992. "Quantifying the neighborhood preservation of self-organizing feature maps," *IEEE Transactions on Neural Networks,* vol. 3, pp. 570–579.

Bauer, H.-U., R. Der, and M. Hermman, 1996. "Controlling the magnification factor of self-organizing feature maps," *Neural Computation,* vol. 8, pp. 757–771.

Baum, E.B., and F. Wilczek, 1988. "Supervised learning of probability distributions by neural networks," in D.Z. Anderson, ed., pp. 52–61, New York: American Institute of Physics.

Beaufays, F., and E.A. Wan, 1994. "Relating real-time backpropagation and backpropagation-through-time: An application of flow graph interreciprocity," *Neural Computation,* vol. 6, pp. 296–306.

Becker, S., 1996. "Mutual information maximization: models of cortical self-organization," *Network: Computation in Neural Systems,* vol. 7, pp. 7–31.

Becker, S., 1991. "Unsupervised learning procedures for neural networks," *International Journal of Neural Systems,* vol. 2, pp. 17–33.

Becker, S., and G.E. Hinton, 1992. "A self-organizing neural network that discovers surfaces in random-dot stereograms," *Nature (London),* vol. 355, pp. 161–163.

Becker, S., and Y. LeCun, 1989. "Improving the convergence of back-propagation learning with second order methods," In D. Touretzky, G.E. Hinton, and T.J. Sejnowski, eds., *Proceedings of the 1988 Connectionist Models Summer School,* pp. 29–37, San Fransisco: Morgan Kaufmann.

Beckerman, M., 1997. *Adaptive Cooperative Systems,* New York: Wiley (Interscience).

Belkin, M., 2003. *Problems of Learning on Manifolds,* Ph.D. thesis, The University of Chicago.

Belkin, M., P. Niyogi, and V. Sindhwani, 2006. "Manifold regularization: A geometric framework for learning from labeled and unlabeled examples," *J. Machine Learning Research,* vol. 7, pp. 2399–2434.

Bell, A.J. and T.J. Sejnowski, 1997. "The 'Independent Components' of natural scenes are edge filters," *Vision Research,* vol. 37, pp. 3327–3338.

Bell, A.J., and T.J. Sejnowski, 1995. "An information-maximization approach to blind separation and blind deconvolution," *Neural Computation,* vol. 6, pp. 1129–1159.

Bellman, R., 1961. *Adaptive Control Processes: A Guided Tour,* Princeton, NJ: Princeton University Press.

Bellman, R., 1957. *Dynamic Programming,* Princeton, NJ: Princeton University Press.

Bellman, R., and S.E. Dreyfus, 1962. *Applied Dynamic Programming,* Princeton, NJ: Princeton University Press.

Bengio, Y., and Y. LeCun, 2007. "Scaling learning algorithms toward AI," in L. Bottou, O. Chapelle, D. DeCosta, and J. Weston, eds., *Large-Scale Kernel Machines*, pp. 321–359, Cambridge, MA: MIT Press.

Bengio, Y., P. Simard, and P. Frasconi, 1994. "Learning long-term dependencies with gradient descent is difficult," *IEEE Transactions on Neural Networks*, vol. 5, pp. 157–166.

Bengtsson, T., P. Bickel, and B. Li, 2008. "Curse-of-dimensionality revisited: Collapse of the particle filter in very large scale systems," *IMS Collections, Probability and Statistics: Essays in Honor of David A. Freedman*, vol. 2, pp. 316–334.

Benveniste, A., M. Métivier, and P. Priouret, 1987. *Adaptive Algorithms and Stochastic Approximation*, New York: Springer-Verlag.

Bertsekas, D.P., 2007. *Dynamic Programming and Optimal Control*, vol. II, 3d ed., Nashua, NH: Athena Scientific.

Bertsekas, D.P., 2005. *Dynamic Programming and Optimal Control*, vol. I, 3d ed., Nashua, NH: Athena Scientific.

Bertsekas, D.P., A. Nedich, and V.S. Borkar, 2004. "Improved temporal difference methods with linear function approximation," in J. Si, A.G. Barto, W.B. Powell, and D. Wunsch II, eds., *Handbook of Learning and Approximate Dynamic Programming*, pp. 235–259, Hobken, NJ: Wiley-Interscience.

Bertsekas, D.P., with A. Nedich and A.E. Ozdaglar, 2003. *Convex Analysis and Optimization*, Nashua, NH: Athena Scientific.

Bertsekas, D.P., and J.N. Tsitsiklis, 2002. *Introduction to Probability*, Nashua, NH: Athena Scientific.

Bertsekas, D.P., 1995. *Nonlinear Programming*. Belmont, MA: Athenas Scientific.

Bertsekas, D.P., and J.N. Tsitsiklis, 1996. *Neuro-Dynamic Programming*, Belmont, MA: Athena Scientific.

Bierman, G.J., and C.L. Thornton, 1977. "Numerical comparison of Kalman filter algorithms: Orbit determination case study," *Automatica*, vol. 13, pp. 23–35.

Bishop, C.M., 1995. *Neural Networks for Pattern Recognition*. Oxford, U.K.: Clarendon Press.

Blahut, R., 1972. "Computation of channel capacity and rate distortion functions," *IEEE Trans. Information Theory*, vol. IT-18, pp. 460–473.

Bobrowski, O., R. Meir, and Y.C. Eldor, 2007. "Bayesian filtering in spiking neural networks: Noise, adaptation, and multisensory integration," *Neural Information Processing Systems (NIPS) Conference*, Vancouver: December.

Bodenhausen, U., and A. Waibel, 1991. "The tempo 2 algorithm: Adjusting time-delays by supervised learning," *Advances in Neural Information Processing Systems*, vol. 3, pp. 155–161, San Mateo, CA: Morgan Kaufmann.

Boltzmann, L., 1872. "Weitere studien über das Wärmegleichgewicht unter gasmolekülen," *Sitzungsberichte der Mathematisch-Naturwissenschaftlichen Classe der Kaiserlichen Akademie der Wissenschaften*, vol. 66, pp. 275–370.

Boothby, W.M., 1986. *An Introduction to Differentiable Manifolds and Riemannian Geometry*, 2d ed., Orlando, FL: Academic Press.

Boser, B., I. Guyon, and V.N. Vapnik, 1992. "A training algorithm for optimal margin classifiers," *Fifth Annual Workshop on Computational Learning Theory*, pp. 144–152. San Mateo, CA: Morgan Kaufmann.

Bottou, L., 2007. *Learning Using Large Datasets*, NIPS 2007 Conference Tutorial Notes, Neural Information Processing Systems (NIPS) Conference, Vancouver: December.

Bottou, L., and C. Lin, 2007. "Support vector machine solvers," in L. Bottou, O. Chapelle, D. DeCosta, and J. Weston, eds., *Large-Scale Kernel Machines*, pp. 1–27, Cambridge, MA: MIT Press.

Boyan, J.A., 2002. "Technical update: Least-squares temporal difference learning," *Machine Learning*, vol. 49, pp. 1–15.

Boyd, S., and L. Vandenberghe, 2004. *Convex Optimization*. Cambridge, U.K., and New York: Cambridge University Press.

Bradtke, S.J., and A.G. Barto, 1996. "Linear least-squares algorithms for temporal difference learning," *Machine Learning*, vol. 22, pp. 33–57.

Braitenberg, V., 1990. "Reading the structure of brains," *Network: Computation in Neural Systems*, vol. 1, pp. 1–12.

Braitenberg, V., 1986. "Two views of the cerebral cortex," in *Brain Theory*, G. Palm and A. Aertsen, eds., pp. 81–96. New York: Springer-Verlag.

Braitenberg, V., 1984. *Vehicles: Experiments in Synthetic Psychology*, Cambridge, MA: MIT Press.

Braitenberg, V., 1977. *On the Texture of Brains*, New York: Springer-Verlag.

Braitenberg, V., 1967. "Is the cerebella cortex a biological clock in the millisecond range?" in *The Cerebellum. Progress in Brain Research*, C.A. Fox and R.S. Snider, eds., vol. 25 pp. 334–346, Amsterdam: Elsevier.

Bregman, A.S., 1990. *Auditory Scene Analysis: The Perceptual Organization of Sound*, Cambridge, MA: MIT Press.

Brodal, A., 1981. *Neurological Anatomy in Relation to Clinical Medicine*, 3d ed., New York: Oxford University Press.

Brogan, W.L., 1985. *Modern Control Theory*, 2d ed., Englewood Cliffs, NJ: Prentice-Hall.

Broomhead, D.S., and D. Lowe, 1988. "Multivariable functional interpolation and adaptive networks," *Complex Systems*, vol. 2, pp. 321–355.

Brown, T.H., E.W. Kairiss, and C.L. Keenan, 1990. "Hebbian synapses: Biophysical mechanisms and algorithms," *Annual Review of Neuroscience*, vol. 13, pp. 475–511.

Bruck, J., 1990. "On the convergence properties of the Hopfield model," *Proceedings of the IEEE*, vol. 78, pp. 1579–1585.

Bryson, A.E., Jr., and Y.C. Ho, 1969. *Applied Optimal Control*, Blaisdell. (Revised printing, 1975, Hemisphere Publishing, Washington, DC).

Cacoullos, T., 1966. "Estimation of a multivariate density," *Annals of the Institute of Statistical Mathematics (Tokyo)*, vol. 18, pp. 179–189.

Caianiello, E.R., 1961. "Outline of a theory of thought-processes and thinking machines," *Journal of Theoretical Biology*, vol. 1, pp. 204–235.

Cameron, S.H., 1960. Tech. Report 60–600, *Proceedings of the Bionics Symposium*, pp. 197–212, Wright Air Development Division, Dayton, Ohio.

Cappé, O., S.J. Godsill, and E. Moulines, 2007. "An overview of existing methods and recent advances in sequential Monte Carlo," *Proc. IEEE*, vol. 95, pp. 899–924.

Cappé, O., E. Moulines, and T. Rydén, 2005. *Inference in Hidden Markov Models*, New York and London: Springer.

Cardoso, J.F., 2003. "Dependence, correlation and Gaussianity in independent component analysis," *J. Machine Learning Research*, vol. 4, pp. 1177–1203.

Cardoso, J.F., 2001. "The three easy routes to independent component analysis: Contrasts and geometry," *Proceedings of 3rd International Conference on Independent Component Analysis and Blind Source Separation*, San Diego, December.

Cardoso, J.-F., 1998. "Blind signal separation: A review," *Proceedings of the IEEE*, vol. 86, pp. 2009–2025.

Cardoso, J-F., 1997. "Infomax and maximum likelihood for blind source separation," *IEEE Signal Processing Letters,* vol. 4, pp. 112–114.

Cardoso, J.-F., and B. Laheld, 1996. "Equivariant adaptive source separation," *IEEE Transactions on Signal Processing,* vol. 44, pp. 3017–3030.

Carpenter, G.A., M.A. Cohen, and S. Grossberg, 1987. Technical comments on "Computing with neural networks," *Science,* vol. 235, pp. 1226–1227.

Černy, V., 1985. "Thermodynamic approach to the travelling salesman problem," *Journal of Optimization Theory and Applications,* vol. 45, pp. 41–51.

Changeux, J.P., and A. Danchin, 1976. "Selective stabilization of developing synapses as a mechanism for the specification of neural networks," *Nature,* vol. 264, pp. 705–712.

Chapelle, O., B. Schölkopf, and A. Zien, 2006. *Semi-Supervised Learning,* Cambridge, MA: MIT Press.

Charlin, L., P. Poupart, and R. Shoida, 2007. "Automated hierarchy discovery for planning in partially observable environments," *Advances in Neural Information Processing Systems,* vol. 19, pp. 225–232.

Chatterjee, C., V.P. Roychowdhhury, and E.K.P. Chong, 1998. "On relative convergence properties of principal component algorithms," *IEEE Transactions on Neural Networks,* vol. 9, pp. 319–329.

Chechik, G., A. Globerson, N. Tishby, and Y. Weiss, 2004. "Information bottleneck for Gaussian variables," *Advances in Neural Information Processing Systems,* vol. 16, pp. 1213–1220.

Chen, S., S. Billings, and P. Grant, 1990. "Non-linear system identification using neural networks," *International Journal of 'Control,* vol. 51, pp. 1191–1214.

Chen, Z., S. Haykin, J.J. Eggermont, and S. Becker, 2007. *Correlative Learning: A Basis for Brain and Adaptive Systems,* New York: Wiley-Interscience.

Cherkassky, V., and F. Mulier, 1998. *Learning from Data: Concepts, Theory and Methods,* New York: Wiley.

Cherry, E.G., 1953. "Some experiments on the recognition of speech, with one and with two ears," *Journal of the Acoustical Society of America,* vol. 25, pp. 975–979.

Cherry, E.C., and W.K. Taylor, 1954. "Some further experiments upon the recognition of speech, with one and with two ears," *Journal of Acoustical Society of America,* vol. 26, pp. 554–559.

Chester, D.L., 1990. "Why two hidden layers are better than one," *International Joint Conference on Neural Networks,* vol. I, pp. 265–268, Washington, D.C.

Chigirev, D. and W. Bialek, 2004. "Optimal manifold representation of data: An information-theoretic approach," *Advances in Neural Information Processing Systems,* vol. 16, pp. 161–168.

Choi, H., and R.G. Baraniuk, 1999. "Multiple basis wavelet denoising using Besov projections," *Proceedings of IEEE International Conference on Image Processing,* pp. 595–599.

Choi, S., A. Cichoki, H.M. Park, and S.Y. Lee, 2005. "Blind source separation and independent component analysis: A review," *Neural Information Processing-Letters and Reviews,* vol. 6, pp. 1–57.

Chung, R.K., 1997. *Spectral Graph Theory,* Regional Conference Series in Mathematics, Number 92, Providence, RI: American Mathematical Society.

Churchland, P.S., and T.J. Sejnowski, 1992. *The Computational Brain,* Cambridge, MA: MIT Press.

Cichocki, A., and S. Amari, 2002. *Adaptive Blind Signal and Image Processing: Learning Algorithms and Applications,* Chichester, NY: Wiley-Interscience.

Cleeremans, A., D. Servan-Schreiber, and J.L. McClelland, 1989. "Finite state automata and simple recurrent networks," *Neural Computation,* vol. 1, pp. 372–381.

Cohen, L., 2005. "The history of noise [on the 100th anniversary of its birth]," *IEEE Signal Processing Magazine,* vol. 22, issue 6, pp. 20–45, November.

Cohen, M. A., and S. Grossberg, 1983. "Absolute stability of global pattern formation and parallel memory storage by competitive neural networks," *IEEE Transactions on Systems, Man, and Cybernetics,* vol. SMC-13, pp. 815–826.

Collins, M., S. Dasgupta, and R.E. Schapire, 2002. "A generation of principal components analysis to the exponential family," *Advances in Neural Information Processing Systems,* vol. 14-1, pp. 617–624, Cambridge, MA: MIT Press.

Comon, P., 1994. "Independent component analysis: A new concept?" *Signal Processing,* vol. 36, pp. 287–314.

Comon, P., 1991. "Independent component analysis," *Proceedings of International Signal Processing Workshop on Higher-order Statistics,* pp. 111–120, Chamrousse, France.

Cook, A.S., 1971. "The complexity of theorem-proving procedures," *Proceedings of the 3rd Annual ACM Symposium on Theory of Computing,* pp. 151–158, New York.

Cook, P.A., 1986. *Nonlinear Dynamical Systems,* London: Prentice-Hall International.

Cools, R., 2002. "Advances in multidimensional integration," *J. Comput. and Applied Math.,* vol. 149, pp. 1–12.

Cools, R., 1997. "Computing cubature formulas: The science behind the art," *Acta Numerica,* vol. 6, pp. 1–54, Cambridge, U.K.: Cambridge University Press.

Cormen, T.H., C.E. Leiserson, and R.R. Rivest, 1990. *Introduction to Algorithms.* Cambridge, MA: MIT Press.

Cortes, C, and V. Vapnik, 1995. "Support vector networks," *Machine Learning,* vol. 20, pp. 273–297.

Cottrell, M., J.C. Fort, and G. Pagés, 1997. "Theoretical aspects of the SOM algorithm," *Proceedings of the Workshop on Self-Organizing Maps,* Espoo, Finland.

Courant, R., and D. Hilbert, 1970. *Methods of Mathematical Physics,* vol. I and II, New York: Wiley Interscience.

Cover, T.M., and J.A. Thomas, 2006. *Elements of Information Theory,* 2d ed., Hoboken, NJ: Wiley-Interscience.

Cover, T.M., 1968. "Capacity problems for linear machines," In L. Kanal, ed., *Pattern Recognition,* pp. 283–289, Washington, DC: Thompson Book Co.

Cover, T.M., 1965. "Geometrical and statistical properties of systems of linear inequalities with applications in pattern recognition," *IEEE Transactions on Electronic Computers,* vol. EC-14, pp. 326–334.

Cover, T.M., and P.E. Hart, 1967. "Nearest neighbor pattern classification," *IEEE Transactions on Information Theory,* vol. IT-13, pp. 21–27.

Cowan, J.D., 1968. "Statistical mechanics of nervous nets," in *Neural Networks,* E.R. Caianiello, ed., pp. 181–188, Berlin: Springer-Verlag.

Cragg, B.G., and H.N.V. Tamperley, 1954. "The organization of neurons: A cooperative analogy," *EEG Clinical Neurophysiology,* vol. 6, pp. 85–92.

Craik, K.J.W., 1943. *The Nature of Explanation,* Cambridge, U.K.: Cambridge University Press.

Craven, P., and G. Wahba, 1979. "Smoothing noisy data with spline functions: Estimating the correct degree of smoothing by the method of generalized cross-validation," *Numerische Mathematik.,* vol. 31, pp. 377–403.

Crisan, D., and A. Doucet, 2002. "A survey of convergence results on particle filtering methods for practitioners," *IEEE Trans. Signal Processing,* vol. 50, pp. 736–746.

Crites, R.H., and A.G. Barto, 1996. "Improving elevator performance using reinforcement learning," *Advances in Neural Information Processing Systems,* vol. 8, pp. 1017–1023, Cambridge, MA: MIT Press.

Csiszár, I., and G. Tusnády, 1984. "Information geometry and alternating minimization procedures," *Statistics and Decisions,* Supplement Issue, vol. I, 205–237.

Cucker, F., and S. Smale, 2001. "On the mathematical foundations of learning," *Bulletin (New Series) of the American Mathematical Society,* vol. 39, pp. 1–49.

Cybenko, G., 1995. "Q-learning: A tutorial and extensions." Presented at *Mathematics of Artificial Neural Networks,* Oxford University, Oxford, U.K., July 1995.

Cybenko, G, 1989. "Approximation by superpositions of a sigmoidal function," *Mathematics of Control, Signals, and Systems,* vol. 2, pp. 303–314.

Cybenko, G., 1988. "Approximation by superpositions of a sigmoidal function," Urbana, IL.: University of Illinois.

Dan, Y., J.J. Atick, and R.C. Reid, 1996. "Efficient coding of natural scenes in the lateral geniculate nucleus: Experimental test of a computational theory," *J. of Neuroscience,* vol. 16, pp. 3351–3362.

Darken, C., and J. Moody, 1992. "Towards faster stochastic gradient search," *Advances in Neural Information Processing Systems,* vol. 4, pp. 1009–1016, San Mateo, CA: Morgan Kaufmann.

Darken, C., and J. Moody, 1991. "Note on learning rate schedules for stochastic optimization," in R.P. Lippmann, J.E. Moody, and D.S. Touretzky, *Advances in Neural Information Processing Systems,* pp. 832–838, San Mateo, CA: Morgan Kaufmann.

Darmois, G., 1953. "Analyse générale des liaisons stochastiques," *Rev. Inst. Internal. Stat.,* vol. 21, pp. 2–8.

Daubechies, I., ed., 1993. *Different Perspectives on Wavelets,* American Mathematical Society Short Course, San Antonio, January 11–12.

Daubechies, I., 1992. *Ten Lectures on Wavelets,* SIAM.

Daubechies, I., 1990. "The wavelet transform, time-frequency," *IEEE Transactions on Information Theory,* vol. IT-36, pp. 961–1005.

Daum, F. and J. Huang, 2003. "Curse of dimensionality and particle filters," *Proceedings, IEEE Aerospace Conference,* vol. 4, pp. 1979–1993, March.

Davis, P.J., 1963. *Interpolation and Approximation,* New York: Blaisdell.

Debnath, L., and P. Mikusiński, 1990. *Introduction to Hilbert Spaces with Applications,* New York: Academic Press.

de Figueiredo, R.J.P., and G. Chen, 1993. *Nonlinear Feedback Control Systems,* New York: Academic Press.

Dempster, A.P., N.M. Laird, and D.B. Rubin, 1977. "Maximum likelihood from incomplete data via the EM algorithm," (with discussion), *Journal of the Royal Statistical Society.,* B, vol. 39, pp. 1–38.

Denardo, E.V., 1967. "Contraction mappings in the theory underlying dynamic programming," *SIAM,* Review, vol. 9, pp. 165–177.

DeSieno, D., 1988. "Adding a conscience to competitive learning," *IEEE International Conference on Neural Networks,* vol. I, pp. 117–124, San Diego.

deSilva, C.J.S., and Y. Attikiouzel, 1992. "Hopfield networks as discrete dynamical systems," *International Joint Conference on Neural Networks,* vol. III, pp. 115–120, Baltimore.

DeVito, E., L. Rosasco, A. Caponnetto, U. DeGiovannini, and F. Odone, 2005. "Learning from examples as an inverse problem." *J. Machine Learning Research*, vol. 6, pp. 883–904.

deVries, B., and J.C. Principe, 1992. "The gamma model—A new neural model for temporal processing," *Neural Networks,* vol. 5, pp. 565–576.

Diamantaras, K.I., and S.Y. Kung, 1996. *Principal Component Neural Networks: Theory and Applications,* New York: Wiley.

Ding, C., 2004. *Spectral Clustering,* Tutorial Notes, ICML, Banff, Alberta, Canada, July.

Ding, C., and X. He, 2004. "K-means clustering via principal component analysis," *Proceedings of the Twenty-first International Conference on Machine Learning,* pp. 225–240, Banff, Alberta, Canada.

Diniz, P.S.R., 2002. *Adaptive Filtering: Algorithms and Practical Implementation,* 2d ed., Boston: Kluwer Academic Publishers.

Dong, D.W., and J.J. Atick, 1995. "Temporal decorrelation: A theory of lagged and non-lagged responses in the lateral geniculate nucleus," *Network: Computation in Neural Systems,* vol. 6, pp. 159–178.

Dony, R.D., and S. Haykin, 1995. "Optimally adaptive transform coding," *IEEE Transactions on Image Processing,* vol. 4, pp. 1358–1370.

Dorny, C.N., 1975. *A Vector Space Approach to Models and Optimization,* New York: Wiley (Interscience).

Doucet, A., N. deFreitas, and N. Gordon, eds., 2001. *Sequential Monte Carlo Methods in Practice,* New York: Springer.

Doucet, A., S. Godsill, and C. Andrieu, 2000. "On sequential Monte Carlo sampling methods for Bayesian filtering," *Statistics and Computing,* vol. 10, pp. 197–208.

Doya, K., S. Ishi, A. Pouget, and R.P.N. Rao, eds., 2007. *Bayesian Brain: Probabilistic Approaches to Neural Coding,* Cambridge, MA: MIT Press.

Drineas, P., and M.W. Mahoney, 2005. "On the Nyström method for approximating a Gram matrix for improved kernel-based learning," *J. Machine Learning Research,* vol. 6, pp. 2153–2175.

Duda, R.O., P.E. Hart, and D.G. Stork, 2001. *Pattern Classification,* 2d ed., New York: Wiley-Interscience.

Duda, R.O., and P.E. Hart, 1973. *Pattern Classification and Scene Analysis,* New York: Wiley.

Durbin, R., and G. Michison, 1990. "A dimension reduction framework for understanding cortical maps," *Nature,* vol. 343, pp. 644–647.

Durbin, R., C. Miall, and G. Mitchison, eds, 1989. *The Computing Neuron,* Reading, MA. Addison-Wesley.

Durdanovic, I., E. Cosatto, and H. Graf, 2007. "Large-scale Parallel SVM implementation". In L. Bottou, O. Chapelle, D. DeCosta, and J. Weston, editors, *Large-Scale Kernel Machines,* pp. 105–138, MIT Press.

Eggermont, J.J., 1990. *The Correlative Brain: Theory and Experiment in Neural Interaction,* New York: Springer-Verlag.

Elhilali, M., 2004. *Neural Basis and Computational Strategies for Auditory Processing,* Ph.D. thesis, University of Maryland.

Elliott, R.J., L. Aggoun, and J.B. Moore, 1995. *Hidden Markov Models: Estimation and Control,* New York: Springer-Verlag.

Elman, J.E., E.A. Bates, M.H. Johnson, A. Karmiloff-Smith, D. Parisi, and K. Plinket, 1996. *Rethinking Innateness: A Connectionist Perspective on Development,* Cambridge, MA: MIT Press.

Elman, J.L., 1990. "Finding structure in time," *Cognitive Science,* vol. 14, pp. 179–211.

Erwin, E., K. Obermayer, and K. Schulten, 1995. "Models of orientation and ocular dominance columns in the visual cortex: A critical comparison," *Neural Computation,* vol. 7, pp. 425–468.

Erwin, E., K. Obermayer, and K. Schulten, 1992a. "I: Self-organizing maps: Stationary states, metastability and convergence rate," *Biological Cybernetics,* vol. 67, pp. 35–45.

Erwin, E., K. Obermayer, and K. Schulten, 1992b. "II: Self-organizing maps: Ordering, convergence properties and energy functions," *Biological Cybernetics,* vol. 67, pp. 47–55.

Feldkamp, L.A., T.M. Feldkamp, and D.V. Prokhorov, 2001. "Neural network training with the nprKF," *Proceedings of the International Joint Conference on Neural Networks,* Washington, DC.

Feldkamp, L., and G., Puskorius, 1998. "A signal processing framework based on dynamic neural networks with application to problems in adaptation, filtering, and classification," *Proc. IEEE,* vol. 86, pp. 2259–2277.

Feldkamp, L.A., G.V. Puskorius, and P.C. Moore, 1997. "Adaptation from fixed weight networks," *Information Sciences,* vol. 98, pp. 217–235.

Feller, W., 1968. *An Introduction to Probability Theory and its Applications,* vol. 1, 3d ed., New York: John Wiley; 1st printing, 1950.

Feller, W., 1971. *An Introduction to Probability Theory and its Applications,* 3d ed., vol. II, New York: Wiley; 1st printing, 1967.

Field, D.J., 1994. "What is the goal of sensory coding?" *Neural computation,* vol. 6, pp. 559–601.

Fischler, M.A., and O. Firschein, 1987. *Intelligence: The Eye, The Brain, and The Computer,* Reading, MA: Addison-Wesley.

Fisher, R.A., 1925. "Theory of statistical estimation," *Proceedings of the Cambridge Philosophical Society,* vol. 22, pp. 700–725.

Fletcher, R., 1987. *Practical Methods of Optimization,* 2d ed., New York: Wiley.

Forgey, E., 1965. "Cluster analysis of multivariate data: Efficiency vs. interpretability of classification," *Biometrics,* vol. 21, p. 768 (abstract).

Földiak, P., 1989. "Adaptive network for optimal linear feature extractions," *IEEE International Joint Conference on Neural Networks,* vol. I, pp. 401–405, Washington, DC.

Forney, G.D., Jr., 1973. "The Viterbi algorithm," *Proceedings of the IEEE,* vol. 61, pp. 268–278.

Forte, J.C., and G. Pagés, 1996. "Convergence of stochastic algorithm: From the Kushner and Clark theorem to the Lyapunov functional," *Advances in Applied Probability,* vol. 28, pp. 1072–1094.

Forte, J.C., and G. Pagés, 1995. "On the a.s. convergence of the Kohonen algorithm with a general neighborhood function," *Annals of Applied Probability,* vol. 5, pp. 1177–1216.

Frasconi, P., and M. Gori, 1996. "Computational capabilities of local-feedback recurrent networks acting as finite-state machines," *IEEE Transactions on Neural Networks,* vol. 7, pp. 1521–1524.

Frasconi, P., M. Gori, and G. Soda, 1992. "Local feedback multilayered networks," *Neural Computation,* vol. 4, pp. 120–130.

Fraser, A.M., 1989. "Information and entropy in strange attractors," *IEEE Transactions on Information Theory,* vol. 35, pp. 245–262.

Freeman, W.J., 1975. *Mass Action in the Nervous System,* New York: Academic Press.

Friedman, J.H., 1995. "An overview of prediction learning and function approximation," In V. Cherkassky, J.H. Friedman, and H. Wechsler, eds., *From Statistics to Neural Networks: Theory and Pattern Recognition Applications,* New York: Springer-Verlag.

Fukunaga, K., 1990. *Statistical Pattern Recognition,* 2d ed., New York: Academic Press.

Fukushima, K., 1995. "Neocognitron: A model for visual pattern recognition," in M.A. Arbib, ed., *The Handbook of Brain Theory and Neural Networks,* Cambridge, MA: MIT Press.

Fukushima, K., 1980. "Neocognitron: A self-organizing neural network model for a mechanism of pattern recognition unaffected by shift in position," *Biological Cybernetics,* vol. 36, 193–202.

Funahashi, K., 1989. "On the approximate realization of continuous mappings by neural networks," *Neural Networks,* vol. 2, pp. 183–192.

Fyfe, C., 2005. *Hebbian Learning and Negative Feedback Networks,* New York: Springer.

Gabor, D., 1954. "Communication theory and cybernetics," *IRE Transactions on Circuit Theory,* vol. CT-1, pp. 19–31.

Gabor, D., W.P.L. Wilby, and R. Woodcock, 1960. "A universal non-linear filter, predictor, and simulator which optimizes itself by a learning process," *Proceedings of the Institution of Electrical Engineers,* London, vol. 108, pp. 422–435.

Galland, C.C., 1993. "The limitations of deterministic Boltzmann machine learning," *Network,* vol. 4, pp. 355–379.

Gallant, A.R., and H. White, 1988. "There exists a neural network that does not make avoidable mistakes," *IEEE International Conference on Neural Networks,* vol. I, pp. 657–664, San Diego.

Garey, M.R., and D.S. Johnson, 1979. *Computers and Intractability,* New York: W.H. Freeman.

Gee, A.H., 1993. "Problem solving with optimization networks," Ph.D. dissertation, University of Cambridge.

Gee, A.H., S.V.B. Aiyer, and R. Prager, 1993. "An analytical framework for optimizing neural networks." *Neural Networks,* vol. 6, pp. 79–97.

Geisser, S., 1975. "The predictive sample reuse method with applications," *Journal of the American Statistical Association,* vol. 70, pp. 320–328.

Gelfand, A.E., and A.F.M. Smith, 1990. "Sampling-based approaches to calculating marginal densities," *Journal of the American Statistical Association,* vol. 85, pp. 398–409.

Geman, S., and D. Geman, 1984. "Stochastic relaxation, Gibbs distributions, and the Bayesian restoration of images," *IEEE Transactions on Pattern Analysis and Machine Intelligence,* vol. PAMI-6, pp. 721–741.

Geman, S., E. Bienenstock, and R. Doursat, 1992. "Neural networks and the bias/variance dilemma," *Neural Computation,* vol. 4, pp. 1–58.

Genest, C., and J. MacKay, 1989. "The joy of copulas: Bivariate distributions with uniform marginals," *The American Statistician,* vol. 40, pp. 280–285.

Gersho, A., and R.M. Gray, 1992. *Vector Quantization and Signal Compression,* Norwell, MA: Kluwer.

Gibbs, J.W., 1902. "Elementary principles in statistical mechanics," reproduced in vol. 2 of *Collected Works of J. Willard Gibbs in Two Volumes,* New York: Longmans, Green and Co., 1928.

Gidas, B., 1985. "Global optimization via the Langevin equation," *Proceedings of 24th Conference on Decision and Control,* pp. 774–778, Ft. Lauderdale, FL.

Giles, C.L., 1996. "Dynamically driven recurrent neural networks: Models, learning algorithms, and applications," Tutorial #4, *International Conference on Neural Networks,* Washington, DC.

Giles, C.L., D. Chen, G.Z. Sun, H.H. Chen, Y.C. Lee, and M.W. Goudreau, 1995. "Constructive learning of recurrent neural networks: Limitations of recurrent cascade correlation with a simple solution," *IEEE Transactions on Neural Networks,* vol. 6, pp. 829–836.

Giles, C.L., and B.G. Horne, 1994. "Representation of learning in recurrent neural network architectures," *Proceedings of the Eighth Yale Workshop on Adaptive and Learning Systems,* pp. 128–134, Yale University, New Haven, CT.

Giles, C.L., G.Z. Sun, H.H. Chen, Y.C. Lee, and D. Chen, 1990. "Higher order recurrent networks and grammatical inference," *Advances in Neural Information Processing Systems,* vol. 2, pp. 380–387, San Mateo CA: Morgan Kaufmann.

Girosi, F., 1998. "An equivalence between sparse approximation and support vector machines," *Neural Computation*, vol. 10, pp. 1455–1480.

Girosi, F, M. Jones, and T. Poggio, 1995. "Regularization theory and neural networks architectures," *Neural Computation*, vol. 7, pp. 219–269.

Glauber, R.J., 1963. "Time-dependent statistics of the Ising model," *Journal of Mathematical Physics*, vol. 4, pp. 294–307.

Golden, R.M., 1986. "The 'Brain-State-in-a-Box' neural model is a gradient descent algorithm," *Journal of Mathematical Psychology*, vol. 30, pp. 73–80.

Goles, E., and S. Martinez, 1990. *Neural and Automata Networks*, Dordrecht, The Netherlands: Kluwer.

Golub, G.H., and C.G. Van Loan, 1996. *Matrix Computations*, 3d ed., Baltimore: Johns Hopkins University Press.

Goodwin, G.C., and K.S. Sin, 1984. *Adaptive Filtering Prediction and Control*, Englewood Cliffs, NJ: Prentice-Hall.

Gordon, N.J., D.J. Salmond, and A.F.M. Smith, 1993. "Novel approach to nonlinear/non-Gaussian Bayesian state estimation," *IEE Proceedings-F*, vol. 140, pp. 107–113.

Goudreau, M.W., C.L. Giles, S.T. Chakradhar, and D. Chen, 1994. "First-order vs. second-order single-layer recurrent neural networks," *IEEE Transactions on Neural Networks*, vol. 5, pp. 511–513.

Grassberger, I., and I. Procaccia, 1983. "Measuring the strangeness of strange attractors," *Physica D*, vol. 9, pp. 189–208.

Gray, R.M., 1984. "Vector quantization," *IEEE ASSP Magazine*, vol. 1, pp. 4–29.

Green, M., and D.J.N. Limebeer, 1995. *Linear Robust Control*, Englewood Cliffs, NJ: Prentice Hall.

Greenberg, H.J., 1988. "Equilibria of the brain-state-in-a-box (BSB) neural model," *Neural Networks*, vol. 1, pp. 323–324.

Grenander, U., 1983. *Tutorial in Pattern Theory*, Brown University, Providence, RI.

Griffiths, L.J., and C.W. Jim, 1982. "An alternative approach to linearly constrained optimum beamforming," *IEEE Transactions on Antennas and Propagation*, vol. AP-30, pp. 27–34.

Grossberg, S., 1990. "Content-addressable memory storage by neural networks: A general model and global Liapunov method," In *Computational Neuroscience*, E.L. Schwartz, ed., pp. 56–65, Cambridge, MA: MIT Press.

Grossberg, S., 1988. *Neural Networks and Natural Intelligence*, Cambridge, MA: MIT Press.

Grossberg, S., 1982. *Studies of Mind and Brain*, Boston: Reidel.

Grossberg, S., 1969. "On learning and energy-entropy dependence in recurrent and nonrecurrent signed networks," *Journal of Statistical Physics*, vol. 1, pp. 319–350.

Grossberg, S., 1968. "A prediction theory for some nonlinear functional-difference equations," *Journal of Mathematical Analysis and Applications*, vol. 21, pp. 643–694, vol. 22, pp. 490–522.

Grossberg, S., 1967. "Nonlinear difference—differential equations in prediction and learning theory," *Proceedings of the National Academy of Sciences*, USA, vol. 58, pp. 1329–1334.

Grünwald, P.D., 2007. *the Minimum Description Length principle*, Cambridge, MA: MIT Press.

Guestrin, C., and G. Gordon, 2002. "Distributed planning in hierarchical factored MDPs," *Proceedings of 18th Conference on Uncertainty in Artificial Intelligence*, pp. 197–206, August.

Hadamard, J., 1902. "Sur les problèmes aux derivées partielles et leur signification physique," *Bulletin, Princeton University*, vol. 13, pp. 49–52.

Haft, M., and I.L. van Hemmen, 1998. "Theory and implementations of infomax filters for the retina." *Network: Computations in Neural Systems*, vol. 9, pp. 39–71.

Hagiwara, M., 1992. "Theoretical derivation of momentum term in back-propagation," *International Joint Conference on Neural Networks*, vol. I, pp. 682–686, Baltimore.

Hampson, S.E., 1990. *Connectionistic Problem Solving: Computational Aspects of Biological Learning,* Berlin: Birkhäuser.

Härdle, W., 1990. *Applied Nonparametric Regression,* Cambridge: Cambridge University Press.

Hardy, R.L., 1971. "Multiquadric equations of topography and other irregular surfaces," *Journal of Geophysics Research,* vol. 76, pp. 1905–1915.

Harel, D., 1987. *"Algorithmics: The Spirit of Computing,"* Reading, MA: Addison-Wesley.

Hartline, H.K., 1940. "The receptive fields of optic nerve fibers," *American Journal of Physiology,* vol. 130, pp. 690–699.

Harvey, A., 1989. *Forecasting, Structural Time Series Models and the Kalman Filter,* Cambridge, U.K., and New York: Cambridge University Press.

Hassibi, B., A.H. Sayed, and T. Kailath, 1999. *Indefinite-Quadratic Estimation and Control: A Unified Approach to H^2 and H^∞ Theories,* Studies in Applied and Numerical Mathematics, SIAM, Philadelphia: Society for Industrial and Applied Mathematics.

Hassibi, B., A.H. Sayed, and T. Kailath, 1996. "The H^∞ optimality of the LMS algorithm," *IEEE Transactions on Signal Processing,* vol. 44, pp. 267–280.

Hassibi, B., A.H. Sayed, and T. Kailath, 1993. "LMS is H^∞ optimal," *Proceedings of the IEEE Conference on Decision and Control,* pp. 74–79, San Antonio.

Hassibi, B., and D.G. Stork, 1993. "Second-order-derivatives for network pruning: Optimal brain surgeon," in S.H. Hanson, J.D. Cowan, and C.L. Giles, eds. *Advances in Neural Information Processing Systems,* vol. 5, pp. 164–171, San Francisco: Morgan Kaufmann.

Hassibi, B., D.G. Stork, and G.J. Wolff, 1992. "Optimal brain surgeon and general network pruning," *IEEE International Conference on Neural Networks,* vol. 1, pp. 293–299, San Francisco.

Hassibi, B., and T. Kailath, 1995. "H^∞ optimal training algorithms and their relation to back propagation," *Advances in Neural Information Proccessing Systems,* vol. 7, pp. 191–198.

Hastie, T., R. Tibshirani, and J. Friedman, 2001. *The Elements of Statistical Learning: Data Mining, Inference, and Prediction,* New York: Springer.

Hastie, T., and W. Stuetzle, 1989. "Principal curves," *Journal of the American Statistical Association,* vol. 84, pp. 502–516.

Hastings, W.K., 1970. "Monte Carlo sampling methods using Markov chains and their applications," *Biometrika,* vol. 87, pp. 97–109.

Haykin, S., and K. Kan, 2007. "Coherent ICA: Implications for Auditory Signal Processing," WASPA'07, New Paltz, NY, October.

Haykin, S., 2006. "Statistical Learning Theory of the LMS Algorithm Under Slowly Varying Conditions, Using the Langevin Equation," *40th Asilomar Conference on Signals, Systems, and Computers,* Pacific Grove, CA.

Haykin, S., and Z. Chen, 2006. "The machine cocktail party problem," in S. Haykin, J.C. Principe, T.J. Sejnowski, and J. McWhirter, eds., *New Directions in Statistical Signal Processing: From Systems to Brain,* pp. 51–75, Cambridge, MA: MIT Press.

Haykin, S., and B. Widrow, 2003. *Least-Mean-Square Adaptive Filters,* New York: Wiley-Interscience.

Haykin, S., 2002. *Adaptive Filter Theory,* 4th ed., Englewood Cliffs, NJ: Prentice Hall.

Haykin, S., and C. Deng, 1991. "Classification of radar clutter using neural networks," *IEEE Transactions on Neural Networks,* vol. 2, pp. 589–600.

Haykin, S., and B. Van Veen, 1998. *Signals and Systems,* New York: Wiley.

Hebb, D.O., 1949. *The Organization of Behavior: A Neuropsychological Theory,* New York: Wiley.

Hecht-Nielsen, R., 1995. "Replicator neural networks for universal optimal source coding," *Science,* vol. 269, pp. 1860–1863.

Hecht-Nielsen, R., 1990. *Neurocomputing,* Reading, MA: Addison-Wesley.

Hecht-Nielsen, R., 1987. "Kolmogorov's mapping neural network existence theorem," *First IEEE International Conference on Neural Networks,* vol. III, pp. 11–14, San Diego.

Helstrom, C.W., 1968. *Statistical Theory of Signal Detection,* 2nd edition, Pergamon Press.

Herault, J., and C. Jutten, 1986. "Space or time adaptive signal processing by neural network models," in J.S. Denker, ed., *Neural Networks for Computing.* Proceedings of the AIP Conference, American Institute of Physics, New York, pp. 206–211.

Herault, J., C. Jutten, and B. Ans, 1985. "Detection de grandeurs primitives dans un message composite par une architecture de calcul neuromimetique un apprentissage non supervise." *Procedures of GRETSI,* Nice, France.

Herbrich, R., 2002. *Learning Kernel Classifiers: Theory and Algorithms,* Cambridge, MA: MIT Press.

Hertz, J., A. Krogh, and R.G. Palmer, 1991. *Introduction to the Theory of Neural Computation,* Reading, MA: Addison-Wesley.

Heskes, T.M., 2001. "Self-organizing maps, vector quantization, and mixture modeling," *IEEE Trans. on Neural Networks,* vol. 12, pp. 1299–1305.

Heskes, T.M. and B. Kappen, 1991. "Learning processes and neural networks," *Phys. Rev.,* A44, pp. 2718–2726.

Hestenes, M.R., and E. Stiefel, 1952. "Methods of conjugate gradients for solving linear systems," *Journal of Research of the National Bureau of Standards,* vol. 49, pp. 409–436.

Hiller, F.S., and G.J. Lieberman, 1995. *Introduction to Operations Research,* 6th ed., New York: McGraw-Hill.

Hinton, G.E., 2007. *Deep Belief Nets,* 2007 NIPS Tutorial Notes, *Neural Information Processing Systems Conference,* Vancouver, BC, December.

Hinton, G.E., S. Osindero, and Y. Teh, 2006. "A fast learning algorithm for deep belief nets," *Neural Computation,* vol. 18, pp. 1527–1554.

Hinton, G.E., 1989. "Connectionist learning procedures," *Artificial Intelligence,* vol. 40, pp. 185–234.

Hinton, G.E., and T.J. Sejnowski, 1986. "Learning and relearning in Boltzmann machines," in *Parallel Distributed Processing: Explorations in Microstructure of Cognition,* D.E. Rumelhart and J.L. McClelland, eds., Cambridge, MA: MIT Press.

Hinton, G.E., and T.J. Sejnowski, 1983. "Optimal perceptual inference," *Proceedings of IEEE Computer Society Conference on Computer Vision and Pattern Recognition,* pp. 448–453, Washington, DC.

Hirsch, M.W., 1989. "Convergent activation dynamics in continuous time networks," *Neural Networks,* vol. 2, pp. 331–349.

Hirsch, M.W., and S. Smale, 1974. *Differential Equations, Dynamical Systems, and Linear Algebra,* New York: Academic Press.

Ho, Y.C., and R.C.K. Lee, 1964. "A Bayesian approach to problems in stochastic estimation and control," *IEEE Trans. Automatic Control,* vol. AC-9, pp. 333–339.

Hochreiter, S., 1991. *Untersuchungen zu dynamischen neuronalen Netzen,* diploma thesis, Technische Universität Munchen, Germany.

Hodgkin, A.L., and A.F. Huxley, 1952. "A quantitative description of membrane current and its application to conduction and excitation in nerve," *Journal of Physiology,* vol. 117, pp. 500–544.

Holland, J.H., 1992. *Adaptation in Natural and Artificial Systems,* Cambridge, MA: MIT Press.

Holmström, L., P. Koistinen, J. Laaksonen, and E. Oja, 1997. "Comparison of neural and statistical classifiers—taxonomy and two case studies," *IEEE Trans. on Neural Networks,* vol. 8, pp. 5–17.

Honkela, T., 2007. "Philosphical aspects of neural, probabilistic and fuzzy modeling of language use and translation," *Proceedings of IJCNN, International Joint Conference on Neural Networks,* pp. 2881–2886, Orlando, FL, August.

Honkela, T., V. Pulkki, and T. Kohonen, 1995. "Contextual relations of words in Grimm tales, analyzed by self-organizing maps," *Proceedings of International Conference on Artificial Neural Networks,* ICANN-95, vol. II, pp. 3–7, Paris.

Hopcroft, J., and U. Ullman, 1979. *Introduction to Automata Theory, Languages and Computation,* Reading MA: Addison-Wesley.

Hopfield, J.J., 1995. "Pattern recognition computation using action potential timing for stimulus representation," *Nature,* vol. 376, pp. 33–36.

Hopfield, J.J., 1994. "Neurons, dynamics and computation," *Physics Today,* vol. 47, pp. 40–46, February.

Hopfield, J.J., 1987. "Learning algorithms and probability distributions in feed-forward and feedback networks," *Proceedings of the National Academy of Sciences, USA,* vol. 84, pp. 8429–8433.

Hopfield, J.J., 1984. "Neurons with graded response have collective computational properties like those of two-state neurons," *Proceedings of the National Academy of Sciences, USA,* vol. 81, pp. 3088–3092.

Hopfield, J.J., 1982. "Neural networks and physical systems with emergent collective computational abilities," *Proceedings of the National Academy of Sciences, USA,* vol. 79, pp. 2554–2558.

Hopfield, J.J., and T.W. Tank, 1985. "'Neural' computation of decisions in optimization problems," *Biological Cybernetics,* vol. 52, pp. 141–152.

Hornik, K., M. Stinchcombe, and H. White, 1990. "Universal approximation of an unknown mapping and its derivatives using multilayer feedforward networks," *Neural Networks,* vol. 3, pp. 551–560.

Hornik, K., M. Stinchcombe, and H. White, 1989. "Multilayer feedforward networks are universal approximators," *Neural Networks,* vol. 2, pp. 359–366.

Hotelling, H., 1936. "Relations between two sets of variates," *Biometrika,* vol. 28, pp. 321–377.

Hotelling, H., 1935. "The most predictable criterion," *J. Educational Psychology,* vol. 26, pp. 139–142.

Hotelling, H., 1933. "Analysis of a complex of statistical variables into principal components," *Journal of Educational Psychology,* vol. 24, pp. 417–441, 498–520.

Howard, R.A., 1960. *Dynamic Programming and Markov Processes,* Cambridge, MA: MIT Press.

Hubel, D.H., 1988. *Eye, Brain, and Vision,* New York: Scientific American Library.

Hubel, D.H., and T.N. Wiesel, 1977. "Functional architecture of macaque visual cortex," *Proceedings of the Royal Society,* B, vol. 198, pp. 1–59, London.

Hubel, D.H., and T.N. Wiesel, 1962. "Receptive fields, binocular interaction and functional architecture in the cat's visual cortex," *Journal of Physiology,* vol. 160, pp. 106–154, London.

Huber, P.J., 1985. "Projection pursuit," *Annals of Statistics,* vol. 13, pp. 435–475.

Huber, P.J., 1981. *Robust Statistics,* New York: Wiley.

Huber, P.J., 1964. "Robust estimation of a location parameter," *Annals of Mathematical Statistics,* vol. 35, pp. 73–101.

Hush, D., P. Kelly, C. Scovel, and I. Steinwart, 2006. "QP algorithms with guaranteed accuracy and run time for support vector machines," *J. Machine Learning Research,* vol. 7, pp. 733–769.

Hush, D.R., and B.G. Home, 1993. "Progress in supervised neural networks: What's new since Lippmann?" *IEEE Signal Processing Magazine,* vol. 10, pp. 8–39.

Hush, D.R., and J.M. Salas, 1988. "Improving the learning rate of back-propagation with the gradient reuse algorithm," *IEEE International Conference on Neural Networks,* vol. I, pp. 441–447, San Diego.

Hyvärinen, A., J. Karhunen, and E. Oja, 2001. *Independent Component Analysis,* New York: Wiley-Interscience.

Hyvärinen, A. and E. Oja, 2000. "Independent component analysis: Algorithms and applications," *Neural Networks,* vol. 13, pp. 411–430.

Hyvärinen, A. and E. Oja, 1997. "A fast fixed-point algorithm for independent component analysis," *Neural Computation,* vol. 9, pp. 1483–1492.

Ito, K., and K. Xing, 2000. "Gaussian filters for nonlinear filtering problems," *IEEE Trans. Automatic Control,* vol. 45, pp. 910–927.

Izhikevich, E., and G.M. Edelman, 2008. "Large-scale model of mammalian thalamocortical systems," *Proceedings of the National Academy of Sciences,* vol. 105, pp. 3593–3598.

Izhikevich, E.M., 2007a. *Dynamical Systems in Neuroscience: The Geometry of Excitability and Bursting,* Cambridge, MA: MIT Press.

Izhikevich, E.M., 2007b. "Solving the distal reward problem through linkage of STDP and dopamine signaling", Cerebral Cortex, vol. 17, pp. 2443–2452.

Jackson, E.A., 1989. *Perspectives of Nonlinear Dynamics,* vol. 1, Cambridge, U.K.: Cambridge University Press.

Jackson, E.A., 1990. *Perspectives of Nonlinear Dynamics,* vol. 2, Cambridge, U.K.: Cambridge University Press.

Jackson, J.D., 1975. *Classical Electrodynamics,* 2d ed., New York: Wiley.

Jacobs, R.A., 1988. "Increased rates of convergence through learning rate adaptation," *Neural Networks,* vol. 1, pp. 295–307.

Jayant, N.S., and P. Noll, 1984. *Digital Coding of Waveforms,* Englewood Cliffs, NJ: Prentice-Hall.

Jaynes, E.T., 2003. *Probability Theory: The Logic of Science,* Cambridge, U.K., and New York: Cambridge University Press.

Jaynes, E.T., 1982. "On the rationale of maximum-entropy methods," *Proceedings of the IEEE,* vol. 70, pp. 939–952.

Jaynes, E.T., 1957. "Information theory and statistical mechanics," *Physical Review,* vol. 106, pp. 620–630; "Information theory and statistical mechanic II," *Physical Review,* vol. 108, pp. 171–190.

Jazwinski, A.H., 1970. *Stochastic Processes and Filtering Theory,* New York: Academic Press.

Jelinek, F., 1997. *Statistical Methods for Speech Recognition,* Cambridge, MA: MIT Press.

Joachims, T., 1999. "Making large-scale SVM learning practical," in B. Schölkopf, C.J.C. Burges, and A.J. Smola, eds., *Advances in Kernel Methods—Support Vector Learning,* pp. 169–184, Cambridge, MA: MIT Press.

Johansson, E.M., F.U. Dowla, and D.M. Goodman, 1990. "Back-propagation learning for multi-layer feedforward neural networks using the conjugate gradient method," Report UCRL-JC-104850, Lawrence Livermore National Laboratory, CA.

Johnson, D.S., C.R. Aragon, L.A. McGeoch, and C. Schevon, 1989. "Optimization by simulated annealing: An experimental evaluation," *Operations Research,* vol. 37, pp. 865–892.

Jolliffe, I.T., 1986. *Principal Component Analysis,* New York: Springer-Verlag.

Jordan, M.I., 1986. "Attractor dynamics and parallelism in a connectionist sequential machine," *The Eighth Annual Conference of the Cognitive Science Society,* pp. 531–546, Amherst, MA.

Jordan, M.I., ed., 1998. *Learning in Graphical Models,* Boston: Kluwer.

Joseph, R.D., 1960. "The number of orthants in n-space intersected by an s-dimensional subspace," Technical Memo 8, Project PARA, Cornell Aeronautical Lab., Buffalo.

Julier, S.J., and J.K. Ulhmann, 2004. "Unscented filtering and nonlinear estimation," *Proc. IEEE,* vol. 92, pp. 401–422.

Julier, S.J., J.K. Ulhmann, and H.F. Durrent-Whyte, 2000. "A new method for nonlinear transformation of means and covariances in filters and estimation," *IEEE Trans. Automatic Control,* vol. 45, pp. 472–482.

Jutten, C. and A. Taleb, 2000. "Source separation: from dusk till dawn," *Proceedings of 2nd International Workshop on Independent Component Analysis and Blind Source Separation,* Helsinki, June.

Jutten, C., and J. Herault, 1991. "Blind separation of sources, Part I: An adaptive algorithm based on neuromimetic architecture," *Signal Processing,* vol. 24, pp. 1–10.

Kaas, J.H., M.M. Merzenich, and H.P. Killackey, 1983. "The reorganization of somatosensory cortex following peripheral nerve damage in adult and developing mammals," *Annual Review of Neurosciences,* vol. 6, pp. 325–356.

Kailath, T., 1980. *Linear Systems,* Englewood Cliffs, NJ: Prentice-Hall.

Kailath, T., 1971. "RKHS approach to detection and estimation problems—Part I: Deterministic signals in Gaussian noise," *IEEE Transactions of Information Theory,* vol. IT-17, pp. 530–549.

Kailath, T., 1968. "An innovations approach to least-squares estimation: Part 1. Linear filtering in additive white noise," *IEEE Transactions of Automatic Control,* vol. AC-13, pp. 646–655.

Kakade, S., 2002. "A natural policy gradient," *Advances in Neural Information Processing Systems,* vol. 14-2, pp. 1531–1538, Cambridge, MA: MIT Press.

Kalman, R.E., 1960. "A new approach to linear filtering and prediction problems," *Transactions of the ASME, Journal of Basic Engineering,* vol. 82, pp. 35–45.

Kaminski, P.G., A.E. Bryson, Jr., and S.F. Schmidt, 1971. "Discrete square root filtering: A survey of current techniques," *IEEE Trans. Automatic Control,* vol. AC-16, pp. 727–735.

Kammler, D. W., 2000, *A First Course in Fourier Analysis,* Prentice-Hall

Kan, K., 2007. *Coherent Independent Component Analysis: Theory and Applications,* M.Eng. thesis, McMaster University, Hamilton, Ontario, Canada.

Kandel, E.R., J.H. Schwartz, and T.M. Jessell, eds., 1991. *Principles of Neural Science,* 3d ed., Norwalk, CT: Appleton & Lange.

Kaplan, J.L., and J.A. Yorke, 1979. "Chaotic behavior of multidimensional difference equations," in H.-O. Peitgen and H.-O. Walker, eds., *Functional Differential Equations and Approximations of Fixed Points,* pp. 204–227, Berlin: Springer.

Kappen, H.J., and F.B. Rodriguez, 1998. "Efficient learning in Boltzmann machines using linear response theory," *Neural Computation,* vol. 10, pp. 1137–1156.

Karhunen, J., and J. Joutsensalo, 1995. "Generalizations of principal component analysis, optimization problems, and neural networks," *Neural Networks,* vol. 8, pp. 549–562.

Karhunen, J. and E. Oja, 1982. "New methods for stochastic approximation of truncated Karhunen–Loève expansions," *IEEE Proceedings of the 6th International Conference on Pattern Recognition,* pp. 550–553, October.

Karhunen, K., 1947. "Über lineare methoden in der Wahrscheinlichkeitsrechnung," *Annales Academiae Scientiarum Fennicae, Series AI: Mathematica-Physica,* vol. 37, pp. 3–79, (Transl.: RAND Corp., Santa Monica, CA, Rep. T-131, Aug. 1960).

Karush, W., 1939. "Minima of functions of several variables with inequalities as side conditions," master's thesis, Department of Mathematics, University of Chicago.

Katz, B., 1966. *Nerve, Muscle and Synapse,* New York: McGraw-Hill.

Kawamoto, A.H., and J.A. Anderson, 1985. "A neural network model of multistable perception," *Acta Psychologiea,* vol. 59, pp. 35–65.

Kearns, M., 1996. "A bound on the error of cross validation using the approximation and estimation rates, with consequences for the training-test split," *Advances in Neural Information Processing Systems,* vol. 8, pp. 183–189, Cambridge, MA: MIT Press.

Kearns, M.J., and U.V. Vazirani, 1994. *An Introduction to Computational Learning Theory,* Cambridge, MA: MIT Press.

Kechriotis, G., E. Zervas, and E.S. Manolakos, 1994. "Using recurrent neural networks for adaptive communication channel equalization," *IEEE Transactions on Neural Networks,* vol. 5, pp. 267–278.

Kerlirzin, P., and F. Vallet, 1993. "Robustness in multilayer perceptrons," *Neural Computation,* vol. 5, pp. 473–482.

Khalil, H.K., 1992. *Nonlinear Systems,* Englewood Cliffs, NJ: Prentice Hall.

Kim, K.I., M.O. Franz, and B. Schölkopf, 2005. "Iterative kernel principal component analysis for image denoising," *IEEE Trans. Pattern Analysis and Machine Intelligence,* vol. 27, pp. 1351–1366.

Kimeldorf, G.S., and G. Wahba, 1971. "Some results on Tchebycheffian spline functions," *J. Math. Apal. Appli.,* vol. 33, pp. 82–95.

Kimeldorf, G.S., and G. Wahba, 1970, "A correspondence between Bayesian estimation on stochastic processes and smoothing by splines," *Annals of Mathematical Statistics,* vol. 41, pp. 495–502.

Kirkpatrick, S., 1984. "Optimization by simulated annealing: Quantitative studies," *Journal of Statistical Physics,* vol. 34, pp. 975–986.

Kirkpatrick, S., and D. Sherrington, 1978. "Infinite-ranged models of spin-glasses," *Physical Review,* Series B, vol. 17, pp. 4384–4403.

Kirkpatrick, S., C.D. Gelatt, Jr., and M.P. Vecchi, 1983. "Optimization by simulated annealing," *Science,* vol. 220, pp. 671–680.

Kirsch, A., 1996. *An Introduction to the Mathematical Theory of Inverse Problems,* New York: Springer-Verlag.

Kleene, S.C., 1956. "Representation of events in nerve nets and finite automata," in C.E. Shannon and J. McCarthy, eds., *Automata Studies,* Princeton, NJ: Princeton University Press.

Kline, M., 1972. *Mathematical Thought from Ancient to Modern Times,* Oxford University Press.

Kmenta, J., 1971. *Elements of Econometrics,* New York: Macmillan.

Knill, D.C., and W. Richards, eds., 1996. *Perception as Bayesian Inference,* Cambridge, U.K., and New York: Cambridge University Press.

Knudsen, E.I., S. duLac, and S.D. Esterly, 1987. "Computational maps in the brain," *Annual Review of Neuroscience,* vol. 10, pp. 41–65.

Koch, C., 1999. *Biophysics of Computation: Information Processing in Single Neurons,* New York: Oxford University Press.

Kohonen, T., 1997a. "Exploration of very large databases by self-organizing maps," *1997 International Conference on Neural Networks,* vol. I, pp. PL1–PL6, Houston.

Kohonen, T., 1997b. *Self-Organizing Maps,* 2d ed., Berlin: Springer-Verlag.

Kohonen, T., 1993. "Things you haven't heard about the self-organizing map," *Proceedings of the IEEE International Conference on neural networks,* pp. 1147–1156, San Francisco.

Kohonen, T., 1990. "The self-organizing map," *Proceedings of the Institute of Electrical and Electronics Engineers,* vol. 78, pp. 1464–1480.

Kohonen, T., 1982. "Self-organized formation of topologically correct feature maps," *Biological Cybernetics,* vol. 43, pp. 59–69.

Kohonen, T., 1972. "Correlation matrix memories," *IEEE Transactions on Computers,* vol. C-21, pp. 353–359.

Kolen, J., and S. Kremer, eds., 2001. *A Field Guide to Dynamical Recurrent Networks,* New York: IEEE Press.

Kollias, S., and D. Anastassiou, 1989. "An adaptive least squares algorithm for the efficient training of artificial neural networks," *IEEE Transactions on Circuits and Systems,* vol. 36, pp. 1092–1101.

Kolmogorov, A., 1965. "Three approaches to the quantitative definition of information," *Problems of Information Transmission,* vol. 1, issue 1, pp. 1–7.

Kolmogorov, A.N., 1942. "Interpolation and extrapolation of stationary random sequences," translated by the Rand Corporation, Santa Monica, CA., April 1962.

Kramer, M.A., 1991. "Nonlinear principal component analysis using autoassociative neural networks," *AIChE Journal,* vol. 37, pp. 233–243.

Kramer, A.H., and A. Sangiovanni-Vincentelli, 1989. "Efficient parallel learning algorithms for neural networks," *Advances in neural Information Processing Systems,* vol. 1, pp. 40–48, San Mateo, CA: Morgan Kaufmann.

Kremer, S.C., 1996. "Comments on constructive learning of recurrent neural networks: Limitations of recurrent cascade correlation and a simple solution," *IEEE Transactions on Neural Networks,* vol. 7, pp. 1047–1049.

Kremer, S.C., 1995. "On the computational power of Elman-style recurrent networks," *IEEE Transactions on Neural Networks,* vol. 6, pp. 1000–1004.

Kreyszig, E., 1988. *Advanced Engineering Mathematics,* 6th ed., New York: Wiley.

Krzyżak, A., T. Linder, and G. Lugosi, 1996. "Nonparametric estimation and classification using radial basis functions," *IEEE Transactions on Neural Networks,* vol. 7, pp. 475–487.

Kuffler, S.W., J.G. Nicholls, and A.R. Martin, 1984. *From Neuron to Brain: A Cellular Approach to the Function of the Nervous System,* 2d ed., Sunderland, MA: Sinauer Associates.

Kullback, S., 1968. *Information Theory and Statistics,* Gloucester, MA: Peter Smith.

Kuhn, H.W., 1976. "Nonlinear programming: A historical view," in R.N. Cottle and C.E. Lemke, eds., *SIAM-AMS Proceedings,* vol. IX, American Mathematical Society, pp. 1–26.

Kuhn, H.W., and A.W. Tucker, 1951. "Nonlinear programming," in J. Neyman, ed., *Proceedings of the 2nd Berkley Symposium on Mathematical Statistics and Probabilities,* pp. 481–492, Monterey CA: University of California Press.

Kung, S.Y., and K.I. Diamantaras, 1990. "A neural network learning algorithm for adaptive principal component extraction (APEX)." *IEEE International Conference on Acoustics, Speech, and Signal Processing,* vol. 2, pp. 861–864, Albuquerque, NM.

Kushner, H.J., and D.S. Clark, 1978. *Stochastic Approximation Methods for Costrained and Unconstrained Systems,* New York: Springer-Verlag.

Laaksonen, J., and V. Viitanieni, 2006. "Emergence of ontological relations from visual data with self-organizing maps," *Proceedings of SCAI'06, the 9th Scandanavian Conference on Artificial Intelligence,* pp. 31–38, Espoo, Finland, October.

Laaksonen, J.T., J.M. Koskela, and E. Oja, 2004. "Class distributions on SOM surfaces for feature extraction and object retrieval," *Neural Networks,* vol. 17, pp. 1121–1133.

Lagoudakis, M.G., and R. Parr, 2003. "Least-squares policy iteration," *J. Machine Learning Research,* vol. 4, pp. 1107–1149.

Lanczos, C., 1964. *Linear Differential Operators,* London: Van Nostrand.

Landau, Y.D., 1979. *Adaptive Control: The Model Reference Approach,* New York: Marcel Dekker.

Landau, L.D., and E.M. Lifshitz, 1980. *Statistical Physics: Part 1,* 3d ed., London: Pergamon Press.

Lanford, O.E., 1981. "Strange attractors and turbulence," in H.L. Swinney and J.P. Gollub, eds., *Hydrodynamic Instabilities and the Transition to Turbulence,* New York: Springer-Verlag.

Lang, S. 2002. *Introduction to Differentiable Manifolds,* New York: Springer.

LeCun, Y., 1993. *Efficient Learning and Second-order Methods, A Tutorial at NIPS 93,* Denver.

LeCun, Y., 1989. "Generalization and network design strategies," Technical Report CRG-TR-89-4, Department of Computer Science, University of Toronto, Ontario, Canada.

LeCun, Y., 1985. "Une procedure d'apprentissage pour reseau a seuil assymetrique." *Cognitiva,* vol. 85, pp. 599–604.

LeCun, Y., and Y., Bengio, 2003. "Convolutional Networks for Images, Speech, and Time Series," in M.A. Arbib, ed., *The Handbook of Brain Theory and Neural Networks,* 2d ed., Cambridge, MA: MIT Press.

LeCun, Y., B. Boser, J.S. Denker, D. Henderson, R.E. Howard, W. Hubbard, and L.D. Jackel, 1990. "Handwritten digit recognition with a back-propagation network," *Advances in Neural Information Processing,* vol. 2, pp. 396–404, San Mateo, CA: Morgan Kaufmann.

LeCun, Y., L. Bottou, and Y. Bengio, 1997. "Reading checks with multilayer graph transformer networks," *IEEE International Conference on Acoustics, Speech and Signal Processing,* pp. 151–154, Munich, Germany.

LeCun, Y., L. Bottou, Y. Bengio, and R. Haffner, 1998. "Gradient-based learning applied to document recognition," *Procedings of the IEEE,* vol. 86, pp. 2278–2324.

LeCun, Y., J.S. Denker, and S.A. Solla, 1990. "Optimal brain damage," *Advances in Neural Information Processing Systems,* vol. 2, pp. 598–605, San Mateo, CA: Morgan Kaufmann.

LeCun, Y, I. Kanter, and S.A. Solla, 1991. "Second order properties of error surfaces: Learning time and generalization," *Advances in Neural Information Processing Systems,* vol. 3, pp. 918–924, Cambridge, MA: MIT Press.

Lee, T.S., and D. Mumford, 2003. "Hierarchical Bayesian inference in the visual cortex," *J. Optical Society of America,* vol. 20, pp. 1434–1448.

Lefebvre, W.C., 1991. *An Object Oriented Approach for the Analysis of Neural Networks,* master's thesis, University of Florida, Gainesville, FL.

Leon-Garcia, A., 1994. *Probability and Random Processes for Electrical Engineering,* 2d ed., Reading, MA: Addison-Wesley.

Leontaritis, I., and S. Billings, 1985. "Input–output parametric models for nonlinear systems: Part I: Deterministic nonlinear systems," *International Journal of Control,* vol. 41, pp. 303–328.

Levenberg, K., 1944. "A method for the solution of certain non-linear problems in least squares," *Quart. Appl. Math.,* vol. 12, pp. 164–168.

Levin, A.V., and K.S. Narendra, 1996. "Control of nonlinear dynamical systems using neural networks—Part II: Observability, identification, and control," *IEEE Transactions on Neural Networks,* vol. 7, pp. 30–42.

Levin, A.V., and K.S. Narendra, 1993. "Control of nonlinear dynamical systems using neural networks—Controllability and stabilization," *IEEE Transactions on Neural Networks,* vol. 4, pp. 192–206.

Lewis, F.L., and V.L. Syrmas, 1995. *Optimal Control,* 2d ed., New York: Wiley (Interscience).

Li, M., and P. Vitányi, 1993. *An Introduction to Kolmogorov Complexity and Its Applications,* New York: Springer-Verlag.

Lichtenberg, A.J., and M.A. Lieberman, 1992. *Regular and Chaotic Dynamics,* 2d ed., New York: Springer-Verlag.

Light, W.A., 1992a. "Some aspects of radial basis function approximation," in *Approximation Theory, Spline Functions and Applications,* S.P. Singh, ed., NATO ASI vol. 256, pp. 163–190, Boston: Kluwer Academic Publishers.

Light, W., 1992b. "Ridge functions, sigmoidal functions and neural networks," in E.W. Cheney, C.K. Chui, and L.L. Schumaker, eds., *Approximation Theory VII,* pp. 163–206, Boston: Academic Press.

Lin, S., and D.J. Costello, 2004. *Error Control Coding,* 2d ed., Upper Saddle River, NJ: Prentice Hall.

Lin, J.K., D.G. Grier, and J.D. Cowan, 1997. "Faithful representation of separable distributions," *Neural Computation,* vol. 9, pp. 1305–1320.

Lin, T., B.G. Horne, P. Tino, and C.L. Giles, 1996. "Learning long-term dependencies in NARX recurrent neural networks," *IEEE Transactions on Neural Networks,* vol. 7, pp. 1329–1338.

Linsker, R., 1993. "Deriving receptive fields using an optimal encoding criterion," *Advances in Neural Information Processing Systems,* vol. 5, pp. 953–960, San Mateo, CA: Morgan Kaufmann.

Linsker, R., 1990a. "Designing a sensory processing system: What can be learned from principal components analysis?" *Proceedings of the International Joint Conference on Neural Networks,* vol. 2, pp. 291–297, Washington, DC.

Linsker, R., 1990b. "Perceptual neural organization: Some approaches based on network models and information theory," *Annual Review of Neuroscience,* vol. 13, pp. 257–281.

Linsker, R., 1989a. "An application of the principle of maximum information preservation to linear systems," *Advances in Neural Information Processing Systems,* vol. 1, pp. 186–194, San Mateo, CA: Morgan Kaufmann.

Linsker, R., 1989b. "How to generate ordered maps by maximizing the mutual information between input and output signals," *Neural computation,* vol. 1, pp. 402–411.

Linsker, R., 1988a. "Self-organization in a perceptual network," *Computer,* vol. 21, pp. 105–117.

Linsker, R., 1988b. "Towards an organizing principle for a layered perceptual network," in *Neural Information Processing Systems,* D.Z. Anderson, ed., pp. 485–494, New York: American Institute of Physics.

Linsker, R., 1987. "Towards an organizing principle for perception: Hebbian synapses and the principle of optimal neural encoding," *IBM Research Report RC12820,* IBM Research, Yorktown Heights, NY.

Linsker, R., 1986. "From basic network principles to neural architecture" (series), *Proceedings of the National Academy of Sciences, USA,* vol. 83, pp. 7508–7512, 8390–8394, 8779–8783.

Lippmann, R.P., 1987. "An introduction to computing with neural nets," *IEEE ASSP Magazine,* vol. 4, pp. 4–22.

Lippmann, R.P., 1989a. "Review of neural networks for speech recognition," *Neural Computation,* vol. 1, pp. 1–38.

Lippmann, R.P., 1989b. "Pattern classification using neural networks," *IEEE Communications Magazine,* vol. 27, pp. 47–64.

Little, W.A., 1974. "The existence of persistent states in the brain," *Mathematical Biosciences,* vol. 19, pp. 101–120.

Little, W.A., and G.L. Shaw, 1978. "Analytic study of the memory storage capacity of a neural network," *Mathematical Biosciences,* vol. 39, pp. 281–290.

Little, W. A., and G.L. Shaw, 1975. "A statistical theory of short and long term memory," *Behavioral Biology,* vol. 14, pp. 115–133.

Littman, M.L., R.S. Sutton, and S. Singh, 2002. "Predictive representations of state," *Advances in Neural Information Processing Systems,* vol. 14, pp. 1555–1561.

Liu, J.S., and R. Chen, 1998. "Sequential Monte Carlo methods for dynamical systems," *J. American Statistical Association,* vol. 93, pp. 1032–1044.

Liu, J.S., 1996. "Metropolized independent sampling with comparisons to rejection sampling and importance sampling," *Statistics and Computing,* vol. 6, pp. 113–119.

Liu, W., P.P. Pokharel, and J.C. Principe, 2008. "The kernel least-mean-square algorithm," *IEEE Trans. Signal Processing,* vol. 56, pp. 543–554.

Livesey, M., 1991. "Clamping in Boltzmann machines," *IEEE Transactions on Neural Networks,* vol. 2, pp. 143–148.

Ljung, L., 1987. *System Identification: Theory for the User.* Englewood Cliffs, NJ: Prentice-Hall.

Ljung, L., 1977. "Analysis of recursive stochastic algorithms," *IEEE Transactions on Automatic Control,* vol. AC-22, pp. 551–575.

Ljung, L., and T. Glad, 1994. *Modeling of Dynamic Systems,* Englewood Cliffs, NJ: Prentice Hall.

Lloyd, S.P., 1957. "Least squares quantization in PCM," unpublished Bell Laboratories technical note. Published later under the same title in *IEEE Transactions on Information Theory,* vol. IT-28, pp. 127–135, 1982.

Lo, J.T., 2001. "Adaptive vs. accommodative neural networks for adaptive system identification," *Proceedings of the International Joint Conference on Neural Networks,* pp. 2001–2006, Washington, DC.

Lo, J.T., and L. Yu, 1995a. "Recursive neural filters and dynamical range transformers," *Proc. IEEE,* vol. 92, pp. 514–535.

Lo, J.T., and L. Yu, 1995b. Adaptive neural filtering by using the innovations process, *Proceedings of the 1995 World Congress on Neural Networks,* vol. II, pp. 29–35, July.

Lo, J.T., 1993. "Dynamical system identification by recurrent multilayer perceptrons," *Proceedings of the 1993 World Congress on Neural Networks,* Portland, OR.

Lo, Z.-P., M. Fujita, and B. Bavarian, 1991. "Analysis of neighborhood interaction in Kohonen neural networks," *6th International Parallel Processing Symposium Proceedings,* pp. 247–249, Los Alamitos, CA.

Lo, Z.-P., Y. Yu and B. Bavarian, 1993. "Analysis of the convergence properties of topology preserving neural networks," *IEEE Transactions on Neural Networks,* vol. 4, pp. 207–220.

Lockery, S.R., Y. Fang, and T.J. Sejnowski, 1990. "A dynamical neural network model of sensorimotor transformations in the leech," *International Joint Conference on Neural Networks,* vol. I, pp. 183–188, San Diego, CA.

Loève, M., 1963. *Probability Theory,* 3d ed., New York: Van Nostrand.

Lorentz, G.G., 1976. "The 13th problem of Hilbert," *Proceedings of Symposia in Pure Mathematics,* vol. 28, pp. 419–430.

Lorentz, G.G., 1966. *Approximation of Functions,* Orlando, FL: Holt, Rinehart & Winston.

Lorenz, E.N., 1963. "Deterministic non-periodic flows," *Journal of Atmospheric Sciences,* vol. 20, pp. 130–141.

Lowe, D., 1989. "Adaptive radial basis function nonlinearities, and the problem of generalisation," *First IEE International Conference on Artificial Neural Networks,* pp. 171–175, London.

Lowe, D., 1991a. "What have neural networks to offer statistical pattern processing?" *Proceedings of the SPIE Conference on Adaptive Signal Processing*, pp. 460–471, San Diego.

Lowe, D., 1991b. "On the iterative inversion of RBF networks: A statistical interpretation," *Second IEE International Conference on Artificial Neural Networks*, pp. 29–33, Bournemouth, U.K.

Lowe, D., and A.R. Webb, 1991a. "Time series prediction by adaptive networks: A dynamical systems perspective," *IEE Proceedings (London), Part F*, vol. 138, pp. 17–24.

Lowe, D., and A.R. Webb, 1991b. "Optimized feature extraction and the Bayes decision in feedforward classifier networks," *IEEE Transactions on Pattern Analysis and Machine Intelligence*, PAMI-13, 355–364.

Luenberger, D.G., 1984. *Linear and Nonlinear Programming*, 2d ed., Reading, MA: Addison-Wesley.

Luttrell, S.P., 1994. "A Bayesian analysis of self-organizing maps," *Neural Computation*, vol. 6, pp. 767–794.

Luttrell, S.P., 1991. "Code vector density in topographic mappings: Scalar case," *IEEE Transactions on Neural Networks*, vol. 2, pp. 427–436.

Luttrell, S.P., 1989a. "Hierarchical vector quantization," *IEE Proceedings (London)*, vol. 136 (Part I), pp. 405–413.

Luttrell, S.P., 1989b. "Self-organization: A derivation from first principle of a class of learning algorithms," *IEEE Conference on Neural Networks*, pp. 495–498, Washington, DC.

Lyapunov, A.M., 1892. *The General Problem of Motion Stability* (in Russian). (Translated in English by F. Abramovici and M. Shimshoni, under the title *Stability of Motion*, New York: Academic Press, 1966.)

Maass, W., 1993. "Bounds for the computational power and learning complexity of analog neural nets," *Proceedings of the 25th Annual ACM Symposium on the Theory of Computing*, pp. 335–344, New York: ACM Press.

MacKay, D.J.C., 2003. *Information Theory, Inference, and Learning Algorithms*, Cambridge, U.K., and New York: Cambridge University Press.

Mackey, M.C., and L. Glass, 1977. "Oscillations and chaos in physiological control systems," *Science*, vol. 197, pp. 287–289.

MacQueen, J., 1967. "Some methods for classification and analysis of multivariate observation," in *Proceedings of the 5th Berkeley Symposium on Mathematical Statistics and Probability*, L.M. LeCun and J. Neyman, eds., vol. 1, pp. 281–297, Berkeley: University of California Press.

Mahowald, M.A., and C. Mead, 1989. "Silicon retina," in *Analog VLSI and Neural Systems* (C. Mead), Chapter 15. Reading, MA: Addison-Wesley.

Mallat, S., 1998. *A Wavelet tour of signal processing*, San Diego: Academic Press.

Mandelbrot, B.B., 1982. *The Fractal Geometry of Nature*, San Francisco: Freeman.

Mañé, R., 1981. "On the dimension of the compact invariant sets of certain non-linear maps," in D. Rand and L.S. Young, eds., *Dynamical Systems and Turbulence*, Lecture Notes in Mathematics, vol. 898, pp. 230–242, Berlin: Springer-Verlag.

Marquardt, D.W. 1963. "An algorithm for least-squares estimation of nonlinear parameters," *J. Soc. Indust. Appli. Math.*, vol. 11, no. 2, pp. 431–441, June.

Marr, D., 1982. *Vision*, New York: W.H. Freeman and Company.

Mason, S.J., 1953. "Feedback theory—Some properties of signal-flow graphs," *Proceedings of the Institute of Radio Engineers*, vol. 41, pp. 1144–1156.

Mason, S.J., 1956. "Feedback theory—Further properties of signal-flow graphs," *Proceedings of the Institute of Radio Engineers,* vol. 44, pp. 920–926.

Maybeck, P.S., 1982. *Stochastic Models, Estimation, and Control,* vol. 2, New York: Academic Press.

Maybeck, P.S., 1979. *Stochastic Models, Estimation, and Control,* vol. 1, New York: Academic Press.

Mazaika, P.K., 1987. "A mathematical model of the Boltzmann machine," *IEEE First International Conference on Neural Networks,* vol. III, pp. 157–163, San Diego.

McBride, L.E., Jr., and K.S. Narendra, 1965. "Optimization of time-varying systems," *IEEE Transactions on Automatic Control,* vol. AC-10, pp. 289–294.

McCulloch, W.S., 1988. *Embodiments of Mind,* Cambridge, MA: MIT Press.

McCulloch, W.S., and W. Pitts, 1943. "A logical calculus of the ideas immanent in nervous activity," *Bulletin of Mathematical Biophysics,* vol. 5, pp. 115–133.

McLachlan, G.J., and T. Krishnan, 1997. *The EM Algorithm and Extensions,* New York: Wiley (Interscience).

McQueen, J., 1967. "Some methods for classification and analysis of multivariate observations," *Proceedings of the 5th Berkeley Symposium on Mathematical Statistics and Probability,* vol. 1, pp. 281–297, Berkeley, CA: University of California Press.

Mead, C.A., 1989. *Analog VLSI and Neural Systems,* Reading, MA: Addison-Wesley.

Mendel, J.M., 1995. *Lessons in Estimation Theory for Signal Processing, Communications, and Control.* Englewood Cliffs, NJ: Prentice Hall.

Mennon, A., K. Mehrotra, C.K. Mohan, and S. Ranka, 1996. "Characterization of a class of sigmoid functions with applications to neural networks," *Neural Networks,* vol. 9, pp. 819–835.

Mercer, J., 1909. "Functions of positive and negative type, and their connection with the theory of integral equations," *Transactions of the London Philosophical Society (A),* vol. 209, pp. 415–446.

Metropolis, N., A. Rosenbluth, M. Rosenbluth, A. Teller, and E. Teller, 1953. Equations of state calculations by fast computing machines, *Journal of Chemical Physics,* vol. 21, pp. 1087–1092.

Meyer, Y., 1993. *Wavelets: Algorithms and Applications,* SIAM (translated from French and revised by R.D. Ryan), Philadelphia: Society for Industrial and Applied Mathematics.

Micchelli, C.A., 1986. "Interpolation of scattered data: Distance matrices and conditionally positive definite functions," *Constructive Approximation,* vol. 2, pp. 11–22.

Miller, D., A.V. Rao, K. Rose, and A. Gersho, 1996. "A global optimization technique for statistical classifier design," *IEEE Transactions on Signal Processing,* vol. 44, pp. 3108–3122.

Miller, D., and K. Rose, 1994. "Combined source-channel vector quantization using deterministic annealing," *IEEE Transactions on Communications,* vol. 42, pp. 347–356.

Miller, R., 1987. "Representation of brief temporal patterns, Hebbian synapses, and the left-hemisphere dominance for phoneme recognition," *Psychobiology,* vol. 15, pp. 241–247.

Minsky, M.L., 1986. Society of Mind, New York: Simon and Schuster.

Minsky, M.L., 1967. *Computation: Finite and Infinite Machines.* Englewood Cliffs, NJ: Prentice-Hall.

Minsky, M.L., 1954. "Theory of neural-analog reinforcement systems and its application to the brain-model problem," Ph.D. thesis, Princeton University, Princeton, NJ.

Minsky, M.L., and S.A. Papert, 1988. *Perceptrons,* expanded edition, Cambridge, MA: MIT Press.

Minsky, M.L., and S.A. Papert, 1969. *Perceptrons,* Cambridge, MA: MIT Press.

Minsky, M.L., and O.G. Selfridge, 1961. "Learning in random nets," *Information Theory, Fourth London Symposium,* London: Buttenvorths.

Møller, M.F., 1993. "A scaled conjugate gradient algorithm for fast supervised learning," *Neural Networks*, vol. 6, pp. 525–534.

Moody, J., and C.J. Darken, 1989. "Fast learning in networks of locally-tuned processing units," *Neural Computation*, vol. 1, pp. 281–294.

Morita, M., 1993. "Associative memory with nonmonotonic dynamics," *Neural Networks*, vol. 6, pp. 115–126.

Morozov, V.A., 1993. *Regularization Methods for Ill-Posed Problems*, Boca Raton, FL: CRC Press.

Müller, K., A. Ziehe, N. Murata, and S. Amari, 1998. "On-line learning in switching and drifting environments with application to blind source separation," in D. Saad, ed., *On-line Learning in Neural Networks*, pp. 93–110, Cambridge, U.K., and New York: Cambridge University Press.

Mumford, D., 1994. "Neural architectures for pattern-theoretic problems," in C. Koch and J. Davis, eds., *Large-Scale Theories of the Cortex*, pp. 125–152, Cambridge, MA: MIT Press.

Murata, N., 1998. "A statistical study of on-line learning," in D. Saad, ed., *On-line Learning in Neural Networks*, pp. 63–92, Cambridge, U.K., and New York: Cambridge University Press.

Murray, M.K., and J.W. Rice, 1993. *Differential Geometry and Statistics*, New York: Chapman and Hall.

Nadal, J.-P., and N. Parga, 1997, "Redundancy reduction and independent component analysis: Conditions on cumulants and adaptive approaches," *Neural Computation*, vol. 9, pp. 1421–1456.

Nadal, J.-P., and N. Parga, 1994, "Nonlinear neurons in the low-noise limit: A factorial code maximizes information transfer, *Network*, vol. 5, pp. 565–581.

Nadaraya, E.A. 1965. "On nonparametric estimation of density functions and regression curves," *Theory of Probability and its Applications*, vol. 10, pp. 186–190.

Nadaraya, É.A., 1964. "On estimating regression," *Theory of Probability and its Applications*, vol. 9, issue 1, pp. 141–142.

Narendra, K.S., and A.M. Annaswamy, 1989. *Stable Adaptive Systems*, Englewood Cliffs, NJ: Prentice Hall.

Narendra, K.S., and K. Parthasarathy, 1990. "Identification and control of dynamical systems using neural networks," *IEEE Transactions on Neural Networks*, vol. 1, pp. 4–27.

Neal, R.M., 1995. *Bayesian Learning for Neural Networks*, Ph.D. Thesis, University of Toronto, Canada.

Neal, R.M., 1993. "Bayesian learning via stochastic dynamics," *Advances in Neural Information Processing Systems*, vol. 5, pp. 475–482, San Mateo, CA: Morgan Kaufmann.

Neal, R.M., 1992. "Connectionist learning of belief networks," *Artificial Intelligence*, vol. 56, pp. 71–113.

Nelsen, R.B., 2006. *An Introduction to Copulas*, 2d ed., New York: Springer.

Newcomb, S., 1886. "A generalized theory of the combination of observations so as to obtain the best result," *American Journal of Mathematics*, vol. 8, pp. 343–366.

Newell, A., and H.A. Simon, 1972. *Human Problem Solving*, Englewood Cliffs, NJ: Prentice-Hall.

Nguyen, D., and B. Widrow, 1989. "The truck backer-upper: An example of self-learning in neural networks," *International Joint Conference on Neural Networks*, vol. II, pp. 357–363, Washington, DC.

Nie, J., and S. Haykin, 1999. "A Q-learning-based dynamic channel assignment technique for mobile communication systems," *IEEE Transactions on Vehicular Technology*, vol. 48, p. 1676–1687.

Nilsson, N.J., 1980. *Principles of Artificial Intelligence*, New York: Springer-Verlag.

Nilsson, N.J., 1965. *Learning Machines: Foundations of Trainable Pattern-Classifying Systems*, New York: McGraw-Hill.

Niyogi, P., and F. Girosi, 1996. "On the relationship between generalization error, hypothesis complexity, and sample complexity for radial basis functions," *Neural Computation,* vol. 8, pp. 819–842.

Novikoff, A.B.J., 1962. "On convergence proofs for perceptrons," in *Proceedings of the Symposium on the Mathematical Theory of Automata,* pp. 615–622, Brooklyn, NY: Polytechnic Institute of Brooklyn.

Nørgaard, M., N.K. Poulsen, and O. Ravn, 2000. "New developments in state estimation for nonlinear systems," *Automatica,* vol. 36, pp. 1627–1638.

Obermayer, K., H. Ritter, and K. Schulten, 1991. "Development and spatial structure of cortical feature maps: A model study," *Advances in Neural Information Processing Systems,* vol. 3, pp. 11–17, San Mateo, CA: Morgan Kaufmann.

Oja, E., 1992. "Principal components, minor components, and linear neural networks," *Neural Networks,* vol. 5, 927–936.

Oja, E., 1983. *Subspace Methods of Pattern Recognition,* Letchworth, England: Research Studies Press.

Oja, E., 1982. "A simplified neuron model as a principal component analyzer," *Journal of Mathematical Biology,* vol. 15, pp. 267–273.

Oja, E., and J. Karhunen, 1985. "A stochastic approximation of the eigenvectors and eigenvalues of the expectation of a random matrix," *Journal of Mathematical Analysis and Applications,* vol. 106, pp. 69–84.

Olshausen, B.A., and D.J. Field, 1997. Sparse coding with an overcomplete basis set: A strategy employed by VI? *Vision Research,* vol. 37, pp. 3311–3325.

Olshausen, B.A., and D.J. Field, 1996. "Emergence of simple-cell receptive field properties by learning a sparse code for natural images," *Nature,* vol. 381, pp. 607–609.

Omlin, C.W., and C.L. Giles, 1996. "Constructing deterministic finite-state automata in recurrent neural networks," *Journal of the Association for Computing Machinery,* vol. 43, pp. 937–972.

Omura, J.K., 1969. "On the Viterbi decoding algorithm," *IEEE Trans. Information Theory,* vol. IT-15, pp. 177–179.

Opper, M., 1996. "Online versus offline learning from random examples: General results," *Phys. Rev. Lett.,* vol. 77, pp. 4671–4674.

Orr, G.B., and K. Müller, 1998. *Neural Networks: Tricks of the Trade* (Outgrowth of a 1996 NIPS Workshop), Berlin and New York: Springer.

Osuna, E., R. Freund, and F. Girosi, 1997. "An improved training algorithm for support vector machines," *Neural Networks for Signal Processing* VII, Proceedings of the 1997 IEEE Workshop, pp. 276–285, Amelia Island, FL.

Ott, E., 1993. *Chaos in Dynamical Systems,* Cambridge, MA: Cambridge University Press.

Packard, N.H., J.P. Crutchfield, J.D. Farmer, and R.S. Shaw, 1980. "Geometry from a time series," *Physical Review Letters,* vol. 45, pp. 712–716.

Palm, G., 1982. *Neural Assemblies: An Alternative Approach,* New York: Springer-Verlag.

Papoulis, A., 1984. *Probability, Random Variables, and Stochastic Processes,* 2d ed., New York: McGraw-Hill.

Parisi, G., 1988. *Statistical Field Theory,* Reading, MA: Addison-Wesley.

Park, J., and I.W. Sandberg, 1991. "Universal approximation using radial-basis-function networks," *Neural Computation,* vol. 3, pp. 246–257.

Parker, D.B., 1987. "Optimal algorithms for adaptive networks." Second order back propagation, second order direct propagation and second order Hebbian learning." *IEEE 1st International Conference on Neural Networks,* vol. 2, pp. 593–600, San Diego, CA.

Parker, T.S., and L.O., Chua, 1989. *Practical Numerical Algorithms for Chaotic Systems,* New York: Springer.

Parzen, E., 1962. "On estimation of a probability density function and mode," *Annals of Mathematical Statistics,* vol. 33, pp. 1065–1076.

Paulin, M.G., 1997. "Neural representations of moving systems," *International Journal of Neurobiology,* vol. 41, pp. 515–533.

Pavlov, I.P., 1927. *Conditional Reflexes: An Investigation of the Physiological Activity of the Cerebral Cortex,* (Translation from the Russian by G.V. Anrep), New York: Oxford University Press.

Pearl, J., 1988. *Probabilistic Reasoning in Intelligent Systems,* San Mateo, CA: Morgan Kaufmann. (revised 2nd printing, 1991).

Pearlmutter, B.A., 1994. "Fast exact multiplication by the Hessian," *Neural Computation,* vol. 6, issue 1, pp. 147–160.

Pearson, K., 1901. "On lines and planes of closest fit to systems of points in space," *Philosophical Magazine,* vol. 2, pp. 559–572.

Peretto, P. 1984. "Collective properties of neural networks: A statistical physics approach," *Biological Cybernetics,* vol. 50, pp. 51–62.

Peretto, P., and J.-J Niez, 1986. "Stochastic dynamics of neural networks," *IEEE Transactions on Systems, Man, and Cybernetics,* vol. SMC-16, pp. 73–83.

Perrin, D., 1990. "Finite automata," in J. van Leeuwen, ed., *Handbook of Theoretical Computer Science, Volume B: Formal Models and Semantics,* Chapter 1, pp. 3–57, Cambridge, MA: MIT Press.

Pham, D.T., and P. Garrat, 1997. "Blind separation of mixture of independent sources through a quasi-maximum likelihood approach," *IEEE Transactions on Signal Processing,* vol. 45, pp. 1712–1725.

Pham, D.T., P. Garrat, and C. Jutten, 1992. "Separation of a mixture of independent sources through a maximum likelihood approach," *Proceedings of EUSIPCO,* pp. 771–774.

Phillips, D., 1962. "A technique for the numerical solution of certain integral equations of the first kind," *Journal of Association for Computing Machinery,* vol. 9, pp. 84–97.

Pineau, J., G. Gordon, and S. Thrun, 2006. "Anytime point-based approximations for large POMDPs." *Journal of Artificial Intelligence Research,* Vol. 27, pp. 335–380.

Pineda, F.J., 1988a. "Generalization of backpropagation to recurrent and higher order neural networks," in *Neural Information Processing Systems,* D.Z. Anderson, ed., pp. 602–611, New York: American Institute of Physics.

Pineda, F.J., 1988b. "Dynamics and architecture in neural computation," *Journal of Complexity,* vol. 4, pp. 216–245.

Pineda, F.J., 1987. "Generalization of back-propagation to recurrent neural networks," *Physical Review Letters,* vol. 59, pp. 2229–2232.

Pitts, W., and W.S. McCulloch, 1947. "How we know universals: The perception of auditory and visual forms," *Bulletin of Mathematical Biophysics,* vol. 9, pp. 127–147.

Pizurica, A., and W. Phillips, 2006. "Estimating the probability of the presence of a signal of interest in multiresolution single- and multiband image denoising," *IEEE Trans. on Image Processing,* vol. 15, pp. 654–665.

Platt, J., 1999. "Fast training of support vector machines using sequential minimal optimization," in B. Schölkopf, C.J.C. Burges, and A.J. Smola, eds., *Advances in Kernel Methods—Support Vector Learning,* pp. 185–208, Cambridge, MA: MIT Press.

Poggio, T., and F. Girosi, 1990a. "Networks for approximation and learning," *Proceedings of the IEEE,* vol. 78, pp. 1481–1497.

Poggio, T., and F. Girosi, 1990b." Regularization algorithms for learning that are equivalent to multilayer networks," *Science,* vol. 247, pp. 978–982.

Poggio, T., and C. Koch, 1985. "Ill-posed problems in early vision: From computational theory to analogue networks," *Proceedings of the Royal Society of London,* Series B, vol. 226, pp. 303–323.

Poggio, T., V. Torre, and C. Koch, 1985. "Computational vision and regularization theory," *Nature,* vol. 317, pp. 314–319.

Polak, E., and G. Ribiére, 1969. "Note sur la convergence de méthodes de directions conjuguées," *Revue Française d' Informatique et de Recherche Opérationnelle* vol. 16, pp. 35–43.

Powell, M.J.D., 1992. "The theory of radial basis function approximation in 1990," in W. Light, ed., *Advances in Numerical Analysis Vol. II: Wavelets, Subdivision Algorithms, and Radial Basis Functions,* pp. 105–210, Oxford: Oxford Science Publications.

Powell, M.J.D., 1988. "Radial basis function approximations to polynomials," *Numerical Analysis 1987 Proceedings,* pp. 223–241, Dundee, UK.

Powell, M.J.D., 1987. "A review of algorithms for nonlinear equations and unconstrained optimization," *ICIAM'87: Proceedings of the First International Conference on Industrial and Applied Mathematics,* Philadelphia, Society for Industrial and Applied Mathematics, pp. 220–264.

Powell, M.J.D., 1985. "Radial basis functions for multivariable interpolation: A review," *IMA Conference on Algorithms for the Approximation of Functions and Data,* pp. 143–167, RMCS, Shrivenham, U.K.

Prechelt, L., 1998. *Early Stopping—But When?* in *Neural Networks: Tricks of the Trade,* ed. G. Orr and K. Müller, Lecture Notes in Computer Science, no. 1524. Berlin: Springer, pp. 55–69.

Preisendorfer, R.W., 1988. *Principal Component Analysis in Meteorology and Oceanography,* New York: Elsevier.

Press, W.H., and S.A. Teukolsky, 1990. "Orthogonal polynomials and Gaussian quadrature with nonclassical weighting functions," *Computers in Physics,* pp. 423–426.

Press, W.H., P.B. Flannery, S.A. Teukolsky, and W.T. Vetterling, 1988. *Numerical Recipes in C: The Art of Scientific Computing,* Cambridge and New York: Cambridge University Press.

Prokhorov, D.V., 2007. "Training recurrent neurocontrollers for real-time applications," *IEEE Trans. Neural Networks,* vol. 16, pp. 1003–1015.

Prokhorov, D.V., 2006. "Training recurrent neurocontrollers for rubustness with derivation-free Kalman filter," *IEEE Trans. Neural Networks,* vol. 17, pp. 1606–1616.

Prokhorov, D.V., L.A. Feldkamp, and I.Y. Tyukin, 2002. "Adaptive behavior with fixed weights in RNN: An overview," *Proceedings of the International Joint Conference on Neural Networks,* Hawaii.

Prokhorov, D., G. Puskorius, and L. Feldkamp, 2001. "Dynamical neural networks for control," in J. Kolen and S. Kremer, eds., *A Field Guide to Dynamical Recurrent Networks,* New York: IEEE Press, pp. 257–289.

Prokhorov, D.V., and D.C. Wunsch, II, 1997. "Adaptive critic designs," *IEEE Transactions on Neural Networks,* vol. 8, pp. 997–1007.

Puskorius, G., and L. Feldkamp, 2001. "Parameter-based Kalman filter training: Theory and implementation," in S. Haykin, ed., *Kalman Filtering and Neural Networks,* New York: Wiley.

Puskorius, G.V., L.A. Feldkamp, and L.I. Davis, Jr., 1996. "Dynamic neural network methods applied to on-vehicle idle speed control," *Proceedings of the IEEE,* vol. 84, pp. 1407–1420.

Puskorius, G.V., and L.A. Feldkamp, 1994. "Neurocontrol of nonlinear dynamical systems with Kalman filter-trained recurrent networks," *IEEE Transactions on Neural Networks,* vol. 5, pp. 279–297.

Puskorius, G.V., and L.A. Feldkamp, 1991. "Decoupled extended Kalman filter training of feedforward layered networks," *International Joint Conference on Neural Networks,* vol. 1, pp. 771–777, Seattle.

Rabiner, L.R., 1989. "A tutorial on hidden Markov models," *Proceedings of the IEEE,* vol. 73, pp. 1349–1387.

Rabiner, L.R., and B.H. Juang, 1986. "An introduction to hidden Markkov models," *IEEE ASSP Magazine,* vol. 3, pp. 4–16.

Ramón y Cajál, S., 1911, *Histologie du Systéms Nerveux de l'homme et des vertébrés,* Paris: Maloine.

Rao, A., D. Miller, K. Rose, and A. Gersho, 1997a. "Mixture of experts regression modeling by deterministic annealing." *IEEE Transactions on Signal Processing,* vol. 45, pp. 2811–2820.

Rao, A., K. Rose, and A. Gersho, 1997b. "A deterministic annealing approach to discriminative hidden Markov model design," *Neural Networks for Signal Processing VII, Proceedings of the 1997 IEEE Workshop,* pp. 266–275, Amelia Island, FL.

Rao, C.R., 1973. *Linear Statistical Inference and Its Applications,* New York: Wiley.

Rao, R.P.N., B.A. Olshausen, and M.S. Lewicki, eds., 2002. *Probabilistics Models of the Brain,* Cambridge, MA: MIT Press.

Rao, R.P.N., and T.J. Sejnowski, 2003. "Self-organizing neural systems based on predictive learning," *Philosophical Transactions of the Royal Society of London,* vol. A.361, pp. 1149–1175.

Rao, R.P.N., and D.H. Ballard, 1999. "Predictive coding in the visual cortex: A functional interpretation of some extra-classical receptive-field effects," *Nature Neuroscience,* vol. 3, pp. 79–87.

Rao, R.P.N., and D.H. Ballard, 1997. "Dynamic model of visual recognition predicts neural response properties in the visual cortex," *Neural Computation,* vol. 9, pp. 721–763.

Rashevsky, N., 1938. *Mathematical Biophysics,* Chicago: University of Chicago Press.

Reed, R.D., and R.J. Marks, II, 1999. *Neural Smithing: Supervised Learning in Feedforward Artificial Neural Networks,* Cambridge, MA: MIT Press.

Reif, F., 1965. *Fundamentals of Statistical and Thermal Physics,* New York: McGraw-Hill.

Renals, S., 1989. "Radial basis function network for speech pattern classification," *Electronics Letters,* vol. 25, pp. 437–439.

Rényi, A., 1970. *Probability Theory,* North-Holland, Amsterdam.

Rényi, A. 1960. "On measures of entropy and information," *Proceedings of the 4th Berkeley Symposium on Mathematics, Statistics, and Probability,* pp. 547–561.

Richards, W., ed., 1988. *Natural Computation,* Cambridge, MA: MIT Press.

Rieke, F., D. Warland, R. van Stevenginck, and W. Bialek, 1997. *Spikes: Exploring the Neural Code,* Cambridge, MA: MIT Press.

Rifkin, R.M., 2002. *Everything old is new again: A fresh look at historical approaches in machine learning,* Ph.D. thesis, MIT.

Rissanen, J., 1989. *Stochastic Complexity in Statistical Inquiry,* Singapore: World Scientific.

Rissanen, J., 1978. "Modeling by shortest data description," *Automatica,* vol. 14, pp. 465–471.

Ristic, B., S. Arulampalam, and N. Gordon, 2004. *Beyond the Kalman Filter: Particle Filters for Tracking Applications,* Boston: Artech House.

Ritter, H., 2003. "Self-organizing feature maps." In M.A. Arbib, editor, *The Handbook of Brain Theory and Neural Networks,* 2nd edition, pp. 1005–1010.

Ritter, H., 1991. "Asymptotic level density for a class of vector quantization processes," *IEEE Transactions on Neural Networks,* vol. 2, pp. 173–175.

Ritter, H., and T. Kohonen, 1989. "Self-organizing semantic maps," *Biological Cybernetics,* vol. 61, pp. 241–254.

Ritter, H., T. Martinetz, and K. Schulten, 1992. *Neural Computation and Self-Organizing Maps: An Introduction,* Reading, MA: Addison-Wesley.

Robbins, H., and S. Monro, 1951. "A stochastic approximation method," *Annals of Mathematical Statistics,* vol. 22, pp. 400–407.

Robert, C.P., 2001. *The Bayesian Choice,* New York: Springer.

Robert, C.P., and G. Casella, 1999. *Monte Carlo Statistical Methods,* New York: Springer.

Roberts, S., and R. Everson, editors, 2001. *Independent Component Analysis: Principles and Practice*, Cambridge, U.K., and New York: Cambridge University Press.

Rochester, N., J.H. Holland, L.H. Haibt, and W.L. Duda, 1956. "Tests on a cell assembly theory of the action of the brain, using a large digital computer," *IRE Transactions on Information Theory*, vol. IT-2, pp. 80–93.

Rose, K., 1998. "Deterministic annealing for clustering, compression, classification, regression, and related optimization problems," *Proceedings of the IEEE*, vol. 86, pp. 2210–2239.

Rose, K., 1991. *Deterministic Annealing, Clustering, and Optimization*, Ph.D. Thesis, California Institute of Technology, Pasadena, CA.

Rose, K., E. Gurewitz, and G.C. Fox, 1992. "Vector quantization by deterministic annealing," *IEEE Transactions on Information Theory*, vol. 38, pp. 1249–1257.

Rose, K., E. Gurewitz, and G.C. Fox, 1990. "Statistical mechanics and phase transitions in clustering," *Physical Review Letters*, vol. 65, pp. 945–948.

Rosenberg, S., 1997. *The Laplacian on a Riemannian Manifold*, Cambridge, U.K., and New York: Cambridge University Press.

Rosenblatt, F., 1962. *Principles of Neurodynamics*, Washington, DC: Spartan Books.

Rosenblatt, F., 1958. "The Perceptron: A probabilistic model for information storage and organization in the brain," *Psychological Review*, vol. 65, pp. 386–408.

Rosenblatt, M., 1970. "Density estimates and Markov sequences," in M. Puri, ed., *Nonparametric Techniques in Statistical Inference*, pp. 199–213, London: Cambridge University Press.

Rosenblatt, M., 1956. "Remarks on some nonparametric estimates of a density function," *Annals of Mathematical Statistics.*, vol. 27, pp. 832–837.

Ross, S.M., 1983. *Introduction to Stochastic Dynamic Programming*, New York: Academic Press.

Roth, Z., and Y. Baram, 1996. "Multi-dimensional density shaping by sigmoids," *IEEE Transactions on Neural Networks*, vol. 7, pp. 1291–1298.

Roussas, G., ed., 1991. *Nonparametric Functional Estimation and Related Topics*, The Netherlands: Kluwer.

Roy, N., and G. Gordon, 2003. "Exponential family PCA for belief compression in POMDPs," *Advances in Neural Information Processing Systems*, vol. 15, pp. 1667–1674.

Roy, S., and J.J. Shynk, 1990. "Analysis of the momentum LMS algorithm," *IEEE Transactions on Acoustics, Speech, and Signal Processing*, vol. ASSP-38, pp. 2088–2098.

Rubin, D.B., 1988. "Using the SIR algorithm to simulate posterior distribution," in J.M. Bernardo, M.H. DeGroot, D.V. Lindley, and A.F.M. Smith, eds., *Bayesian Statistics*, vol. 3, pp. 395–402, Oxford, U.K.: Oxford University Press.

Rubner, J., and K. Schulten, 1990. "Development of feature detectors by self-organization," *Biological Cybernetics*, vol. 62, pp. 193–199.

Rubner, J., and P. Tavan, 1989. "A self-organizing network for principal component analysis," *Europhysics Letters*, vol. 10, pp. 693–698.

Ruderman, D.L., 1997. "Origins of scaling in natural images," *Vision Research*, vol. 37, pp. 3385–3395.

Rueckl, J.G., K.R. Cave, and S.M. Kosslyn, 1989. "Why are 'what' and 'where' processed by separate cortical visual systems? A computational investigation," *J. Cognitive Neuroscience*, vol. 1, pp. 171–186.

Rumelhart, D.E., and J.L. McClelland, eds., 1986. *Parallel Distributed Processing: Explorations in the Microstructure of Cognition*, vol. 1, Cambridge, MA: MIT Press.

Rumelhart, D.E., and D. Zipser, 1985. "Feature discovery by competitive learning," *Cognitive Science*, vol. 9, pp. 75–112.

Rumelhart, D.E., G.E. Hinton, and R.J. Williams, 1986a. "Learning representations of back-propagation errors," *Nature (London)*, vol. 323, pp. 533–536.

Rumelhart, D.E., G.E. Hinton, and R.J. Williams, 1986b. "Learning internal representations by error propagation," in D.E. Rumelhart and J.L. McCleland, eds., vol 1, Chapter 8, Cambridge, MA: MIT Press.

Russell, S.J., and P. Novig, 1995. *Artificial Intelligence: A Modem Approach,* Upper Saddle River, NJ: Prentice Hall.

Saarinen, S., R.B. Bramley, and G. Cybenko, 1992. "Neural networks, backpropagation, and automatic differentiation," in *Automatic Differentiation of Algorithms: Theory, Implementation, and Application,* A. Griewank and G.F. Corliss, eds., pp. 31–42, Philadelphia: SIAM.

Saarinen, S., R. Bramley, and G. Cybenko, 1991. "The numerical solution of neural network training problems," *CRSD Report No. 1089,* Center for Supercomputing Research and Development, University of Illinois, Urbana, IL.

Saerens, M., and A. Soquet, 1991. "Neural controller based on back-propagation algorithm," *IEE Proceedings (London), Part F,* vol. 138, pp. 55–62.

Salomon, R., and J.L. van Hemmen, 1996. "Accelerating backpropagation through dynamic self-adaptation," *Neural Networks,* vol. 9, pp. 589–601.

Samuel, A.L., 1959. "Some studies in machine learning using the game of checkers," *IBM Journal of Research and Development,* vol. 3, pp. 211–229.

Sandberg, I.W., 1991. "Structure theorems for nonlinear systems," *Multidimensional Systems and Signal Processing,* vol. 2, pp. 267–286.

Sandberg, I.W., L. Xu, 1997a. "Uniform approximation of multidimensional myopic maps," *IEEE Transactions on Circuits and Systems,* vol. 44, pp. 477–485.

Sandberg, I.W., and L. Xu, 1997b. "Uniform approximation and gamma networks," *Neural Networks,* vol. 10, pp. 781–784.

Sanger, T.D., 1990. "Analysis of the two-dimensional receptive fields learned by the Hebbian algorithm in response to random input," *Biological Cybernetics,* vol. 63, pp. 221–228.

Sanger, T.D., 1989a. "An optimality principle for unsupervised learning," *Advances in Neural Information Processing Systems,* vol. 1, pp. 11–19, San Mateo, CA: Morgan Kaufmann.

Sanger, T.D., 1989b. "Optimal unsupervised learning in a single-layer linear feedforward neural network," *Neural Networks,* vol. 12, pp. 459–473.

Sauer, T., J.A. Yorke, and M. Casdagli, 1991. "Embedology," *Journal of Statistical Physics,* vol. 65, pp. 579–617.

Saul, L.K., and M.I. Jordan, 1995. "Boltzmann chains and hidden Markov models," *Advances in Neural Information Processing Systems,* vol. 7, pp. 435–442.

Scharf, L.L., 1991. *Statistical Signal Processing: Detection, Estimation, and Time Series Analysis,* Reading, MA: Addison-Wesley.

Schei, T.S., 1997. "A finite-difference method for linearization in nonlinear estimation algorithms," *Automatica,* vol. 33, pp. 2051–2058.

Schiffman, W.H., and H.W. Geffers, 1993. "Adaptive control of dynamic systems by back propagation networks," *Neural Networks,* vol. 6, pp. 517–524.

Schölkopf, B., and A.J. Smola, 2002. *Learning with Kernels: Support Vector Machines, Regularization, Optimization, and Beyond,* Cambridge, MA: MIT Press.

Schölkopf, B., A.J. Smola, and K. Müller, 1998. "Nonlinear component analysis as a kernel eigenvalue problem," *Neural Computation,* vol. 10, pp. 1299–1319.

Schölkopf, B., 1997. *Support Vector Learning,* Munich, Germany: R. Oldenbourg Verlag.

Schraudolf, N.N., J. Yu, and S. Günter, 2007. "A stochastic quasi-Newton method for on-line convex optimization," *Proceedings of 11th Intl. Conf. Artificial Intelligence and Statistics,* Puerto Rico, pp. 433–440.

Schraudolph, N.N., 2002. "Fast curvature matrix–vector products for second-order gradient descent," *Neural Computation,* vol. 4, pp. 1723–1738.

Schultz, W., 2007. "Reward signals", *Scholarpedia,* vol. 2, issue 6, 16 pages.

Schultz, W., 1998. "Predictive reward signal of dopamine neurons", *J. Neurophysiology,* vol. 80, pp. 1–27.

Schumaker, L.L., 1981, *Spline Functions: Basic Theory,* New York: Wiley.

Seber, G.A.F., and C.J. Wild, 1989. *Nonlinear Regression,* New York: Wiley.

Sejnowski, T.J., 1977a. "Strong covariance with nonlinearly interacting neurons," *Journal of Mathematical Biology,* vol. 4, pp. 303–321.

Sejnowski, T.J., 1977b. "Statistical constraints on synaptic plasticity," *Journal of Theoretical Biology,* vol. 69, pp. 385–389.

Sejnowski, T.J., and C.R. Rosenberg, 1987. "Parallel networks that learn to pronounce English text," *Complex Systems,* vol. 1, pp. 145–168.

Selfridge, O.G., 1958. "Pandemonium: A paradigm for learning," *Mechanization of Thought Processes, Proceedings of a Symposium held at the National Physical Laboratory,* pp. 513–526, London, November. (Reproduced in J.A. Anderson and E. Rosenfeld, editors, *Neurocomputing,* pp. 117–122, Cambridge, MA: MIT Press, 1988.)

Shah, S., and F. Palmieri, 1990. "MEKA—A fast, local algorithm for training feedforward neural networks," *International Joint Conference on Neural Networks,* vol. 3, pp. 41–46, San Diego.

Shamma, S.A., 2001. "On the role of space and time in auditory processing," *Trends in Cognitive Sciences,* vol. 5, pp. 340–348.

Shamma, S., 1989. "Spatial and temporal processing in central auditory networks," in *Methods in Neural Modeling,* C. Koch and I. Segev, Eds., Cambridge, MA: MIT Press.

Shanno, D.F., 1978. "Conjugate gradient methods with inexact line searches," *Mathematics of Operations Research,* vol. 3, pp. 244–256.

Shannon, C.E., 1948. "A mathematical theory of communication," *Bell System Technical Journal,* vol. 27, pp. 379–423, 623–656.

Shannon, C.E., and W. Weaver, 1949. *The Mathematical Theory of Communication,* Urbana, IL: The University of Illinois Press.

Shannon, C.E., and J. McCarthy, eds., 1956. *Automata Studies,* Princeton, NJ: Princeton University Press.

Shawe-Taylor, J., and N. Cristianini, 2004. *Kernel Methods for Pattern Analysis,* Cambridge, U.K., and New York: Cambridge University Press.

Shepherd, G.M., 1988. *Neurobiology,* 2d ed., New York: Oxford University Press.

Shepherd, G.M., ed., 1990. *The Synoptic Organization of the Brain,* 3d ed., New York: Oxford University Press.

Shepherd, G.M., and C. Koch, 1990. "Introduction to synaptic circuits," in *The Synaptic Organization of the Brain,* G.M. Shepherd, ed., pp. 3–31. New York: Oxford University Press.

Sherrington, C.S., 1933. *The Brain and Its Mechanism,* London: Cambridge University Press.

Sherrington, C.S., 1906. *The Integrative Action of the Nervous System,* New York: Oxford University Press.

Sherrington, D., and S. Kirkpatrick, 1975. "Spin-glasses," *Physical Review Letters,* vol. 35, p. 1972.

Shewchuk, J.R., 1994. *An Introduction to the Conjugate Gradient Method Without the Agonizing Pain,* School of Computer Science, Carnegie Mellon University, Pittsburgh, August 4, 1994.

Shore, J.E., and R.W. Johnson, 1980. "Axiomatic derivation of the principle of maximum entropy and the principle of minimum cross-entropy," *IEEE Transactions on Information Theory,* vol. IT-26, pp. 26–37.

Shynk, J.J., 1990. "Performance surfaces of a single-layer perceptron," *IEEE Transactions or Neural Networks,* 1, 268–274.

Shynk, J.J. and N.J. Bershad, 1991. Steady-state analysis of a single-layer perceptron based on a system identification model with bias terms," *IEEE Transactions on Circuits and Systems,* vol. CAS-38, pp. 1030–1042.

Si, J., A.G. Barto, W.B. Powell, and D. Wunsch II, eds., 2004. *Handbook of Learning and Approximate Dynamic Programming,* Hoboken, NJ: Wiley-Interscience.

Siegelmann, H.T., B.G. Home, and C.L. Giles, 1997. "Computational capabilities of recurrent NARX neural networks," *Systems, Man, and Cybernetics, Part B: Cybernetics,* vol. 27, pp. 208–215.

Siegelmann, H.T., and E.D. Sontag, 1991. "Turing computability with neural nets," *Applied Mathematics Letters,* vol. 4, pp. 77–80.

Silver, D., R.S. Sutton, and M. Müller, 2008. "Sample-based learning and search with permanent and transient memories," *Proceedings of the 25th International Conference on Machine Learning,* Helsinki, Finland.

Simmons, J.A., P.A. Saillant, and S.P. Dear, 1992. "Through a bat's ear," *IEEE Spectrum,* vol. 29, issue 3, pp. 46–48, March.

Sindhwani, V., M. Belkin, and P. Niyogi, 2006. "The geometric basis of semi-supervised learning," in O. Chapelle, B. Schölkopf, and A. Zien, eds., *Semi-Supervised Learning,* pp. 217–235, Cambridge, MA: MIT Press.

Sindhwani, V., P. Niyogi, and M. Belkin, 2005. "Beyond the point cloud: From transductive to semi-supervised learning," *Proceedings of the 22nd International Conference on Machine Learning,* Bonn, Germany.

Singh, S., and D. Bertsekas, 1997. "Reinforcement learning for dynamic channel allocation in cellular telephone systems," *Advances in Neural Information Processing Systems,* vol. 9, pp. 974–980, Cambridge, MA: MIT Press.

Singhal, S., and L. Wu, 1989. "Training feed-forward networks with the extended Kalman filter," *IEEE International Conference on Acoustics, Speech, and Signal Processing,* pp. 1187–1190, Glasgow, Scotland.

Sklar, A. (1959), "Fonctions de repartition 'a n dimensions et leurs marges," Publ. Inst. Statist. Univ. Paris 8, pp. 229–231.

Slepian, D., 1973. *Key papers in the development of information theory,* New York: IEEE Press.

Sloane, N.J.A., and A.D. Wyner, 1993. *Claude Shannon: Collected Papers,* New York: IEEE Press.

Slonim, N., N. Friedman, and N. Tishby, 2006. "Multivariate information bottleneck," *Neural Computation,* vol. 18, pp. 1739–1789.

Slotine, J.-J., and W. Li, 1991. Applied Nonlinear Control, Englewood Cliffs, NJ: Prentice Hall.

Smith, T. 2007. *Probabilistic Planning for Robotic Exploration,* Ph.D. thesis, Carnegie Mellon University, Pittsburgh.

Smolensky, P., 1986. "Information processing in dynamical systems: Foundations of Information Theory," in D.E. Rumelhart, J.L. McLelland, and the PDP Research Group, *Parallel Distributed Processing, Volume 1: Foundations,* Chapter 6, pp. 194–281, Cambridge, MA: MIT Press.

Snyder, D.L., 1975. *Random Point Processes,* New York: Wiley-Interscience.

Snyder, D.L., 1972. "Filtering and detection for doubly stochastic Poisson processes," *IEEE Trans. Information Theory,* vol. IT-18, pp. 91–102.

Sompolinsky, H., N. Barkai, and H.S. Seung, 1995. "On-line learning and dicotomies: Algorithms and learning curves," in J.-H. Oh, C. Kwon, and S. Cho, eds., *Neural Networks: The Statistical Mechanics Perspective,* pp. 105–130, Singapore and River Edge, NJ: World Scientific.

Sondik, E.J., 1971. *The Optimal Control of Partially Observable Markov Processes,* Ph.D. thesis, Stanford University.

Sontag, E.D., 1992. "Feedback stabilization using two-hidden-layer nets," *IEEE Transactions on Neural Networks,* vol. 3, pp. 981–990.

Sontag, E.D., 1990. *Mathematical Control Theory: Deterministic Finite Dimensional Systems,* New York: Springer-Verlag.

Sontag, E.D., 1989. "Sigmoids distinguish more efficiently than Heavisides," *Neural Computation,* vol. 1, pp. 470–472.

Southwell, R.V., 1946. *Relaxation Methods in Theoretical Physics,* New York: Oxford University Press.

Specht, D.F., 1991. "A general regression neural network," *IEEE Transactions on Neural Networks,* vol. 2, pp. 568–576.

Sperduti, A., 1997. "On the computational power of recurrent neural networks for structures," *Neural Networks,* vol. 10, pp. 395–400.

Sprecher, D.A., 1965. "On the structure of continuous functions of several variables," *Transactions of the American Mathematical Society,* vol. 115, pp. 340–355.

Steinbuch, K., 1961. "Die Lernmatrix." *Kybernetik,* vol. 1, pp. 36–45.

Steinwart, I., 2003. "Sparseness of support vector machines," *J. Machine Learning Research*, vol. 4, pp. 1071–1105.

Stent, G.S., 1973. "A physiological mechanism for Hebb's postulate of learning," *Proceedings of the National Academy of Sciences, USA,* vol. 70, pp. 997–1001.

Sterling, P., 1990. "Retina," in *The Synoptic Organization of the Brain,* G.M. Shepherd, ed., 3d ed., pp. 170–213, New York: Oxford University Press.

Stewart, G.W., 1973. *Introduction to Matrix Computations,* New York: Academic Press.

Stone, M., 1978. "Cross-validation: A review," *Mathematische Operationsforschung Statistischen, Serie Statistics,* vol. 9, pp. 127–139.

Stone, M., 1974. "Cross-validatory choice and assessment of statistical predictions," *Journal of the Royal Statistical Society,* vol. B36, pp. 111–133.

Strang, G., 1980. *Linear Algebra and its Applications,* New York: Academic Press.

Stroud, A.H., 1971. *Approximate Calculation of Multiple Integrals,* Englewood Cliffs, NJ: Prentice-Hall.

Stroud, A.H., 1966. *Gaussian Quadrature Formulas,* Englewood Cliffs, NJ: Prentice-Hall.

Su, H.-T., and T. McAvoy, 1991. "Identification of chemical processes using recurrent networks," *Proceedings of the 10th American Controls Conference,* vol. 3, pp. 2314–2319, Boston.

Su, H.-T., T. McAvoy, and P. Werbos, 1992. "Long-term predictions of chemical processes using recurrent neural networks: A parallel training approach," *Industrial Engineering and Chemical Research,* vol. 31, pp. 1338–1352.

Suga, N., 1990a. "Cortical computational maps for auditory imaging," *Neural Networks,* vol. 3, pp. 3–21.

Suga, N., 1990b. "Computations of velocity and range in the bat auditory system for echo location," in *Computational Neuroscience,* E.L. Schwartz, ed., pp. 213–231, Cambridge, MA: MIT Press.

Suga, N., 1990c. "Biosonar and neural computation in bats," *Scientific American,* vol. 262, pp. 60–68.

Suga, N., 1985. "The extent to which bisonar information is represented in the bat auditory cortex," in *Dynamic Aspects of Neocortical Function*, G.M. Edelman, W.E. Gall, and W.M. Cowan, eds. pp. 653–695, New York: Wiley (Interscience).

Suga, N., 2003, "Echolocation: Chocleotopic and computational maps," in M.A. Arbib, ed., *The Handbook of Brain Theory and Neural Networks*, 2d edition, pp. 381–387, Cambridge, MA: MIT Press.

Sutton, R.S., 1988. "Learning to predict by the methods of temporal differences," *Machine Learning*, vol. 3, pp. 9–44.

Sutton, R.S., 1984. "Temporal credit assignment in reinforcement learning," Ph.D. dissertation, University of Massachusetts, Amherst, MA.

Sutton, R.S., ed., 1992. Special Issue on Reinforcement Learning, *Machine Learning*, vol. 8, pp. 1–395.

Sutton, R.S., and A.G. Barto, 1998. *Reinforcement Learning: An Introduction*, Cambridge, MA: MIT Press.

Sutton, R.S., and B. Tanner, 2005. "Temporal Difference Networks," *Advances in Neural Information Processing Systems*, vol. 17, pp. 1377–1384.

Suykens, J.A., T. Van Gestel, J. DeBrabanter, B. DeMoor, and J. Vanderwalle, 2002. *Least-Squares Support Vector Machines*, River Edge, NJ: World Scientific.

Suykens, J.A.K., J.P.L. Vandewalle, and B.L.R. DeMoor, 1996. *Artificial Neural Networks for Modeling and Control of Non-Linear Systems*, Dordrecht, The Netherlands: Kluwer.

Takens, F., 1981. "On the numerical determination of the dimension of an attractor," in D. Rand and L.S. Young, eds., *Dynamical Systems and Turbulence*, Annual Notes in Mathematics, vol. 898, pp. 366–381, Berlin: Springer-Verlag.

Tapia, R.A., and J.R. Thompson, 1978. *Nonparametric Probability Density Estimation*, Baltimore: The Johns Hopkins University Press.

Tesauro, G., 1995. "Temporal difference learning and TD-gamma," *Communications of the Association for Computing Machinery*, vol. 38, pp. 58–68.

Tesauro, G., 1994. "TD-Gammon, A self-teaching Backgammon program, achieves master-level play," *Neural Computation*, vol. 6, pp. 215–219.

Tesauro, G., 1992. "Practical issues in temporal difference learning," *Machine Learning*, vol. 8, pp. 257–277.

Tesauro, G., 1989. "Neurogammon wins computer olympiad," *Neural Computation*, vol. 1, pp. 321–323.

Tesauro, G., and R. Janssens, 1988. "Scaling relationships in back-propagation learning," *Complex Systems*, vol. 2, pp. 39–44.

Theodoridis, S., and K. Koutroumbas, 2003. *Pattern Recognition*, 2d ed., Amsterdam and Boston: Academic Press.

Thorndike, E.L., 1911. *Animal Intelligence*, Darien, CT: Hafner.

Thrun, S.B., 1992. "The role of exploration in learning control," in *Handbook of Intelligent Control*, D.A. White and D.A. Sofge, eds., pp. 527–559, New York: Van Nostrand Reinhold.

Tichavsky, P., Z. Koldovsky, and E. Oja, 2006. "Performance analysis of FastICA algorithm and Cramér–Rao bounds for linear independent component analysis," *IEEE Trans. Signal Processing*, vol. 54, pp. 1189–1203.

Tikhonov, A.N., 1973. "On regularization of ill-posed problems," *Doklady Akademii Nauk USSR*, vol. 153, pp. 49–52.

Tikhonov, A.N., 1963. "On solving incorrectly posed problems and method of regularization," *Doklady Akademii Nauk USSR*, vol. 151, pp. 501–504.

Tikhonov, A.N., and V.Y. Arsenin, 1977. *Solutions of Ill-posed Problems,* Washington, DC: W.H. Winston.

Tishby, N., and N. Slonim, 2001. "Data Clustering by Markovian relaxation and the information bottleneck method," *Advances in Neural Information Processing Systems,* vol. 13, pp. 640–646.

Tishby, N., F.C. Pereira, and W. Bialek, 1999. "The information bottleneck method," *Proceedings of the 37th Annual Allerton Conference on Communications, Control and Computing,* pp. 368–377.

Touretzky, D.S., and D.A. Pomerleau, 1989. "What is hidden in the hidden layers?" *Byte,* vol. 14, pp. 227–233.

Tsitsiklis, J.N., 1994. "Asynchronous stochastic approximation and Q-learning," *Machine Learning,* vol. 16, pp. 185–202.

Tsoi, A.C., and A.D. Back, 1994. "Locally recurrent globally feedforward networks: A critical review," *IEEE Transactions on Neural Networks,* vol. 5, pp. 229–239.

Tu, Z.W., X. R. Chen, A.L. Yiulle, and S.C. Zhu, 2005. "Image parsing: Unifying segmentation, detection, and recognition," *International J. Computer Vision,* vol. 63, pp. 113–140.

Turing, A.M., 1952. "The chemical basis of morphogenesis," *Philosophical Transactions of the Royal Society, B,* vol. 237, pp. 5–72.

Turing, A.M., 1950. "Computing machinery and intelligence," *Mind,* vol. 59, pp. 433–460.

Turing, A.M., 1936. "On computable numbers with an application to the Entscheidungs problem," *Proceedings of the London Mathematical Society,* Series 2, vol. 42, pp. 230–265. Correction published in vol. 43, pp. 544–546.

Ukrainec, A.M., and S. Haykin, 1996. "A modular neural network for enhancement of cross-polar radar targets," *Neural Networks,* vol. 9, pp. 143–168.

Ukrainec, A., and S. Haykin, 1992. "Enhancement of radar images using mutual information based unsupervised neural networks," *Canadian Conference on Electrical and Computer Engineering,* pp. MA6.9.1–MA6.9.4, Toronto, Canada.

Uttley, A.M., 1979. *Information Transmission in the Nervous System,* London: Academic Press.

Uttley, A.M., 1970. "The informon: A network for adaptive pattern recognition," *Journal of Theoretical Biology,* vol. 27, pp. 31–67.

Uttley, A.M., 1966. "The transmission of information and the effect of local feedback in theoretical and neural networks," *Brain Research,* vol. 102, pp. 23–35.

Uttley, A.M., 1956. "A theory of the mechanism of learning based on the computation of conditional probabilities," *Proceedings of the First International Conference on Cybernetics,* Namur, Gauthier-Villars, Paris.

Valiant, L.G., 1984. "A theory of the learnable," *Communications of the Association for Computing Machinery,* vol. 27, pp. 1134–1142.

Van Essen, D.C., C.H. Anderson, and D.J. Felleman, 1992. "Information processing in the primate visual system: An integrated systems perspective," *Science,* vol. 255, pp. 419–423.

Van Hulle, M.M., 2005. "Maximum likelihood topographic map formation," *Neural Computation,* vol. 17, pp. 503–513.

Van Hulle, M.M., 2002a. "Kernel-based topographic map formation by local density modeling," *Neural Computation,* vol. 14, pp. 1561–1573.

Van Hulle, M.M., 2002b. "Joint entropy maximization in kernel-based topographic maps," *Neural Computation,* vol. 14, pp. 1887–1906.

Van Hulle, M.M., 1997. "Nonparametric density estimation and regression achieved with topographic maps maximizing the information-theoretic entropy of their outputs," *Biological Cybernetics,* vol. 77, pp. 49–61.

Van Hulle, M.M., 1996. "Topographic map formation by maximizing unconditional entropy: A plausible strategy for "on-line" unsupervised competitive learning and nonparametric density estimation," *IEEE Transactions on Neural Networks,* vol. 7, pp. 1299–1305.

van Laarhoven, P.J.M., and E.H.L. Aarts, 1988. *Simulated Annealing: Theory and Applications,* Boston: Kluwer Academic Publishers.

Van Trees, H.L., 1968. *Detection, Estimation, and Modulation Theory,* Part I, New York: Wiley.

Vapnik, V.N., 1998. *Statistical Learning Theory,* New York: Wiley.

Vapnik, V.N., 1995. *The Nature of Statistical Learning Theory,* New York: Springer-Verlag.

Vapnik, V.N., 1992. "Principles of risk minimization for learning theory," *Advances in Neural Information Processing Systems,* vol. 4, pp. 831–838, San Mateo, CA: Morgan Kaufmann.

Vapnik, V.N., 1982. *Estimation of Dependences Based on Empirical Data,* New York: Springer-Verlag.

Vapnik, V.N., and A.Ya. Chervonenkis, 1971. "On the uniform convergence of relative frequencies of events to their probabilities," *Theoretical Probability and Its Applications,* vol. 17, pp. 264–280.

Vapnik, V.N., and A. Ya. Chervonenkis, 1964. "A note on a class of perceptrons," *Automation and Remote Control,* vol. 25, pp. 103–109.

Venkataraman, S., 1994. "On encoding nonlinear oscillations in neural networks for locomotion," *Proceedings of the 8th Yale Workshop on Adaptive and Learning Systems,* pp. 14–20, New Haven, CT.

Vidyasagar, M., 1997. *A Theory of Learning and Generalization,* London: Springer-Verlag.

Vidyasagar, M., 1993. *Nonlinear Systems Analysis,* 2d ed., Englewood Cliffs, NJ: Prentice Hall.

Viterbi, A.J., 1967. "Error bounds for convolutional codes and an asymptotically optimum decoding algorithm," *IEEE Transactions on Information Theory,* vol. IT-13, pp. 260–269.

von der Malsburg, C., 1990a. "Network self-organization," in *An Introduction to Neural and Electronic Networks,* S.F. Zornetzer, J.L. Davis, and C. Lau, eds., pp. 421–432, San Diego: Academic Press.

von der Malsburg, C., 1990b. "Considerations for a visual architecture," in *Advanced Neural Computers,* R. Eckmiller, ed., pp. 303–312, Amsterdam: North-Holland.

von der Malsburg, C., 1981. "The correlation theory of brain function," *Internal Report 81–2,* Department of Neurobiology, Max-Plak-Institute for Biophysical Chemistry, Göttingen, Germany.

von der Malsburg, C., 1973. "Self-organization of orientation sensitive cells in the striate cortex," *Kybernetik,* vol. 14, pp. 85–100.

von der Malsburg, C., and W. Schneider, 1986. "A neural cocktail party processor," *Biological Cybernetics,* vol. 54, pp. 29–40.

von Neumann, J., 1986. *Papers of John von Neumann on Computing and Computer Theory,* W. Aspray and A. Burks, eds., Cambridge, MA: MIT Press.

von Neumann, J., 1958. *The Computer and the Brain,* New Haven, CT: Yale University Press.

von Neumann, J., 1956. "Probabilistic logics and the synthesis of reliable organisms from unreliable components," in *Automata Studies,* C.E. Shannon and J. McCarthy, eds., pp. 43–98, Princeton, NJ: Princeton University Press.

Wahba, G., 1990. *Spline Models for Observational Data,* SIAM.

Wahba, G., D.R. Johnson, F. Gao, and J. Gong, 1995. "Adaptive tuning of numerical weather prediction models: Randomized GCV in three and four dimensional data assimilation," *Monthly Weather Review,* vol. 123, pp. 3358–3369.

Watkins, C.J.C.H., 1989. *Learning from Delayed Rewards,* Ph.D. thesis, University of Cambridge, Cambridge, U.K.

Watkins, C.J.C.H., and P. Dayan, 1992. "Q-leaming," *Machine Learning,* vol. 8, pp. 279–292.

Watrous, R.L. 1987. "Learning algorithms for connectionist networks: Applied gradient methods of nonlinear optimization," *First IEEE International Conference on Neural Networks*, vol. 2, pp. 619–627, San Diego.

Watson, G.S., 1964. "Smooth regression analysis," *Sankhyā: The Indian Journal of Statistics, Series A*, vol. 26, pp. 359–372.

Wax, W., and T. Kailath, 1985. "Detection of signals by information theoretic criteria," *IEEE Trans. Acoustics, Speech and Signal Processing*, vol. ASSP32, pp. 387–392.

Webb, A.R., 1994. "Functional approximation by feed-forward networks: A least-squares approach to generalisation," *IEEE Transactions on Neural Networks*, vol. 5, pp. 480–488.

Webb, A.R., and D. Lowe, 1990. "The optimal internal representation of multilayer classifier networks performs nonlinear discriminant analysis," *Neural Networks*, vol. 3, pp. 367–375.

Weierstrass, K., 1885. "Uber die analytische Darstellbarkeit sogenannter willkurlicher Funktionen einer reellen veranderlichen," *Sitzungsberichte der Akademie der Wissenschaften, Berlin*, pp. 633–639, 789–905.

Werbos, P., 2004. "ADP: Goals, opportunities and principles," in J. Si, A.G. Barto, W.B. Powell, and D. Wunsch II, eds., *Handbook of Learning and Approximate Dynamic Programming*, Hoboken, NJ: Wiley-Interscience.

Werbos, P.J., 1992. "Neural networks and the human mind: New mathematics fits humanistic insight," *IEEE International Conference on Systems, Man, and Cybernetics*, vol. 1, pp. 78–83, Chicago.

Werbos, P.J., 1990. "Backpropagation through time: What it does and how to do it," *Proceedings of the IEEE*, vol. 78, pp. 1550–1560.

Werbos, P.J., 1989. "Backpropagation and neurocontrol: A review and prospectus," *International Joint Conference on Neural Networks*, vol. I, pp. 209–216, Washington, DC.

Werbos, P., 1977. "Advanced forecasting for global crisis warning and models of intelligence," *General Systems Yearbook*, vol. 22, pp. 25–38.

Werbos, P.J., 1974. "Beyond regression: New tools for prediction and analysis in the behavioral sciences," Ph.D. thesis, Harvard University, Cambridge, MA.

Whitney, H., 1936. "Differentiable manifolds," *Annals of Mathematics*, vol. 37, pp. 645–680.

Whittaker, E.T., 1923. "On a new method of graduation," *Proceedings of the Edinburgh Mathematical Society*, vol. 41, pp. 63–75.

Widrow, B., N.K. Gupta, and S. Maitra, 1973. "Punish/reward: Learning with a critic in adaptive threshold systems," *IEEE Transactions of Systems, Man, and Cybernetics*, vol. SMC-3, pp. 455–465.

Widrow, B., and M.E. Hoff, Jr., 1960. "Adaptive Switching Circuits," *IRE WESCON Conv. Rec.*, Pt. 4, pp. 96–104.

Widrow, B., and M.A. Lehr, 1990. "30 years of adaptive neural networks: Perceptron, madaline, and back-propagation," *Proceedings of the Institute of Electrical and Electronics Engineers*, vol. 78, pp. 1415–1442.

Widrow, B., P.E. Mantey, L.J. Griffiths, and B.B. Goode, 1967. "Adaptive antenna systems," *Proceedings of the IEEE*, vol. 55, pp. 2143–2159.

Widrow, B., and S.D. Stearns, 1985. *Adaptive Signal Processing*, Englewood Cliffs, NJ: Prentice-Hall.

Widrow, B., and E. Walach, 1996. *Adaptive Inverse Control*, Upper Saddle River, NJ: Prentice Hall.

Wieland, A., and R. Leighton, 1987. "Geometric analysis of neural network capabilities," first *IEEE International Conference on Neural Networks*, vol. III, pp. 385–392, San Diego.

Wiener, N., 1961. *Cybernetics*, 2d ed., New York: Wiley.

Wiener, N., 1958. *Nonlinear Problems in Random Theory,* New York: Wiley.

Wiener, N., 1949. *Extrapolation, Interpolation, and Smoothing of Stationary Time Series with Engineering Applications,* Cambridge, MA: MIT Press. (This was originally issued as a classified National Defense Research Report, February 1942).

Wiener, N., 1948. *Cybernetics: Or Control and Communication in the Animal and the Machine,* New York: Wiley.

Wilks, S.S., 1962. *Mathematical Statistics,* New York: Wiley.

Williams, R.J., and J. Peng, 1990. "An efficient gradient-based algorithm for on-line training of recurrent network trajectories," *Neural Computation,* vol. 2, pp. 490–501.

Williams, R.J., and D. Zipser, 1995. "Gradient-based learning algorithms for recurrent networks and their computational complexity," in Y. Chauvin and D.E. Rumelhart, eds., *Backpropagation: Theory, Architectures, and Applications,* pp. 433–486, Hillsdale, NJ: Lawrence Erlbaum.

Williams, R.J., and D. Zipser, 1989. "A learning algorithm for continually running fully recurrent neural networks," *Neural Computation,* vol. 1, pp. 270–280.

Willshaw, D.J., O.P. Buneman, and H.C. Longuet-Higgins, 1969. "Non-holographic associative memory," *Nature (London),* vol. 222, pp. 960–962.

Willshaw, D.J., and C. von der Malsburg, 1976. "How patterned neural connections can be set up by self-organization," *Proceedings of the Royal Society of London Series B,* vol. 194, pp. 431–445.

Wilson, G.V., and G.S. Pawley, 1988. "On the stability of the travelling salesman problem algorithm of Hopfield and Tank," *Biological Cybernetics,* vol. 58, pp. 63–70.

Wilson, H.R., and J.D. Gowan, 1972. "Excitatory and inhibitory interactions in localized populations of model neurons," *Journal of Biophysics,* vol. 12, pp. 1–24.

Winder, R.O., 1961. "Single stage threshold logic," *Switching Circuit Theory and Logical Design,* AIEE Special Publications, vol. S-134, pp. 321–332.

Winograd, S., and J.D. Cowan, 1963. *Reliable Computation in the Presence of Noise,* Cambridge, MA: MIT Press.

Wood, N.L., and N. Cowan, 1995. "The cocktail party phenomenon revisited: Attention and memory in the classic selective listening procedure of Cherry (1953)," *Journal of Experimental Psychology: General,* vol. 124, pp. 243–262.

Woods, W.A., 1986. "Important issues in knowledge representation," *Proceedings of the Institute of Electrical and Electronics Engineers,* vol. 74, pp. 1322–1334.

Wu, C.F.J., 1983. "On the convergence properties of the EM algorithm," *Annals of Statistics,* vol. 11, pp. 95–103.

Wylie, C.R., and L.C. Barrett, 1982. *Advanced Engineering Mathematics,* 5th ed., New York: McGraw-Hill.

Xu, L., A. Krzyzak, and A. Yuille, 1994. "On radial basis function nets and kernel regression: Statistical consistency, convergency rates, and receptive field size," *Neural Networks,* vol. 7, pp. 609–628.

Xu, L., E. Oja, and C.Y. Suen, 1992. "Modified Hebbian learning for curve and surface fitting," *Neural Networks,* vol. 5, pp. 441–457.

Yee, P., and S. Haykin, 2001. *Regularized Radial Basis Function Networks: Theory and Applications,* New York: Wiley-Interscience.

Yockey, H.P., 1992. *Information Theory and Molecular Biology,* Cambridge, U.K.: Cambridge University Press.

Yom-Tov, E., 2007. "A distributed sequential solver for large-scale SVMs." In L. Bottou, O. Chapelle, D. DeCosta, and J. Weston, editors, *Large-Scale Kernel Machines*, pp.139–154, Cambridge: MIT Press.

Yoshizawa, S., M. Morita, and S. Amari, 1993. "Capacity of associative memory using a nonmonotonic neuron model," *Neural Networks,* vol. 6, pp. 167–176.

Young, P.C., 1984. *Recursive Estimation and Time-Series Analysis,* Berlin and New York: Springer-Verlag.

Younger, S., S. Hockreiter, and P. Conwell, 2001. "Meta-learning with backpropagation," *Proceedings of the International Joint Conference on Neural Networks,* pp. 2001–2006, Washington, DC.

Younger, S., P. Conwell, and N. Cotter, 1999. "Fixed-weight on-line learning," *IEEE Trans. Neural Networks,* vol. 10, pp. 272–283.

Zadeh, L.A., and C.A. Desoer, 1963. *Linear System Theory: The State Space Approach,* New York: McGraw-Hill.

Zames, G., 1981. "Feedback and optimal sensitivity: Model reference transformations, multiplicative seminorms, and approximate inverses," *IEEE Transactions on Automatic Control,* vol. AC-26, pp. 301–320.

Zames, G., and B.A. Francis, 1983. "Feedback, minimax, sensitivity, and optimal robustness," *IEEE Transactions on Automatic Control,* vol. AC-28, pp. 585–601.

Zhou, K., and J.C. Doyle, 1998. *Essentials of Robust Control,* Englewood Cliffs, NJ: Prentice Hall.

Index

Abbreviations and Symbols

ABBREVIATIONS

AR	autoregressive
BBTT	back propagation through time
BM	Boltzmann machine
BP	back propagation
b/s	bits per second
BSB	brain-state-in-a-box
BSS	Blind source (signal) separation
cmm	correlation matrix memory
CV	cross-validation
DFA	deterministic finite-state automata
EKF	extended Kalman filter
EM	expectation-maximization
FIR	finite-duration impulse response
FM	frequency-modulated (signal)
GCV	generalized cross-validation
GHA	generalized Hebbian algorithm
GSLC	generalized sidelobe canceler
Hz	hertz
ICA	independent-components analysis
Infomax	maximum mutual information
Imax	variant of Infomax
Imin	another variant of Infomax
KSOM	kernel self-organizing map
KHA	kernel Hebbian algorithm
LMS	least-mean-square
LR	likelihood ratio

LS	Least-squares
LS-TD	Least-squares, temporal-difference
LTP	long-term potentiation
LTD	long-term depression
LR	likelihood ratio
LRT	Likelihood ratio test
MAP	Maximum a posteriori
MCA	minor-components analysis
MCMC	Markov Chan Monte Carlo
MDL	minimum description length
MIMO	multiple input–multiple output
ML	maximum likelihood
MLP	multilayer perceptron
MRC	model reference control
NARMA	nonlinear autoregressive moving average
NARX	nonlinear autoregressive with exogenous inputs
NDP	neuro-dynamic programming
NW	Nadaraya–Watson (estimator)
NWKR	Nadaraya–Watson kernal regression
OBD	optimal brain damage
OBS	optimal brain surgeon
OCR	optical character recognition
PAC	probably approximately correct
PCA	principal-components analysis
PF	Particle Filter
pdf	probability density function
pmf	probability mass function
QP	quadratic programming
RBF	radial basis function
RLS	recursive least-squares
RLS	regularized least-squares
RMLP	recurrent multilayer perceptron
RTRL	real-time recurrent learning
SIMO	single input–multiple output
SIR	sequential importance resampling
SIS	sequential important sampling
SISO	single input–single output
SNR	signal-to-noise ratio
SOM	self-organizing map
SRN	simple recurrent network (also referred to as Elman's recurrent network)

SVD	singular value decomposition
SVM	support vector machine
TD	temporal difference
TDNN	time-delay neural network
TLFN	time-lagged feedforward network
VC	Vapnik–Chervononkis (dimension)
VLSI	very-large-scale integration
XOR	exclusive OR

IMPORTANT SYMBOLS

a	action
$\mathbf{a}^T\mathbf{b}$	inner product of vectors $\mathbf{a}$ and $\mathbf{b}$
$\mathbf{a}\mathbf{b}^T$	outer product of vectors $\mathbf{a}$ and $\mathbf{b}$
$\begin{pmatrix} l \\ m \end{pmatrix}$	binomial coefficient
$A \cup B$	unions of A and B
B	inverse of temperature
b_k	bias applied to neuron k
$\cos(\mathbf{a},\mathbf{b})$	cosine of the angle between vectors $\mathbf{a}$ and $\mathbf{b}$
$c_{u,v}(u, v)$	probability density function of copula
D	depth of memory
$D_{f\|g}$	Kullback–Leibler divergence between probability density functions f and g
$\tilde{\mathbf{D}}$	adjoint of operator $\mathbf{D}$
E	energy function
E_i	energy of state i in statistical mechanics
$\mathbb{E}$	statistical expectation operator
$\langle E \rangle$	average energy
$\exp$	exponential
$\mathscr{E}_{av}$	average squared error, or sum of squared errors
$\mathscr{E}(n)$	instantaneous value of the sum of squared errors
$\mathscr{E}_{total}$	total sum of error squares
F	free energy
$\mathscr{F}^*$	subset (network) with minimum empirical risk
$\mathbf{H}$	Hessian (matrix)
$\mathbf{H}^{-1}$	inverse of Hessian $\mathbf{H}$
i	square root of -1, also denoted by j
$\mathbf{I}$	identity matrix
$\mathbf{I}$	Fisher's information matrix
J	mean-square error
$\mathbf{J}$	Jacobian (matrix)

$\mathbf{P}^{1/2}$	square root of matrix $\mathbf{P}$
$\mathbf{P}^{T/2}$	transpose of square root of matrix $\mathbf{P}$
$\mathbf{P}n,n-1$	error covariance matrix in Kalman filter theory
k_B	Boltzmann constant
log	logarithm
$L(\mathbf{w})$	log-likelihood function of weight vector $\mathbf{w}$
$\mathscr{L}(\mathbf{w})$	log-likelihood function of weight vector $\mathbf{w}$ based on a single example
$\mathbf{M}_c$	controllability matrix
$\mathbf{M}_o$	observability matrix
n	discrete time
p_i	probability of state i in statistical mechanics
p_{ij}	transition probability from state i to state j
$\mathbf{P}$	stochastic matrix
$P(e|\mathscr{C})$	conditional probability of error e given that the input is drawn from class $\mathscr{C}$
P_α^+	probability that the visible neurons of a Boltzmann machine are in state α , given that the network is in its clamped condition (i.e., positive phase)
P_α^-	probability that the visible neurons of a Boltzmann machine are in state α, given that the network is in its free-running condition (i.e., negative phase)
$\hat{r}_x(j, k;n)]$	estimate of autocorrelation function of $x_j(n)$ and $x_k(n)$
$\hat{r}_{dx}(k;n)$	estimate of cross-correlation function of $d(n)$ and $x_k(n)$
$\mathbf{R}$	correlation matrix of an input vector
t	continuous time
T	temperature
$\mathscr{T}$	training set (sample)
tr	operator denoting the trace of a matrix
var	variance operator
$V(\mathbf{x})$	Lyapunov function of state vector $\mathbf{x}$
v_j	induced local field or activation potential of neuron j
$\mathbf{w}_o$	optimum value of synaptic weight vector
w_{kj}	weight of synapse j belonging to neuron k
$\mathbf{w}^*$	optimum weight vector
$\overline{\mathbf{x}}$	equilibrium value of state vector $\mathbf{x}$
$\langle x_j \rangle$	average of state x_j in a "thermal" sense
$\hat{x}$	estimate of x, signified by the use of a caret (hat)
$|x|$	absolute value (magnitude) of x
x^*	complex conjugate of x, signified by asterisk as superscript
$\|\mathbf{x}\|$	Euclidean norm (length) of vector $\mathbf{x}$
$\mathbf{x}^T$	transpose of vector $\mathbf{x}$, signified by the superscript T
z^{-1}	unit-time delay operator
Z	partition function
$\delta_j(n)$	local gradient of neuron j at time n
Δw	small change applied to weight w
∇	gradient operator

∇^2	Laplacian operator
$\nabla_w J$	gradient of J with respect to w
$\nabla \cdot \mathbf{F}$	divergence of vector $\mathbf{F}$
η	learning-rate parameter
κ	cumulant
μ	policy
θ_k	threshold applied to neuron k (i.e., negative of bias b_k)
λ	regularization parameter
λ_k	kth eigenvalue of a square matrix
$\varphi_k(\cdot)$	nonlinear activation function of neuron k
$\in$	symbol for "belongs to"
$\cup$	symbol for "union of"
$\cap$	symbol for "intersection of"
$*$	symbol for convolution
$+$	superscript symbol for pseudoinverse of a matrix
$+$	superscript symbol for updated estimate

Open and closed intervals

- The open interval (a, b) of a variable x signifies that $a < x < b$.
- The closed interval $[a, b]$ of a variable x signifies that $a \leq x \leq b$.
- The closed-open interval $[a, b)$ of a variable x signifies that $a \leq x < b$; likewise for the open-closed interval $(a, b], a < x \leq b$.

Minima and Maxima

- The symbol arg $\min_{\mathbf{w}} f(\mathbf{w})$ signifies the minimum of the function $f(\mathbf{w})$ with respect to the argument vector $\mathbf{w}$.
- The symbol arg $\max_{\mathbf{w}} f(\mathbf{w})$ signifies the maximum of the function $f(\mathbf{w})$ with respect to the argument vector $\mathbf{w}$.